G000145012

BlackBerry

iPhone / iPad

◎**Harden's** **21st** YEAR

UK Restaurant Survey 2012

"The UK's most helpful and informative guide"
The Sunday Times

In association with **RÉMY MARTIN**
FINE CHAMPAGNE COGNAC

The Heart of Cognac

Survey driven reviews of nearly 3,000 restaurants

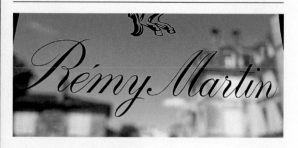

The appreciation of excellence

Few business partnerships last as long as the co-operation between Rémy Martin and Harden's. This is based on many things, but particularly on authenticity, integrity and reliability, which are important to both of us.

Harden's derives its authenticity from its annual nationwide survey of restaurant-goers, leading to the creation of the UK's definitive democratic restaurant guides and now, in association with The Sunday Times, the UK's definitive Top 100 list. For Rémy Martin, it comes from three centuries of tradition, its origins in the heart of Cognac and the unique know-how of the cellar-master.

The Heart of Cognac

Since 1724, Rémy Martin – the only grand cognac house still in family ownership – has produced cognacs of exceptional quality and taste. Alone, it sources 100% of its grapes from the very 'heart of Cognac'. The 'heart' has its own official designation: 'Appellation Fine Champagne Contrôllée'. 'Fine Champagne' indicates a blend of cognac from the two best areas in the centre of the Cognac region, Grande Champagne (at least half the blend) and Petite Champagne.

Champagne lends its name to these two Cognac areas because, like the famous sparkling wine region, the soil is chalky. Over 80% of all the Fine Champagne cognac produced in this designated area is used in Rémy Martin Fine Champagne cognacs.

The result is three main characteristics which distinguish Rémy Martin: the harmony between the complex aromas and the sweetness of the flavours; the elegant richness of the aromas and palate; and the supreme length of the finish.

Please enjoy Rémy Martin responsibly

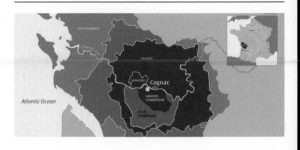

This is why we believe that Rémy Martin captures the very heart of Cognac and it is this unswerving dedication to quality over nearly three centuries that has led Rémy Martin to become the worldwide leader in the most premium of cognacs.

The Centaur

The Sagittarius Centaur – a symbol of the alliance of man and nature – was adopted by the Rémy Martin family in 1870. Not only is Sagittarius the star sign of Rémy Martin's founding father, Paul-Émile Rémy Martin, but it is also representative of many of the values that the family upholds – courage, energy, audacity and generosity.

Artist and Artisan

The role of the cellar master commands huge respect. It demands a special combination of skills: knowledgeable viticultualist, skilled wine maker, master blender, and expert taster, all whilst never losing sight of the house style. Thanks to the skilled craftsmanship of generations of cellar masters, Rémy Martin has been able to anticipate the evolution of consumer tastes and adapt and innovate accordingly.

Spirit for Life

Much more than a digestif, Rémy Martin has a cognac to suit every mood and occasion from celebrations to moments of solace. Throw out the rule book: aperitif, digestif, cocktail or frozen, Rémy Martin captures the spirit for living.

Rémy Martin V.S.O.P

This is the world's favourite V.S.O.P (Very Superior Old Pale) cognac and the benchmark by which all other V.S.O.P's are measured. Rémy Martin V.S.O.P shows near perfect balance of the three cornerstones of great cognac: floral, fruity and spice. Blended from over 240 eaux-de-vie, the result is a wonderfully balanced and smooth V.S.O.P.

Much more than simply a traditional digestif, the versatility of Rémy Martin V.S.O.P means it is perfect for many occasions. Why not try the recent trend from the US and impress friends by pulling a bottle out of the freezer and serving it chilled?

Enjoying Rémy Martin

Not only are Rémy Martin Fine Champagne cognacs the ideal choice to round off a wonderful meal, but Rémy Martin can also be enjoyed as a long drink before dinner or as the perfect accompaniment to fine food.

French Mojito

50 ml of Rémy Martin VSOP
Half a lime
4 small cane sugar cubes
(white or brown)
10 mint leaves
Crushed ice
Soda water

Method: build in a highball glass
Muddle (mash) the mint, lime and sugar together
Fill your glass with crushed ice
Pour the Remy Martin VSOP cognac and stir gently
Top up with a splash of soda water
Garnish with a mint sprig

RÉMY MAR

FINE CHAMPAGNE C

V.S.O.

Fondée en 1724

PRODUCT OF FRA

The Rémy Martin V.S.O.P Award for the Best-Rated Newcomer remains the industry's most coveted recognition of up-and-coming restaurants. Rémy Martin is once again proud to be associated with the development of such a dynamic category.

Rémy Martin VSOP Award for Best Rated Newcomer

Winner

Dinner

Heston Blumenthal burst out of Bray – until then home to all his operations – to open this British restaurant inspired by years of historical research. The resulting menu - a celebration of select British dishes from the 14th century onwards – includes such quirky delights as Meat Fruit, Powdered Duck and Tipsy Cake. Heading up the kitchen is Ashley Palmer-Watts, who brings with him not only his own experience and creativity, but also the benefit of 10 years' experience at the fabled Fat Duck.

Runners Up
Morito
Yashin
Pollen Street Social
Brawn

Rémy Martin XO

Sophisticated and beautifully balanced, Rémy Martin XO Excellence (Extra Old) combines aromatic richness and complexity with a wonderful velvety texture. The nose yields hints of jasmine, ripe fig and candied orange and the palate shows notes of cinnamon and freshly baked brioche.

Rémy Martin XO is aged for up to 37 years in Limousin oak cask to achieve its maturity and balance.

XO is a wonderful digestif and the perfect partner to rich hazelnut and cinnamon desserts. Rémy Martin XO truly is the taste of extravagance.

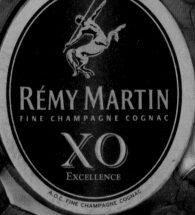

RÉMY MARTIN
FINE CHAMPAGNE COGNAC

The Heart of Cognac

Now it its third year, the Rémy Martin XO Excellence Award is for the Best All Round Restaurant. This award is the result of painstaking analysis of the survey results, to identify the true crème de la crème – having regard to food, service and ambience – of the UK's dining scene.

Rémy Martin XO Excellence Award for Best All-Round Restaurant – London

Winner

Le Gavroche

It would be difficult to overstate the important of this London institution. More than 40 years after it first opened its doors (at a different address), it remains the case that the 'family trees', so to speak, of most major chefs wend their way back to this Mayfair legend. Now led by Michel Roux Jr., son of founder Albert, the restaurant remains an unashamed bastion of Gallic classicism. As the Award confirms, the old ways can still be the best ways!

Runners Up
The Ledbury
The Ritz
Chez Bruce
Min Jiang

Rémy Martin XO Excellence Award for Best All-Round Restaurant – Rest of UK

Winner

Gidleigh Park, Chagford

This grand country house may have an idyllic location on the fringe of Dartmoor, but it's Michael Caines's cooking that has really put it on the map. Michael is a 'local boy', trained in Exeter, and subsequently worked with some of the greats – including Raymond Blanc at Great Milton, and the late Bernard Loiseau in Saulieu – before become head chef at Gidleigh in 1994. He has subsequently gone into partnership with Andrew Brownsord (originally of greeting card fame) to establish the ABode hotel chain, each of whose outposts has a Michael Caines restaurant.

Runners Up
Waterside Inn, Bray
Le Manoir aux Quat' Saisons, Great Milton
Mr Underhill's, Ludlow
Restaurant Martin Wishart, Edinburgh

Remy Martin Coeur de Cognac

Through expert blending, Rémy Martin has created a fruit-driven and succulent spirit – Coeur de Cognac. Fresher and lighter in taste than traditional cognacs, the predominant flavours are of apricot, honey and vanilla. The first taste is like biting into a succulent, juicy apricot whilst the nose bursts with ripe summer fruits and the palate is rich and soft – without the fiery finish usually associated with spirits.

Coeur de Cognac is intended for sheer drinking pleasure to be enjoyed anytime, anywhere. Try it with an ice cube or two which will help to reveal all its complex flavours and make an ideal aperitif.

Developed with people who appreciate fine food and dining in mind, it is a natural accompaniment to fruity deserts like apricot tart or petits fours such as macaroons or fruit jellies.

RÉMY MARTIN
FINE CHAMPAGNE COGNAC

The Heart of Cognac

Now it its third year, the Rémy Martin Coeur de Cognac Award for the Best Dessert rewards a much overlooked, yet sublime, aspect of a complete dining experience.

Coeur de Cognac Award for Best Dessert

Winner

Marcus Wareing at the Berkeley
Custard tart, plum, crumble, plum ice cream

As a native Lancastrian – and having won recognition as London's top chef – it's particularly appropriate that Marcus Wareing should once again also carry off the prize for that most essential course in British cuisine: pudding. Marcus's skill for creating food that's both flawlessly presented and big on taste is showcased perfectly in his desserts. Indeed, with his warm chocolate moelleux, he won the Award last year too.

Runners Up
Dinner *(Tipsy Cake with spit-roast pineapple)*
Chez Bruce *(Cheeseboard)*
Le Gavroche *(Tarte Tatin)*
The Ledbury *(Gingerbread soufflé)*

THE SUNDAY TIMES

The UK's 100 Best Restaurants

1   The Ledbury, London W11

2   Le Manoir aux Quat' Saisons, Great Milton

3   Gidleigh Park, Chagford
    Winner Rémy Martin XO Award (Rest of UK)

4   Le Gavroche, London W1
    Winner Rémy Martin XO Award (London)

5   Waterside Inn, Bray

6   One-O-One, Sheraton Park Tower, London SW1

7   Andrew Fairlie, Gleneagles Hotel, Auchterarder

8   Restaurant Martin Wishart, Edinburgh

9   Pied à Terre, London W1

10 The Fat Duck, Bray

11 Hambleton Hall, Hambleton

12 Midsummer House, Cambridge

13 John Campbell At Coworth Park, Coworth Park, Ascot

14 Yorke Arms, Ramsgill-in-Nidderdale

15 The Square, London W1

16 L'Enclume, Cartmel

17 The Hambrough, Ventnor

18 Restaurant Nathan Outlaw, The St Enodoc Hotel, Rock

19 Marcus Wareing, The Berkeley, London SW1
    Winner Rémy Martin Coeur de Cognac Award

20 The Kitchin, Edinburgh

21 Dinner, Mandarin Oriental Hyde Park, London SW1
    Winner Rémy Martin VSOP Award

22 Simon Radley, The Chester Grosvenor, Chester

RÉMY MARTIN

FINE CHAMPAGNE COGNAC

The Heart of Cognac

THE SUNDAY TIMES

The UK's 100 Best Restaurants

THE SUNDAY TIMES

The UK's 100 Best Restaurants

49 Rasoi, London SW3

50 Morston Hall, Morston

51 Roussillon, London SW1

52 Texture, London W1

53 The Castle Terrace, Edinburgh

54 Paris House, Woburn

55 Drakes, Ripley

56 21212, Edinburgh

57 L'Ortolan, Shinfield

58 Hélène Darroze, The Connaught Hotel, London W1

59 Simpsons, Birmingham

60 Club Gascon, London EC1

61 Hibiscus, London W1

62 La Petite Maison, London W1

63 Artichoke, Amersham

64 The Vineyard at Stockcross, Stockcross

65 Min Jiang, The Royal Garden Hotel, London W8

66 Morgan M, London N7

67 The River Café, London W6

68 The French Horn, Sonning-on-Thames

69 Scott's, London W1

70 L'Oranger, London SW1

71 Hakkasan, London W1

72 Summer Isles Hotel, Achiltibuie

73 Ramsons, Ramsbottom

74 The Latymer, Pennyhill Park Hotel, Bagshot

RÉMY MARTIN
FINE CHAMPAGNE COGNAC

The Heart of Cognac

THE SUNDAY TIMES

The UK's 100 Best Restaurants

75 Dorchester Grill, Dorchester Hotel, London W1

76 Tyddyn Llan, Llandrillo

77 Gauthier Soho, London W1

78 Gordon Ramsay, London SW3

79 Van Zeller, Harrogate

80 Bohemia, The Club Hotel & Spa, Jersey

81 Apsleys, Lanesborough Hotel, London SW1

82 Yauatcha, London W1

83 Theo Randall, InterContinental Hotel, London W1

84 La Trompette, London W4

85 Angelus, London W2

86 Purnells, Birmingham

87 J Sheekey, London WC2

88 Wiltons, London SW1

89 Pearl, London WC1

90 The Crown at Whitebrook, Whitebrook

91 Roux At The Landau, The Langham, London W1

92 Read's, Faversham

93 Pétrus, London W1

94 Nobu, London SW1

95 Benares, London W1

96 Chewton Glen, New Milton

97 Turners, Birmingham

98 St John, London EC1

99 Pollen Street Social, London W1

100 Trinity, London SW4

Put us in your pocket!

Try our editions for BlackBerry and iPhone.

visit BlackBerry app world or the istore for more details.

___

Follow Harden's on Twitter – @hardensbites

© **Harden's Limited 2011**

British Library Cataloguing-in-Publication data: a catalogue record for this book is available from the British Library.

Printed in Spain by Graphy Cems

Design: Margaret Vanschaemelhout

Content Manager & Layout: Helen Teschauer

Research assistants: Sarah Ashpole, Tom Kochavi, Gilles Talarek

Harden's Limited
Golden Cross House
8 Drummond Street
London WC2N 4JF

The views expressed in the editorial section of this guide are exclusively those of Harden's Limited

Would restaurateurs (and PRs) please address communications to 'Editorial' at the above address, or ideally by email to:
editorial@hardens.com

The contents of this book are believed correct at the time of printing. Nevertheless, the publisher can accept no responsibility for errors or changes in or omissions from the details given.

CONTENTS

RATINGS & PRICES

Ratings

Our rating system is unlike those found in other guides (most of which tell you nothing more helpful than that expensive restaurants are, as a general rule, better than cheap ones).

What we do is to compare each restaurant's performance – as judged by the average ratings awarded by reporters in the survey – with other restaurants in the same price-bracket.

This approach has the advantage that it helps you find – whatever your budget for any particular meal – where you will get the best 'bang for your buck'.

The following qualities are assessed:

> **F** — Food
> **S** — Service
> **A** — Ambience

The rating indicates that, *in comparison with other restaurants in the same price-bracket*, performance is…

> **❶** — Exceptional
> **❷** — Very good
> **❸** — Good
> ④ — Average
> ⑤ — Poor

In the **UK section**, some restaurants are worth a mention but, for some reason (typically low feedback) we do not think a rating is appropriate. These are indicated as follows:

> **❶** — Tip

Prices

The price shown for each restaurant is the cost for one (1) person of an average three-course dinner with half a bottle of house wine and coffee, any cover charge, service and VAT. Lunch is often cheaper. With BYO restaurants, we have assumed that two people share a £6 bottle of off-licence wine.

Telephone number – within London all numbers should be prefixed with '020' if dialling from outside the London area.

Map reference – London after the telephone number; UK next to location.

Rated on Editors' visit – indicates ratings have been determined by the Editors personally, based on their visit, rather than derived from the survey.

Website – the first entry in the small print (after any note about Editors' visit)

Last orders time – listed after the website (if applicable); Sunday may be up to 90 minutes earlier.

Opening hours – unless otherwise stated, restaurants are open for lunch and dinner seven days a week.

Credit and debit cards – unless otherwise stated, Mastercard, Visa, Amex and Maestro are accepted.

Dress – where appropriate, the management's preferences concerning patrons' dress are given.

Special menus – if we know of a particularly good value set menu we note this (e.g. "set weekday L"), together with its formula price (FP) calculated exactly as in 'Prices' above. Details change, so always check ahead.

FROM THE EDITORS

The first things regular readers of this guide will note is that it has a new title. The guide formerly known as *Harden's UK Restaurant Guide* is now called *Harden's UK Restaurant Survey*.

To an extent, this change is cosmetic. This guide has always been based on a survey – indeed, it is the only guide based on a detailed annual survey of restaurant-goers – and that hasn't changed. Changes in the media environment have made it truer than ever that the only economically feasible way to cover the restaurants of an entire country is – in our view – to enlist the support of thousands of helpers.

We have also, however, decided to make a real change: the guide now includes the full published results of our 2012 research initiative – all our London entries (as already published separately), plus all the out-of-town results.

We're entirely conscious that the result is a book which, those who only visit the capital rarely might say is biased towards London. That may be true, but we still offer almost as many 'country' entries as *The Good Food Guide* offers for London and the country combined!

And, for the future, we'd like to think that the answer is to get people to help us to 'level up': we'd like to cover the whole country in the same degree of detail!

We are very grateful to each of our thousands of reporters, without whose input this guide could simply not have been written. Many of our reporters express views about a number of restaurants at some length, knowing full well that – given the concise format of the guide – we can seemingly never 'do justice' to their observations. We must assume that they do so in the confidence that the short – and we hope snappy – summaries we produce are as fair and as well-informed as possible.

You, the reader, must judge – restaurant guides are not works of literature, and should be assessed on the basis of utility. This is a case where the proof of the pudding really is in the eating.

Given the growing scale of our task, we are particularly grateful for the continuing support we have received from Rémy Martin Fine Champagne Cognac in the publication of this guide. We are also developing an important relationship with the Sunday Times, and are pleased to record, in the front section of the guide, the list we prepare for them of the Top 100 restaurants in the UK.

All restaurant guides are the subject of continual revision, and the more input we have, the more accurate and comprehensive future editions will be. If you are not already signed up, please do join the www.hardens.com mailing list – we will then ensure that you are invited to take part in future surveys.

Richard Harden   **Peter Harden**

HOW THIS BOOK IS ORGANISED

The guide begins in *London*, and contains the full text of the guide already published as *London Restaurants 2012*. Thereafter, the guide is organised strictly alphabetically by location, without regard to national divisions– Beaumaris, Belfast and Birmingham appear together under 'B'.

For *cities and larger towns*, you should therefore be able to turn straight to the relevant section. In addition to the entries for the restaurants themselves, cities which have significant numbers of restaurants also have a brief introductory overview.

In *less densely populated areas*, you will generally find it easiest to start with the relevant map at the back of the book, which will guide you to the appropriate place names.

If you are looking for a specific restaurant, the alphabetical index at the very back of the book lists all of the restaurants – London and UK – in this guide.

YOUR CONTRIBUTION

This book is the result of a research effort involving thousands of 'reporters'. As a group, you are 'ordinary' members of the public who share with us summary reviews of the best and the worst of your annual dining experiences. This year, over 8,000 of you again gave us some 85,000 reviews in total.

The density of the feedback on London (where many of the top places attract several hundred reviews each) is such that the ratings for the restaurants in the capital are almost exclusively statistical in derivation. (We have, as it happens, visited almost all the restaurants in the London section, anonymously, and at our own expense, but we use our personal experiences only to inform the standpoint from which to interpret the consensus opinion.)

In the case of the more commented-upon restaurants away from the capital, we have adopted an essentially statistical approach very similar to London. In the case of less-visited provincial establishments, however, the interpretation of survey results owes as much to art as it does to science.

In our experience, smaller establishments are – for better or worse – generally quite consistent, and we have therefore felt able to place a relatively high level of confidence in a lower level of commentary. Conservatism on our part, however, may have led to some smaller places being under-rated compared to their more-visited peers.

SURVEY MOST MENTIONED

These are the restaurants which were most frequently mentioned by reporters. (Last year's position is given in brackets.) An asterisk* indicates the first appearance in the list of a recently-opened restaurant.

1	J Sheekey (1)
2	Scott's (2)
3	Marcus Wareing at the Berkeley (4)
4	Chez Bruce (3)
5	Le Gavroche (5)
6	The Ledbury (10)
7=	Clos Maggiore (13)
7=	Galvin Bistrot de Luxe (8)
9	The Wolseley (6)
10	Les Deux Salons*

11	Terroirs (11)
12	Bleeding Heart (8)
13	The Cinnamon Club (15)
14	The Square (20)
15	Bar Boulud*
16	La Trompette (12)
17	Le Caprice (16)
18	Galvin La Chapelle (36)
19	Oxo Tower (Rest') (19)
20	La Poule au Pot (18)

21	The Ivy (14)
22	Benares (29)
23	The River Café (22)
24=	Dinner*
24=	Bocca Di Lupo (21)
26	Zuma (26)
27	Amaya (35)
28	Koffmann's*
29	Gordon Ramsay (17)
30	Andrew Edmunds (24)

31	Moro (30)
32=	L'Atelier de Joel Robuchon (32)
32=	Gordon Ramsay at Claridge's (25)
34	Bistrot Bruno Loubet (-)
35	Pied à Terre (-)
36	Murano (33)
37	Yauatcha (36)
38	Arbutus (23)
39	Galvin at Windows (31)
40	The Anchor & Hope (27)

SURVEY NOMINATIONS

Top gastronomic experience

1. Marcus Wareing At The Berkeley (1)
2. Le Gavroche (2)
3. The Ledbury (3=)
4. Chez Bruce (3=)
5. Dinner*
6. La Trompette (5=)
7= The Square (7)
7= Pied à Terre (-)
9. Viajante (-)
10 Gordon Ramsay (5=)

Favourite

1. Chez Bruce (1)
2. The Wolseley (5)
3. Le Caprice (3)
4. Galvin Bistrot de Luxe (2)
5. The Ledbury (9)
6. La Trompette (3)
7. Le Gavroche (-)
8. Marcus Wareing At The Berkeley (-)
9. J.Sheekey (6)
10 Trinity (-)

Best for business

1. The Wolseley (1)
2. The Don (5)
3. The Square (3)
4. Bleeding Heart (4)
5. Galvin La Chapelle (9)
6. Coq d'Argent (2)
7. L'Anima (6)
8= Galvin Bistrot de Luxe (7)
8= Scott's (8)
10 The Ivy (10)

Best for romance

1. Clos Maggiore (2)
2. La Poule au Pot (1)
3. Andrew Edmunds (3)
4. Bleeding Heart (4)
5. Chez Bruce (6)
6. Galvin at Windows (5)
7. Le Caprice (9)
8. Le Gavroche (10)
9. The Ledbury (-)
10 Oxo Tower (Rest') (-)

Best breakfast/brunch

1   The Wolseley (1)
2   Roast (3)
3   Smiths (Ground Floor) (-)
4   Cecconi's (4)
5   Automat (9)
6   Simpsons-in-the-Strand (5)
7   Caravan (-)
8   The Goring Hotel (9)
9   Providores (Tapa Room) (-)
10 Tom's Kitchen (8)

Best bar/pub food

1   The Anchor & Hope (1)
2   Harwood Arms (2)
3   Bull & Last (3)
4   Canton Arms*
5   The Orange (8)
6   The Gun (-)
7   The Anglesea Arms (4)
8   The Thomas Cubitt (6)
9   The Eagle (8)
10 The Pantechnicon (-)

Most disappointing cooking

1   Gordon Ramsay at Claridge's (2)
2   Oxo Tower (Rest') (1)
3   The Ivy (4)
4   Marcus Wareing at the Berkeley (-)
5   Gordon Ramsay (3)
6   Les Deux Salons*
7   The Wolseley (-)
8=   Skylon (-)
8=   Hibiscus (-)
8=   maze (-)

Most overpriced restaurant

1   Oxo Tower (1)
2   Gordon Ramsay at Claridge's (2)
3   Gordon Ramsay (3)
4   Marcus Wareing at the Berkeley (-)
5   The River Café (5)
6   Hakkasan (6)
7   Alain Ducasse (7)
8=   maze (10)
8=   Le Gavroche
10   Nobu (-)

SURVEY HIGHEST RATINGS

FOOD   SERVICE

£85+

	FOOD			SERVICE
1	The Ledbury		1	Le Gavroche
2	Le Gavroche		2	The Ledbury
3	One-O-One		3	The Ritz Restaurant
4	The Square		4	Marcus Wareing
5	Marcus Wareing		5	The Square

£65-£84

	FOOD			SERVICE
1	Chez Bruce		1	Chez Bruce
2	Zuma		2	The Goring Hotel
3	Min Jiang		3	Angelus
4	Gauthier Soho		4	Texture
5	Yauatcha		5	Le Caprice

£50-£64

	FOOD			SERVICE
1	Morgan M		1	Oslo Court
2	Hunan		2	Trinity
3	Trinity		3	La Trompette
4	La Trompette		4	Brula
5	Pollen Street Social		5	Pollen Street Social

£40-£49

	FOOD			SERVICE
1	Dinings		1	Upstairs Bar
2	Sushi-Say		2	Caraffini
3	Buen Ayre		3	Sushi-Say
4	Sukho Fine Thai Cuisine		4	Emile's
5	Barrafina		5	About Thyme

£39 or less

	FOOD			SERVICE
1	Café Japan		1	Uli
2	Ragam		2	Yoshino
3	New Tayyabs		3	Kaffeine
4	Pham Sushi		4	Adams Café
5	500		5	Tinello

SURVEY HIGHEST RATINGS

AMBIENCE

1	The Ritz Restaurant
2	Le Gavroche
3	The Ledbury
4	L'Atelier de Joel Robuchon
5	Marcus Wareing

1	Min Jiang
2	Les Trois Garçons
3	Paramount
4	Scott's
5	Belvedere

1	Clos Maggiore
2	La Poule au Pot
3	Café du Marché
4	The Wallace
5	Galvin La Chapelle

1	Wapping Food
2	Andrew Edmunds
3	Upstairs Bar
4	The Oak
5	Barrafina

1	Gordon's Wine Bar
2	Paradise
3	El Pirata
4	La Buvette
5	Polpetto

OVERALL

1	Le Gavroche
2	The Ledbury
3	The Ritz Restaurant
4	Marcus Wareing
5	Dinner

1	Chez Bruce
2	Min Jiang
3	Scott's
4	J Sheekey
5	The Goring Hotel

1	Trinity
2	Clos Maggiore
3	Pollen Street Social
4	La Trompette
5	Galvin La Chapelle

1	Upstairs Bar
2	Barrafina
3	J Sheekey Oyster Bar
4	Sushi-Say
5	Babur

1	Kaffeine
2	Paradise
3	Ganapati
4	500
5	Tinello

SURVEY BEST BY CUISINE

These are the restaurants which received the best average food ratings (excluding establishments with a small or notably local following).

Where the most common types of cuisine are concerned, we present the results in two price-brackets. For less common cuisines, we list the top three, regardless of price.

For further information about restaurants which are particularly notable for their food, see the cuisine lists starting on page 268. These indicate, using an asterisk*, restaurants which offer exceptional or very good food.

British, Modern

£50 and over
1. The Ledbury
2. Chez Bruce
3. Trinity
4. Pollen Street Social
5. The Glasshouse

Under £50
1. Inside
2. Tom Ilic
3. Lamberts
4. Emile's
5. The Sands End

French

£50 and over
1. Le Gavroche
2. Pied à Terre
3. Morgan M
4. La Trompette
5. The Square

Under £50
1. Upstairs Bar
2. Brawn
3. Bistrot Bruno Loubet
4. Le Cercle
5. Comptoir Gascon

Italian/Mediterranean

£50 and over
1. Murano
2. The River Café
3. Assaggi
4. Enoteca Turi
5. Bocca Di Lupo

Under £50
1. Zucca
2. 500
3. Dehesa
4. Le Querce
5. Latium

Indian & Pakistani

£50 and over
1. Zaika
2. Amaya
3. Trishna
4. Café Spice Namaste
5. The Cinnamon Club

Under £50
1. Ragam
2. Babur
3. New Tayyabs
4. Indian Zing
5. Lahore Kebab House

Chinese

£50 and over
1 Hunan
2 Min Jiang
3 Yauatcha
4 Kai Mayfair
5 Royal China Club

Under £50
1 Taiwan Village
2 Pearl Liang
3 Ba Shan
4 Barshu
5 Ken Lo's Memories

Japanese

£50 and over
1 Roka W1
2 Zuma
3 Umu
4 Yashin
5 Nobu

Under £50
1 Dinings
2 Café Japan
3 Sushi-Say
4 Jin Kichi
5 Pham Sushi

British, Traditional
1 Dinner
2 Scott's
3 Bull & Last

Vegetarian
1 Vanilla Black
2 Roussillon
3 Mildred's

Burgers, etc
1 Lucky Seven
2 Automat
3 Joe Allen

Pizza
1 Franco Manca
2 Santa Maria
3 Donna Margherita

Fish & Chips
1 Golden Hind
2 Toff's
3 Two Brothers

Thai
1 Sukho Fine Thai Cuisine
2 Nahm
3 Isarn

Steaks & Grills
1 Buen Ayre
2 Hawksmoor
3 Goodman City

Fish & Seafood
1 One-O-One
2 J.Sheekey
3 Scott's

Fusion
1 Viajante
2 E&O
3 Caravan

Spanish
1 Barrafina
2 Dehesa
3 El Parador

Turkish
1 Mangal 1
2 Cyprus Mangal
3 Gem

Lebanese
1 Maroush
2 Yalla Yalla
3 Al-Waha

TOP SPECIAL DEALS

The following menus allow you to eat in the restaurants concerned at a significant discount when compared to their evening à la carte prices.

The prices used are calculated in accordance with our usual formula (i.e. three courses with house wine, coffee and tip).

Special menus are by their nature susceptible to change – please check that they are still available.

Weekday lunch

£60+ Gordon Ramsay
Hélène Darroze
Marcus Wareing
Rib Room

£55+ L'Atelier de Joel Robuchon
Dinner
Sketch (Lecture Rm)
The Square

£50+ The Bingham
The Capital Restaurant
Dorchester Grill
Le Gavroche
Gordon Ramsay at Claridge's
Hibiscus
Kai Mayfair
maze
maze Grill
Murano
Rasoi
Roussillon

£45+ Blakes
Cassis Bistro
The Greenhouse
Pearl
Pied à Terre
Roux At Parliament Square
Texture
Viajante

£40+ Athenaeum
Babylon
Belvedere
China Tang
Galvin at Windows
Kicca
Paramount
Quaglino's
Rhodes W1 Restaurant
Seven Park Place
Spice Market

£35+ Criterion
Daphne's
Frederick's
Goodman
High Timber
Kitchen W8
Little Italy

Lucio
Mitsukoshi
Momo
Mon Plaisir
Montpeliano
Notting Hill Brasserie
Pellicano
Tamarind
Les Trois Garçons
Verta
The Warrington

£30+ Arbutus
The Ark
L'Aventure
Bistro K
Bocca Di Lupo
Café Luc
Caponata
Chabrot Bistrot d'Amis
Charlotte's Bistro
Charlotte's Place
Cinnamon Kitchen
City Miyama
Colony
Le Deuxième
Essenza
Fish Place
The Forge
Frantoio
Harrison's
Kiku
The Meat & Wine Co
Rock & Rose
Suk Saran
Timo
Verru

£25+ Admiral Codrington
Ambassador
Benja
Café des Amis
Cantina del Ponte
Carnevale
Chez Patrick
Les Deux Salons
Electric Brasserie
Franklins
Fratelli la Bufala
Gastro
Grumbles

Hix Oyster & Chop House
The Hoxton Grill
Lots Road
Market
Polish Club
Ozer
Princess Victoria
The Rose & Crown
Rossopomodoro
Sonny's
Sophie's Steakhouse
Venosi
Wine Gallery
XO
Zayna

Origin Asia
La Petite Auberge
El Pirata
Le Sacré-Coeur
Sapori
Seasons Dining Room
Tentazioni
Thali
Woodlands
Yming

£20+ Al Forno
Chez Lindsay
Cocotte
Ganapati
Gessler at Daquise
Giraffe
Mogul
Naga
The Old Bull & Bush

£15+ The Bountiful Cow
Café Japan
Fairuz
54 Farringdon Road
Fish in a Tie
Galicia
Kolossi Grill
Mona Lisa
Sagar

£10+ Inshoku
Mirch Masala

Pre/post theatre (and early evening)

£55+ Pied à Terre

Quo Vadis
Zaika

£50+ L'Atelier de Joel Robuchon
Galvin at Windows
Massimo
maze Grill

£30+ The Almeida
Arbutus
Bocca Di Lupo
Le Deuxième
L'Escargot
The Forge
Mon Plaisir

£40+ Indigo
Spice Market

£35+ The Avenue
Bank Westminster
Brasserie Joël
Brasserie Roux
Christopher's
Circus
Criterion
Daphne's
Dean Street Townhouse
Franco's
Frederick's
Little Italy
Orso

£25+ Les Deux Salons
54 Farringdon Road
Grumbles
Hix
Menier Chocolate Factory
Ozer

£20+ Yming

Sunday lunch

£60+ The Capital Restaurant

£45+ Launceston Place

£30+ Como Lario
The Spread Eagle

£25+ Elephant Royale
Lots Road

THE RESTAURANT SCENE

Openings finally show the strain

This year we record 107 openings, well down on last year (140) and somewhat below the range generally observed during the 'noughties' (120 to 142). At 71, however, closings are barely changed from last year (72), and well within the usual range. (See lists on pages 40 and 41.)

The ratio of openings to closings stands at an historically low level of 1.5:1. If the normal five year trough-to-trough cycle we have observed for the past two decades is followed, however, next year looks set to see an even lower ratio of openings to closings. In short, in purely numerical terms, things may get worse before they get better.

… as diners turn away from hype and celebrity, and towards quality

Let's not get too hung up on the numbers, though: the most important thing about the current restaurant scene is that it's maturing, and maturing in a very good way too.

Back in the '90s, the restaurants 'everyone' was talking about were Sir Terence Conran's big, brash 'gastrodromes'. This was an age when the food pages talked a lot about 'Modern British' cooking, and every dish came with a raspberry coulis. The fad soon passed.

Then, in the early noughties, Gordon Ramsay hogged the limelight. His bright idea was to perfect and popularise – but not much to advance – classic 'haute cuisine'. We found ourselves fretting in this introduction five years ago about the f-word chef's dominance at the top end of the market; potentially stultifying, we said. As it turns out, his dominance of the London market was then at a high point from which it has subsequently rapidly receded.

There were other interesting developments, of course, such as the march of gastropubs, and the 'grass roots' trends in British cooking, often twinned with a focus on sustainability and provenance. But many of the supposed improvements in the quality of London dining were of style rather than substance.

But now London's restaurateurs seem to be doing some serious work. One emblematic trend is the gradual reclaiming of Covent Garden as a 'proper' restaurant destination. Another is the remedying of one of London's longest-standing and most puzzling deficiencies – the (until recently) remarkably poor steakhouse scene.

But most significantly, there's a tangible growth in the pursuit of 'real cooking'. Take a glance at our Editor's top ten picks on the page opposite. With the exception of the *Riding House Café* – none the worse for being a 'fashionable' debut – this year has been all about serious food-led operations. These restaurants are about pursuing the best ingredients, and doing something imaginative with them. London has lagged appallingly on that front. Perhaps 2012 will be remembered for Olympian achievements in the kitchen as well as on the track!

Market trends

The following seem to us to be the trends of the moment:

● London is seeing the launch of a wave of high-class restaurants which emphasise innovative cooking of high quality. Examples include such new openings as *Dinner, Galoupet, Hedone, Medlar, Pollen Street Social* and *Roganic*

● Hotels are investing a lot to make their restaurants relevant to wider audiences. Many are succeeding – four out of the five recent openings debuting on our most-mentioned list (p11) are in hotels

● 'Petits-plats' formulae are becoming so common as to be unremarkable, especially at the upper end of the market

● The most popular flavour for new restaurants, especially in the mid-range, is London's original restaurant comfort-cuisine: Italian

● The culinary spotlight appears to be turning away from 'new' areas, and towards the rejuvenation of long-established restaurant areas, and especially Covent Garden

● The steakhouse boom continues. The more we are told we should eat less meat for the good of the planet, the more of it London diners seem determined to consume.

● America, and in particular New York, is the origin of, or provides the inspiration for, many recent and forthcoming openings – these include *Balthazar, Bar Boulud, Cut* and *Sushisamba,* as well as Russell Norman's *Polpo* empire

● Some variety of the brasserie format remains popular in the middle market, perhaps with most obvious success at *Les Deux Salons* and the *Riding House Café.*

Every year, we select what seem to us personally to be the ten most significant openings of the preceding 12 months. This year, our selection is as follows:

Brawn	Medlar
Les Deux Salons	Pollen Street Social
Dinner	Riding House Cafe
Galoupet	Roganic
Hedone	Yashin

This is a very strong field. Difficult economic conditions have not impacted adversely on the quality of new openings.

Prices

The average price of dinner for one at establishments listed in the guide is £45.01. Prices have risen by an unprecedented 11.1% in the past 12 months. Just over 2% of this may be attributed to the January 2011 increase in the rate of VAT. Pre-tax prices are therefore up some 9% year-on-year. This extraordinary rise has to be seen as a 'rebound' after a very marginal (0.3%) increase in pre-tax prices the year before: if we look back at the past *two* years together, prices are seen to have risen by 'only' 4.5% per annum over the period.

OPENINGS AND CLOSURES

Openings (107)

Alyn Williams
Amaranto
Anokha Restaurant (EC4)
Antidote
Aurelia
Balthazar
Benito's Hat (W1)
Bennett Oyster Bar & Brasserie
Bistro du Vin (W1, EC1)
Boisdale of Canary Wharf
Brawn
Bread Street Kitchen
Caffé Vergnano (EC4)
Canonbury Kitchen
Canta Napoli (N12)
Cantinetta
Capote Y Toros
Casa Malevo
Cavallino
Cây Tre (W1)
Chabrot Bistrot d'Amis
Charm
Chiswell Street Dining Rooms
Le Cigalon
Cocorino (W1)
Cocotte
Corner Room
Cut
da Polpo
La Delizia (SW18)
Dragoncello
El leven Park Walk
Eighty-Six Bar and Restaurant
The English Pig
Entrée
Fish Place
Four Seasons (W1)
Fox & Grapes
Frankie's Italian Bar & Grill (SW6)
Fulham Wine Rooms
The Gallery
Galoupet
Geales Chelsea Green (SW3)
Gilbert Scott

The Grand Imperial
Grazing Goat
Hawksmoor (EC2)
Hedone
The Henry Root
Homa
Ibérica (E14)
Ilia
Inamo (SW1)
Indian Zilla
Jam Tree (SW6)
José
Kateh
Kazan (Cafe) (SW1)
Kentish Canteen
Kerbisher & Malt
Kimchee
Kopapa
Ladurée (WC2)
Lahore Kebab House (SW16)
Lupita
Made In Camden
Mar I Terra (W1)
Massimo
Medlar
Mill Lane Bistro
Morito
Nizuni
Nopi
Nordic Bakery (W1)
Novikov
Opera Tavern
Otto Pizza
Pizarro
Pizza East Portobello
Pollen Street Social
Quantus
Le Querce (SE3)
Quince
Raoul's Café & Deli (W6)
Riding House Café
Rocca Di Papa (SE21)
Roganic
Roots At N1
Samarqand
Smith Square Bar & Restaurant
La Sophia

Openings (cont'd)

Spice Market
Spuntino
Sushisamba
Tempo
Thali
34 Grosvenor Square
Tsuru *(EC4)*
Union Street Café
Venosi

Verru
Verta
Vinoteca Seymour
    Place *(W1)*
Watatsumi
Yalla Yalla *(W1)*
Yashin

Closures (71)

Artisan
Arturo
Atma
Aubergine
Battery
Bermondsey Kitchen
Blue Elephant
Bombay Bicycle Club
    (SW10, NW3)
Café Mozart
Cantina Italia
Carpaccio's
Chez Kristof
Coast
Cocoon
Donzoko
Eastside Inn
Emni
Faro
Fat Badger
Fish Shop
Frankie's Italian
    Bar & Grill *(W4)*
Friends
Fung Shing
Garbo's
Gem & I
Gilmour's
Green & Red Bar & Cantina
Green Chilli
Izakaya Aki
Just St James
Kastoori
Kazan *(EC3)*
Konstam
L-Restaurant & Bar

Langan's Coq d'Or Bar
    & Grill
Il Locale *(EC3)*
Ma Cuisine *(TW1,TW9)*
Maroush III *(W1)*
Metrogusto
Michael Moore
Monsieur M.
More
101 Pimlico Road
Osteria Emilia
Otarian
Red Pepper *(SW1)*
Rooburoo
The Rye
S & M Café *(SE10)*
Sargasso
Seasons Dining Room
Story Deli
Sushi-Hiro
Taman Gang
Tampopo
Tartufo Trattoria
Taste of McClements
La Trouvaille
Urban Turban
Via Condotti
Villandry Kitchen *(WC1,W4)*
Vineria
W55
Wine Factory
Wódka

EATING IN LONDON FAQs

How should I use this guide?

You will often wish to use this guide in a practical way.
At heart, the issue will usually be geographical – where can
we eat near…? To answer such questions, the London Maps
(from page 324) and Area Overviews (from page 286) are
the place to start. The latter tell you all the key facts about
the restaurants – perhaps dozens of 'em – in a given area in
the space of a couple of pages. These Area Overviews are
unique, so please do spend a second to have a look!

This section, though, is about seeking out new places when
you want to be inspired to make a culinary adventure for its
own sake, or you need to find a venue for a special event.

What makes London special?

Each year in recent times we've had to re-write this section!
In the old days, the answer was always easy. London was like
New York: it offered lots of cuisines (good), but few done
especially well (bad). It was the very opposite of Paris, where
essentially one cuisine was endlessly elaborated.

Nowadays, the London story is both more interesting and
more positive. Not only is there cosmopolitanism, there is also
quality. It is the combination of the two which – at long last –
is making London a city which can genuinely claim to be one of
the world's best places to eat. We'll cover some culinary fields
particularly worth exploring on the following two pages, but
first let's dispose of that hoary old chestnut…

Which is London's best restaurant?

It's getting more and more difficult to say, because the old
certainties are breaking down. But let's stick with the
traditional 'haute cuisine' definition. On that basis, the safest
choice is the oldest – Le Gavroche is London's original grand
restaurant of the modern era, and it remains the very best
place to eat in the centre of town.

The second best restaurant – The Ledbury – is interesting
precisely because it's everything that the Gavroche is not.
The chef is Antipodean, not of French descent. It is in
Notting Hill, not Mayfair. The style is svelte and modern, not
the very essence of classicism. The Ledbury, in short, is a
worthy champion of the newer style that has begun to
transform London's restaurant scene of late.

For our third choice, though, we go back in time to The Ritz.
It has always been famous for its Louis XVI-style interior
but improving food is beginning to make this a destination
for any sort of celebration, not just for romance.

For other truly tip-top suggestions, please use the lists on
pages 32-33.

What about something a little more reasonably priced?

Although no one would say that London is a cheap place to eat, it is getting much easier to find food well worth eating without paying a fortune for it.

Most notable in this category is the group formed around 'London's favourite restaurant' for the 7th successive year, *Chez Bruce* (Wandsworth), plus its siblings *La Trompette* (Chiswick) and the *Glasshouse* (Kew). (That group also includes the Ledbury, mentioned on the previous page.)

Other hidden jewels out in Zones 2 and 3 include *Chez Liline* (Finsbury Park), *Morgan M* (Islington), *Trinity* (Clapham), *Lambert's* (Balham) and that wonderful '70s period-piece, *Oslo Court* (St John's Wood)

What about some really good suggestions in the heart of the West End?

It used to be practically impossible to find a really good meal in the heart of London at any reasonable cost! No longer, fortunately.

Names particularly to consider include *Arbutus*, *Giaconda Dining Room*, *Galvin Bistrot de Luxe* and *Wild Honey*. If you're happy to eat more in tapas style, add to this list *Barrafina* (be prepared to queue), *Bocca di Lupo*, *Dehesa*, *Polpo* and *Terroirs*.

If you want a little more comfort and style, as well as pretty good food you're unlikely to go far wrong at the restaurant which attracts most survey attention, *J Sheekey*, a fish specialist hidden-away in the very heart of Theatreland, or at *Scott's*, a celebrity magnet on one of the grandest streets in Mayfair. These last are hardly bargain suggestions, but they do offer all-round value. For pure theatre, a visitor should probably try to eat at the *Wolseley* – the nation's 'grand café', by the Ritz – at some point. Breakfast or tea provide excellent opportunities!

It is a symbol of the recent improvements in Covent Garden that *Clos Maggiore* – newly-crowned as 'London's most romantic restaurant', and with an extraordinary wine list – is on full public view just a few paces from the market itself! A more recent opening of note is the *Opera Tavern*.

And don't forget to lunch!

Lunch in London can be a great bargain. Restaurants don't come much grander than *Le Gavroche*, for example, and it famously offers a superb-value all-in lunch – even including some very decent wine – for less than many relatively run-of-the-mill establishments end up charging for a basic dinner. For further top value suggestion, see the list on pages 36 and 37.

And for the best of British?

British food – long confined to a sort of tourist ghetto – has recently become very fashionable. The change all began with the Smithfield restaurant *St John*, whose bravery and dedication to old-fashioned (and usually offal-heavy) British cooking has won it international acclaim. The trend that St John kicked off when it opened back in 1994 has recently culminated in the opening of Heston Blumenthal's much-heralded *Dinner* (Knightsbridge) – it is not meant as a backhanded compliment to describe it as an opening which has almost lived up to the hype! Tables do need to be booked weeks, and possibly months, ahead.

Other restaurants which may to be said to be from the school of St John include *Magdalen* (South Bank), *Great Queen Street* (Covent Garden), *Hereford Road* (Bayswater) and *St John Bread & Wine* (Shoreditch). In a different idiom, the recently opened *Gilbert Scott* reflects another 'take' on the reviving interest in more obscure British recipes.

But a lot of 'British' cooking is taking place in gastropubs…

What are gastropubs?

These are essentially bistros in pub premises. They come in a variety of styles. What many people think of as the original gastropub (*The Eagle*, 1991) still looks very much like a pub with a food counter. At the other end of the scale, however, the 'pub' element is almost redundant, and the business is really just a restaurant housed in premises that happen once to have been a pub.

Few of the best gastropubs are particularly central. The handy location of the *Anchor & Hope*, on the South Bank, is no doubt part of the reason for its great popularity. Other stars include the *Bull & Last* (Kentish Town), the *Canton Arms* (Stockwell) and the *Harwood Arms* (Fulham).

Isn't London supposed to be a top place for curry?

London has a reasonable claim to being the world's top Indian restaurant city. Leading lights such as *Amaya*, *The Painted Heron*, *The Cinnamon Kitchen*, *Benares*, *Rasoi*, *Trishna* and *Zaika* are pushing back the frontiers, but – perfectly reasonably – charge the same as their European equivalents.

What's more exciting in terms of value are the many Indian restaurants where you can eat much more cheaply than you could eat European. There are too many of them to list here – search out the asterisked restaurants in the Indian and Pakistani lists commencing on pages 281 and 283 respectively.

Two top names in the East End are, however, almost legendary 'value' experiences – the *Lahore Kebab House* and *New Tayyabs*. The *Rasa* group also includes some very good value options.

Any money-saving tips?

● The top tip, already noted, is to lunch not dine. If you're a visitor, you'll find that it's better for your wallet, as well as your digestion, to have your main meal in the middle of the day. In the centre of town, it's one of the best ways you can be sure of eating 'properly' at reasonable cost. See the spread on pages 36 and 37.

● Think ethnic – for a food 'experience' at modest cost, you'll almost always be better off going Indian, Thai, Chinese or Vietnamese (to choose four of the most obvious cuisines) than French, English or Italian. The days when there was any sort of assumption that ethnic restaurants were – in terms of comfort, service and décor – in any way inferior to European ones is long gone, but they do still tend to be cheaper.

● Don't assume the West End is the obvious destination. That's not to say that – armed with this book – you shouldn't be able to eat well in the heart of things, but you'll almost certainly do better in value terms outside the Circle line. Many of the best and cheapest restaurants in this guide are easily accessible by tube. Use the maps at the back of this book to identify restaurants near tube stations on a line that's handy for you.

● If you must dine in the West End, try to find either pre-theatre (generally before 7 pm) or post-theatre (generally after 10 pm) menus. You will generally save at least the cost of a cinema ticket, compared to dining à la carte. Many of the more upmarket restaurants in Theatreland do such deals. For some of our top suggestions, see page 37.

● Use this book! Don't take pot luck, when you can benefit from the pre-digested views of thousands of other diners-out. Choose a place with a ❶ or ❷ for food, and you're very likely to eat much better than if you walk in somewhere 'on spec' – this is good advice anywhere, but is most particularly so in the West End.

● Once you have decided that you want to eat within a particular area, use the Area Overviews (starting on page 286) to identify the restaurants that are offering top value. We have gone to a lot of trouble to boil down a huge amount of data into the results which are handily summarised in such lists. Please use them! You are unlikely to regret it.

● Visit our website, www.hardens.com for the latest reviews, and restaurant news, and to sign up for our annual spring survey.

A Cena TW1 £48 ❷❷❷
418 Richmond Rd 8288 0108 1–4A
One of the best restaurants round Richmond, this "first-class local Italian", in St Margaret's, combines a "delightful" setting and "superb" service, with "enjoyable" food and an "impressive" selection of "well-priced" wine. / www.acena.co.uk; 10 pm; closed Mon L & Sun D; booking: max 6, Fri & Sat.

A La Cruz EC1 £49 ❸❸④
42 Northampton Rd 7837 1999 9–1A
"Superb steak, awesome chips and outstanding red wine" – all help inspire enthusiasm for this "good-value" Argentinian parilla, in Farringdon. / www.alacruz.com; 10pm, Sat & Sun 9.30pm; closed weekday L; no Amex.

The Abbeville SW4 £45 ④❸❷
67-69 Abbeville Rd 8675 2201 10–2D
An "exceptionally welcoming" Clapham local, which draws fans from numerous nearby postcodes with its "lovely" ambience; the food is "frustratingly variable", but "more often good than bad". / www.renaissancepubs.co.uk; 10.30 pm, Sun 9 pm.

Abeno £36 ❸❷④
47 Museum St, WC1 7405 3211 2–1C
17-18 Great Newport St, WC2 7379 1160 4–3B
"Having the food cooked at your table is a fun bonus", at these rather "different" okonomi-yaki (fancy Japanese omelettes) parlours in the West End – "friendly little places", and in "handy" locations too; they can, though, "get a bit hot and crowded". / www.abeno.co.uk; 10 pm-midnight; WC2 no booking.

The Abingdon W8 £52 ❸❷❷
54 Abingdon Rd 7937 3339 5–2A
"Perfectly suiting the needs of its locale", this "gently buzzing" pub-conversion, off Kensington High Street, offers food "at the finer end of gastropub", and "accommodating" service too; it makes a great choice for a "casual" meal – try to book a booth at the back. / www.theabingdon.co.uk; Mon 10.30 pm, Sun 9.30 pm.

Abokado £16 ④❸④
16 Newman St, W1 7636 9218 2–1B
160 Drury Ln, WC2 7242 5600 4–2D
The Lexington, 40-56 City Rd, EC1 7608 2620 12–1A
63 Cowcross St, EC1 7490 4303 9–1A
33 Fleet St, EC4 7353 8284 9–2A
"A novel and interesting lunchtime option" – these good alternatives to Pret offer "no-hassle, healthy bites" (udon-noodle soups, wraps, and so on) to "eat on the run". / www.abokado.com; 7.30 pm; no Amex; no booking.

About Thyme SW1 £45 ❷④④
82 Wilton Rd 7821 7504 2–4B
"Classy" by local standards, this Pimlico restaurant serves an "enjoyable mix" of Spanish-influenced dishes, and some "superb regional wines"; tables are rather "packed-in", but staff are particularly "friendly and professional". / www.aboutthyme.co.uk; 10.30 pm; closed Sun.

L'Absinthe NW1 £38 ❸❷❷
40 Chalcot Rd 7483 4848 8–3B
"So French it hurts!"; service that's authentic "almost to the point of parody" breathes character into this "delightful" Primrose Hill corner spot, which serves a sensibly "limited" menu of "good-value" bistro fare. / www.labsinthe.co.uk; 10.30 pm, Sun 9.30 pm; closed Mon.

Abu Zaad W12   £24   ❸❸④
29 Uxbridge Rd 8749 5107 7–1C
*"A long-running Syrian favourite", near Shepherd's Bush Market;
its "fresh and beautifully-prepared" dishes – including "super grills
and juices", and excellent mezze – offer "great value".*
/ www.abuzaad.co.uk; 11 pm; no Amex.

L'Accento Italiano W2   £42   ❸❷❸
16 Garway Rd 7243 2201 6–1B
*"Genuine family-Italian cooking", a "well-chosen fixed-price menu"
and a "decent" wine list – the features which continue to satisfy the
small fan club of this "solid" Bayswater fixture, recently revamped.*
/ www.laccentorestaurant.co.uk; 11 pm, Sun 6 pm; closed Sun L.

Acorn House WC1   £45   ④④⑤
69 Swinton St 7812 1842 8–3D
*In "an odd location on a busy Bloomsbury road", an "interesting little
organic place", where eco-consciousness is a theme, and "excellent
seasonal ingredients are the focus"; even fans feel the cooking "needs
to sharpen up", though, and the "squashed-in" dining room, in the
style of a "railway carriage", is no particular advantage.*
/ www.acornhouserestaurant.com; 10 pm; closed Sat L & Sun.

Adam Street WC2   £60   ④④❷
9 Adam St 7379 8000 4–4D
*It's the relaxing and enjoyable vibe of this "discreet" private members'
club, "tucked-away off the Strand", which makes it a handy venue for
business lunches (and the wine list is pretty good too) – the food
"is not impressive". / www.adamstreet.co.uk; L only, closed Sat & Sun.*

Adams Café W12   £29   ❸❶❷
77 Askew Rd 8743 0572 7–1B
*"Delicious" tagines, couscous and grills in "plentiful" quantities have
made a firm "local favourite" of this "super-friendly" Tunisian café,
in the backwoods of Shepherd's Bush; by day, it's a greasy spoon;
licensed, or you can BYO (£3 corkage). / www.adamscafe.co.uk; 11 pm;
closed Sun.*

Addie's Thai Café SW5   £30   ❷❷❸
121 Earl's Court Rd 7259 2620 5–2A
*A "fast and furious" joint, near Earl's Court tube, worth seeking out
for its "extraordinarily good Thai food", and "at bargain prices too".
/ www.addiesthai.co.uk; 11 pm; closed Sat L & Sun L; no Amex.*

Admiral Codrington SW3   £47   ❸④❸
17 Mossop St 7581 0005 5–2C
*"Excellent" steaks are a "surprise menu highlight" at this airy and
"pleasant" dining room attached to a "noisy" (and perennially
fashionable) Chelsea pub; with its sliding roof, it makes a "delightful
summer location" too. / www.theadmiralcodrington.co.uk; 11 pm;
set weekday L £29 (FP).*

Afghan Kitchen N1   £21   ❷④④
35 Islington Grn 7359 8019 8–3D
*A "teeny" café, by Islington Green, serving a "limited menu"
of "cheap and delicious" Afghani curries; service can be "short",
and the interior is very "cramped" and "crowded", so "take-away
is an option worth bearing in mind". / 11 pm; closed Mon & Sun;
no credit cards.*

Aglio e Olio SW10 £37 ❸❸❸
194 Fulham Rd   7351 0070   5–3B
"A jam-packed" café, by the Chelsea & Westminster Hospital, that's "the epitome of cheap 'n' cheerful"; "it may be noisy and cramped", but – "year in, year out" – it serves "outstanding" pasta, and other reliable fare. / 11.30 pm.

Al Duca SW1 £45 ④④⑤
4-5 Duke of York St   7839 3090   3–3D
Prepare yourself for "small portions", "tightly-packed tables" and a "lack of atmosphere", but the "simple, modern food" on offer at this low-key Italian comes at bargain prices – well, St James's-style bargain prices anyway. / www.alduca-restaurant.co.uk; 11 pm; closed Sun.

Al Forno £39 ❸❷❷
349 Upper Richmond Rd, SW15   8878 7522   10–2A
2a King's Rd, SW19   8540 5710   10–2B
"Hilarious staff and cosy surroundings" all contribute to the "quirky" experience of visiting these busy traditional Italians – "a perfect place with friends", and "excellent for kids" too, with "biiiggg pizza" the star of the "tasty" menu. / SW15 11 pm; SW19 11.30 pm, Sun & Mon 10.30 pm; set weekday L £23 (FP).

Al Hamra W1 £46 ④⑤④
31-33 Shepherd Mkt   7493 1954   3–4B
"For a true taste of Lebanon", say fans, seek out this Shepherd Market "classic" (which benefits from some fine al fresco tables); as ever, though, it can seem "seriously overpriced", and service is sometimes "terrible". / www.alhamrarestaurant.co.uk; 11.30 pm.

Al Sultan W1 £43 ❷❸⑤
51-52 Hertford St   7408 1155   3–4B
"Let the wonderful Lebanese food beguile you", when you visit this "professional" little place, near Shepherd Market; if you're looking for atmosphere, though, you might want to try elsewhere. / www.alsultan.co.uk; midnight.

Al Volo
The Old Truman Brewery E1 £32 ❷④❸
Hanbury St   7377 0808   12–2C
A "perennial favourite", in the heart of Brick Lane; this trendy Italian café "continues to serve up delicious food at very reasonable prices" – cognoscenti go for the calzone. / www.alvolo.co.uk; Sun-Wed 10 pm, Thu-Sat 11 pm.

Al-Waha W2 £42 ❷❸④
75 Westbourne Grove   7229 0806   6–1B
"Squashed" and anonymous-looking the premises may be, but this Bayswater "stand-out" offers "unexpectedly fabulous" Lebanese food, and at "affordable prices" too. / www.alwaharestaurant.com; 11 pm; no Amex.

Alain Ducasse
Dorchester W1 £111 ④④④
53 Park Ln   7629 8866   3–3A
"How is this three Michelin Stars?"; the notion that this opulent but "slightly dead" Mayfair dining room is one of London's best is a joke – reporters do have some "fabulous" experiences, of course, but there are far too many visits which "lack flair"; either way, your wallet is pretty much guaranteed "a heart attack". / www.alainducasse-dorchester.com; 10 pm; closed Mon, Sat L & Sun; jacket.

Alba EC1 £52 ❸②④
107 Whitecross St 7588 1798 12–2A
*"Precise Piedmontese cooking", a "very good Italian wine list",
and "the friendliest service" have won a super-loyal following for this
"upmarket" (but slightly "sterile") stalwart, especially as a "business
lunch and post-Barbican stand-by". / www.albarestaurant.com; 11 pm;
closed Sat & Sun.*

Albannach WC2 £51 ⑤⑤⑤
66 Trafalgar Sq 7930 0066 2–3C
*As a cocktail bar it's fine, but the food at this Scottish-themed venue,
on Trafalgar Square, can be "quite dreadful"; service is "slow" too,
and don't expect to hear any Caledonian accents among the kilted
staff! / www.albannach.co.uk; 10.45 pm, Sun 6 pm; closed Sun D.*

Albertine W12 £33 ④②⓿
1 Wood Ln 8743 9593 7–1C
*OK, it's "more a wine bar with food than a restaurant with wine",
but this "cramped" fixture makes a "quirky" and "Bohemian" refuge
from "the urban desert of Shepherd's Bush Green"; there are "lots of
interesting bottles" on offer too. / 10.30 pm; closed Sat L & Sun; no Amex.*

The Albion N1 £42 ④④❷
10 Thornhill Rd 7607 7450 8–3D
*"In a quiet and leafy part of Islington", this "lovely" boozer is famous
for its "wonderful" garden; otherwise, though, it's pretty ordinary –
service can be "slow", and the food is only "moderately good".
/ www.the-albion.co.uk; 10 pm, Sun 9 pm.*

Albion E2 £44 ❸❸❷
2-4 Boundary St 7729 1051 12–1B
*"A Formica heaven for the casual scoffer!" – Sir Terence Conran's
"brilliant" neighbourhood caff "fits like a glove into Shoreditch",
and succeeds in "accommodating mums in prams and local arty
types alike"; its "ribsticking British food" is "unpretentious, and tasty"
too. / www.albioncaff.co.uk; 11 pm.*

Ali Baba NW1 £19 ❸❷❸
32 Ivor Pl 7723 5805 2–1A
*"Recently the TV has been focused on current affairs" –
understandable enough, at this "family-run and very authentic"
Egyptian, in a front room behind a Marylebone take-away; BYO.
/ midnight; no credit cards.*

Alisan HA9 £35 ⓿②④
The Junction, Engineers Way, Wembley 8903 3888 1–1A
*"Granted, it's not the best location" – "in an industrial estate,
opposite Wembley Stadium" – but this contemporary-style Chinese
is worth a trip for its "very interesting and different dim sum";
and there's "free, easy parking" too! / www.alisan.co.uk; 11 pm,
Sat 11.30 pm, Sun 10.30 pm; closed Tue.*

All Star Lanes £45 ④⑤❸
Victoria Hs, Bloomsbury Pl, WC1 7025 2676 2–1D
Whiteley's, 6 Porchester Gdns, W2 7313 8363 6–1C
Old Truman Brewery, 95 Brick Ln, E1 7426 9200 12–2C
*"Considering the food is incidental to the bowling", the cooking
at these "fun" 10-pin venues could be a lot worse, with "fab burgers"
the top tip; they are "a little overpriced", though, and the waiters
"don't have a great attitude". / www.allstarlanes.co.uk; WC1 10.30 pm,
Fri & Sat midnight, Sun 9 pm; E1 10 pm; W2 10.30 pm, Fri-Sun 11 pm;
WC1 & W2 closed L Mon-Thu.*

Alloro W1 £57 ❸❸❸
19-20 Dover St   7495 4768   3–3C
"Ideal for business", this "smart" and "spacious" Mayfair Italian offers a "high standard" of cooking; the downside? – it can seem a little "dull". / www.alloro-restaurant.co.uk; 10.30 pm; closed Sat L & Sun.

Alma SW18 £39 ❹❺❸
499 Old York Rd   8870 2537   10–2B
The year that's seen the revamp of this "madly-popular" Wandsworth boozer has inspired very mixed feedback – let's hope for fewer reports of "disastrous" meals next year! / www.thealma.co.uk; 10.30 pm, Sun 9 pm.

The Almeida N1 £59 ❹❸❹
30 Almeida St   7354 4777   8–2D
"One of the D&D stable's better restaurants", this large Islington dining room is a "civilised" venue, serving "competent" Gallic fare, and as a pre-theatre option – prior to a show opposite – it works perfectly; on the downside, the decor can seem "cold", and the cooking "mediocre, for the price". / www.almeida-restaurant.co.uk; 10.30 pm; closed Mon L & Sun D; set pre theatre £33 (FP).

Alounak £27 ❸❹❸
10 Russell Gdns, W14   7603 1130   7–1D
44 Westbourne Grove, W2   7229 0416   6–1B
"Superb" kebabs and other "lovely, fresh Persian dishes", all in "ample portions", help explain the "regular queues" for these "inexpensive" BYO Iranian cafés, in Bayswater and Olympia. / 11.30 pm; no Amex.

Alyn Williams
Westbury Hotel W1 NEW
Bond St   7629 7755   3–2C
Good omens for this late-2011 'fine dining' opening, in Mayfair; until recently, Williams headed up Marcus Wareing's kitchen, and the hotel seems to have had quite a success with its other recent dining debut, the Gallery. / www.westburymayfair.com.

Amaranth SW18 £30 ❷❷❸
346 Garratt Ln   8874 9036   10–2B
"Always a winner" – this "busy" Thai café, in Earlsfield, makes "a great cheap and cheerful place to eat", with "ever-fresh" dishes and "helpful" staff ; you can BYO too (corkage £2.50). / 10.30 pm; D only, closed Sun; no Amex.

Amaranto
Four Seasons Hotel W1 NEW £75
Hamilton Pl   7319 5206   3–4A
Reporter excitement about this luxurious new Mayfair dining room seems to be in inverse proportion to the vast expenditure on its blingy decor – too little, in fact, even for a rating; such feedback as there is is talks of "flappy" service of Italian food that's "fussy" and "overpriced". / www.fourseasons.com; 10.30 pm.

Amaya SW1 £63 ❶❷❷
Halkin Arc, 19 Motcomb St   7823 1166   5–1D
"Style and flair" abound at this "simply outstanding" nouvelle Indian – one of London's best – tucked-away in Belgravia; many of its "innovative", "light" and "flavourful" tapas-style dishes come from a central grill. / www.realindianfood.com; 11.30 pm, Sun 10.30 pm.

Ambassador EC1 £41 ❸❸❸
55 Exmouth Mkt   7837 0009   9–1A
With its "stripped-down bistro look", this Clerkenwell venture strikes harsher reporters as looking "a little uncared-for"; "it does what it does well", though, including "solid and flavourful" dishes, and "well-matched wine". / www.theambassadorcafe.co.uk; 10.15 pm; set weekday L £26 (FP).

Amerigo Vespucci E14 £43 ❹❹❸
25 Cabot Sq   7513 0288   11–1C
A "decent" traditional Italian which has particular attractions for Canary Wharf chain-o-phobes – "the best thing going for it is that it's not part of a larger group". / www.amerigovespucci.co.uk; 11 pm; closed Sat L & Sun L.

Amico Bio EC1 £37 ❹❹❹
43-44 Cloth Fair   7600 7778   9–2B
"Tucked-away behind Bart's", this meat-free Italian is "such a good concept"; it's a "shame, then, that it doesn't quite deliver" – the food "may sound fantastic", but the results can be "rather patchy". / www.amicobio.co.uk; 10.30 pm; closed Sat L & Sun.

Anarkali W6 £32 ❸❷❸
303-305 King St   8748 1760   7–2B
"At last it's back, and back on form!"; to the relief of regulars, this Hammersmith curry classic has re-opened following a flood – "I've been going for over 30 years, and the food's even better than before". / www.anarkalirestaurant.co.uk; midnight, Sun 11.30 pm.

The Anchor & Hope SE1 £39 ❶❸❷
36 The Cut   7928 9898   9–4A
"Other gastropubs pale in comparison", say fans of London's No.1 boozer, near the Old Vic – "a winner on many levels", but most importantly for the "exciting twist" it puts on "big-flavoured" British dishes (many with offal); arrive early – "its popularity is its own worst enemy!" / 10.30 pm; closed Mon L & Sun D; no Amex; no booking.

Andrew Edmunds W1 £43 ❸❷❶
46 Lexington St   7437 5708   3–2D
"Gorgeously scruffy, yet atmospheric", this delightfully "quirky" candlelit Soho favourite is as perfect as ever for "an intimate tête-à-tête" – sit upstairs if you can; the "simple" food is reasonably "inventive", but it's the "superb" wines that offer "outstanding value". / 10.30 pm; no Amex; booking: max 6.

Angels & Gypsies
Church Street Hotel SE5 £38 ❷❸❷
29-33 Camberwell Church St   7703 5984   1–3C
"A surprise find in a Camberwell hotel!" – this "cool" but "friendly" hang-out is "well worth a detour" for its "super-fresh and interesting" tapas, plus a range of other "fairly-priced" Spanish "classics". / www.churchstreethotel.com; 10.30 pm; closed Mon L.

Angelus W2 £78 ❷❶❸
4 Bathurst St   7402 0083   6–2D
"On the way to classic status" – this "cosy" ex-pub, near Lancaster Gate, is a "very Gallic" and "intimate" spot, serving many "brilliant" dishes; service is at its best when patron Thierry Thomasin ("the sommelier's sommelier") is there, presiding over his "fantastic" wine list. / www.angelusrestaurant.co.uk; 11 pm, Sun 10 pm.

The Anglesea Arms SW7   £40   ❸❹❷
15 Sellwood Ter   7373 7960   5–2B
*A very "buzzy" South Kensington hostelry, which boats a "cosy back restaurant", but is perhaps best known for its bijou terrace; the food's "good value" too... "and all the better for not being at all 'gastro-'"!
/ www.angleseaarms.com; 10 pm, Sun 9.30 pm.*

The Anglesea Arms W6   £45   ❷❹❷
35 Wingate Rd   8749 1291   7–1B
"It's great now you can book!", say fans of this "unfussy" tavern, near Ravenscourt Park – one of London's original gastropubs and still, for most reporters, "one of the best"; the occasional report of "appalling" meals this year, however, denied it an 'outstanding' food rating. / Mon 10 pm, Tue-Sat 10.30 pm, Sun 9.30 pm; no Amex; no booking.

Anglo Asian Tandoori N16   £34   ❷❶❷
60-62 Stoke Newington Church St   7254 3633   1–1C
"Still a cut above most Indian restaurants" – this surprisingly romantic Stoke Newington veteran is showing impressive longevity! / 11.45 pm.

L'Anima EC2   £69   ❸❸❸
1 Snowden St   7422 7000   12–2B
*With its "clean" and "craftsmanlike" cooking, Francesco Mazzei's "slick" and "airy" Italian is undoubtedly "a great City restaurant"; of late, however, it's "gone slightly off the boil", and is taking ever more flak for "inconsistent" food and a rather "corporate" ambience.
/ www.lanima.co.uk; 10.30 pm; closed Sat L & Sun.*

Annie's   £45   ❹❷❷
162 Thames Rd, W4   8994 9080   1–3A
36-38 White Hart Ln, SW13   8878 2020   10–1A
*"For a lazy weekend brunch" – in the company of "kids of all ages" – these "cosy" and "eclectically-furnished" havens of shabby-chic, in Chiswick and Barnes, come in to their own; "filling" food of a "comfort" nature plays something of a supporting role.
/ www.anniesrestaurant.co.uk; 10 pm, Sat 10.30 pm, Sun 9.30 pm.*

Anokha Restaurant   £42   ❷❸❸
2 Creechurch Lane, EC3   7283 7729   9–2D
4 Burgeon St, EC4   7236 3999   9–3B **NEW**
These small Indian restaurants – one in a basement near Fenchurch Street station, the other "hidden-away between St Paul's and Blackfriars" – offer some "brilliant" cooking. / 11 pm; EC3 closed Sat-Sun; EC4 closed Sat L and Sun.

Antelope SW17   £36   ❷❸❷
76 Mitcham Rd   8672 3888   10–2C
The Victorian-style dining room at this Tooting pub, recently relaunched, makes "a surprisingly good find", and wins praise for its "interesting" menu, well-chosen wine and "great" beers; the staff attitude is "accommodating" too. / www.antic-ltd.com/antelope; 10.30 pm; closed Mon-Fri L & Sun D; no Amex.

Antidote W1 **NEW**   £45   ❸❹❸
12a Newburgh St   7287 8488   3–2C
The tucked-away Soho site of La Trouvaille (RIP) has now been relaunched (same owners) as a simple and very Gallic wine bar; the food is decent enough, and there's an entertaining list of 'biodynamique' wines, but service on our own early-days visit was Clouseau-meets-Keystone Kops. / Rated on Editors' visit; www.antidotewinebar.com; 10.30 pm; closed Sun D.

Antipasto & Pasta SW11 £38 **❸❷❸**
511 Battersea Park Rd 7223 9765 10–1C
"Nothing is too much hassle" for staff at this *"manically busy but entertaining"* Battersea Italian, which offers *"great food at very reasonable prices"*. / 11.30 pm, Sun 11 pm; need 4+ to book.

Apostrophe £17 **❹❸❸**
Branches throughout London
A Gallic café-multiple that's still often seen as "a cut above other coffee house chains", thanks not least to its *"terrific coffee"* and its *"interesting"* snacks; sliding ratings, however, support those who say it's *"not quite at the level it once was"*. / www.apostropheuk.com; most branches 6 pm, Sat 5.30 pm; no booking.

Applebee's Cafe SE1 £40 **❷❸❹**
5 Stoney St 7407 5777 9–4C
A wet fish counter as you enter advertises the "specialist" attractions of this "friendly" Borough Market fixture, where the dishes are "wonderfully fresh and well-prepared". / www.applebeesfish.com; 10 pm, Fri 10.30 pm.

Apsleys
Lanesborough Hotel SW1 £90 **❸❷❸**
1 Lanesborough Pl 7333 7254 5–1D
This "opulent" dining room by Hyde Park Corner, governed from afar by hot-shot Roman chef Heinz Beck, is starting to win more acclaim; critics still find it "unexciting" and "nose-bleedingly expensive", but on many accounts the Italian cooking – pasta in particular – is "simply incredible". / www.apsleys.co.uk; 10.30 pm; booking: max 12.

aqua kyoto W1 £72 **❸❸❶**
240 Regent St (entrance 30 Argyll St) 7478 0540 3–2C
"Set in a beautifully cool, black and red space" – and with a "wonderful rooftop terrace" – this "lovely" (if "touristy") Japanese is definitely the better part of this rooftop complex, near Oxford Circus; the food is "pretty pricey", but usually matches up.
/ www.aqua-london.com; Mon-Wed 10.45 pm, Thu-Sat 11.15pm; closed Sun.

aqua nueva W1 £62 **❹❹❹**
240 Regent St (entrance 30 Argyll St) 7478 0540 3–2C
"For the amazing roof terrace" alone, it's worth a visit to this "large" and "glamorous" – but sometimes "lifeless" – venue, near Oxford Circus (sibling to 'aqua kyoto', see also); more generally, though, the standards – including of the Spanish cuisine – are indifferent.
/ www.aqua-london.com; 11 pm.

Arbutus W1 £52 **❷❷❸**
63-64 Frith St 7734 4545 4–2A
This "thoroughly accomplished" Soho bistro has won a big name with its "no-nonsense" dishes, often based on cheaper cuts, plus "stunning wines" (by the glass or carafe), and all at very "sensible" prices (particularly at lunch); the interior is rather "dull", but it does get a boost from "lots of happy diners". / www.arbutusrestaurant.co.uk; set weekday L £32 (FP), set dinner & pre-theatre £34 (FP).

Archduke Wine Bar SE1 £46 **❺❹❹**
Concert Hall Approach, South Bank 7928 9370 2–3D
New owners the Black & Blue group don't seem hugely to have changed the spirit of this South Bank 'institution' (their word), which inhabits atmospheric railway arches near the Festival Hall – it's still "not a foodie destination", but "good live jazz" adds to its "reliable" pre-concert appeal. / www.thearchduke.co.uk; Sun-Wed 11 pm, Fri & Sat 1 am.

The Arches NW6 £41 ④❸❷
7 Fairhazel Gdns 7624 1867 8–2A
"You go for the vino more than anything else" (a marvellous list at miraculous prices), when you seek out this "electric and wonderful" Swiss Cottage wine bar; "OK" food plays a supporting role. / 10.30 pm; no Amex.

Archipelago W1 £56 ❸❸❶
110 Whitfield St 7383 3346 2–1B
"Exotic" decor contributes to the "magical" aura of this "eccentric and fun little venue", near the Telecom Tower – "a must-do if your life will be incomplete never having eaten pan-fried zebra, or gnu Stroganoff". / www.archipelago-restaurant.co.uk; 10.15 pm; closed Sat L & Sun.

The Ark W8 £55 ❸❸❷
122 Palace Gardens Ter 7229 4024 6–2B
"Perfect for a romantic night out" – this tightly-packed Italian, just off Notting Hill Gate, inspires only limited feedback, but fans applaud its cosy style and its "refined" cooking. / www.ark-restaurant.com; 10.30 pm; closed Mon L & Sun; set weekday L £32 (FP).

Ark Fish E18 £46 ❶❷④
142 Hermon Hill 8989 5345 1–1D
"Quality is unsurpassed, and quantity more than adequate" – this brilliant fish restaurant, in South Woodford, is sometimes claimed as "the best place on the London/Essex borders"; "no booking, so arrive early and expect a wait". / www.arkfishrestaurant.co.uk; Tue-Thu 9.45 pm, Fri & Sat 10.15 pm, Sun 8.45 pm; closed Mon; no Amex.

L'Art du Fromage SW10 £47 ❸❷④
1a Langton St 7352 2759 5–3B
"Cheese, cheese... and more cheese", from "wonderful fondues" to "a good variety on the board" – the "brilliant" formula, say fans, of this year-old World's End venture, where service which is "so knowledgeable" takes the edge off a rather "basic" setting. / www.artdufromage.co.uk; 10.30 pm; closed Mon L & Sun.

Artigiano NW3 £48 ④❸④
12a Belsize Ter 7794 4288 8–2A
This Belsize Park Italian inspires a variety of opinions – on the downside, it's "fairly standard" and "rather pricey", but the overall verdict is that it's "worth looking out for... if you're in the area". / www.etruscarestaurants.com; 10.30 pm, Sun 10 pm; closed Mon L.

L'Artista NW11 £36 ④④❸
917 Finchley Rd 8731 7501 1–1B
This "buzzing" Italian may have a "grim location (under the tube bridge by Golder's Green station)", but it "always puts a smile on your face", thanks to its "cheerful" ("cheesy") style and its "huge, tasty pizzas" – "fantastic for a family outing!" / www.lartistapizzeria.com; midnight.

L'Artiste Musclé W1 £39 ④❸❸
1 Shepherd Mkt 7493 6150 3–4B
"A super-secret little bistro in Mayfair's Shepherd Market", which is "quite stylish, in a falling-down sort of way" – "as in Paris, the ambience makes you feel the food is better than it is!" / 10.30 pm; closed Sun L.

Asadal WC1 £46 ❸④④

227 High Holborn   7430 9006   2–1D

A "spacious" cellar, under Holborn tube, which offers "simple but well-cooked" Korean food – "a huge surprise, given the grotty entrance and unpromising location". / www.asadal.co.uk; 11 pm; closed Sun L.

Asakusa NW1 £33 ❶④④

265 Eversholt St   7388 8533   8–3C

"It may not look much from the outside" ("or the inside, for that matter!"), but this "authentically Japanese-feeling" establishment, near Euston Station, is worth seeking out for its "amazing, cheap food". / 11.30 pm, Sat 11 pm; D only, closed Sun.

Asia de Cuba
St Martin's Lane Hotel WC2 £91 ④⑤④

45 St Martin's Ln   7300 5588   4–4C

A "funky" haunt of (surprisingly) long standing, which still has a fan club, who applaud its "vibrant" style and its fusion fare "to die for"; for sceptics, though, it's "past its prime" – "blindingly expensive for food that's only moderately OK, and snootily served too". / www.stmartinslane.com; midnight, Sun 11 pm.

Ask £36 ⑤④④

Branches throughout London

An ongoing refurbishment programme aims to recapture the "lost reputation" of this pizza-multiple; no uptick in ratings just yet, though – they average out somewhere "between OK and dreadful". / www.askcentral.co.uk; most branches 11 pm, Fri & Sat 11.30 pm; some booking restrictions apply.

Assaggi W2 £69 ❷❷❸

39 Chepstow Pl   7792 5501   6–1B

"My favourite London Italian!" – still how many reporters feel about this famously "unglitzy" room, over a Bayswater pub, which has won renown for "simple" dishes, "brilliantly" executed, and wonderfully "warm" service too; in recent times, however, even some of its most dedicated fans have found it "slightly below usual standards". / 11 pm; closed Sun; no Amex.

Les Associés N8 £41 ④❷④

172 Park Rd   8348 8944   1–1C

Long-established in a Crouch End front room, this very Gallic outfit is still "always reliable, and really great value", says its fans; doubters, though, say "they've let things slip", and that it's now "really ordinary". / www.lesassocies.co.uk; 10 pm; closed Mon, Tue L, Sat L & Sun D; 24 hr notice for L bookings.

Atari-Ya £28 ❶❷④

20 James St, W1   7491 1178   3–1A

1 Station Pde, W5   8896 3175   1–3A **NEW**

31 Vivian Ave, NW4   8202 2789   1–1B

75 Fairfax Road, London, NW6   7328 5338   8–2A

Some of the best sushi in London is to be found at these "busy" and "utilitarian" café/take-aways, which are usually packed with Japanese diners; the new Ealing branch takes over where Sushi Hiro (RIP) left off, but regulars still "cry with pleasure" – it's so "amazing". / www.atariya.co.uk; W1 8.30 pm, NW4 9.30 pm, NW6 10.30 pm, W5 9 pm; NW4 closed Mon.

L'ATELIER DE JOEL ROBUCHON WC2 £90   ❷❸❷
13-15 West St   7010 8600   4–2B
*"Sitting at the bar, watching the expert chefs at work" adds to the
frisson of "the amazing taste sensations" delivered by the "magical"
small plates on offer at Joël Robuchon's "chic" Covent Garden
outpost (which has a "more formal" dining room upstairs); "go for
the set lunch, unless you want a heart attack when the bill arrives…"
/ www.joelrobuchon.co.uk; 10.45 pm, Sun 10.30 pm; no trainers;
set pre-theatre £52 (FP), set weekday L £58 (FP).*

Athenaeum
Athenaeum Hotel W1   £69   ❷❷❸
116 Piccadilly   7499 3464   3–4B
*This little-sung Mayfair dining room is winning quite a following
among reporters, especially as a business rendezvous; service
is "attentive", the food "delicious", the Art Deco-ish decor
is "classy"… and "during the week, the set menu really is excellent!"
/ www.athenaeumhotel.com; 10.30 pm; set weekday L £40 (FP).*

The Atlas SW6   £41   ❷❸❸
16 Seagrave Rd   7385 9129   5–3A
*"Imaginative" and "gutsy" Mediterranean cuisine has helped win
a widespread fan club for this "bustling" boozer (with garden),
"tucked-away" near Earl's Court 2. / www.theatlaspub.co.uk; 10 pm.*

Aubaine   £53   ④④④
4 Heddon St, W1   7440 2510   3–2C
260-262 Brompton Rd, SW3   7052 0100   5–2C
37-45 Kensington High St, W8   7368 0950   5–1A **NEW**
*Morning visitors to this trendy bakery/bistro chain are rewarded
by "outstanding" pastries, and a "great atmosphere" too; later on,
however, the experience is much more "ordinary" – it doesn't help
that "you almost have to pay to breath". / www.aubaine.co.uk;
SW3 10 pm; W1 11 pm, W1A 9 pm, W8 10 pm, Sun 6 pm; W8 no booking.*

Aurelia W1 **NEW**
13-14 Cork St   awaiting tel   3–3C
*The owners of Zuma, Roka and so on only 'do' quality productions,
so this Mayfair newcomer – scheduled to open around the publication
date of this guide – should be one to watch; following in the footsteps
of one of their other properties, La Petite Maison, it's to be a
Mediterranean petits-plats affair.*

Aurora W1   £45   ❸❸❷
49 Lexington St   7494 0514   3–2D
*A "lovely" Soho spot, with a "great courtyard" – it's eclipsed
in popularity by Andrew Edmunds (opposite), but this is also
a "romantic" place, and has a similarly "decent" food offer too.
/ 10.30 pm, Sun 9 pm.*

Automat W1   £59   ④④④
33 Dover St   7499 3033   3–3C
*A "charismatic" but "noisy" American "diner-style-restaurant", in the
heart of Mayfair, which draws a "lively" crowd; it's a big hit for
breakfast, and for "great hamburgers" too, but it does have critics,
who say it's "more a useful rendezvous than a place you'd actually
choose to eat!" / www.automat-london.com; midnight; closed Sat D & Sun D.*

L'Autre Pied W1 £62 ❷❷❸
5-7 Blandford St 7486 9696 2–1A
*"The superb little sister of Pied à Terre" – a "serious but fun"
Marylebone venture founded on a small-plate formula
of "adventurous" and "exquisite" dishes; the set lunch, in particular,
is "a steal". / www.lautrepied.co.uk; 10.45 pm; closed Sun D;
set weekday L & pre theatre £37 (FP).*

Avalon SW12 £40 ❹❸❷
16 Balham Hill 8675 8613 10–2C
*It's the "incredible" outside space that really sets this large and trendy
Balham gastroboozer apart, even if its supporters do insist that the
food is "a notch above the usual". / www.theavalonlondon.co.uk;
10.30 pm, Sun 9 pm.*

L'Aventure NW8 £56 ❷❷❶
3 Blenheim Ter 7624 6232 8–3A
*St John's Wood's "little piece of France" is an "unfailing" and
"romantic" classic – especially the "blissful terrace on a balmy
summer's evening"; its "unashamedly traditional" cuisine is dished
up under the "ever-watchful eye" of owner Catherine Parisot. / 11 pm;
closed Sat L & Sun; set weekday L £34 (FP).*

The Avenue SW1 £55 ❹❸❸
7-9 St James's St 7321 2111 3–4D
*"A stunning legacy of '90s restaurant design", this "light" and "airy"
– "Manhattan-esque" – St James's brasserie remains a popular
business choice; not everyone's impressed though – it can still seem
a "soulless" and "incredibly noisy" place, where the food is simply
"dull". / www.theavenue-restaurant.co.uk; 10.30 pm; closed Sat L & Sun;
set pre theatre £36 (FP).*

Awana SW3 £56 ❹❹❹
85 Sloane Ave 7584 8880 5–2C
*London's most upscale Malaysian, in Chelsea, is still "very busy";
reporters, though, can't really discern why – prices are "sky high",
service can "border on rude", and the food is often rather "average".
/ www.awana.co.uk; Mon-Wed 11 pm, Thu-Sat 11.30 pm, Sun 10.30 pm.*

Axis
One Aldwych Hotel WC2 £57 ❹❷❹
1 Aldwych 7300 0300 2–2D
*A grand Covent Garden basement that makes a "useful" spot for
a "competent" business or pre-theatre meal; despite the best efforts
of the "very helpful staff", though, ambience can seem "lacking".
/ www.onealdwych.com; 10.30 pm; closed Sat & Sun.*

Azou W6 £33 ❸❸❷
375 King St 8563 7266 7–2B
*An appearance on the 'f-word' boosted the profile of this tiny family-
run Hammersmith café; it remains a "lovely" and "intimate" spot,
serving "large helpings" of Moroccan fare in a manner that's
"cordial", "endearing" and "occasionally chaotic". / www.azou.co.uk;
11 pm; no Amex.*

Ba Shan W1 £34 ❷❹❸
24 Romilly St 7287 3266 4–3A
*"Just as good as Bar Shu... but cheaper!" – a spin-off from the
restaurant opposite, this Soho café dishes up some "blisteringly hot
and unusual" Sichuanese dishes, with "real Chinese flavours". / 11 pm,
Fri 11.30 pm.*

Babbo W1 £70 ④④⑤
39 Albermarle St   3205 1099   3–3C
*"Why so expensive?" – the prices at this "crushed" Mayfair Italian
(unrelated to the famous NYC establishment of the same name)
leave reporters mystified; all it really has going for it is a "great
location", not far from the Ritz.* / www.babborestaurant.co.uk; 11 pm;
closed Sun.

Babur SE23 £41 ❶❶❷
119 Brockley Rise   8291 2400   1–4D
*"Thank you Harden's for helping us discover Babur!" – this Honor
Oak Park "star" continues to offer "extraordinarily imaginative and
interesting" Indian cooking, a "great wine list", and "fantastic" service
too... for "about half the cost you'd pay in the West End"!*
/ www.babur.info; 11 pm, 10.30 pm.

Babylon
Kensington Roof Gardens W8 £69 ④④❷
99 Kensington High St   7368 3993   5–1A
*"A sense of drama" heightens a visit to this eighth-floor "haven" –
"the most wonderful spot", with "super views", and also, of course,
"huge roof gardens for a romantic pre-prandial stroll"; shame
it "trades on its location", though – the food is "dull", and the prices
are "daylight robbery".* / www.virgin.com/roofgardens; 10.30 pm; closed
Sun D; set weekday L £41 (FP).

Il Bacio £42 ❸④④
61 Stoke Newington Church St, N16   7249 3833   1–1C
178-184 Blackstock Rd, N5   7226 3339   8–1D
*Those in search of a "great family hang-out" in Highbury or Stoke
Newington should seek out these "frantic" Sardinians; topping the
menu: "super pizzas in massive portions".* / www.ilbaciohighbury.co.uk;
10 pm-11 pm; N5, Mon-Fri L; no Amex.

Back to Basics W1 £48 ❷❷④
21a Foley St   7436 2181   2–1B
*A "cramped and bustling" Marylebone corner-spot, whose "simple
but great-tasting fish" makes it "a real find" – especially if you can
get a pavement table; "the day's specials on the blackboard are
particularly interesting".* / www.backtobasics.uk.com; 10.30 pm.

Baker & Spice £41 ❸❸❷
54-56 Elizabeth St, SW1   7730 5524   2–4A
47 Denyer St, SW3   7225 3417   5–2D
20 Clifton Rd, W9   7289 2499   8–4A
*"The best baked goods", "divine scrambled eggs" and light bites
"so nutritious you can almost feel the vitamins" make these
"informal" deli/bakeries popular with many reporters – even those
who find the product "outstanding", though, may feel prices are
so high that it just "isn't worth it".* / www.bakerandspice.uk.com; 7 pm,
Sun 5 pm-6 pm; closed D; no Amex; no booking.

Balans £44 ④❸❸
34 Old Compton St, W1 7439 3309 4–2A
60 Old Compton St, W1 7439 2183 4–3A
239 Old Brompton Rd, SW5 7244 8838 5–3A
Westfield, Ariel Way, W12 8600 3320 7–1C
214 Chiswick High Rd, W4 8742 1435 7–2A
187 Kensington High St, W8 7376 0115 5–1A
These "buzzy" diners go on till late, and are really all about the vibe
("almost like a club") and the "people-watching" – nowhere more
so than at the 24/7 heart-of-gay-Soho HQ; food quality can be a
"roller coaster", but the "good-value" brunch is a highpoint.
/ www.balans.co.uk; midnight-2 am; 34 Old Compton St 24 hrs; some booking
restrictions apply.

Bald Faced Stag N2 £43 ❸❷❷
69 High Rd 8442 1201 1–1B
"A delicious meal is guaranteed", say the many fans of East Finchley's
"fantastic local gastropub", which goes "from strength to strength".
/ www.thebaldfacedstagn2.co.uk; 10.30 pm, Sun 9.30 pm; no Amex.

Balthazar WC2 **NEW**
4-6 Russell St awaiting tel 4–3D
Englishman in New York Keith McNally has established his famous
SoHo brasserie as a Big Apple perennial; in conjunction with Richard
Caring, he's to launch a London offshoot in 2012 – which may well
cement the revival of Covent Garden as a fashionable restaurant
destination.

Baltic SE1 £45 ④④④
74 Blackfriars Rd 7928 1111 9–4A
For a "fun night out" – "as long as the vodka keeps on flowing" –
this "spacious" and "airy" post-industrial venue, by Southwark tube,
still has many fans; it "seems to have lost direction", though – it feels
more "barn-like" nowadays, and the "unusual Baltic-inspired" food
seems no better than incidental. / www.balticrestaurant.co.uk; 11.15 pm,
Sun 10.15 pm.

Bam-Bou W1 £48 ❸❸❷
1 Percy St 7323 9130 2–1C
It's the "colonial styling" and the "buzzy and fun" vibe that make this
seductive Fitzrovia townhouse such an ideal spot for romance (or a
party), but the Franco-Vietnamese food is "interesting" too, even if
some say "you pay a bit over the odds" for it. / www.bam-bou.co.uk;
midnight; closed Sat L & Sun; booking: max 6.

The Banana Tree Canteen £32 ❸❷❸
103 Wardour St, W1 7479 4790 3–2D **NEW**
21-23 Westbourne Grove, W2 7221 4085 6–1C
166 Randolph Ave, W9 7286 3869 8–3A **NEW**
237 West End Ln, NW6 7431 7808 1–1B
75-79 Battersea Rise, SW11 7228 2828 10–2C
412-416 St John St, EC1 7278 7565 8–3D
"A lovely oriental mini-chain"; you may have to endure
"uncomfortable bench-seating", but the fare is "reliable, tasty and
inexpensive". / 11 pm, Sun 10.30 pm; booking: min 6.

Bangalore Express £34 ④❸❷
103-107 Waterloo Rd, SE1 7021 0886 9–4A
1 Corbet Ct, EC3 7220 9195 9–3C
*"Fun table-booths up ladders" (SE1) is just part of the "interesting
concept" of these "buzzy" modern Indians, which feature "Indian fish
'n' chips with tangy mushy peas" alongside traditional thalis;
most reporters feel they're "good value", but the occasional disastrous
report on EC3 drags ratings down overall. / www.bangaloreexpress.co.uk;
11 pm; closed Sun.*

Bangkok SW7 £35 ❷❷❸
9 Bute St 7584 8529 5–2B
*"They've been doing the same thing for pretty much 30 years,
and they do it pretty well" – the UK's oldest Thai restaurant continues
to satisfy and, for somewhere in South Kensington, it's very
"reasonably priced" too. / 10.45 pm; no Amex.*

Bank Westminster
St James Court Hotel SW1 £59 ④❸④
45 Buckingham Gate 7630 6644 2–4B
*"There's not a lot of competition round here", so this large but
"unexciting" joint has established itself as the undoubted "staple"
of the Victoria Street business crowd; "sunny-day tables in the
conservatory" are the most sought-after. / www.bankrestaurants.com;
10.30 pm; closed Sat L & Sun; set pre theatre £37 (FP).*

Banners N8 £43 ④④❸
21 Park Rd 8348 2930 1–1C
*"The food's only OK, the service snarky, and the setting authentically
shabby, but I could eat here every week!" – this world-food bistro
is an 'institution' in Crouch End; famously, it's at its best for
breakfast and/or with kids; indeed, "it's almost too family-friendly".
/ www.bannersrestaurant.com; 11.30 pm, Fri & Sat midnight, Sun 11 pm;
no Amex.*

Baozi Inn WC2 £17 ❷⑤④
25 Newport Ct 7287 6877 4–3B
*"It's a bit rough 'n' ready, in-and-out" – and with "hilariously rude"
staff too – but this pint-sized Chinatown three-year-old serves
up Sichuan bites that are both "cheap" and "incredibly tasty".
/ 10 pm, Fri-Sat 10.30 pm; no credit cards; no booking.*

BAR BOULUD
MANDARIN ORIENTAL SW1 £50 ❷❷❸
66 Knightsbridge 7201 3899 5–1D
*Daniel B's "buzzy" NYC-import is proving a "great addition to the
London scene" – an "efficient" basement operation that's "good-
value" too (especially by Knightsbridge standards); "divine" burgers
are – perhaps curiously – the highlight of its "old-fashioned and
unfussy" French menu, on which "fine charcuterie" also rates
a mention. / www.barboulud.com; 10.45 pm Mon-Sat, Sun 9.45 pm.*

Bar Italia W1 £28 ❸④❶
22 Frith St 7437 4520 4–2A
*A "crazy, old-fashioned Italian coffee bar" that's become the definitive
24/7 Soho institution – "THE place after clubbing for a caffeine shot
to get you home". / www.baritaliasoho.co.uk; open 24 hours, Sun 4 am;
no Amex; no booking.*

Bar Trattoria Semplice W1 £43 ④④⑤
22-23 Woodstock St   7491 8638   3–2B
*The (remarkably inferior) trattoria-style offshoot of Mayfair's Semplice
divides views – fans do insist it offers "simple but tasty" dishes in a
"very informal setting", but there's a fair-sized gang of critics who find
portions "small" and standards "mediocre".*
/ www.bartrattoriasemplice.com; 11 pm, Fri-Sat 11.30 pm, Sun 9.30 pm.

Barbecoa EC4 £58 ④④④
20 New Change Pas   3005 8555   9–2B
*Jamie O has never run a truly impressive upmarket restaurant,
and this "cavernous" and "noisy" City BBQ looks unlikely to break the
mould; the view (St Paul's) may be "unbeatable", and the vibe may
be "fun", but – for too many reporters – it's a "vacuous" and
"overpriced" operation that's "worth giving a miss".*
/ www.barbecoa.com; 11 pm.

La Barca SE1 £58 ④❸❷
80-81 Lower Marsh   7928 2226   9–4A
*Near Waterloo, an "old-established Italian with a loyal following";
critics may find it "old-fashioned", and "pricey" for what it is,
but devotees prefer to think of it as "a wonderful throw-back to the
'60s and '70s". / www.labarca-ristorante.com; 11.15 pm; closed Sat L & Sun.*

Il Baretto W1 £55 ❷④④
43 Blandford St   7486 7340   2–1A
*An "improved" Marylebone Italian, whose "simple and delicious"
dishes are generally reckoned to be worth their "high" prices;
the service can be a touch "variable", though, and the "noisy"
basement setting is something of a drawback. / www.ilbaretto.co.uk;
10.45 pm, Sun 10 pm; closed Sun.*

The Barnsbury N1 £42 ❸④❸
209-211 Liverpool Rd   7607 5519   8–2D
*A "friendly" and "relaxed" gastroboozer (with garden) that's "worth
the walk from Upper Street"; Sunday lunch is a particular highlight.
/ www.thebarnsbury.co.uk; 10 pm, Sun 8 pm; closed Sun D.*

Barrafina W1 £40 ❶❶❷
54 Frith St   7813 8016   4–2A
*"Still the go-to place in the West End"; the Hart brothers' inspired
take-off of Barcelona's famous Cal Pep is an ongoing blockbuster,
with "a wonderful vibe" and "zen-perfect" tapas ("zingy seafood" the
highlight); NB: only 23 seats, so consider "dining solo" – "you can
sometimes jump the queue!" / www.barrafina.co.uk; 11 pm, Sun 10.30 pm;
no booking.*

Barrica W1 £30 ❸❸❷
62 Goodge St   7436 9448   2–1B
*"Vibrant", but sometimes "chaotic" – this Fitzrovia yearling "feels as if
it has been airlifted straight from Barcelona"; it offers some
"outstanding" dishes and "an ample, well-chosen wine list",
all "at reasonable prices". / www.barrica.co.uk; 10.30 pm; closed Sun.*

Bar Shu W1 £46 ❷④❸
28 Frith St   7287 6688   4–3A
*"Give your tongue a kicking", at this Soho café, whose "mouth-
numbing" Sichuanese cuisine is arguably "the best of its type
in London"; the culinary experience may be "amazing", but sadly the
"moody" service is "average at best". / www.bar-shu.co.uk; 11 pm, Fri-Sat
11.30 pm.*

Basilico £32 ❷❸④
690 Fulham Rd, SW6 0800 028 3531 10–1B
26 Penton St, N1 0800 093 4224 8–3D
51 Park Rd, N8 8616 0290 1–1C **NEW**
515 Finchley Rd, NW3 0800 316 2656 1–1B
175 Lavender Hill, SW11 0800 389 9770 10–2C
178 Upper Richmond Rd, SW14 0800 096 8202 10–2B
"It's impossible to contemplate ordering any other take-away pizza",
say fans of this "excellent" chain, and its "awesome, thin and crispy"
offerings. / www.basilico.co.uk; 11 pm; no booking.

Bayee Village SW19 £36 ❸❸❷
24 High St 8947 3533 10–2B
In the chain-hell which is Wimbledon Village, this "efficient" operation
is all the more worth knowing about – it offers "solid" Chinese
cooking ("with a few interesting specialities too"). / www.bayee.co.uk;
11 pm.

Beach Blanket Babylon £62 ⑤⑤❶
45 Ledbury Rd, W11 7229 2907 6–1B
19-23 Bethnal Green Rd, E1 7749 3540 12–1C
"Worth a visit for the decor alone" – these "exotic" and "fun"
Gaudiesque hang-outs, in Notting Hill and Shoreditch, offer "divine"
cocktails, and plenty of scope for romance too; the food, though,
can be "truly awful". / www.beachblanket.co.uk; 10 pm; W2 some booking
restrictions apply Fri & Sat.

Bedlington Café W4 £25 ④❷⑤
24 Fauconberg Rd 8994 1965 7–2A
"Sound" cooking and friendly service – plus a BYO policy – ensure
a devoted following for this little Thai caff in deepest Chiswick; no one
minds too much about its "unchanging" menu, or the "dreary" decor.
/ 10 pm; closed Sun L; no credit cards.

Beirut Express £39 ❷④④
65 Old Brompton Rd, SW7 7591 0123 5–2B
112-114 Edgware Rd, W2 7724 2700 6–1D
"Authentic fresh cuisine" – lovely shawarmas and zingy mezze,
in "generous portions" – makes these "reasonably-priced" Lebanese
cafés, in South Kensington and Bayswater, well worth seeking out.
/ www.maroush.com; W2 2 am; SW7 midnight.

Beiteddine SW1 £46 ❸④⑤
8 Harriet St 7235 3969 5–1D
A "very good basic Lebanese"; having avoided the glitzification that's
engulfed the area, this rather dowdy veteran remains – by the
standards of Sloane Street – notably modestly-priced.
/ www.beiteddine.com; midnight.

Belgo £37 ④④❸
50 Earlham St, WC2 7813 2233 4–2C
67 Kingsway, WC2 7242 7469 2–2D
72 Chalk Farm Rd, NW1 7267 0718 8–2B
44-48 Clapham High Rd, SW4 7720 1118 10–2D
"Stick to the moules, frites and beers", and you can have a "fun"
time at this "basic" but "bustling" Belgian chain (where the waiters
dress as monks); when it comes to more adventurous fare, however
"the law of diminishing returns" quickly sets in.
/ www.belgo-restaurants.co.uk; most branches 10.30 pm-11.30 pm;
SW4 midnight, Thu 1 am, Fri & Sat 2 am, Sun 12.30 am.

Bellamy's W1 £70 ❸❷❸
18-18a Bruton Pl   7491 2727   3–2B
"Quiet and luxurious, in a nicely old-fashioned way" – this "discreet" Mayfair mews operation is a "well-spaced" room with service that's "friendly without being familiar", and it offers Gallic fare that's "reliable but not too adventurous". / www.bellamysrestaurant.co.uk; 10.15 pm; closed Sat L & Sun.

Bellevue Rendez-Vous SW17 £40 ❷❷❷
218 Trinity Rd   8767 5810   10–2C
"A perfect local"; "straightforward French classics" are "done well and without pretensions", at this "reliably enjoyable" and "reasonably-priced" family-run spot, near Wandsworth Common. / www.bellevuerendezvous.com; 10.30 pm; closed Mon L; no Amex.

Belvedere W8 £68 ❹❸❶
Holland Pk, off Abbotsbury Rd   7602 1238   7–1D
"Looks like a Hollywood film set!"; this "delightful" Art Deco "gem" is certainly very "plush", and it enjoys a "really stunning" setting, actually in Holland Park – shame the cooking is no more than "fairly reliable". / www.belvedererestaurant.co.uk; 10.30 pm; closed Sun D; set weekday L £40 (FP).

Benares W1 £75 ❷❷❸
12a Berkeley Square Hs, Berkeley Sq   7629 8886   3–3B
"Nobody uses spices better than Atul Kochar", and his "new slant on Indian cuisine" helps create some "intense" and "totally harmonious" dishes at this "sleek" Mayfair dining room; it's "very pricey", though, and can seem slightly "soulless". / www.benaresrestaurant.co.uk; 10.45 pm, Sun 10.15 pm; no trainers.

Bengal Clipper SE1 £39 ❸❹❸
Shad Thames   7357 9001   9–4D
"One of the Butler's Wharf pioneers", this South Bank Indian is "still serving remarkably good food, 15 years on" (and the Sunday buffet, in particular, is "an incredible bargain"); "aloof service lets it down" though – it can "kill the ambience of what's otherwise a classy room". / www.bengalclipper.co.uk; 11.30 pm, Sun 11 pm.

Benihana £61 ❹❸❸
37 Sackville St, W1   7494 2525   3–3D
77 King's Rd, SW3   7376 7799   5–3D
"Go in a big group of family and friends" – especially with teens – to get the most out of this "fun" US-style teppan-yaki chain, whose "entertaining" staff include knife-wielding chefs who cook at your table; the food is "actually quite good", if "expensive" for what it is. / www.benihana.co.uk; 10.30 pm, Sun 10 pm.

Benito's Hat £20 ❸❷❹
12 Great Castle St, W1   7636 6560   3–1C **NEW**
56 Goodge St, W1   7637 3732   2–1B
19 New Row, WC2   awaiting tel   4–3C
"Hats off to you, Señor Benito!"; these "efficient" Mexican operations have "lovely" staff, and offer "outstanding" made-to-order burritos and tacos at "fair prices"; "arrive early, or the queue can be long". / 10 pm, Thu-Sat 11 pm.

Benja W1 £47 ❷❷❸
17 Beak St   7287 0555   3–2D
Just off Regent Street, but oddly little-known, this lavishly-furnished (but quite cramped) townhouse-Thai is of special note for its "outstanding-value" prix-fixe lunch. / www.benjarestaurant.com; 10.45 pm; closed Sun; set weekday L £28 (FP).

Bennett Oyster Bar & Brasserie SW11 NEW £50   ④⑤④
7-9 Battersea Sq   7223 5545   10–1C
Battersea reporters are torn between delight that "this graveyard site has finally re-opened" and concern that its latest incarnation as a smart seafood brasserie still has "a lot of work to do"; our own visit confirmed that standards leave lots of scope for 'tightening up'. / bennettsbrasserie.com; 10 pm, Fri-Sat 10.30 pm.

Bentley's W1   £67   ❷❸❸
11-15 Swallow St   7734 4756   3–3D
Richard Corrigan's "polished" seafood dishes – amongst the capital's best – have put this "civilised" stalwart, near Piccadilly Circus, back on the map in recent years; the "glamorous yet informal" oyster bar downstairs (with great outside seats) is, however, a better bet than the "rather stuffy" dining room above. / www.bentleys.org; 10.30 pm; no jeans; booking: max 8.

Bento Cafe NW1   £32   ❷❷④
9 Parkway   7482 3990   8–3B
"Stuff yourself silly at a thoroughly reasonable price" – this "always-busy" but "efficient" Camden Town pit stop serves "sushi and noodles a-plenty". / bentocafe.co.uk; 10.15 pm, Fri-Sat 11 pm.

Benugo   £34   ④⑤❸
14 Curzon St, W1   7629 6246   3–4B
23-25 Gt Portland St, W1   7631 5052   3–1C
V&A Museum, Cromwell Rd, SW7   7581 2159   5–2C
Natural History Museum, Cromwell Rd, SW7   7942 5011   5–2B NEW
Westfield, Unit 1070 Ariel Way, W12   8746 9490   7–1C
St Pancras International, , NW1   7833 0201   8–3C
BFI Southbank, Belvedere Rd, SE1   7401 9000   2–3D
116 St John St, EC1   7253 3499   9–1A
82 City Rd, EC1   7253 1295   12–1A
These potentially classy cafés occupy some great sites, such as the "terrific space" in the V&A, and the "happening" BFI branch; too often, however, the setting is a "wasted asset", given the "awful" service, and food (from sarnies and coffee to grander fare) that's "so ordinary and expensive". / www.benugo.com; 4 pm-10 pm; W1 & EC1 branches closed Sat & Sun; W1 & EC1 branches, no credit cards.

Bertorelli   £46   ⑤⑤⑤
5 Argyll St, W1   7437 2503   3–1C NEW
37 St Martin's Ln, WC2   7836 5837   4–4C
15 Mincing Ln, EC3   7283 3028   9–3D NEW
"Why does it still exist when it's so consistently bad?" – a question too often on the lips of reporters on this middle-of-the-road Italian chain; the raison d'être of the West End branches is particularly hard to discern. / www.bertorelli.co.uk; 10 pm; EC3 closed Sat & Sun; booking: W1 max 10, WC2 max 6; set always available £30 (FP).

Best Mangal   £31   ❸❸❸
104 North End Rd, W14   7610 1050   7–2D
66 North End Rd, W14   7602 0212   7–2D
619 Fulham Rd, SW6   7610 0009   5–4A
"Fantastic for a regular meat-fest", these "buzzing" Turkish joints, near West Kensington tube, serve "well-charred, super-moist kebabs" cooked in front of you on the charcoal BBQ; there's also a Fulham branch. / www.bestmangal.com; midnight, Sat 1 am; no Amex.

Bevis Marks EC3 £63 ❸❸❸
Bevis Marks 7283 2220 9–2D
An intriguing annex to London's oldest synagogue houses this "high-quality" kosher venture; it is "perfect for business discussions" and makes "an interesting change from other City restaurants"… although "it is a little expensive for what it is". / www.bevismarkstherestaurant.com; 8.30 pm; closed Fri D, Sat & Sun.

Beyoglu NW3 £34 ❸④④
72 Belsize Ln 7435 7733 8–2A
"In an area not well served by restaurants" (Belsize Park), an establishment whose "very tasty" and affordable Turkish food ensures consistent popularity. / www.beyoglu.co.uk; 11 pm; no Amex.

Bibendum SW3 £79 ❸❷❷
81 Fulham Rd 7581 5817 5–2C
"The airy beauty of the space" – "fantastic on a sunny day" – has made this first-floor Brompton Cross dining room a modern-day classic; "professional" service and notable wine also play their part but, of late, the "superior Gallic cuisine" has played rather a supporting role. / www.bibendum.co.uk; 11 pm, Sun 10.30 pm; booking: max 12 at L, 10 at D.

Bibendum Oyster Bar SW3 £63 ❸❷❷
81 Fulham Rd 7589 1480 5–2C
"Lovely fruits-de-mer" in Art Deco surroundings – the makings of a treat at this Brompton Cross fixture, albeit one which comes "at a price"; "get a table in the original space", though, "not in the lobby of the Conran Shop". / www.bibendum.co.uk; 10.30 pm, Sun 10 pm; no booking.

Big Easy SW3 £51 ④④❷
332-334 King's Rd 7352 4071 5–3C
This "roll-up-your-sleeves" American 'crab shack' in Chelsea – jazzed up with live music some evenings – is "a great place to go with friends", and it serves "huge portions" of ribs, steak and seafood; some long-term fans do feel, though, that it has "gone downhill" of late. / www.bigeasy.uk.com; Mon-Thu 11 pm, Fri & Sat 11.30 pm Sun 10.30 pm.

Bincho Yakitori W1 £33 ❸④④
16 Old Compton St 7287 9111 4–2A
Even fans may admit "you need to choose carefully", but this Soho Japanese skewer-specialist pleases most reporters with its dainty dishes – "the tiny lamb chops are particularly good". / www.bincho.co.uk; 11.30 pm, Sun 10.30 pm; closed Mon L.

The Bingham TW10 £85 ④④❸
61-63 Petersham Rd 8940 0902 1–4A
"Gorgeous" Thames views (and a "lovely terrace") set an "elegant" tone at this "handsome" dining room, near Richmond Bridge; fans say it's a "perfect all-rounder", but critics complain that it's a "formal" sort of place, with "fussy, fussy" food and "unfocused" service. / www.thebingham.co.uk; 10 pm; closed Sun D; no trainers; set weekday L £50 (FP).

Bistro 1 £20 ④❸④
27 Frith St, W1 7734 6204 4–3A
75 Beak St, W1 7287 1840 3–2D
33 Southampton St, WC2 7379 7585 4–3D
"Nothing fancy, but all good!"; this "no-nonsense" chain may be a bit "humdrum", but – if you're on a budget – it's hard to beat "for a quick and well-priced Mediterranean meal". / www.bistro1.co.uk; midnight.

Bistro Aix N8 £50 ❷❷❷
54 Topsfield Pde, Tottenham Ln   8340 6346   8–1C
*"Step through the door, and you're in France" – not Crouch End –
at this "very friendly and welcoming" bistro; it's "always full and
buzzing", and the food is often "excellent" too. / www.bistroaix.co.uk;
midnight; closed Mon, Tue-Fri D only, Sat & Sun open L & D; set always
available £29 (FP).*

Bistro du Vin £54 ④❸④
36 Dean St, W1   7432 4800   4–2A **NEW**
40 St John St, EC1   7490 9230   9–1B **NEW**
*Take the Hotel du Vin concept, lose the hotel, and... bingo! you have
this new Gallic bistro, on the Clerkenwell site of the sadly ill-fated
Eastside Inn (RIP); early-day feedback is mixed – for a place that feels
like a French-themed hotel coffee shop, prices are certainly high;
now in Soho too. / Rated on Editors' visit; Mon-Sat 10.30 pm, Sun 10 pm;
W1 closed Sun L.*

Bistro K SW7 £50 ④④④
117-119 Old Brompton Rd   7373 7774   5–2B
*The Gallic cuisine is "decent" and the setting is "elegant" too –
shame, then, that the main impression some reporters take away
from this South Kensington yearling is its "astronomical prices".
/ www.bistro-k.co.uk; 10.30 pm; closed Mon; set weekday L £31 (FP).*

Bistrot Bruno Loubet
The Zetter EC1 £47 ❷❷❸
St John's Square 86-88 Clerkenwell Rd   7324 4455   9–1A
*Bruno Loubet's "magnificent" cuisine – "gutsy" Gallic bistro fare,
with an "Asian-fusion twist" – inspires continuing raves for this
"urban-chic" Clerkenwell yearling; main problem? – even fans may
fear the place is getting "a bit up itself". / www.thezetter.com; 10.30 pm,
Sat & Sun 11 pm.*

Bistrotheque E2 £50 ④④❶
23-27 Wadeson St   8983 7900   1–2D
*Quite a "mainstream" crowd nowadays frequents this once-edgy
East End warehouse-conversion; it "still feels like a bit of a secret",
though, and makes a "great venue for brunch" (or, of course,
the drag-cabaret). / www.bistrotheque.com; 10.30 pm, Fri 11 pm; closed
weekday L; set always available £32 (FP).*

Black & Blue £45 ④④④
37 Berners St, W1   7436 0451   2–1B
90-92 Wigmore St, W1   7486 1912   3–1A
127 King's Rd, SW3   7351 1661   5–3C **NEW**
105 Gloucester Rd, SW7   7244 7666   5–2B
215-217 Kensington Church St, W8   7727 0004   6–2B
1-2 Rochester Walk, SE1   7357 9922   9–4C
*"A good stand-by for carnivores"; its branches may rarely set the
pulse racing, but this "easy-going" and "no-nonsense" chain offers
"reliable steak" and "decent-enough burgers", and at a "decent
price" too. / www.blackandbluerestaurant.com; most branches 11 pm, Fri &
Sat 11.30 pm; SE1 (South Bank) closed Sun; no booking.*

Blakes
Blakes Hotel SW7 £86 ④❸❷
33 Roland Gdns   7370 6701   5–2B
*"Hidden-away" in South Kensington, this "quiet and romantic"
basement remains a "very sexy" destination for a date; even if its
East/West cuisine is "surprisingly good", though, the prices
"are enough to quell anyone's ardour". / www.blakeshotels.com;
11.30 pm, Sun 10 pm; set weekday L £49 (FP).*

BLEEDING HEART EC1 £60 ❷❷❷
Bleeding Heart Yd, Greville St 7242 8238 9–2A
*"For a discreet liaison of a business or romantic nature", this "cosy",
"mysterious" and "olde-worlde" den, hidden-way off Holborn, remains
phenomenally popular; "high-quality" Gallic fare and "superb" wines
are served in a warren or rooms, comprising tavern, bistro and
restaurant.* / www.bleedingheart.co.uk; 10.30 pm; closed Sun.

Blue Jade SW1 £32 ❸⓿❸
44 Hugh St 7828 0321 2–4B
*This "comfy" Thai, in the backwoods of Pimlico, is a "good, regular
neighbourhood spot" par excellence – "it's stuck in a time warp,
but the homely food never disappoints, and service is unfailingly
charming".* / 10.30 pm; closed Sat L & Sun.

Blue Legume N16 £33 ❸❹❷
101 Stoke Newington Church St 7923 1303 1–1C
*"For an old-time hippy experience", try this "tiny" but "very busy",
Stoke Newington café, long known for its "perfect" breakfasts; it has
sprouted a new Islington branch – "a welcome addition to the less
exciting end of Upper Street".* / 11 pm, Sun 6 pm; no Amex; no bookings
Sat & Sun.

Bluebird SW3 £55 ⑤④④
350 King's Rd 7559 1000 5–3C
*"A total disaster!" – the setting may be "airy" and "glamorous",
but this "overpriced" Chelsea landmark continues to dish up "bland
bistro-food" of a sometimes "abominable" standard; on a bad day,
service is "eye-wateringly poor" too.* / www.bluebird-restaurant.co.uk;
10.30 pm.

Bluebird Café SW3 £38 ⑤⑤④
350 King's Rd 7559 1000 5–3C
*"A waste of time and money!" – the D&D group's "notoriously
terrible" and "overpriced" King's Road café has "a nice location"
(largely al fresco)… "but that's about it".* / www.bluebird-restaurant.co.uk;
10 pm, Sun 9.30 pm.

**Blueprint Café
Design Museum SE1** £50 ❸❸⓿
28 Shad Thames, Butler's Wharf 7378 7031 9–4D
*"Get a window seat to enjoy one of London's best views" –
"impressive even to the well-travelled" – at this Tower Bridge-side
operation; as ever, though, there's an odd split in opinion between
those who say Jeremy Lee's "seasonal" cuisine really "does the
business" and those who find it "underwhelming".*
/ www.danddlondon.com; 10.45 pm; closed Sun D.

Bob Bob Ricard W1 £55 ④❷❷
1 Upper James St 3145 1000 3–2D
*"Glamorous", if "slightly weird!" – "imagine Savoy Grill-meets-
American diner" – this Soho two-year-old boasts highlights such
as "comfy private booths" and "divine" cocktails; the Anglo-Russian
"comfort" food is no more than OK… but "how can you not like
a place where each table comes complete with its own champagne
buzzer?"* / www.bobbobricard.com; 11.15 pm; closed Mon & Sun.

Bocca Di Lupo W1 £52 ❷❷❷
12 Archer St 7734 2223 3–2D
"London's most interesting Italian!"; this "cool" (if "cramped" and very "clattery") Soho two-year-old is "worth the hype", say fans, thanks to its "breathtaking" use of "top-class ingredients" to create "earthy" tapas-style dishes; sitting at the bar is "particularly special". / www.boccadilupo.com; 11 pm; closed Sun D; booking: max 10; set weekday L & pre-theatre £31 (FP).

Bodean's £45 ❹❺❹
10 Poland St, W1 7287 7575 3–1D
Fulham Broadway, SW6 7610 0440 5–4A
169 Clapham High St, SW4 7622 4248 10–2D
16 Byward St, EC3 7488 3883 9–3D
"If you like ribs" (not to mention pulled pork and burnt ends), these "quick and easy", American-style "BBQ-houses" are a rapid route to "guilty pleasure"; standards are "slipping away", though, with reports of "faux" food and lacklustre service on the rise. / www.bodeansbbq.com; 11 pm, Sun 10.30 pm; EC3 10 pm; 8 or more.

Boisdale SW1 £61 ❹❹❷
13-15 Eccleston St 7730 6922 2–4B
"A top cigar terrace", "an outstanding whisky selection", "blaring jazz" and "East European girls in kilts" set the scene at this "faux-Scottish" Belgravian – this may all make for good male-bonding opportunities, but the "traditional" fare (highlighting steak) can seem pretty "indifferent", given the "steep" prices. / www.boisdale.co.uk; 11.30 pm; closed Sat L & Sun.

Boisdale of Bishopsgate EC2 £54 ❸❸❸
202 Bishopsgate, Swedeland Ct 7283 1763 9–2D
"Top burgers" and "fantastic game in season" are among the pluses winning praise for this Scottish-themed bar (upstairs)/restaurant (cellar), near Liverpool Street, which fans say is a "hidden gem". / www.boisdale.co.uk; 9 pm; closed Sat & Sun; set always available £35 (FP).

Boisdale of Canary Wharf E14 NEW £58 ❹❹❸
Cabot Pl 7715 5818 11–1C
This latest addition to laird Ranald Macdonald's faux-Scottish empire occupies a "large and airy space", with "good views" of Canary Wharf; its "fun" style and "fabulous" steaks have won it some early-days praise, but – like the sibling establishments – it's certainly no bargain. / www.boisdale.co.uk; 11.30 pm; closed Sun.

The Bolingbroke SW11 £42 ❸❸❸
174 Northcote Rd 7228 4040 10–2C
"A perfect place to meet with friends, especially with little ones" – this "reliable" Battersea gastropub is of particular note as "an absolute must for Sunday lunch". / www.renaissancepubs.co.uk; 10.30 pm, Sun 9 pm.

Bombay Bicycle Club £41
128 Holland Park Ave, W11 7727 7335 6–2A
95 Nightingale Ln, SW12 8673 6217 10–2C
A 'mystery buyer' bought this financially-troubled subcontinental chain – where standards have sometimes been "dire" of late – in the summer of 2011; let's hope the new owner can get a grip of what was once a good-quality operation. / www.thebombaybicycleclub.co.uk; 11 pm, Sun 10.30 pm.

Bombay Brasserie SW7 £65 ❸❸❸
Courtfield Close, Gloucester Rd   7370 4040   5–2B
Views divide rather oddly on this vast and once-celebrated South
Kensington Indian, which was refurbished a couple of years ago;
fans find it a "bright and airy" place with "amazing" cuisine –
for detractors, though, "the charm's gone", and food-quality with it.
/ www.bombaybrasserielondon.com; 11.30 pm, Sun 10.30 pm.

Bombay Palace W2 £44 ❷❷⑤
50 Connaught St   7723 8855   6–1D
There's certainly "no arty modern presentation", at this "traditional"
Indian veteran, in a quiet Bayswater Square; its "beautifully-spiced"
cuisine, however, "hits the spot time and again".
/ www.bombay-palace.co.uk; 11.30 pm.

Bonds
Threadneedles Hotel EC2 £62 ④④④
5 Threadneedle St   7657 8088   9–2C
A "great location" ("right in the middle of the City") helps make the
dining room of this trendy – by local standards – hotel a popular
business lunch destination… even if it "does nothing particularly
well". / www.theetoncollection.com/restaurants/bonds/; 10 pm; closed
Sat & Sun.

Il Bordello E1 £42 ❷⓪❷
81 Wapping High St   7481 9950   11–1A
"Fresh", "no-nonsense" fare is served in "huge" portions, by "fun"
and "personable" staff, at this "traditional" and "relaxed" Wapping
favourite, where "fantastic" pizzas are just one highlight of the
"extensive" menu. / 11 pm, Sun 10.30 pm; closed Sat L.

La Bota N8 £29 ❸❷❸
31 Broadway Pde   8340 3082   1–1C
"Bringing a real, rural taste of Spain to Crouch End"; well, the owners
are from Barcelona, and this "noisy" bar is a "comforting" place,
offering consistently "good value for money". / www.labota.co.uk; 11 pm,
Fri-Sun 11.30 pm; no Amex.

The Botanist SW1 £57 ⑤⑤⑤
7 Sloane Sq   7730 0077   5–2D
Thanks to its "prime Sloane Square location", the bar area of this
smart, younger-scene hang-out is always "heaving"; avoid the
adjoining restaurant, though – it's "loud" too, with "nonchalant"
service and "bad", "overpriced" cooking.
/ www.thebotanistonsloanesquare.com; 10.30 pm.

La Bottega £16 ❸❸❸
20 Ryder St, SW1   7839 5789   3–4C **NEW**
25 Eccleston St, SW1   7730 2730   2–4B
65 Lower Sloane St, SW1   7730 8844   5–2D
14 Gloucester Rd, SW7   7581 6980   5–1B
97 Old Brompton Rd, SW7   7581 6622   5–2B **NEW**
Springing up in a number of "well-heeled" postcodes, this smart, little
café/deli chain offers "a slice of Italian life" – "simple", "expertly-
sourced" dishes, "delightful" staff… and "great coffee" too.
/ www.labottega65.com; Lower Sloane St 8 pm, Sat 6 pm, Sun 5 pm; Eccleston
St 7 pm; SW7 8 pm; Ryder St closed Sat & Sun; no booking.

La Bouchée SW7 £48 ❸④❷
56 Old Brompton Rd   7589 1929   5–2B
"Still a great place to take a date" – this South Kensington bistro
"perennial" continues to exert its very own brand of "crowded" and
"authentically French" charm, and its fare is suitably "solid"; service,
though, can be "haphazard". / www.boudinblanc.co.uk; 10.45 pm.

Le Bouchon Breton E1 £61 ④⑤⑤
8 Horner Sq   0800 019 1704   12–2B
A Spitalfields venture that's "let down massively" by its "cavernous" quarters – "it's just wrong to put a serious French brasserie in a soulless modern unit"; "hit-and-miss" cooking and "chaotic" service do the place no favours either, but "exceptional cheese" and a huge wine list offer some compensation. / www.lebouchon.co.uk; 10 pm; closed Sun D.

Boudin Blanc W1 £58 ❸④❷
5 Trebeck St   7499 3292   3–4B
"Paris comes to London", at this "cosy and conspiratorial" ("cramped") Shepherd Market fixture, ever-popular for its "buzzing" ambience and its "delicious" (if rather "unadventurous") Gallic cuisine; great al fresco tables. / www.boudinblanc.co.uk; 11 pm.

Boulevard WC2 £38 ⑤⑤④
40 Wellington St   7240 2992   4–3D
Fans tout this "fun" brasserie, in the heart of tourist-ville, as a "cheap" Covent Garden "staple"; even they can concede that service is often "slapdash", however, and harsher critics feel the place is "dire". / www.boulevardbrasserie.co.uk; Mon-Thu 11 pm, Fri & Sat 11.30 pm, Sun 10.30 pm.

The Boundary E2 £63 ❸❸❷
2-4 Boundary St   7729 1051   12–1B
"A Conran classic" – Sir Tel's "cool" and "classy" Shoreditch basement is applauded by most reporters for its "faultless" brasserie-style fare (although, true to form, it's a bit "expensive for what you get"); NB: the rooftop terrace is "the place to be" in summer, but nabbing a table is "a nightmare". / www.theboundary.co.uk; 10.30 pm; closed Mon-Fri L & Sun D.

The Bountiful Cow WC1 £45 ❸④④
51 Eagle St   7404 0200   2–1D
"Superb steaks" and "absolutely fantastic burgers" draw fans to this carnivorous haven near Holborn; service, though, can be "disinterested" and "slow". / www.thebountifulcow.co.uk; 10.30 pm; closed Sun; set weekday L £17 (FP).

Boyd's Brasserie
The Northumberland WC2 £47 ④④④
8 Northumberland Ave   7808 3344   2–3C
It has "such a great location" (just off Trafalgar Square) and hugely "impressive" (marbled) decor too, but this "cavernous" brasserie still feels "impersonal" – it doesn't help that the cooking offers "little in the way of excitement". / www.boydsbrasserie.co.uk; 10 pm; closed Sun D.

Bradley's NW3 £53 ④④❸
25 Winchester Rd   7722 3457   8–2A
"Quiet but lovely", say fans, this Swiss Cottage stalwart is an "utterly reliable" choice after a show at the nearby Hampstead Theatre; a crowd of sceptics, though, insist "it's gone right down", offering "very boring" food and "erratic" service too. / www.bradleysnw3.co.uk; 11 pm; closed Sat L & Sun D.

Brady's SW18 £34 ❸❸❸
513 Old York Rd   8877 9599   10–2B
"Exactly how a fish 'n' chip shop should be!"; the "colourful" Mr Brady's "honest and cheerful" Wandsworth bistro offers "excellent" renditions of the national staple (grilled or fried), plus "good, old-fashioned puds". / www.bradysfish.co.uk; 10 pm; closed Mon-Thu L & Sun; no Amex; no booking.

La Brasserie SW3   £48   ⑤④❸
272 Brompton Rd   7581 3089   5–2C
*"London's most authentic Parisian brasserie" is – say fans – simply
"humming" since the installation of its "impressive" new bar;
for critics, though, the fare on offer at this South Kensington fixture
is not just "massively overpriced", but "rubbish" too!*
/ www.labrasserielondon.co.uk; 11.30 pm; no booking, Sat L & Sun L.

Bar Battu EC2   £42   ❸❸❸
48 Gresham St   7036 6100   9–2B
*"A true find in the heart of the City"; thanks to its "esoteric wines
at sensible prices" – and its "honest bistro cooking" too – this "vibey"
year-old bar/restaurant is already being hailed as "a real lunchtime
staple". / 10 pm; closed Sat & Sun.*

Brasserie Blanc EC2   £41   ❸❸❸
60 Threadneedle St   7710 9440   9–2C
*The "buzzing and competent" EC2 branch of Raymond B's national
brasserie chain is "good for business lunches", and handy for "early
dinners" too; "it's not fine dining, though, nor an especially warm
experience". / www.brasserieblanc.com; 10 pm; closed Sat & Sun.*

Brasserie James SW12   £43   ④❸④
47 Balham Hill   8772 0057   10–2C
*"A little local brasserie" that's established itself as "a reliable part
of Clapham life"; it doesn't attract universal praise, but the "great
tasting-menus" have their fans. / www.brasseriejames.com; 10 pm,
Sun 9 pm; closed Sun D; no Amex.*

Brasserie Joël
Park Plaza Westminster Bridge SE1   £69   ❷④⑤
Westminster Bridge Rd   7620 7272   2–3D
*Prices are high, ambience "totally lacking" and service "indifferent",
at the dining room of this 1000+ bedroom hotel, at the south end
of Westminster Bridge; bizarrely, though, Joël Antunes's Gallic dishes
are often "excellent"! / www.brasseriejoel.co.uk; 10.30 pm, Sun 9.30 pm;
closed Sat L; set pre theatre £36 (FP).*

Brasserie Roux
Sofitel St James SW1   £61   ❸❷❸
8 Pall Mall   7968 2900   2–3C
*"It's hard to find decent food at a fair price near Trafalgar Square",
so this "convenient" dining room in a "well-spaced" former banking
hall is worth knowing about; it offers "genuine" Gallic cooking,
"polished" service, and a "civilised" setting (and they do a "fantastic"
brunch too). / www.sofitelstjames.com; 11 pm, Sat & Sun 10.30 pm; set pre
theatre £36 (FP).*

Brasserie St Jacques SW1   £52   ④❸④
33 St James's St   7839 1007   3–4C
*"Conveniently located", just off Piccadilly, this "little piece of France"
continues to divide opinion; fans love its "comfy" setting, "jovial"
maitre d' and "very competent" brasserie fare, but critics just say the
whole show is "rubbish". / www.brasseriestjacques.co.uk; 11 pm; closed
Sat & Sun; no jeans or trainers.*

Brasserie Toulouse-Lautrec SE11   £39   ④❷❷
140 Newington Butts   7582 6800   1–3C
*"What it lacks in food" – the Gallic fare is rather "overpriced and
average" – is "made up for in atmosphere and jovial service",
say fans of this "off-the-beaten-track" Elephant & Castle bistro;
it's run by the same family as the Lobster Pot, next door.
/ www.brasserietoulouselautrec.co.uk; 10.30 pm.*

Brawn E2 NEW £43 ❶❷❷
49 Columbia Rd 7729 5692 12–1C
"An East End version of Terroirs… and even better!" – this "airy"
corner site has been an instant mega-hit, thanks to its "gutsy"
selection of dishes that supporters say are "a pure joy", twinned with
a "funky" (and sometimes "challenging") range of 'natural' wines.
/ www.brawn.co; 11 pm; closed Sun D; no Amex.

Bread Street Kitchen EC4 NEW
1 New Change awaiting tel 9–2B
Gordon Ramsay's late-2011 debutant opens in a shiny new City mall,
by St Paul's, where there is seemingly much competition (such as
Jamie O's Barbecoa), but nothing yet of real quality – a perfect
opportunity for his new fast-food venture to shine?

Brick Lane Beigel Bake E1 £7 ❶④⑤
159 Brick Ln 7729 0616 12–1C
"The best beigels in London" (especially the ones "with huge chunks
of salt beef, slathered in mustard") draw crowds night-and-day to this
24/7 East End phenomenon; "don't worry about the queue, it moves
fast!" / open 24 hours; no credit cards; no booking.

Brilliant UB2 £37 ❶❷❸
72-76 Western Rd 8574 1928 1–3A
"You have to to go Southall for the real deal", say fans of this huge
and sometimes "overcrowded" Indian veteran, who are prepared
to brave a trip to the suburbs for the "memorable" curries it offers.
/ www.brilliantrestaurant.com; 11 pm; closed Mon, Sat L & Sun L.

Brinkley's SW10 £50 ⑤④❸
47 Hollywood Rd 7351 1683 5–3B
A "wonderful courtyard" is the only undoubted plus of this side-street
haunt, whose bar is always packed with Chelsea Lotharios and their
molls – well, it can't be the food, which is "far too expensive for what
it is". / www.brinkleys.com; 11 pm; closed weekday L.

Brinkley's Kitchen SW17 £44 ④❸❸
35 Bellevue Rd 8672 5888 10–2C
"A reliable destination for a simple dining experience" –
John Brinkley's "comfortable" and "child-friendly" bistro,
by Wandsworth Common, is an "ideal local"; as well as "a wide and
attractive" menu, it offers a "particularly interesting and keenly-priced
wine list". / www.brinkleys.com; 11 pm; closed Sun D.

La Brocca NW6 £37 ④④❸
273 West End Ln 7433 1989 1–1B
Fans of this "cheery" cellar Italian, in West Hampstead, still tout it as
"a great neighbourhood haunt", not least for the quality of its pizza;
the view is growing, however, that it's "not what it used to be" –
"must try harder!" / www.labrocca.co.uk; 10.30 pm, Fri & Sat 11 pm.

Brompton Bar & Grill SW3 £48 ④❸❸
243 Brompton Rd 7589 8005 5–2C
A "buzzy" Knightsbridge brasserie whose customer base seems
largely to be drawn from the offspring of those who went there in the
site's 'St Quentin' days; a "warm and welcoming" sort of place,
it offers food that's "uncomplicated", but consistently "OK".
/ www.bromptonbarandgrill.com; 10.30 pm, Sun 10 pm; set always available
£32 (FP).

Brouge £37 ④❸❷
241 Hampton Rd, TW2 8977 2698 1–4A
5 Hill St, TW9 8332 0055 1–4A
A duo of quite "classy-looking" Belgian bistros, in Richmond and
Twickenham, serving "solidly-prepared" moules frites in "generous
portions", washed down with "excellent" Continental beers.
/ www.brouge.co.uk; TW2 10 pm; TW9 11 pm; no Amex.

The Brown Dog SW13 £45 ❸❷❷
28 Cross St 8392 2200 10–1A
"In the back streets of what Barnes estate agents call 'Little
Chelsea'", this "stylish and dog-friendly" pub is "a firm favourite with
families"; the menu may be "limited", but the food is "well-cooked".
/ www.thebrowndog.co.uk; 10 pm, Sun 9.30 pm.

(Hix at Albemarle)
Brown's Hotel W1 £75 ❸❷❷
Albemarle St 7493 6020 3–3C
For a "quiet environment for a good conversation" – especially
on business – you won't do better than this "very professional" and
"bustle-free" panelled chamber, in Mayfair; "Mark Hix has created
an outstanding menu featuring great British classics alongside many
lighter dishes". / www.roccofortecollection.com; 11 pm, 10.30 pm.

(The English Tea Room)
Brown's Hotel W1 £26 ❸❷❶
Albemarle St 7493 6020 3–3C
"Where else would you go for afternoon tea?" – this long-established
Mayfair hotel "makes you feel like you're in an Agatha Christie novel",
and is well-known for its "elegant" panelled tea room; even fans,
though, can find it "expensive".
/ www.brownshotel.com/dining/english_tea_room.htm; 11 pm; no jeans
or trainers; only for afternoon tea.

Browns £42 ⑤④④
2 Cardinal Pl, SW1 7821 1450 2–4B **NEW**
47 Maddox St, W1 7491 4565 3–2C
82-84 St Martin's Ln, WC2 7497 5050 4–3B
9 Islington Grn, N1 7226 2555 8–3D
Butler's Wharf, SE1 7378 1700 9–4D
Hertsmere Rd, E14 7987 9777 11–1C
8 Old Jewry, EC2 7606 6677 9–2C
"Seemingly trading on a combination of past glories and the lovely
locations of many of its branches", this national brasserie chain yet
again takes a drubbing for food "some school canteens would
be ashamed of". / www.browns-restaurants.co.uk; most branches
10 pm-11 pm; EC2 closed Sat & Sun; W1 closed Sun D.

Brula TW1 £51 ❷❶❶
43 Crown Rd 8892 0602 1–4A
"Everything is done beautifully", at this "romantic" and slightly old-
fashioned bistro in St Margaret's – service is "utterly delightful" and
the "simple" Gallic care is "top-grade". / www.brula.co.uk; 10.30 pm;
closed Sun D.

Buen Ayre E8 £45 ❶❸❸
50 Broadway Mkt 7275 9900 1–2D
"I had been a vegetarian for 23 years... but couldn't resist a teeny
weeny taste!" – this "barebones" Hackney 'parilla' is acclaimed by all
for its "buzzy" vibe, and for steak "so succulent" it's very often hailed
as "the best in London". / www.buenayre.co.uk; 10.30 pm; no Amex.

Buenos Aires Cafe £53 ❸❸❸
86 Royal Pde, SE10 8488 6764 1–3D
17 Royal Pde, SE3 8318 5333 1–4D
"For a decent steak" (and also *"good pizza and pasta"*), this *"casual"*
Blackheath Argentinian is just the job, although service can be a bit
"haphazard"; it also has a simpler café/deli sibling, in Greenwich.
/ www.buenosairesltd.com; SE3 10.30 pm; SE10 7 pm, Sat & Sun 6 pm;
no Amex.

The Builders Arms SW3 £41 ❸❸❷
13 Britten St 7349 9040 5–2C
"A neighbourhood treasure"; *"tucked-away"* in Chelsea, this *"warm"*,
"friendly" and *"reliably good"* gastroboozer is the jewel in the crown
of the Geronimo Inns chain. / www.geronimo-inns.co.uk; 10 pm, Sat 11 pm,
Sun 9 pm; no booking.

Bull & Last NW5 £48 ❶❷❷
168 Highgate Rd 7267 3641 8–1B
"Still the best North London gastropub" – this Kentish Town mega-hit
is a *"perfect local"*, where the attractions include *"utterly delicious"*
food, *"humorous"* staff and a *"great location next to the Heath"*;
"the only drawback is that it's always way too loud".
/ www.thebullandlast.co.uk; 10 pm, Sun 9 pm; no Amex.

Bumbles SW1 £48 ❸❷④
16 Buckingham Palace Rd 7828 2903 2–4B
Long written-off as a tourist trap, this *"old-fashioned"* operation near
Buckingham Palace is tipped by fans as a *"hidden gem worthy
of more attention"*; they praise its *"inventive approach to traditional"*
dishes, and especially its *"excellent £10 set lunch"*.
/ www.bumbles1950.com; 10 pm; closed Sat L & Sun.

Bumpkin £47 ⑤④❸
102 Old Brompton Rd, SW7 7341 0802 5–2B
209 Westbourne Park Rd, W11 7243 9818 6–1B
"Underwhelming on all fronts", say critics of these Notting Hill and
South Kensington pub-conversions; fans insist, though, that they're
"congenial" places, and that, if you *"stick to the basics"* of the
"staple" menu, you'll have *"a nice time"*; *"epic"* English breakfasts
are a highlight. / www.bumpkinuk.com; 11 pm.

Buona Sera £36 ❸❶❶
289a King's Rd, SW3 7352 8827 5–3C
22 Northcote Rd, SW11 7228 9925 10–2C
"Fun and energetic", this Battersea fixture always delights its family-
centric following with a *"cheerful welcome"* and its *"unfailingly tasty,
good-value fare"*; the Chelsea offshoot (*"perfect pre-cinema"*) benefits
from bizarre two-level seating – a hang-over from its '70s origins
as 'The Jam'. / midnight; WC2 11.30 pm, Sun 10 pm; SW3 closed Mon L.

Busaba Eathai £35 ❸❸❷
35 Panton St, SW1 7930 0088 4–4A
106-110 Wardour St, W1 7255 8686 3–2D
8-13 Bird St, W1 7518 8080 3–1A
22 Store St, WC1 7299 7900 2–1C
Westfield, Ariel Way, W12 3249 1919 7–1C **NEW**
313-319 Old St, EC1 7729 0808 12–1B
"A cut above the Wagamamas of the world" (and notably
"less sterile"), these *"communal"* canteens are *"lovely"* and *"vibrant"*
places, where the *"classic Thai dishes"* deliver *"bags of flavour for
your money"*; perhaps no surprise, then, that *"the queues never seem
to get shorter…"* / www.busaba.co.uk; 11 pm, Fri & Sat 11.30 pm,
Sun 10 pm; W1 no booking; WC1 booking: min 10.

Arbutus

Brawn

Clos Maggiore

Butcher & Grill £45 ④❸④
39-41 Parkgate Rd, SW11 7924 3999 5–4C
33 High St, SW19 8944 8269 10–2B
"Stick to the steak 'n' chips", and results can be "first-class", say fans
of these "unfussy" bistro/butchers, in Battersea and Wimbledon;
critics, though, still find the performance resolutely "average".
/ www.thebutcherandgrill.com; 11 pm, Sun 9 pm; SW11 closed Sun D;
SW19 closed Mon L.

Butcher's Hook SW6 £39 ❸❸❸
477 Fulham Rd 7385 4654 5–4A
"Don't go when Chelsea are playing at home!"... but otherwise this
very decent gastropub, opposite Stamford Bridge, serves "surprisingly
good" food – "nothing complicated, just simple dishes done well".
/ www.thebutchershook.co.uk; 10.30 pm; no Amex.

Butlers Wharf Chop House SE1 £61 ④④❸
36e Shad Thames 7403 3403 9–4D
The combination of "iconic" Tower Bridge views and a meaty British
menu helps make this D&D-group venue "a good place to entertain
foreign clients" – hopefully, they won't mind its often "slapdash"
standards; paying your own way? – head for the bar.
/ www.chophouse.co.uk; 10.45 pm, Sun 9.45 pm.

La Buvette TW9 £37 ❸❷❶
6 Church Walk 8940 6264 1–4A
"Tucked-away in a church courtyard" (with al fresco dining when
weather permits), this "charming" Gallic bistro, in Richmond, offers
"comforting food, in calm and cosy surroundings", and "good value
for money" too! / www.labuvette.co.uk; 10 pm.

Byron £31 ❸❸❸
11 Haymarket, SW1 7925 0276 4–4A NEW
97-99 Wardour St, W1 7297 9390 3–2D
24-28 Charing Cross Rd, WC2 7557 9830 4–4B NEW
33-35 Wellington St, WC2 7420 9850 4–3D
300 King's Rd, SW3 7352 6040 5–3C
242 Earl's Court Rd, SW5 7370 9300 5–2A NEW
75 Gloucester Rd, SW7 7244 0700 5–2B
93-95 Old Brompton Rd, SW7 7590 9040 5–2B
Westfield, Ariel Way, W12 8743 7755 7–1C
222 Kensington High St, W8 7361 1717 5–1A
341 Upper St, N1 7704 7620 8–3D
46 Hoxton Sq, N1 3487 1230 12–1B NEW
22 Putney High St, SW15 8246 4170 10–2B NEW
Cabot Place East, E14 7715 9360 11–1C
7 One New Change, EC2 7246 2580 9–2B NEW
"The new king of burgers!" – this phenomenal chain (part of the
PizzaExpress empire) is achieving massive growth, yet maintaining its
impressive formula of "stylish" decor, "cheery and efficient" staff...
plus "chunky" and "honest" fare that's "full of flavour".
/ www.byronhamburgers.com.

C London (formerly Cipriani) W1 £88 ⑤⑤④
25 Davies St 7399 0500 3–2B
"Berlusconi would love it!"; "Eurotrash... WAGs... a scrum through
the paparazzi!" – this "tasteless" but "hilarious" Mayfair Italian
is simply "the worst"; the prices for the "terrible" food and "fake"
service? – "think of a number and double it!" / www.clondon.com;
11.45 pm.

C&R Cafe £18 ③④⑤
3-4 Rupert Ct, W1   7434 1128   4–3A
52 Westbourne Grove, W2   7221 7979   6–1B
"Huge portions of good, cheap Malaysian food" – that's the simple
but compelling proposition of these "authentic" joints, in Chinatown
and Bayswater. / 11 pm.

The Cabin W4 £42 ④④④
148 Chiswick High Rd   8994 8594   7–2A
Especially as a daytime or early-evening destination – when 'bargain'
set deals are available – this surf 'n' turf Chiswick diner generally
pleases the locals; as a dinner-destination, though, it doesn't seem
it always measures up. / www.cabinrestaurants.co.uk; 10.30 pm, Fri & Sat
11 pm; no Amex; No toddlers after 7pm; set until 6.30 pm £28 (FP).

The Cadogan Arms SW3 £48 ③④③
298 King's Rd   7352 6500   5–3C
A "friendly and bustling" Chelsea gastropub, offering "enjoyable" –
and sometimes "outstanding" – fare. / www.thecadoganarmschelsea.com;
10.30 pm, Sun 9 pm.

Café 209 SW6 £22 ③②②
209 Munster Rd   7385 3625   10–1B
"Joy, the proprietor, is quite mad, but she tries hard to please";
her BYO café, in deepest Fulham, is "beyond cramped", but the
dishes are "priced cheaper than you could make at home!"
/ 10.30 pm; D only, closed Sun, closed Dec; no Amex.

Le Café Anglais
Whiteley's W2 £53 ③③③
8 Porchester Gdns   7221 1415   6–1C
The new oyster-bar has been "a great addition" to Rowley Leigh's
"airy" Art Deco-style brasserie, above Bayswater's landmark mall –
"one of London's nicer daytime venues", especially for a "family-
friendly" Sunday lunch; a long and "pricey" menu
of "straightforward" classic fare is realised to a reliable standard.
/ www.lecafeanglais.co.uk; 11 pm, Sun 10 pm.

Café Below EC2 £37 ③③③
St Mary-le-Bow, Cheapside   7329 0789   9–2C
A "quirky" self-service café in an "atmospheric" crypt, "tucked-away"
under one of Wren's greatest City churches; the food (which has
a veggie slant) can be "surprisingly tasty", especially considering its
"very reasonable" prices. / www.cafebelow.co.uk; 9 pm; closed Sat & Sun;
no Amex.

Café Bohème W1 £45 ④②①
13 Old Compton St   7734 0623   4–2A
"A great buzz" distinguishes this "very French-feeling"
café/bar/brasserie, in the heart of Soho – a popular all-hours haunt
for anything from a coffee to a full meal. / www.cafeboheme.co.uk;
2.45 am, Sun midnight; booking: max 12.

Café del Parc N19 £19 ③②②
167 Junction Road   7281 5684   8–1C
An "utterly improbable and totally fab" find in Tuffnell Park –
a "closely packed" café with "fantastic" staff, producing "brilliant"
tapas "with a twist" from its "very public" kitchen. / www.delparc.co.uk;
10.30 pm; open D only, Wed-Sun; no Amex.

Café des Amis WC2 £53 ④④④
11-14 Hanover Pl 7379 3444 4–2D
"It's time they pulled their socks up", at this cutely-located bistro, by the Royal Opera House – "it's been trading on its old reputation" for years; the best bet is still the "lively" cellar wine bar. / www.cafedesamis.co.uk; 11.30 pm; closed Sun; set weekday L £29 (FP), set dinner £33 (FP).

Café du Marché EC1 £52 ❷❷❶
22 Charterhouse Sq 7608 1609 9–1B
"Down a quaint Smithfield alleyway", this "petit coin de Paris" oozes "charm and a sense of calm"; its "unabashedly French" cuisine is a benchmark of consistency, striking just the right note for business by day, or romance by night (when there's jazz). / www.cafedumarche.co.uk; 10 pm; closed Sat L & Sun; no Amex.

Café Emm W1 £35 ④④❸
17 Frith St 7437 0723 4–2A
A "bustling" younger-crowd Soho canteen that, say fans, "still can't be beat for a cheap eat" – it doesn't, however, seem to inspire the excitement it once did. / www.cafeemm.com; 11.30 pm, Sun 10.30 pm; no Amex.

Café España W1 £27 ❸❷❷
63 Old Compton St 7494 1271 4–3A
"Bustling with tourists and locals nightly" (till late) – this tapas bar in seediest Soho offers "surprisingly good food for such reasonable prices" ("and you can't beat a £2 glass of wine to wash it down!"). / 11.45 pm, Sun 10.30 pm; closed Mon.

Café in the Crypt
St Martin's in the Fields WC2 £29 ④④❸
Duncannon St 7766 1158 2–2C
The crypt of Trafalgar Square's great church provides "a lovely and unusual" setting for this self-service cafeteria; the food may "look more promising than it is", but fans say that – for somewhere so central – the prices are "excellent". / www.smitf.org; Sun 6 pm, Mon-Tue 8 pm, Wed-Sat 9 pm; no Amex; no booking.

Café Japan NW11 £30 ❶❷④
626 Finchley Rd 8455 6854 1–1B
"My Japanese wife says this is the best-value sushi in London!" – the lady is not alone, and this "basic" Golder's Green spot is extolled by reporters for "fantastic-quality" fare that's among the best, affordable sushi in town. / 10 pm; closed Mon; no Amex; only D; set weekday L £18 (FP).

Café Laville W2 £36 ④④❶
453 Edgware Rd 7706 2620 8–4A
The "picture perfect" setting – "perched above Regent's Canal" – creates a "pretty special" atmosphere at this Maida Vale spot; best go for brunch or a cuppa, though – more substantial fare tends to be "mediocre". / 10 pm; no Amex.

Café Luc W1 £56 ④④❷
50 Marylebone High St 7258 9878 2–1A
An "inviting" setting has helped make this stylish and "buzzing" yearling a "great addition to Marylebone"; even those who find the brasserie fare "decent", though, may admit that it's also rather "unexciting" – brunch is arguably the forte. / www.cafeluc.com; 10.45 pm; closed weekday L; set weekday L £34 (FP).

Café Pacifico WC2 £43 ⑤④❸
5 Langley St 7379 7728 4–2C
A "vibrant" Covent Garden cantina of long standing; it survives by virtue of its "cosy" style, though, rather than its "stereotypical" Tex-Mex scoff. / www.cafepacifico-laperla.com; 11.45pm, Sun 10.45 pm.

Café Rouge £36 ⑤⑤④
Branches throughout London
With kids in tow (to whom staff can be "lovely"), or for "coffee and pastries", this faux-Gallic brasserie chain has its uses; in other respects, though, it feels like a fairly "cynical" operation, whose guiding principle is too often the lowest common denominator. / www.caferouge.co.uk; 11 pm, Sun 10.30 pm.

Café Spice Namaste E1 £52 ❶❶❸
16 Prescot St 7488 9242 11–1A
Its debut seemed so path-breaking in the mid-'90s, but – after all these years – practically every meal at Cyrus & Pervin Todiwala's "quirky" East End HQ is still "a delight", thanks to "innovative" Indian-fusion cuisine that's "beyond superb", and "charming" service too. / www.cafespice.co.uk; 10.30 pm; closed Sat L & Sun.

Cafe Strudel SW14 £43 ❸④④
429 Upper Richmond Road 8487 9800 1–4A
Scrumptious coffee and pastries, and some slightly 'different' Austro-Hungarian food (and wine) make this East Sheen spot a handy local stand-by. / www.cafestrudel.co.uk; 11 pm, Sun 4 pm; closed Mon & Sun D.

Caffè Caldesi W1 £53 ④❷❸
118 Marylebone Ln 7487 0754 2–1A
It's perhaps as a "lovely" lunch venue that this Marylebone Italian – a "bustling bar" with dining room above – is of most interest; it attracts little feedback, often to the effect that results are "average". / www.caldesi.com; 10.30 pm.

Caffè Nero £13 ④❸❸
Branches throughout London
"The most authentic chain coffee" – "close to the genuine Italian article" – is the special draw to these "friendly and efficient" pit stops; the pastries and panini, though, are "only standard". / most branches 7 pm; City branches earlier; most City branches closed all or part of weekend; some branches no credit cards; no booking.

Caffé Vergnano £12 ④❸❸
62 Charing Cross Rd, WC2 7240 8587 4–3B
Royal Festival Hall, SE1 7921 9339 2–3D
2 New Street Sq, EC4 7936 3404 9–2A **NEW**
The "best coffee this side of Italy" makes this Covent Garden café a "West End stand-out" for caffeine addicts; the larger Royal Festival Hall outpost – whose offer includes "pasta as an Italian might recognise it" – is "one of the better places on the South Bank" too. / www.caffevergnano.com; SE1 midnight; WC2 8 pm, Fri & Sat midnight, EC4 11 pm; EC4 Sat & Sun; no Amex.

La Cage Imaginaire NW3 £43 ④❷❸
16 Flask Walk 7794 6674 8–1A
A mega-cute Hampstead lane provides the setting for this old-school Gallic stalwart; the food can seem "ordinary and expensive", but the overall experience is "very pleasant" nonetheless. / www.la-cage-imaginaire.co.uk/; 11 pm.

Cah-Chi £34 ❸⓪❸
394 Garratt Ln, SW18 8946 8811 10–2B
34 Durham Rd, SW20 8947 1081 10–2B
These "brilliant" local Koreans, in Earlsfield and Raynes Park, are "so welcoming"; their food – "including the at-table barbecue" – is "deliciously fresh" too. / www.cahchi.com; SW18 11 pm, Sat & Sun 11.30 pm; SW20 11 pm; SW20 closed Mon; cash only.

Cambio de Tercio SW5 £57 ❷❷❷
163 Old Brompton Rd 7244 8970 5–2B
Hailed by some as "the best Spanish restaurant in the UK!", this "buzzy" South Kensington "gem" wins adulation for its "inspiring" – "El Bulli-esque", even! – dishes, and "stunning" wines; it's "crowded", though, and the two-sittings policy is a continuing source of complaints. / www.cambiodetercio.co.uk; 11.30 pm.

Camden Brasserie NW1 £40 ④❸④
9-11 Jamestown Rd 7482 2114 8–3B
A "welcoming" Camden Town stand-by, which has long lived up to its name; "the best frites" aside, however, its whole performance can seem a little "anodyne". / www.camdenbrasserie.co.uk; 10.45 pm.

Camino N1 £44 ④⑤❸
3 Varnishers Yd, Regent Quarter 7841 7331 8–3C
This "stylish" tapas bar – a couple of minutes' walk from King's Cross – is one of the best places round the station, and it's "always busy"; drooping ratings, though, support those who say: "popularity has been its downfall!" / www.camino.uk.com; 11 pm, Sun 10 pm.

Cannizaro House SW19 £65 ④④❸
West Side, Wimbledon Common 8879 1464 10–2A
A "simply fabulous location" is the trump card of this Wimbledon Common-side hotel, where the "very expensive" food attains a standard that's "only OK"; for afternoon tea, however, it is a "wonderful little secret". / www.cannizarohouse.com; 9.30 pm.

Canonbury Kitchen N1 NEW £45 ❸②④
19 Canonbury Ln 7226 9791 8–2D
A new Italian, near Highbury & Islington tube, where "a short and simple rustic menu" comes "well-executed"; ambience-wise, however, we're talking "sub-PizzaExpress". / www.canonburykitchen.com; 11 pm; closed Mon-Fri L, Sat D & Sun D; no Amex.

Canta Napoli £34 ❸❸④
9 Devonshire Rd, W4 8994 5225 7–2A
932-934 North Finchley, N12 8445 1351 1–1B NEW
"Italian regionally-themed evenings" are a top time to visit this Chiswick Neapolitan, which also has quite a name for its pizza; the harsh view, however, is that it's "an OK local, but doesn't really stand out"; the North Finchley sibling inspires no feedback. / 10.30 pm; no Amex.

Canteen £39 ④④④
55 Baker St, W1 0845 686 1122 2–1A
Royal Festival Hall, SE1 0845 686 1122 2–3D
Park Pavilion, 40 Canada Sq, E14 0845 686 1122 11–1C
Crispin Pl, Old Spital'fds Mkt, E1 0845 686 1122 12–2B
"A good formula gone wrong" – fans may like the "simple but effective" cuisine at these "reinvented British caffs", but more striking is the number of critics, who complain of "woefully inconsistent" cooking, sometimes "laughable" service, and "the lack of any real atmosphere". / www.canteen.co.uk; 11 pm; no booking weekend L.

Cantina del Ponte SE1   £46   ⑤④④
Butler's Wharf Building, 36c Shad Thames   7403 5403   9–4D
"Lovely views of Tower Bridge" make this D&D-group Italian a useful
South Bank destination for first-time visitors to London; it has its fans
among the natives too, but the feeble overall ratings tend to bolster
those who think its attractions primarily touristic. / www.cantina.co.uk;
11 pm, Sun 10 pm; set weekday L £27 (FP).

Cantina Laredo WC2   £45   ③④⑤
10 Upper St Martin's Ln   7420 0630   4–3B
Fans of this US import to Covent Garden, part of an "upmarket
Mexican" chain, hail its dishes as "impressively executed" –
"they make the guacamole at your table!"; for sceptics, though,
the food is "underwhelming", and the interior so "bland" it "feels like
a Travelodge lobby". / www.cantinalaredo.co.uk; 11.30 pm, Sat midnight,
Sun 10.30 pm; over 7 people.

Cantina Vinopolis
Vinopolis SE1   £50   ④④④
1 Bank End   7940 8333   9–3C
As you might hope at a museum of wine, the wine list at this "bistro-
style" venue – set in attractive South Bank vaults – is "to die for";
otherwise, however, the experience can seem "pricey" and "generic".
/ www.cantinavinopolis.com; 10.30 pm; closed Mon-Wed D & Sun.

Cantinetta SW15 **NEW**   £42   ④⑤❸
162-164 Lower Richmond Rd   8780 3131   10–1A
"So much potential", as yet unfulfilled, at this Putney newcomer,
formerly called the Phoenix (and under unchanged ownership) –
it may have a "lovely" ambience, but its Italian menu is realised to a
"distinctly average" standard, and service "seemingly can't cope".
/ www.cantinetta.co.uk; 10.30 pm, Fri-Sat 11 pm; closed Sun D; set always
available £28 (FP).

Canton Arms SW8   £37   ❷❷❶
177 South Lambeth Rd   7582 8710   10–1D
"Just how a gastropub should be" – this Anchor & Hope sibling would
be "a terrific asset" anywhere, but seems particularly "awesome"
in "the Stockwell desert"; its "rough and ready" style only adds to the
ambience, as does the "enthusiastic" service, and the "superb" and
"hearty" British cuisine. / www.cantonarms.com; 10 pm; closed Mon L;
no Amex; no booking.

Cape Town Fish Market W1   £49   ❸④④
5 & 6 Argyll St   7437 1143   3–1C
Decorated in garish shopping-mall style, this off-beat South African-
backed concept, near Oxford Circus, offers a "quirky" menu ranging
from "traditional" dishes to sushi ; the (few) reports it attracts
suggest the food is "good", if perhaps "overpriced". / www.ctfm.com;
10.45 pm, Fri-Sat 11.15 pm.

The Capital Restaurant
Capital Hotel SW3   £92   ❸④④
22-24 Basil St   7589 5171   5–1D
"After a slight wobble" on the departure of the previous chef,
this grand but compact Knightsbridge chamber appears to be getting
back on track, and Jerome Ponchelle's cuisine is often "superb";
the atmosphere, though, remains too "library-like" for some tastes.
/ www.capitalhotel.co.uk; 10.30 pm, Sun 10 pm; no jeans or trainers;
set weekday L £54 (FP), set Sun L £60 (FP).

Caponata NW1   £46   ❸❷❷
3-7 Delancey St   7387 5959   8–3B
*"A real surprise in the middle of Camden"; this "modern and airy"
restaurant and music venue – laid-out round a glazed courtyard,
complete with a 'living wall' – offers some "interesting" and "good-
value" Sicilian cooking, and some "lovely" service too.
/ www.caponatacamden.co.uk; 10.30 pm, Sun 10 pm; set weekday L £30 (FP).*

Capote Y Toros SW5 NEW   £39
157 Old Brompton Rd   7373 0567   5–2B
*The new tapas bar offshoot of South Kensington's estimable Cambio
de Tercio, nearby; it opened too late for much survey commentary
(or to receive a rating), but an early reporter hails "great food... but
an even better list of sherries". / www.cambiodetercio.co.uk; 11.30 pm;
D only, closed Mon & Sun.*

LE CAPRICE SW1   £65   ❸❶❷
Arlington Hs, Arlington St   7629 2239   3–4C
*"Never putting a foot wrong" has long underpinned the "classic"
status of this "swish" and "vibrant" '80s-minimalist brasserie behind
the Ritz; it's been "slipping" of late, though – let's hope the major
refurbishment in mid-2011 marks a turning point.
/ www.le-caprice.co.uk; midnight, Sun 11 pm; set always available £43 (FP).*

Caraffini SW1   £45   ❸❶❷
61-63 Lower Sloane St   7259 0235   5–2D
*"Why change a winning formula?"; ebullient staff greet you "like the
Prodigal Son" when you visit this "old-faithful" trattoria, near Sloane
Square; the food may be "unadventurous", but it's "always reliable",
and "honestly priced" too. / www.caraffini.co.uk; 11.30 pm; closed Sun.*

Caravaggio EC3   £60   ④④④
107-112 Leadenhall St   7626 6206   9–2D
*"Expense accounts must still be thriving!" – otherwise, reporters are
hard put to explain the survival of this "pricey" but "average-all-
round" City Italian; or perhaps it has something to do with the
"convenient location"? / www.etruscarestaurants.com; 10 pm; closed
Sat & Sun; set always available £36 (FP).*

Caravan EC1   £39   ❷❷❶
11-13 Exmouth Mkt   7833 8115   9–1A
*"Awesome" home-roasted coffee, and "brilliant" Antipodean
breakfasts inspire many raves for this "busy" but chilled Clerkenwell
café; its main, fusion-tapas menu is also "full of interesting ideas",
and realisation – though it can be slightly "hit-and-miss" – is often
"top notch". / www.caravanonexmouth.co.uk; Sat 5 pm; closed Sun D;
set always available £7 (FP).*

Carluccio's   £38   ④④④
Branches throughout London
*Love 'em or hate 'em, these "bright" cafés inspire unusually
passionate feelings for a chain; to fans, their "snappy fare" makes
them a great "cheap 'n' cheerful" stand-by, especially with the family
or for brunch – critics just find them "faux-Italian" and "dull".
/ www.carluccios.com; most branches 11 pm, Sun 10.30 pm; no booking
weekday L.*

Carnevale EC1   £42   ❸❷④
135 Whitecross St   7250 3452   12–2A
*A well-established veggie, by the Barbican, commended by its small
fan club for its "original" fare. / www.carnevalerestaurant.co.uk; 11 pm;
closed Sat L & Sun; no Amex; set weekday L £26 (FP).*

Carob Tree NW5 £32 ④❷④
15 Highgate Rd 7267 9880 8–1B
"Fresh and tasty" dishes win praise for this Greek spot, in Dartmouth Park; of late, however, has it "lost its sparkle"? / 10.30 pm, Sun 9 pm; closed Mon; no Amex.

The Carpenter's Arms W6 £41 ❸④④
91 Black Lion Ln 8741 8386 7–2B
Tucked away in a Hammersmith backwater, this stylishly-converted pub pleases most reporters with its "interesting" and "well-cooked" food; there's a "great" garden too. / 10 pm, Sun 9 pm.

Carvosso's W4 £41 ⑤④❸
210 Chiswick High Rd 8995 9121 7–2A
A "cosy" hang-out – in Chiswick's former police station! – where the stand-out attraction is the "terrific courtyard garden"; well, it certainly isn't the food... / www.carvossosat210.co.uk; 11 pm.

Casa Brindisa SW7 £36 ❸④❸
7-9 Exhibition Rd 7590 0008 5–2C
Yet to be re-badged under the 'Tapas Brindisa' brand, this South Kensington two-year-old is a "high-quality" Spanish operation – even those who feel it's "not in the same league as nearby Tendido Cero" say it's a "fun" spot, offering "decent" fare. / www.casabrindisa.com; 10.45 pm.

Casa Malevo W2 NEW £45 ④④④
23 Connaught St 7402 1988 6–1D
Middling ratings for this Bayswater débutant; most reports applaud a "convivial" joint, offering "good steaks" – to the odd critic, though, it's just a "me-too Argie steakhouse". / www.casamalevo.com; 10.30 pm.

Cassis Bistro SW3 £71 ④④④
232-236 Brompton Rd 8581 1101 5–2C
Marlon Abela's slick new bistro, on the former Knightsbridge site of Oratory (RIP), seduces some reporters with its "crowd-pleasing" Gallic fare – sceptics, however, find its whole style "pretentious", and say prices are "outrageous" too. / 11 pm; set weekday L £45 (FP).

Le Cassoulet CR2 £48 ❸④❸
18 Selsdon Rd 8633 1818 10–2D
"Putting Croydon on the gastronomic map!" – Malcolm John's "honest" and "traditional" Gallic cooking makes this "buzzing" city-centre bistro "the best restaurant for miles around", say fans; cynics, sensing local hype, say the place "doesn't really live up". / www.lecassoulet.co.uk; 10.30 pm, Sat 11 pm, Sun 10 pm.

Catch
Andaz Hotel EC2 £52 ④④④
40 Liverpool St 7618 7200 12–2B
The "beautiful" interior is a high point of this business-friendly fish specialist, that forms part of a Liverpool Street hotel; the food is "good" but it's "overpriced", and the noise from the adjacent bar does little for the atmosphere. / www.andazdining.com; 10.30 pm; closed Sat & Sun.

Cattle Grid £41 ④④④
76 Northcote Rd, SW11 7228 4188 10–2C
1 Balham Station Rd, SW12 8673 9099 10–2C
A small and "relaxed" steak and burger chain that's yet to excite much in the way of reports – such as there are tend to the view that the food is "good, if not great". / www.cattlegridrestaurant.com; 10 pm, Fri & Sat 10.30 pm; no Amex.

Cavallino SW3 NEW £56
4 Sydney St 7352 3435 5–2C
*Jockey Franco Dettori is the PR-friendly backer of this mid-2011
Italian newcomer, in Chelsea; unfortunately we didn't fit in a visit
before this guide went to press, but the overall concept seems rather
similar to the former occupant of the site, Carpaccio's (RIP).*
/ www.cavallino-restaurant.com; 11 pm, Sun 10 pm.

Cây Tre £36 ❷④④
42-43 Dean St, W1 7317 9118 4–2A NEW
301 Old St, EC1 7729 8662 12–1B
*"Confused service doesn't get in the way of some unbelievable
flavours", at this "plastic"-looking Shoreditch Vietnamese; it now has
a stylish café-style Soho sibling, where an early visit found very harsh
acoustics, but dishes of cracking quality.* / 11 pm, Fri-Sat 11.30 pm,
Sun 10.30; no Amex.

Cecconi's W1 £62 ❸❷❶
5a Burlington Gdns 7434 1500 3–3C
*"Hedge-fund-alley-meets-ladies-who-lunch", at this "fun" and
"fashionable" Italian brasserie – a "safe, reliable and very smooth"
hub of Mayfair life, at any time of day (and especially popular for
breakfast).* / www.cecconis.co.uk; 1am, Sun midnight.

Cellar Gascon EC1 £35 ❸❸❷
59 West Smithfield Rd 7600 7561 9–2B
*A slightly "Spartan" spin-off from Farringdon's nearby Club Gascon,
featuring some "unbelievably interesting" SW French wines
to complement its tapas menu; the prix-fixe lunch is "unbeatable
value".* / www.cellargascon.com; midnight; closed Sat & Sun.

Le Cercle SW1 £49 ❷❷❷
1 Wilbraham Pl 7901 9999 5–2D
*"Hits the mark every time!" – this "chic" Gascon basement,
near Sloane Square, is an "elegant" sort of place, offering "eclectic"
tapas-style cuisine and "fascinating" wine; if you grab a booth, it can
be "wonderfully romantic" too.* / www.lecercle.co.uk; 10.45 pm; closed
Mon & Sun.

Cha Cha Moon W1 £29 ④④❸
15-21 Ganton St 7297 9800 3–2C
*It opened to a blaze of hype a couple of years ago, but this "canteen-
style" Cantonese noodle concept – a Chinese Wagamama, if you like
– has never really made waves; "for a quick West End bite", though,
you could do worse.* / www.chachamoon.com; 10.30 pm, Fri & Sat
11.20 pm, Sun 10.20 pm.

Chabrot Bistrot d'Amis SW1 NEW £54 ❸❶❸
9 Knightsbridge Grn 7225 2238 5–1D
*"A truly French feel" distinguishes this "very welcome addition
to Knightsbridge", which wins fans with its "honest" fare, and its
impeccably friendly service; critics can find the food a bit "safe",
though, and the cramped setting "too busy and noisy".*
/ www.chabrot.co.uk; 11 pm; closed Sun; set weekday L £33 (FP).

Chamberlain's EC3 £61 ❸❸④
23-25 Leadenhall Mkt 7648 8690 9–2D
*With its "excellent" fish and "attentive" service, this well-established
City seafood parlour is sometimes said to be "better than expected";
critics, though, insist that "you're just paying for its Leadenhall Market
location".* / www.chamberlains.org; 9.15 pm; closed Sat & Sun.

Chamomile NW3 £28 ❸❷❸
45 England's Ln 7586 4580 8–2B
A "bubbly" café, in the heart of Belsize Park, where "smiley" staff
dish up "the best breakfast in the area", and "great sandwiches and
salads" too. / 6 pm; L only; no Amex.

Champor-Champor SE1 £48 ❷❷❷
62 Weston St 7403 4600 9–4C
Be "magically transported to another world", when you visit this
"weird and wonderful" hide-away, near London Bridge – the staff are
"lovely", and the Malaysian cuisine is usually "intense and complex"
("if occasionally baffling"). / www.champor-champor.com; midnight; D only,
closed Sun.

The Chancery EC4 £50 ❷❸④
9 Cursitor St 7831 4000 9–2A
"Well-considered" cuisine and "fair prices" have made a big,
business-lunching hit of this "professional" joint in the back streets
of legal-land – "one of those rare places where the food is actually
better than it sounds on the menu!" / www.thechancery.co.uk; 10.30 pm;
closed Sat L & Sun.

Chapters SE3 £42 ④❸④
43-45 Montpelier Vale 8333 2666 1–4D
Long a linchpin of the area, this Blackheath brasserie still serves
up "solid" food (including a "stand-out" breakfast); overall, though,
standards are "pretty ordinary nowadays".
/ www.chaptersrestaurants.com; 11 pm, Sun 9 pm.

Le Chardon £46 ④⑤④
65 Lordship Ln, SE22 8299 1921 1–4D
32 Abbeville Rd, SW4 8673 9300 10–2D
A duo of "charming" south London bistros, nowadays in Clapham
as well as East Dulwich; fans praise their "well-executed, traditional
Gallic fare", but even they can find results "variable", and critics slam
"indifferent" food and "appalling" service. / www.lechardon.co.uk; 11 pm.

Charles Lamb N1 £39 ❸❸❷
16 Elia St 7837 5040 8–3D
"A hilarious annual Bastille Day boules tournament" hints at the
"good-humoured" Gallic ownership of this "classic, small
neighbourhood pub", "hidden-away" near Angel – a "charming" place
with "interesting" food, and "well-kept" beer too.
/ www.thecharleslambpub.com; 9.30 pm; closed Mon L, Tue L & Sun D;
no Amex; no booking.

Charlotte's Bistro W4 £50 ④④④
6 Turnham Green Ter 8742 3590 7–2A
This Chiswick yearling inspires mixed feedback – fans proclaim
a "lovely", stylish modern bistro offering "surprisingly interesting"
food, but for sceptics "the cooking looks better than it tastes" and
is "appallingly expensive" for what it is too. / www.charlottes.co.uk;
10.30 pm, Sun 9 pm; set weekday L £31 (FP).

Charlotte's Place W5 £48 ❸❸❸
16 St Matthew's Rd 8567 7541 1–3A
"It's Ealing's best!", say delighted locals, who love this "intimate"
bistro "gem", by the Common, and praise its "imaginative" fare;
bad (ie "awful") days, however, are not entirely unknown.
/ www.charlottes.co.uk; 10 pm, Sun 9 pm; set weekday L £30 (FP).

Charm W6 NEW £46 ❸❷❷
270-272 King St 8741 8863 7–2B
*"It feels like a Hong Kong bankers' playground", so this "extremely
smart and well-appointed" bar/restaurant makes an odd find on the
mid-market restaurant strip near Ravenscourt Park tube; it's by
no means a bad place, but some critics feel it's "not as good
as others nearby". / 10.30 pm.*

Chella W4 £39 ❸❷❸
142 Chiswick High Rd 8994 6816 7–2A
*"A more interesting take on Middle Eastern food than usual" –
plus attractive decor and "efficient" service – have made this year-old
Iranian "a welcome addition to the Chiswick scene".
/ www.chella-restaurant.co.uk; midnight; no Amex.*

The Chelsea Brasserie
Sloane Square Hotel SW1 £54 ❹❹❹
7-12 Sloane Sq 7881 5999 5–2D
*A prime location ("incredibly convenient for the Royal Court") helps
keep this percussive Sloane Square brasserie very busy; the food can
be good too, but those unable to avail themselves of special menus
may find it "overpriced". / www.chelsea-brasserie.co.uk; 10.30 pm;
no Amex.*

Chelsea Bun Diner SW10 £26 ❸❷❸
9a Lamont Rd 7352 3635 5–3B
*The "American-sized" breakfasts at this World's End diner are
legendary in their hang-over-curative properties; indeed, its reputation
for "honest nosh at good and sensible prices" has long made it a
"crowded" destination at any hour; BYO. / www.chelseabun.co.uk; 6 pm;
L only; no Amex; no booking, Sat & Sun.*

The Chelsea Kitchen SW10 £28 ❹❸❸
451 Fulham Rd 3055 0088 5–3B
*"Cheap, cheap, cheap… for Chelsea"; this resurrected joint –
relocated to a pub-conversion at the far end of the Royal Borough –
may offer only basic fodder, but fans say it's "still amazing value,
after all these years". / www.chelseakitchen.com; 11.30 pm, Sun 11 pm.*

Cheyne Walk Brasserie SW3 £68 ❸❹❸
50 Cheyne Walk 7376 8787 5–3C
*With its "trendy" decor and "fabulous" Gallic food – much of
it cooked on an open grill – this "romantic" Chelsea venture, in a
former pub, can seem quite a "find"; you can think a visit here
"enjoyable", though, and still feel the experience is "no match for the
bill!" / www.cheynewalkbrasserie.com; 10.30 pm; closed Mon L & Sun D.*

CHEZ BRUCE SW17 £68 ❶❶❷
2 Bellevue Rd 8672 0114 10–2C
*For the 7th year, Bruce Poole's "astonishingly consistent"
(yet "reasonably-priced") neighbourhood restaurant, by Wandsworth
Common, is the survey's favourite, thanks to its "artful but unfussy"
cooking, "amazing" wine, "spectacular" cheese and "genuine" staff;
it's "less crowded" too, after the recent expansion.
/ www.chezbruce.co.uk; 10.30 pm, Sun 9.30 pm.*

Chez Gérard £55 ⑤⑤⑤
31 Dover St, W1 7499 8171 3–3C
8 Charlotte St, W1 7636 4975 2–1C
119 Chancery Ln, WC2 7405 0290 2–2D
45 Opera Ter, Covent Garden, WC2 7379 0666 4–3D
9 Belvedere Rd, SE1 7202 8470 2–3D
64 Bishopsgate, EC2 7588 1200 9–2D
14 Trinity Sq, EC3 7480 5500 9–3D
1 Watling St, EC4 7213 0540 9–2B
"Oh dear!"; as steakhouses become ever more popular,
this *"uninspiring"* steak/frites chain goes from bad to worse –
it incites rather too many reports of food that's *"not very nice"*,
and service that's *"a joke"*. / www.chezgerard.co.uk; 10 pm-11.30 pm;
City branches closed all or part of weekend; some booking restrictions apply.

Chez Liline N4 £44 ❶⑤⑤
101 Stroud Green Rd 7263 6550 8–1D
"London's best-kept fish secret!" – Sylvain Hong's *"deliciously-sauced"*
Mauritian seafood is *"sensational"*, and service is *"lovely"* too, at this
Finsbury Park stalwart; shame about the *"awful"* location and *"dead"*
ambience – *"in a better bit of town, it would be famous"*.
/ ww.chezliline.co.uk; 11 pm; closed Mon.

Chez Lindsay TW10 £42 ④❸④
11 Hill Rise 8948 7473 1–4A
"Pancakes galore", *"good seafood plates"* and *"delicious ciders"* too –
all attractions of this *"busy"* bistro of long standing, near Richmond
Bridge; even fans, though, can find the cooking *"inconsistent"*.
/ www.chezlindsay.co.uk; 11 pm; no Amex; set weekday L £22 (FP).

Chez Marcelle W14 £28 ❶⑤⑤
34 Blythe Rd 7603 3241 7–1D
*"Marcelle has delegated more, but you can still expect a lengthy
wait"*, at her *"eccentric"* café, behind Olympia; at least your meal –
"wonderful, home-cooked Lebanese dishes", at very *"restrained"*
prices – will be *"worth waiting for"*. / 10 pm; closed Mon, Tue-Thu D only,
Fri-Sun open L & D; no credit cards.

Chez Patrick W8 £45 ❸②❸
7 Stratford Rd 7937 6388 5–2A
"Patrick is a complete Gallic charmer", and – for a small but devoted
fan club – his presence helps make it worth seeking out this old-
fashioned fish restaurant, in a quiet Kensington backwater, where the
"well executed" cuisine is *"very similar to what you'd find at parallel
establishments in France"*. / www.chezpatrickinlondon.co.uk; 10.45 pm;
closed Sun D; set weekday L £25 (FP), set dinner £29 (FP).

Chilango £13 ❶②④
76 Chancery Ln, WC2 7430 1231 2–1D **NEW**
27 Upper St, N1 7704 2123 8–3D
142 Fleet St, EC4 7353 6761 9–2A
As *"snaking queues"* attest, *"the best London burritos"*, and *"quick"*
service too, have made these *"buzzy"* Mexicans a big hit; let's hope
"creeping prices" don't spoil it all! / www.chilango.co.uk; EC4 9 pm;
N1 10 pm, Fri & Sat midnight; EC4 closed Sat & Sun; no booking.

Chilli Cool WC1 £27 ❷⑤④
15 Leigh St 7383 3135 2–1D
"Not for the faint-hearted", *"the chilli-hot dishes"* at this packed
Bloomsbury café are hailed by fans as *"the best Sichuan food this
side of Chongqing"*; no-one seems too phased by the *"shockingly bad"*
service. / www.chillicool.com; 10.15 pm.

China Tang

Dorchester Hotel W1 £75 ④④❸

53 Park Ln 7629 9988 3–3A

"The best Peking duck" is a highlight, at Sir David Tang's surprisingly "old-school" Mayfair basement Chinese, which feels "like a neat and tidy opium den… but without the opium!"; given the prices, however, critics feel the food is "nothing special at all" – don't, however, miss the glamorous cocktail bar. / www.thedorchesterhotel.com; 11.30 pm; set weekday L £41 (FP).

Chinese Cricket Club EC4 £38 ❸④⑤

19 New Bridge St 7438 8051 9–3A

It may feel "like an airport departure lounge", but this room in a "bland hotel" can seem like "an absolute find" – "in the desert around Blackfriars", anywhere serving "delicious" Chinese cooking is well worth knowing about! / www.chinesecricketclub.com; 10 pm; closed Sun; no Amex.

Chipotle WC2 £19 ❸④④

114-116 Charing Cross Rd 7836 8491 4–1A

Much-ballyhooed when it opened, a year or so ago, this Mexican import (which has 1000 US branches) inspired remarkably little survey feedback this year; such reports as there were on the initial, fringe-of-Covent-Garden branch are weakly positive, however, and further openings are seemingly planned. / www.chipotle.com; 11 pm, Sun 10 pm; no bookings.

Chisou W1 £43 ❷❸④

4 Princes St 7629 3931 3–1C

"Fantastic" sushi and "a good range of izakaya-style dishes done very well" inspire enthusiastic reports on this "proper" Japanese café, near Oxford Circus; there's a "wide selection of sakes" too – "the owner is happy to talk you through them". / www.chisou.co.uk; 10.30 pm; closed Sun.

Chiswell Street Dining Rooms EC1 NEW £53 ❸❷❸

56 Chiswell St 07872 456 090 12–2A

The latest addition to the empire of the Martin brothers (of 'Gun' and so on fame), this comfortable, if quite loud, newcomer was already doing impressive City-lunching business on our early-days visit; service was notably good. / Rated on Editors' visit.

Chiswick House Cafe W4 £24 ④⑤❸

Burlington Ln 8995 6356 10–1A

"You love or hate the new building" (a symphony in concrete), but this year-old park café undoubtedly occupies "such an idyllic spot"; "why didn't an independent get it", though? – the menu's "very limited", and service "breaks down" at peak times. / www.chiswickhousecafe.com; 5 pm; L only; no Amex.

Cho-San SW15 £40 ❷❸④

292 Upper Richmond Rd 8788 9626 10–2A

"An authentic slice of Japan"; this Putney veteran may seem a little worn nowadays, but compensates with "lovely, family service" and "utterly dependable" fare, including some "great sushi". / 10.30 pm; closed Mon.

Chop'd £12 ❸❸④
52 Curzon St, W1   7495 1014   3–3B
St Pancras International, NW1   7837 1603   8–3C
Unit 1 34 The North Colonnade, E14   3229 0087   11–1C
2 Horner Sq, Old Spitalfields Mkt, E1   7247 8757   12–2B
1 Leadenhall Mkt, EC3   7626 3706   9–2D
"Choose from pre-made or pick-your-own", at this "efficient" chain, which serves a "huge variety of fresh and healthy salads", and "with a smile" too; "they're a bit pricey for every day, though". / www.chopd.co.uk; most branches 4 pm, NW1 9 pm; most branches Sat & Sun; no Amex.

Chor Bizarre W1 £43 ④④❷
16 Albemarle St   7629 9802   3–3C
"Kitsch" but "comfortable", this Mayfair Indian is "crammed" with bric-a-brac; fans say it's "an excellent venue for business or pleasure", but service can be "brusque" or "dippy", and its "good-but-not-outstanding" food comes "at a price". / www.chorbizarre.com; 11.30 pm, Sun 10.30 pm.

Choys SW3 £38 ④④④
172 King's Rd   7352 9085   5–3C
The "fairly standard" menu is never going to set the world on fire, but this "well-established" (1952!) Chelsea Chinese is a "friendly" place that "rarely surprises or disappoints". / 11 pm.

Christopher's WC2 £64 ④❸❸
18 Wellington St   7240 4222   4–3D
It's still sometimes hailed as a top brunch or business venue, but this grand surf 'n' turf American, in a gorgeous Covent Garden townhouse, has had a lot of "bad days" of late, with its pricey fare seeming "very unimaginative" – "the bar menu may be the best option". / www.christophersgrill.com; 11.30 pm, Sun 10.30 pm; booking: max 12; set pre theatre £36 (FP).

Chuen Cheng Ku W1 £33 ❸④④
17 Wardour St   7437 1398   4–3A
"Trolleys of steaming dim sum" weaving around the "busy" dining rooms are a trademark of this Chinatown landmark – a "fun", "fast" and "reasonably-priced" experience ("brilliant with young kids, as there's no hanging about"). / www.chuenchengku.co.uk; 11.45 pm.

Churchill Arms W8 £26 ❷❸❷
119 Kensington Church St   7792 1246   6–2B
"Always busy, always fun, always good value!" – this "bustling" but "lovely" pub-annex, near Notting Hill Gate, is "an institution" of over 20 years' standing, serving "incredibly cheap" Thai scoff that's "tasty well beyond its price". / 10 pm, 9.30 pm.

Chutney SW18 £29 ❷❷❸
11 Alma Rd   8870 4588   10–2B
Food that's "full of fresh flavours" helps make this "always-busy" Wandsworth local "much better than your average curry house". / www.chutneyrestaurant.co.uk; 11.30 pm; D only.

Chutney Mary SW10 £55 ❷❷❷
535 King's Rd   7351 3113   5–4B
An "upmarket" World's End Indian of over 20 years' standing that still "consistently delivers" an excellent all-round experience; service is "wonderful" and the "interesting" cooking "subtly aromatic" too – "not just spicy". / www.realindianfood.com; 11.30 pm, Sun 10.30 pm; closed weekday L; booking: max 10.

Chutneys NW1 £29 ❸❸❸
124 Drummond St 7388 0604 8–4C
*The "tasty" all-you-can-eat buffet (lunch and all-day Sunday) is the
main draw to this long-serving south Indian veggie, near Euston
station – it's "incredible value". / www.chutneyseuston.co.uk; 11 pm;
no Amex; need 5+ to book.*

Ciao Bella WC1 £41 ❹❷❷
86-90 Lamb's Conduit St 7242 4119 2–1D
*"You are always greeted like a long-lost relative", at this "noisy and
bustling" Bloomsbury veteran; the food's main virtue is arguably that
it's "cheap", but fans like its "reliability", and in any case a visit
is usually "great fun". / www.ciaobellarestaurant.co.uk; 11.30 pm,
Sun 10.30 pm.*

Cibo W14 £44 ❸❸❹
3 Russell Gdns 7371 6271 7–1D
*Fans proclaim "exciting" food and "wonderful" wines at this once-
famous Italian, in the backwoods of Olympia; given that no one has
a bad word to say about the place, it's a bit of a mystery why
it incites so few reports. / www.ciborestaurant.net; 11 pm; closed Sun D.*

Cicada EC1 £40 ❷❷❸
132-136 St John St 7608 1550 9–1B
*Will Ricker's early-wave pan-Asian fusion hang-out, in Shoreditch, still
manages to be "trendy and eclectic"; hey, after all these years the
food – with "extra heat and zing" – has even "got better of late" too!
/ www.rickerrestaurants.com; 11 pm; closed Sat L & Sun; set always available
£25 (FP).*

Cigala WC1 £48 ❸❸❹
54 Lamb's Conduit St 7405 1717 2–1D
*"Humming and popular", this Bloomsbury corner spot is of note for
its "real" ("if not entirely consistent") Spanish cooking and some
"exciting" wines to go with it; service is "friendly" too, if sometimes
"over-stretched". / www.cigala.co.uk; 10.45 pm, Sun 9.30 pm.*

Le Cigalon WC2 NEW £50 ❷❷❷
115 Chancery Ln 7242 8373 2–2D
*In a "light and airy" room, this new Provençal addition to the Club
Gascon stable "fills a real gap in Midtown", especially as a place
to wine and dine legal types – the lunch menu is particularly
"good value"; downstairs, in the bar, check out the pétanque court!
/ www.cigalon.co.uk/; 10 pm; closed Sat & Sun.*

THE CINNAMON CLUB SW1 £67 ❷❸❷
Old Westminster Library, Great Smith St 7222 2555 2–4C
*"Full of MPs, union leaders and spin-doctors... otherwise excellent!";
this "beautiful" former library, near Westminster Abbey, is renowned
as one of London's foremost subcontinentals thanks to the "exquisite"
twists it puts on Indian cuisine; prices are "hefty", though – look out
for lunch and early-evening deals. / www.cinnamonclub.com; 10.45 pm;
closed Sun; no trainers.*

Cinnamon Kitchen EC2 £56 ❷❸❹
9 Devonshire Sq 7626 5000 9–2D
*After a cracking debut, this "slick" two-year-old sibling
to Westminster's famous Cinnamon Club ("hidden-away near
Liverpool Street") is losing some ground – the "very clever" cooking
is still "fabulous", but the style seems ever more "corporate".
/ www.cinnamon-kitchen.com; 11 pm; closed Sat L & Sun; set weekday L
£34 (FP).*

Book*a*table ♥

If you're eating out
bookatable.com

Circus WC2 £58 ④④②
27-29 Endell St 7420 9300 4–2C
*You watch circus acts while you eat – often right in front of your nose
– at this year-old Covent Garden burlesque-joint; the few reports
it attracts suggest it's a "vibrant" experience, from which the cooking
does not positively detract. / www.circus-london.co.uk; midnight, Fri & Sat
2 am; closed Sun; no Amex; set pre theatre £38 (FP).*

City Café
Mint Westminster SW1 £46 ④③④
30 John Islip St 7932 4600 2–4C
*"Great-value buffets" – on Sunday and for breakfast – are the
highlights at this "spacious and comfortable", if "atmosphere-free",
dining room, near Tate Britain. / www.citycafe.co.uk; 10.30pm, Sun 10 pm.*

City Miyama EC4 £52 ②④⑤
17 Godliman St 7489 1937 9–3B
*"The space is so dull, but the food is always good", at this "authentic"
Japanese basement, in the City; "superb sushi" at the upstairs bar
is a highlight. / www.miyama.co.uk; 9.30 pm; closed Sat D & Sun;
set weekday L £31 (FP).*

Clarke's W8 £62 ②②③
124 Kensington Church St 7221 9225 6–2B
*Sally Clarke's once-"pioneering" California-inspired veteran,
near Notting Hill Gate, remains for most reporters a "fantastic" spot,
with "elegant" decor and "refined" cuisine; a disgruntled minority,
though, fear it's becoming "tired", and "trading on its reputation".
/ www.sallyclarke.com; 10 pm; closed Sun D; booking: max 14.*

Clifton E1 £26 ③③③
1 Whitechapel Rd 7377 5533 9–2D
*One of the better-known Brick Lane Indians – it doesn't inspire 'raves'
from reporters, but it is consistently well-rated.
/ www.cliftonrestaurant.com; midnight.*

The Clissold Arms N2 £44 ④④④
Fortis Grn 8444 4224 1–1C
*"Some food shows real flair", at this popular Muswell Hill gastropub,
which benefits from a "beautiful" outside area; it's "expensive"
though, and not everyone likes the reintroduction of the "garish"
Kinks memorabilia to pep up the "uninspiring" modern interior.
/ 10 pm, Sun 9 pm.*

CLOS MAGGIORE WC2 £54 ②①①
33 King St 7379 9696 4–3C
*"Like an enchanted garden", the "breathtaking" conservatory of this
Covent Garden "oasis" is the survey's newly-crowned 'top spot for
romance'; that's not its only attraction, though – reports consistently
praise its "delicious" cooking and "unbeatable" service, not to
mention a wine list of over 2000 bins. / www.closmaggiore.com; Mon-Sat
11 pm, Sun 10 pm.*

Club Gascon EC1 £75 ②②③
57 West Smithfield 7796 0600 9–2B
*"Unforgettable" foie-gras, and "small plates" of other "very rich" and
"crazily good" Gascon delicacies – complemented by "amazing"
SW France wines – make this "elegant" and "romantic", if "tightly-
packed", Smithfield favourite "an experience to savour".
/ www.clubgascon.com; 10 pm, Fri-Sat 10.30 pm; closed Sat L & Sun.*

Coach & Horses EC1 £40 ❷❷❸
26-28 Ray St 7278 8990 9–1A
*"Tucked-away in Clerkenwell", a "reliable" and "unfussy"
gastroboozer, offering "a short menu full of seasonal food that sounds
lovely and tastes better". / www.thecoachandhorses.com; 10 pm; closed
Sat L & Sun D.*

Cochin Brasserie SW15 £30 ❷④④
193 Lower Richmond Rd 8785 6004 10–1A
*"Eclectic" south Indian dishes are "beautifully prepared" – and some
are "absolutely exceptional" – at this low-key Putney curry house;
"the kitchen can be slow, but waiting staff are as helpful as can be".
/ www.cochinbrasserie.com; 11 pm; D only.*

Cochonnet W9 £43 ❸❷❸
1 Lauderdale Pde 7289 0393 1–2B
*"A great little local", in Maida Vale, "which is busy every night of the
week", thanks to its "good, standard Italian fare",
not least "the best pizza". / www.cochonnet.co.uk; 10.30 pm.*

Cock Tavern EC1 £29 ❸④④
Smithfield Mkt 7236 4923 9–2A
*"The butchers eat here, which says it all!" – this café-like pub,
actually under Smithfield market, offers "superb full English
breakfasts", with meat "straight from the market"; Guinness on tap
too. / www.thecocktavern.com; 7.30pm; L only, closed Sat & Sun.*

Cocorino £15 ❶❶❸
18 Chilton St, W1 7935 0860 2–1A NEW
18 Thayer St, W1 7935 0810 3–1A
*"A tiny hole in the wall", off Marylebone High Street, serving "world-
beating ice creams" and "delicious" focaccia-based snacks,
from breakfast onwards; there's now a nearby 'espresso room' too.
/ Thayer Street 8 pm; Chilton Street Mon-Sat 6 pm, Sun 5 pm; no Amex;
no bookings.*

Cocotte NW3 NEW £43 ④④❸
85b Fleet Rd 7433 3317 8–2A
*Owners who are "friendly, relaxed and utterly charming" add much
to the mood at this "lovely" Gallic newcomer, by South End Green,
which serves up "fairly-priced traditional bistro fare". / 11 pm; closed
Mon, Tue L, Wed L, Thu L & Sun D; set weekday L £24 (FP).*

Cocum SW20 £30 ❸❸❸
9 Approach Rd 8540 3250 10–2B
*A Raynes Park Keralan that's "improved" in recent times, and of note
for the "consistent, well-balanced flavours" of its cuisine.
/ www.cocumrestaurant.co.uk; 10.30 pm, Sun 10 pm; no Amex.*

La Collina NW1 £47
17 Princess Rd 7483 0192 8–3B
*New owners took over this Primrose Hill Italian (which has a lovely
garden for the summer) just as our survey for the year was
concluding; let's hope the first (and so far only) report – of "delicious"
cooking and "great value for money" – is the start of a trend! / 11 pm.*

Le Colombier SW3 £58 ❸❷❷
145 Dovehouse St 7351 1155 5–2C
*"Very genteel and Parisian", Didier Garnier's "discreet" Chelsea
brasserie remains "very popular with the locals"; the food, though,
is an attraction rather incidental to the "professional" service,
the "very good and reasonably-priced wines", and the exceptional
terrace. / www.le-colombier-restaurant.co.uk; 10.30 pm, Sun 10 pm.*

Colony W1   £54   ❸④⑤
7-9 Paddington St   7935 3353   2–1A
Star chef Atul Kochar is no longer involved in this low-lit Indian
yearling, in Marylebone, which is based around a tapas-style concept
that's yet to catch fire; fans applaud its "exquisite" dishes, but to
critics the small plates here are just "a good example of how not
to do it!" / www.colonybarandgrill.com; 10.45 pm, Sun 10.30 pm;
set weekday L £30 (FP).

Como Lario SW1   £47   ⑤④❸
18-22 Holbein Pl   7730 2954   5–2D
Diehard fans say "it always has a happy atmosphere", but this
trattoria "classic", off Sloane Square, is badly on the slide – the food's
"gone downhill fast", and service has sometimes been notably "off-
hand" of late. / www.comolario.uk.com; 11.30 pm, Sun 10 pm; set Sun L
£30 (FP).

The Compass N1   £38   ❸④❸
58 Penton St   7837 3891   8–3D
"A little Chapel Market gem", this "cheerful" gastropub has a "cosy"
interior, and offers "accurate" cooking too. / thecompassn1.co.uk;
9.45 pm, Sun 7.45 pm; closed Mon L & Tue L; no Amex.

Comptoir Gascon EC1   £47   ❷❸❷
63 Charterhouse St   7608 0851   9–1A
"Duck and gamey delights abound", on the "hearty" and
"wonderfully simple" menu of SW French fare on offer at at this
"lovely" Smithfield bistro; it's "well priced" too.
/ www.comptoirgascon.com; 10 pm, Thu & Fri 11 pm; closed Mon & Sun.

Comptoir Libanais   £18   ④⑤④
65 Wigmore St, W1   7935 1110   3–1A
Westfield, The Balcony, W12   8811 2222   7–1C
Fans still tout these "fun"-looking Middle Easterners as a decent
"cheap 'n' cheerful" experience; too many reporters, however,
now talk of food that's "tasteless", and service that's "unacceptably
slow". / www.lecomptoir.co.uk; W12 9 pm, Thu & Fri 10 pm, Sun 6 pm;
W1 9.30 pm; W12 closed Sun D; no Amex; no bookings.

Constancia SE1   £42   ❷❶❷
52 Tanner St   7234 0676   9–4D
"Everyone needs a local steakhouse like this", say fans of this
"very authentic" Argentinian, just south of Tower Bridge; highlights
of the "relatively short" menu include "fabulous" meat (of course)
and "tasty" puddings. / www.constancia.co.uk; 10.30 pm; D only; no Amex.

Il Convivio SW1   £56   ❸❸④
143 Ebury St   7730 4099   2–4A
"Why don't more people know about this wonderful restaurant?",
wonder fans of this swish Belgravia Italian; critics, though, see the
glass as half-empty – they cite "nothing special on the food front",
"slow service", and an interior that feels "like a rehash of a typical
'90s trattoria". / www.etruscarestaurants.com; 10.45 pm; closed Sun.

Coq d'Argent EC2   £66   ④⑤④
1 Poultry   7395 5000   9–2C
"Formulaic" food, "unhelpful" service and a "lifeless" dining room,
all at "sky-high prices" – no once could say a visit to this 6th-floor
D&D group venue is without its pitfalls; it remains popular for City
entertaining, though, thanks not least to its "memorable" rooftop
gardens (for drinks). / www.coqdargent.co.uk; 9.45 pm; closed
Sat L & Sun D.

Cork & Bottle WC2   £42   ⑤④❷
44-46 Cranbourn St   7734 7807   4–3B
"You don't come for the food" (not even the 'famous' cheese 'n' ham pie!) to this "secret" but "handy" hide-away, by a Leicester Square sex shop – it's the "fantastic" wine which is the real draw; "don't delay your trip, as Don, the owner, is going to retire at some point". / www.corkandbottle.net; 11.30 pm, Sun 10.30 pm; no booking after 6.30 pm.

Corner Room E2 NEW   £37
Patriot Sq   7871 0461   1–2D
Don't fancy the outré fare on offer at Bethnal Green's ambitious Viajante? – try this adjacent mid-2011 newcomer, where Nuno Mendes offers a much simpler and more accessible cuisine; we sadly didn't have the opportunity to visit before this guide went to press. / www.viajante.co.uk.

Corrigan's Mayfair W1   £70   ❸❸❸
28 Upper Grosvenor St   7499 9943   3–3A
"Fish and game done to perfection" head up the list of attractions, at this Irish chef's "luxurious" Mayfair dining room; its performance "dropped off" notably this year, however, with a number of "disastrous" reports, exacerbated by "wince-making" prices. / www.corrigansmayfair.com; 11 pm, Sun 9 pm; closed Sat L; booking: max 8; set always available £44 (FP).

Costa's Grill W8   £25   ④❸④
12-14 Hillgate St   7229 3794   6–2B
An "unpretentious" and inexpensive taverna of aeons standing, just off Notting Hill Gate, with a "charming garden"; "it may be average, but I'd still happily eat here every day!" / www.costasgrill.com; 10.30 pm; closed Sun.

Côte   £38   ④❸❷
124-126 Wardour St, W1   7287 9280   3–1D
17-21 Tavistock St, WC2   7379 9991   4–3D
98 Westbourne Grove, W2   7792 3298   6–1B NEW
50-54 Turnham Green Ter, W4   8747 6788   7–2A NEW
47 Kensington Ct, W8   7938 4147   5–1A
Hays Galleria, Tooley St, SE1   7234 0800   9–4D
8 High St, SW19   8947 7100   10–2B
45-47 Parsons Green Ln, SW6   7736 8444   10–1B
26 Ludgate Hill, EC4   7236 4399   9–2A NEW
"What Café Rouge used to aspire to be"; Richard Caring's burgeoning group of Gallic bistros may seem increasingly "formulaic", but it can still offer some "pleasant surprises" on the food front, and "by high street chain standards, service and atmosphere are excellent too". / www.cote-restaurants.co.uk; 11 pm.

The Courtauld Gallery Café
The Courtauld Gallery WC2   £27   ④❸❸
Somerset Hs, Strand   7848 2527   2–2D
Off a sunken courtyard, just a few feet from the Strand, a "convenient" café serving "a good choice of good-value dishes" – it's especially worth seeking out on a sunny day, when the al fresco tables offer one of London's nicest surprises. / 3 pm; no Amex.

The Cow W2   £49   ❸④❷
89 Westbourne Park Rd   7221 0021   6–1B
Tom Conran's "busy and buzzy" faux-Irish boozer, in Bayswater, continues to pack in a hip crowd with its "consistently good" realisation of simple seafood dishes – "no reservations, expect to wait"; upstairs, the formula is more formal. / www.thecowlondon.co.uk; 11 pm, Sun 10.30 pm; no Amex.

Crazy Bear W1   £53   ❸❸❶
26-28 Whitfield St   7631 0088   2–1C
Kick off with a cocktail in the "fun" and "vibey" basement bar, if you
visit this glamorously opulent Fitzrovia venue; there's a "great range"
of pan-Asian food too, but it's "expensive" and "rather overshadowed
by the decor". / www.crazybeargroup.co.uk; 10.30 pm; no shorts.

Crazy Homies W2   £42   ❸❹❶
125 Westbourne Park Rd   7727 6771   6–1B
Tom Conran's "fun and buzzy" – read "loud" and "squashed" –
Bayswater cantina is "mostly about the vibe"; but while
"good Mexican food is hard to find in London", this place "makes
a decent stab at it". / www.crazyhomieslondon.co.uk; 11 pm; closed
weekday L; no Amex.

Criterion W1   £66   ❹❹❷
224 Piccadilly   7930 0488   3–3D
"Opulent" and "very spacious", this neo-Byzantine chamber, right
on Piccadilly Circus, is a "stunning" space; its ambience can still seem
surprisingly "low-key", though, not helped by iffy service and food that
"at the price, should be better". / www.criterionrestaurant.com; 11.30 pm,
Sun 9 pm; set weekday L & pre-theatre £39 (FP).

Crussh   £14   ❸❷❹
Branches throughout London
"Healthy alternatives to your usual sandwiches" – including "great
salads and soups" – win universal praise for this "innovative" small
chain; "fresh juices and smoothies too", of course. / www.crussh.com;
4.30 pm-8 pm,; many branches closed all or part of weekend; no credit cards
in many branches.

Cumberland Arms W14   £41   ❸❸❸
29 North End Rd   7371 6806   7–2D
"Unpretentious" and "mellow", this Olympia spot ticks all of the
obvious boxes for a congenial local gastropub.
/ www.thecumberlandarmspub.co.uk; 10 pm, Sun 9.30 pm.

Curve / Manhattan Grill
London Marriott W' India Quay E14
22 Hertsmere Rd   7517 2808   11–1C
As this guide goes to press, this large waterside dining room by
Canary Wharf is to be reformatted from a fish restaurant, into a
steak house. / www.marriothotel.co.uk; 10.30 pm, Sun 10 pm; closed
Sat L & Sun L; set always available £37 (FP).

Cut
45 Park Lane W1 NEW
45 Park Ln   7493 4545   3–4A
Opening in late-2011, this grand surf 'n' turf specialist, in a new
Mayfair hotel, will be the first European venture of eminent
Austrian/Californian restaurateur Wolfgang Puck.
/ www.45parklane.com.

Cyprus Mangal SW1   £29   ❷❸❹
45 Warwick Way   7828 5940   2–4B
A "cramped" Pimlico dive, where the neighbouring parking bays are
"clogged with black cabs", attracted by "big plates of shish kebab"
at "cheap" prices. / Sun-Thu midnight, Fri & Sat 1 am.

Da Mario SW7 £39 ④❷❸
15 Gloucester Rd 7584 9078 5–1B
*Proximity to the Albert Hall and a "buzzing" atmosphere are prime
selling points of this long-established and family-friendly Italian;
its pizza 'n' pasta fare is "reliable, but not outstanding in any way".
/ www.damario.co.uk; 11.30 pm.*

Da Mario WC2 £39 ④❷❷
63 Endell St 7240 3632 4–1C
*In touristy Covent Garden, it's "a joy", say fans, to stumble upon this
"tiny", age-old, family-run trattoria – a "genuine Italian" serving
"speedy pre-performance meals" in a "cramped" interior with
"real buzz".*

da Polpo WC2 NEW £30 ❸❷④
6 Maiden Ln 7836 8448 4–3D
*The fourth member of Russell Norman's quickly-created Venetian
tapas empire makes a handy addition to Covent Garden's improving
dining-out scene; by the group's vibey standards, though, the interior
is bare and rather lacking in character. / Rated on Editors' visit.*

Dalchini SW19 £36 ❸❸④
147 Arthur Rd 8947 5966 10–2B
*"A great cross-over of Indian and Chinese cuisine" – the 'Hakka'
dishes at this "different" local, opposite Wimbledon Park tube,
are "really interesting", and "super value" too. / www.dalchini.co.uk;
10.30 pm, Fri & Sat 11 pm; no Amex.*

Dans le Noir EC1 £70 ⑤④❶
29 Clerkenwell Grn 7253 1100 9–1A
*"If you're looking for something different", try a meal in the pitch
black, at this crackpot Farringdon theme-restaurant, where "you eat
as if you were blind" (as the staff actually are); "the novelty wears off
quickly", though – the food is "diabolical" and "overpriced", and the
staff can be "grumpy" too! / www.danslenoir.com; 9.30 pm; D only.*

Daphne NW1 £34 ❸❶❶
83 Bayham St 7267 7322 8–3C
*"Without question, the friendliest Greek in London!" – fans aren't shy
in their praise for this veteran Camden Town taverna, where the
"tasty" cuisine includes some "interesting specials"; pleasant roof
terrace. / 11.30 pm; closed Sun; no Amex.*

Daphne's SW3 £57 ❸❷❷
112 Draycott Ave 7589 4257 5–2C
*This "timeless Italian", near Brompton Cross, remains a "must-visit"
for many reporters, thanks to its "lovely", "romantic" style and its
"warm" and "professional" service; prices are "not for the faint-
hearted", but the food – "while not trail-blazing" – is "amazingly
consistent". / www.daphnes-restaurant.co.uk; 11.30 pm; set weekday L &
pre-theatre £36 (FP).*

The Dartmouth Arms SE23 £36 ❸❸❷
7 Dartmouth Rd 8488 3117 1–4D
*"Still the best for miles around" – a "gem" of a Forest Hill
gastroboozer, which wins quite a following with its "deliciously
consistent" cuisine. / www.thedartmoutharms.com; 10 pm, Sun 9 pm;
no Amex.*

Daylesford Organic £40 ④⑤④
44b Pimlico Rd, SW1 7881 8060 5–2D
208-212 Westbourne Grove, W11 7313 8050 6–1B
These "smart" deli/cafés are often "full of yummy mummies and
their adorable children"; fans plug breakfasts as being of "top-quality
simplicity", and say the other fare is "delicious" too – critics are more
inclined to note "truly absurd" prices, and "the worst ever" service.
/ www.daylesfordorganic.com; 5 pm-8 pm, Sun 4 pm-6 pm; W11 no booking L.

Dean Street Townhouse W1 £58 ④❸❷
69-71 Dean St 7434 1775 4–2A
"Slightly Manhattanite, but very British", this panelled Soho dining
room (part of the trendy Soho House group) is "the place to go for
people-watching and general glamour"; the food – "homely" or "plain
and unimaginative", according to your viewpoint – is rather incidental.
/ www.deanstreettownhouse.com; midnight; set pre theatre £36 (FP).

Defune W1 £46 ❷⓪④
34 George St 7935 8311 3–1A
A long-established Marylebone Japanese where the story never
changes – the sushi is "excellent", but you pay "silly prices" to endure
sitting in either a "dreary basement", or on the "characterless
first floor". / 10.30 pm.

Dehesa W1 £41 ❶❶❷
25 Ganton St 7494 4170 3–2C
"Superbly moreish" Italian/Spanish tapas, "perceptive" staff and
a "lively" atmosphere make this small bar/café, off Carnaby Street,
a "wonderful" all-rounder (now eclipsing its elder sibling, Salt Yard);
seating is limited (and "cramped" too), so "booking is essential".
/ www.dehesa.co.uk; 11 pm; closed Sun D.

Del'Aziz £41 ④⑤❷
24-32 Vanston Pl, SW6 7386 0086 5–4A
Westfield, Ariel Way, W12 8740 0666 7–1C
Swiss Cottage Leis' C', Adelaide Rd, NW3 7586 3338 8–2A
11 Bermondsey Sq, SE1 7407 2991 9–4D
5 Canvey St, SE1 7633 0033 9–3B
Fans really take to the "trendy" and "vibrant" style of this Moroccan-
inspired chain, whose culinary attractions include an "unusual
brunch", "a great mezze selection", and cakes and coffee; "awful"
service, though, can take the edge off the experience, and critics find
the grub "very average" too. / www.delaziz.co.uk; SW6 10.30 pm;
NW3 9.30 pm; SE1 11 pm; W12 10.45 pm, Sun 9.45 pm; SE1 11 pm;
NW3 D sat, sun.

Delfina SE1 £47 ❸❸❸
50 Bermondsey St 7357 0244 9–4D
"Vast and starkly white", this Bermondsey gallery creates
a "fantastically airy and uncluttered space" for a meal; the cooking
doesn't hit the heights it once did, but most reports still praise it as
"thoughtful". / www.thedelfina.co.uk; 10 pm; closed Sun-Thu D, Fri open
L & D, closed Sat.

Delfino W1 £43 ❷④④
121 Mount St 7499 1256 3–3B
"The thin-crust pizzas are historic!", at this "utilitarian" Mayfair
basement-Italian – a particularly "handy" stand-by in a
"stratospherically expensive part of town". / www.finos.co.uk; 11 pm;
closed Sun.

La Delizia £34 ❸❸❸

63-65 Chelsea Manor St, SW3   7376 4111   5–3C
314 Trinity Rd, SW18   88759 595   10–2C **NEW**

*It may be "cramped", but this "small, very Italian-feeling local", in a
Chelsea back street, "has been making authentic, wood-oven pizzas
since long before it was the fancy thing to do, and still turns out some
of the best"; it now has an offshoot in Wandsworth too. / 11 pm,
Sun 10.30; no Amex.*

The Depot SW14 £40 ❸❷❶

Tideway Yd, Mortlake High St   8878 9462   10–1A

*"Radically improved" service of late and better-rated cooking too
make this local favourite, near Barnes Bridge, more than
just an "atmosphere" recommendation nowadays – you still shouldn't
forget, though, to "ask for a window table overlooking the Thames".
/ www.depotbrasserie.co.uk; 10 pm, Sun 9.30 pm.*

LES DEUX SALONS WC2 £54 ❸❹❸

40-42 William IV St   7420 2050   4–4C

*"It could be Paris!"; handily located near Charing Cross, Will Smith
and Anthony Demetre's hugely popular new brasserie – a sibling
to Arbutus – is, say fans, "a brilliant addition to London"; critics,
though, "don't think the food's that exciting", and find the survey's
most-mentioned newcomer "massively overhyped".
/ www.lesdeuxsalons.co.uk; 11 pm; set weekday L & pre-theatre £28 (FP).*

Le Deuxième WC2 £55 ❹❸❺

65a Long Acre   7379 0033   4–2D

*"A reliable stand-by, near the Royal Opera House"; it may have
"no decor at all", but it's an "efficient" operation, offering "solid
bistro-cooking". / www.ledeuxieme.com; midnight, Sun 11 pm; set weekday
L & pre-theatre £31 (FP).*

dim T £31 ❺❹❸

56-62 Wilton Rd, SW1   7834 0507   2–4B
32 Charlotte St, W1   7637 1122   2–1C
1 Hampstead Ln, N6   8340 8800   8–1B
3 Heath St, NW3   7435 0024   8–2A
Tooley St, SE1   7403 7000   9–4D

*"After a bright start, quality has fallen off a cliff", at this budget pan-
Asian chain; positives include stylish interiors (and "great views"
in SE1), but the downsides can include "tasteless" food and
amateurish service. / www.dimt.co.uk; most branches 11 pm, Sun 10.30pm.*

Diner £31 ❺❺❸

18 Ganton St, W1   7287 8962   3–2C
21 Essex Rd, N1   7226 4533   8–3D
64-66 Chamberlayne Rd, NW10   8968 9033   1–2B
2 Jamestown Rd, NW1   7485 5223   8–3B
128 Curtain Rd, EC2   7729 4452   12–1B

*Such a shame these "lively" American diners – with the possible
exception of the Shoreditch original – so often fail to live up to the
dream; on a bad day, the food is "like cardboard", and the service
"can be pretty trying too". / www.thedinershoreditch.com; midnight; W1 &
NW1 Sun 11.30 pm; EC2 Sun & Mon 10.30 pm; booking: max 10.*

Dinings W1 £42 ❶❷❺

22 Harcourt St   7723 0666   8–4A

*"OK, it's in a bunker", but Tomonari Chiba's "brutalist" Japanese
basement, "tucked-away" in Marylebone, is nonetheless
an "overwhelmingly excellent" place, offering sushi and sashimi that
are "cutting-edge" creative, and "super, super, super fresh" too.
/ www.dinings.co.uk; 10.30 pm; closed Sat L & Sun.*

DINNER
MANDARIN ORIENTAL SW1   £94   ❷❷❷
66 Knightsbridge   7201 3833   5–1D
"Surprisingly it lives up to the hype!"; Heston B's "modern Olde English food" – "beautifully executed with a dash of showmanship" – has made his Knightsbridge newcomer the hit of the year; prices are "remarkable" too, though, and the room is a bit "hotel-like" (even if some lucky lunchers do get "amazing" park-views).
/ www.dinnerbyheston.com; 10.45 pm; set weekday L £56 (FP).

Dishoom WC2   £35   ❷❸❶
12 Upper St Martins Ln   7420 9320   4–3B
"Just like Bombay in the 1950s!" – the "delightfully elegant" interior of this Covent Garden chain-prototype has a suitably "energetic" atmosphere; its "spicy" street food is generally "very flavoursome", and hailed as "quite authentic" too. / www.dishoom.com; 11 pm, Fri & Sat midnight, Sun 10 pm; booking 6+ D.

Diwana Bhel-Poori House NW1   £28   ❸⑤⑤
121-123 Drummond St   7387 5556   8–4C
"A lunchtime buffet worth travelling for" is still the top tip at this "absurdly cheap", '60s-survivor, veggie canteen, in the Little India near Euston; it's "not as marvellous as it was a few years ago" though, and still gets "no prizes for decor"; BYO.
/ diwanabhelpoori.co.uk; 11.45 pm, Sun 11 pm; need 10+ to book.

The Dock Kitchen
Portobello Dock W10   £49   ❸❸❶
344 Ladbroke Grove   8962 1610   1–2B
Steve Parle's "funky" café, by the canal in North Kensington, offers "thoughtful" food from an "eclectic" and ever-changing set menu; it's "gone downhill" since it opened, though – results can be "patchy depending on the night", and "amateurish" service increasingly "seems to believe its own PR". / www.dockkitchen.co.uk; 10 pm; closed Sun D.

Dockmaster's House E14   £50   ④④❸
1 Hertsmere Rd   7345 0345   11–1C
An "out-of-the-way" nouvelle Indian, near Canary Wharf, praised by fans for its "inventive" cuisine, and its "relaxed" setting in a lovely Georgian house; service is increasingly "erratic", though, and "some dishes work better than others".
/ www.dockmastershouse.com; 11 pm; closed Sat L & Sun.

Dolada W1   £51   ❸❸④
13 Albermarle St   7409 1011   3–3C
Fans of this Mayfair basement venture applaud its "proper" Italian cooking, "stylish" decor and "discreet yet friendly" staff… or, to put it another way, it's "a pretty dull place, with OK food, and suited to business lunches". / www.dolada.co.uk; 10.30 pm; closed Sat L & Sun.

$ EC1   £42   ④④❸
2 Exmouth Mkt   7278 0077   9–1A
Dwindling feedback supports those who say this attractive Clerkenwell haunt has "gone massively downhill" – "it used to do the best burger around", but now "it's a place for cocktails rather than food". / www.dollargrills.com; 11.30 pm, Tue & Wed 11 pm, Sun & Mon 10 pm.

The Don EC4 £58 ❸❷❸
20 St Swithin's Ln 7626 2606 9–3C
The Square Mile's "best business option" – in "characterful" premises near Bank – has a "top-quality" restaurant on the ground floor, and a "convivial" bistro below ("in the old port cellar"); overall, it's a very "professional" operation, but the "outstanding" wines and sherries are a greater draw than the "competent" cuisine.
/ www.thedonrestaurant.com; 10 pm; closed Sat & Sun; no trainers.

don Fernando's TW9 £42 ❸❷❸
27f The Quadrant 8948 6447 1–4A
This large family-run "Spanish tapas restaurant", by the railway station, "has served Richmond incredibly well over the years" – it's a "fun" place, with "responsive" service and "ever-reliable" food.
/ www.donfernando.co.uk; 11 pm; no Amex; no booking.

Don Pepe NW8 £34 ❸❷❸
99 Frampton St 7262 3834 8–4A
A stalwart St John's Wood tapas bar where "everything looks so tasty, the only problem is choosing"; "revisiting after 20 years, I found just the same waiters – they seemed a little older, but were still just as friendly". / 11.30 pm; closed Sun; no Amex.

Donna Margherita SW11 £41 ❷❸❷
183 Lavender Hill 7228 2660 10–2C
"Antipasto and pizza just like they serve back in Naples" make this "jolly" and "easy-going" Battersea spot very popular; it helps that it's "very reasonably priced" too. / www.donna-margherita.com; 10.30 pm, Fri-Sat 11 pm; closed weekday L.

**Dorchester Grill
Dorchester Hotel W1** £89 ❹❸❹
53 Park Ln 7629 8888 3–3A
"Hideous" tartan decor aside, this "opulent" Mayfair grill room has attracted (somewhat) more praise of late for its straightforward cuisine, and its often "excellent" service – prices, though, still tend to "exorbitant". / www.thedorchester.com; 10.45 pm, Sun 10.15 pm; no trainers; set weekday L £52 (FP).

Dose EC1 £10 ❷❹❹
70 Long Ln 7600 0382 9–1B
"The best of London's Antipodean coffee shops" now occupies larger premises next door to its original site; it's "a great place to grab and go" at any time, with "super breakfasts" a highlight.
/ www.dose-espresso.com; L only; no Amex.

Dotori N4 £26 ❷❸❸
3 Stroud Green Rd 7263 3562 8–1D
"Book early, and expect to wait for a table even so", at this "minuscule" Finsbury Park outfit, where "charming" (if "harried") staff serve up some "super-fresh" and "authentic" Korean and Japanese fare. / 10.30 pm; closed Mon; no Amex.

Doukan SW18 £37 ❸❷❷
350 Old York Rd 8870 8280 10–2B
"Tasty and varied" Moroccan grub is part of the all-round formula that makes this friendly and atmospheric Wandsworth spot a very superior local. / www.doukan.co.uk; Tue-Thu 10 pm, Fri-Sat 10.30 pm, Sun 5 pm; closed Mon & Sun D; no Amex.

Dragon Castle SE17 £35 ❷④④
100 Walworth Rd 7277 3388 1–3C
In unlovely Elephant & Castle, this "huge" Chinese "oasis" has carved
out quite a name, especially for dim sum that's "hard to beat";
its ratings slid this year, though, with service sometimes seeming
"overbearing" of late. / www.dragoncastle.eu; 11 pm.

Dragoncello W2 NEW £51 ④❷❸
104a, Chepstow Rd 7221 1821 6–1B
"A tiny little Notting Hill gem" which gives an impression rather like
"being served in your own front room"; the Italian fare shows
"potential", but critics find prices "astronomical". / 10.30 pm, Sat & Sun
11 pm; closed Mon, Tue-Fri L.

The Drapers Arms N1 £43 ④④❸
44 Barnsbury St 7619 0348 8–3D
"I was rather hoping they'd have revamped the revamp by now!" –
this elegant, well-known Islington gastropub (with garden) is still
on many accounts a "lovely local", yet it too often falls short
nowadays; despite the "steep" prices, the service can be "appalling",
and the food is regularly "wide of the mark". / www.thedrapersarms.com;
10.30 pm; no Amex.

The Duke of Cambridge N1 £48 ④④❸
30 St Peter's St 7359 3066 1–2C
"All-organic, low food-miles, low carbon..." – "every right-on
requirement you can think of" is catered for at this "buzzy"
gastropub; even by trendy-Islington standards, though, service can
seem a bit "casual", and cynics say the "outrageously expensive"
menu "isn't actually that good". / www.dukeorganic.co.uk; 10.30 pm,
Sun 10 pm; no Amex.

Duke of Sussex W4 £41 ❸❷❷
75 South Pde 8742 8801 7–1A
A "gorgeous" interior (and "great outdoor space") adds to the appeal
of this "lively" tavern on the Chiswick/Acton borders; it "stands apart
from the usual gastropub suspects", thanks not least to a Spanish-
influenced cuisine, which is often realised to a "high" standard.
/ 10.30 pm, Sun 9.30 pm; closed Mon L; no Amex.

The Duke of Wellington W1 £44 ❸④❸
94a, Crawford St 7723 2790 2–1A
A "lovely little gastropub", in the heart of Marylebone, offering food
that's "a notch up from the average". / www.thedukew1.co.uk; 10 pm,
Sun 9 pm; no Amex.

E&O W11 £52 ❷❸❷
14 Blenheim Cr 7229 5454 6–1A
"Still buzzing!" – Will Ricker's "cool and clubby" Notting Hill hang-
out still delivers up "delectable" Asian-fusion dishes in a "trendy"
setting whose vibe is buoyed by a "busy" bar; "the clientele is a bit
west London-Boho, but then you can't have everything".
/ www.rickerrestaurants.com; 11 pm, Sun 10.30 pm; booking: max 6.

E11even Park Walk SW10 NEW £56 ❸④④
11 Park Wk 7352 3449 5–3B
Gordon Ramsay initially found fame at this Chelsea site, which
continued to trade as Aubergine (RIP) until recently; in its new guise,
it's a comfortable sort of place, but the Italian cuisine seems to have
no aspirations much beyond "competence", and the service can
be "very slow". / Rated on Editors' visit;
www.atozrestaurants.com/11parkwalk; midnight.

The Eagle EC1 £27 ❸❹❶
159 Farringdon Rd   7837 1353   9–1A
The "no-frills" Clerkenwell "origin of the gastropub movement" is "still the best", say fans, and still "crazy-busy at times"; its Mediterranean cooking is "not as good as it once was", but still "surprisingly hearty and enjoyable". / 10.30 pm; closed Sun D; no Amex; no booking.

Eagle Bar Diner W1 £37 ❸❸❷
3-5 Rathbone Pl   7637 1418   4–1A
"From the quality and flavour of the beef, to the superlative side-dishes", this trendy boothed hang-out, just off Oxford Street, is worth seeking out for its "brilliant" burgers; they do a mean cocktail too. / www.eaglebardiner.com; 11 pm, Thu-Sat 1 am; closed Sun; need 6+ to book.

Ealing Park Tavern W5 £44 ❸❸❹
222 South Ealing Rd   8758 1879   1–3A
"Ealing is severely lacking in the quality restaurant department", so this "cavernous" gastropub – with its "well-cooked and well-presented dishes" – certainly stands out. / www.ealingparktavern.com; 10 pm, Sun 9 pm.

Earl Spencer SW18 £41 ❸❸❸
260-262 Merton Rd   8870 9244   10–2B
"Easy-going and spacious", this Southfields gastropub "gem" delights the locals with its "foodie" menu and its "friendly" staff; the secret, though, is well and truly out – "get there by noon at weekends or you won't get a table!" / www.theearlspencer.co.uk; 10 pm, Sun 9.30 pm; no booking Sun.

The East Hill SW18 £39 ❸❸❷
21 Alma Rd   8874 1833   10–2B
It's "the perfect local boozer", say fans of this "fun" Wandsworth hostelry, which continues to go down well with the denizens of the Nappy Valley. / www.geronimo-inns.co.uk; 10 pm, Thu-Sat 10.30 pm, Sun 9 pm.

The Easton WC1 £41 ❷❷❸
22 Easton St   7278 7608   9–1A
"A little gem off Easton Street, opposite the better-known Exmouth Market" – this "great gastropub" is "run by chef/proprietors who know what they're doing", and who serve up some "delicious" fare. / 10 pm, Sun 9.30 pm.

Eat £12 ❹❸❹
Branches throughout London
"Tasty" and "healthy" soups (in particular) and "invariably fresh" sandwiches lead fans to hail these "reliable lunch stops" as "better than Pret"; in the survey as a whole, however, their rivals just pip 'em to the post on all counts. / www.eat.co.uk; 4 pm-8 pm; most City branches closed all or part of weekend; no credit cards; no booking.

The Ebury SW1 £47 ❹❹❸
11 Pimlico Rd   7730 6784   5–2D
"A lovely atmosphere" helps make this large Pimlico bar/brasserie a "super place to hang out"; the food, though, is no more than "fine", and it's "pricey" too. / www.theebury.co.uk; 10.30 pm, Sun 10 pm.

Ebury Wine Bar SW1 £46 ❹❸❸
139 Ebury St   7730 5447   2–4A
This age-old Belgravia haunt remains an "agreeable" sort of place; not everyone is convinced by the "average" food, though – "it's more somewhere you go for the wine". / www.eburywinebar.co.uk; 10.15 pm.

Eco SW4 £36 ❸❹❸
162 Clapham High St 7978 1108 10–2D
"Still the best pizza", say fans, but this once-trendy Clapham hang-out can seem a little long-in-the-tooth nowadays, and inspires only middling levels of satisfaction overall. / www.ecorestaurants.com; 11 pm, Fri & Sat 11.30 pm.

Ed's Easy Diner £27 ❹❸❷
12 Moor St, W1 7434 4439 4–2A
Trocadero, 19 Rupert St, W1 7287 1951 3–3D
Sedley Pl, 14 Woodstock St, W1 7493 9916 3–2B **NEW**
These *"glorious"*, *"hyper-retro"* diners serve *"good burgers and cheesy fries, plus milkshakes to die for"* – *"OK, it's not the most gourmet burger, but the place can't be beaten for fun!"*
/ www.edseasydiner.co.uk; Rupert St 11 pm, Fri & Sat midnight; Moor St midnight, Sun 10 pm, Sedley place 9 pm; no Amex; Moor St no booking.

Edera W11 £61 ❷❶❸
148 Holland Park Ave 7221 6090 6–2A
In chichi Holland Park, this *"classy local Italian"*, serves food that's *"more upmarket than most"*; particularly *"charming"* service contributes to an all-round performance that can only be characterised as *"excellent"*. / www.atozrestaurants.com/edera/; 11 pm, Sun 10 pm.

Edokko WC1 £46 ❷❶❸
50 Red Lion St 7242 3490 2–1D
"No one's heard of the place", yet fans say the *"beautifully executed"* sushi and other *"delicious"* and *"authentic"* fare on offer at this cosy and *"traditional"* (*"dingy"*) Japanese, off Holborn, are among the best in town; *"the only drawback is two sittings at lunchtime"*.
/ 10 pm; closed Sat & Sun.

Eight Over Eight SW3 £52 ❷❸❷
392 King's Rd 7349 9934 5–3B
"Back in its stride" after the fire (well, almost), this *"buzzy"* Chelsea pan-Asian is again a *"fabulous sibling to E&O"*, serving *"imaginative"*, *"fusion/Asian"* fare; *"delicious"* cocktails help fuel a *"fantastic vibe"* – is that why everyone seems *"so good-looking"*?
/ www.rickerrestaurants.com; 11 pm, Sun 10.30 pm; closed Sun L.

Eighty-Six SW3 **NEW** £47 ❹❺❸
86 Fulham Rd 7052 9620 5–2C
The site of Chelsea's long-established Cactus Blue (RIP) has been attractively revamped to create a bar for the local jeunesse dôrée – judged as a restaurant, though, reporters (small in number, admittedly) find the new incarnation *"truly dreadful"*.
/ www.86restaurant.co.uk; 10 pm; D only, closed Sun.

Electric Brasserie W11 £49 ❹❹❷
191 Portobello Rd 7908 9696 6–1A
"Always buzzing with locals, families and Notting Hillbillies" – this *"vibrant"*, *"heart-of-Portobello"* hang-out offers *"top people-watching possibilites"*, especially at weekends; *"very good"* breakfasts aside, however, the food is *"distinctly average"*.
/ www.electricbrasserie.com; 11 pm, Sun 10 pm; Max 8; set weekday L £28 (FP).

Elena's L'Etoile W1 £51 ⑤④④
30 Charlotte St 7636 7189 2–1C

"Sadly Elena is no longer in attendance", at this "faded" and "elegant" Fitzrovia old-timer, and the place is in "sad decline" – the "basic" brasserie fare is "very ordinary", with "subdued and not particularly helpful staff" contributing to an ambience that's rather "flat". / www.elenasletoile.co.uk; 10.30 pm; closed Sat L & Sun.

Elephant Royale
Locke's Wharf E14 £44 ④❸❸
Westferry Rd 7987 7999 11–2C

"Perfect on a summer evening", when you can enjoy the "great views" towards Greenwich – this rather glitzy Isle of Dogs venue may not astonish with the quality of its Thai food, but it rarely disappoints. / www.elephantroyale.com; 11.30 pm, Fri & Sat midnight, Sun 11 pm; set Sun L £28 (FP).

Élysée W1 £49 ④❸❷
13 Percy St 7636 4804 2–1C

Potentially a real hidden gem, this recently-relaunched Greek restaurant, in Fitzrovia, has a truly "beautiful" period-townhouse interior and an "exceptional" roof garden too; so why has no one ever heard of it? – the "mundane" cooking can't help. / Rated on Editors' visit; www.elyseerestaurant.com; 2 am; closed Sun.

Emile's SW15 £40 ❷⓿❸
96-98 Felsham Rd 8789 3323 10–2B

"Emile is the perfect host", say fans of this "intimate" Putney "gem" – a stalwart establishment that's currently going "from strength to strength"; "superb beef Wellington" is a long-standing highlight on a menu that's "in a good way, rather old-fashioned". / www.emilesrestaurant.co.uk; 11 pm; D only, closed Sun; no Amex.

The Empress of India E9 £45 ❸❸❷
130 Lauriston Rd 8533 5123 1–2D

Nothing Indian except the name, about this popular and "good-value" gastropub, near Victoria Park. / www.theempressofindia.com; 10 pm; closed Sun D.

Empress of Sichuan WC2 £43 ❸❸④
6 Lisle St 7734 8128 4–3A

With its "robust" Sichuanese cuisine, this "plush" spot offers "a spicy alternative to your standard Chinatown Cantonese"; this year, however, a minority of reporters encountered "below par" food. / 11 pm.

The Engineer NW1 £45 ④④❷
65 Gloucester Ave 7722 0950 8–3B

"On a sunny day, the garden comes into its own", at this once-celebrated – and still "atmospheric" – Primrose Hill gastropub; while the food's still "fine", though, "prices have gone crazy", and service "could do with smartening up". / www.the-engineer.com; 10.30 pm, Sun 10 pm; no Amex.

The English Pig EC1 NEW £43 ❷❷④
171-176 Aldersgate St 7600 9707 9–2B

"A crazy and charismatic chef/host" helps breath life into this "not very promising" venue – a "barn-like" site (formerly a Slug & Lettuce) "on a roundabout at the end of London Wall"; it's generally a "convivial" enough place, though, offering "wholesome" cuisine realised to a "high standard". / theenglishpig.co.uk; Mon-Fri 9.30 pm, Sat 10 pm; closed Sat L & Sun.

Enoteca Turi SW15 £50 ❶❶❸
28 Putney High St 8785 4449 10–2B
"Passionate owners", Giuseppe and Pamela Turi, run this *"hidden gem"*, near Putney Bridge; *"the best Italian wine list outside Italy"* is *"cleverly matched"* with *"expertly prepared"* dishes in a *"lovely"*, if low key, setting. / www.enotecaturi.com; 10.30 pm, Fri-Sat 11 pm; closed Sun.

The Enterprise SW3 £50 ❸❸❷
35 Walton St 7584 3148 5–2C
"Shame you can't book", at this *"busy"* but *"cosy"* and perennially fashionable Knightsbridge corner hang-out – *"the food is always good"*. / www.theenterprise.co.uk; 10 pm, Sat 10.30 pm; no booking, except weekday L.

Entrée SW11 NEW £46 ❸❹❸
2 Battersea Rise 7223 5147 10–2C
"A great addition to Battersea Rise"; it may occupy a *"difficult site"*, but the locals are rooting for this *"unlikely"* outfit, which encompasses a *"speakeasy-style"* bar (below), and a restaurant above, serving *"well-executed modern European fare"*. / www.entreebattersea.co.uk/; 10.30 pm; closed weekday L.

Eriki NW3 £38 ❷❶❸
4-6 Northways Pde, Finchley Rd 7722 0606 8–2A
"Not to be expected on such an ugly road", this *"gem among the Swiss Cottage dross"* offers notably *"imaginative"* Indian cooking (in 'nouvelle' style) and *"sparkling and smiley"* service. / www.eriki.co.uk; 10.45 pm; closed Sat L.

Esarn Kheaw W12 £30 ❶❸❹
314 Uxbridge Rd 8743 8930 7–1B
"Unexpectedly terrific" cooking – with *"superb Northern Thai specialities you won't find elsewhere"* – provide ample reason to truffle out this *"treasure"* of a café, in spite of its location in a tatty corner of Shepherd's Bush. / www.esarnkheaw.co.uk; 11 pm; closed Sat L & Sun L; no Amex.

L'Escargot W1 £54 ❸❷❷
48 Greek St 7437 2679 4–2A
This *"romantic"*, art-filled Soho stalwart keeps a low-profile nowadays, but it's still a *"reliable"* and professional operation, offering *"accomplished"* Gallic cuisine; lunch and pre-theatre menus are *"very good value"*. / www.whitestarline.org.uk; 11.15 pm; closed Sat L & Sun; set pre theatre £34 (FP).

Essenza W11 £53 ❸❸❹
210 Kensington Park Rd 7792 1066 6–1A
"Great and honest", or *"surprisingly unoriginal and ordinary"*? – the former view predominates, but the puzzlingly few reports on this Notting Hill Italian are notably mixed; *"very good fish dishes"*, though, do seem to be a highlight. / www.essenza.co.uk; 11.30 pm; set weekday L £33 (FP).

L'Etranger SW7 £64 ❸❷❸
36 Gloucester Rd 7584 1118 5–1B
"Superb wine, with hidden treasures from across the globe" is matched up with *"unusual and interesting French/Japanese fusion cuisine"*, at this South Kensington venture; for critics, though, *"ridiculous"* prices can rather take the edge off the experience. / www.etranger.co.uk; 11 pm, Sun 10 pm.

Euphorium Bakery N1 £9 ❸④❸
26a Chapel Mkt   7837 7010   8–3D
*A place to "chill out with a book" on "one of the comfy sofas",
this high-quality Islington café/bakery serves up "lovely, if expensive",
sarnies, cakes and pastries. / www.euphoriumbakery.com; 6 pm; no Amex.*

Everest Inn SE3 £33 ❷❸❷
41 Montpelier Vale   8852 7872   1–4D
*"A super Blackheath curry option" – the "varied" menu of this
"refined", "friendly" and "welcoming" Nepalese establishment
is notable for the "clean" and "fresh" flavours it offers.
/ www.everestinn.co.uk; midnight, Sun 11 pm.*

Eyre Brothers EC2 £55 ❸❸❸
70 Leonard St   7613 5346   12–1B
*"Fine Iberian cooking" – well-matched with some "wonderful" wines
– justifies the toppish prices at this "modern yet welcoming"
Shoreditch bar/restaurant; lunches attract a business crowd,
but evenings are "more relaxed". / www.eyrebrothers.co.uk; 10.30 pm;
closed Sat L & Sun.*

Faanoos £25 ❸❸❸
472 Chiswick High Rd, W4   8994 4217   7–2A
481 Richmond Road, SW14   8878 5738   1–4A
*"Succulent kebabs", "gorgeous home-made bread" and fresh dips
(served in "large portions" and at "good prices") win praise for these
"very cheerful" Persians, in Sheen and more recently Chiswick;
BYO (£4 corkage). / SW14 11 pm; W4 Fri & Sat midnight.*

Fabrizio EC1 £41 ❷⓿④
30 Saint Cross St   7430 1503   9–1A
*"Fabrizio is a star", and his "great-value" Italian, in the "Diamond
District", is making a name for its "warm hospitality and delicious
food"; the interior is "a bit shabby" though – "only go with business
associates you know pretty well!" / www.fabriziorestaurant.co.uk; 10 pm;
closed Sat L & Sun.*

Fairuz W1 £44 ❸❸④
3 Blandford St   7486 8108   2–1A
*"The quality of the mezze" is the particular reason to seek out this
"friendly" Marylebone Lebanese – "stick to them, and you'll easily fill
up". / www.fairuz.uk.com; 11.30 pm, Sun 10.30 pm; set weekday L £16 (FP).*

Fakhreldine W1 £55 ④④④
85 Piccadilly   7493 3424   3–4C
*Only modest feedback on this glitzy Lebanese, where lunchers get
impressive Green Park views; reports, better than last year, are still
a little up-and-down, but most reporters find the food at least "well-
executed". / www.fakhreldine.co.uk; midnight, Sun 11 pm.*

Falconiere SW7 £42 ④❸⑤
84 Old Brompton Rd   7589 2401   5–2B
*Even fans can find the food "average", but this "friendly" Italian
stalwart, near South Kensington tube, still has its plus points –
notably the "terrific-value" set lunch. / www.ilfalconiere.co.uk; 11.15 pm;
closed Sun.*

La Famiglia SW10 £50 ❸❸❸
7 Langton St   7351 0761   5–3B
*Fans (some of 40 years' standing) still love this ancient Chelsea
trattoria, its "relaxed, Italian-style romance", its "delightful" garden,
and its food which, if "hardly cutting-edge", is generally "enjoyable";
an impression of drift, though, is unavoidable. / www.lafamiglia.co.uk;
11.45 pm.*

The Farm Collective EC1 £8 ❷❸❸
91 Cowcross St   7253 2142   9–1A
"You can tell they use good ingredients" – this Farringdon café/bistro attracts positive reports overall, but it's the "great-tasting food" which really stands out. / www.farmcollective.com; L only, closed Sat & Sun.

Fat Boy's £33 ❸❹❸
10a-10b Edensor Rd, W4   8742 0249   10–1A
33 Haven Grn, W5   8998 5868   1–2A
201 Upper Richmond Rd, SW14   8876 0644   1–4A
431-433 Richmond Rd, TW1   8892 7657   1–4A
68 High St, TW8   8569 8481   1–3A
With their "freshly-cooked" and "reliable" Thai (and Chinese) fare, these simple joints in west London generally hit the spot, even if the service "can be a bit hit-and-miss". / www.fatboysthai.co.uk; 11 pm.

Faulkner's E8 £29 ❷❷❸
424-426 Kingsland Rd   7254 6152   1–1D
"Fantastic fish at prices you could barely buy it uncooked!", and "a very wide selection" too, help ensure this comfy, if dated, Dalston chippy practically "never disappoints". / 10 pm; no Amex; need 8+ to book.

The Fellow N1 £43 ❹❹❹
24 York Way   7833 4395   8–3C
"Very handy for travellers passing through King's Cross", this "bustling" gastropub is probably the top all-purpose choice immediately around the station – no wonder it is "usually crammed". / www.thefellow.co.uk; 10 pm; closed Sun D.

The Fentiman Arms SW8 £39 ❸❸❷
64 Fentiman Rd   7793 9796   10–1D
A "worthy" Vauxhall gastropub, with "open fires in winter and an amazing terrace for the summer"; reports (limited) suggest the food "has upped its game" of late. / www.geronimo-inns.co.uk; 10 pm, Sun 9 pm.

Fernandez & Wells £30 ❷❷❷
16a, St Anne's Ct, W1   7494 4242   3–1D
43 Lexington St, W1   7734 1546   3–2D
73 Beak St, W1   7287 8124   3–2D
"Small, and full of trendies", these "rustic" Soho pit stops offer "mouth-watering" sarnies, tapas and nibbles, plus – in Lexington Street – "excellent" Spanish wines; in St Anne's Court, it's all about "beautiful" coffee and "outstanding" cakes.
/ www.fernandezandwells.com; Lexington St 10 pm; Beak St 5 pm; St Anne's Court closed Sun.

Ffiona's W8 £47 ❹❷❶
51 Kensington Church St   7937 4152   5–1A
"Eccentric" owner Ffiona offers "a personal and idiosyncratic welcome to all", at her "candlelit, small and intimate" Kensington bistro; the "homely" English cuisine may be "average", but fans say the experience is second to none; weekend brunch is a "welcome innovation". / www.ffionas.com; 11 pm, Sun 10 pm; D only, closed Mon; no Amex.

Fifteen Dining Room N1 £75 ❺❺❺
15 Westland Pl   3375 1515   12–1A
"Simply dreadful", "you must warn people away!"; this "extraordinarily overpriced" Hoxton basement (in part staffed by disadvantaged trainees) offers up "diabolical" Italian food and notably "careless" service – if it couldn't "live off Jamie Oliver's name", it wouldn't last a week! / www.fifteen.net; 10 pm; booking: max 12.

Fifteen Trattoria N1 £51 ④⑤④
15 Westland Pl   3375 1515   12–1A
Fans are "pleasantly surprised" by the "really relaxed" vibe on the
cheaper ground floor of Jamie's Hoxton training-venture, and say the
food is "fabulous" too; doubters, however, may "admire the concept"
but still say the reality is "no better than most local Italians",
just much more expensive. / www.fifteen.net; 10.45 pm; booking: max 16.

**The Fifth Floor Restaurant
Harvey Nichols SW1** £65 ④❸④
109-125 Knightsbridge   7235 5250   5–1D
From "outstanding" to "really disappointing" – reports on this stark
'90s dining room are not only mixed, but also amazingly
modest in number nowadays; an "excellent" wine list is the only
undisputed attraction. / www.harveynichols.com; 10.45 pm; closed Sun D.

54 Farringdon Road EC1 £43 ❸❸④
54 Farringdon Rd   7336 0603   9–1A
"Good and original Malay cuisine" is one of the features making this
rather oddly-decorated spot a very useful Farringdon stand-by.
/ www.54farringdon.com; 10.30 pm; closed Sun-Mon, Tue & Wed L, Sat L;
set weekday L £17 (FP), set pre-theatre £28 (FP).

Fig N1 £46 ❶❷❷
169 Hemingford Rd   7609 3009   8–3D
"How do they produce such good meals in such a tiny space?"; for a
"leisurely romantic meal", this "neighbourhood gem" is just the job –
it hasn't suffered at all from its "simpler" approach since the owner
shifted his main focus to 'North Road'. / www.fig-restaurant.co.uk; 10 pm;
D only, open Sun L only; no Amex.

La Figa E14 £36 ❸❷❸
45 Narrow St   7790 0077   11–1B
This "cheery and bustling", pizza 'n' pasta joint, in Wapping,
continues to impress all who comment on it, not least with its
"huge portions" of "freshly-cooked" fare – "you might not cross
London for it, but you'd cross the East End!" / www.lafigarestaurant.co.uk;
11 pm, Sun 10.30 pm.

Fine Burger Company £33 ④④④
330 Upper St, N1   7359 3026   8–3D
St Pancras International, Pancras Rd, NW1   7278 8056   8–3C
O2 Centre, Finchley Rd, NW3   7433 0700   8–2A
An "average-to-good" chain, whose "good thick burgers" get the
thumbs-up from most reporters. / www.fineburger.co.uk; 10 pm-11 pm,
NW1 1am, Fri-Sat midnight.

Fino W1 £52 ❷❷❷
33 Charlotte St   7813 8010   2–1C
"A real eye-opener" when it comes to "authentically Spanish" cuisine
– the Hart Brothers' "understated" yet "spectacularly good" all-
rounder, in a Fitzrovia basement, offers "tremendous" tapas,
"personable" service, "super" wines, and a list of sherries that's
simply "an education". / www.finorestaurant.com; 10.30 pm; closed
Sat L & Sun; booking: max 12.

Fire & Stone £35 ④❸❸
31-32 Maiden Ln, WC2 08443 712550 4–3D
Westfield, Ariel Way, W12 0844 371 2550 7–1C
4 Horner Sq, E1 0844 371 2550 12–2B
*"Weird and wonderful" pizzas (a "nice change from PizzaExpress!")
please fans of this small chain (whose "cavernous" and very concrete
Covent Garden branch is the most interesting); for some reporters,
though, the "novelty" is wearing thin – its "bizarre" creations,
they say, are "really gross". / www.fireandstone.com; WC2 11 pm;
W12 11 pm, Sat & Sun 11.30 pm; E1 11pm, Sun 8 pm.*

The Fire Stables SW19 £50 ④④❷
27-29 Church Rd 8946 3197 10–2B
*In the heart of ultra-cute but under-served Wimbledon Village,
a buzzy Young's gastropub worth knowing about for decent food
at "sensible prices". / www.firestableswimbledon.co.uk; 10.30 pm,
Sun 10 pm.*

Firezza £31 ❷❸④
116 Finborough Rd, SW10 7370 2255 5–3A
12 All Saints Rd, W11 7221 0020 6–1B
48 Chiswick High Rd, W4 8994 9494 7–2B
276 St Paul's Rd, N1 7359 7400 8–2D
40 Lavender Hill, SW11 7223 5535 10–1C
205 Garrett Ln, SW18 8870 7070 10–2B
*"The best take-away pizzas, bar none", thanks to their "wonderful,
crisp, thin bases" and "yummy" toppings; in some outlets you could
eat in... but "don't bother!" / www.firezza.com; 11 pm, Fri & Sat midnight;
N1 closed Sun; no Amex.*

First Floor W11 £42 ❸❷❶
186 Portobello Rd 7243 0072 6–1A
*"Shabby-chic" styling doesn't come more "romantic" than at this high-
ceilinged and candlelit Portobello Market dining room, and the food,
if a touch "hit-and-miss", is pretty good too; NB: upstairs, there's one
of London's nicer private rooms. / www.firstfloorportobello.co.uk; 11 pm;
closed Sun D.*

Fish Central EC1 £28 ❷❷❸
149-155 Central St 7253 4970 12–1A
*"The name says it all" about this "informal and friendly" East End
venture – all you get is "extremely fresh fish, cooked to perfection".
/ www.fishcentral.co.uk; 10.30 pm, Fri & Sat 11 pm; closed Sun.*

Fish Club £35 ❷❷④
189 St John's Hill, SW11 7978 7115 10–2C
57 Clapham High St, SW4 7720 5853 10–2D
*"Nothing's fancy, but everything's extremely tasty", at these "basic"
south London refectories (with wet fish counters attached); their "top-
notch", "upmarket" fish 'n' chips offer "a good twist on the traditional
formula". / www.thefishclub.com; 10 pm, Sun 9 pm; SW4 & SW11 closed
Mon L; no bookings.*

Fish in a Tie SW11 £30 ④❷❶
105 Falcon Rd 7924 1913 10–1C
*"Hidden-away in a non-glamorous road behind Clapham Junction",
this "great little Italian" makes a good "cheap 'n' cheerful" choice –
"it could charge double", say fans, "and still be as busy!"
/ www.fishinatie.co.uk; midnight; no Amex; set weekday L £18 (FP), set always
available £19 (FP).*

Fish Place SW11 NEW £51 ❷❷⑤

Vicentia Ct, Bridges Ct   7095 0410   10–1C

"A real discovery", this hidden-away Battersea newcomer – a "small glass-fronted" spot, with "amazing Thames views" – is well worth seeking out for its "interesting" menu (which includes the "lovely" fish dishes you'd hope for); it's not yet found the following it deserves, though, and atmosphere can be elusive. / www.thefishplace.co.uk; 10.30 pm; closed Mon; set weekday L £33 (FP).

fish! SE1 £48 ④⑤⑤

Cathedral St   7407 3803   9–4C

Would this glass-and-steel shed survive, were it not for its prominent Borough Market location? – the setting is clattery, the service "poor", prices "steep", and the fish "very average" – "avoid!" / www.fishkitchen.com; 10.45 pm, Sun 10.30 pm.

Fishworks £47 ❸❸④

7-9 Swallow St, W1   7734 5813   3–3D
89 Marylebone High St, W1   7935 9796   2–1A

"Good-quality fish, correctly prepared" is helping this café/fishmonger group stage something of a 'comeback' – it also benefits from an ambience "less chain-like than some of its rivals", and service that's more "efficient" too. / www.fishworks.co.uk; 10.30pm.

Fitou's Thai Restaurant W10 £24 ❷❸④

1 Dalgarno Gdns   8968 0558   6–1A

"There's no way you'd just stumble upon this bizarrely hidden-away BYO Thai" – formerly called Number One Café – opposite Little Wormwood Scrubs ; if you do, you'll find "cracking food at ridiculously cheap prices". / www.numberonethaicafe.co.uk; 10.30 pm; closed Sun L.

Five Hot Chillies HA0 £27 ❷④⑤

875 Harrow Rd   8908 5900   1–1A

Prices at this grungy café, on a busy Sudbury highway, are "hard to beat"; its very authentic Indian fare can be "excellent" too, "especially the grills"; BYO. / www.fivehotchillies.co.uk; midnight; no Amex.

500 N19 £38 ❶❶❷

782 Holloway Rd   7272 3406   8–1C

"The real biz!" – this "terrific" trattoria, "tucked-away" in an "unlikely" Archway location, is a "crowded" but really "charming" place, where a "small but original" Sicilian menu is realised "with flair"; star turn: "sublime" pasta. / www.500restaurant.co.uk; 10 pm; closed Mon & Sun L.

5 Pollen Street W1 £75 ④❸❸

5 Pollen St   7629 1555   3–2C

Opposite Pollen Street Social, and already rather eclipsed by it, this stylish Mayfair newcomer is a pleasant sort of place in a rather old-fashioned and comfortable sort of way; most aspects of the operation though seem to have struck early-days reporters (and ourselves) as rather lacking 'oomph'. / www.pollenst.com; 10.30 pm; closed Sun.

The Flask N6 £41 ❸❸❷

77 Highgate West Hill   8348 7346   1–1C

It's the "nice location and lovely beer garden" ("very busy on warm days") that make this historic Highgate coaching inn of particular note; fans insist, however, that its cooking is "above average" too. / www.theflaskhighgate.com; 10 pm, Sun 9 pm.

Flat White W1 £10 ❷❷❸
17 Berwick St 7734 0370 3–2D
You get "the most amazing coffee, plus a large dollop of chilled-out
Antipodean charm", at this "hipsters' paradise" Soho coffee shop;
"nice cakes" too. / www.flat-white.co.uk; L only; no credit cards.

Florence SE24 £38 ❹❸❸
131-133 Dulwich Rd 7326 4987 10–2D
Down Brockwell Park way, an attractive pub which – in addition
to some decent food – boasts "a wide selection of beers",
a "nice little garden", and an "enormous playroom" for the kids.
/ www.capitalpubcompany.com/the-florence/florence; 10 pm, Sun 9.30 pm;
no Amex.

Floridita W1 £61 ❹❹❹
100 Wardour St 7314 4000 3–2D
OK, "you can't hear yourself think", but this cavernous Cuban-themed
Soho joint generally gets the thumbs-up for its "vibrant" ambience;
the food, though, is "average" and "overpriced".
/ www.floriditalondon.com; 3 am, Tue & Wed 2 am; D only, closed Mon & Sun.

Food for Thought WC2 £19 ❷❹❺
31 Neal St 7836 0239 4–2C
It's "invariably crowded", but this battered Covent Garden basement
remains a "wonderful gem" thanks to its "nourishing, tasty veggie
fare in large portions", and at "rock-bottom prices" too; beware
queues; BYO. / www.foodforthought-london.co.uk; 8 pm, Sun 5 pm; no credit
cards; no booking.

The Forge WC2 £50 ❹❹❹
14 Garrick St 7379 1531 4–3C
Fans of this traditional Gallic fixture, in Covent Garden, accept it's
"nothing spectacular", but say it's a "solid performer" that's "perfect"
pre- or post-theatre; its ratings dipped this year, though,
with numerous gripes about "disappointingly average" food and
"uncaring" service. / www.theforgerestaurant.co.uk; midnight, Sun 11 pm;
set weekday L & pre-theatre £31 (FP).

Forman's E3 £52 ❷❷❹
Stour Rd, Fish Island 8525 2365 1–1D
A "great view of the Olympic Stadium" is destined to provide a major
draw, during 2012, to the dining room of this East End, canal-side,
smoked salmon factory; service is "attentive" and the "limited" menu
of "simple" fish and seafood is typically realised to an "excellent"
standard. / www.formans.co.uk; 11 pm; Closed Mon-Wed, Thu & Fri D only,
Sat open L & D, closed Sun D.

Formosa Dining Room
The Prince Alfred W9 £45 ❸❹❸
5a Formosa St 7286 3287 6–1C
A huge Victorian tavern in Maida Vale, with some "simply amazing"
architecture; its dining annex is quite a simple, modern affair,
however, offering "good, solid British food". / www.theprincealfred.co.uk;
10 pm, Fri & Sat 11 pm, Sun 9 pm; no Amex; set dinner £29 (FP).

(The Fountain)
Fortnum & Mason W1 £62 ❹❸❸
181 Piccadilly 7734 8040 3–3D
"Incredibly under-rated" as a breakfast destination, the "genteel"
buttery of this posh St James's institution is also worth seeking out for
its "scrumptious" afternoon tea, or a spot of Welsh rarebit at any
time of day; NB "very good lunchtime deals" – see also 1707.
/ www.fortnumandmason.com; 10.45 pm; closed Sun D.

Fortune Cookie W2   £28   ②④⑤
1 Queensway   7727 7260   6–2C
"Authentic Cantonese food", at *"good-value"* prices, wins praise for this grungy Bayswater veteran. / 11 pm; no Amex.

Four O Nine SW9   £55   ❸②②
409 Clapham Rd   7737 0722   10–1D
This *"quirky, concealed room"*, above a pub near Clapham North, *"really feels like a find"* – with its *"sexy" decor*, *"flickering candles"*, *"delicious" cocktails*, and *"beautifully-presented" food*, it has *"all the ingredients for romance"*. / www.fouronine.co.uk; 10.30 pm; closed weekday L.

Four Regions TW9   £41   ❸②④
102-104 Kew Rd   8940 9044   1–4A
"Reliable and down-to-earth", this Chinese restaurant, on the Kew/Richmond border, is quite a *"neighbourhood favourite"*, thanks not least to its *"friendly" style* and its *"fair prices"*. / 11.30 pm, Sun 11 pm.

The Four Seasons   £27   ②④⑤
12 Gerrard St, W1   7494 0870   4–3A
23 Wardour St, W1   7287 9995   4–3A **NEW**
84 Queensway, W2   7229 4320   6–2C
Service may be off-hand and the setting scruffy, but *"the best roast duck ever"* still makes quite a name for this *"bustling"* Bayswater Chinese – beware the *"inevitable queue"*; its lesser-known Chinatown siblings are *"well worth a special visit too"*. / www.ukfourseasons.com; Queensway and Gerrard St 1 am, Sun 11 pm, Wardour St 3.30 am.

The Fox EC2   £39   ❸④❸
28 Paul St   7729 5708   12–2B
"Handy for both the City and trendy Shoreditch" – a traditional-looking boozer where the Mediterranean cuisine can be *"really good"*… even if the service is sometimes *"all over the show"*; the panelled upstairs dining room is a better option than the bar below. / www.thefoxpublichouse.com; 10 pm; closed Sat L & Sun D.

Fox & Grapes SW19 **NEW**   £48   ❸④❸
9 Camp Rd   8619 1300   10–2A
"It's a relief finally to have something half-decent in Wimbledon", so Claude ('Hibiscus') Bosi's *"uncluttered"* make-over of this picturesque inn near the Common has been a *"welcome"* arrival; not everyone is wowed though – it's *"expensive for what it is"*, and suffers from an *"identity crisis"*: *"is it a restaurant or a pub?"* / foxandgrapeswimbledon.co.uk; 9.30pm; no Amex.

The Fox & Hounds SW11   £40   ❷❷❷
66 Latchmere Rd   7924 5483   10–1C
"It isn't trying to be anything other than a great pub!" – this *"fabulous"* Battersea boozer may be just that, but its *"continuously-updated"* cuisine is *"ever-reliable"* nonetheless. / www.thefoxandhoundspub.co.uk; 10 pm; Mon-Thu D only, Fri-Sun open L & D.

The Fox and Anchor EC1   £42   ❸②❶
115 Charterhouse St   7250 1300   9–1B
"Everything a pub should be" – this *"cosy and beautiful"* Victorian gem, tucked-away in Smithfield, serves *"very British"* food, executed *"with a rarely found lightness of touch"*, and *"delivered with a smile"* too. / www.foxandanchor.co.uk; 9.30 pm; closed Sun D.

Foxtrot Oscar SW3   £50   4️⃣3️⃣4️⃣
79 Royal Hospital Rd   7352 4448   5–3D
"Nothing hits the right note", say critics of Gordon Ramsay's tenure
of this long-established Chelsea bistro; it would be fair to say, though,
that it *"was never really known as a destination for amazing food"*,
and that the cooking – while still *"entirely unmemorable"* –
has improved somewhat of late. / www.gordonramsay.com/foxtrotoscar/;
10 pm, Sun 9 pm.

Franco Manca   £20   1️⃣3️⃣3️⃣
144 Chiswick High Rd, W4   8747 4822   7–2A
Unit 4 Market Row, SW9   7738 3021   10–2D
"The best pizza outside Italy" – using *"amazing"* Neapolitan
sourdough bases – again wins raves for this teeny and *"stupidly
cheap"* Brixton Market pizzeria, and its Chiswick offshoot (*"a big hit
with local yummy mummies"*) is almost as good; expansion to Covent
Garden, Brick Lane and Westfield coming soon – can quality survive?
/ www.francomanca.com; SW9 5 pm; W4 11 pm; sw9 no bookings.

Franco's SW1   £64   4️⃣4️⃣4️⃣
61 Jermyn St   7499 2211   3–3C
A *"plush"* modern trattoria, in St James's, that can fit the bill if you're
looking for *"a good solid option for a business lunch"*; critics feel its
"rich" cuisine is *"not the most inspiring"*, though, and fear prices
verge on *"ridiculous"*. / www.francoslondon.com; 11 pm; closed Sun; set pre
theatre £36 (FP).

Frankie's Italian Bar & Grill   £45   5️⃣5️⃣4️⃣
3 Yeomans Row, SW3   7590 9999   5–2C
Stamford Bridge, Fulham Rd, SW6   7957 8298   5–4A **NEW**
Given its *"pedestrian cooking"* and *"unwarranted prices"*, it's hard
to see the appeal – expect possibly with kids in tow – of MPW and
Franco Dettori's pizza chain, *"bizarrely decorated"* in Vegas-bling
style; the former Chiswick branch now trades under different
management – but with very similar branding – as Bardolino.
/ www.frankiesitalianbarandgrill.com; 11 pm; W4 closed Mon-Fri L.

Franklins SE22   £46   3️⃣4️⃣3️⃣
157 Lordship Ln   8299 9598   1–4D
A *"wonderful local bistro"*, in East Dulwich – a *"friendly"* sort
of place, it offers a *"marvellously tasty"* menu, on which *"meaty"*
dishes are a speciality. / www.franklinsrestaurant.com; 10.30 pm;
set weekday L £29 (FP).

Frantoio SW10   £50   4️⃣3️⃣3️⃣
397 King's Rd   7352 4146   5–3B
A *"retro"* menu is served *"with gusto"*, at this *"always-cheerful"* and
"noisy" Italian, near World's End; critics, though find it *"all-round
mediocre"* – *"what do regulars see we don't?"* / www.frantoio.com;
11.15 pm, Sun 10.15 pm; set weekday L £32 (FP).

Fratelli la Bufala NW3   £41   3️⃣4️⃣4️⃣
45a South End Rd   7435 7814   8–2A
*"Part of a global chain, but you'd think it was run by some local
Italians!"* – this *"indispensable"* Hampstead fixture serves some
"amazing" wood-fired pizza (plus a whole range of dishes featuring
buffalo mozzarella). / 11 pm; closed Mon L & Tue L; no Amex;
set weekday L £26 (FP).

Frederick's N1 £56 ④④❷
106 Islington High St 7359 2888 8–3D
"The conservatory is lovely", at this "spacious, light and airy" Islington "staple", whose "formal" but "sociable" style suits a special occasion; fans insist its cooking is "top-notch" too, but the overall view is that it's merely "acceptable". / www.fredericks.co.uk; 11 pm; closed Sun; set weekday L & pre-theatre £35 (FP).

Freemasons Arms NW3 £41 ⑤④❷
32 Downshire Hill 7433 6811 8–2A
"On the edge of Hampstead Heath", a popular pub – with a "cosy" interior, a "lovely" conservatory and "excellent garden tables" – that's "consistently packed with local families"; performance, however, is "schizophrenic", and when things go wrong the food can be "atrocious". / www.freemasonsarms.co.uk; 10 pm.

Fresco W2 £20 ❸❷❸
25 Westbourne Grove 7221 2355 6–1C
"A great variety of fresh juices", plus "amazing" Lebanese wraps – all at bargain prices – make this "modest-looking" pit stop a handy Bayswater stand-by. / www.frescojuices.co.uk; 10.30 pm.

Frizzante at City Farm
Hackney City Farm E2 £28 ❸❸❷
1a Goldsmiths Row 7729 6381 12–1D
A "busy" but "really relaxed" Italian café, on the East End's "weekend trail" between Columbia Road and Broadway Market; its "freshly-made" fare includes some good cakes and breakfasts – "don't forget to take the kids to look at the animals". / www.frizzanteltd.co.uk; D only, closed Mon; no Amex.

Frizzante Cafe
Surrey Docks Farm SE16 £23 ❸④❸
South Whf, Rotherhithe St 7231 1010 11–2B
In deepest Rotherhithe, the sweet café of a Thames-side working farm, which serves "fresh, tasty Italian-based food", plus "good coffee and lovely cakes" – "watch out for wandering chickens!" / www.frizzanteltd.co.uk; 4.30 pm; closed Mon & Tue, Wed-Sun D.

La Fromagerie Café W1 £38 ❷❸❷
2-6 Moxon St 7935 0341 3–1A
"Delectable cheeses and other gourmet delights" – including "fresh salads", "good charcuterie" and "great wine" – are on offer at the "glorious" café attached to the famous Marylebone shop; "yummy breakfasts" too. / www.lafromagerie.co.uk; 7 pm, Sat 6.30 pm, Sun 5.30 pm; L only; no booking.

The Frontline Club W2 £48 ❸❷❷
13 Norfolk Pl 7479 8960 6–1D
All the more notable "in the Paddington restaurant desert", a "leading media club" (dining room open to all) whose menu "showcases the best of British" (much of it from the owner's farm), accompanied by a "delightful" wine list ; war-reporting is the house speciality – "the photos on the wall certainly make an impression". / www.frontlineclub.com; 11 pm; closed Sun D.

Fryer's Delight WC1 £10 ❸④④
19 Theobald's Rd 7405 4114 2–1D
Views on this "cramped", "no-frills" Holborn chippy are becoming more mixed – supporters still vaunt its "classic" style, but critics are adamant that "Londoners (and tourists) have much better choices for their fish 'n' chips"; BYO. / 11 pm; closed Sun; no credit cards; no booking.

Fujiyama SW9 £28 ❸❸④
5-7 Vining St 7737 2369 10–2D
A "cheap 'n' cheerful" Brixton Japanese, popular for "steaming bowls
of noodle soup", and "fresh sushi" too. / www.newfujiyama.com; 11 pm.

Fulham Wine Rooms SW6 NEW £46 ④❸❸
871-873 Fulham Rd 7042 9440 10–1B
The food can "miss", but "full marks for effort", at this Fulham
newcomer, which – like its Kensington sibling – offers "a fun way
to sample an extensive choice of wine" (served by the glass from
an Enomatic machine). / www.greatwinesbytheglass.com; 11 pm.

Furnace N1 £36 ❸❸❸
1 Rufus St 7613 0598 12–1B
A "reliable" hang-out for Hoxton trendies – a "cheerful" and
"welcoming" pizzeria, just off the Square. / www.hoxtonfurnace.com;
11 pm; closed Sun L; no Amex.

Fuzzy's Grub £13 ④④④
6 Crown Pas, SW1 7925 2791 3–4D
10 Well Ct, EC4 7236 8400 9–2B
62 Fleet St, EC4 7583 6060 9–2A
"The 'roast-dinner-in-a-bap' is a king amongst sandwiches", and –
along with "fab, high-quality breakfasts" – helps make this British
diner/take-out chain a "pretty good-value" choice; in its own
lunchtime, though, it was a legend, and some old fans feel it's
"gone rapidly downhill" in recent years. / www.fuzzysgrub.com; 3 pm;
no Amex; no booking.

Gaby's WC2 £28 ❸④⑤
30 Charing Cross Rd 7836 4233 4–3B
It certainly offers "no frills", but this "excellent refuelling spot", right
by Leicester Square tube, is worth seeking out for its "top falafels",
"great salt beef sarnies" and "super prices"; fans go further –
"it's not at all as grotty as you suggest", they claim,
and "its reputation for surly service is undeserved!" / midnight,
Sun 10 pm; no Amex.

Gail's Bread £25 ❸❸④
138 Portobello Rd, W11 7460 0766 6–1B
282 Chiswick High Rd, W4 8995 2266 7–2A NEW
64 Hampstead High St, NW3 7794 5700 8–1A
5 Circus Rd, NW8 7722 0983 8–3A
64 Northcote Rd, SW11 7924 6330 10–2C
33-35 Exmouth Mkt, EC1 7713 6550 9–1A NEW
"First-rate coffee", "yummy cakes" and "interesting sarnies" (using
"lovely" bread) help make these attractive and "bustling"
café/bakeries worth seeking out, even if their prices are rather "high".
/ www.gailsbread.co.uk; W11 7 pm; NW3 & NW6 8 pm; no booking.

Galicia W10 £34 ❸④❸
323 Portobello Rd 8969 3539 6–1A
"An unassuming treat"; this "no-frills" North Kensington veteran may
look "shabby" from the street, but it's a "warm and buzzing"
neighbourhood spot, offering competent tapas at "cheap" prices.
/ 11.15 pm; closed Mon; set weekday L £17 (FP).

6

daPolpo

a Polpo

Gilbert Scott

Jose

The Gallery
Westbury Hotel W1 NEW   £65   ❷⓿④
Old Bond St   7629 7755   3–2C
*Ignore (if you can!) the operatic-bling styling of this large and
comfortable Mayfair newcomer (and the elevator music which goes
with it) – this is a mega-professional operation, dispensing 'hotel food'
of a very high quality; our early-days visit was for a top-value set
lunch – perfect for Bond Street shoppers. / Rated on Editors' visit;
www.westburymayfair.com.*

Gallery Mess
Saatchi Gallery SW3   £50   ④④④
Duke of Yorks HQ, Kings Rd   7730 8135   5–2D
*A fabulous Chelsea location, with an attractive terrace overlooking
a large leafy square, adds appeal to this big and "buzzing" gallery-
café – "not bad" overall, then, even if service can "struggle", and the
straightforward food is "decent" but "uninspiring" (and a bit
"overpriced") too). / www.saatchi-gallery.co.uk; Mon-Sat 9.30 pm, Sun 6 pm.*

Gallipoli   £32   ❸④❸
102 Upper St, N1   7359 0630   8–3D
107 Upper St, N1   7226 5333   8–3D
120 Upper St, N1   7226 8099   8–3D
*"Great as a cheap and cheerful stand-by with friends" – these
"vibrant" ("rammed-in") Turkish bistros, in the heart of Islington,
may be "rough and ready", but they "always have a good buzz",
and their food is "reliable" too. / www.cafegallipoli.com; 11 pm, Fri & Sat
midnight.*

Galoupet SW3 NEW   £50   ❶❷❸
13 Beauchamp Pl   7036 3600   5–1C
*Galoupet, a vineyard from SW France, launched this Knightsbridge
restaurant in the summer of 2011, but don't assume the food is an
afterthought – on the evidence of our own early-days visit, the petits-
plats here (from an ex-Zuma chef) are spectacular. / Rated on Editors'
visit; www.galoupet.co.uk; Sun-Thu 10:30 pm, Fri-Sat 11:30 pm.*

Galvin at Windows
Park Lane London Hilton Hotel W1   £83   ❸❷❷
22 Park Ln   7208 4021   3–4A
*It's not just the "terrific" views that make this 28th-floor Mayfair eyrie
"a wonderful place for a special occasion"; the food is "surprisingly
good" too, and "to seal the deal" – be it of a business or romantic
nature – the overall package is hard to beat. / www.galvinatwindows.com;
Mon-Wed 10.30 pm, Thu-Sat 11 pm; closed Sat L & Sun D; no Maestro;
no shorts; set weekday L £43 (FP), set pre-theatre £54 (FP).*

GALVIN BISTROT DE LUXE W1   £59   ❷⓿❷
66 Baker St   7935 4007   2–1A
*"A little slice of Paris… minus the waiters!"; the Galvin brothers'
"magnificent" Marylebone "all-rounder" remains "a benchmark
of bistro-style cuisine" – "beautifully judged", and "professionally
served", in a "smart" but "convivial" setting.
/ www.galvinrestaurants.com; Mon-Wed 10.30 pm, Thu-Sat 10.45 pm,
Sun 9.30 pm.*

GALVIN LA CHAPELLE E1   £62   ❷⓿⓿
35 Spital Sq   7299 0400   12–2B
*"Your first thought is: 'wow!'", and the Galvin brothers' "spectacular"
and "luxurious" Spitalfields yearling doesn't let you down thereafter –
their "beautifully sympathetic" conversion of a high-vaulted Victorian
school hall offers "impeccable" brasserie fare that's "inventive" but
"unfussy". / www.galvinrestaurants.com; Mon-Sat 10.30 pm, Sun 9.30 pm.*

Ganapati SE15 £33 **❶❶❷**
38 Holly Grove 7277 2928 1–4C
"Peckham's finest!" – this very small communal diner, where "table-sharing is de rigueur", continues to impress and amaze with its "personable" service, and with "exciting" cooking that "compares well with what you actually get in south India".
/ www.ganapatirestaurant.com; 10.30 pm, Sun 10 pm; closed Mon; no Amex; set weekday L £21 (FP).

Gandhi's SE11 £29 **❸❷❸**
347 Kennington Rd 7735 9015 1–3C
It can seem "ordinary" – and lives somewhat in the shadow of the nearby Kennington Tandoori – but this "friendly" Indian is generally tipped for its "high-quality curry selection". / www.gandhis.co.uk; 11.30 pm.

Garrison SE1 £44 **❸❸❶**
99-101 Bermondsey St 7089 9355 9–4D
"Cramped" but "vibey", this "stalwart" early-wave Bermondsey gastropub, near the Antiques Market, still "manages to hold its own"; "buzzy" brunches a speciality. / www.thegarrison.co.uk; 10 pm, Sun 9.30 pm.

Garufa N5 £42 **❸④❸**
104 Highbury Pk 7226 0070 8–1D
"Satisfying steaks" – the raison d'être of this "charming" Argentinian outfit, in Highbury, where the food is "sound", if "nothing exceptional". / www.garufa.co.uk; 10.30 pm; no Amex.

Gastro SW4 £44 **④⑤❸**
67 Venn St 7627 0222 10–2D
"Très français" and romantic, this shabby-chic café/bistro, by the Clapham Picture House, is often tipped as a breakfast destination; overall, however, feedback has become rather mixed. / midnight; no Amex; set weekday L £27 (FP).

The Gate W6 £44 **❷❸④**
51 Queen Caroline St 7748 6932 7–2C
"Surprising" dishes – "enjoyable even to dedicated carnivores" – have made a big name for this church-hall-style veggie, near the Hammersmith Odeon (and it has a "lovely courtyard" for the summer too); ratings slid this year, though, reflecting dissatisfaction with "OK but overpriced" food, and a "clinical" ambience. / www.thegate.tv; 10.30 pm, Sat 11 pm; closed Sat L & Sun.

Gaucho £59 **❸④❸**
25 Swallow St, W1 7734 4040 3–3D
60 Charlotte St, W1 7580 6252 2–1C
125 Chancery Ln, WC2 7242 7727 2–2D
89 Sloane Ave, SW3 7584 9901 5–2C
64 Heath St, NW3 7431 8222 8–1A
02 Centre, Peninsular Sq, SE10 8858 7711 11–2D
Tooley St, SE1 7407 5222 9–4D
Tow Path, TW10 8948 4030 1–4A
29 Westferry Circus, E14 7987 9494 11–1B
93a Charterhouse St, EC1 7490 1676 9–1B
5 Finsbury Ave, Broadgate, EC2 7256 6877 12–2B
1 Bell Inn Yd, EC3 7626 5180 9–2C
"Decent steak" wins many admirers for these "darkly-decorated" and "dependable" Argentinian-themed outfits, not least "for business lunching"; "crazy" prices put off quite a few reporters, though, and – on off-days – service can be "painfully bad".
/ www.gauchorestaurants.co.uk; 11 pm, Fri & Sat 11.30 pm, SE10, Piccadilly midnight, Sun 11 pm; EC3 & EC2 closed Sat & Sun; WC2 7 EC1 closed Sun.

Gauthier Soho W1 £65 **①②③**

21 Romilly St 7494 3111 4–3A

"A Theatreland show-stopper!"; with its "warm" welcome and "memorable" Gallic cuisine, Alexis Gauthier's "intimate" yearling "makes better use of this Soho townhouse than its illustrious predecessor" (Richard Corrigan's Lindsay House, RIP); the atmosphere of the "cramped" interior, however, can sometimes seem rather "muted". / www.gauthiersoho.co.uk; 10.30 pm; closed Sun.

LE GAVROCHE W1 £115 **①②②**

43 Upper Brook St 7408 0881 3–2A

"Still cutting it after all these years", Michel Roux's "remarkable" Mayfair basement (established by father Albert in 1967) stands out for its "sheer professionalism", and its "peerless" realisation of "classic" Gallic cuisine; it's "astronomically expensive", of course, making "the best-value set lunch in town" all the more of a "bargain". / www.le-gavroche.co.uk; 11 pm; closed Sat L & Sun; jacket required; set weekday L £51 (FP).

Gay Hussar W1 £46 **⑤③②**

2 Greek St 7437 0973 4–2A

It still has its fans – especially as a venue for a "sustaining" winter lunch – but this "once-great" Soho townhouse-institution is "living on its former reputation"; "I hope Hungarians eat better than this!" / www.gayhussar.co.uk; 10.45 pm; closed Sun.

Gaylord W1 £42 **③④④**

79-81 Mortimer St 7580 3615 2–1B

A "venerable" and rather "grand" Indian, just off Regent Street, serving "good, traditional anglicised food"; even some fans, though, rail at its "highfalutin" prices and sometimes iffy service. / www.gaylordlondon.com; 11.30 pm, Sun 11 pm.

Gazette £38 **④④②**

79 Riverside Plaza, Chatfield Rd, SW11 7223 0999 10–1C

100 Balham High St, SW12 8772 1232 10–2C

Especially "as a Saturday morning retreat, with coffee, eggs and the papers", these sarf London bistros win support with their "authentic" scoff and "reasonable" prices; service is "erratic" though, and critics find the food simply "pseudo". / www.gazettebrasserie.co.uk; 11 pm; set always available £25 (FP).

Geales £49 **③③④**

1 Cale St, SW3 7965 0555 5–2C **NEW**

2 Farmer St, W8 7727 7528 6–2B

Tucked-away off Notting Hill Gate, this rejuvenated grand chippy is "not what it was" in the old days, but a "reliable" option nonetheless; fans are "impressed" by its "appallingly cramped" Chelsea Green sibling (on the site of Tom's Place, RIP) too, but others (with whom we tend to agree) find it "nothing to write home about". / www.geales.com; 10.30, Sun 9.30-10 pm; Mon L.

Geeta NW6 £18 **③③⑤**

57-59 Willesden Ln 7624 1713 1–1B

"You'll double-take when you see how small the bill is!" – no wonder this ultra-grungy Kilburn café still has quite a following for its "really authentic" South Indian cuisine; not everyone, however, is convinced that standards are being maintained; BYO. / 10.30 pm, Fri-Sat 11 pm; no Amex.

Gelupo W1 £9 ❷❷④
7 Archer St   7287 5555   3–2D
*"MMMMMmmmmmm!"; this "cool" new Soho ice cream parlour –
sorry, 'Gelateria' – from the team at Bocca di Lupo (opposite) offers
"an amazing array" of ices, sorbets and granitas, which many
reporters tip as "the best in London". / www.gelupo.com; Sun-Wed
11 pm, Thu-Sat 1 am.*

Gem N1 £24 ❷❶❷
265 Upper St   7359 0405   8–2D
*"Incredibly fresh and tasty mezze at ridiculously low prices" make
it worth seeking out this Kurdish "staple", in Islington; the recent
renovation "has really lifted the interior". / www.gem-restaurant.co.uk;
11 pm, Fri & Sat midnight, Sun 10.30 pm.*

La Genova W1 £63 ❸❷❸
32 North Audley St   7629 5916   3–2A
*"You're made to feel part of the family", say fans of this "old-style"
Mayfair trattoria; it's "hugely expensive", though, and the odd former
fan fears it's losing its edge. / www.lagenovarestaurant.com; 11 pm;
closed Sun.*

George & Vulture EC3 £43 ⑤④❷
3 Castle Ct   7626 9710   9–3C
*"A splendidly Dickensian location" wins hearts for this historic tavern,
"tucked-away" in the City; its comfort food menu, however, ranges
from "barely adequate… to far worse". / www.georgeandvulture.com;
2.45 pm; L only, closed Sat & Sun.*

Gessler at Daquise SW7 £39 ④❷❸
20 Thurloe St   7589 6117   5–2C
*"This old friend has had quite a facelift", but not everyone loves the
new régime at this WWII-era Polish émigrés' café in South
Kensington; some reporters do praise its "honest and different" fare,
but critics find the approach "fussy", and say that results overall are
only "OK". / gesslerlondon.com; 11 pm; no Amex; set weekday L £24 (FP).*

The Giaconda Dining Room WC2 £41 ❷❷④
9 Denmark St   7240 3334   4–1A
*"Behind an unprepossessing façade", near Centre Point,
this "cramped" and "entirely unpretentious" café is an absolute
"knock-out" – the "friendly" service is incredibly "professional",
and the "tiny kitchen" turns out "probably the best-value bistro-
cooking in central London". / www.giacondadining.com; 9.15 pm; closed
Mon, Sat D & Sun.*

Giant Robot EC1 £39 ❸④❷
45 Clerkenwell Rd   7065 6810   9–1A
*A "very cool" Clerkenwell haunt, where "superb meatballs" are the
highlight of "a menu suited to sharing"; service, though, can be "a bit
random". / www.gntrbt.com; midnight.*

Gifto's Lahore Karahi UB1 £24 ❷❸④
162-164 The Broadway   8813 8669   1–3A
*"Rushed at weekends, when there are queues out the door" –
this large and "buzzy" Southall diner offers "great Punjabi" food
at "the best prices". / www.gifto.com; 11.30 pm, Sat & Sun midnight.*

Gilbert Scott
St Pancras Renaissance NW1 NEW £67 ④❷❷
Euston Rd 7278 3888 8–3C
*It may occupy an "amazing" room in a "spectacular" Victorian
building, but Marcus Wareing's much-hyped British brasserie "hasn't
yet found its stride"; service is "personable", but the "semi-historical"
menu "promises much" but is "rather less exciting on the plate".
/ www.thegilbertscott.co.uk; 10.30 pm.*

Gilgamesh NW1 £62 ❸④❷
The Stables, Camden Mkt, Chalk Farm Rd 7428 4922 8–3B
*It's not just the giant scale that makes it an "OTT" experience to visit
this "opulent" venue, over Camden Market… the bill's super-sized
too; that said, the pan-Asian food is sometimes surprisingly "great".
/ www.gilgameshbar.com; midnight; no trainers.*

Ginger & White NW3 £8 ❸❷❷
4a-5a, Perrins Ct 7431 9098 8–2A
*"Small", "cosy" and "sociable", this Hampstead café is "thriving" –
breakfasts are a highlight, but it's the coffee which really gets fans
revved up. / www.gingerandwhite.com; L only; no Mastercard.*

Giraffe £40 ⑤④④
120 Wilton Rd, SW1 7233 8303 2–4B
6-8 Blandford St, W1 7935 2333 2–1A
19-21 The Brunswick Centre, WC1 7812 1336 8–4C
120 Holland Park Ave, W11 7229 8567 6–2A
270 Chiswick High Rd, W4 8995 2100 7–2A
7 Kensington High St, W8 7938 1221 5–1A
29-31 Essex Rd, N1 7359 5999 8–3D
196-198 Haverstock Hill, NW3 7431 3812 8–2A
46 Rosslyn Hill, NW3 7435 0343 8–2A
Royal Festival Hall, Riverside, SE1 7928 2004 2–3D
27 Battersea Rise, SW11 7223 0933 10–2C
1 Crispin Pl, E1 3116 2000 12–2B
*"Even the messiest toddler is welcomed", at this "accommodating"
and very "family-focussed" chain of 'World Food' cafés; it's also worth
seeking out for a "great brunch" but, more generally, "the accent
is on quantity not quality". / www.giraffe.net; 10.45 pm, Sun 10.30pm;
no booking, Sat & Sun 9am-5pm; set weekday L £21 (FP).*

La Giralda HA5 £27 ❸❷❸
66-68 Pinner Grn 8868 3429 1–1A
*"Waiters who've been there for decades" add to the "loud and fun"
style of this stalwart tapas bar, in a Pinner shop parade.
/ www.lagiralda.co.uk; 10 pm; closed Mon & Sun D.*

The Glasshouse TW9 £57 ❶❶❸
14 Station Pde 8940 6777 1–3A
*"Living in the shadow of sibling Chez Bruce, but holding its own!";
this "discreet" spot, by Kew Gardens, transcends its "airy" but slightly
"anodyne" interior, thanks to its "exceptional" service and its
"consistently outstanding" cuisine (to which "bright" Asian notes add
interest). / www.glasshouserestaurant.co.uk; 10.30 pm, Sun 10 pm.*

Golden Dragon W1 £30 ❸❸❸
28-29 Gerrard St 7734 2763 4–3A
*"A large and busy Chinese" in the "heart of Chinatown" where
"the classics are done very well"; top tip: "steaming hot" dim sum.
/ 11 pm, Fri & Sat 11.30 pm, Sun 10.20 pm.*

Golden Hind W1 £21 ❶❷❸
73 Marylebone Ln 7486 3644 2–1A
The owner Mr Christou "welcomes you back like family" to this "irresistible" Marylebone chippy, which offers some of the West End's best "cheap 'n' cheerful" scoff; fortunately, "recent expansion hasn't dented the warmth of the place"; BYO. / 10 pm; closed Sat L & Sun.

Goldfish £45 ❷❸④
82 Hampstead High St, NW3 7794 6666 8–2A
46 Gresham St, EC2 7726 0308 9–2B
"Extremely innovative" cuisine has won quite a fan club for this stylish Chinese duo, although the "dinky" Hampstead original outlet remains better-known than its City offshoot; conditions are "overcrowded", though, and staff sometimes "pushy". / 10.30 pm, NW3 Sat & Sun 11 pm; EC2V closed Sat & Sun.

Good Earth £52 ❸❸⑤
233 Brompton Rd, SW3 7584 3658 5–2C
143-145 The Broadway, NW7 8959 7011 1–1B
"A cut above" – this smart Chinese mini-chain "has maintained high standards for many years"; unfortunately, however, its prices "have got a little out of hand" of late, especially as both the Knightsbridge and Mill Hill branches look "in need of a revamp". / www.goodearthgroup.co.uk; 11 pm, Sun 10.30 pm.

Goodman £60 ❷❷❸
26 Maddox St, W1 7499 3776 3–2C
11 Old Jewry, EC2 7600 8220 9–2C
"Brilliant steaks" – London's best, for many reporters – plus "out-of-this-world burgers", and "a wine list of full-bodied reds" win legions of rave reviews (especially from business types) for these "New York-style power steakhouses". / 11 pm; W1 Sun, EC2 Sat & Sun; set weekday L £36 (FP).

Gopal's of Soho W1 £31 ❸❸❸
12 Bateman St 7434 1621 4–2A
Just the job when you're in need of a "classic" curry house – one of the few traditional West End joints where you can be reasonably sure of getting some "great Indian food". / www.gopalsofsoho.co.uk; 11.30 pm.

GORDON RAMSAY SW3 £121 ④❸④
68-69 Royal Hospital Rd 7352 4441 5–3D
Fans insist the cooking "maintains top marks", but Gordon Ramsay's worldwide HQ, in Chelsea, can seem a "very formulaic" operation nowadays, as well as an "eye-wateringly expensive" one; when, we wonder, will Michelin finally feel obliged to notice that its poster boy's flagship barely deserves two stars on current form, never mind three? / www.gordonramsay.com; 11 pm; closed Sat & Sun; no jeans or trainers; booking: max 8; set weekday L £61 (FP).

Gordon Ramsay at Claridge's
Claridge's Hotel W1 £100 ⑤④⑤
55 Brook St 7499 0099 3–2B
This grand Mayfair dining room is so clearly "living on its reputation" that you do have to wonder why its parent hotel recently extended the lease; the potentially wonderful Deco chamber feels "about as exciting as a post office" nowadays, and the food is too often "shockingly bad". / www.gordonramsay.com; 11 pm, Sun 10 pm; no jeans or trainers; booking: max 8; set weekday L £52 (FP).

Gordon's Wine Bar WC2 £27 ⑤④❶
47 Villiers St 7930 1408 4–4D
"Magical old arches" add much to the romance of this *"insanely
busy"* wine bar, near Embankment, which also benefits from one
of central London's biggest terraces; its barbecue, deli platters and
cheeses are *"incidental"* – *"it's all about quaffing the wines"*.
/ www.gordonswinebar.com; 11 pm, Sun 10 pm; no booking.

The Goring Hotel SW1 £78 ❸❶❶
15 Beeston Pl 7396 9000 2–4B
"Hopefully Royal Wedding fame won't change it!" – the *"properly old-
fashioned"* dining room of this *"quiet and refined"* family-owned hotel,
near Victoria, offers a *"well-spaced"* environment, *"Rolls-Royce"*
service and *"splendid"* cooking (including a tremendous breakfast)
in *"traditional"* style. / www.thegoring.com; 10 pm; closed Sat L; no jeans
or trainers; table of 8 max; set brunch £49 (FP).

Gourmet Burger Kitchen £27 ❸④④
Branches throughout London
For its (dwindling) army of fans, this once path-breaking Kiwi-inspired
chain remains a *"failsafe"* option for a *"proper"* burger (with *"a good
range of toppings"* too); it's hard to disagree, though, with those who
feel *"the formula looks a bit worn, especially versus newcomers,
such as Byron"*. / www.gbkinfo.com; 10.45 pm; EC4 10 pm; SW19 11 pm,
Sun 10 pm; no booking.

Gourmet Pizza Company £31 ❸❸❸
Gabriels Wharf, 56 Upper Ground, SE1 7928 3188 9–3A
18-20 Mackenzie Walk, E14 7345 9192 11–1C
"Well-made pizza with interesting toppings" – plus *"smiling"* and
"efficient" staff – again win praise for these superior pizza-stops;
the outside tables at the SE1 branch enjoy great views of the City and
St Paul's. / www.gourmetpizzacompany.co.uk; E14 10.30 pm; SE1 10.45 pm,
Fri, Sat 11.15; E14 closed Sun; booking: min 7.

Gourmet San E2 £21 ❷④⑤
261 Bethnal Green Rd 7729 8388 12–1D
Ignore the *"grim-looking exterior in a grim location"* – it's the
"deliciously spicy" and *"fiery"* Sichuan cooking that makes this *"no-
frills"* East End dive so *"startlingly good"*; it's *"cheap as chips"* too.
/ www.oldplace.co.uk; 11 pm; D only.

Govinda's W1 £13 ❸④④
9 Soho St 7437 4928 4–1A
"Especially for a cheap lunch" near Oxford Street, the no-frills café
of the Radha-Krishna Temple, just north of Soho Square, makes
a great bet, thanks to its good-quality, *"authentically Indian"* veggie
fare. / www.iskcon-london.org; 8 pm; closed Sun; no Amex.

Gow's EC2 £49 ④❸❸
81 Old Broad St 7920 9645 9–2C
"Undemanding", but *"reliable for a business lunch"* –
this *"unreconstructed City fish place"*, near Liverpool Street, continues
to exert its rather *"club-like"* charm. / www.ballsbrothers.co.uk; 9.30 pm;
closed Sat & Sun.

The Gowlett SE15 £35 ❷④❷
62 Gowlett Rd 7635 7048 1–4C
"Amazing pizza" – with *"Rizla-thin crusts"* – is the highlight at this
"neighbourhood gem", in Peckham; *"and you get a great array of real
ales"* too – *"what's not to like?"* / www.thegowlett.com; 10.30 pm,
Sun 9 pm.

Goya SW1 £40 ④④④
34 Lupus St   7976 5309   2–4C
"Reliable" tapas help make this "laid-back" Pimlico bar a "busy" local rendezvous; it may also help that there's precious little else hereabouts... / www.goyarestaurant.co.uk; 11.30 pm.

Gran Paradiso SW1 £46 ④❸④
52 Wilton Rd   7828 5818   2–4B
"The menu hasn't changed much in 30 years", at this Pimlico trattoria; everyone says the food's "thoroughly reliable" though, and this remains a "much-loved local", even if service has seemed a little "weary" of late. / 10.45 pm; closed Sat L & Sun.

The Grand Imperial
Guoman Grosvenor Hotel SW1 NEW £49 ④❸④
101 Buckingham Palace Rd   7821 8898   2–4B
The scale of this grand new Chinese restaurant – in a Victorian hotel by Victoria Station – can make it feel a bit like a "mausoleum"; service tries hard, though, and strengths include lots of space for business meetings, and good-value lunchtime dim sum. / www.grandimperiallondon.com; 10 pm; no trainers.

The Grapes E14 £44 ❸❸❷
76 Narrow St   7987 4396   11–1B
"A Dickensian interior and great Thames views" make this "intimate" Docklands inn "a big hit with visitors from abroad"; upstairs there's a "small but perfectly formed restaurant", serving simple, fishy fare – "if you can, get a window seat". / 9.30 pm; closed Sat L & Sun D.

Grazing Goat W1 NEW £55 ❸❷❷
6 New Quebec St   7724 7243   2–2A
"Beautifully refurbished" (by the 'Thomas Cubitt' group), this new Marylebone gastropub is – say fans – "a breath of fresh air" locally; critics, however, find the "uncomplicated" cuisine "overpriced", and say it comes in "minuscule portions" too. / www.thegrazinggoat.co.uk; 10 pm; .

Great Eastern Dining Room EC2 £42 ❷❸❷
54-56 Great Eastern St   7613 4545   12–1B
Will Ricker must be proud of this ever-"trendy" Shoreditch hang-out – thanks to its "creative" pan-Asian tapas that are "every bit as good as the vibe", and "brilliant cocktails" too, it really has stood the test of time. / www.rickerrestaurants.com; 10.45 pm; closed Sat L & Sun.

Great Nepalese NW1 £28 ❸❷⑤
48 Eversholt St   7388 6737   8–3C
"Specialities not found in your average Indian" add interest to this "always reliable" and "very welcoming" Nepalese stalwart, in the grim shadow of Euston Station. / www.great-nepalese.co.uk; 11.30 pm, Sun 10 pm.

Great Queen Street WC2 £44 ❷❸❸
32 Great Queen St   7242 0622   4–1D
"Showcasing the best of British food!" – this "deceptively simple" (or perhaps "self-consciously basic") Covent Garden pub-conversion gives its famous sibling the Anchor & Hope a good run for its money, and its "lively" ("noisy") interior is more atmospheric too. / 10.15 pm; closed Sun D; no Amex.

The Greedy Buddha SW6   £33   ❸②❸
144 Wandsworth Bridge Rd   7751 3311   10–1B
"Delicious, freshly-made food" – and "staff who work hard" too –
win strong local praise for this "good-value" Fulham Nepalese.
/ www.thegreedybuddha.com; 10.30 pm, Fri & Sat 11.30 pm; closed
weekday L; no Amex.

Green & Blue SE22   £34   ④②②
38 Lordship Ln   8693 9250   1–4D
"Wine heaven!" – in fact, no one bothers to mention the deli scoff
on offer at this "chilled" East Dulwich wine store at all; indeed, for a
small per capita charge, you can even BYO – the food, that is! –
to accompany your choice of bottle (sold, earlier in the week, at retail
prices). / www.greenandbluewines.com; Thu 11 pm, Fri & Sat midnight,
Sun 8 pm; no Amex.

Green Cottage NW3   £28   ②④⑤
9 New College Pde   7722 5305   8–2A
Ignore the "dingy" setting and the "slightly supercilious" service –
it's the "great no-frills Chinese food", at "reasonably prices" too,
that makes it worth visiting this busy stalwart, near Swiss Cottage.
/ 11 pm, Sun 10 pm; no Amex.

Green Papaya E8   £30   ②②②
191 Mare St   8985 5486   1–1D
An "authentic" Hackney Vietnamese, where "food of a surprisingly
high standard" is just part of a package that enthuses its (small) fan
club. / www.green-papaya.com; 11 pm; Closed L, Mon; no Amex.

Green's   £62   ②②②
36 Duke St, SW1   7930 4566   3–3D
14 Cornhill, EC3   7220 6300   9–2C
Simon Parker Bowles's "old-fashioned" St James's bastion has traded
less on its "clubby" credentials of late, and more on the attractions
of some "first-class" fish and seafood; its offshoot – in an
"impressive" banking hall by Bank – offers "one of the most civilised
settings for a City lunch". / www.greens.org.uk; SW1 11 pm; SW1 closed
Sun (May-Sep), EC3 Sat & Sun.

The Greenhouse W1   £98   ❸❸②
27a Hays Mews   7499 3331   3–3B
An "astonishing" cellar ("the wine list is two heavy tomes"),
"faultless" cuisine, and overall "attention to detail" win high praise –
especially from expense accounters – for Marlon Abela's "well-
spaced" and "discreet" venture, "in a lovely Mayfair mews".
/ www.greenhouserestaurant.co.uk; 11 pm; closed Sat L & Sun; booking:
max 12; set weekday L £47 (FP).

Grumbles SW1   £42   ⑤④④
35 Churton St   7834 0149   2–4B
Diehard fans see this "cramped" Pimlico local as "a delightful
harking-back to the bistros of the '60s and '70s"; harsher critics,
however, fear it has merely "lost its way".
/ www.grumblesrestaurant.co.uk; 10.45 pm; set weekday L & pre-theatre
£27 (FP).

Guerilla Burgers W1   £30   ❸②②
35 James St   7486 1511   3–1A
"Che Guevara would be a fan", say those whose praise the
"humorous" decor of this funky spot near Selfridges; it offers burgers
which are decent enough, but arguably not up to the other "excellent,
fresh-Mex" fare. / www.guerillaburgers.com; 11 pm, Sun 10.30 pm.

The Guinea Grill W1 £63 ❷❸❸
30 Bruton Pl 7499 1210 3–3B
A "meat-lover's haven"; this "old-school" pub, "hidden-away" in a
Mayfair mews, serves up some "excellent" and "very traditional"
steaks and pies, in a "cramped" and "atmospheric" dining room
which "harks back to Edwardian days"; even fans, however, can find
it "expensive". / www.theguinea.co.uk; 10.30 pm; closed Sat L & Sun;
booking: max 8.

The Gun E14 £50 ❷④❷
27 Coldharbour 7515 5222 11–1C
With its "lovely views" ("across the Thames to the O2 dome"),
this "beautifully-located" riverside pub is a hugely popular refuge from
nearby Canary Wharf; its "upmarket British gastropub fare" is "top-
quality" too, although it's "expensive", and service can be "slow".
/ www.thegundocklands.com; 10.30 pm, Sun 9.30 pm.

Gung-Ho NW6 £36 ❸❷❸
328-332 West End Ln 7794 1444 1–1B
"It does have its off days", but this "always-buzzing"
West Hampstead Chinese veteran is "still above-average for a local",
and "when it's good, it's very good". / www.stir-fry.co.uk; 11.30 pm;
no Amex.

Haandi SW3 £47 ❷❷④
7 Cheval Pl 7823 7373 5–1C
Oddly 'hidden-away' in a mews opposite Harrods, this long-
established Indian offers some "terrific" Punjabi cooking that's well
worth seeking out. / www.haandi-restaurants.com; 11 pm.

Haché £35 ❸❸❸
329-331 Fulham Rd, SW10 7823 3515 5–3B
24 Inverness St, NW1 7485 9100 8–3B
"Better than Byron!" – these "cool" but "friendly" Camden Town and
Chelsea bistros have acquired a massive following by dint of their
"huge selection" of "fantastically juicy" and "well-seasoned" burgers,
that are amongst "the best in town". / www.hacheburgers.com; 10.30 pm,
Fri-Sat 11 pm, Sun 10 pm.

HAKKASAN £82 ❷④❷
17 Bruton St, W1 7907 1888 3–2C
8 Hanway Pl, W1 7927 7000 4–1A
For a "sexy night out", these "slick", "noisy" and "über-expensive"
Chinese hotspots "still rock", not least for those in search
of "London's most finely executed dim sum"; the "très flash" new
branch in Mayfair "raises the bar even higher than the original"
(near Tottenham Court Road). / www.hakkasan.com; midnight, Sun 11 pm.

Halepi W2 £44 ❸❶❸
18 Leinster Ter 7262 1070 6–2C
"You just feel as if you are on a charming Greek island" – well,
you do need a bit of imagination – when you visit this veteran
Bayswater taverna; its diehard fan club love the hearty fare, and the
staff who "greet you like family". / www.halepi.co.uk; midnight.

Haozhan W1 £39 ❸④⑤
8 Gerrard St 7434 3838 4–3A
Is this "mould-breaking" Chinatown three-year-old beginning
to "slack"? – fans still say its "original" modern Asian cooking is "in a
different league" from its competitors, enabling it to transcend its
"drab", IKEA-esque decor; sceptics say it's on the verge of becoming
"bog-standard". / www.haozhan.co.uk; 11.30 pm, Fri & Sat midnight,
Sun 11 pm.

Harbour City W1 £30 ❷④④
46 Gerrard St 7439 7859 4–3B
"Still Gerrard Street's best for dim sum" – this Chinatown fixture
offers *"amazing value"* at lunchtime, and its *"other traditional dishes"*
are *"reliable"* too. / 11.30 pm, Fri-Sat midnight, Sun 10 pm.

Hard Rock Café W1 £47 ④❷❷
150 Old Park Ln 7629 0382 3–4B
"Still grooving after all these years", the *"fun"* Mayfair original branch
of this global chain still pleases kids of all ages; its *"basic"* food
is cooked only *"reasonably well"*, but *"it's the rock 'n' roll you go for"*.
/ www.hardrock.com; midnight; need 10+ to book.

Hardy's Brasserie W1 £44 ④④❸
53 Dorset St 7935 5929 2–1A
"Nicely tucked-away in a side street", this *"old-fashioned"* wine bar
is strong on atmosphere; it offers *"OK"* food too, and some *"diverse"*
wines to go with it. / www.hardysbrasserie.co.uk; 10.30 pm; closed
Sat & Sun.

Hare & Tortoise £28 ❸❸❸
11-13 The Brunswick, WC1 7278 9799 2–1D
373 Kensington High St, W14 7603 8887 7–1D
38 Haven Grn, W5 8810 7066 1–2A
296-298 Upper Richmond Rd, SW15 8394 7666 10–2B
90 New Bridge St, EC4 7651 0266 9–2A
"Always busy", these pan-Asian canteens are great *"for a quick exotic
meal"*; they serve *"great-value sushi"*, but it's the *"fine noodles"* that
are the *"real bargain"* – *"go early to avoid the queues"*.
/ www.hareandtortoise-restaurants.co.uk; 10.45 pm, Fri & Sat 11.15 pm;
EC4 10 pm; EC4 Sun; W14 no bookings.

Harrison's SW12 £47 ④④❸
15-19 Bedford Hill 8675 6900 10–2C
It's *"buzzy and consistent"*, but you don't go to Sam Harrison's
"neighbourhood" hang-out (formerly Balham Bar & Grill) for
memorable cuisine – it's at its best as *"a venue for a lazy Sunday"*.
/ www.harrisonsbalham.co.uk; 10.30 pm, Sun 10 pm; set weekday L £30 (FP).

(Georgian Restaurant)
Harrods SW1 £68 ❸❸❸
87-135 Brompton Rd 7225 6800 5–1D
Of the many eating options at the Knightsbridge department store,
the *"quiet"* and elegant top-floor main dining room is probably the
best – once you're there, the enormous buffet is worth serious
consideration. / www.harrods.com; 5 pm; L only.

Harry Morgan's NW8 £37 ❷❸❸
31 St John's Wood High St 7722 1869 8–3A
Back on top form post-refurbishment – this *"buzzing"* kosher
institution, in St John's Wood, is *"your classic deli"*, and rightly praised
for its *"famous chicken soup"* and *"the best salt beef in town!"*
/ www.harryms.co.uk; 10 pm.

Harwood Arms SW6 £49 ❷❷❷
Walham Grove 7386 1847 5–3A
"A REAL gastropub!"; the *"superb"* British cooking – including
"magnificent" game and *"the best Scotch eggs"* – has made a huge
name for this Fulham backstreet boozer; it's a *"laid-back"* kind
of place too, with staff who are *"so welcoming"*.
/ www.harwoodarms.com; 9.30 pm, Sun 9 pm; closed Mon L.

The Havelock Tavern W14 £43 ②④②
57 Masbro Rd   7603 5374   7–1C
"Back, after a rocky patch", this "genuine" gastropub, in an Olympia back street, is "always humming"; the food can be "outstanding" – service is still "slow", though, but at least "it's not surly, like it used to be". / www.thehavelocktavern.co.uk; 10 pm, Sun 9.30 pm; no booking.

The Haven N20 £47 ④④④
1363 High Rd   8445 7419   1–1B
Views on "Whetstone's finest joint" have become very mixed; for fans, this is still a "great" and "boisterous" neighbourhood place – for quite a few critics, though, it's "very mediocre" nowadays.
/ www.haven-bistro.co.uk; 11 pm; no Amex.

Hawksmoor £59 ②②②
11 Langley St, WC2   7856 2154   4–2C
157 Commercial St, E1   7247 7392   12–2B
10-12 Basinghall St, EC2   awaiting tel   9–2C **NEW**
"Terrific steaks" ("mind you, you pay for 'em"), "crazy-good triple-cooked chips" and "the best cocktails" – three potent ingredients that are carving a formidable and growing reputation for these Spitalfields, Covent Garden and (from late-2011) City steakhouses.
/ www.thehawksmoor.com; 10.30 pm; both Sun D; no Amex.

Haz £36 ③③②
9 Cutler St, E1   7929 7923   9–2D
34 Foster Ln, EC2   7600 4172   9–2B
112 Hounsditch, EC3   7623 8180   9–2D
6 Mincing Ln, EC3   7929 3173   9–3D
"Fresh" and "good-value" mezze and kebabs and "brisk" service have won a big City following for these "cramped" but "efficient" Turkish operations – thanks to their "ever-reliable" charms, they're always "buzzing". / www.hazrestaurant.co.uk; 11.30 pm; EC3 Sun.

Hazev E14 £30 ④④④
2 South Quay Sq, Discovery Dock West   7515 9467   11–1C
"Nothing special, but it's nice to have more variety in Canary Wharf" – this large and "noisy" Turkish water-sider, near South Quay DLR, "draws in the crowds" with its "tasty mezze and other dishes".
/ www.hazev.com; 11.30 pm, Wed-Sat 11 pm.

Hazuki WC2 £35 ②②④
43 Chandos Pl   7240 2530   4–4C
An "unassuming" café, near Charing Cross, that's well worth knowing about if you're looking for "interesting" Japanese food at "reasonable prices"; its interior "isn't that great", but "the grub makes up".
/ www.hazukilondon.co.uk; 10.30 pm, Sun 9.30 pm; closed Sat L & Sun L.

Hedone W4 **NEW** £79 ②④④
301 Chiswick High Rd   8747 0377   7–2A
Foodie cognoscenti are enraptured by this ambitious, ingredient-led Chiswick newcomer, which opened in summer 2011; Mikael Jonsson's cooking undoubtedly shows huge promise, but – on our very early-days visit – all aspects of the operation needed more polish, yet prices were already sky high. / Rated on Editors' visit.

Hélène Darroze
The Connaught Hotel W1   £105   ❸❹❸
Carlos Pl   3147 7200   3–3B
"Elaborate" cuisine and "elegant" surroundings win fans for this
Mayfair outpost of the acclaimed Parisienne chef; service "veers from
friendly to stuffy", though, and quite a few reporters still yearn for the
"good old days" (before celebrity nonsense took hold), when this was
one of the classiest and most consistent destinations in town.
/ www.the-connaught.co.uk; 10.30 pm; closed Mon & Sun; jacket & tie;
set weekday L £63 (FP).

Hellenic W1   £43   ❹❷❸
30 Thayer St   7935 1257   2–1A
In Fitzrovia, an "old-fashioned" Greek restaurant – straight from
Central Casting – whose "authentic" charms still win it a small fan
club. / 10.45 pm; closed Sun; no Amex.

The Henry Root SW10 NEW   £46   ❹❷❸
9 Park Walk   7352 7040   5–3B
With a feel a bit like "an upmarket gastropub", this heart-of-Chelsea
newcomer is heartily praised for its "cosy and welcoming" interior,
its "very attentive" staff and its "great selection of tasty dishes";
detractors, though, just find the whole show rather too "average".
/ www.thehenryroot.com; 11 pm.

Hereford Road W2   £42   ❷❷❹
3 Hereford Rd   7727 1144   6–1B
"No-nonsense, robust British dishes" – from "good-quality
ingredients", including "good offal and game" – have won a huge fan
club for Tom Pemberton's Bayswater bistro; best place to sit: the
"booths-à-deux", at the front. / www.herefordroad.org; 10.30 pm,
Sun 10 pm.

Hibiscus W1   £110   ❸❹❹
29 Maddox St   7629 2999   3–2C
"Brilliant" cuisine that "thinks outside the box" wins "10/10" ratings
from fans of Claude Bosi's "calm" Mayfair HQ; not everyone
is persuaded, though, and critics perennially complain of "ridiculous"
prices for food that's "nothing special", and an ambience like
a "funeral parlour" (albeit a rather comfortable one).
/ www.hibiscusrestaurant.co.uk; 9.45 pm; closed Mon L & Sun; set weekday L
£53 (FP).

High Road Brasserie W4   £48   ❹❹❷
162-166 Chiswick High Rd   8742 7474   7–2A
A "fantastic" (and "family-friendly") brunch is a highlight at this
"atmospheric" and "very popular" hang-out, on Chiswick's main drag;
critics find its approach a bit too "strenuously trendy", though,
especially as the "very expensive" food is "nothing special at all".
/ www.sohohouse.co.uk; 10.30 pm, Fri & Sat 11.30 pm, Sun 9.30 pm.

High Timber EC4   £59   ❸❷❸
8 High Timber   7248 1777   9–3B
"Wonderful South African wines" – you choose by "nipping down
to the cellar" – are the highlight of this City spot, hidden-away near
the wobbly bridge, and it enjoys "fine" Thames views; in comparison,
the food – "excellent" steaks apart – can seem "a tasty sideline".
/ www.hightimber.com; 10 pm; closed Sat & Sun; set weekday L £38 (FP).

Hilliard EC4 £27 ❷❷❸
26a Tudor St 7353 8150 9–3A
"A foodie haven, just off chain-infested Fleet Street" – this "absolute
joy" of a pit stop is packed with lawyers getting their daily fix
of "gourmet sarnies", "imaginative salads" and "yummy coffee and
cakes"; oh, and "interesting wines" too. / www.hilliardfood.co.uk; 6 pm;
L only, closed Sat & Sun; no booking.

Hix W1 £61 ❸❹❸
66-70 Brewer St 7292 3518 3–2D
"Adopted by the entire Soho media class", this "buzzing" yearling
is extolled for its "sophisticatedly simple" British cuisine and its
"outstanding" basement bar too – no denying, though, that there are
still refuseniks who find the whole experience "very average".
/ www.hixsoho.co.uk; 10.15 pm.

Hix Oyster & Chop House EC1 £60 ❷❸❸
36-37 Greenhill Rents, Cowcross St 7017 1930 9–1A
Mark Hix's sparsely-furnished Smithfield operation is at
last establishing itself as "a seriously good place to eat"; service has
"improved", as has the cooking, which majors in the "great treatment
of quality ingredients", including "the freshest oysters",
and "a fantastic selection of chops and steaks".
/ www.restaurantsetcltd.com; 10.45 pm; closed Sat L; set always available,
weekday L & pre-theatre £26 (FP).

Hole in the Wall W4 £40 ❸❹❸
12 Sutton Lane North 8742 7185 7–2A
Tucked-away in Gunnersbury, an "unpretentious" gastroboozer,
almost invariably hailed by locals for its "restaurant-quality" food;
super garden too. / 9.45 pm, Sun 9.15 pm; closed Mon L & Tue L; no Amex.

Holly Bush NW3 £44 ❸❸❶
22 Holly Mount 7435 2892 8–1A
"Snuggle up in a nook", at this "old and atmospheric" boozer, which
benefits from a gorgeous Hampstead location; the "simple, comfort
food menu" goes nicely "with a pint of ale". / 10 pm, Sun 9 pm.

Homa N16 NEW £48 ❸❸❸
71-73 Stoke Newington Church St 7254 2072 1–1C
"At last, a decent European restaurant to add to Stokey's inner-city
mix!" – its "stylish" and "friendly" charms have already won quite
a following (...to the extent there's already the occasional fear it's
'coasting'). / www.homalondon.co.uk; 11.30 pm; closed Mon.

The Horseshoe NW3 £47 ❹❸❸
28 Heath St 7431 7206 8–2A
"Wholesome, hearty fare" and "friendly" service make this
"pleasant" gastropub a handy heart-of-Hampstead stand-by;
increasingly, though, "it's merging into the culinary averageness
of NW3". / www.thehorseshoehampstead.com; 10pm, Fri & Sat 11 pm.

Hot Stuff SW8 £20 ❷❶❷
23 Wilcox Rd 7720 1480 10–1D
"Unless you want swanky decor", this BYO Indian in deepest Vauxhall
is "brilliant", thanks to its super-"welcoming" owner, and food that's
"so zingy", and "really cheap"; it's now two doors down from the
original, so there's "more room now" too. / www.eathotstuff.com;
9.30 pm; no Amex.

Hoxton Apprentice N1 £45 ❸④❷
16 Hoxton Sq 7749 2828 12–1B
The ethos – a training project for the disadvantaged – "is part of the
attraction" of this Hoxton hang-out, which benefits from a pleasant
terrace, and quite a stylish interior; even fans, though, can find the
food "expensive for what it is". / www.hoxtonapprentice.com; 11 pm.

The Hoxton Grill EC2 £46 ❸❸❷
81 Great Eastern St 7739 9111 12–1B
The Soho House group is making quite a go of the bar/restaurant
at this hip Shoreditch-fringe hotel; "great steak and chips"
("especially cheap at lunchtimes") are a highlight, and breakfasts can
be "excellent" too. / www.hoxtongrill.com; 11.45 pm; set weekday L
£29 (FP).

Hudsons SW15 £35 ④④❸
113 Lower Richmond Rd 8785 4522 10–1A
A "reliable" Putney bistro, that "continues to deliver the goods,
year after year"; breakfasts – which come in "rower-sized portions" –
are "a must". / www.hudsonsrestaurant.co.uk; 10 pm, Sun 9.30 pm.

Hummus Bros £17 ❷❷④
88 Wardour St, W1 7734 1311 3–2D
36-67 Southampton Row, WC1 7404 7079 2–1D
128 Cheapside, EC2 7726 8011 9–2B
"I had no idea the humble chickpea could be lifted to such heights!"
– this hummus-mad chain is perfect for a snack that's "quick, cheap,
tasty, satisfying and healthy". / www.hbros.co.uk; W1 10 pm, Thu-Sat
11 pm; WC1 9 pm; WC1, EC2 closed Sat & Sun; no booking.

Hunan SW1 £50 ❶❷④
51 Pimlico Rd 7730 5712 5–2D
"Simply the best Chinese food in London!" – leave it to the chef
to choose, and the "spectacular", "tapas-style" courses "just never
stop coming", at the Peng family's "bizarre" (and decidedly
unspectacular-looking) Pimlico legend; even the wine list is – in a good
way – "full of unusual surprises". / www.hunanlondon.com; 11 pm;
closed Sun.

**Huong-Viet
An Viet House N1** £26 ④❺❺
12-14 Englefield Rd 7249 0877 1–1C
"Full of Dalston hip kids", this "fun" BYO Vietnamese, in a
De Beauvoir Town community-centre, has long been known
as "an absolute bargain"; "the food's not as good as it once was",
though, and "service and decor have never been strong points".
/ www.huongviet.co.uk; 11 pm; closed Sun; no Amex.

Hush W1 £55 ❺❺④
8 Lancashire Ct 7659 1500 3–2B
"Trading on its prime location", just off Bond Street – and with
a "hidden courtyard" too – this trendy bar/brasserie remains
a "hit with the Sotheby's set"; rather worryingly, that crowd doesn't
seem to mind that the food is "mediocre" and prices "absurd".
/ www.hush.co.uk; 11 pm; closed Sun; booking: max 12.

Ibérica £43 ❸❸❸
195 Great Portland St, W1 7636 8650 2–1B
10 Cabot Sq, E14 awaiting tel 11–1C **NEW**
"Sophisticated but authentic dishes", and "enthusiastic" service
inspire fans of this "smart" and "buzzy" tapas bar, near Great
Portland Street tube; it can seem "a bit pricey" for what it is, though,
and critics find the setting a tad "soulless"; a Canary Wharf offshoot
opens in late-2011. / 11 pm; W1 closed Sun D.

Ida W10   £38   ❸❷❷

167 Fifth Ave   8969 9853   1–2B
A "cheap 'n' cheerful" North Kensington café, hailed by fans as a
"fantastic local", where the Italian menu offers "incredible value".
/ www.idarestaurant.co.uk; 11 pm; closed Sat L & Sun; no Amex.

Ikeda W1   £85   ❷❷⑤

30 Brook St   7629 2730   3–2B
"Dismal" decor ("like a cheap motel lounge") and "chronic" prices
do not quite succeed in discouraging fans of this veteran Mayfair
Japanese, where the sushi in particular is often "excellent".
/ 10.20 pm; closed Sat L & Sun.

Ilia SW3 NEW   £67   ❸④④

96 Draycott Ave   7225 2555   5–2C
Most of the (surprisingly few) early-days reports on this new Chelsea
Italian (on the ex-Papillon, RIP, site) share our repeated experience
that it's a "friendly" place, offering "fresh" food in a "smart" and
"lively" setting; there's also a small band of critics, though,
who just find it "average" across the board. / www.ilia-london.com;
10.30 pm, Fri-Sat 11 pm; closed Mon L.

Imli W1   £36   ④❸④

167-169 Wardour St   7287 4243   3–1D
"For a novel and light approach" to Indian cooking, fans tip this
"buzzy" Soho canteen, and its "inventive" tapas formula; critics think
the idea is great too, but complain that the food is descending
to "chain-like" standards. / www.imli.co.uk; 11 pm, Sun 10 pm.

Imperial China WC2   £42   ❸❸④

25a Lisle St   7734 3388   4–3B
"Beyond a little bridge, over an ornamental pond", you enter this
large operation in a Chinatown side street; fans say it's "better than
the places on the main drag", thanks to its civilised style, and its
"presentable" cuisine. / www.imperial-china.co.uk; midnight, Sun 10.30 pm.

Imperial City EC3   £46   ④❸❸

Royal Exchange, Cornhill   7626 3437   9–2C
"In the atmospheric vaults of the Royal Exchange", this "classy"-
looking Cantonese continues to dish up "consistently good" cooking;
"it would get higher ratings, were it not for its typical high-end City
pricing". / www.orientalrestaurantgroup.co.uk; 10.30 pm; closed Sat & Sun.

Inaho W2   £43   ❶⑤⑤

4 Hereford Rd   7221 8495   6–1B
Thanks not least to its "irreproachable" sushi, this "tiny" and
"homely" Bayswater shack is hailed by fans as "the best Japanese
restaurant on the planet"; service, though, has only two speeds –
"slow" or "rushed". / 11 pm; closed Sat L & Sun; no Amex or Maestro.

Inamo   £43   ④④❷

4-12 Regent St, SW1   7499 8558   3–3D NEW
134-136 Wardour St, W1   7851 7051   3–1D
Kids of all ages love the gimmick – your touch-sensitive table-top
takes orders, changes pattern, plays games and so on – at these
"fun" West End diners; the pan-Asian fare is "uninspiring and pricey"
or "perfectly good", to taste. / 10.45 pm, SW1 12 am.

Incognico WC2   £56   ④④④

117 Shaftesbury Ave   7836 8866   4–2B
"Go for the set menus", say regulars, if you visit this heart-of-
Theatreland brasserie – if you choose its "decent, old-fashioned Gallic
fare" à la carte, you may come to the view that it is "hugely
overpriced". / www.incognico.com; 11 pm; closed Sun.

Indali Lounge W1 £34 ❸❸❸
50 Baker St 7224 2232 2–1A
With its "much lighter" (no-ghee) cooking, and contemporary styling, this large Marylebone two-year-old is "an Indian unlike any other"; critics find the food "bland" and the place "lacking buzz", but the attractions of the "excellent-value prix-fixe lunch" are undoubted. / www.indalilounge.com; midnight, Sun 11 pm; closed Sat L.

India Club
Strand Continental Hotel WC2 £25 ❹❹❹
143 Strand 7836 0650 2–2D
"Pretend you're in India!", when you visit this "old-style-colonial" canteen, near the High Commission – a "rather extraordinary" throwback, where the food is not only basic, but also "dirt cheap"; BYO. / www.strand-continental.co.uk; 10.50 pm; no credit cards; booking: max 6.

Indian Moment SW11 £34 ❸❸❹
44 Northcote Rd 7223 6575 10–2C
"An extremely busy and packed-in" Battersea curry house, which locals say is "a real cut above average"; it "doesn't break the bank" either.

Indian Ocean SW17 £25 ❷❸❸
216 Trinity Rd 8672 7740 10–2C
"Around for years, but consistently of a high standard" – this Wandsworth curry house continues to go down well with its local fan club. / 11.30 pm.

Indian Rasoi N2 £34 ❶❷❷
7 Denmark Ter 8883 9093 1–1B
"Lovely, fresh, spicy flavours" are a hallmark of the "wonderful" and "unusual" cuisine at this Muswell Hill Indian; "it's always packed, so make sure you book". / www.indian-rasoi.co.uk; 11 pm.

Indian Zilla SW13 NEW £43 ❷❶❸
2-3 Rocks Ln 8878 3989 10–1A
Indian Zing's new offshoot may occupy (formerly) "jinxed" Barnes premises, but most reporters are confident that its "exotic" and "heavenly" Indian cuisine will see it through; perhaps inevitably, though, one or two critics perceive "slightly less zing" than at the original. / www.indianzilla.co.uk; 11 pm, Sun 10.30 pm.

Indian Zing W6 £43 ❶❷❸
236 King St 8748 5959 7–2B
"Knocking many so-called top Indians out of the water!" – Manoj Vasaikar's "terrific" outfit, near Ravenscourt Park, "pleases even Michael Winner" with its "light" and "punchy" cooking, and its "civilised", if rather "cramped", setting. / www.indianzing.co.uk; 11 pm, Sun 10.30 pm.

Indigo
One Aldwych WC2 £63 ❹❷❸
1 Aldwych 7300 0400 2–2D
With its view of the cocktail bar below, this "comfortable" mezzanine makes a "pleasant" Covent Garden venue for a "business lunch" or a "pre-theatre meal"; the food was also once quite an attraction, but nowadays seems a little "uninspired". / www.onealdwych.com; 11.15 pm; set pre theatre £41 (FP).

Inn the Park SW1 £48 ④⑤❸
St James's Pk 7451 9999 2–3C
"You can't beat St James's Park for a backdrop", and this striking modern café, with its many outside tables, has huge potential; sadly, though, this is true "tourist hell", offering "pricy" and "inconsistent" food, and "inexplicably poor" service. / www.innthepark.com; 9 pm; no Amex.

Inside SE10 £43 ❷❷④
19 Greenwich South St 8265 5060 1–3D
"For years, the best food in Greenwich" – it may be "cramped", "noisy" and "uncomfortably minimalist", but this "friendly" and "professional" local is adored in SE10 as a rare source of "astonishingly dependable" cooking. / www.insiderestaurant.co.uk; 10.30 pm, Fri & Sat 11 pm; closed Mon & Sun D.

Isarn N1 £43 ❷❶❸
119 Upper St 7424 5153 8–3D
An "out-of-this-world" fish curry is a culinary highlight at this Islington fixture, which is a real "cut above" the standards of your usual "local Thai"; the "speedy" service is "immensely friendly" too, but the "corridor-like" setting can feel "oddly squeezed". / www.isarn.co.uk; 11 pm; no Amex.

Ishbilia SW1 £50 ❷④⑤
9 William St 7235 7788 5–1D
Near Harvey Nics, an authentic Lebanese café with good outside seating and offering "very good mezze"; the interior, though, could do with "a bit of a refurb"'. / www.ishbilia.com; 11 pm.

Ishtar W1 £39 ❸❷❸
10-12 Crawford St 7224 2446 2–1A
What this "cheap 'n' cheerful" Marylebone Turk may lack in fireworks it makes up for with impressive consistency – it's especially worth seeking out for the prix-fixe lunch, which is "an amazing bargain". / www.ishtarrestaurant.com; 11 pm, Sun 10.30 pm.

Isola del Sole SW15 £46 ❸❶❷
16 Lacy Rd 8785 9962 10–2B
What's not to like about this "so welcoming" and "cosy" Italian, off Putney High Street, especially when its "traditional Sardinian cuisine" is "tasty", and rather "unusual" too? / www.isoladelsole.co.uk; 10.30 pm; closed Sun.

Itsu £31 ④④④
118 Draycott Ave, SW3 7590 2400 5–2C
100 Notting Hill Gate, W11 7229 4016 6–2B
Level 2, Cabot Place East, E14 7512 5790 11–1C
"For a healthful, rapid lunch", at "cheap" prices, most reports still say this "slick"-looking sushi, soup and salad chain is a "boon"; its ratings are still sliding, though – "what was once innovative, is now indifferent, and not that tasty". / www.itsu.co.uk; 11 pm; E14 10 pm; some are closed Sat & Sun; no booking.

THE IVY WC2 £65 ④❷❷
1-5 West St 7836 4751 4–3B
It's still "magical" for its army of fans, but this cosy, panelled Theatreland legend often seems a "shadow of its former self" nowadays, and its comfort food, in particular, has "really gone downhill" – those in the know say the (private) Ivy Club, adjacent, "is much better". / www.the-ivy.co.uk; midnight, Sun 11 pm; no shorts; booking: max 6.

Izgara N3 £33 ❸❷❸
11 Hendon Lane 8371 8282 1–1B
"Very popular and so it should be" – a Turkish café-take-away,
in North Finchley, where the basic dishes are *"very good, for a
'local'".* / www.izgararestaurant.net; midnight.

Jai Krishna N4 £20 ❸❷❸
161 Stroud Green Rd 7272 1680 8–1D
*"It's evolved from its previous canteen setting to a more comfortable
experience"*, but this *"inexpensive"* Stroud Green favourite still has
"no pretentions", and its Indian veggie dishes are still *"brilliant"*.
/ 10.30 pm; closed Sun; no credit cards.

The Jam Tree £44 ❹❷❸
58 Milson Rd, W14 7371 3999 7–1C
541 King's Rd, SW6 3397 3739 5–4B **NEW**
"Tucked-away in Olympia", a *"lovely little gastropub"*, praised
by locals for its *"decent"* cooking and its *"sweet"* staff; it has a new
sibling at the Fulham end of the King's Road. / W14 11 pm,
Sun 10.30 pm; SW6 Mon-Thu 11 pm, Fri-Sat 2 am, Sun 10.30 pm.

Jamie's Italian £41 ❹❸❹
10-12 Upper St Martin's Ln, WC2 3326 6390 4–3B
Westfield, Ariel Way, W12 8090 9070 7–1C
2 Churchill Pl, E14 3002 5252 11–1C
Jamie Oliver's chain of *"buzzy"* and *"fun"* Italians started off as the
best restaurant venture he'd ever been associated with by far; as the
group grows, however, gravity is re-asserting itself, and gripes about
"overpriced" and *"average"* food are gaining momentum.
/ www.jamiesitalian.com; 11.30 pm, Sun 10.30 pm; over 6.

Jenny Lo's Tea House SW1 £33 ❸❶❹
14 Eccleston St 7259 0399 2–4B
The chow is *"always fresh and exciting"*, at this *"excellent, cheap,
and no-frills"* noodle house – a *"canteen-style"* veteran, near Victoria.
/ www.jennylo.co.uk; 9.55 pm; closed Sat & Sun; no credit cards; no booking.

Jin Kichi NW3 £41 ❶❷❹
73 Heath St 7794 6158 8–1A
"As good as eating in Tokyo" – London's *"homeliest and
most delicious Japanese"* may occupy *"tiny"* Hampstead premises,
but it continues to thrill its disproportionately large fan club with
"fabulous sushi and yakitori". / www.jinkichi.com; 11 pm, Sun 10 pm;
closed Mon, Tue-Fri D only, Sat & Sun open L & D.

Joanna's SE19 £44 ❸❷❷
56 Westow Hill 8670 4052 1–4D
"Stick to the basics and you won't go wrong", at this *"cramped"* but
"pleasant and welcoming" Crystal Palace favourite; its home cooking
"is a little variable", but it *"can be lovely"*. / www.joannas.uk.com; 11 pm,
Sun 10.30 pm.

Joe Allen WC2 £51 ❹❹❷
13 Exeter St 7836 0651 4–3D
Still *"vaguely glamorous"*, this *"fun"* Theatreland basement serves
*"pretty much the same menu as when it was cloned from the NYC
original in the '70s"* – the food's *"nothing special"*, except for
a burger (*"famously not on the menu"*) that's
amongst *"the best in town"*. / www.joeallen.co.uk; 12.45 am,
Sun 11.45 pm; booking: max 10 Fri & Sat.

Joe's Brasserie SW6 £41 ❸❸❸
130 Wandsworth Bridge Rd   7731 7835   10–1B
John Brinkley's long-established deepest-Fulham stalwart was "always fun"; as this guide goes to press, however, it is undergoing repairs after a fire. / www.brinkleys.com; 11 pm, Sat 11.30 pm, Sun 10.30 pm.

Jom Makan £27 ❹❺❺
5-7 Pall Mall East, SW1   7925 2402   2–2C
South Terrace Westfields, W12   8735 5870   7–1C
This "canteen-y and rather pricey" Malaysian chain is perfectly at home in Westfield; in Trafalgar Square – with Chinatown two minutes' walk away – its raison d'être is harder to discern. / www.jommakan.co.uk; SW1 11 pm, W12 10 pm.

José SE1 NEW £45
104 Bermondsey St   7403 4902   9–4D
Brindisa's restaurant empire was built with the help of chef José Pizarro, who has now struck out on his own at these cute Bermondsey corner premises; we had yet to visit when this guide went to press, but he's doing so well, he's already on to his next opening: Pizarro.

Joy King Lau WC2 £31 ❸❹❹
3 Leicester St   7437 1132   4–3A
"Better than average for Chinatown"; this "buzzy" veteran, just off Leicester Square, is "not the smartest" place, but, for supporters, it remains a "regular bolt-hole", thanks to its "excellent-value dim sum" and other "tasty" fare. / 11.30 pm, Sun 10.30 pm.

Julie's W11 £58 ❹❹❶
135 Portland Rd   7229 8331   6–2A
"Little booths and dark corners" add charm to the "magical" setting of this "gorgeous" and "labyrinthine" Holland Park stalwart; you need to hope, though, that "the best dish is the one sat opposite you" – the cooking can be "woeful", and it comes at "criminal" prices too. / www.juliesrestaurant.com; 11 pm; closed Sun L.

The Junction Tavern NW5 £39 ❸❷❷
101 Fortress Rd   7485 9400   8–2B
A "lovely" garden, "dependable" food and notably "friendly" staff too – no wonder this "large and comfortable" Kentish town pub is always pretty "busy". / www.junctiontavern.co.uk; 10.30 pm, Sun 9.30 pm; no Amex.

Juniper Dining N5 £39 ❷❸❸
100 Highbury Pk   7288 8716   8–1D
A chef who's "a genuine enthusiast" adds style to this café-style Highbury yearling; locals rave over its keen young staff and "superb-value" bistro fare – "I'd certainly travel, if I didn't live nearby!" / www.juniperdining.co.uk; 10.30 pm; closed Mon & Sun D.

JW Steakhouse
Grosvenor House Hotel W1 £66 ❹❹❹
86 Park Ln   7399 8460   3–3A
"Not disappointing, but nothing special" – this "large and airy" American steakhouse, right on Park Lane, does win praise for its USDA-certified steaks and "BIG" portions; it seems too "expensive" for what it is, though, to gain a widespread following among reporters. / www.jwsteakhouse.co.uk; 10.30 pm, Fri & Sat 11 pm.

K10 EC2 £37 ❸❸❹
20 Copthall Ave   7562 8510   9–2C
"Perfect for a quick lunch"; with its good sushi and other "fresh" dishes, this reliable City conveyor-café is "worth the (inevitable) queue". / www.k10.net; L only, closed Sat & Sun; no booking.

Kaffeine W1   £10   ❷❶❶
66 Great Titchfield St   7580 6755   3–1C
*"The top place for Noho's caffeine-addict creatives", this "über-small"
and "super-friendly" café is winning a big name for its "superb
Antipodean coffee", "interesting cakes", and "brilliant, and classy
sandwiches, served Sydney-style". / www.kaffeine.co.uk; 6 pm; L only,
closed Sun; no Amex; no bookings.*

Kai Mayfair W1   £100   ❸❸④
65 South Audley St   7493 8988   3–3A
*"Stunning" Chinese food – "off the scale for simplicity and subtlety" –
inspires rave reviews for this swanky Mayfair joint; prices, however,
are equally mind-numbing, and the "glamorous" interior can seem
"somewhat lacking on the atmosphere front". / www.kaimayfair.com;
10.45 pm, Sun 10.15 pm; set weekday L £51 (FP).*

Kaifeng NW4   £61   ❷❷④
51 Church Rd   8203 7888   1–1B
*"Expensive, but worth it", this "excellent kosher Chinese", in Hendon,
attracts impressively positive reports. / www.kaifeng.co.uk; 10.30 pm;
closed Fri & Sat.*

kare kare SW5   £41   ❸❸④
152 Old Brompton Rd   7373 0024   5–2B
*Fated always to be eclipsed by the neighbouring 'Star', this South
Kensington Indian nonetheless offers some "reliable" and
"imaginative" dishes, and "good value" too. / www.karekare.co.uk;
11 pm; D only.*

Karma W14   £38   ❷❶④
44 Blythe Rd   7602 9333   7–1D
*"Different and creative" Indian cooking – "with interesting regional
dishes" – rewards the discovery of this "contemporary"-style
operation, whose "friendly" and "efficient" style helps overcome its
"quiet" backstreet location, in Olympia. / www.k-a-r-m-a.co.uk; 11 pm;
no Amex.*

Kateh W9 NEW   £39   ❸❷❸
5 Warwick Pl   7289 3393   8–4A
*"A super little Persian", newly opened in the cute, if cramped, Little
Venice site that was once Green Olive (RIP), where zesty dishes are
brought by "enthusiastic" staff. / www.kateh.co.uk; 10.45 pm,
Sun 9.30 pm; closed Mon, Tue L, Wed L & Thu L.*

Kazan   £41   ❷❷❸
77 Wilton Rd, SW1   7233 8298   2–4B NEW
93-94 Wilton Rd, SW1   7233 7100   2–4B
*"Sumptuously-decorated" and "noisy", these "heaving" but "friendly"
Turkish bistros, in Pimlico, offer "reasonably-priced kebabs" that are
"a feast for both eyes and palate". / www.kazan-restaurant.com; 10 pm.*

Ken Lo's Memories SW1   £56   ❷❸❸
65-69 Ebury St   7730 7734   2–4B
*It's sometimes said to be "fading", but this "steadfast" and
"comfortable" Chinese veteran, in Belgravia, is still a favourite choice
for many reporters; it's the food – "classy and at its best truly
outstanding" – which is the prime attraction.
/ www.londonfinedininggroup.com; 11 pm, Sun 10.30 pm.*

Ken Lo's Memories of China W8 £46 ❶❷❸
353 Kensington High St 7603 6951 7–1D
*"Absolutely sensational-tasting food" and "very helpful" service win
the highest praise for this Chinese operation, on the
Olympia/Kensington borders – an even better destination, nowadays,
than the still-excellent Belgravia original.* / www.memories-of-china.co.uk;
11 pm, Sun 10 pm.

Kennington Tandoori SE11 £36 ❸❷❷
313 Kennington Rd 7735 9247 1–3C
*"Popular with the neighbourhood yuppies" (and the politicos too) –
this "stalwart curry house" emerged from a "refreshing" refit
a couple of years ago, with a "charming" interior, "super-polite"
service and cooking's that's "a cut above".*
/ www.kenningtontandoori.co.uk; midnight; no Amex.

Kensington Place W8 £50 ❸❸④
201-209 Kensington Church St 7727 3184 6–2B
*It may nowadays lack its former 'buzz', but this once trail-blazing
modern British 'goldfish bowl', off Notting Hill Gate, bounced back
this year – reports are still a bit mixed, but the "classic, well-prepared
dishes" (especially fish) have often been "very enjoyable" of late.*
/ www.kensingtonplace-restaurant.com; 10.30 pm, Sun 10 pm.

Kensington Square Kitchen W8 £33 ❸❷❸
9 Kensington Sq 7938 2598 5–1A
*"The best brunch for miles around" – the main reason to seek out
this sweet little café, nicely hidden-away from the mêlée which
is Kensington High Street.* / www.kensingtonsquarekitchen.co.uk; 5 pm,
Sun 4 pm; L only.

The Kensington Wine Rooms W8 £47 ④❷❷
127-129 Kensington Church St 7727 8142 6–2B
*"Does exactly what it says on the – smart – tin"; this "cracking"
(if "noisy") haunt, near Notting Hill Gate tube, offers "stunning"
wines, with 40 options by the glass (from an 'Enomatic' machine);
it also does a "nice line in tapas", but "food isn't the main event".*
/ www.greatwinesbytheglass.com; 10.45 pm.

Kentish Canteen NW5 NEW £38 ❸❷❸
300 Kentish Town Rd 7485 7331 8–2C
*A "buzzy" Kentish Town newcomer that lives up to its name;
it's "not trying to do too much", but it's "a very safe option" that
"pitches good food at affordable prices".* / www.kentishcanteen.co.uk;
10.30 pm.

(Brew House)
Kenwood House NW3 £28 ④④❷
Hampstead Heath 8341 5384 8–1A
*"On a bright day, nothing is better than sitting out in the peaceful
garden" – that's the star attraction of this "refined" self-service café,
at the top of Hampstead Heath; "the food isn't bad, but isn't really
the point".* / www.companyofcooks.com; 6 pm (summer), 4 pm (winter);
no Amex.

Kenza EC2 £52 ④④❸
10 Devonshire Sq 7929 5533 9–2D
*For "a fun and lively dining experience" – "like being in Beirut!" –
this "entertaining" cellar-Lebanese, near Liverpool Street, can be quite
a "find"; the belly-dancing music can be "ear-splitting", though,
and not all reporters are impressed by the food.*
/ www.kenza-restaurant.com; 10 pm; closed Sun.

Kerbisher & Malt W6 NEW £13 ❷❸④
164 Shepherd's Bush Rd 3556 0228 7–1C
At last! – Brook Green finally has a good chippy, in the shape of this
stylish but Spartan new café/take-away, on the former site of Snows
on the Green (RIP); the fish is very good if not generous-portioned –
top tip is the home made curry sauce! / Rated on Editors' visit;
www.kerbisher.co.uk; 10 pm; closed Mon.

Kettners W1 £47 ④❸❸
29 Romilly St 7734 6112 4–2A
"Eat down the road first!" – it's for the champagne bar (with its
"amazing list at reasonable prices") that this rambling and historic
Soho "time warp" is worth seeking out; as a place to eat, it "needs
serious work". / www.kettners.com; Mon-Thu 11 pm, Fri & Sat 11.30 pm,
Sun 9.30 pm.

Kew Grill TW9 £53 ❸❷④
10b Kew Grn 8948 4433 1–3A
Antony Worral Thompson's small grill-restaurant, on Kew Green,
put in a better showing this year, attracting general (if not quite
universal) praise for its "juicy" steaks, and "attentive" service.
/ www.awtrestaurants.com; 10.30 pm, Fri-Sat 11 pm, Sun 10 pm; closed
Mon L.

Khan's W2 £21 ❸④❸
13-15 Westbourne Grove 7727 5420 6–1C
"Unchanging standards" of "always-delicious" food make this
"chaotic" and cavernous – but "fun" and "really good value" – Indian
an ongoing Bayswater institution; no alcohol! / www.khansrestaurant.com;
11.30 pm, Sat-Sun midnight.

Khan's of Kensington SW7 £39 ❸❸❸
3 Harrington Rd 7584 4114 5–2B
"A reliable and well-established curry house", very handily located
by South Kensington tube; it may rarely excite, but it rarely
disappoints either. / www.khansofkensington.co.uk; 11.30 pm.

Khoai £31 ❸❸④
362 Ballards Ln, N12 8445 2039 1–1B
6 Topsfield Pde, N8 8341 2120 1–1C
A duo of "basic" Vietnamese cafés – in Crouch End and North
Finchley – consistently praised by reporters for their "tasty" and
"good-value" fare. / 11.30 pm; N12 closed Mon; no booking Fri & Sat after
7.30 pm.

Kiasu W2 £29 ❸④④
48 Queensway 7727 8810 6–2C
A decent "cheap 'n' cheerful" Bayswater pan-Asian stand-by;
it seemingly offers a "lengthy" menu, but "quite a few of the popular
dishes aren't always available". / www.kiasu.co.uk; 11 pm; no Amex.

Kiku W1 £60 ❷❷④
17 Half Moon St 7499 4208 3–4B
"A genuine Tokyo experience, all the way down to the bad lighting";
this little-known heart-of-Mayfair spot offers "expertly-prepared sushi
and sashimi", and at "great-value" prices too.
/ www.kikurestaurant.co.uk; 10.15 pm; closed Sun L; set weekday L £33 (FP).

Kimchee WC1 NEW £31 ❸❸❸
71 High Holborn 7430 0956 2–1D
"Bringing a taste of Korea to London" – this "airy", "sleek" and
"buzzing" newcomer is "in a similar mould to Ping Pong, Busaba and
Wagamama", and serves food that's "fresh and extremely tasty, if a
little spicy". / www.kimchee.uk.com; 10.20 pm.

Kings Road Steakhouse & Grill SW3 £56 ④④④
386 King's Rd 7351 9997 5–3B
*"An expensive dinner which failed to excite…", "never been
somewhere with such rude staff…" – ah yes, Marco Pierre White
has quickly put his inimitable stamp on this year-old Chelsea
steakhouse.* / www.kingsroadsteakhouseandgrill.com; 11 pm, Sun 10 pm.

Kipferl N1 £30 ❸②②
20 Camden Pas 77041 555 9–1B
*This Austrian operation, now re-located to Islington, still has "lovely
staff" and "delicious coffee and cakes", but it now also offers a "well-
prepared, if limited, menu" of more ambitious fare, plus Austrian
wines and beers.* / www.kipferl.co.uk; 7.30 pm, Sat 9.30 pm, Tue and Sun
5.30 pm; closed Tue D & Sun D; no Amex.

Kiraku W5 £33 ❶②❸
8 Station Pde 8992 2848 1–3A
*"Always busy and full of Japanese people", this unassuming café,
near Ealing Common tube, offers "meltingly delicious" cooking
(not least "amazing sushi") at "outstanding-value" prices; ambience
is "slightly lacking", but this is somewhat offset by the "lovely and
helpful" service.* / www.kiraku.co.uk; 10 pm; closed Mon; no Amex.

Kitchen W8 W8 £59 ❶②②
11-13 Abingdon Road 7937 0120 5–1A
*"Who could want a better local restaurant than this?"; the interior
is admittedly "a bit John Lewis", but – when it comes to offering
"exceptional, seasonal food" at "superb-value" prices – this "smart
but informal" Kensington outfit, just off the High Street, is never
knowingly undersold; "it has improved greatly since launch".*
/ www.kitchenw8.com; 10.15 pm, Sun 9.15 pm; set weekday L £35 (FP).

Koba W1 £40 ❸❸④
11 Rathbone St 7580 8825 2–1C
*Fans say you get "the best Korean food in London" – and in
a "handy" location too – at this "bustling" table-BBQ, in Fitzrovia;
not everyone is quite so wowed, but even sceptics say the scoff
is "serviceable".* / 10.30 pm; closed Sun L.

**Koffmann's
The Berkeley SW1** £75 ②②④
The Berkeley, Wilton Pl 7235 1010 5–1D
*"Classic Gallic bistro cooking" (including "magnificent stuffed pig's
trotter") is executed "with aplomb" at Pierre K's "elegant" (if "hotel-
ish") Knightsbridge basement yearling; those who remember him
from La Tante Claire (London's best restaurant of its day), however,
may still find the new operation a little underwhelming.*
/ www.the-berkeley.co.uk; set always available £45 (FP).

Kolossi Grill EC1 £29 ④②②
56-60 Rosebery Ave 7278 5758 9–1A
*A survivor from the '60s, this Farringdon Greek/Cypriot is somewhere
between rough 'n' ready and cheap 'n' cheerful – "I have been eating
here for over 40 years", says one reporter, and "just love the fact it's
so unpretentious!"* / www.kolossigrill.com; 11 pm; closed Sat L & Sun;
set weekday L £16 (FP).

Konditor & Cook £24 ❷❸❸
Curzon Soho, 99 Shaftesbury Ave, W1 7292 1684 4–3A
46 Gray's Inn Rd, WC1 7404 6300 9–1A
10 Stoney St, SE1 7407 5100 9–4C
22 Cornwall Road, SE1 7261 0456 9–4A
63 Stamford St, SE1 7921 9200 9–4A
30 St Mary Axe, EC3 0845 262 3030 9–2D
"Truly irresistible cakes", "first-class coffee" and "interesting" savouries certainly make these café/take-aways a tempting option; even fans can find them "expensive" though, or feel their service is rather "variable". / www.konditorandcook.com; 6 pm – W1 11 pm; WC1 & EC3 closed Sat & Sun; SE1 branches closed Sun; no booking.

Kopapa WC2 NEW £48 ❸❸④
32-34 Monmouth St 7240 6076 4–2B
"Inventive and tasty" small plates – with some "zingy" Pacific Rim "fusion-combinations" – have made Peter Gordon's café-style newcomer a useful addition to Covent Garden; it's "pricey", though, service can be "disjointed", and the hard-surfaced interior can be "deafening". / www.kopapa.co.uk; 10.45 pm, Fri & Sat 11.15 pm.

Kovalam NW6 £25 ❷④⑤
12 Willesden Ln 7625 4761 1–2B
"Hidden-away in a side street, but a great find" – this Kilburn Indian may occupy "a standard curry house setting", but it dishes up some "fantastic" Keralan cuisine; the bill comes as "a happy surprise" too. / www.kovalamrestaurant.co.uk; 11 pm, Fri & Sat midnight; no Amex.

Koya W1 £24 ❷❷❸
49 Frith St 7434 4463 4–2A
You get "the best udon noodles in London" (with "authentic broths" too), say fans of this popular and "bustling" Soho yearling; "expect to queue, eat and go". / www.koya.co.uk; 10.30 pm; closed Sun; no booking.

Kulu Kulu £29 ④④⑤
76 Brewer St, W1 7734 7316 3–2D
51-53 Shelton St, WC2 7240 5687 4–2C
39 Thurloe Pl, SW7 7589 2225 5–2C
They're "nothing innovative" nowadays – and they look "scruffy" – but these "no-frills" conveyor-canteens still get the thumbs-up from most reporter for their "cheap" and "relatively authentic" sushi. / 10 pm; SW7 10.30 pm; closed Sun; no Amex; no booking.

Kurumaya EC4 £37 ❷❷④
76-77 Watling St 7236 0236 9–2B
Thanks to "some of the City's best sushi" (as well as "good" hot dishes) and "smiling" service too, this "pleasant" Japanese is always "packed", both in its street-level bar and downstairs restaurant. / www.kurumaya.co.uk; 9.30 pm; closed Sat & Sun.

Kyashii WC2 £55 ④④❸
4a Upper St Martin's Ln 7836 5211 4–3B
This "futuristic" Japanese yearling ("love the fish tanks") is hailed by fans as "a welcome addition to Covent Garden"; perhaps because it's so "expensive", though, it's yet to generate much buzz, and critics see it simply as a "massive disappointment". / www.kyashii.co.uk; 10.30 pm; no shorts.

The Ladbroke Arms W11 £44 ❷❸❷
54 Ladbroke Rd 7727 6648 6–2B
This "lovely" and "upmarket" boozer, near Ladbroke Grove, serves "more than pub food" – it's always "busy" and, on a sunny day, you'll find it "hard to get a table in the garden". / www.capitalpubcompany.com; 9.30 pm; no booking after 8 pm.

Ladurée £70 ④④❸
Harrods, 87-135 Brompton Rd, SW1   7730 1234   5–1D
71-72 Burlington Arc, Piccadilly, W1   7491 9155   3–3C
1 Covent Garden Mkt, WC2   7240 0706   4–3D **NEW**
With its "delicate pâtisserie and 'macarons'", this OTT Knightsbridge grand café is a worthy outpost of the famed Parisian fixture – no great surprise that it's a tad "overpriced"; also in Covent Garden (new) and Piccadilly (mainly retail). / www.laduree.com; SW1 8.45 pm, Sun 5.45 pm; W1 6.30 pm, Sun 5 pm; W1 no booking, SW1 no booking 3 pm-6 pm; set always available £44 (FP).

Lahore Karahi SW17 £17 ❶④④
1 Tooting Hill, London   8767 2477   10–2C
This "bustling" BYO canteen, in Tooting, is known for its "tremendous" Pakistani cuisine – "expect no luxury, but the food is genuine and the place is mobbed". / www.lahorekarahi.co.uk; midnight; no Amex.

Lahore Kebab House £22 ❶⑤④
668 Streatham High Rd, SW16   8765 0771   10–2D **NEW**
2-10 Umberston St, E1   7488 2551   11–1A
"The king-pin of East End curry houses"; this "warehouse"-like "legend" is often "as busy as a Pakistani street", thanks to its "unbelievably good" scoff at dirt-cheap prices – with "fabulous" lamb chops a highlight; now also in Streatham (and, coming soon, other branches); BYO. / midnight.

Lamberts SW12 £48 ❶❶❷
2 Station Pde   8675 2233   10–2C
"Second only to Chez Bruce... and not that far behind!" – this Balham "beacon" remains a "good-value" and "professional" destination, where the "sure-footed" cuisine uses "carefully-sourced" ingredients to "great effect", and the service is "attentive, personal and jolly". / www.lambertsrestaurant.com; 10.30 pm, Sun 5 pm; closed Mon, Tue-Fri L & Sun D; no Amex.

(Winter Garden)
The Landmark NW1 £79 ④❸❷
222 Marylebone Rd   7631 8000   8–4A
"Three hours of non-stop champagne and buffet" in a "spectacular" covered atrium – the makings of the "fabulous Sunday jazz brunch" at this Marylebone hotel, which is also tipped for afternoon tea; otherwise, though, it's "expensive for what it is". / www.landmarklondon.co.uk; 10.30 pm; no trainers; booking: max 12.

Langan's Bistro W1 £44 ❸❷❷
26 Devonshire St   7935 4531   2–1A
Despite the odd hiccup, it seems to have been a good year for this "beautiful" and "cosy" pint-sized Marylebone veteran; the bistro fare may not be the main point, but it rarely disappoints. / www.langansrestaurants.co.uk; 11 pm; closed Sat L & Sun.

Langan's Brasserie W1 £61 ④④❷
Stratton St   7491 8822   3–3C
"So yesterday!"; although there's still "a real buzz" about this Mayfair old-timer, and fans do still say it's "always enjoyable", the "tasteless" food and "can't-be-bothered" service really aren't funny any more – can someone please hurry up and buy it! / www.langansrestaurants.co.uk; 11 pm, Fri & Sat 11.30 pm, Sun 4pm.

The Lansdowne NW1 £43 ❸❸❷
90 Gloucester Ave 7483 0409 8–3B
*You get a taste of "Primrose Hill, without the snobbery", at this
"true gastropub", which serves "hearty, but well-executed food in a
bustling setting"; top tip: "top-notch" pizza.
/ www.thelansdownepub.co.uk; 10 pm, Sun 9.30 pm; no Amex.*

Lantana Cafe W1 £30 ❸❸❸
13-14 Charlotte Pl 7323 6601 2–1C
*"Great Aussie coffee" attracts "hordes" of caffeine-fiends to this
"busy" but "relaxed" Fitzrovia joint, where brunch (a speciality)
is done "with aplomb". / www.lantanacafe.co.uk; 9.30 pm; closed
Mon D & Tue D; no Amex; no booking.*

La Lanterna SE1 £39 ❸❶❸
6-8 Mill St 7252 2420 11–2A
*"Portions are massive, and the staff always friendly and helpful",
at this good-value Italian, just over Tower Bridge; pizza is the best bet.
/ www.pizzerialalanterna.co.uk; 11 pm, Sun 10.30 pm; closed Sat L.*

The Larder EC1 £46 ❹❸❹
91-93 St John St 7608 1558 9–1A
*"Bustling at lunchtime" ("fairly quiet" at night) – this Clerkenwell
bar/bakery/take-away/restaurant is regularly tipped "for a business
meal near the City", thanks not least to its "reliable" cuisine, served
in "brasserie style". / www.thelarderrestaurant.com; 10.30 pm; closed
Sat L & Sun.*

Latium W1 £48 ❷❶❸
21 Berners St 7323 9123 3–1D
*Maurizio Morelli's very "civilised" Italian, north of Oxford Street, is an
"authentic and honest" sort of place, with notably "charming and
well-informed" service; signature dish: "ravioli to die for".
/ www.latiumrestaurant.com; 10.30 pm, Sat 11 pm; closed Sat L & Sun.*

Launceston Place W8 £72 ❷❷❷
1a Launceston Pl 7937 6912 5–1B
*A "very intimate" townhouse, "on the corner of a beautiful
Kensington street", where "everything is polished and understated";
staff are "extremely charming", and Tristan Welch's highly "original"
food is "incredibly fresh" and "perfectly executed" – can this really
be a member of the D&D group? / www.danddlondon.com; 10.30 pm;
closed Mon L; set Sun L £46 (FP).*

THE LEDBURY W11 £90 ❶❶❷
127 Ledbury Rd 7792 9090 6–1B
*"It just gets better!"; Brett Graham's "genius" cuisine – the highest-
rated in London this year – is beginning to secure international
recognition for this Notting Hill pub-conversion, where "marvellous"
and "unstuffy" service tops off a "staggeringly good all-round
experience". / www.theledbury.com; 10.30 pm, Sun 10 pm; closed Mon L.*

Lemonia NW1 £40 ❺❷❷
89 Regent's Park Rd 7586 7454 8–3B
*"It's hard to criticise, what with it always being full", but – although
this "stalwart" Primrose Hill "mega-taverna" does indeed remain
"fantastically buzzy" – the food it offers can seem very "jaded"
nowadays. / www.lemonia.co.uk; 11.30 pm; closed Sat L & Sun D; no Amex.*

Leon £22 ❸❸❸
275 Regent St, W1 7495 1514 3–1C
35-36 Gt Marlborough St, W1 7437 5280 3–2C
36-38 Old Compton St, W1 7434 1200 4–2A **NEW**
73-76 The Strand, WC2 7240 3070 4–4D
7 Canvey St, SE1 7620 0035 9–4B
Cabot Place West, E14 7719 6200 11–1C
3 Crispin Pl, E1 7247 4369 12–2B
12 Ludgate Circus, EC4 7489 1580 9–2A
86 Cannon St, EC4 7623 9699 9–3C
"The most convincing effort to re-invent fast food!" – these *"cheerful"*
retro-styled cafés are *"brilliant for a quick, cheap and healthy bite
on the move"*. / www.leonrestaurants.co.uk; 10 pm; W1 8.45 pm; E14 8 pm;
EC4 closed Sun; W1 closed Sat & Sun; no booking L.

Leong's Legends £33 ❹❹❸
4 Macclesfield St, W1 7287 0288 4–3A
82 Queensway, W2 7221 2280 6–2C
*"A slightly more unusual Taiwanese take on the typical Chinatown
offering"*; this *"tacky, but oddly-endearing"* place has quite a following
among reporters, not least for its *"sublime"* dumplings; there's also
an offshoot in Bayswater. / www.leongslegend.com; 11 pm, Sat 11.30 pm;
no bookings.

Levant W1 £54 ❸❸❶
Jason Ct, 76 Wigmore St 7224 1111 3–1A
"Be transported from London to the Middle East!" – this *"darkly-lit"*
Marylebone basement offers a *"superb"* atmosphere for those with
a party (or romance) in mind, plus, for nourishment, *"a great
selection of mezze"*. / www.levant.co.uk; 11 pm, Sat 11.30 pm.

The Light House SW19 £46 ❸❸❸
75-77 Ridgway 8944 6338 10–2B
"Off the beaten track", near Wimbledon Village, this modern bistro
has long been a top option locally; the minimalist styling creates
"bad acoustics", though, and critics find the *"eclectic"* cuisine
almost *"too imaginative"*! / www.lighthousewimbledon.com; 10.30 pm;
closed Sun D.

The Lighthouse SW11 £38 ❸❷❷
441 Battersea Park Rd 7223 7721 10–1C
A Battersea gastropub which attracts most praise for its *"fabulous
atmosphere"*; the *"hearty"* fare is *"sometimes very good"* too,
but *"lacks a little in consistency"*. / www.thelighthousebattersea.com;
11 pm, Sun 10.30 pm Fri-Sat midnight.

Lisboa Pâtisserie W10 £8 ❷❸❹
57 Golborne Rd 8968 5242 6–1A
"Unrivalled custard tarts" and *"the best latte in the world"*! –
no wonder this *"no-nonsense"* Portuguese café/pâtisserie in North
Kensington is always heaving. / 7.30 pm; L & early evening only;
no booking.

Little Bay £30 ❹❷❶
228 Belsize Rd, NW6 7372 4699 1–2B
228 York Rd, SW11 7223 4080 10–2B
171 Farringdon Rd, EC1 7278 1234 9–1A
"Wild", *"boudoir-esque"* decor and *"smiling"* staff set a *"celebratory"*
tone at these *"quirky and fun"* budget bistros; as for the *"tasty"*
fodder – *"how do they do it"* for the *"stupidly cheap"* prices?
/ www.little-bay.co.uk; 11.30 pm, sun 11 pm; no Amex, NW6 no credit cards.

Little Georgia Café E2 £26 ❸❸❸
87 Goldsmiths Row   7739 8154   1–2D
This "tiny" Bethnal Green café is "a lovely local", serving
an "interesting" Georgian menu (on which the mezze and
cheeseboard star); "BYO is a bonus". / 9.30 pm.

Little Italy W1 £66 ❹❹❸
21 Frith St   7734 4737   4–2A
Fans of this "pricey" late-night Soho Italian bar/restaurant/club say it's
"great", even if "the food's rather beside the point", because
"the dancing is the draw"; for critics, though, it's just "shockingly bad
in every respect". / www.littleitalysoho.co.uk; 4 am, Sun 11.30 pm;
set weekday L & pre-theatre £36 (FP).

Livebait £48 ❹❹❺
21 Wellington St, WC2   7836 7161   4–3D
43 The Cut, SE1   7928 7211   9–4A
"A whiff of the production line" hangs over this "predictable" and
"formulaic" fish chain; its "latrine"-like decor is no great attraction
either. / www.santeonline.co.uk; 11 pm; SE1 Sun 9 pm; WC2 Sun 7.30 pm;
set always available £28 (FP).

LMNT E8 £35 ❸❷❶
316 Queensbridge Rd   7249 6727   1–2D
Bonkers, pharaoh-kitsch decor and "very romantic booths" boost the
vibe at this "cheap 'n' cheerful" Dalston destination – always
"an enjoyable evening out". / www.lmnt.co.uk; 10.45 pm; no Amex.

Lobster Pot SE11 £56 ❸❸❸
3 Kennington Ln   7582 5556   1–3C
"Seagulls piped through the stereo" have long added to the "seaside
atmosphere", at this "fantastically Gallic" Kennington stalwart, run by
Hervé et sa famille; it's a "fun" place with "warm" service and
sometimes "excellent" seafood, but ratings overall are not quite what
they once were. / www.lobsterpotrestaurant.co.uk; 10.30 pm; closed
Mon & Sun; booking: max 8.

Locanda Locatelli
Hyatt Regency W1 £72 ❸❸❸
8 Seymour St   7935 9088   2–2A
Giorgio Locatelli's "chic and buzzy" Marylebone Italian still wows
most reporters with its "deceptively simple" dishes, "cooked
to perfection", and some "superb" wines too; "extreme" prices are
beginning to take the edge off the experience, however, as are
incidents of "I'm-doing-you-a-favour" service. / www.locandalocatelli.com;
11 pm, Fri & Sat 11.30 pm, Sun 10.15 pm; booking: max 8.

Locanda Ottomezzo W8 £69 ❹❷❸
2-4 Thackeray St   7937 2200   5–1B
The "best breakfast menu ever", the "best coffee around" and some
"delicious" Italian dishes at lunch and dinner too... – so why isn't this
"cramped" Kensington café/bistro more popular?; "I'd be there daily",
says one reporter, "if it wasn't so expensive!"
/ www.locandaottoemezzo.co.uk; 10.30 pm, Fri & Sat 10.45 pm; closed
Sat L & Sun.

Loch Fyne £40 ④④④
2-4 Catherine St, WC2 7240 4999 2–2D
77-78 Gracechurch St, EC3 7929 8380 9–3C
*"Always a good stand-by"; "you know what you're going to get",
at this "straightforward" fish and seafood chain, which sets
"consistently high" standards – even critics tend not to find anything
actively wrong with it, they just gripe that it's too "unexciting"!*
*/ www.lochfyne-restaurants.com; 10 pm; WC2 10.30 pm; set always available
£24 (FP).*

Lola & Simón W6 £49 ❸❷❸
278 King St 8563 0300 7–2B
*A "very friendly" Hammersmith café that makes a handy haunt for
a "fabulous" brunch, or "fantastic" coffee and cakes; its main, quasi-
Argentinian menu is good too, if rather "unchanging" and "pricey",
and there are "gorgeous" wines to go with it. / www.lolaandsimon.co.uk;
10 pm; no Amex.*

Lola Rojo £39 ❷❸❷
140 Wandsworth Bridge Rd, SW6 7371 8396 10–1B
78 Northcote Rd, SW11 7350 2262 10–2C
*"Very creative" tapas and "lovely" wines too have won quite
a following for this "pretty, if cramped", Battersea spot; its lesser-
known Fulham outpost, gets good reports too. / www.lolarojo.net;
SW11 11 pm; SW6 11 pm; SW6 Mon-Fri D only; no Amex.*

London Wall Bar & Kitchen EC2 £35 ④④❸
150 London Wall 7600 7340 9–2B
*Thanks to its "interesting" ("foolhardy") location – "a podium of the
Barbican, near the Museum of London" – this year-old Benugo-group
brasserie can be quiet; it's undoubtedly "useful" in a thin area though,
and its menu of staples is realised to a "pretty good" standard.
/ www.londonwallbarandkitchen.com; 9 pm; closed Sat & Sun.*

Lots Road SW10 £45 ❸❷④
114 Lots Rd 7352 6645 5–4B
*The "best burger" is the foodie highlight at this pub by the entrance
to Chelsea Harbour; "very helpful" staff help pep up a rather low-key
atmosphere. / www.lotsroadpub.com; 10 pm, Sun 9.30 pm; set weekday
L £28 (FP), set Sun L £29 (FP).*

Lotus Chinese Floating Restaurant E14 £38 ④④❸
5 Baltimore Walk 7515 6445 11–2C
*Floating placidly near Canary Wharf, this large Asian barge lives up to
its name; "excellent" dim sum is the highlight of a "solid" menu
selection, which includes a buffet. / www.lotusfloating.co.uk; 10.30 pm.*

Luc's Brasserie EC3 £46 ④❸❷
17-22 Leadenhall Mkt 7621 0666 9–2D
*"Get a window seat to look down on Leadenhall Market", if you visit
this "genuine"-feeling Gallic bistro, whose "classic" cuisine is praised
by most, if not quite all, reporters. / www.lucsbrasserie.com; 9 pm; closed
Mon D, Fri D, Sat & Sun.*

Lucio SW3 £60 ❸❸❸
257 Fulham Rd 7823 3007 5–3B
*"Lucio and his family are so welcoming", and fans of this "jam-
packed" Chelsea Italian say it's a "class act" that "never fails
to deliver"; it's "cramped" however, and a small band of critics finds
the whole performance "pricey" and "dull". / 10.45 pm; set weekday L
£36 (FP).*

Lucky Seven W2 £44 ❸❸❷
127 Westbourne Park Rd 7727 6771 6–1B
Tom Conran's "funky" homage to the US diner has wonderful, retro-
styling, and it "takes some beating for great burgers and shakes" too
– it's a tiny place, though, so "be prepared to share a booth",
and note it's "not easy to get a seat at peak times".
/ www.tomconranrestaurants.com; 10.15 pm, Sun 10 pm; no Amex;
no booking.

Lupita WC2 NEW £36 ④④④
13-15 Villiers St 7930 5355 4–4D
Divergent views on this 'Mexico City' street-food newcomer, on a
slightly tatty strip near Charing Cross; a slight majority hail food that's
"fresh", "flavourful" and "cheap", but doubters dismiss this "strangely
laid-out" place as a "poor Wahaca rip-off", with "uncomfy" seating.
/ www.lupita.co.uk; 11 pm, Sun 8 pm.

Lutyens EC4 £62 ❸❸④
85 Fleet St 7583 8385 9–2A
Though much-touted as a "safe" haven for an "obviously businessy"
lunch, Sir Terence Conran's "austere" City-fringe brasserie
is "somehow less than the sum of its parts" – the interior's "pleasant,
but functional", the food's "good, but formulaic", and the service
"prompt, but without personality". / www.lutyens-restaurant.com; 9.45 pm;
closed Sat & Sun.

The Luxe E1 £48 ⑤⑤④
109 Commercial St 7101 1751 12–2B
"He'd get kicked off the show for food like this!" – ex-Masterchef
judge John Torode wins poor ratings for his Smithfield yearling; fans do
praise the "good choice of breakfasts" and other British fare,
but critics say "he should be ashamed" of the "woeful" cooking and
"shambolic" service. / www.theluxe.co.uk; 10.30 pm; closed Sun D; booking:
max 10.

Ma Cuisine TW9 £44 ④❸④
9 Station Approach 8332 1923 1–3A
"In a pretty parade of shops", by Kew Gardens station, an archetypal
bistro where "all the classic French dishes are served"; it's "always
humming", but reporters have a feeling that while "not bad, it could
do so much better". / www.macuisinekew.co.uk; 10 pm, Fri & Sat 10.30 pm;
no Amex.

Ma Goa SW15 £37 ❷①❸
242-244 Upper Richmond Rd 8780 1767 10–2B
"Wonderful and original Goan home cooking" – at a
"very reasonable price" and served by "outstanding" staff –
wins continuing rave reviews for this "charming" family-run Putney
fixture. / www.ma-goa.com; 11 pm, Sun 10 pm; closed Mon L & Sat L.

**Made In Camden
Roundhouse NW1** NEW £31 ❸❸④
Chalk Farm Rd 7424 8495 8–2B
"A great excuse to go to a gig at the Roundhouse" – this "stripped-
down" canteen is proving a "neat newcomer", thanks to its
"unexpectedly good" food at "reasonable prices".
/ www.madeincamden.com; 10.30 pm.

Medlar

Moro

Pollen Street Social

Made in China SW1   £45   ④④④
37 Monck St   7222 2218   2–4C
"Fresh" Chinese cooking – some of "the only decent, affordable food in Westminster" – wins fans for this potentially "attractive" yearling, near the Home Office; the occasional reporter, however, has found declining standards of late. / www.madeinchinarestaurant.co.uk; 10.15 pm; closed Sun; no Amex.

Made in Italy SW3   £39   ❷❸❷
249 King's Rd   7352 1880   5–3C
"Divine" thin-crust pizzas (by the metre) make this "crowded" and "fun" Chelsea spot – now with spin-offs in Soho and near Selfridges – a popular destination for all the family; in warm weather, seek out the first-floor terrace. / www.madeinitalygroup.co.uk; 11.30 pm, Sun 10.30 pm; Mon-Thu D only, Fri-Sun open L & D; no Amex.

Madhu's UB1   £35   ❷❸❸
39 South Rd   8574 1897   1–3A
The quality of this superior Southall Indian has helped spawn a major outside catering empire; here at HQ, fans approve the "proper" cooking – "lovely dishes" that "don't leave you feeling over-stuffed". / www.madhusonline.com; 11.30 pm; closed Tue, Sat L & Sun L.

Madsen SW7   £47   ④④④
20 Old Brompton Rd   7225 2772   5–2B
If Copenhagen is currently the centre of the culinary world, there's no sign of it at this "pleasant" Danish two-year-old in South Kensington, which serves "simple", "home-style" fare – it has its fans, but quite a few reporters find its offering all-embracingly "pale". / www.madsenrestaurant.com; 10 pm, Fri & Sat 10.45 pm; closed Sun D; no Amex.

Magdalen SE1   £51   ❶❷❷
152 Tooley St   7403 1342   9–4D
"Inspired and interesting" British cooking ("very much in the style of St John, with an abundance of offal"), draws fans – especially from the City – to this "unassuming" and "relaxed" establishment, "hidden-away" near City Hall. / www.magdalenrestaurant.co.uk; 10 pm; closed Sat L & Sun.

Maggie Jones's W8   £60   ⑤④❶
6 Old Court Pl   7937 6462   5–1A
This "very '70s" bistro, hidden-away near Kensington Gardens, is a "lovely cosy hide-away", often tipped for romance; the cooking really is stuck in a "time warp", though, and critics find it plain "dull". / www.maggie-jones.co.uk; 11 pm, Sun 10.30 pm.

Magic Wok W2   £32   ❸❸⑤
100 Queensway   7792 9767   6–1C
"Doing the staples well, and with some great speciality dishes" – the cooking at this Queensway Chinese is "always reliable", so its "lacklustre" setting may be worth putting up with. / 11 pm.

Maison Bertaux W1   £14   ❷❸❶
28 Greek St   7437 6007   4–2A
For a "richly Bohemian" setting, you won't beat this "wildly idiosyncratic!" Soho pâtisserie (est 1871) – a "jammed-in" place, with "super-charming" service and "cakes to die for" ("and with enough calories that you probably will…"). / www.maisonbertaux.com; 10.30 pm, Sun 8 pm.

Malabar W8 £45 ❷❷❸

27 Uxbridge St 7727 8800 6–2B

This "old-faithful" Indian, hidden-away off Notting Hill Gate, "always delivers"; despite the increasing sophistication of its rivals, it still, after all these years, manages – thanks to its "muted" decor, and food that's "inventive, fresh and perfectly seasoned" – to feel "just a bit different from the run-of-the-mill". / www.malabar-restaurant.co.uk; 11.15 pm, Sun 10.30 pm.

Malabar Junction WC1 £41 ❸❸❸

107 Gt Russell St 7580 5230 2–1C

This "Tardis-like" Bloomsbury veteran has a surprisingly large and pleasant conservatory interior; its "very varied" South Indian menu – including "many veggie options" – is "well executed", and "reasonably priced" too. / www.malabarjunction.com; 11 pm.

The Mall Tavern W8 £42 ❸❸❷

71-73 Palace Gardens Ter 7229 3374 6–2B

Despite its "awkward location", just off Notting Hill Gate, this "little neighbourhood pub" has a "relaxed" and "intimate" interior (and a "pretty, small courtyard" too); its menu includes some "nice examples of modernised British staples". / www.themalltavern.com; 10 pm.

Malmaison Brasserie EC1 £52 ④❸❸

18-21 Charterhouse St 7012 3700 9–1B

A useful City-fringe business option – an attractively-located and "discreet" hotel dining room, where "you can hear yourself think". / www.malmaison.com; 10.15 pm.

La Mancha SW15 £40 ❸❷❸

32 Putney High St 8780 1022 10–2B

A "no-nonsense" Putney veteran, known for a "reliable and jolly tapas experience"; "you can't have a conversation without screaming", but that's all part of the fun. / www.lamancha.co.uk; 11 pm; need 6+ to book.

Mandalay W2 £25 ❸❸⑤

444 Edgware Rd 7258 3696 8–4A

"Still a favourite", this long-established café, near Edgware Road tube, offers "a good introduction to Burmese food", and "one of the cheapest lunches in London" too; fair to say, though, that the scoff isn't a patch on what it used to be, and the decor is, as ever, "nothing to write home about" either. / www.mandalayway.com; 10.30 pm; closed Sun.

Mandarin Kitchen W2 £37 ❷④⑤

14-16 Queensway 7727 9012 6–2C

"The best lobster noodles in London" justify braving the "curt" service and the "crammed" and "very shabby" dining room of this Bayswater "stalwart"; while it's still often tipped as "THE place for Chinese seafood", however, its food rating is not quite what it once was. / 11.30 pm.

Mangal 1 E8 £28 ❶❷❸

10 Arcola St 7275 8981 1–1C

"Incredibly good value!" – yes, that's the very worst comment anyone made this year on this "fun, no-frills Turkish BBQ", in Dalson, which serves "the juiciest kebabs ever"; "the atmosphere is best if you can sit near the hot coals"; BYO. / www.mangal1.com; midnight, Sat-Sun 1 am; no credit cards.

Mangal II N16 £39 ❸❸④
4 Stoke Newington Rd 7254 7888 1–1C
"Check if Gilbert & George are on the next table" ("they're regulars"), at this "utterly reliable" Turkish ocakbasi restaurant in Dalston; "the Mangal around the corner gets all the plaudits, but this is better", fans insist. / www.mangal2.com; 1 am; no Amex or Maestro.

Mango & Silk SW14 £36 ④④❸
199 Upper Richmond Rd 8876 6220 1–4A
"Blinding" cooking and "smiling" service win acclaim from fans of Udit Sarkhel's East Sheen Indian; sadly, however, there are almost as many critics who find it a disappointment, especially in comparison to his days in Southfields. / www.mangoandsilk.co.uk; 10 pm, Fri & Sat 10.30 pm; closed weekday L.

Mango Room NW1 £41 ❸❷❷
10-12 Kentish Town Rd 7482 5065 8–3B
It's not just the "wonderful" cocktails and "always-buzzing" style that wins fans for this "unpressurised" Camden Town haunt; "it's just the place for some good West Indian food", mixing dishes both "modern and traditional". / www.mangoroom.co.uk; 11 pm.

Mango Tree SW1 £53 ❸④④
46 Grosvenor Pl 7823 1888 2–4B
Look out for "frequent offers", if you're thinking of visiting this "barn" of a place, on the edge of Belgravia – if you pay full whack, the prices for its "very tasty" Thai fare can seem rather "steep", and you may be more prone to notice the rather "soulless" and "conveyor-belt-esque" ambience too. / www.mangotree.org.uk; 11 pm, Thu-Sat 11.30 pm, Sun 10.30 pm.

Mango Tree SE1 £48 ❷❸④
5-6 Cromwell Buildings, Red Cross Way 7407 0333 9–4C
Thanks to its "interesting" and "value-for-money" cooking – and in spite of its rather "uninspiring" contemporary decor – this hidden-away Indian, near Borough Market, is always "packed". / www.justmangotree.co.uk; 11 pm.

Manicomio £56 ❸④❸
85 Duke of York Sq, SW3 7730 3366 5–2D
6 Gutter Ln, EC2 7726 5010 9–2B
Some of "the best al fresco eating in town" is to be had on the terraces of these "stylish" Italians – in Chelsea and, more implausibly, the City; their "seasonal" cuisine is "fresh"-tasting too, if on the "expensive" side for what it is. / www.manicomio.co.uk; SW3 10.30 pm, Sun 10 pm; EC2 10 pm; EC2 closed Sat & Sun.

Manna NW3 £51 ⑤④④
4 Erskine Rd 7722 8028 8–3B
This well-worn Primrose Hill veggie – the UK's oldest (1968) – needs to buck up its act; even some fans say the food is "less enticing than it was", and for critics it's just a "bitter disappointment" – "I've been veggie for 20 years, but its tasteless offerings made me want to go home and have a fry-up!" / www.mannav.com; 10.30 pm; closed Mon, Tue-Fri D only, Sat & Sun open L & D.

Manson SW6 £50 ❶④❸
676 Fulham Rd 7384 9559 10–1B
"It's an absolute treasure", say fans of Fulham's "brilliant local"; note, however, that the chef changed as our survey for the year was coming to an end - let's hope new boy Alan Stewart is keeping up the good work! / www.mansonrestaurant.co.uk; 10.30 pm, Sun 6 pm.

Mao Tai SW6 £60 ③④③
58 New King's Rd   7731 2520   10–1B
A Parson's Green oriental that was trendy long before the idea of a 'trendy-oriental' became commonplace; fans insist that it's a "sound old favourite", but the cuisine of late has been rather "hit-and-miss". / www.maotai.co.uk; 11.30 pm; D only, ex Sun open L & D.

Mar I Terra £29 ③②③
17 Air St, W1   7734 1992   3–3D **NEW**
14 Gambia St, SE1   7928 7628   9–4A
"Tucked-away in railway arches near Southwark tube", this "fairly ordinary-looking" ex-pub offers "authentic" tapas in a "relaxing" setting; the Soho branch – not nearly as well-known – can also be "useful". / SE1 10.30 pm; W1 11 pm; SE1 closed Sat L, Sun; W1 closed Sun-Mon & Tue-Sat L.

Marco
Stamford Bridge SW6 £59 ④⑤⑤
Fulham Rd   7915 2929   5–4A
The little feedback inspired by this ambitious Gallic two-year-old, by Stamford Bridge, suggests it's a soulless and overpriced sort of place – we presume it survives solely by virtue of its backer, MPW's 'celebrity' status... on which he has primarily traded for over a decade! / www.marcorestaurant.co.uk; 10.30 pm; D only, closed Mon & Sun.

Marco Pierre White Steakhouse & Grill
East India House E1 £52 ④④⑤
109-117 Middlesex St   7247 5050   9–2D
A "very underwhelming" City-fringe basement where (as usual) MPW-branding portends nothing particularly positive – indeed, with its "bistro food at restaurant prices" some reporters think the place is just a plain "rip-off". / www.mpwsteakandalehouse.org; 10 pm; closed Sun.

MARCUS WAREING
THE BERKELEY SW1 £115 ②②②
Wilton Pl   7235 1200   5–1D
Marcus Wareing's "sensational" cuisine again won his "luxurious", if "formal" Knightsbridge HQ the most survey nominations as 'London's No. 1 dining room'; this year, however, a small but vocal minority also found it "hyped" and "unjustifiably pricey" – perhaps a blip due to losing Alyn Williams and/or launching the Gilbert Scott? / www.marcus-wareing.com; 10.30 pm; closed Sat L & Sun; no jeans or trainers; booking: max 8; set weekday L £60 (FP).

Marine Ices NW3 £35 ③②②
8 Haverstock Hill   7482 9003   8–2B
"There's no better ice cream in London", say fans of this Camden Town "institution", run by the Manzi family "since forever..." (the 1920s); it's a "dependable" pizza 'n' pasta stop too, and "always buzzing with all the generations mixing happily together". / www.marineices.co.uk; Sun 10 pm; closed Mon; no Amex.

Market NW1 £46 ③③④
43 Parkway   7267 9700   8–3B
"Normally full to the brim", this "simple" and "buzzy" Camden Town bistro has made quite a name with its "hearty" British fare; it's "a bit expensive", though, for a place that's so "very noisy" and "cramped". / www.marketrestaurant.co.uk; 10.30 pm; closed Sun D; set weekday L £29 (FP).

Maroush £45 ❷④④
I) 21 Edgware Rd, W2 7723 0773 6–1D
II) 38 Beauchamp Pl, SW3 7581 5434 5–1C
IV) 68 Edgware Rd, W2 7224 9339 6–1D
V) 3-4 Vere St, W1 7493 5050 3–1B
'Garden') 1 Connaught St, W2 7262 0222 6–1D
*"A fun place to visit, even at 2am!"; London's longest-established
"posh" Lebanese chain offers a range of culinary possibilities,
of which the best are arguably the handy café/take-aways (at I, II and
V); expect "zingy" mezze, "lovely light flat breads", and kebabs and
grills that are "sooooo tasty".* / www.maroush.com; 12.30 am-5 am.

The Marquess Tavern N1 £40 ❸❸❸
32 Canonbury St 7354 2975 8–2D
*In leafy Canonbury, an "elegant" gastroboozer, on an impressive
scale; the food is "consistently good" (in particular the "superb
Sunday lunch").* / www.marquesstavern.com; 10 pm; closed weekday L.

Masala Zone £30 ❸❸❸
9 Marshall St, W1 7287 9966 3–2D
48 Floral St, WC2 7379 0101 4–2D
147 Earl's Court Rd, SW5 7373 0220 5–2A
583 Fulham Rd, SW6 7386 5500 5–4A
71-75 Bishop's Bridge Rd, W2 7221 0055 6–1C
80 Upper St, N1 7359 3399 8–3D
25 Parkway, NW1 7267 4422 8–3B
*"Big yummy thalis", composed of "interesting" and "different" Indian
dishes, maintain a large and enthusiastic following for this "smarter-
than-average" chain – "yes, it's a production line, but for value and
flavour it's solidly reliable".* / www.realindianfood.com; 11 pm,
Sun 10.30 pm; no Amex; booking: min 10.

Massimo
Corinthia Hotel SW1 **NEW** £77 ④❷❷
10 Northumberland Ave 7930 8181 2–3D
*This stupendously grand 5-star newcomer, near Embankment tube,
makes a splendid venue to impress, especially on business; Roman
chef, Massimo Riccioli's fish-heavy menu is dextrously realised too –
shame that, unless you go for the 'steal' of a set lunch menu,
it's really very overpriced.* / Rated on Editors' visit;
www.massimorestaurant.co.uk; 10.45 pm; closed Sun; set pre theatre £50 (FP).

Masters Super Fish SE1 £28 ❷④⑤
191 Waterloo Rd 7928 6924 9–4A
*A "very busy" chippy near the Old Vic, where you can hope to find
"some of the best fish 'n' chips of your life", served "in large portions,
and with all the extras"; "you certainly don't come for the terrible
ambience", however.* / 10.30 pm; closed Sun, Mon L; no Amex; no booking
Fri D.

Matsuba TW9 £43 ❷❸④
10 Red Lion St 8605 3513 1–4A
*This low-key, family-run Japanese café, in Richmond, is worth seeking
out for its "delicious", if "pricey", selection of dishes, notably some
"outstanding" sashimi and sushi.* / 10.30 pm; closed Sun.

Matsuri SW1 £84 ❷❷⑤
15 Bury St 7839 1101 3–3D
*The "excellent teppan-yaki" helps "make for a fun and different
experience", at this "very reliable" St James's Japanese; "shame
about the dreary subterranean space", though.*
/ www.matsuri-restaurant.com; 10.30 pm, Sun 10 pm.

Maxim W13 £33 ③④④
153-155 Northfield Ave   8567 1719   1–3A
"A decent Chinese in a neighbourhood without much decent Chinese food" – this Ealing stalwart is "always busy", although "dishes range from great to lacklustre". / 11.30 pm, Sun 11 pm.

maze W1 £78 ④④④
10-13 Grosvenor Sq   7107 0000   3–2A
"Little plates/big prices"; since Jason Atherton's departure, the "inventive" Mayfair tapas-restaurant he set up for Gordon Ramsay "seems to have lost its dynamism" – the ratio of supporters ("stunning", "slick") to critics ("ridiculous money", "zero ambience") is moving rapidly the wrong way. / www.gordonramsay.com/maze; 10.30 pm; set weekday L £51 (FP).

maze Grill W1 £82 ④④④
10-13 Grosvenor Sq   7495 2211   3–2A
It's always been "unatmospheric" and "pricey", but this Ramsay-group Mayfair steakhouse inspires ever more erratic feedback in all respects – for every reporter who finds the steak "fabulous" there's another who speaks in terms of "huge disappointment". / www.gordonramsay.com; 10.30 pm; no shorts; set weekday L & pre-theatre £50 (FP).

The Meat & Wine Co Westfield W12 £58 ④①④
Unit 1026 Ariel Way   8749 5914   7–1C
This "meatilicious" operation, by the entrance to Westfield, has its fans, though it leaves many reporters "full but dissatisfied" – prices are "very high", and the "flashy" interior contributes to an overall impression which is "formulaic" and "soulless". / www.themeatandwineco.com; 11.30 pm, Sun 10.30 pm; no Maestro; set weekday L £31 (FP).

Mediterraneo W11 £53 ❸❸❸
37 Kensington Park Rd   7792 3131   6–1A
A "reliable" Notting Hill "stalwart", this "lively" corner Italian – sibling to nearby Osteria Basilico – is a "cosy" sort of place, where the cooking is generally "really solid". / www.mediterraneo-restaurant.co.uk; 11.30 pm, Sun 10.30 pm; booking: max 10.

Medlar SW10 NEW £57 ❶❷❸
438 King's Rd   7349 1900   5–3B
"First and foremost, the food is incredible", at this "fantastic newcomer" – a plainish but comfortable dining room near World's End, created by a team that's broken away from Chez Bruce and The Square; "the atmosphere will doubtless improve as Chelsea locals find and love it". / 10.30 pm; closed Mon & Sun D.

Mekong SW1 £32 ❸②④
46 Churton St   7630 9568   2–4B
"Great fun and excellent value" are to be had at this "tiny" Pimlico veteran, where "helpful" staff serve up "strongly-flavoured" Vietnamese food in "generous portions"; claustrophobes should avoid the basement. / 11.30 pm.

Mela WC2 £38 ❸❸❸
152-156 Shaftesbury Avenue   7836 8635   4–2B
A large but "friendly" curry house, just north of Cambridge Circus, that offers "good value" by West End standards; even long-term fans, however, may find that the cuisine is "reasonable, but no longer outstanding". / www.melarestaurant.co.uk; 11.30 pm, Sun 10.30 am.

Melati W1 £35 ④❸⑤
21 Gt Windmill St 7437 2745 3–2D
A "simple" canteen, off Piccadilly Circus, which serves "authentic
SE Asian food", and has long been "a great cheap eat in the heart
of London"; it also has a nearby namesake – unrelated! – at 30-31
Peter Street, which "overcomes a tatty first impression to deliver fine
Indonesian classics". / www.melati.co.uk; 11 pm, Sat-Sun 11.30 pm.

Mem & Laz N1 £28 ④❷❷
8 Theberton St 7704 9089 8–3D
"Cheap, fun and certainly entertaining", this "buzzy" joint,
near Angel, serves a "huge menu" which mixes Turkish and
Mediterranean dishes, all cooked to a "reliable" standard; lunch is a
particular "bargain". / www.memlaz.com; 11.30 pm, Fri & Sat midnight;
no Amex.

Memories of India SW7 £33 ❸④④
18 Gloucester Rd 7581 3734 5–1B
"It's not got the most attractive exterior (or interior!)", but this South
Kensington curry house has long been a local favourite, thanks to its
"surprisingly good" food. / www.memoriesofindia.com; 11.30 pm.

Memsaheb on Thames E14 £30 ④❷❸
65-67 Amsterdam Rd 7538 3008 11–2D
"Nothing is too much trouble" for staff at this Isle of Dogs Indian,
which benefits from "good views" of the river; the food can
be "patchy", but it mostly gets the thumbs-up. / www.memsaheb.net;
11 pm; closed Sat L; no Amex.

Menier Chocolate Factory SE1 £44 ⑤④❷
51-53 Southwark St 7407 4411 9–4B
"A meal here before a show is a special experience", say fans of this
Bohemian Southwark playhouse; viewed as a culinary performance,
however, it's most definitely "not worth crossing town for".
/ www.menierchocolatefactory.com; 11 pm; closed Mon & Sun D; set pre
theatre £29 (FP).

Mennula W1 £52 ❷❸④
10 Charlotte St 7636 2833 2–1C
"Creative" and "accomplished" cooking – from an "engaging" chef
and "sincere" staff – win high praise for this "homely" Sicilian
yearling, in Fitzrovia; service can be "erratic", though, and conditions
are "squashed". / www.mennula.com; 11 pm, Sun 9.30 pm; closed Sat L.

The Mercer EC2 £53 ❸❷❸
34 Threadneedle St 7628 0001 9–2C
"Comfortable", "elegant" and "welcoming", this former banking hall
has carved out a big reputation as a "favourite" City rendezvous,
thanks to its "unobtrusive and efficient service", and its "well-
executed" and "straightforward" cooking. / www.themercer.co.uk;
9.30 pm; closed Sat & Sun.

Le Mercury N1 £27 ④❸❷
140a Upper St 7354 4088 8–2D
"Unbeatable for romance on a budget" – this "remarkable survivor",
by Islington's Almeida Theatre, is a "cosy and candlelit spot", offering
"consistently good food" at prices that seem "unchanged since the
last century". / www.lemercury.co.uk; 1 am, Sun 11.30 pm.

Meson don Felipe SE1　　　£38　　④④❷
53 The Cut　7928 3237　9–4A
"Affordable" tapas and "gluggable Sangria" – plus an infamous guitarist – have long made this "fun" bar a "bustling" South Bank "bolt hole"; admittedly, it's "not a patch on the Barrafinas of the world", but that's not really the point. / www.mesondonfelipe.com; 11 pm; closed Sun; no Amex; no booking after 8 pm.

Mestizo NW1　　　£40　　❷❷④
103 Hampstead Rd　7387 4064　8–4C
"An unassuming eatery that tries (and often succeeds) in bringing Londoners a taste of true Mexican food" (and a "wide variety of Tequilas" to go with it); only its obscure location – a short walk north of Warren Street tube – prevents it from being better known. / www.mestizomx.com; 10.45 pm.

Mews of Mayfair W1　　　£56　　④❸❸
10 Lancashire Ct, New Bond St　7518 9388　3–2B
The location (just off Bond Street) and the "metro-casual" vibe make this "quirky" and hidden-away joint a natural for ladies-who-lunch, especially as the midday set menus offer "particularly good value"; dinner à la carte is a less compelling proposition. / www.mewsofmayfair.com; 11 pm; closed Sun D.

Mezzanine
Royal National Theatre SE1　　　£41　　④❸④
Royal National Theatre, Belvedere Rd　7452 3600　2–3D
The RNT's in-house restaurant "could be better", but by and large "does what it says on the tin"; puddings (which you can take during the interval) are "the best bit". / www.nationaltheatre.org.uk; 11 pm; closed Mon L, Fri L & Sun D.

Michael Nadra W4　　　£48　　❶❸④
6-8 Elliott Rd　8742 0766　7–2A
M. Nadra's cuisine "improves with every menu", and his Chiswick yearling is starting to give the nearby La Trompette (where he used to be head chef) a good "run for its money"; ambience-wise, though, overcoming the constraints of these "cramped" premises is always going to be a challenge. / www.restaurant-michaelnadra.co.uk; 10 pm, Fri & Sat 10.30 pm.

Mien Tay　　　£23　　❶④④
180 Lavender Hill, SW11　7350 0721　10–1C
122 Kingsland Rd, E2　7729 3074　12–1B
"Genius" Vietnamese cooking – at "unbelievably low prices for the quality" – inspire nothing but adulation for these "bustling", if slightly "tacky", BYO cafés in Battersea and, now, Shoreditch. / 11 pm, Fri & Sat 11.30 pm, sun 10.30 pm; cash only.

Mildreds W1　　　£40　　❷④④
45 Lexington St　7494 1634　3–2D
"Almost worth giving up bacon sarnies for!" – the veggie cuisine at this buzzing Soho diner is so "innovative and exciting" (and "affordable" too) it would "please the most ardent meat eater"; staff, though, "operate on the principle that you need to win them over, not vice versa…" / www.mildreds.co.uk; 11 pm; closed Sun; no Amex; no booking.

Mill Lane Bistro NW6 NEW £41 ❸❷④
77 Mill Ln 7794 5577 1–1B
"A decent addition to the impoverished West Hampstead scene"; this Gallic yearling may have an "unprepossessing location", but it offers "good French bistro grub" and "drinkable wines", all at "affordable" prices. / www.milllanebistro.com; 10 pm, Fri & Sat 10.30 pm, Sun 9 pm; closed Mon, Tue-Fri D only; no Amex.

Min Jiang
The Royal Garden Hotel W8 £68 ❶❷❶
2-24 Kensington High St 7361 1988 5–1A
*"Legendary Peking duck", "excellent dim sum", and "one of London's best panoramic views" (of Kensington Gardens and beyond) are amongst the many attractions of this "superbly sophisticated" eighth-floor restaurant; remember to book the bird well ahead.
/ www.minjiang.co.uk; 10 pm.*

Mint Leaf £63 ❸④❸
Suffolk Pl, Haymarket, SW1 7930 9020 2–2C
Angel Ct, Lothbury, EC2 7600 0992 9–2C
*"Solid cocktails" and "fresh modern cuisine" give these clubby subcontinentals – in a Theatreland basement, and near Bank – all the makings of "an enjoyable night out"; "extortionate" prices can take the edge off the experience, though, making the "good-value" prix-fixe lunch (WC2) especially worth looking out for.
/ www.mintleafrestaurant.com; SW1 10.30 pm, Sun 10 pm; EC2 10.30 pm; SW1 closed Sat & Sun L; EC2 closed Sat & Sun; set always available £36 (FP).*

Miran Masala W14 £18 ❷❷⑤
3 Hammersmith Rd 7602 4555 7–1D
"Very good grilled meats and breads" – "the lamb chops are special" – win rave reviews for this little Pakistani café, by Olympia; its "friendly" service compensates for an interior that decidedly "nothing special". / www.miranmasala.co.uk; midnight; D only; no Amex.

Mirch Masala £23 ❷④④
171-173 The Broadway, UB1 8867 9222 1–3A
1416 London Rd, SW16 8679 1828 10–2C
213 Upper Tooting Rd, SW17 8767 8638 10–2D
111 Commercial Rd, E1 7247 9992 12–2D
"So cheap, and absolutely brilliant!" – these "busy and bustling" Pakistani canteens offer "no frills", just "amazing-tasting" grills, naans and curries; BYO. / www.mirchmasalarestaurant.co.uk; midnight; set weekday L £10 (FP).

Misato W1 £32 ④④⑤
11 Wardour St 7734 0808 4–3A
"It runs by numbers nowadays", but this "cheap 'n' cheerful" Soho Japanese still offers "very fast and filling" fodder, and "the queue's just as long as it ever was". / 10.30 pm; no credit cards.

Mitsukoshi SW1 £55 ❷❷⑤
Dorland Hs, 14-20 Lower Regent St 7930 0317 3–3D
*"Dated, functional and really in need of a make-over" – no change, then, at this Japanese department store basement, near Piccadilly Circus; the food, though, "remains very good", especially if you visit what's arguably "the best sushi bar in the West End".
/ www.mitsukoshi-restaurant.co.uk; 10 pm; set weekday L £35 (FP).*

Miyama W1 £60 ❷④⑤
38 Clarges St 7499 2443 3–4B
"Top-quality sushi and sashimi", but "less-than-average decor" – the trade-off at this "quiet" Mayfair veteran Japanese is just the same as ever. / www.miyama-restaurant.co.uk; 10.15 pm; closed Sat L & Sun L.

The Modern Pantry EC1 £48 ❸❸❸
47-48 St Johns Sq 7553 9210 9–1A
Anna Hansen's "very light and airy" and "laid-back" Clerkenwell
venture is set in "a lovely peaceful courtyard"; the "innovative" cuisine
can be "brilliant", but critics find it "inconsistent" – there's no doubt,
though, that brunch is "outstanding". / www.themodernpantry.co.uk;
Mon-Sat 11 pm, Sun 10 pm.

Mogul SE10 £33 ❸❷❸
10 Greenwich Church St 8858 1500 1–3D
A "good Greenwich Indian" whose "very reliable" all-round charms
include a "wonderful selection of curries, perfectly cooked"; "for the
best atmosphere, book a table downstairs". / www.mogulindian.co.uk;
11.30 pm; set weekday L £21 (FP).

Mohsen W14 £27 ❷❸❺
152 Warwick Rd 7602 9888 7–1D
"Fresh and filling" Persian dishes (accompanied by "amazing bread")
make up for the "lacklustre" decor of this Kensington outfit;
its location – opposite Homebase – isn't much to write home about
either; BYO. / midnight; no credit cards.

Momo W1 £65 ❹❺❸
25 Heddon St 7434 4040 3–2C
"With all its nooks, crannies and dancers", Mourad Mazouz's "fun"
and "buzzy" Moroccan, off Regent Street, is "perfect for a date" or a
party; the "hit-and-miss" cuisine is rather beside the point
(and service may not win any prizes either…) / www.momoresto.com;
11.30 pm, Sun 11 pm; closed Sun L; set weekday L £35 (FP).

Mon Plaisir WC2 £54 ❹❹❸
19-21 Monmouth St 7836 7243 4–2B
This rambling and "very French" Covent Garden veteran (est. 1945)
"still delivers the goods" for most reporters, who love its "romantic"
style and "traditional" fare (especially the "well-priced theatre
menu"); ratings aren't a patch on a few years ago, however,
and sceptics feel that "as prices have gone up, quality has gone
down". / www.monplaisir.co.uk; 11.15 pm; closed Sun; set pre-theatre £33
(FP), set weekday L £35 (FP).

Mona Lisa SW10 £27 ❹❶❷
417 King's Rd 7376 5447 5–3B
"A great mixed clientele" ("from local Chelsea ladies to footie fans")
adds to the charm of this family-run Italian "greasy spoon",
near World's End, where "marvellous cheap food is served with
a smile". / 11 pm, Sun 5.30 pm; closed Sun D; no Amex; set weekday L
£17 (FP).

Monmouth Coffee Company £11 ❷❷❷
27 Monmouth St, WC2 7379 3516 4–2B
2 Park St, SE1 7940 9960 9–4C
34 Maltby St, SE1 7232 3010 9–4D
"Go, drink, buzz"; rivals are legion, but these "packed" Covent
Garden and Borough Market cafés are "London's reigning coffee
champions" – with their "perfect croissants and cakes", they are also
"cult" Saturday destinations, so beware the queues!
/ www.monmouthcoffee.co.uk; 6 pm-6.30 pm; SE1 2 pm; closed Sun,
Maltby St SE1 open Sat only; no Amex; no booking.

Montpeliano SW7 £62 ④④④
13 Montpelier St 7589 0032 5–1C
"Stuck in the '80s", it may be, but this Knightsbridge trattoria is still,
for its fans, a "reliable" and "lively" classic; for critics, however, there's
"just one word for it" – "terrible!" / www.montpelianorestaurant.com;
11.45 pm, Sun 11.30 pm; set weekday L £36 (FP).

Monty's £32 ❸❸④
692 Fulham Rd, SW6 0872 148 1291 10–1B
54 Northfield Ave, W13 8567 6281 1–2A
1 The Mall, W5 8567 8122 1–2A
"Always-reliable" local curry houses, mainly located in Ealing; opinions
differ on which is best – ownership varies – but all offer well-rated
Nepalese fare. / 11 pm.

Mooli's W1 £12 ❷❷④
50 Frith St 7494 9075 4–2A
"Zingy" Indian rotis ("go for the goat", it's "sublime") and "colourful"
salads at "staggeringly low" prices make this "inventive" Soho yearling
a hot spot for a "really distinctive" bite; ratings have dipped since
opening, though, with sceptics fearing it's becoming "overhyped".
/ www.moolis.com; Mon-Wed 10 pm, Thu-Sat 11.30 pm; closed Sun.

The Morgan Arms E3 £44 ❸❷❷
43 Morgan St 8980 6389 1–2D
"Less and less like a pub", this "good, local East End joint" has
a strong local following, thanks not least to its "consistent" culinary
standards. / www.capitalpubcompany.com/The-Morgan-Arms; 10 pm,
Sun 9 pm.

Morgan M N7 £64 ❶❶❸
489 Liverpool Rd 7609 3560 8–2D
Almost "Alice-in-Wonderlandish" in its improbability, Morgan
Meunier's "phenomenal" conversion of a "dull"-looking Holloway pub
is "one of London's best French restaurants" – "if it was in Soho,
you'd need to book months ahead!" / www.morganm.com; 9 pm; closed
Mon, Tue L, Sat L & Sun D; no Amex; booking: max 8.

Morito EC1 **NEW** £24 ❷❷❷
32 Exmouth Mkt 7278 7007 9–1A
Thanks to its "divine" dishes, this new "Moro-lite" operation –
a "cramped" and "very authentic tapas bar" – has been "rammed"
since the day it opened: "arrive early!" / www.morito.co.uk; 11 pm; closed
Sun; no booking for D.

MORO EC1 £48 ❷❷❸
34-36 Exmouth Mkt 7833 8336 9–1A
"Superb, simple food, with zero pretentiousness" and an "always
stimulating" (if "hellishly noisy") vibe have won a legendary following
for this "inspiring" Spanish/Moorish favourite in Exmouth Market;
its ratings dipped a bit this year, however – is it becoming
"less focussed"? / www.moro.co.uk; 10.30 pm; closed Sun.

Mosaica
The Chocolate Factory N22 £46 ❸❷❸
Unit C005, Clarendon Rd 8889 2400 1–1C
The industrial-estate location couldn't be more "unpromising",
but this "eccentric" Wood Green venue rewards the adventurous with
its "exotic" interior and "first-class" service; the food is usually "well-
executed" too, but this year did see the occasional "grim" report.
/ www.mosaicarestaurants.com; 9.30 pm, Sat 10 pm; closed Mon,
Sat L & Sun D.

Motcombs SW1 £58 ④④❸
26 Motcomb St 7235 6382 5–1D
On an ever-trendier corner, a welcoming establishment of long standing, comprising a "casual" upstairs bar (with al fresco tables) and a "country house"-style dining room downstairs; "the food's not really up with the prices, but this is Belgravia". / www.motcombs.co.uk; 11 pm; closed Sun D.

Moti Mahal WC2 £52 ❷❸④
45 Gt Queen St 7240 9329 4–2D
"Is this the most under-rated curry house in London?" – this increasingly well-known Covent Garden outpost of a Delhi-based group offers "exquisite" dishes which are "up with the best in India itself"; prices, however, are "decidedly high" and the interior is "not the most exciting". / www.motimahal-uk.com; 11 pm; closed Sat L & Sun.

Mount Street Deli W1 £20 ④④④
100 Mount St 7499 6843 3–3A
"Mayfair prices" somewhat colour views of this Caprice group deli/café yearling, but fans say that "limited seating is the only drawback" of a place that's "great for a quick bite" (and there aren't many of those round here…) / www.themountstreetdeli.co.uk; 6 pm, Sat 5 pm; closed Sun; no bookings.

Mr Chow SW1 £74 ④④④
151 Knightsbridge 7589 7347 5–1D
Once a glamorous Knightsbridge linchpin, this Chinese restaurant can seem "a little passé" nowadays, but it still turns out "decent" chow in a "civilised" setting, say fans; critics, though, find the whole experience "so overpriced, you're left wondering whether the food was nice after all". / www.mrchow.com; 11.45 pm.

Mr Kong WC2 £32 ❸❸④
21 Lisle St 7437 7341 4–3A
"One of the safer bets in Chinatown", this "hustling and bustling" veteran benefits from a "charming" manager and a very "dependable" standard of cooking – "avoid the obvious menu choices, and go for the specials". / www.mrkongrestaurant.com; 2.45 am, Sun 1.45 am.

Mr Wing SW5 £45 ❸④❷
242-244 Old Brompton Rd 7370 4450 5–2A
"Dark alcoves" and "novel" décor (lots of fish tanks and plants) have long made this Earl's Court Chinese a "fun" option for a party – especially when jazz is playing – or romance; "with the old manager gone", however, there are several concerns about "slipping" standards, particularly on the service front. / www.mrwing.com; 11.30 pm.

Mrs Marengos W1 £18 ❶❸④
53 Lexington St 7287 2544 3–2D
"Great breakfasts, tasty lunches and amazing cakes" are on offer at this "cute" Soho spot; it's not as well known as its big sister, Mildred's, but – as it's so small – that's perhaps a blessing. / www.mrsmarengos.co.uk; L only, closed Sun; no Amex; no booking.

Mugen EC4 £40 ❸❷❸
26 King William St 7929 7879 9–3C
"Pleasantly bustling", "extremely reliable" and with "brilliant" service, this Japanese restaurant, near Monument, is "ideal for a quick lunch". / 10.30 pm; closed Sat & Sun.

Murano W1 £90 ❸❷❸
20-22 Queen St 7495 1127 3–3B
*Maybe it is "now free of the Ramsay empire", but since Angela
Hartnett's October 2010 buy-out, the ratings of this "classy",
if slightly "impersonal", Mayfair dining room, have drifted; her cuisine
is still often acclaimed as "first-rate", but those who find it "nothing
special" are becoming more vociferous.* / www.angela-hartnett.com;
10.15 pm; closed Sun; set weekday L £50 (FP).

My Old Place E1 £34 ❷⑤④
88-90 Middlesex St 7247 2200 9–2D
*Overlook the "grotty" setting and the "reluctant" service – "cheap
and fiery Sichuan cooking" makes this "authentic" spot,
near Liverpool Street, a "jewel".* / www.myoldplace.co.uk; 11 pm; no Amex.

Nahm
Halkin Hotel SW1 £80 ❸❸⑤
5 Halkin St 7333 1234 2–3A
*Shame that a "weird" ambience and "exorbitant" prices continue
to handicap David Thompson's renowned Thai dining room,
in Belgravia – the food may strike its critics as merely "pleasant
enough", but most reporters reckon it's "phenomenal".*
/ www.nahm.como.bz; 10.30 pm; closed Sat L & Sun L.

Namo E9 £30 ❸❸❸
178 Victoria Park Rd 8533 0639 1–2D
*"Authentic pho" is one of the "good range of options" on offer at this
Vietnamese local, in Hackney; "the back terrace is best in summer".*
/ www.namo.co.uk; 11 pm; no Amex.

Nando's £28 ④④④
Branches throughout London
*"Basic, simple, quick… and OK-quality for a cheap meal";
this "reliable" peri-peri chicken chain "is hardly a destination for
a night out", but its "fuss-free" charms make it "a good alternative
to a pizza", in particular for those with families in tow.*
/ www.nandos.co.uk; 11.30 pm, Sun 10.30 pm; no Amex; no booking.

Napket £20 ④④❸
5 Vigo St, W1 7734 4387 3–3D
6 Brook St, W1 7495 8562 3–2B
61 Piccadilly, W1 7493 4704 3–3C
342 King's Rd, SW3 7352 9832 5–3C
34 Royal Exchange, EC3 7621 1831 9–2C
*A growing chain of glamorous cafés, praised as "a good place for
a coffee and a sandwich", and offering "lots of bespoke options";
it's really "not cheap" though.* / www.napket.com; 7 pm; W1 10 pm,
EC3 5 pm; Brook St closed Sun; EC3 closed Sat & Sun; W1 no Amex;
no bookings.

Napulé SW6 £39 ❸④❸
585 Fulham Rd 7381 1122 5–4A
*"Still authentic, even though it's now part of a chain"; this convivial
member of the 'Made in Italy' family, by Fulham Broadway, scores
most highly for its "excellent" pizza-by-the-metre.* / 11.30 pm,
Sun 10.30 pm; closed weekday L; no Amex.

The Narrow E14 £57 ④④④
44 Narrow St 7592 7950 11–1B
*A potentially atmospheric riverside boozer in Docklands, where the
food is "uninspiring", and service too often "couldn't care less" –
in short, it's the sort of 'Kitchen Nightmare' that the proprietor,
Gordon Ramsay, is famous for fixing; so why doesn't he?*
/ www.gordonramsay.com; 11 pm, Sun 10.30 pm.

The National Dining Rooms
National Gallery WC2   £50   ⑤⑤④
Sainsbury Wing, Trafalgar Sq   7747 2525   2–2C
*"Great views" reward those who bag one of the "lovely" window seats
in this first-floor dining room, overlooking Trafalgar Square; generally,
"the food is not so good" – the afternoon tea, though, can be
"excellent".* / www.thenationaldiningrooms.co.uk; 7 pm; Sat-Thu closed
D, Fri open L & D; no Amex.

National Gallery Café
National Gallery WC2   £50   ④④④
East Wing, Trafalgar Sq   7747 5942   4–4B
*This panelled café on Trafalgar Square (no view) is ideally placed as a
central rendezvous; its wide-ranging menu – from sandwiches
to more ambitious dishes – is realised only to an "average" standard,
but it makes a handy option for a light bite or breakfast.*
/ www.thenationaldiningrooms.co.uk; 11 pm, Sun 6 pm; no Amex.

Natural Kitchen   £32   ❸❸❸
77-78 Marylebone High St, W1   3012 2123   2–1A
15-17 New Street Sq, Fetter Ln, EC4   3012 2123   9–2A
*For "casual lunches", these "friendly" and "always-packed" diners
"fill a gap" with their "interesting" salads, soups, sarnies and quiches;
who cares if purists decry the fare as "faux-Mediterranean"?* / EC4
10 pm; W1 8 pm, Sat 7 pm, Sun 5 pm; EC4 closed Sat Sun.

Nautilus NW6   £37   ❷❷④
27-29 Fortune Green Rd   7435 2532   1–1B
*"North London's best fish 'n' chips" (fried in matzo meal) are,
say fans, to be found at this West Hampstead veteran; well, it's not
the "lousy" interior which draws the crowds!* / 10 pm; closed Sun;
no Amex.

Navarro's W1   £38   ❸④❷
67 Charlotte St   7637 7713   2–1C
*An eye-catching tiled interior helps make this Fitzrovia haunt central
London's leading traditional-style tapas bar; it offers "delicious" food,
too, which comes in "surprisingly generous portions".*
/ www.navarros.co.uk; 10 pm; closed Sat L & Sun.

Nazmins SW18   £33   ❸❷④
398 Garratt Ln   8944 1463   10–2B
*"Always busy", this Earlsfield Indian has a big name locally for its
"reliable and tasty" food.* / www.nazmins.com; midnight.

Needoo E1   £25   ❶❸④
87 New Rd   7247 0648   12–2D
*"On a par with the legendary Tayyabs, but less busy" – this "brilliant"
Pakistani yearling is acclaimed for its "amazing grilled meats and
curries at low prices"; "staff actually smile" too.* / www.needoogrill.co.uk;
6 pm; closed Sun; no Amex.

New Culture Revolution   £31   ❸④④
305 King's Rd, SW3   7352 9281   5–3C
157-159 Notting Hill Gate, W11   7313 9688   6–2B
42 Duncan St, N1   7833 9083   8–3D
*"Totally reliable and good-quality", this small and basic chain
impresses almost all reporters with its "tasty noodles, soups and
dumplings".* / www.newculturerevolution.co.uk; 10.30 pm.

New Mayflower W1   £30   ②❸④
68-70 Shaftesbury Ave   7734 9207   4–3A
*Consistently one of Chinatown's best performers – and traditionally
one of London's best places to eat post-midnight too –
this nondescript-looking Cantonese serves up "excellent" food;
service, though, is "businesslike, rather than friendly". / 4 am; D only;
no Amex.*

New Tayyabs E1   £27   ❶④❸
83 Fieldgate St   7247 9543   9–2D
*The "horrific" queues at this "hectic" East End Pakistani classic are
legendary, and no wonder – its "awesome" but "absurdly cheap"
lamb chops and curries offer "one of London's great eating
experiences"; "thank God they now take bookings!"; BYO.
/ www.tayyabs.co.uk; 11.30 pm.*

New World W1   £33   ④④❸
1 Gerrard Pl   7734 0396   4–3A
*"Easy to imagine you're in Hong Kong", when you visit this "giant"
and "noisy" Chinatown fixture; the lunchtime dim sum, served from
trolleys, is "excellent and very cheap" – "ignore everything else!"
/ 11.45 pm, Sun 11 pm; no booking, Sun L.*

1901
Andaz Hotel EC2   £62   ④❸❸
40 Liverpool St   7618 7000   12–2B
*"Very elegant" surroundings and an "impressive" wine list help qualify
this "very comfortable" dining room, by Liverpool Street, as a power-
dining haunt; fans find the food "sound" too, but critics dismiss it as
"pretentious". / www.andazdining.com; 10 pm; closed Sat L & Sun; booking:
max 12.*

19 Numara Bos Cirrik N16   £24   ❸❸④
34 Stoke Newington Rd   7249 0400   1–1C
*"Perhaps it's unhealthy, but by gosh it's good"; this "cheap" and "fun"
kebab house, by Hackney Central, serves up "enormous plates
of tasty grilled meat", and "fresh" mezze too. / midnight; no Amex.*

Nizuni W1 NEW   £37   ❷❷❸
22 Charlotte St   7580 7447   2–1C
*Surprisingly few reports on this Fitzrovia newcomer, which offers
"really good Asian-fusion food, much, much cheaper than nearby
Roka", and "very good sushi" too – perhaps it's because the interior's
a little "bland". / www.nizuni.com; 10.45 pm; closed Sun L; .*

Nobu
Metropolitan Hotel W1   £80   ❷④④
19 Old Park Ln   7447 4747   3–4A
*"Some now think it naff", but this epic Mayfair Japanese – which
back in 1997 kicked off a wave of trendy Asian high-flyers – still
delivers many "divine" sushi and fusion dishes; it's "eye-wateringly
expensive", though, and menu, service and decor are all now arguably
"in need of an update". / www.noburestaurants.com; Mon-Thu 10.15 pm,
Fri & Sat 11 pm, Sun 10 pm.*

Nobu W1   £84   ❸④❸
15 Berkeley St   7290 9222   3–3C
*"Clubbier" – and also a bit more "Footballers' Wives" – than its Park
Lane sibling, the younger of the Mayfair Nobus serves similarly
"exquisite" Japanese-fusion cuisine that's similarly "scandalously
overpriced"; the setting is "way-too-noisy", and "canteen-like",
but "fun"… if you like that sort of thing. / www.noburestaurants.com;
11 pm, Thu-Sat midnight, Sun 9 pm; closed Sat L & Sun L.*

Noor Jahan £36 **②②④**
2a, Bina Gdns, SW5   7373 6522   5–2B
26 Sussex Pl, W2   7402 2332   6–1D
"You will never be disappointed", says one of the many fans of the
"fresh-tasting" Indian food served at this "popular workhorse", whose
South Kensington location draws in a well-heeled crowd at odds with
its "gloomy" curry-house looks; similarly, the W2 spin-off is "definitely
a cut-above". / 11.30 pm, Sun 10.30 pm.

Nopi W1 **NEW** £55 **②②③**
21-22 Warwick St   7494 9584   3–2D
Yotam Ottolenghi's has a "magical touch", say fans of this "beautiful
and casual" Soho newcomer, which offers "exotic" but "clean-tasting"
tapas displaying a "brilliant combination of Middle Eastern and Asian
influences"; we do have some sympathy , though, with those who find
it "way overpriced". / www.nopi-restaurant.com; 11.30 pm; closed Sun D.

Nordic Bakery £15 **③②②**
14a, Golden Sq, W1   3230 1077   3–2D
37b, New Cavendish St, W1   7935 3590   2–1A **NEW**
"The antidote to everything to do with chains and Italio/American
coffee shops!" – this "minimalist", "relaxed" and "blissfully music-
free" Soho café offers "great coffee" and "cinnamon buns to die for";
a second outlet recently opened, north of Oxford Street. / Golden
Square 8 pm, Sat 7 pm, Sun 6 pm; Cavendish Street 7 pm, Sun 6 pm.

The Norfolk Arms WC1 £37 **④④③**
28 Leigh St   7388 3937   8–4C
A "casual" (going-on "erratic") Bloomsbury boozer whose "quirky"
menu offers "a choice of Spanish-style tapas or modern British
mains" – the former seem the better bet. / www.norfolkarms.co.uk;
10.15 pm.

North China W3 £36 **②②③**
305 Uxbridge Rd   8992 9183   7–1A
"By far the best food in Acton" is to be had at this "friendly" and
"high-quality" family-run Chinese – "worth a trip" for its "deeply
satisfying" cooking. / www.northchina.co.uk; 11 pm, Fri & Sat 11.30 pm.

The North London Tavern NW6 £43 **③④③**
375 Kilburn High Rd   7625 6634   1–2B
A "beautifully restored" Kilburn boozer that's still "a real pub",
but where the cooking is of "good quality". / www.realpubs.co.uk;
10.30 pm, Sun 9.30 pm; no Amex.

North Road EC1 £54 **②③④**
69-73 St John St   3217 0033   9–1B
"Fascinating" – that's the verdict on Christoffer Hruskova's "sterile"-
feeling Danish newcomer, in Clerkenwell; some of his "challenging"
("weird") flavours and food combos seem "misconceived", but a
striking number of reporters feel this is a "genuinely unique"
experience that "really lives up to the hype!"
/ www.northroadrestaurant.co.uk; Mon -Thu 10.30 pm, Fri-Sat 11 pm;
closed Sun.

North Sea Fish WC1 £34 **③③③**
7-8 Leigh St   7387 5892   8–4C
"Top-class fish 'n' chips" maintain the wide-ranging appeal of this
"old-fashioned" Bloomsbury chippy. / www.northseafishrestaurant.co.uk;
10.30 pm; closed Sun; no Amex.

Northbank EC4 £50 ❸❸❷
1 Paul's Walk 7329 9299 9–3B
*"An excellent position, just by the Millennium Bridge" – with fine
Thames views and an "unbeatable summer terrace" –
has traditionally been the highlight at this "friendly" bar/café;
the "creative" food, however, shows some signs of beginning
to "measure up". / www.northbankrestaurant.co.uk; 10.30 pm.*

The Northgate N1 £36 ❷❷❸
113 Southgate Rd 7359 7392 1–1C
*A De Beauvoir Town gastroboozer, hailed by the locals for its
"interesting" menu, its "consistently good" food and its "charming"
service. / 10.30 pm, Sun 9.30 pm; closed Mon L.*

Notting Hill Brasserie W11 £70 ❸④❸
92 Kensington Park Rd 7229 4481 6–2B
*In spite of a recent revamp, this potentially very "special" and
"romantic" west London townhouse-restaurant (not brasserie) is still
putting in a much more erratic performance than it once did; reports
– especially on the service – are noticeably up-and-down.
/ www.nottinghillbrasserie.co.uk; 11 pm, Mon & Sun 10.30 pm; set weekday L
£36 (FP).*

Nottingdale W11 £37 ❷④❷
11 Evesham St 7221 2223 6–2A
*Think River Café-lost-in-the-backwoods-of-Notting Hill, and you have
something of the flavour of this "interesting" canteen (which is part-
owned by Charles Dunstone of Carphone Warehouse fame);
its "simply-prepared" dishes offer "good flavours" from ingredients
of "high quality". / www.nottingdale.com; 7 pm; closed Sat & Sun.*

Noura £50 ❸④④
122 Jermyn St, SW1 7839 2020 3–3D
16 Hobart Pl, SW1 7235 9444 2–4B
2 William St, SW1 7235 5900 5–1D
16 Curzon St, W1 7495 1050 3–4B
*The style ("all shiny mirrors") is somewhere between "classy" and
"impersonal", but these "bustling" brasseries still win praise for their
"genuine" Lebanese cuisine. / www.noura.co.uk; 11.30 pm, sun 10 pm.*

Novikov W1 NEW
50 Berkeley St awaiting tel 3–3C
*Breezing in from Moscow – from a restaurateur already claiming
50 spectacular establishments to his name – this major new Mayfair
venture, with dining rooms both Italian and Asian in style,
is scheduled to open in late-2011. / www.novikovrestaurant.co.uk.*

Nozomi SW3 £71 ④⑤④
14-15 Beauchamp Pl 7838 1500 5–1C
*An allegedly in-crowd Knightsbridge Japanese, of note for its
"very stylish bar scene"; the reporters who comment on its cuisine
(few) however, tend to find the whole show rather "pretentious".
/ www.nozomi.co.uk; 11.30 pm, Sun 10.30 pm; closed Mon L.*

Number Twelve WC1 £50 ❸④④
12 Upper Woburn Pl 7693 5425 8–4C
*A handy Bloomsbury address – this little-known hotel dining room,
near Euston, is "fairly formal", and so "good for business"; it serves
up "simple but tasty" cuisine "with an Italian bent".
/ www.numbertwelverestaurant.co.uk; 10.15 pm; closed Sat L & Sun.*

Numero Uno SW11 £48 ❸❷❸
139 Northcote Rd 7978 5837 10–2C
*"The menu never changes, but that's a good thing", say the fans
of this "friendly and efficient" Nappy Valley Italian — "we're lucky
to have it as a local". / 11.30 pm; no Amex.*

Nuovi Sapori SW6 £43 ❷❶④
295 New King's Rd 7736 3363 10–1B
*Staff are "particularly warm and welcoming", at this Fulham Italian,
and the cooking is "well above average" too; shame "the ambience
leaves something to be desired". / 11 pm; closed Sun.*

Nusa Kitchen £10 ❷④④
9 Old St, EC1 7253 3135 9–1B
2 Adam's Ct, EC2 7628 1149 9–2C
*"Queues out the door, even in the rain!" attest to the power of these
City pit stops' addictive staple — "absolutely delicious soups, in a huge
range of flavours, and with no duff choices". / www.nusakitchen.co.uk;
4 pm; Sat & Sun; no booking.*

O'Zon TW1 £30 ❸④④
33-35 London Rd 8891 3611 1–4A
*"A good range" of "well-cooked" oriental food at "reasonable prices"
remains a winning proposition for this friendly Chinese in downtown
Twickenham; it's "very popular with kids" too. / www.justchinese.co.uk;
11 pm, Fri & Sat 11.30 pm.*

The Oak W2 £49 ❷❸❶
137 Westbourne Park Rd 7221 3355 6–1B
*"Airy and always buzzing" – this gorgeous Bayswater pub-conversion
is just the place if you're looking for a "relaxed and stylish" meal,
with a menu including "some of the best – if not the cheapest –
pizzas in town!" / www.theoaklondon.com; 10.30 pm, Sun 10 pm;
Mon-Thu D only, Fri-Sun open L & D; no booking.*

Odette's NW1 £57 ❷❷❷
130 Regent's Park Rd 7586 8569 8–3B
*"Going places!"; Bryn Williams's "superb" and "beautifully presented"
cuisine – "more consistent", of late – won renewed support this year
for this "elegant" neighbourhood restaurant, which benefits from
a "romantic" Primrose Hill setting. / www.odettesprimrosehill.com;
10.30 pm.*

Odin's W1 £52 ④❷❷
27 Devonshire St 7935 7296 2–1A
*"Utterly delightful, in an old-school, clubby sort of way" –
this "civilised", art-filled Marylebone "time warp" is "just the place
to take your aunt", and also perfect "for business"; the traditional
cuisine is no more than "OK", but no one really seems to mind.
/ www.langansrestaurants.co.uk; 11 pm; closed Sat L & Sun; booking: max 12.*

Okawari W5 £34 ❸❸④
13 Bond St 8566 0466 1–3A
*An "always-reliable" little café, in central Ealing, which offers "simple,
fresh and tasty" sushi (and so on), eaten at sunken tables.
/ www.okawari.co.uk; 11.15 pm, Sun 10.45 pm.*

The Old Brewery SE10   £39   ④④❷
The Pepys Building, Old Royal Naval College   3327 1280   1–3D
It's "hard to find better beers in London", says fans of this converted
brewery within the old Naval College – "a great-looking place with big
copper vats", and "a huge sun trap terrace"; it's proving
a "very useful addition to Greenwich" even if the food – burgers aside
– is "not massively special". / www.oldbrewerygreenwich.com; Fri & Sat
10.30 pm, Sun-Thu 10 pm; D only; no Amex.

The Old Bull & Bush NW3   £38   ⑤⑤❷
North End Rd   8905 5456   8–1A
"After a trip to Hampstead Heath", this "always-busy" gastropub,
opposite Golder's Hill Park, makes an atmospheric destination; "it's a
bit of a production line" though – the food's "not so impressive",
and service "needs a major lift" too. / www.thebullandbush.co.uk;
9.30 pm, Sat 10 pm, Sun 9 pm; set weekday L £24 (FP).

Old Parr's Head W14   £23   ④④❸
120 Blythe Rd   7371 4561   7–1C
"Did the old Thai family go back to Thailand?" – "quality seems to be
falling and prices rising", in the restaurant of this Olympia boozer;
it still benefits from its "hidden beer garden", though, and fans still
find it a "great local". / www.theoldparrshead.co.uk; 10 pm, Sat & Sun
9.30 pm; no Amex.

Ye Olde Cheshire Cheese EC4   £36   ④④❶
145 Fleet St   7353 6170   9–2A
"A very scenic tourist-trap"; this famous Fleet Street inn – rebuilt after
the Great Fire, and Dr Johnson's local – is also popular with the
locals, and its pub fodder, though pretty ordinary, could be a lot
worse. / 9.30 pm; closed Sun D; no booking, Sat & Sun.

Oliveto SW1   £50   ❶③④
49 Elizabeth St   7730 0074   2–4A
"The best pizza in Europe!" (well almost); no wonder that,
at weekends, this not-exactly-cheap Belgravia Sardinian is "teeming
with smartly-dressed tots and their glamorous parents" –
book ahead! / www.olivorestaurants.com; 11 pm, Sun 10.30 pm; booking:
max 7 at D.

Olivo SW1   £55   ❸③⑤
21 Eccleston St   7730 2505   2–4B
"Lots of regulars, including a fair number of Italians" maintain the
"neighbourhood" style of this Belgravia fixture, which is still "going
strong", thanks to the quality of its "honest" Sardinian fare;
the "jaded" interior, though, is "crowded", "noisy" and
"uncomfortable". / www.olivorestaurants.com; 11 pm, Sun 10.30 pm; closed
Sat L & Sun L.

Olivomare SW1   £64   ❷③④
10 Lower Belgrave St   7730 9022   2–4B
"Simple" but "heavenly" fish and seafood have won a major fan club
for this "brilliant" Belgravia Sardinian; not everyone, though, likes its
"snazzy interior design" – it's "like eating in a posh fridge!"
/ www.olivorestaurants.com; 11 pm, Sun 10.30 pm; booking: max 10.

Olley's SE24   £39   ❸③④
65-69 Norwood Rd   8671 8259   10–2D
This eclectically-decorated Brockwell Park chippy is one of the
best in south London, and it raises our native dish to a standard
"well above the norm". / www.olleys.info; 10 pm, Sun 9.30 pm; closed Mon;
no Amex.

Olympus Fish N3 £28 ②②④
140-144 Ballards Ln 8371 8666 1–1B
You can have "expertly-prepared" fish – either classic-style or char-grilled – at this Turkish chippy, in Finchley; it maintains "high standards", and is always "very busy". / 11 pm; closed Mon.

I Lombard Street EC3 £62 ④④④
I Lombard St 7929 6611 9–3C
A heart-of-the-City rendezvous for expense-accounters (with a more "power lunch"-style restaurant attached); its cooking "has improved of late", but it is still "not exceptional", and the banking hall setting can – at peak times – seem "too much like a railway terminus" for some tastes. / www.1lombardstreet.com; 10 pm; closed Sat & Sun.

One-O-One
Sheraton Park Tower SW1 £90 ①③⑤
101 Knightsbridge 7290 7101 5–1D
"Quite simply the best fish restaurant in the UK"; Pascal Proyart's "stunning" cuisine can be enjoyed à la carte, tapas-style or – perhaps best of all for Knightsbridge shoppers – at a "bargain" set lunch; the "dead" interior, though, is an object lesson in "uninspiring" hotel-design. / www.oneonerestaurant.com; 10 pm; booking: max 6.

The Only Running Footman W1 £46 ❸❸❸
5 Charles St 7499 2988 3–3B
"Quiet and spacious enough upstairs to have a relaxed meal", this seemingly "packed" pub is a Mayfair destination well worth knowing about, thanks not least to its "fresh" and "seasonal" cuisine. / www.therunningfootmanmayfair.com; 10 pm.

Opera Tavern WC2 **NEW** £40 ❷❸❸
23 Catherine St 7836 3680 4–3D
"A great addition to the options near the Royal Opera House" – this "stylish" (but "closely-packed") sibling to Salt Yard serves up some "tantalising" Mediterranean small dishes that "burst with flavour"; don't get too carried away, though – "the bills can add up". / www.operatavern.co.uk; 11.30 pm; closed Sun D.

The Orange SW1 £48 ❸❸❷
37 Pimlico Rd 7881 9844 5–2D
It may be "cheap only by Belgravia standards", but this elegantly "stripped-back" boozer is now starting to out-do its parent, the Thomas Cubitt, in the popularity stakes; the secret? – a "decent" menu of staples, and a scene that's always "buzzing". / www.theorange.co.uk; Mon-Thu 10 pm, Fri & Sat 10.30 pm, Sun 9.30 pm.

Orange Pekoe SW13 £19 ❸❷❷
3 White Hart Ln 8876 6070 10–1A
A "pretty" tea and coffee shop with a "sun trap terrace", near the river in Barnes, serving "tempting" cakes, sarnies and salads. / www.orangepekoeteas.com; L only.

The Orange Tree N20 £38 ❸❸❷
7 Totteridge Ln 8343 7031 1–1B
Being "beautifully located" and "very child-friendly/forgiving" – two particular virtues of this Totteridge inn (and garden), which was well-rated this year for its "above-average" gastropub fare. / www.theorangetreetotteridge.co.uk; 9.30 pm, Fri & Sat 10.30 pm, Sun 9 pm.

L'Oranger SW1 £86 ❸❸❷
5 St James's St 7839 3774 3–4D
A "blissful, hidden courtyard", for the summer months, bolsters the "stylish" appeal of this "smart" St James's fixture; after a sticky patch, it won renewed praise this year for cuisine that's generally "fine", and sometimes "outstanding". / www.loranger.co.uk; 11 pm; closed Sat L & Sun; no jeans or trainers.

Origin Asia TW9 £37 ❷❷❸
100 Kew Rd 8948 0509 1–4A
"Unusually light and unusually delicate" dishes have created a strong name locally for this Richmond "modern Indian"; even so, "it can lack atmosphere at times". / www.originasia.co.uk; 11 pm; no Amex; set weekday L £22 (FP).

Orrery W1 £68 ❸❷❷
55 Marylebone High St 7616 8000 2–1A
"The luxury of space between tables" adds to the "light and airy" charms – especially for business – of this first-floor room, overlooking a churchyard; service is "exemplary" (a rarity for the D&D group), and the Gallic cuisine is "delightful" too – if "less imaginative" than in previous years. / www.orreryrestaurant.co.uk; 10.30 pm, Fri & Sat 11 pm.

Orso WC2 £56 ❸❸④
27 Wellington St 7240 5269 4–3D
"Once a flagship for regional Italian cooking", this Covent Garden "old-time" basement is looking a bit "faded" nowadays; fans still find it a "very reliable" stand-by, though, especially post-theatre, thanks to its "personable" service and its "rustic" and "hearty" fare. / www.orsorestaurant.co.uk; midnight; set pre theatre £35 (FP).

Oscar
Charlotte Street Hotel W1 £60 ④❸❷
15 Charlotte St 7806 2000 2–1C
This Fitzrovia haunt is a 'happening' linchpin for local meedjah types – "it's a shame the restaurant doesn't live up to the bar", but it is sometimes tipped for breakfast, or for business, nonetheless. / www.charlottestreethotel.com; 10.45 pm, Sun 9.45 pm.

Oslo Court NW8 £57 ❷❶❷
Charlbert St, off Prince Albert Rd 7722 8795 8–3A
"The dessert trolley is pure theatre", at this "real 1970's"-style "time warp", at the foot of a Regent's Park apartment block – the preferred birthday-party venue locally for those of a certain age; its "hilarious" (but highly professional) staff serve up an "amazingly large" menu that delivers surprisingly "excellent" results – "you simply have to love it!" / 11 pm; closed Sun; no jeans or trainers.

Osteria Antica Bologna SW11 £39 ❸❸❸
23 Northcote Rd 7978 4771 10–2C
Rustic Italian bistro of long standing, a short step from Clapham Junction; for fans, it's a "really great" destination, and is certainly often a "busy" one too, but standards are still rather up-and-down. / www.osteria.co.uk; 10.30 pm, Sat & Sun 10 pm.

Osteria Appennino EC2 £44 ❷④④
8 Devonshire Sq 7247 4472 9–2D
A "cramped" family-run Italian near Liverpool Street, offering "beautifully thin" pizza, and "beautifully authentic" pasta too. / www.osteriarestaurants.co.uk; 10.15 pm; closed Sat & Sun.

Osteria Basilico W11   £56   ❸❸❷
29 Kensington Park Rd   7727 9957   6–1A
*"Still a fun place", this "chaotic" neighbourhood Italian (specialising
in pizza) remains a linchpin of the Notting Hill dining scene, and is
"always busy"; sit on the ground-floor (or outside) if you can –
the basement tables aren't nearly as nice. / www.osteriabasilico.co.uk;
11.30 pm, Sun 10.30 pm; no booking, Sat L.*

Osteria Dell'Angolo SW1   £54   ❸❸⑤
47 Marsham St   3268 1077   2–4C
*Not everyone likes the "formal, rarefied and businessy" style of this
Westminster Italian – a shame, as its "classic Tuscan dishes" are
"robust" and of "good quality", and complemented by an
"enterprising" wine list. / www.osteriadellangolo.co.uk; 10.30 pm; closed
Sat L & Sun.*

Osteria dell'Arancio SW10   £53   ❸❸❸
383 King's Rd   7349 8111   5–3B
*A "casual" World's End trattoria offering "real Italian country
cooking"; it's the "amazing" wine list, though – "with many choices
one rarely sees outside Italy" – that's the biggest attraction, enhanced
by guidance from a "knowledgeable manager/sommelier".
/ www.osteriadellarancio.co.uk; 11 pm; closed Mon L & Sun D.*

Otto Pizza W2 🆕   £25   ❷❷❸
6 Chepstow Rd   7792 4088   6–1B
*"Filling and delicious pizzas with a difference" ("the cornmeal
crust is somewhere between pizza and pie") earn applause for this
small and basic Bayswater newcomer. / www.ottopizza.com; 11 pm,
Sun 10 pm.*

Ottolenghi   £47   ❶❸❸
13 Motcomb St, SW1   7823 2707   5–1D
63 Ledbury Rd, W11   7727 1121   6–1B
1 Holland St, W8   7937 0003   5–1A
287 Upper St, N1   7288 1454   8–2D
*"OK, £10 for a few bits of aubergine is expensive... but I love it!";
Yotam Ottolenghi's "cramped" designer cafés/delis may
be "shockingly pricey" (and "queueing is a bore"), but "who can
resist" their "over-indulgent" cakes, "tempting" salads and amazing
"upmarket tapas"; a wow for brunch too. / www.ottolenghi.co.uk;
10.15 pm; W8 & W11 8 pm, Sat 7 pm, Sun 6 pm; N1 closed Sun D; Holland
St takeaway only; W11 & SW1 no booking, N1 booking for D only.*

(Brasserie)
Oxo Tower SE1   £70   ⑤④❸
Barge House St   7803 3888   9–3A
*It can be "romantic on a sunny summer evening" (or "perfect for out-
of-town clients"), but otherwise "why would you want to go" even
to the cheaper section of this South Bank landmark, where "you pay
for the view"... and get little else besides?
/ www.harveynichols.com/restaurants/oxo-tower-london; 11 pm, Sun 10.30 pm;
set always available £43 (FP).*

(Restaurant)
Oxo Tower SE1   £81   ⑤⑤④
Barge House St   7803 3888   9–3A
*"A criminal waste of one of London's best views"; the grander section
on the sixth floor of this South Bank landmark serves up "dreadful"
food and service is "below-average" too; it's also "wildly overpriced" –
"only go if someone deep-pocketed wants to take you!"
/ www.harveynichols.com; 11 pm, Sun 10 pm.*

Ozer W1 £42 ④④④
5 Langham Pl   7323 0505   3–1C
"Reliable, if unexciting" – this well-appointed Turkish restaurant,
just north of Oxford Circus, is a popular canteen for "BBC types"
(Broadcasting House being opposite), theatre-goers and shoppers.
/ www.sofra.co.uk;   11 pm; set weekday L & pre-theatre £27 (FP).

Le P'tit Normand SW18 £37 ❸②❸
185 Merton Rd   8871 0233   10–2B
"A little gem" of a Gallic bistro, "hidden-away in the depths
of Southfields"; its "charming patron" presides over an old-fashioned
experience worth seeking out for its consistent "good value".
/ www.leptitnormand.co.uk;   10 pm; closed Mon, Sat L & Sun D.

Pacific Oriental EC2 £48 ④❸❸
52 Threadneedle St   0871 704 4060   9–2C
"Assembly line" pan-Asian dishes come at "pretty astronomical"
prices, at this large-scale bar/brasserie/restaurant; but, hey, this is the
City, and the attractive conversion of a former banking hall helps
create a "relaxed and informal" atmosphere.
/ www.orientalrestaurantgroup.co.uk;   10.30 pm; closed Sat & Sun; no trainers.

The Paddyfield SW12 £25 ❷④❸
4 Bedford Hill   8772 1145   10–2C
This "closely-packed" Balham canteen has "incredibly friendly
(if erratic) service", and serves "delicious Vietnamese food for very
little money"; "BYO is a massive bonus". / www.thepaddyfield.co.uk;
11.30 pm; D only, closed Mon; no credit cards.

Il Pagliaccio SW6 £34 ④❸❶
182-184 Wandsworth Bridge Rd   7371 5253   10–1B
"Opera nights are the best", but – thanks to the "friendly singing
waiters" – the atmosphere at this "cheap and cheerful" Sands End
pizzeria is "always lively"; a visit here is "always an easy option with
kids". / www.paggs.co.uk; midnight; no Amex.

Le Pain Quotidien £34 ④④❸
Branches throughout London
"Lovely coffee in bowls", served with "yummy bread and a huge array
of spreads", helps make these "relaxed" Belgian communal-cafés
a good place to start the day, even if they are a trifle
"more expensive than they should be"; "great salads and
sandwiches" too. / www.painquotidien.com; 7 pm-10 pm; no booking
at some branches, especially at weekends.

The Painted Heron SW10 £53 ❶❷❸
112 Cheyne Walk   7351 5232   5–3B
"Unconventional", "very refined" food from "market-fresh"
ingredients puts this "hidden gem" (by Chelsea Embankment) well
up London's premier league of top subcontinentals – it's "not as
flashy" as the bigger names, but "every bit as good".
/ www.thepaintedheron.com; 11 pm, Sun 10.30 pm; D only, Sun open L & D.

The Palm SW1 £80 ④④⑤
1 Pont St   7201 0710   5–1D
Fans of this NYC-to-Knightsbridge steakhouse concede it's "pricey",
buy say it offers "the best USDA sirloin in town"; there are many
sceptics, however, for whom it's just "stupidly expensive".
/ www.thepalm.com/london; 11 pm, Sun 10 pm; closed weekday L.

The Palmerston SE22 £39 ❷❷❸
91 Lordship Ln 8693 1629 1–4D
*"The secret is well and truly out" – the "seasonal" food at this
"bubbly" East Dulwich gastropub is "darn good"; best place to sit
is the "comforting wood-panelled back room".* / www.thepalmerston.net;
10 pm, Sun 9.30 pm.

Palmyra TW9 £36 ❸❷④
277 Sandycombe Rd 8948 7019 1–3A
*"The best falafels" are a highlight of the "very fresh" and "carefully
cooked" dishes on offer at this "well-kept, quiet and pleasant"
Lebanese local, in Kew.* / www.palmyrarestaurant.co.uk; 10.30 pm; no Amex.

The Pantechnicon SW1 £53 ❸❸❷
10 Motcomb St 7730 6074 5–1D
*"What a smart pub!" – this "comfy" and "convivial" Belgravia boozer
could easily double as a gentleman's club; it may be "a little
overpriced", but the food is "consistently good".*
/ www.thepantechnicon.com; 10 pm downstairs/9.30 pm upstairs.

Pantry SW18 £18 ❸❸❸
342 Old York Rd 8871 0713 10–2B
*"Much-loved and frequented", this Wandsworth café is ideal "for a
quick salad or sandwich".* / www.thepantrylondon.com; L only; no Amex.

Paolina Café WC1 £24 ❸④⑤
181 Kings Cross Rd 7278 8176 8–3D
*In King's Cross, a "shabby", "order-by-numbers" Thai café where
you're unlikely to spot the man from Michelin – "for those brave
enough to step in, however, it's a real find".* / 10 pm; closed Sat L & Sun;
no credit cards.

Pappa Ciccia £34 ❸❸④
105-107 Munster Rd, SW6 7384 1884 10–1B
41 Fulham High St, SW6 7736 0900 10–1B
*These "cheap 'n' cheerful" pizzerias have quite a local following;
the Fulham High Street branch is perhaps the better of the two
(and Putney is no more).* / www.pappaciccia.com; 11 pm, Sat & Sun
11.30 pm; SW6 no credit cards.

Paradise by Way of Kensal Green W10 £38 ❷❷⓿
19 Kilburn Ln 8969 0098 1–2B
*"There's always a fun time to be had", at this "lovely" Kensal Green
stalwart – a "sprawling" places with many rooms, terraces and
a garden; the cooking's "almost too good to be called pub food" –
"go early to avoid the scrum" (especially at weekends).*
/ www.theparadise.co.uk; 10.30 pm, Sun 9 pm; no Amex.

El Parador NW1 £34 ❷⓿❸
245 Eversholt St 7387 2789 8–3C
*"A real find"; this "lovely little tapas bar", near Mornington Crescent,
combines "shockingly good" food (including "a fantastic selection for
veggies"), with an "interesting wine list"; there's even a "wonderful
garden" too.* / www.elparadorlondon.com; 11 pm, Fri-Sat 11.30 pm,
Sun 9.30 pm; closed Sat L & Sun L; no Amex.

**Paramount
Centre Point WC1** £66 ④④⓿
101-103 New Oxford St 7420 2900 4–1A
*"You're definitely paying for the view" ("stunning"), when you visit the
32nd floor of Centre Point; the food is "distinctly average" and service
"random"… "but you won't notice, as you'll be staring out of the
window".* / www.paramount.uk.net; 10.30 pm; set weekday L £42 (FP).

The Parlour Bar E14 £40 ⑤⑤⑤
Park Pavillion, 40 Canada Square Pk 0845 468 0100 11–1C
*"Standards have dropped", at this "once-impressive" yearling, in a
Canary Wharf pavilion – service is "poor", and "the food gets more
mediocre with every visit". / www.theparlourbar.co.uk; 10 pm, Sun 6 pm.*

Pasha SW7 £50 ⑤④❷
1 Gloucester Rd 7589 7969 5–1B
*"Lovely, exotic decor" has long been the highlight at this low-profile
South Kensington Moroccan – just as well, as service is "not that
observant", and "some of the food looks like school dinners".
/ www.pasha-restaurant.co.uk; 10.45 pm, Sat & Sun 11.45 pm.*

Patara £47 ❷❸❸
15 Greek St, W1 7437 1071 4–2A
3-7 Maddox St, W1 7499 6008 3–2C
181 Fulham Rd, SW3 7351 5692 5–2C
9 Beauchamp Pl, SW3 7581 8820 5–1C
*"My Thai government pals take me here, so they must be authentic!"
– these "smart" and "bustling" Asian havens make a very "reliable"
option, thanks to their "polite" service and "wonderfully flavoursome"
cooking. / www.pataralondon.com; 10.30 pm.*

Paternoster Chop House EC4 £53 ⑤⑤④
Warwick Ct, Paternoster Sq 7029 9400 9–2B
*A D&D group operation, by St Paul's, whose "macho" meat-driven
approach "suits City business"; it has "perfect" al fresco tables too,
but the interior is "noisy", service "incredibly amateurish", the food
"very ordinary" and prices "ridiculous"! / www.danddlondon.com;
10.30 pm; closed Sat & Sun D.*

Patio W12 £30 ❸❷❶
5 Goldhawk Rd 8743 5194 7–1C
*"A chat with the owner is a 'must'", when visiting this very
"welcoming" Polish restaurant, right on Shepherd's Bush; its "solid,
honest, homely food", and range of vodkas – all at bargain prices –
help make it a great budget party venue. / www.patiolondon.com;
11.30 pm; closed Sat L & Sun L.*

Pâtisserie Valerie £28 ⑤⑤④
Branches throughout London
*"It looks the same, but oh dear it's lost its way!"; as it goes national,
this expanding pâtisserie chain (whose original Soho branch allegedly
introduced '30s-Britain to the croissant) still does "reliable" breakfasts
and "yummy" cakes, but in other respects is now "very ordinary".
/ www.patisserie-valerie.co.uk; 5 pm-8 pm; Old Compton St 7.30 pm, Wed-Sat
10.30 pm; Hans Cr 11.30 pm; no booking except Old Compton St Sun-Thu.*

Patogh W1 £14 ❷❸④
8 Crawford Pl 7262 4015 6–1D
*It looks a little "shabby" (like a "hole in the wall") but this
Marylebone Iranian really is "a joy" – its "fresh-grilled meats" and its
"home-made flat breads" all come "for an absolute pittance"; BYO.
/ 11 pm; no credit cards.*

Patterson's W1 £71 ❸❸④
4 Mill St 7499 1308 3–2C
*A "low-key family-run eatery" like this is a rarity in Mayfair, and many
fans seek out its "hidden-away" location (near Savile Row),
not least as a venue for business; the food has drifted a bit in recent
times, but is still often "superb". / www.pattersonsrestaurant.co.uk; 11 pm;
closed Sat L & Sun.*

Paul £32 ❸④❸
115 Marylebone High St, W1   7224 5615   2–1A
29-30 Bedford St, WC2   7836 3304   4–3C
*"Fabulous sandwiches" (using "proper French bread"), "lovely"
pastries, and "stand-out" macaroons make it worth braving the oft-
"appalling" service of these café-outposts of France's biggest high
street bakery; "the nicest London branch is the Bedford St WC2
original". / www.paul-uk.com; 7 pm-8.30 pm; no booking.*

Pearl WC1 £85 ④④❸
252 High Holborn   7829 7000   2–1D
*This is "a jewel of a restaurant", say fans of this "impressive" ("rather
cavernous") and "sumptuously furnished" Holborn dining room;
but while Jun Tanaka's cuisine is "witty" and "adventurous",
"massive" bills depress reporter satisfaction to only a middling level
overall. / www.pearl-restaurant.com; 10 pm; closed Sat L & Sun; set weekday L
£46 (FP).*

Pearl Liang W2 £39 ❶❷❷
8 Sheldon Sq   7289 7000   6–1C
*"A great find… if you can find it!"; this "upmarket" Chinese
basement, hidden-away "in the Paddington Basin complex",
is "a revelation" that's "worth the trek" – the cuisine, in particular
the "wonderful" dim sum, is "simply exceptional".
/ www.pearlliang.co.uk; 11 pm.*

The Peasant EC1 £45 ④❸❸
240 St John St   7336 7726   8–3D
*All the more worth knowing about in the "no-man's-land" north
of Smithfield, a fine Victorian pub, which offers "decent" –
and sometimes "adventurous" – cooking; "the upstairs dining room
is preferable to the draughty downstairs bar". / www.thepeasant.co.uk;
10.45 pm, Sun 9.30 pm.*

Pellicano SW3 £58 ❸❸④
19-21 Elystan St   7589 3718   5–2C
*This backstreet Italian is, say fans, "the best local in Chelsea" –
"the sort of place where you eat two or three times a week";
even they can find its ambience a bit "bland", though, and critics say
this is "surely the establishment for which the term 'curate's egg' was
invented". / www.pellicanorestaurant.co.uk; 11 pm, Sun 9.30 pm;
set weekday L £37 (FP).*

E Pellicci E2 £14 ❸❷❶
332 Bethnal Green Rd   7739 4873   12–1D
*"The perfect East End Italian greasy spoon", this Art Deco gem
(the interior is listed) is "well worth a trip across town", especially for
breakfast; staff "treat you like family" and, crowd-wise, "this is where
old and new East End meet". / 4.15 pm; L only, closed Sun; no credit cards.*

**Peninsular
Holiday Inn Express SE10** £34 ❷④④
85 Bugsbys Way   8858 2028   1–3D
*"Terrific-value dim sum" makes it worth seeking out this crushed-in
Greenwich spot – something of "a find", at the foot of a Holiday Inn
(even if the premises are as atmospheric as that description
suggests). / www.mychinesefood.co.uk/; 11.30 pm, Sun 11 pm.*

The Pepper Tree SW4 £25 ❸❸❸
19 Clapham Common S'side 7622 1758 10–2D
An "excellent", cheap 'n' cheerful Thai canteen, by Clapham South, that "does exactly what it says on the tin" – "they get you in, the food takes literally seconds to come, and it always tastes great". / www.thepeppertree.co.uk; 11 pm, Sun & Mon 10.30 pm; no Amex; no booking at D.

Pescatori £50 ❸❷④
11 Dover St, W1 7493 2652 3–3C
55-57 Charlotte St, W1 7580 3289 2–1C
To critics, these West End Italians are "dull" and "too commercialised"; to their friends, though, they're an "institution", offering "reliable" fish dishes, and "smart, helpful and attentive" service. / www.pescatori.co.uk; 11 pm; closed Sat L & Sun.

Petek N4 £30 ❷❷❷
94-96 Stroud Green Rd 7619 3933 8–1D
"Miles better than most Turkish restaurants in London", this "family-friendly" Finsbury Park spot has been firing impressively on all cylinders since its expansion, and it's still "always busy". / www.petekrestaurant.co.uk; 11 pm.

Petersham Hotel TW10 £61 ❸❷❷
Nightingale Ln 8940 7471 1–4A
This "classy old-school dining room" has a "beautiful location overlooking the Thames", and is especially known as a "scenic Sunday lunch destination"; the occasional off-day, however, is not unknown. / www.petershamhotel.co.uk; Mon-Sat 9.30 pm, Sun 8.30 pm.

Petersham Nurseries TW10 £56 ❷④❶
Church Ln, Off Petersham Rd 8605 3627 1–4A
A "rustic-chic" greenhouse provides the "beautiful" setting for Skye Gyngell's "unique" café, where the "simple" and "seasonal" cooking can be "unbelievably wonderful"; the "mountainous" prices seem increasingly "silly" though – "it is, at the end of the day, in a garden centre"! / www.petershamnurseries.com; L only, closed Mon.

La Petite Auberge N1 £35 ④❸❷
283 Upper St 7359 1046 8–2D
"It feels like rural France", at this "cosy" joint, near Islington's Almeida Theatre – service is "very friendly" and the food, if rather "retro", is "reasonably priced". / www.petiteauberge.co.uk; 11 pm, Fri & Sat 11.30 pm, Sun 10.30 pm; set weekday L £20 (FP).

La Petite Maison W1 £77 ❷❷❷
54 Brook's Mews 7495 4774 3–2B
"Go through the heavy velvet curtain, and you're in the South of France", at this glamorous Mayfair "oasis", where the "Provençal small plates" are designed for sharing; OK, "prices are nuts", but "everything on the menu is fresh and light, and always amazing". / www.lpmlondon.co.uk; 10.30 pm, Sun 9 pm.

Pétrus SW1 £85 ④❷❸
1 Kinnerton St 7592 1609 5–1D
"It's time to stop Gordon-bashing", say fans of his luxurious Belgravian two-year-old, who see much to praise in the "phenomenal" wine and "impeccable" service, and the "bargain set lunch" too; sceptics say the cuisine is "competent" enough, but they find it "without spirit" – "like in an upmarket international hotel chain". / www.gordonramsay.com/petrus; 10 pm; closed Sun; no trainers; set always available £56 (FP).

Pham Sushi EC1   **£32**   **❶**④④
159 Whitecross St   7251 6336   12–2A
It looks "lacklustre" – "a bare and charmless room" – but this Japanese café, near the Barbican, "goes from strength to strength", offering "some of the best sushi in town", and at "affordable" prices too. / www.phamsushi.co.uk; 10 pm; closed Sat L & Sun.

The Phene SW3   **£43**   ④④**❷**
9 Phene St   7352 9898   5–3C
This leafily-located pub has, post-refurb, taken on "an eclectic and relaxed look", and makes an attractive hang-out for the Chelsea crowd; the food's OK, but – plus ça change – the star of the show is the "fantastic garden" (given a St Tropez-style make-over in recent times). / www.thephene.com; 10 pm.

Pho   **£33**   **❷❸❸**
163-165 Wardour St, W1   7434 3938   3–1D **NEW**
3 Great Titchfield St, W1   7436 0111   3–1C
Westfield, Ariel Way, W12   07824 662320   7–1C
86 St John St, EC1   7253 7624   9–1A
"Big bowls" of "cheap", "simple" and "vibrant" Vietnamese dishes – particularly pho ('feu') to slurp – is making a major hit of these "cramped" and "authentic" cafés, which (unusually for an expanding chain) "just get better year-on-year". / www.phocafe.co.uk; EC1 10 pm, Fri & Sat 10.30 pm; W1 10.30 pm; W12 9 pm, Sat 7 pm, Sun 6 pm; EC1 closed Sat L & Sun; W1 closed Sun; no Amex; no booking.

The Phoenix SW3   **£42**   ④⑤**❸**
23 Smith St   7730 9182   5–2D
A "buzzy" Chelsea gastropub, with an atmospheric dining room, and a handy location, just off the King's Road; "no matter how empty or full the place is", however, "the service lets it down"! / www.geronimo-inns.co.uk; 10 pm.

Phoenix Palace NW1   **£44**   **❷❸❸**
5-9 Glentworth St   7486 3515   2–1A
"Close to an authentic Hong Kong experience"... "but you can book!" – this "just-about-the-right-side-of-gaudy" Baker Street "institution" serves "wonderful, un-Anglicised cooking, with plenty of unusual dishes", plus some of "the finest dim sum in the UK"; "it's always full of Asian families". / www.phoenixpalace.co.uk; 11.15 pm, Sun 10.30 pm.

Piccolino   **£44**   ④④④
21 Heddon St, W1   7287 4029   3–2C
38 High St, SW19   8946 8019   10–2B
11 Exchange Sq, EC2   7375 2568   12–2B
The food may be "nothing out-of-the-ordinary", but this "buzzing" Italian chain has its uses – the Heddon Street branch, for example, is in a "peaceful pedestrianised oasis", off Regent St, with lovely al fresco tables. / www.piccolinorestaurants.co.uk; 11 pm, Sun 10 pm; EC2 closed Sat & Sun.

PIED À TERRE W1   **£96**   **❶❷❷**
34 Charlotte St   7636 1178   2–1C
The former chef has recently departed, but – fingers crossed – we've kept the survey rating of David Moore's "inspiring" Fitzrovia townhouse – a "class act" long known for its "professional" style, "thought-provoking" cuisine, and "incredible" wine; a downside? – the interior can seem "cramped and oddly configured". / www.pied-a-terre.co.uk; 10.45 pm; closed Sat L & Sun; no Maestro; booking: max 7; set weekday L £46 (FP), set pre-theatre £57 (FP).

The Pig's Ear SW3 £48 ❸❸❶
35 Old Church St 7352 2908 5–3C
"Quirky" and "wonderfully atmospheric", the upstairs dining room is the highlight at this "beautiful" Art Nouveau-themed pub, tucked away off the King's Road – a "friendly" spot, with "competent" cooking. / www.thepigsear.info; 10 pm; closed Sun D.

Pinchito EC1 £31 ❹❸❶
32 Featherstone St 7490 0121 12–1A
"For a good night out", near Old Street, this "laid-back and bustling" haunt – with its "decadent cocktails" – may be worth checking out; decent tapas play a supporting role. / www.pinchito.co.uk; 11 pm; closed Sat L & Sun.

ping pong £32 ❹❹❸
10 Paddington St, W1 7009 9600 2–1A
29a James St, W1 7034 3100 3–1A
45 Gt Marlborough St, W1 7851 6969 3–2C
48 Eastcastle St, W1 7079 0550 3–1C
48 Newman St, W1 7291 3080 3–1C
74-76 Westbourne Grove, W2 7313 9832 6–1B
83-84 Hampstead High St, NW3 7433 0930 8–2A
Southbank Centre, SE1 7960 4160 2–3D
3-6 Steward St, E1 7422 7650 9–2D
St Katharine Docks, E1 7680 7850 9–3D
3 Appold St, EC2 7422 0780 12–2B
Bow Bells Hs, 1 Bread St, EC4 7651 0880 9–2B
For a "fun" meal that's "quick and relatively cheap", these "slick" dim sum (and cocktail) specialists have many fans; critics, though, feel the menu "reads better than it tastes" – "what once seemed an exciting new experience now just feels rather like a bland old chain". / www.pingpongdimsum.com; 10 pm-11.30 pm; EC2 & EC4 closed Sat & Sun; booking: min 8.

El Pirata W1 £36 ❹❷❶
5-6 Down St 7491 3810 3–4B
"Fantastic fun!"; especially "worth knowing about in a pricey area", this "packed and buzzing" Mayfair haunt is "so friendly", and it offers many "tasty tapas" too. / www.elpirata.co.uk; 11.30 pm; closed Sat L & Sun; set weekday L £21 (FP).

El Pirata de Tapas W2 £30 ❸❷❷
115 Westbourne Grove 7727 5000 6–1B
"For an edgy, adventurous approach to tapas", some reporters really rate this "narrow" and "very buzzy" Bayswater two-year-old; a few repeat-visitors, though, feel the food's "lost a bit of its early-days pizzazz". / www.elpiratadetapas.co.uk; 11 pm.

Pissarro W4 £47 ❹❹❸
Corney Reach Way 8994 3111 10–1A
Can't help feeling this Thames-side fixture, with an attractive conservatory, trades on its "wonderful setting" – a quiet stretch of towpath near Chiswick House; it does have its fans, but for sceptics its "very unremarkable", and "expensive" too. / www.pissarro.co.uk; 10 pm.

Pizarro SE1 NEW
194 Bermondsey St awaiting tel 9–4D
Ex-Brindisa chef José Pizarro has barely got José open, and he's already planning this new, more restaurant-like operation, to launch in late-2011 on the site recently vacated by the Bermondsey Kitchen (RIP).

Pizza East E1 £46 ③④❶
56 Shoreditch High St 7729 1888 12–1B

"An achingly hip hub for Shoreditch digerati" – Nick Jones's *"industrial-chic"* warehouse-conversion serves *"thick-looking but crisp"* pizza with an array of *"interesting toppings"*; *"non-beautiful people may feel intimidated"*, however, by staff who are *"too trendy to serve"*. / www.pizzaeast.com; Sun-Wed 11 pm, Thu midnight, Fri & Sat 1 am.

Pizza East Portobello W10 NEW £39
310 Portobello Rd 8969 4500 6–1A

Shoreditch-chic comes to North Kensington, at this new offshoot – on the former site of the Fat Badger, RIP – of Nick Jones's too-cool-for-school East End pizzeria; it opened too late to figure in the survey, but press reports suggest it's very like the original, if a touch less 'urban'. / www.pizzaeastportobello.com.

Pizza Metro SW11 £36 ③③❷
64 Battersea Rise 7228 3812 10–2C

"Save on a trip to Naples!" – these *"chaotic"* (and *"bambino-friendly"*) Italians are *"always very busy and relaxed"*, and they serve the *"yummiest"* pizza (on metre-long trays) too; the new Notting Hill branch is *"not as raucous"* as the Battersea original. / www.pizzametropizza.co.uk; 11 pm; closed weekday L; no Amex.

(Ciro's) Pizza Pomodoro SW3 £49 ④④❷
51 Beauchamp Pl 7589 1278 5–1C

"Fun and lively", this late-night Knightsbridge-cellar fixture is really *"all about the entertainment"* – though it's *"cheap 'n' cheerful"*, by local standards, the pizza *"could use an upgrade"*. / www.pomodoro.co.uk; 1 am; D only.

PizzaExpress £36 ④④❸
Branches throughout London

"Excellent new additions to the menu" have helped refresh the offering of these gold-standard pizzerias – the survey's most commented-upon chain; in other respects, however *"it's predictable in the best kind of way"*, including as *"a godsend with kids"*. / www.pizzaexpress.co.uk; 11.30 pm-midnight; most City branches closed all or part of weekend; no booking at most branches.

Pizzeria Malletti £7 ❷❸❸
26 Noel St, W1 7439 4096 3–1D
174-176 Clerkenwell Rd, EC1 7713 8665 2–1D

"Creative" pizzas draw an ardent fan club to these Soho (take-away only) and Clerkenwell Italians; *"delicious risotto"* too. / 4.30 pm; W1 cash only.

Pizzeria Oregano N1 £38 ❸❷❸
19 St Albans Pl 7288 1123 8–3D

Islington's best basic Italian – this "bustling" little café, down an alleyway, is praised for its "huge" pizzas (with "fantastic thin crusts") and its "lovely home-made pasta"; "energetic staff give quick service, and a warm welcome to kids too". / 11 pm, Fri 11.30 pm, Sun 10.30 pm; closed weekday L.

Pizzeria Pappagone N4 £32 ❸❷❸
131 Stroud Green Rd 7263 2114 8–1D

"The owner makes you feel welcome, and there's a strong family vibe", at this *"really buzzing"* Italian, near Crouch End, which serves *"huge portions of honest food"* (in particular, *"proper pizza"*). / www.pizzeriapappagone.co.uk; midnight.

PJ's Bar and Grill SW3 £50 ④④❸
52 Fulham Rd 7581 0025 5–2C
*"Fun, reliable and boisterous", this US-themed South Kensington
bar/diner remains a top Euro/Sloane brunch spot; in general, though,
it can rather seem to be "relying on former glories" nowadays.
/ www.pjsbarandgrill.co.uk; 10.30 pm, Sun 10 pm.*

Plane Food TW6 £49 ④❸④
Heathrow Airport, Terminal 5 8897 4545 1–3A
*Views divide on Gordon Ramsay's airside diner; to critics it "exploits
its captive audience" with "very average" food at "inflated" prices –
for fans it's "a haven of sanity from the mayhem", and serves
"unbeatable breakfasts" (with a "perfect eggs Benedict" singled out
for praise). / www.gordonramsay.com; 9.30 pm.*

Plateau E14 £63 ⑤④④
Canada Pl 7715 7100 11–1C
*With its "huge windows overlooking Canada Square", this D&D
group operation is still – say fans – "probably Canary Wharf's
best restaurant"; critics of its "investment banker prices" and its "bog-
standard" cooking, though, say it "needs to compete better with new
arrivals hereabouts!" / www.plateaurestaurant.co.uk; 10 pm; closed
Sat L & Sun.*

Plum Valley W1 £34 ❸❷❸
20 Gerrard St 7494 4366 4–3A
*"Delicious dim sum all day" is a highlight of this dimly-lit, "cool and
contemporary" Chinatown scene; its more "nouvelle" culinary
aspirations, however, don't always come off. / 11.30 pm.*

Pod £13 ❸④④
124 High Holborn, WC1 3174 0541 2–1D
Tooley St, SE1 3174 0374 9–4D **NEW**
10 St Martin's Le Grand, EC1 3174 0399 9–2B
162-163 London Wall, EC2 7256 5506 9–2C
25 Exchange Sq, EC2 3174 0290 12–2B
Devonshire Sq, EC2 3174 0108 9–2D
5 Lloyds Ave, EC3 3174 0038 9–3D
1 Printer St, EC4 3174 0228 9–2A
75 King William St, EC4 7283 7460 9–3C **NEW**
*For "fresh and zingy" salads and snacks "on the go", this "healthy"
chain still has many fans; it's "not the cheapest", though, and its
ratings dipped a bit this year. / www.podfood.co.uk; 3 pm-4 pm; closed
Sat & Sun; no Amex.*

Poissonnerie de l'Avenue SW3 £67 ❸❸④
82 Sloane Ave 7589 2457 5–2C
*A notably "senior" clientele are drawn to this "elegant" –
but "crowded" and "expensive" – Chelsea "old-timer"; the lure? –
"simple but very palatable fresh fish and seafood".
/ www.poissonneriedelavenue.co.uk; 11.30 pm, Sun 11 pm.*

(Ognisko Polskie)
The Polish Club SW7 £49 ⑤④❸
55 Prince's Gate, Exhibition Rd 7589 4635 5–1C
*"A great dining space" – the time-warped interior of a grandly-housed
South Kensington émigrés' club – is the particular attraction of this
quirky venture; its basic Polish fodder plays a supporting role,
but most reporters have "no complaints". / www.ognisko.com; 11 pm;
no trainers; set weekday L £29 (FP).*

FSA

Pollen Street Social W1 NEW £64 002
8-10 Pollen St 7290 7600 3–2C
*Jason Atherton ('Mr Maze') was always one of the sharpest knives
in the Ramsay drawer, so it's no surprise that his first solo venture –
a "bright and hard-surfaced" Mayfair venue – is an instant smash hit:
dishes – not least the "amazing puds" – offer "excellent explorations
of flavour combinations". / www.pollenstreetsocial.com; 10.45 pm;
closed Sun.*

Polpetto
The French House W1 £35 220
49 Dean St 7734 1969 4–3A
*This "bijou" room, over a "characterful" Soho pub, has a certain
"je ne said quoi" for romantics; there's no booking at dinner (giving
ample scope for a glass of Ricard downstairs) but the Venetian tapas
– "better than at its parent, Polpo" – are "worth the wait".
/ www.polpetto.co.uk; 11 pm; closed Sun; book only at L.*

Polpo W1 £25 320
41 Beak St 7734 4479 3–2D
*"Always rammed" with an "interesting crowd", Russell Norman's
"very-NYC-Meatpacking-District" Soho haunt is just the job if you
want to feel "at the heart of the action"; the tapas-y food (notionally
Venetian) is "fine" too… "but the atmosphere's the thing".
/ www.polpo.co.uk; 11 pm, Sun 4 pm; closed Sun D; no bookings for D.*

Le Pont de la Tour SE1 £64 432
36d Shad Thames 7403 8403 9–4D
*Fans "don't understand the perennially mixed reviews" this guide
gives to this "slick", "feel-good" D&D group Thames-sider, whose
"unbeatable views" of Tower Bridge help make it a 'natural' for
business or romance; there are still quite a few critics, though,
who find it "arrogant", and say it charges "high prices" for food that's
"15 years out of date!" / www.lepontdelatour.co.uk; 11 pm, Sun 10 pm;
no trainers.*

Popeseye £46 023
108 Blythe Rd, W14 7610 4578 7–1C
277 Upper Richmond Rd, SW15 8788 7733 10–2A
*"If you want a great steak, this is the place!" – this "quirky" duo
of west London bistros offer a "simple, meat-based formula that hits
the spot" (with "a fantastic wine list as a bonus"); the sole real
criticism? – "the decor needs improving". / www.popeseye.com;
10.30 pm; D only, closed Sun; no credit cards.*

La Porchetta Pizzeria £32 333
33 Boswell St, WC1 7242 2434 2–1D
141-142 Upper St, N1 7288 2488 8–2D
147 Stroud Green Rd, N4 7281 2892 8–1D
74-77 Chalk Farm Rd, NW1 7267 6822 8–2B
84-86 Rosebery Ave, EC1 7837 6060 9–1A
*Thanks to their "HUGE portions" of "fresh pizza" and other "home-
style dishes" – all "relatively cheap" – these "noisy" north London
Italians are always "very busy"; they're "very welcoming to kids" too.
/ www.laporchetta.net; last orders varies by branch; WC1 closed Sat L & Sun;
N1 closed Mon-Thu L; N4 closed weekday L; no Amex.*

Portal EC1 £61 222
88 St John St 7253 6950 9–1B
*"Portuguese food takes on a new dimension", at Antonio Correia's
"classy" Clerkenwell bar/restaurant, which has a "lovely"
conservatory, with an excellent terrace; there's a "phenomenal wine
list" too. / www.portalrestaurant.com; 10.15 pm; closed Sat L & Sun.*

La Porte des Indes W1 £63 ❸④❷
32 Bryanston St 7224 0055 2–2A
*"Imaginatively decorated" – "think Rainforest Café for adults!" –
this unexpectedly huge, subterranean joint, near Marble Arch, offers
a "plush and exotic" environment in which to enjoy some "light"
(and somewhat "Frenchified") Indian cuisine.* / www.laportedesindes.com;
11.30 pm, Sun 10.30 pm.

Porters English Restaurant WC2 £36 ④❸❸
17 Henrietta St 7836 6466 4–3C
*"Still perhaps mainly for tourists", but Lord Bradford's traditional-
English-styled Covent Garden eatery nonetheless provides hearty pies,
puds and other English fare at affordable prices; excellent-value set
menu.* / www.porters.uk.com; 11.30 pm, Sun 10.30 pm; no Amex.

Il Portico W8 £46 ❸❶❷
277 Kensington High St 7602 6262 7–1D
*It may "really hark back to the Italians of the '60s and '70s",
but that's just how people like this "basic" – but "warm" and
"welcoming" – trattoria, next to the Kensington Odeon.*
/ www.ilportico.co.uk; 11 pm; closed Sun.

Portobello Ristorante W11 £40 ❸④④
7 Ladbroke Rd 7221 1373 6–2B
*"A bit chaotic" – but "too busy to be all that atmospheric!" –
this "wildly popular" Notting Hill Italian offers some good "regional"
cooking, including "proper pizza" (sold by the metre); "the terrace
is lovely in summer".* / www.portobellolondon.co.uk; 11 pm, Sun 10.15 pm;
set dinner £21 (FP).

The Portrait
National Portrait Gallery WC2 £48 ④❷❶
St Martin's Pl 7312 2490 4–4B
*"Flick between your lover's eyes and the views of the London skyline",
as you enjoy your meal at this top-floor venue, which enjoys
a "stunning" West End panorama; the food – "nothing really
to grumble about" – plays rather a supporting role.* / www.searcys.co.uk;
Thu-Fri 8.30 pm; Sat-Wed closed D.

La Poule au Pot SW1 £56 ❸❸❶
231 Ebury St 7730 7763 5–2D
*"Just the kind of place where a girl hopes to be proposed to!" –
this "unashamedly old-fashioned" Pimlico den is a "higgledy piggledy"
sprawl, with "dark, candlelit corners" and "colourful", if somewhat
"arrogant", staff, who offer "rustic" Gallic scoff in "large portions".*
/ 11 pm, Sun 10 pm.

Pret A Manger £13 ❸❷④
Branches throughout London
*"Nowhere else quite matches up", say fans of this "steadfast"
London-based "pit stop" chain, whose empire now spans three
continents; the coffee, soup, sarnies and so on are all "utterly
reliable", but the secret weapon is the same as ever –
the "indefatigable cheeriness" of the staff.* / www.pret.com; generally
4 pm-6 pm; closed Sun (except some West End branches); City branches
closed Sat & Sun; no Amex; no booking.

Prince Albert NW1 £36 ❸❸❸
163 Royal College St 7485 0270 8–3C
*"Whether in the relaxed pub, or the stylish restaurant above", this –
slightly "erratic" – Camden Town boozer is generally "good value".*
/ www.princealbertcamden.com; 11 pm, Sun 10.30 pm; no Amex.

The Prince Albert SW11 £40 ❹❸❷
85 Albert Bridge Rd 7228 0923 5–4C
*"So popular you usually need to book", this "laid-back" boozer
(with good al fresco seating) goes down very well with those who live
round Battersea Park; the "unadventurous pub grub", however,
"doesn't always live up to expectations".*
/ www.theprincealbertbattersea.co.uk; 10 pm, Sun 9 pm.

The Prince Of Wales SW15 £42 ❸❹❸
138 Upper Richmond Rd 8788 1552 10–2B
"Super pub food, great beers, and the best chips" – all factors in the
success of this "upmarket gastropub" near East Putney station;
service, however, "can fluctuate". / www.princeofwalesputney.co.uk; 10 pm.

Princess Garden W1 £59 ❷❷❸
8-10 North Audley St 7493 3223 3–2A
*"Swankily-located", this "well-spaced" and "brightly-lit" Mayfair
Chinese may be, but it is nonetheless applauded for its "friendly"
approach (including to families) and for dim sum that – remarkably –
offers "great value for money"; more substantial fare is "pricey but
worth it".* / www.princessgardenofmayfair.com; 11.45 pm, Sun 10.45 pm.

Princess of Shoreditch EC2 £45 ❷❸❸
76 Paul St 7729 9270 12–1B
*"A favourite gastropub of a very high standard", in Shoreditch; there's
a lively bar or – up the spiral staircase – a quieter mezzanine.*
/ www.theprincessofshoreditch.com; 11 pm, Sun 10.30 pm.

Princess Victoria W12 £46 ❷❷❷
217 Uxbridge Rd 8749 5886 7–1B
*"An incredible find in a shabby bit of Shepherd's Bush";
this "sympathetically restored" gin palace is a "fine local stalwart"
nowadays, offering "surprisingly excellent" food, a notably "classy"
wine list, "enthusiastic" service and "a nice vibe" too.*
/ www.princessvictoria.co.uk; 10.30 pm, Sun 9.30 pm; no Amex; set weekday L
£27 (FP).

Princi W1 £25 ❸❹❷
135 Wardour St 7478 8888 3–2D
*"A younger crowd, who think the place über-cool" hangs out "at all
hours", at this "cosmopolitan" Soho café, where "brilliant" Italian
pastries (and breads) start the day, and "mouthwatering" savouries
and cakes become available later on; the downside? – expect
to stand.* / www.princi.co.uk; midnight, Sun 10 pm; no booking.

Prism EC3 £64 ❹❹❹
147 Leadenhall St 7256 3875 9–2D
"Convenience for business" – and a "smart" interior too –
must explain the continuing existence of this Harvey Nics-owned
restaurant in a former City banking hall; it's certainly not the prices
("not cheap") or the cuisine ("hit-and-miss"). / www.harveynichols.com;
10 pm; closed Sat & Sun.

Prix Fixe W1 £29 ❹❸❸
39 Dean St 7734 5976 4–2A
*The brasserie fare is decent enough, but it is the price which is – in a
good way – "the stand-out feature", at this "noisy" Soho bistro.*
/ www.prixfixe.net; Wed-Sat 11.30 pm, Sun-Tue 11 pm.

The Providores W1 £61 ❸④④
109 Marylebone High St   7935 6175   2–1A
Peter Gordon's fusion menu is "so exciting", and it's "perfectly matched" with "punchy" wines too, say fans of the "rammed" space over the Tapa Room; critics, citing "hefty" bills and "seriously arrogant" service, are less convinced. / www.theprovidores.co.uk; 10.30 pm.

**(Tapa Room)
The Providores W1** £48 ❷④④
109 Marylebone High St   7935 6175   2–1A
"Peter Gordon's fusion-food makes for a terrific brunch" – the top time to visit his "very cramped" but "buzzy" bar/diner, in Marylebone; more serious dining involves "some outlandish food combos" – results can be "bizarre", but more often they are "spectacular". / www.theprovidores.co.uk; 10.30 pm, Sun 10 pm.

The Punch Tavern EC4 £29 ❸④❸
99 Fleet St   7353 6658   9–2A
"A great place for tourists and office-workers", this Victorian tavern, near Ludgate Circus, is "worth a visit for the architecture alone"; by pub standards, the food is generally "better than average" too. / www.punchtavern.com; 10 pm, Sun 7 pm; closed Sat D.

Putney Station SW15 £35 ④④❸
94-98 Upper Richmond Rd   8780 0242   10–2B
One of John Brinkley's lesser-known ventures, this Putney stand-by is nonetheless true to his DNA – its comfort fare is "ordinary", but fans "love it" for its "extensive and reasonably-priced wine list". / www.brinkleys.com; midnight, Sun 4 pm; closed Sun D.

**Quadrato
Four Seasons Hotel E14** £68 ④④⑤
Westferry Circus   7510 1857   11–1B
A grand Canary Wharf hotel where "the brunch buffet is just 'wow'", and the terrace can be "lovely" too; the interior is "very boring and corporate", though – a fact you may dwell on as the sometimes "very slow" service brings "pricey" Italian dishes that are "decent but not outstanding". / www.fourseasons.com; 10.30 pm.

Quaglino's SW1 £69 ⑤⑤⑤
16 Bury St   7930 6767   3–3D
Owned by the D&D (ex-Conran) group, this cavernous '90s basement, in St James's, offers "boring, boring, boring" brasserie fare at prices that too often seem "a complete rip-off"; it doesn't help that some reporters don't feel so much fed as "processed". / www.quaglinos.co.uk; 10.30 pm, Fri & Sat 11 pm; closed Sun; no trainers; set weekday L £44 (FP).

Quantus W4 NEW £41 ❸❷❸
38 Devonshire Rd   8994 0488   7–2A
Almost opposite La Trompette, this Chiswick newcomer inspires mixed views; to fans, its "warm service", "quirky" decor and "short-but-tempting" menu "scores highly in every way" – doubters, though, sensing local hype, say it "lacks flair". / www.quantus-london.com; 11 pm; closed Sat L.

Queen's Head W6 £36 ④❷❷
13 Brook Grn   7603 3174   7–1C
In summer, this picturesque Brook Green boozer comes into its own, thanks to its "most enormous and secluded garden" ("more like you'd expect in the 'burbs"); it serves a notably varied menu – more exotic choices are best avoided... / www.fullers.co.uk; 10 pm, Sun 9 pm.

Queen's Head & Artichoke NW1 £41 ④④❸
30-32 Albany St 7916 6206 8–4B

The "extensive" tapas menu in the bar is the best bet at this "lively" ("manic") boozer, near Regent's Park, whose "attractive" upstairs room also offers a wide menu; it's generally a sound performer, but this past year saw a few 'disasters' too. / www.theartichoke.net; 10.15 pm.

The Queens Arms SW1 £42 ❸❸❸
11 Warwick Way 7834 3313 2–4B

"A real 'find', in something of a culinary desert" – this Pimlico "bistro/pub" is a "home-from-home" for regulars, who proclaim the attractions of its "super" British dishes, and its "super-friendly" staff too. / www.thequeensarmspimlico.co.uk; 10 pm.

Le Querce £37 ❶❷❷
66-68 Brockley Rise, SE23 8690 3761 1–4D
17 Montpelier Vale, SE3 8852 9226 1–3D NEW

"Simply brilliant" and "adventurous" Sardinian fare inspires rave reviews for this family-run Brockely favourite, where culinary highlights include "delicious" pasta, "perfect pizza", and basil-, beetroot- and garlic-flavoured… er, ice cream; early reports say its new Blackheath sibling is "spot on" too. / SE23 10 pm, Sun 9 pm; SE3 10.30 pm, Sun 8.30 pm; SE23 closed Mon & Tue L; SE3 closed Mon.

Quilon SW1 £56 ❶❶④
41 Buckingham Gate 7821 1899 2–4B

"As far from a standard Indian as a Rolls-Royce is from a scooter", this "poised" Goan/Keralan operation offers "perfectly-spiced" food, and service as "magically unobtrusive" as you'd hope to find at nearby Buck House; such a shame, then, that – even by hotel standards – the decor is deadly "dull". / www.quilon.co.uk; 11 pm, Sun 10.30 pm; closed Sat L.

Quince
The May Fair Hotel W1 NEW £73 ④❸⑤
Stratton St 7915 3892 3–3C

A bizarre, low-ceilinged Mayfair newcomer, whose garish interior's supposedly Ottoman character feels as if it's been done 'by numbers'; there's nothing wrong with ex-Baltic chef (and esteemed cookbook-writer) Silvena Rowe's cuisine, but is it really so much better than you could find in Dalston, for a quarter of the price? / Rated on Editors' visit; www.quincelondon.com; 10 pm.

Quirinale SW1 £60 ❷❶❸
North Ct, 1 Gt Peter St 7222 7080 2–4C

"Hidden-away near the Houses of Parliament", this "airy", "discreet" and "comfortable" (if somewhat "corporate") basement "gem" is well worth seeking out for its "interesting" and "eclectic" cucina all'Italiana; "excellent-value" lunchtime prix-fixe. / www.quirinale.co.uk; 10.30 pm; closed Sat & Sun; set weekday L & pre theatre £36 (FP).

Quo Vadis W1 £58 ❷❷❷
26-29 Dean St 7437 9585 4–2A

"Sam and Eddie Hart run a tight ship", and their "club-like" and "polished" Soho spot put in a "first-class" performance this year; the British comfort-food menu is extremely "competently prepared", if perhaps a little "safe". / www.quovadissoho.co.uk; 10.45 pm; closed Sun; set pre theatre £37 (FP).

Racine SW3   £66   ❸❷❸
239 Brompton Rd   7584 4477   5–2C
"You are transported to Paris", when you visit Henry Harris's "old-fashioned-in-a-really-good-way" Knightsbridge bistro, which is widely acclaimed for its "intelligently-realised" cuisine; "prices are high", though, and drifting ratings tend to confirm that it's "getting a bit complacent". / www.racine-restaurant.com; 10.30 pm, Sun 10 pm; set always available £36 (FP).

Ragam W1   £27   ❶❷⑤
57 Cleveland St   7636 9098   2–1B
"Who cares about the dodgy decor?" – and that's after the recent redecoration! – at this "tiny and cramped" BYO dive, near the Telecom Tower; after more than twenty years, the Keralan dishes still "rock", and are still "tremendous value for money". / www.ragam.co.uk; 10.45 pm, Fri & Sat 11 pm, Sun 10 pm.

Randa W8   £45   ❸❸④
23 Kensington Church St   7937 5363   5–1A
An unlikely Lebanese pub-conversion, near Kensington High Street, offering "fresh" and "authentic" fare; service ebbs and flows, but it's "friendly" enough. / www.maroush.com; midnight.

Randall & Aubin W1   £44   ❸❸❷
16 Brewer St   7287 4447   3–2D
"It's great watching the world go by", sitting perched on a stool at this "fun" spot, "edgily-located" in the sleazy heart of Soho – a "loud" and "very buzzy" place, serving "superb", if "pricey", seafood; expect to queue. / www.randallandaubin.co.uk; 11 pm, Sun 10 pm; no booking.

Rani N3   £26   ❷❸④
7 Long Ln   8349 4386   1–1B
The interior may be "dull", but that does nothing to dim the "evergreen" charm of this "very good veggie Indian", whose excellent-value buffet includes "outstanding stuffed breads", plus "an excellent range of chutneys", "all made in-house". / www.raniuk.com; 10 pm; D only, ex Sun open L & D.

Ranoush   £45   ❷④④
22 Brompton Rd, SW1   7235 6999   5–1D
338 King's Rd, SW3   7352 0044   5–3C
43 Edgware Rd, W2   7723 5929   6–1D
86 Kensington High St, W8   7938 2234   5–1A
"The best shawarma in town" is the special reason to seek out these Lebanese café/take-aways – especially in the early hours, they "tick all the boxes for a quick, cheap, tasty bite". / www.maroush.com; 1 am-3 am.

Ransome's Dock SW11   £50   ④❸④
35 Parkgate Rd   7223 1611   5–4C
This Battersea "old-stager" is an œnophile's dream, and its "brilliantly adventurous" wine list offers "amazing value"; perhaps the menu "could do with a shake-up", though? – the faithful may say the food "never disappoints", but critics find it ever more "lacklustre". / www.ransomesdock.co.uk; 11 pm; closed Sun D.

otts

ing House Cafe

he Ritz Restaurant

Raoul's Café £39 ④⑤④
105-107 Talbot Rd, W11 7229 2400 6–1B
113-115 Hammersmith Grove, W6 8741 3692 7–1C **NEW**
13 Clifton Rd, W9 7289 7313 8–4A

"If you can survive the weekend queues", these "cramped" hang-outs,
in Maida Vale and Notting Hill, are renowned for "a great buzz" and
"the best eggs Benedict" (with eggs imported from Italy!); the new
W6 branch, on the former Chez Kristof (RIP) site, is however,
"awful". / www.raoulsgourmet.com; 10.15 pm, W11 6.15 pm; booking after
5 pm only.

Rasa N16 £26 ❶❷❷
55 Stoke Newington Church St 7249 0344 1–1C

"1,000,000 miles from a high street curry"; this "life-affirming" Stoke
Newington Keralan – the original of the chain – has long featured
amongst London's best Indians; it serves "vibrant" veggie dishes fans
find little short of "divine". / www.rasarestaurants.com; 10.45 pm, Fri & Sat
11.30 pm; closed weekday L.

Rasa £36 ❷❷❸
5 Charlotte St, W1 7637 0222 2–1C
6 Dering St, W1 7629 1346 3–2B
Holiday Inn Hotel, 1 Kings Cross, WC1 7833 9787 8–3D
56 Stoke Newington Church St, N16 7249 1340 1–1C
715 High Rd, N1 8859 1700 1–1D

A "vibrant" taste of Kerala (mostly fish and veggie dishes)
at "brilliant" prices, have won huge acclaim for these spin-offs from
the N16 original; their ratings dipped a fraction this year, however –
hopefully just a blip. / www.rasarestaurants.com; 10.45 pm; variable hours
especially on weekends.

Rasoi SW3 £93 ❸④❸
10 Lincoln St 7225 1881 5–2D

"In a class of its own" – Vineet Bhattia's "surprising" Chelsea
townhouse is, say fans, "London's most interesting Indian", thanks
to his "immensely subtle" cuisine; it can feel "a little quiet", though,
and its ratings are undercut by a few sceptics for whom the
experience "doesn't hit the heights", and is "way overpriced" too.
/ www.rasoirestaurant.co.uk; 10.30 pm; closed Sat L; no trainers; set weekday L
£50 (FP).

The Real Greek £37 ⑤⑤④
56 Paddington St, W1 7486 0466 2–1A
60-62 Long Acre, WC2 7240 2292 4–2D
Westfield, Ariel Way, W12 8743 9168 7–1C
15 Hoxton Market, N1 7739 8212 12–1B
1-2 Riverside Hs, Southwark Br Rd, SE1 7620 0162 9–3B
6 Horner Sq, E1 7375 1364 12–2B

A soulless Greek chain whose ratings remain on Skid Row –
even some fans say the food is "nothing special", and service can
be "laughable"; perhaps the new owners – as from mid-2011 –
can perk things up. / www.therealgreek.com; 10.45 pm; WC2 10.30 pm,
E1 Sun 7 pm; EC1 closed Sun; no Amex; WC2 no booking.

Rebato's SW8 £39 ❷❶❶
169 South Lambeth Rd 7735 6388 10–1D

A "jolly Spanish stalwart", in Stockwell, comprising a "busy" tapas bar
and "idiosyncratic" restaurant; the "lovely owner and really solicitous
staff" are the "top draw", but the cooking is seldom less than
"delicious". / www.rebatos.com; 10.45 pm; closed Sat L & Sun.

Red Fort W1 £63 ❷❸❸
77 Dean St 7437 2525 4–2A
*"Refined" Indian cooking – for fans nothing short of "incredible" –
has long created a formidable reputation for this "high end" Soho
veteran, nowadays decorated in "calm", modern style; it can seem
"a little overpriced", even so. / www.redfort.co.uk; 11.30 pm; closed
Sat L & Sun L.*

The Red Pepper W9 £44 ❷❸④
8 Formosa St 7266 2708 8–4A
*"The most outstanding pizza" has long won raves for this "squeezed"
Maida Vale veteran – it's "too small and too busy", but then it always
has been... / theredpepper.net; Sat 11 pm, Sun 10.30 pm; closed weekday L;
no Amex.*

Redhook EC1 £46 ④④❸
89-90 Turnmill St 7065 6800 9–1A
*Benefitting from a wonderfully "funky" setting by Farringdon tube,
this "out-of-the-way" brasserie offered "OK" standards when
it opened last year; ratings have taken "a huge dive", though – there
are too many reports of "dreadful" food, and service that's "very,
very slow". / www.redhooklondon.com; midnight, Thu-Sat 1 am; closed Sun.*

Refettorio
The Crowne Plaza Hotel EC4 £52 ④④④
19 New Bridge St 7438 8052 9–3A
*A City business-hotel dining room that used to stand out from the
crowd (not least with its once-innovative Italian platters); the world
moves on, though, and the formula can now just seem "rather
ordinary". / www.refettorio.com; 10.30 pm, Fri & Sat 10 pm; closed
Sat L & Sun.*

Refuel
Soho Hotel W1 £55 ❸❸❷
4 Richmond Mews 7559 3007 3–2D
*"Great for a lost afternoon" – a buzzing bar is at the heart of this
"lively yet intimate" rendezvous in the heart of Soho; it's not really
what you could call a foodie destination, but fans insist the cooking
is "fabulous" too. / www.firmdale.com; midnight, Sun 11 pm.*

Le Relais de Venise L'Entrecôte £40 ❷❸❸
120 Marylebone Ln, W1 7486 0878 2–1A
5 Throgmorton St, EC2 7638 6325 9–2C
*"Just about the only choice is how you want it cooked!"; these Parisian
"steak/frites factories" have a "simple" but "brilliantly-executed"
formula, enhanced by a "delicious" secret-sauce (and free seconds);
queues are "inevitable", but they usually "move rapidly".
/ www.relaisdevenise.com; W1 11 pm, Sun 10.30 pm; EC2 10 pm; EC2 closed
Sat & Sun; no booking.*

Le Rendezvous du Café EC1 £49 ❸❷❷
22 Charterhouse Sq 7336 8836 9–1B
*"Splendid plats du jour" and "great steak/frites" typify the "simple"
and "well-cooked" fare on offer at this "very French" offshoot
of Smithfield's Café du Marché; be braced, though, for tables which
are "tiny" and "tightly-packed". / www.cafedumarche.co.uk; 10 pm; closed
Sat L & Sun.*

The Restaurant at St Paul's
St Paul's Cathedral EC4   £37   ③④③
St Paul's Churchyard   7248 2469   9–2B
Compared to the magnificence of the Wren setting, this restaurant-in-the-crypt feels a little "homespun"; for a "touristy venue", though, the British dishes can be "surprisingly good" and "interesting".
/ www.restaurantatstpauls.co.uk; L only; no Amex.

Retsina NW3   £41   ③②③
48-50 Belsize Ln   7431 5855   8–2A
"Tasty" Greek fare ("freshly cooked by Mama") and "very friendly" service earn strong local support for this "lively" and "good-value" taverna, in Belsize Park. / www.retsina-london.com; 11 pm; closed Mon L; no Amex.

Reubens W1   £50   ④⑤⑤
79 Baker St   7486 0035   2–1A
"It wouldn't last a minute in Manhattan!"; only by virtue of its rarity value as "the West End's only kosher option" is this stalwart Marylebone deli/restaurant of any interest – of the few reports it incites, rather too many are of the "worst-meal-ever" variety.
/ www.reubensrestaurant.co.uk; 10 pm; closed Fri D & Sat; no Amex.

Rhodes 24 EC2   £80   ③③③
25 Old Broad St   7877 7703   9–2C
"Spectacular views", such as "to impress any business guest", reward visits to Gary R's 24th-floor City-lunching eyrie (and compensate for the slightly "tired" interior); many reporters "flinch" at the "very high" prices, but the "enjoyable" British cooking generally measures up.
/ www.rhodes24.co.uk; 9 pm; closed Sat & Sun; no shorts; booking essential.

Rhodes W1 Restaurant
Cumberland Hotel W1   £68   ④③⑤
Gt Cumberland Pl   7616 5930   2–2A
"Opulent chandeliers" don't succeed in creating a particularly sparkling atmosphere at Gary R's luxurious – but "atmosphere-free" – dining room, near Marble Arch; reports divide on whether the food is "brilliant" or "underwhelming", but the most striking feature is just how little feedback, of any sort, the place inspires.
/ www.rhodesw1.com; 10.15 pm; closed Mon, Sat L & Sun; no jeans or trainers; set weekday L £41 (FP).

Rib Room
Jumeirah Carlton Tower Hotel SW1   £103
Cadogan Pl   7858 7250   5–1D
This swanky Knightsbridge grill room was closed for a major revamp as this guide went to press; long ago, it was the capital's only steakhouse of any note – can it now re-invent itself to ride London's steak revolution? / www.jumeirah.com; 10.45 pm, Sun 10.15 pm; set weekday L £60 (FP).

RIBA Café
Royal Ass'n of Brit' Architects W1   £46   ④⑤②
66 Portland Pl   7631 0467   2–1B
"Wow!"; it's the "impressive surroundings" and the "wonderful Art Deco interior" of the architects' palatial Marylebone HQ that make it of interest – "service can be slow", and the food is "pricey" for what it is. / www.riba-venues.com; L only, closed Sat & Sun.

Riccardo's SW3 £42 ④④④
126 Fulham Rd 7370 6656 5–3B
*"The formula works!", say fans of this "lively" Chelsea Italian, which
has served "a menu of starters" since long before 'petits-plats' menus
became fashionable; it's "rather crowded", though, and the food
is more "variable" than it used to be. / www.riccardos.it; 11.30 pm,
Sun 10.30 pm.*

Riding House Café W1 NEW £44 ❷❷❶
43-51 Great Titchfield St 7927 0840 3–1C
*A superb, snazzy interior – twinned with a "crowd-pleasing" menu
of "comfort food" – is making a smash hit of this "comfy and casual"
new Fitzrovia brasserie; let's hope it doesn't become too popular for
its own good! / www.ridinghousecafe.co.uk; 11 pm.*

El Rincón Latino SW4 £30 ④❷❷
148 Clapham Manor St 7622 0599 10–2D
*"Full Spanish weekend fry-ups!" are a top tip at this good-value
Clapham tapas bar; otherwise, the food's only middling nowadays,
but the "wonderful" staff help create a good buzz.
/ www.rinconlatino.co.uk; 10.30 pm, Fri & Sat 11.30 pm; closed Mon-Fri L.*

Rising Sun NW7 £38 ❷❷❸
137 Marsh Ln, Highwood Hill 8959 1357 1–1B
*"A lovely, picturesque pub in leafy Mill Hill, now run by an Italian
family" – "the owner makes a great host", and the food is "simple
and well-presented". / 9.30 pm, Sun 8.30 pm; closed Mon.*

Ristorante Semplice W1 £64 ❷❷❸
9-10 Blenheim St 7495 1509 3–2B
*A "sophisticated" and "personable" Italian, off the top end of Bond
Street, offering cuisine that's both "expert" and "refined"; only real
problem? – the somewhat "cramped" lay-out.
/ www.ristorantesemplice.com; 10.30 pm; closed Sat L & Sun; booking:
max 12.*

**(Palm Court)
The Ritz W1** £44 ④❸❷
150 Piccadilly 7493 8181 3–4C
*"A once-in-a-lifetime experience everyone should have" –
this St James's grand-hotel afternoon tea is so famous that it has
become a touristic cliché... which is no doubt why critics find
it "totally disappointing and over-rated". / www.theritzlondon.com; 10 pm;
jacket & tie required.*

**The Ritz Restaurant
The Ritz W1** £118 ❸❷❶
150 Piccadilly 7493 8181 3–4C
*"You don't ever forget a date at the Ritz!"; if you're looking for
a "great place for a celebration", especially of a "romantic" nature,
this "incomparable" Louis XVI chamber is a total "wow",
and nowadays the food – traditionally lacklustre – almost lives up!
/ www.theritzlondon.com; 10 pm; jacket & tie required.*

Riva SW13 £56 ❷❷④
169 Church Rd 8748 0434 10–1A
*Andreas Riva's "serious" Barnes venture is one of London's
most idiosyncratic stalwarts; to fans, it's "the perfect Italian",
with "awesome" and "very interesting" cuisine and a "glamorous"
vibe – to the uninitiated, it's an "overhyped" place, with "disdainful"
service and "drab" decor. / 10.30 pm, Sun 9.30 pm; closed Sat L.*

THE RIVER CAFÉ W6 £79 ❷❷❸
Thames Wharf, Rainville Rd 7386 4200 7–2C
"Quality is absolute", at Ruth Rogers's riverside Hammersmith
canteen, world-famous for seasonal fare that's "the quintessence
of Italian cuisine"; even for fans, however, bills are so "brutal" that
the overall experience can be "bittersweet". / www.rivercafe.co.uk; 9 pm,
Sat 9.15 pm; closed Sun D.

**The Riverfront
BFI Southbank SE1** £37 ❷❷❸
Southbank 7928 0808 2–3D
"An excellent place for a quick and tasty meal on the South Bank" –
this attractive Benugo-group café is very handily-located,
and "good value" too. / www.riverfrontbarandkitchen.com; 9.30 pm.

Rivington Grill £50 ❸④④
178 Greenwich High Rd, SE10 8293 9270 1–3D
28-30 Rivington St, EC2 7729 7053 12–1B
The "luxury burger" may be "great", and the brunches "excellent",
but these Caprice-group bar/brasseries offer a "hit-and-miss"
experience overall, and arguably a rather "unexciting" one too.
/ www.rivingtongrill.co.uk; 11 pm, Sun 10 pm; SE10 closed Mon,
Tue L & Wed L.

Roast SE1 £64 ❸④❸
Stoney St 0845 034 7300 9–4C
"Good food... but about 20% overpriced!" – a pretty representative
opinion on this "beautifully light" Borough dining room, which has
"delightful views" over the Market, and serves a "traditional" menu
(focussing on meat); this is a quintessentially British establishment,
however, so "breakfast is much better than lunch!"
/ www.roast-restaurant.com; 10.15 pm, Sun 6 pm.

Rocca Di Papa £30 ④❸❸
73 Old Brompton Rd, SW7 7225 3413 5–2B
75-79 Dulwich Village, SE21 8299 6333 1–4D **NEW**
A large but "friendly" South Kensington pizza spot, which – if you're
looking for a "family meal" in this surprisingly thinly-provided area –
makes a "good-value" choice; on thin feedback, its new Dulwich
sibling (with outside tables) is off to a fair start too. / SW7 11.30 pm;
SE21 11 pm.

Rochelle Canteen E2 £33 ❷❷❷
Arnold Circus 7729 5677 12–1C
Don't leave it to the Bethnal Green trendies!; this small, unlicensed
canteen – "tucked-away in a former school bicycle shed" – is "a real
hidden gem", serving "simple but perfect" cuisine at "cheap" prices;
"great alfresco dining" too. / www.arnoldandhenderson.com; L only, closed
Sat & Sun; no Amex.

Rock & Sole Plaice WC2 £30 ❸④❸
47 Endell St 7836 3785 4–1C
A "great" old-fashioned chippy which is of particular note as one
of the best places for a "cheap 'n' cheerful" group meal in Covent
Garden; "eat in, take away, or eat outside on a warm day". / 11 pm,
Sun 10.30 pm; no Amex; need 4+ to book.

Rock & Rose TW9 £54 ④❸❶
106-108 Kew Rd 8948 8008 1–4A
It's the stylishly "kitsch" decor – "so OTT it's a laugh" – that makes
this "romantic" Richmond destination worth seeking out; prices can
seem "steep", though, and the "global" menu is realised only to a
"mediocre" standard. / www.rockandroserestaurant.co.uk; 10 pm;
set weekday L £33 (FP).

Rocket £43 ④④❸

4-6 Lancashire Ct, W1   7629 2889   3–2B
Churchill Pl, E14   3200 2022   11–1C
6 Adams Ct, EC2   7628 0808   9–2C

"Tucked-away", off Bond Street, this "vibrant" operation is a "simple and central" rendezvous, offering "well-priced" pizzas and salads; visits to the "industrially-styled" Canary Wharf spin-off are also "enjoyable". / 10.30 pm; W1 closed Sun; EC2 closed Sat & Sun; SW15 Mon-Wed D only.

Rodizio Rico £45 ⑤④⑤

111 Westbourne Grove, W2   7792 4035   6–1B
77-78 Upper St, N1   7354 1076   8–3D
11 Jerdan Pl, SW6   7183 6085   5–4A **NEW**

These all-you-can-eat, meat-heavy Brazilian buffets often divide opinion; fans say they're "excellent for groups, and good value for money" too, but for critics, who are more vocal this year, they're simply a "disaster" – "I still have flashbacks!" / www.rodiziorico.com; W2 & N1 midnight, Sun 11 pm; SE10 11 pm, Fri & Sat midnight; W2 & N1 closed weekday L; no Amex.

The Roebuck W4 £42 ❸②②

122 Chiswick High Rd   8995 4392   7–2A

An "unassuming" but "efficient" and "buzzy" Chiswick boozer, serving "classic dishes with an interesting twist"; it has a "lovely garden" too. / www.theroebuckchiswick.co.uk; Fri & Sat 10.30 pm, Mon-Thu, Sun 10 pm.

Roganic W1 NEW £78 ❶❷⑤

19 Blandford St   7486 0380   2–1A

Simon Rogan (of Cumbria's L'Enclume fame) is one of the UK's most innovative chefs, and his talents are impressively demonstrated by the 6-course and 10-course set menus offered at the short-term (two-year) 'pop up' he launched in Marylebone in mid-2011; the setting though – especially the cramped rear room – is bare. / Rated on Editors' visit; www.roganic.co.uk; 9 pm; closed Mon & Sun.

Roka £76 ❶❸❷

37 Charlotte St, W1   7580 6464   2–1C
Unit 4, Park Pavilion, 40 Canada Sq, E14   7636 5228   11–1C

"Stunning" cuisine – highlighting a 'robata' grill which creates "the most wonderful flavours" – takes centre stage at these "exciting" Japanese operations, whose "cool" styling helps create a "great buzz"; NB: the Fitzrovia original (which has a "must-do" basement bar) significantly outclasses the newer Canary Wharf branch. / www.rokarestaurant.com; 11.15 pm, Sun 10.30 pm; closed Sun D; booking: max 8.

Roots At N1 N1 NEW £46 ❷❷④

115 Hemingford Rd   7697 4488   8–3D

"A fantastic addition to Barnsbury"; this stylishly-converted pub "operates far above the level of an average neighbourhood Indian". / www.rootsatn1.com; 10 pm, Sun 9 pm; D only, closed Mon; no Amex.

Rosa's £34 ❸④❸

48 Dean St, W1   7494 1638   4–3A
12 Hanbury St, E1   7247 1093   12–2C

These "fun" budget Thai canteens can be "inconsistent", but mostly win praise for their "vibrant" dishes; the "buzzy" original, near Brick Lane, now has a "cute" Soho sibling. / www.rosaslondon.com; 10.30 pm, Fri & Sat 11 pm; some booking restrictions apply.

The Rose & Crown N6 £45 ④④④

86 Highgate High St 8340 0770 1–1C
This Highgate yearling – "not really a pub", more a restaurant nowadays – does have its fans; it also faces some ominous criticisms though, of "stodgy and bland" food and a "complacent" attitude. / www.roseandcrownhighgate.com; 10 pm; closed Mon L & Sun D; no Amex; set weekday L £29 (FP).

Rossopomodoro £40 ❸④④

50-52 Monmouth St, WC2 7240 9095 4–3B
214 Fulham Rd, SW10 7352 7677 5–3B
184a Kensington Park Rd, W11 7229 9007 6–1A
Often "full of Italian-speaking families", these "very busy and noisy" trattorias feel notably "authentic" (as you'd hope of a group originating in Naples) – the pizza is "noticeably better than at most chains". / www.rossopomodoro.co.uk; 11.30 pm; WC2 Sun 11.30 pm; set weekday L £26 (FP).

The Rôtisserie £51 ④❸④

316 Uxbridge Rd, HA5 8421 2878 1–1A
1288 Whetstone High Rd, N20 8343 8585 1–1B
82 Fortune Green Rd, NW6 7435 9923 1–1B
87 Allitsen Rd, NW8 7722 7444 8–3A
"Great steaks at fair prices" win praise for this "reliable" small chain; there are also quite a few critics, though, who find it "pricey", and say it's merely "OK if you can't be bothered to cook, but not what you could really call a 'night out'". / www.therotisserie.co.uk; 10.30 pm, Sun 9.30 pm; NW6, NW8 & NW20 closed Mon L, NW6 closed Sun; no Amex (except HA5).

Rôtisserie Bute Street SW7 £35 ❸④④

6-8 Bute St 7584 0600 5–2B
"Good, cheap, hearty, simple" fast food is still the order of the day at this basic South Kensington stand-by, where you can choose anything… so long as it's rôtisserie chicken; BYO. / www.rotisseriebutestreet.com; 10.30 pm.

Rotunda Bar & Restaurant
Kings Place N1 £48 ④❸❷

90 York Way 7014 2840 8–3C
The large dining facility of this "buzzy" arts centre/office complex, near King's Cross, undoubtedly makes "a good spot for a pre-concert supper"; on a warm day though, it's the canal-side tables – with their "stunning" views – which are worth a journey in their own right. / www.rotundabarandrestaurant.co.uk; 10.30 pm.

Roussillon SW1 £86 ❸❸④

16 St Barnabas St 7730 5550 5–2D
This "sedate" (but quite "romantic") Gallic operation is still often hailed as a Pimlico "hidden gem", but there's no doubt it has "slightly lost its edge" since its former chef left last year; no reason for despair, though – many reports do speak of "exquisite" dishes, and fans say the new régime is "getting there". / www.roussillon.co.uk; 11 pm; closed Sat L & Sun; no trainers; set weekday L £53 (FP).

Roux At Parliament Square
RICS SW1 £80 ❸④⑤

12 Great George St 7334 3737 2–3C
"Odd" decor and "eccentric" service are not the only peculiarities which have made Michel Roux's "sepulchral" Westminster outpost a "strange" débutante – reports on the cuisine range the whole way from "best meal for many years" to "extremely disappointing". / www.rouxatparliamentsquare.co.uk; 10 pm; closed Sat & Sun; set weekday L £47 (FP).

Roux At The Landau
The Langham W1   £80   ❷❷❷
1c, Portland Pl   7965 0165   2–1B
"The Landau is reborn", thanks to the Roux take-over of this
"palatial" and "truly lovely" dining room – the cuisine is "impeccably
executed" and service "seamless and unobtrusive"; the set lunch,
in particular, is "excellent value". / www.thelandau.com; 10 pm; closed
Sat L & Sun; no trainers.

Rowley's SW1   £62   ⑤⑤⑤
113 Jermyn St   7930 2707   3–3D
"The interior makes the atmosphere", say fans of this "traditional"
St James's steakhouse (whose tiled premises date from its days as the
birthplace of Wall's sausages); even supporters can find
it "disappointingly touristy" nowadays, however, and too many critics
feel it's "cramped", "average" and "way overpriced".
/ www.rowleys.co.uk; 11 pm.

Royal China   £46   ❷④④
24-26 Baker St, W1   7487 4688   2–1A
805 Fulham Rd, SW6   7731 0081   10–1B
13 Queensway, W2   7221 2535   6–2C
30 Westferry Circus, E14   7719 0888   11–1B
"After two years in the East, this is where I come to satisfy my dim
sum cravings!"; London's benchmark Chinese chain is "superbly
authentic", all the way down to its "bordello-glitz" decor,
and "brusque" service; NB: they're "always busy" – expect
"long queues" at peak times. / www.royalchinagroup.co.uk; 10.45 pm,
Fri & Sat 11.15 pm, Sun 9.45 pm; no booking Sat & Sun L.

Royal China Club W1   £55   ❷❸④
40-42 Baker St   7486 3898   2–1A
This "posher" (and "pricier") version of the Royal China formula
serves similarly "fantastic" food, with "phenomenal" dim sum and
lobster (from the tank) among the highlights; another advantage
of this Marylebone outlet? – "you can book!"
/ www.royalchinagroup.co.uk; 11 pm, Fri & Sat 11.30 pm, Sun 10.30 pm.

Royal China SW15   £43   ④④④
3 Chelverton Rd   8788 0907   10–2B
Famously a "very consistent" Putney destination, this "dim sum
favourite" shares roots (but not ownership) with the well-known chain;
ratings are down this year, though, and one long-term fan reports that
"food quality has dived" – hopefully just a blip!
/ www.royalchinaputney.co.uk; 11 pm, Fri-Sat 11.30 pm; only Amex.

The Royal Exchange Grand Café
The Royal Exchange EC3   £49   ④④❶
The Royal Exchange Bank   7618 2480   9–2C
The D&D group's café in the Royal Exchange's magnificent atrium
makes "a good City rendezvous"; with its "small" and "extremely
pricey" portions, it's ideal "for regular business-lunchers who don't
want to get too roly poly!" / www.royalexchange-grandcafe.co.uk; 10 pm;
closed Sat & Sun; no booking at L & D.

RSJ SE1   £49   ❸❷⑤
33 Coin St   7928 4554   9–4A
"Never disappointed in 25 years!"; this "useful" South Bank stalwart
offers an "unchanging" mix of "charming" service, "reliable" cooking,
and – last but not least – an "absolute joy" of a wine list (from the
Loire); the other constant, sadly, is an ambience that's "nothing
to shout about". / www.rsj.uk.com; 11 pm; closed Sat L & Sun.

Rugoletta N2   £36   ❸❸❸
59 Church Ln   8815 1743   1–1B
*"Basic" but "buzzy", this BYO bistro – "tucked-away between shops",
in East Finchley – has made something of a name locally with its
"good-value" Italian cuisine; it's "very small, and you have to book!"
/ 10.30 pm; closed Sun.*

Rules WC2   £74   ❹❸❷
35 Maiden Ln   7836 5314   4–3D
*"Unbeatable for wowing foreigners!" – London's oldest restaurant
(1798) offers "old-world" (Edwardian) "opulence", "relaxed charm"
and "good, solid British food" too; ever more "frightening" prices,
however, risk making it a place for "rich tourists and expense-
accounters". / www.rules.co.uk; 11.30 pm, Sun 10.30 pm; no shorts; booking:
max 6.*

S & M Café   £32   ❹❹❹
4-6 Essex Rd, N1   7359 5361   8–3D
48 Brushfield St, E1   7247 2252   12–2B
*Haute cuisine it ain't, but – "for reliable, solid nourishment" –
the Sausage 'n' Mash on offer at this chain of "'50s-style" British
caffs satisfies most of the (relatively few) reporters who comment
on it. / www.sandmcafe.co.uk; N1 11 pm; E1 10.30 pm; E1 closed Sun;
no Amex.*

Sabor N1   £41   ❸❶❸
108 Essex Rd   7226 5551   8–3D
*OK, it's "scruffily located", but this "vibrant" Islington cantina offers
"fantastic cocktails", "fresh" Latino fare and "a bit of buzz" too.
/ www.sabor.co.uk; 10.45 pm, Sat & Sun 11 pm; closed Mon, Tue-Fri D only,
Sat & Sun open L & D; no Amex.*

Le Sacré-Coeur N1   £37   ❹❷❸
18 Theberton St   7354 2618   8–3D
*Islington locals find their "very own little bit of Montmartre", at this
"crowded neighbourhood bistro" – a place that's "good for what it is",
in its "old-fashioned" sort of way. / www.lesacrecoeur.co.uk; 11 pm,
Sat 11.30 pm, Sun 10.30 pm; set weekday L £24 (FP).*

Saf   £47   ❷❹❹
Whole Foods, 63-97 High St Ken', W8   7368 4555   5–1A
152-154 Curtain Rd, EC2   7613 0007   12–1B
*"I had no idea raw food could be so delicious!" – these vegan outfits
offer "surprisingly varied and intensely-flavoured" dishes; "indifferent"
service can grate, though, and the in-store Kensington branch has less
atmosphere than the Shoreditch original. / www.safrestaurant.co.uk;
EC2 11 pm, Sun 10; W8 10 pm, Sun 5 pm.*

Sagar   £30   ❷❷❹
17a, Percy St, W1   7631 3319   3–2B
31 Catherine St, WC2   7836 6377   4–3D
157 King St, W6   8741 8563   7–2C
*"Subtle yet insistent" South Indian dishes – including "excellent
dosas" and "puri to die for" – again win a hymn of praise for these
"great cheap veggies"; "the ambience is nothing to speak of",
but staff are notably "cheerful". / www.gosagar.com; Sun-Thu 10.45 pm,
Fri & Sat 11.30 pm; set weekday L £19 (FP).*

Saigon Saigon W6 £41 ❷❷❸
313-317 King St 8748 6887 7–2B
*"Surprisingly good" food ("astonishing", say fans) and "delightful"
service draw a large fan club to this "thoroughly enjoyable" and "ever-
popular" Hammersmith Vietnamese – "it looks as if it might be a bit
downmarket, but actually it's good value". | www.saigon-saigon.co.uk;
11 pm, Sun & Mon 10 pm, Fri & Sat 11.30 pm; no Amex.*

ST JOHN EC1 £72 ❷❸④
26 St John St 7251 0848 9–1B
*"An enticing way with unattractive animal parts" has won global fame
for Fergus Henderson's "Spartan" Smithfield offal-shrine; even fans
fear a "smug" attitude is "starting to cast a cloud", though,
and critics say: "one of the World's 50 Best? – you must be joking!"
| www.stjohnrestaurant.com; 11 pm; closed Sat L & Sun D.*

St John Bread & Wine E1 £50 ❶❷❷
94-96 Commercial St 7251 0848 12–2C
*"Yes, it's as good as they say!"; St John's "younger and buzzier"
Spitalfields canteen spin-off is nowadays "a more reliable destination
than its parent" – staff are "competent and helpful", the "austere"
interior is "cool", and the British fare so "adventurous in its simplicity"
as to be really "exciting". | www.stjohnbreadandwine.com; 10.30 pm,
Sun 9.30 pm.*

St John Hotel WC2 £63 ❸❷④
1 Leicester St 3301 8069 4–3A
*The St John team's "stark" make-over of Theatreland veteran Manzi's
(RIP) is off to a mixed start; fans say the "interesting" British fare
makes it "a joy", but detractors can just see a "crowded" place,
where food that's "good, but not that good" comes at "way OTT"
prices; handy in the early hours, though! | 1.30 am.*

St Johns N19 £40 ❷❷❷
91 Junction Rd 7272 1587 8–1C
*The "fantastic old ballroom interior" at this "5-star" tavern,
in Archway, is "quite something", but the "interesting" British menu –
"with great emphasis on provenance" – is quite an attraction in its
own right too. | 11 pm, Sun 9.30 pm; Mon-Thu D only, Fri-Sun open L & D;
booking: max 12.*

Le Saint Julien EC1 £50 ④❷④
62-63 Long Ln 7796 4550 9–1B
*The quality of the fare is at best "typique", but "sparkling" service
livens up this very Gallic bistro, overlooking Smithfield Market. | 10 pm;
closed Sat L & Sun.*

St Moritz W1 £52 ❸④❸
161 Wardour St 7734 3324 3–1D
*In "Swiss-chalet style", this "genuine" stalwart – with its "cosy",
if "rather kitsch", decor – makes a bizarre find in central Soho;
its "filling" fondues and other fare, however, offer "a real taste of the
Alps"! | www.stmoritz-restaurant.co.uk; 11.30 pm; closed Sat L & Sun.*

St Pancras Grand
St Pancras Int'l Station NW1 £51 ⑤⑤④
The Concourse 7870 9900 8–3C
*The "impressive" design of this grand brasserie, within St Pancras
station, may surprise Gallic visitors – shame the "formulaic" food and
"pot luck" service must quickly reinforce their most negative
preconceptions about England! | www.stpancrasgrand.com; 10.30 pm.*

Sake No Hana SW1 £60 ❸④④
23 St James's St 7925 8988 3–4C
"Strange" and "soulless", this would-be trendy St James's Japanese does not seem to have emerged from its 'emergency' early-days revamp especially improved, but the basic problem is that prices can still seem "ludicrous" – one has to wonder if the new owners as of mid-2011, Hakkasan, are the people to put this right!
/ www.sakenohana.com; 11 pm, Fri-Sat 11.30 pm; closed Sat L & Sun.

Saki EC1 £40 ❷❸④
4 West Smithfield 7489 7033 9–2A
Shame it's in a basement that's "a bit on the gloomy side" – this Smithfield Japanese offers some "top cooking", and particularly some "very good set lunch deals". / www.saki-food.com; 10.30 pm; closed Sat L & Sun.

Sakonis HA0 £19 ❸④⑤
127-129 Ealing Rd 8903 9601 1–1A
In the wilds of Wembley, a noisy, no-frills Indian canteen, particularly praised for "fresh and tasty dosas", and its "excellent Bombay street snacks"; there's a big Chinese menu too. / www.sakonis.co.uk; 9.30 pm; no Amex.

Sakura W1 £30 ❷④④
23 Conduit St 7629 2961 3–2C
Now in a new, slightly more modern Mayfair location (a short walk from the old Hanover Street basement), this "authentic" operation – complete with "real Japanese patrons" – still offers "excellent quality and value-for-money". / 10 pm.

Salaam Namaste WC1 £34 ❷❸④
68 Millman St 7405 3697 2–1D
"Everything tastes freshly-made and delicious", say fans of this "excellent local Indian", hidden-away in Bloomsbury; it can sometimes get "very busy". / www.salaam-namaste.co.uk; 11.30 pm, Sun 11 pm.

Sale e Pepe SW1 £55 ④❸❸
9-15 Pavilion Rd 7235 0098 5–1D
"What's happened?" at this "closely-packed" old-favourite trattoria, behind Harrods? – some reporters "still love it", but its "welcoming" and "flamboyant" service risks becoming "slapdash", and "the food has been bland of late". / www.saleepepe.co.uk; 11.30 pm; closed Sun; no shorts.

Salloos SW1 £48 ❷❸④
62-64 Kinnerton St 7235 4444 5–1D
A curious old place, hidden-away in a Belgravia mews, where the "subtly-flavoured Punjabi dishes" – including "simply outstanding" lamb chops – have long made it one of London's top 'Indians'; it's always been "expensive" too. / 11 pm; closed Sun.

The Salt House NW8 £42 ❸❸❷
63 Abbey Rd 7328 6626 8–3A
"Well-lit, with candles and muted decor", this "lovely neighbourhood favourite" delivers "great" gastropub fare, for which fans travel even from beyond St John's Wood; good terrace for the summer. / www.thesalthouse.co.uk; 10 pm, Sun 9.30 pm.

Salt Yard W1 £38 ❸❷❷
54 Goodge St 7637 0657 2–1B
*"Creative" Italian-Spanish tapas and "passionate" staff have made
a smash hit of this "super-busy" (and arguably "too cramped")
Fitzrovia haunt; quality, however, "seems to have gone downhill"
somewhat – the distraction of recent openings elsewhere?*
/ www.saltyard.co.uk; 11 pm; closed Sat L & Sun.

The Salusbury NW6 £41 ❸❸❸
50-52 Salusbury Rd 7328 3286 1–2B
*This "Queen's Park icon" – a "lazy weekend" kind of place with
"consistent" Mediterranean food – has been "re-fitted and revitalised
of late", in particular the adjoining former deli, which is now
an "atmospheric café" serving "good pizza, salads and coffee".*
/ www.thesalusbury.co.uk; 10.15 pm; closed Mon L.

Sam's Brasserie W4 £46 ❹❸❸
11 Barley Mow Pas 8987 0555 7–2A
*"With something for everyone", Sam Harrison's "casual"
bar/brasserie – a "buzzy" factory-conversion, "tucked-away off
Chiswick High Road" – is a "perfect local"; its "simple brasserie fare"
doesn't aim to set the world on fire, but it is "reliable" and "tasty".*
/ www.samsbrasserie.co.uk; 10.30 pm, Sun 9.30 pm; booking: max 26.

Samarqand W1 NEW £46 ❹❹❸
18 Thayer St 7935 9393 3–1A
*"Unique" is a term oft-used to describe this clubby Marylebone
basement newcomer, where "the vodka flows" in the "substantial
bar", and the clientele consists of "Russian oligarchs and leggy
blondes"; the food? – a bit beside the point.*
/ www.samarqand-restaurant.com; Mon-Sat 11 pm, Sun 10 pm.

San Daniele del Friuli N5 £39 ❸❸❷
72 Highbury Park 7226 1609 8–1D
*A long-established Highbury Park trattoria, where fans say the food
is "always good"; "helpful" staff contribute to a "good Italian
atmosphere" too.* / 10.30 pm; closed Mon L, Tue L, Sat L & Sun; no Amex.

San Lorenzo SW3 £65 ❹❹❹
22 Beauchamp Pl 7584 1074 5–1C
*The A-list is not so often seen nowadays at this once-legendary
Knightsbridge Italian, and it inspires little feedback; it is trying harder
("they even take credit cards"), but it's difficult to avoid the feeling
that these improvements are coming "too late".* / 11 pm; closed Sun.

San Lorenzo Fuoriporta SW19 £53 ❹❺❹
38 Wimbledon Hill Rd 8946 8463 10–2B
*This Wimbledon cousin of the once-famous Knightsbridge trattoria
looks like an upmarket PizzaExpress; it benefits for a cute garden but
that's the only undoubted attraction – too many diners report
"terrible" experiences, and ones that are "ridiculously overpriced"
too.* / www.sanlorenzo.com; 10.45 pm, Sun 9.30 pm.

The Sands End SW6 £46 ❷❸❷
135 Stephendale Rd 7731 7823 10–1B
*"A classy restaurant with a pub attached", this Sand's End "hotspot"
– a sibling to Manson – may be "quite expensive", but it offers some
"excellent" cooking (including "great bar nibbles").*
/ www.thesandsend.co.uk; 10 pm, Sun 9 pm.

FSA

Santa Lucia SW10   £41   ❸❹❸
2 Hollywood Rd   7352 8484   5–3B
*"You get a real taste of Italy", at this hectic little Chelsea café –
"if you can bag a space, that is"; its "distracted" staff serve "great"
pizza, by the metre, from the wood-burning oven.*
/ www.madeinitalygroup.co.uk; 11.30 pm, Sun 10.30 pm; closed weekday L.

Santa Maria W5   £25   ❷❷❷
15 St Mary's Rd   8579 1462   1–3A
*"Fantastico!" – "brilliant" and "authentic" Neapolitan pizza has
quickly made a disproportionately big name for this "tiny" Ealing
newcomer; it's "always busy", though, and you can't book.*
/ www.santamariapizzeria.com; 10.30 pm.

Santa Maria del Sur SW8   £45   ❷❹❸
129 Queenstown Rd   7622 2088   10–1C
*The "hype" that's surrounded this Argentinian 'parilla' in Battersea
since it featured on a Ramsay TV show leads some reporters
to suggest it's "over-rated"; even if it's not quite up to its Hackney
sibling (Buen Ayre), though, it's undoubtedly a "jovial" place, offering
"fantastic" steaks. / www.santamariadelsur.co.uk; 11.30 pm; closed
weekday L; no Amex.*

Santini SW1   £69   ❹❹❹
29 Ebury St   7730 4094   2–4B
*This datedly glamorous Belgravian inspires little feedback nowadays;
it's most often tipped as a business lunch venue, but even fans can
find its "proper" Italian cooking "expensive" for what it is, and critics
just say prices are "ridiculous, even for SW1".*
/ www.santini-restaurant.com; 11 pm, Sun 10 pm; closed Sat L & Sun L.

Santore EC1   £37   ❸❷❸
59 Exmouth Mkt   7812 1488   9–1A
*"Almost as good as being in Italy"; this "trendy" and "buzzy"
Exmouth Market spot offers "no fancy nonsense", just "basic" and
"good-value" food – notably the "excellent, thin and crispy pizza",
served by "chatty" staff. / www.santorerestaurant.co.uk; 11 pm.*

Sapori WC2   £41   ❹❸❹
43 Drury Ln   7836 8296   4–2D
*A minute from the Royal Opera House, a "friendly" trattoria –
"run by real Italians!" – that makes a "useful stand-by" for locals and
opera-goers: NB "excellent-value set lunch". / 11.30 pm; no Amex;
set weekday L £22 (FP).*

Sarastro WC2   £42   ❺❺❶
126 Drury Ln   7836 0101   2–2D
*"Opera, violins, and occasional belly-dancing" – plus decor that's
as camp as a row of tents – help make this Theatreland oddity "quite
an experience"; the food, though, is "unmemorable"… if you're lucky.
/ www.sarastro-restaurant.com; 10.30 pm, Thu-Sat 11.30 pm.*

Sardo W1   £48   ❸❸❹
45 Grafton Way   7387 2521   2–1B
*The menu – "with a Sardinian twist" – may seem a little "offbeat",
but fans extol many "unvarnished" but "delicious" meals at this
"genuine" Fitzrovia spot; the similarly "off-piste" wine list is likewise
"a treasure", but even supporters can find the overall experience
"very expensive for what it is". / www.sardo-restaurant.com; 11 pm; closed
Sat L & Sun.*

202

Sardo Canale NW1 £47 ④④④
42 Gloucester Ave 7722 2800 8–3B
It has something of a 'name', but this canal-side (no view) Primrose Hill Italian risks becoming a "former favourite" for many reporters – there was praise for some "fine" Sardinian cooking this year, but it was drowned out by boos from those who found it "lamentable". / www.sardocanale.com; 10 pm.

Sarracino NW6 £41 ❷❷④
186 Broadhurst Gdns 7372 5889 1–1B
The "authentically-prepared" Italian dishes – not least "fabulous" pizza, served by the metre – can come as "quite a surprise" at this "buzzy" West Hampstead Neapolitan. / www.sarracinorestaurant.com; 11 pm; closed weekday L.

Sartoria W1 £59 ❸❸❸
20 Savile Row 7534 7000 3–2C
As "a smart venue for business", the D&D group's "well-spaced and very comfortable" Mayfair dining room comes well recommended, not least for its "light" Italian fare; perhaps that's another way of saying: "while it's a very agreeable place, it's obviously not worth it if you're spending your own money…" / www.sartoria-restaurant.co.uk; 11 pm; closed Sun.

Satay House W2 £38 ❸❸④
13 Sale Pl 7723 6763 6–1D
Radically revamped in recent times, a Paddington backstreet Malaysian of long standing; fans applaud its "surprisingly good" food, but others find in it "nothing noteworthy". / www.satay-house.co.uk; 11 pm.

Satsuma W1 £35
56 Wardour St 7437 8338 3–2D
This heart-of-Soho site is being relaunched in late-2011, with a new concept – katsu curries; the proprietors are the Royal China people, so it would be surprising if it were not at least competent. / www.osatsuma.com; 10.30 pm, Wed & Thu 11 pm, Fri & Sat 10 pm; no booking.

Sauterelle
Royal Exchange EC3 £59 ④❸❸
Bank 7618 2483 9–2C
"Above the glamour of the Royal Exchange", this "beautiful" D&D group mezzanine dining room makes a particularly "useful business venue"; "it doesn't have quite the atmosphere it should", however, not helped by run-of-the-mill standards generally. / www.danddlondon.com; 9.30 pm; closed Sat & Sun.

Savoir Faire WC1 £37 ❸④❸
42 New Oxford St 7436 0707 4–1C
"A 'find' in the Holborn vacuum" – this "friendly" small-scale bistro serves "freshly-prepared French food", at "value-for-money" prices. / www.savoir.co.uk; 11 pm.

(River Restaurant)
The Savoy Hotel WC2 £85 ⑤⑤❸
91 The Strand 7836 4343 4–3D
"How could they make such a special place such a turn-off?" – the window tables still have "gorgeous river views", but the relaunch of this grand-hotel-classic has proved a real damp squib – service is both "over-fussy" and "badly coordinated", and the food "just like in many other hotels"; the wine prices are terrifying too. / www.fairmont.com/savoy/; 10.30 pm.

(Savoy Grill)
The Savoy Hotel WC2 £79 ❸❷❸
Strand 7592 1600 4–3D
This Art Deco power-dining room has had a "superb" refurbishment, and most reporters applaud the Ramsay group for its "enthusiastic" service and "solid" menu of "retro" British "classics" – such a repertoire can also seem "unexciting", though, and critics say the place "doesn't yet live up to its iconic reputation". / www.gordonramsay.com/thesavoygrill/; 11 pm, Sun 10.30 pm; jacket required.

Scalini SW3 £65 ❹❹❸
1-3 Walton St 7225 2301 5–2C
The food "always keeps you coming back", say fans of this ever-"packed" Knightsbridge Italian – who cares if it's "a bit expensive"?; given the "noisy" and "cramped" interior, and staff who "rush you through", however, others are less forgiving. / www.scalinionline.com; 11.45 pm.

Scandinavian Kitchen W1 £12 ❸❷❷
61 Great Titchfield St 7580 7161 2–1B
"Impressive brunches" and "super coffee and cakes" are highlights at this "great, informal community café", in Fitzrovia; as you may possibly have guessed, it celebrates all things Scandi-tastic. / www.scandikitchen.co.uk; L only.

Scarpetta TW11 £40 ❸❸❹
78 High St 8977 8177 1–4A
A "small and authentic" Teddington Italian that's made itself "extremely popular" with its "imaginative" cuisine; "good pizzas" are a highlight. / www.scarpetta.co.uk; 11 pm, Mon & Sun 10 pm; no shorts.

The Scarsdale W8 £38 ❹❸❷
23a Edwardes Sq 7937 1811 7–1D
A "gorgeous sitting area out front" is the highlight at this beautifully-located pub – "the food's nothing special, but it's a lovely oasis away from the hustle of Kensington High Street". / 10 pm, Sun 9.30 pm.

Scoffers SW11 £39 ❹❶❷
6 Battersea Rise 7978 5542 10–2C
A romantic-looking Battersea local – not many places have a "magical indoor tree", after all – which has its fans, particularly as a brunch venue; critics, though, just find it "very average". / www.scoffersrestaurant.co.uk; Mon 10 pm, Tue-Sat midnight, Sun 6 pm; closed Mon & Sun D.

SCOTT'S W1 £73 ❷❶❶
20 Mount St 7495 7309 3–3A
For sheer "A-list" glamour, nowhere beats Richard Caring's magnificent Mayfair all-rounder, with its "very classy", "old-school" décor, "impeccable" service and "fabulous" traditional seafood (amongst the best in town). / www.scotts-restaurant.com; 10.30 pm, Sun 10 pm; booking: max 6.

The Sea Cow SE22 £28 ❸❸❸
37 Lordship Ln 8693 3111 1–4D
"A smart fish 'n' chip shop with bench seating", in East Dulwich, that's long been a local favourite, thanks to its "wide selection of fish, cooked traditional-style or grilled", and its "short but reasonably-priced wine list". / www.theseacow.co.uk; 11 pm, Sun 10 pm; closed Mon L; no Amex.

Sea Pebbles HA5 £27 ❸❸④
348-352 Uxbridge Rd 8428 0203 1–1A
"Superb freshly-cooked fish 'n' chips" is the draw to this "simple and unpretentious" Hatch End chippy; your fish can be grilled, or fried in batter or matzo meal. / 9.45 pm; closed Sun; debit cards only; need 8+ to book.

Seafresh SW1 £33 ❸④⑤
80-81 Wilton Rd 7828 0747 2–4B
"They do more than just fish 'n' chips" – "the extensive menu includes Dover sole and lobster" – at this "no-frills" Pimlico chippy; the style, though, is rather "dated". / www.seafresh-dining.com; 10.30 pm; closed Sun.

Searcy's Brasserie EC2 £54 ④④❸
Level 2, Barbican Centre 7588 3008 12–2A
The name says it all, really – the Barbican's in-house brasserie is "not memorable", but it's a "pleasant" enough room, offering "OK" food and service to its (semi-) captive audience. / www.searcys.co.uk; 10.30 pm; closed Sat L & Sun.

The Sea Shell NW1 £40 ❸❸❸
49 Lisson Grove 7224 9000 8–4A
"Better", as a result of its post-fire refurb, this now rather "pleasant" Marylebone legend is again cooking up "top-rate fish 'n' chips". / www.seashellrestaurant.co.uk; 10.30 pm; closed Sun.

Sedap EC1 £24 ❸④⑤
102 Old St 7490 0200 12–1A
"There's not much elbow room", at this "canteen-like" modern café, in Shoreditch, but fortunately its "home-style" Nyonya (Chinese-Malaysian) cooking is worth squeezing in for, and it comes at "amazingly reasonable" prices. / www.sedap.co.uk; 10.30 pm; closed Sat L & Sun L; no Amex.

Serafino W1 £57 ❸②④
8 Mount St 7629 0544 3–3B
"A good-value Italian in the heart of Mayfair" – and there aren't too many of those! – where "they serve all the standard dishes with flair"; for maximum economy, seek out the café-style operation, hidden-away in the basement. / www.finos.co.uk; 10.45 pm; closed Sat L & Sun.

Seven Park Place SW1 £72 ❶❶❷
7-8 Park Pl 7316 1600 3–4C
*"Little-known", but worth discovering; ex-Aubergine chef William Drabble "really knows his stuff", and cranks out "wonderfully inventive" dishes at this "luxurious" (if oddly broken-up) dining room, "tucked-away in a St James's side street".
/ www.stjameshotelandclub.com; 10 pm; closed Mon & Sun; set weekday L £43 (FP).*

Seven Stars WC2 £33 ④④❷
53 Carey St 7242 8521 2–2D
"Just behind the Royal Courts of Justice, and often filled with denizens of the courts", this "tiny and ancient pub" is at its best when "hilarious" landlady Roxy Beaujolais is in evidence; the "home-cooking" is sometimes "slapdash", though, and the place can feel "crammed-in" and "chaotic". / 11 pm, Sun 10.30 pm.

Seventeen W11 £41 ❷❷❸
17 Notting Hill Gate 7985 0006 6–2B
*Not helped by an unattractive location right on Notting Hill Gate,
and despite considerable investment in night-clubby decor,
this Chinese yearling has attracted little attention; the few reports
there are, however, tend to be rather positive.*
/ www.seventeen-london.co.uk; 11.30 pm.

1707
Fortnum & Mason W1 £47 ❹❸❸
181 Piccadilly 7734 8040 3–3D
*"More than 1,000 wines" – "one of London's best selections", all at
"modest mark-ups" – is the stand-out attraction at this civilised bar,
in the basement of the famously posh St James's grocers; with its
simple "deli"-style fare it makes a handy option for a "light bite".*
/ www.fortnumandmason.co.uk; 7 pm, Sun 5 pm.

Shaka Zulu NW1 £64 ❺❹❷
Stables Mkt 3376 9911 8–3B
*"They spent about a zillion pounds on the decor", at this gigantic,
"loud" Camden Town yearling, where "Las Vegas meets Africa";
shame they didn't invest as much in the service ("truly awful"), or the
cooking ("rubbish").* / www.shaka-zulu.com; 10 pm; closed weekday L.

Shampers W1 £43 ❸❷❷
4 Kingly St 7437 1692 3–2D
*"Always humming", this "welcoming" '70s wine bar is an "unfailing"
Soho institution, serving "good honest food", and where Simon the
owner "looks after you and invariably recommends a decent bottle" –
"great fun".* / www.shampers.net; 10.45 pm; closed Sun.

Shanghai E8 £34 ❸❸❶
41 Kingsland High St 7254 2878 1–1C
*A Dalston Chinese of note for its decor ("make sure you sit in the
former pie 'n' eel shop bit, at the front"), and its sometimes
"fantastic" food ("especially the dim sum"); karaoke, however, is an
ever present risk – "where else can you enjoy top salt 'n' pepper
squid to the sound of Celine Dion being murdered next door...?"*
/ www.wengwahgroup.com; 11 pm; no Amex.

Shanghai Blues WC1 £60 ❷❹❷
193-197 High Holborn 7404 1668 4–1D
*"Dark and intriguing" decor, plus "really superb" cuisine –
not least "fabulous dim sum" – makes this "glossy" conversion of a
former library not only "the best restaurant around Holborn", but also
one of the capital's top Chineses; it's certainly no bargain, but it really
deserves wider recognition.* / www.shanghaiblues.co.uk; 11.30 pm.

J SHEEKEY WC2 £67 ❶❶❷
32-34 St Martin's Ct 7240 2565 4–3B
*"London's finest seafood restaurant"; this "special" but remarkably
"understated" Theatreland veteran remains the survey's most-
mentioned spot – its "suave" staff serve up "simple" but "superb"
dishes in a "bustling" series of "clubby" (if "cramped") chambers.*
/ www.j-sheekey.co.uk; midnight, Sun 11 pm; booking: max 6.

J Sheekey Oyster Bar WC2 £46 ❷❶❶
32-34 St Martin's Ct 7240 2565 4–3B
*"For sheer pleasure and joie-de-vivre", this "glamorous" add-on
to Theatreland's famous fish veteran really is a gem; with its "utterly
charming" staff and "to-die-for seafood", it's "fabulous for a pre-
/post- theatre bite" – if you can, bag a seat at the bar.*
/ www.j-sheekey.co.uk; midnight, Sun 11 pm; booking: max 3.

Shepherd's SW1 £50 ❹❸❸
Marsham Ct, Marsham St 7834 9552 2–4C
"For MPs, and those lunching them", this "discreet" Westminster
dining room can make a "very comfortable" and "quietly efficient"
choice, offering "straightforward" British fare of "steady" quality... or,
to put it another way: "you pay a lot for pretty average comfort food".
/ www.langansrestaurants.co.uk; 10.45 pm; closed Sat & Sun.

Shilpa W6 £30 ❶❸❺
206 King St 8741 3127 7–2B
It looks totally "forgettable", but this Hammersmith Keralan is a
"gem", where "excellent" cooking comes at "amazing" prices –
well worth putting up with the "charmingly chaotic" service.
/ www.shilparestaurant.co.uk; 11 pm, Thu-Sat midnight; no Amex.

The Ship SW18 £46 ❸❸❶
41 Jews Row 8870 9667 10–2B
This "buzzy" and "atmospheric" boozer's special attraction is its large
Thames-side terrace, with spiffing river views and extensive al fresco
seating (so arrive early for your weekend lunch!) – "great food, and in
summer there's the added bonus of a huge BBQ". / www.theship.co.uk;
10 pm; no Amex; no booking, Sun L.

Siam Central W1 £29 ❸❹❸
14 Charlotte St 7436 7460 2–1C
A "decent" and "reasonably-priced" Fitzrovia corner Thai, which
continues to attract praise for cooking which is "packed full
of flavour". / 10.45 pm, Sun 10.15 pm.

Signor Sassi SW1 £62 ❸❸❷
14 Knightsbridge Grn 7584 2277 5–1D
"A trusted favourite"; this "bustling" ("loud") Knightsbridge Italian
earns its enduring popularity with "good" ("if unspectacular") food,
and "warm" service in "traditional style". / www.signorsassi.co.uk;
11.30 pm, Sun 10.30 pm.

Simplicity SE16 £45 ❹❸❸
1 Tunnel Rd 7232 5174 11–2A
"Hidden-away in the back streets of Rotherhithe", this "friendly" and
"intimate" spot pleases most, if not quite all, the locals, with its
"very good breakfast", and other more substantial fare too.
/ www.simplicityrestaurants.com; 10.30 pm; closed weekday L; no Amex.

Simply Indian SE1 £25 ❸❹❹
25 Tabard St 7407 5005 1–3C
"A bargain BYO Indian, conveniently close to London Bridge station" –
the food is "innovative" and "of reasonably good quality", but service
can be "iffy". / www.simplyindian.co.uk; 11.30 pm.

Simpson's Tavern EC3 £37 ❹❸❶
38 1/2 Ball Ct, Cornhill 7626 9985 9–2C
"Still a great institution for City schoolboys" – this cramped
chophouse "classic" (1757) delivers a menu of unreformed British
stodge – don't miss the savoury speciality of 'stewed cheese';
"generally, men love it, and women don't". / www.simpsonstavern.co.uk;
3 pm; L only, closed Sat & Sun.

Simpsons-in-the-Strand WC2 £75 ❹❺❹
100 Strand 7836 9112 4–3D
"Sadly now for (rich) tourists", this "olde-worlde" Covent Garden
classic is "just not what it's cracked up to be" nowadays – its iffy
"traditional" fare is "poorly served", and "overpriced" too; the "meaty
breakfast", however, still comes "thoroughly recommended".
/ www.simpsonsinthestrand.co.uk; 10.45 pm, Sun 9 pm; no trainers.

Singapore Garden NW6 £45 ❷❷❸
83a Fairfax Rd 7624 8233 8–2A
*"London's top Singaporean" (not a tough contest, admittedly) –
this "always-busy" Swiss Cottage veteran is "a cut above" your typical
local, and serves dishes of "consistently high quality".
/ www.singaporegarden.co.uk; 11 pm, Fri & Sat 11.30 pm.*

**(Gallery)
Sketch W1** £64 ⑤⑤④
9 Conduit St 7659 4500 3–2C
*It's "designed to impress" (and has "the best loos in London"),
but few places achieve such dire ratings in the survey as this
"happening" – read hilariously "pretentious" and "overpriced" –
Mayfair venue, where the food is "so bad" it could only ever
be "a sideshow". / www.sketch.uk.com; 11 pm; D only, closed Sun; booking:
max 10.*

**(Lecture Room)
Sketch W1** £102 ⑤⑤❸
9 Conduit St 7659 4500 3–2C
*This "hysterically poncy" dining room, on the first floor of an
impressive Mayfair palazzo, is overseen from afar by Parisian über-
chef Pierre Gagnaire; fans say its OTT formula is "brilliant" –
detractors just find it "shockingly bad", and insanely overpriced too.
/ www.sketch.uk.com; 10.30 pm; closed Mon, Sat L & Sun; no trainers; booking:
max 8; set weekday L £56 (FP).*

**(The Parlour)
Sketch W1** £45 ④④❸
9 Conduit St 7659 4533 3–2C
*The "quirky" pâtisserie of this Mayfair palazzo is arguably the
most useful part – fans proclaim it "a hidden gem for afternoon tea".
/ www.sketch.uk.com; closed Sun; no Amex; no booking.*

Skipjacks HA3 £38 ❶❷⑤
268-270 Streatfield Rd 8204 7554 1–1A
*"Always busy, often with queues out the door" – this family-run
Harrow chippy may look "very ordinary", but the fish (grilled,
steamed or fried) is "amazing", and "great value"; fortunately the
service is "super-fast" too. / 10.30 pm; closed Sun.*

**Skylon
South Bank Centre SE1** £55 ④④❷
Southbank Centre, Belvedere Rd 7654 7800 2–3D
*"To-die-for views" through the huge windows lend quite a "sense
of occasion" to this "light", "airy", and glamorously '50s-tastic
operation, in the Festival Hall; the food, though, too often seems
"around the standard of a company canteen", and "massively
overpriced" too. / www.skylonrestaurant.co.uk; 10.45 pm, Sun 10.30 pm;
no trainers.*

Slurp £26 ❸❸⑤
104-106 Streatham High Rd, SW16 8677 7786 10–2D
138 Merton Rd, SW19 8543 4141 10–2B
*"You wouldn't linger", but – for a quick, filling, delicious bowl of rice
or noodles – check out these "canteen-like" operations,
in Wimbledon and Streatham. / www.slurprestaurant.co.uk; 11 pm;
no Amex.*

Smith Square SW1 NEW £41
St John's, Smith Sq 7222 2779 2–4C
*The new name for the dining operation (fka the Footstool) beneath
the deconsecrated Westminster church that's now a concert hall;
it has as yet inspired no survey commentary, but we include it for its
practical attractions in a thin area. / www.leafi.co.uk; 10 pm depends
on concert; no Amex.*

Smithfield Bar & Grill EC1 £52 ④④④
2-3 West Smithfield 7246 0900 9–2A
*The "louche" and "glitzy" ("'80s-throwback") feel does the place
no favours, but this "buzzy" Smithfield spot has its fans... even
if reports on its steaks and other fare, range from "fantastic"
to "distinctly average". / www.blackhouse.uk.com; 10.30 pm; closed
Sat L & Sun.*

(Ground Floor)
Smiths of Smithfield EC1 £29 ④④❷
67-77 Charterhouse St 7251 7950 9–1A
*"Unrivalled for weekend brunch" – the ground-floor bar/diner of this
warehouse-conversion, by Smithfield Market, does "marvellous"
breakfasts, and has a "brilliant buzz most mornings"; at other times
– little commented-on – it's a place for a "fast, effective bite".
/ www.smithsofsmithfield.co.uk; L only.*

(Dining Room)
Smiths of Smithfield EC1 £50 ④④❸
67-77 Charterhouse St 7251 7950 9–1A
*A certain "infectious vibe" is the only reliable attraction of the
"buzzy" (very "loud") first floor of this Smithfield behemoth; at best,
it offers a "convenient" venue for "OK" burgers and other "simple"
fare, but service is "slow", and the food can be "unexciting".
/ www.smithsofsmithfield.co.uk; 10.45 pm; closed Sat L & Sun; booking:
max 12.*

(Top Floor)
Smiths of Smithfield EC1 £65 ④④❸
67-77 Charterhouse St 7251 7950 9–1A
*"Beautiful views of the City" and "wonderful steaks" have long made
this "bright" dining room a "solid" option for business entertaining;
perhaps that's why prices can seem "very high" – both food and
service are "very ordinary" by comparison.
/ www.smithsofsmithfield.co.uk; 10.45 pm; closed Sat L & Sun D; booking:
max 10.*

Sofra £35 ④④④
1 St Christopher's Pl, W1 7224 4080 3–1A
18 Shepherd St, W1 7493 3320 3–4B
36 Tavistock St, WC2 7240 3773 4–3D
11 Circus Rd, NW8 7586 9889 8–3A
*"Well-prepared" mezze, in particular, still commend this long-
established Turkish bistro-chain to many reporters; they're "variable",
though – when an experience is both "formulaic" and "chaotic",
it arguably offers the worst of all possible worlds! / www.sofra.co.uk;
11 pm-midnight.*

Soho Japan W1 £40 ❸❷④
52 Wells St 7323 4661 2–1B
*It looks like the Irish pub it once was, but this "easy-going" Japanese
spot, just north of Oxford Street, is tipped for some "very good"
dishes. / www.sohojapan.co.uk; 10.30 pm; closed Sat L & Sun; no Amex.*

Solly's NW11   £42   ④⑤⑤
146-150 Golders Green Rd   8455 0004   1–1B
With its "informal" café/take-away, and grander restaurant upstairs, this busy Israeli is a linchpin of the Golder's Green strip, serving "plentiful helpings of standard kosher fare"; it can seem "rather pricey" and complacent, though, and critics fear it's simply "lost the plot". / 10.30 pm; closed Fri D & Sat L; no credit cards.

Somerstown Coffee House NW1   £36   ④❸❸
60 Chalton St   7691 9136   8–3C
Between Euston and King's Cross, a "great boozer/restaurant combo"; it remains a pretty "dependable" destination but, of late, the "previously adventurous French dishes have seemed a little more ordinary than before". / www.somerstowncoffeehouse.co.uk; 10 pm.

Sông Quê E2   £29   ❷⑤⑤
134 Kingsland Rd   7613 3222   12–1B
"OK, so it's scruffy, noisy and chaotic", but this "no-frills" Shoreditch caff still draws queues with its "amazingly fresh" Vietnamese dishes, not least "the best pho" – "and at these prices, who's complaining?" / 11 pm; no Amex.

Sonny's SW13   £48   ④❷❸
94 Church Rd   8748 0393   10–1A
As "a solid, dependable neighbourhood restaurant", this "convivial" Barnes local of (very) long standing still has much going for it; even fans, however, would concede that nowadays "its strength lies in its consistency, not its flair". / www.sonnys.co.uk; 10.30 pm Fri & Sat 11 pm; closed Sun D; set weekday L £29 (FP), set dinner £32 (FP).

La Sophia W10 NEW   £46   ❷❷④
46 Golborne Road   8968 2200   6–1A
An "intimate" Mediterranean newcomer, in North Kensington, already attracting plaudits for its "good food" and its "obliging" service. / www.lasophia.co.uk; Sun 10pm, Fri & Sat 11 pm, 10.30 pm.

Sophie's Steakhouse   £44   ④❸❸
29-31 Wellington St, WC2   7836 8836   4–3D
311-313 Fulham Rd, SW10   7352 0088   5–3B
As "a good place to socialise", this "always-packed" Chelsea steakhouse still has many fans for its "great buzz" and "pretty good" steaks; its ratings are waning, though, with the food at the "more impersonal" Covent Garden sibling reckoned a particular "yawn". / www.sophiessteakhouse.com; SW10 11.45 pm, Sun 11.15 pm; WC2 12.45 pm, Sun 11 pm; no booking; set weekday L £26 (FP).

Soseki EC3   £55   ❷❷❷
1f, 20 Bury St   7621 9211   9–2D
"A Japanese oasis in the heart of the City!" – this "serene" and "beautiful" spot, by the Gherkin, offers "very well-executed" cuisine, with "a rich sense of ceremonial"; it makes a "great place for a business lunch or dinner", but – if you get one of the booths – can be "very romantic" too. / www.soseki.co.uk; 10 pm; closed Sat & Sun; booking: max 12.

Sotheby's Café W1   £52   ❷❷❷
34-35 New Bond St   7293 5077   3–2C
"It's not exactly cheap", but the café off the foyer of the famous Mayfair auction house offers a simple but classy menu, realised to a "consistently excellent" standard. / www.sothebys.com; L only, closed Sat & Sun; booking: max 8.

Spaniard's Inn NW3 £40 ❸❸❶
Spaniards Rd, Hampstead Heath 8731 8406 8–1A
"Quirky" and "most atmospheric", this ancient pub, north
of Hampstead Heath, is "a great spot for those with dogs or kids",
thanks not least to its "huge beer garden"; the food is nothing special,
but that does nothing to dent the place's enormous popularity.
/ www.thespaniardshampstead.co.uk; 10 pm.

Spianata & Co £10 ❷❸④
Tooley St, SE1 8616 4662 9–4D **NEW**
41 Brushfield St, E1 7655 4411 12–2B
20 Holborn Viaduct, EC1 7248 5947 9–2A
17 Blomfield St, EC2 7256 9103 9–2C
29-30 Leadenhall Mkt, EC3 7929 1339 9–2D
73 Watling St, EC4 7236 3666 9–2B
"Panini heaven"; spianata, Roman-style – using "awesome own-baked
bread", with "great quality ingredients and combos" – are the
highlight at these "grab-and-go" pit stops. / www.spianata.com; 3.30 pm;
EC3 11 pm; closed Sat & Sun; E1 closed Sat; no credit cards; no booking.

Spice Market
W Hotel London W1 **NEW** £75 ④④④
10 Wardour St 7758 1088 4–3A
"A shambles"; top NYC chef Jean-Georges Vongerichten's much-hyped
fusion newcomer, off Leicester Square, offers "hit-and-miss" cooking,
"patchy" service and an interior that's "great… if you've never been
inside a boutique hotel before"; drinks prices can seem exorbitant
too. / www.spicemarketlondon.co.uk; Sun-Wed 11 pm, Thu-Sat 11.30 pm;
set weekday L £41 (FP), set pre-theatre £43 (FP).

The Spread Eagle SE10 £51 ④④❸
1-2 Stockwell St 8853 2333 1–3D
This "fine old building" – an olde-worlde Greenwich tavern – offers
a "very comfortable" location for a meal; it may seem rather
"overpriced", though – for critics, "the sumptuous decor only
heightens the disappointment". / www.spreadeaglerestaurant.co.uk;
10.30 pm; no Amex; set Sun L £33 (FP).

Spuntino W1 **NEW** £41 ❸❷❷
61 Rupert St no tel 3–2D
With its "grimy Americana" (Lower East Side-style), its "achingly cool"
staff, and its menu of calorific "US faves", Russell Norman's "studied"
newcomer – "in the sleaziest heart of Soho" – has inspired
"evangelical fervour" amongst fashionista twenty/thirty-somethings;
doubters, though, find the whole shtick "a bit meh". / Rated on Editors'
visit; www.spuntino.co.uk; 11.30 pm, Sun 10.30 pm.

THE SQUARE W1 £106 ❷❷❸
6-10 Bruton St 7495 7100 3–2C
"Superb in every department" – the "complex" cuisine Phil Howard
offers at this acclaimed Mayfair dining room is complemented by an
"immense" wine list of "amazing" quality; the ambience can seem
"sombre", though, not helped by the place's popularity with "Identikit
men in suits". / www.squarerestaurant.com; 9.45 pm, Sat 10.15 pm,
Sun 9.30 pm; closed Sat L & Sun L; booking: max 8; set weekday L £56 (FP).

Sree Krishna SW17 £26 ❶❷❸
192-194 Tooting High St 8672 4250 10–2C
On top form at present, this "friendly" Tooting veteran dishes
up "some of the best south Indian food in London" (including
an "astonishing selection of starters"); "if you want to go off-piste,
they are very good at preparing a feast for you"; BYO.
/ www.sreekrishna.co.uk; 11 pm, Fri & Sat midnight.

FSA

Star of India SW5 £49 ❷❹❸
154 Old Brompton Rd 7373 2901 5–2B
"An old favourite that still delivers"; perhaps surprisingly, though, it's not the characterful ("dated") decor of this South Kensington veteran which attracts attention, nor the "slow" and sometimes "off-hand" service – rather, it's the "lovely, fresh and interesting" cuisine! / www.starofindia.eu; 11.45 pm, Sun 11.15 pm.

Starbucks £14 ❹❸❸
Branches throughout London
Barristas who seem "genuinely happy to serve" and "comfy branches for a chat" create the "welcoming" appeal of this "formulaic" mega-chain; even those who think "the coffee is great", however, may feel its paninis, cakes and other fare "are not". / www.starbucks.com; 6.30 pm-11 pm; most City branches closed all or part of weekend; no booking.

Stein's TW10 £29 ❸❹❷
Towpath (Rear of 55 Petersham Rd) 8948 8189 1–4A
For "a really fun day by the riverside" ("with the added bonus of a gated play area for kids"), try this "lovely" German beer garden, near Richmond Bridge – "a totally relaxed place" with a good-value, if admittedly "rather sausage-heavy", menu. / www.stein-s.com; 9.30 pm; no Amex.

Stick & Bowl W8 £23 ❸❸❸
31 Kensington High St 7937 2778 5–1A
"Unassuming, easily-overlooked and shabby", this handy Chinese chow house, in Kensington, is a "rushed" sort of place where you eat "squashed in on bar stools"; thanks to its "huge" and "cheap" noodle dishes, "it's always busy, mostly with Asians". / 10.45 pm; no credit cards; no booking.

Sticky Fingers W8 £43 ❹❹❸
1a Phillimore Gdns 7938 5338 5–1A
"Good big juicy burgers" and other "fattening" American fare help make this veteran Kensington diner a popular nomination for those with kids in tow; "if you get bored, you can look at the Rolling Stones memorabilia on the walls". / www.stickyfingers.co.uk; 11.30 pm.

Stock Pot £27 ❺❹❹
40 Panton St, SW1 7839 5142 4–4A
273 King's Rd, SW3 7823 3175 5–3C
These "die hard" '60s canteens are "oh-so-dependable" for "old-fashioned, school-dinners scoff at great prices"; "don't linger, though – they're for fuelling up!" / SW1 11.30 pm, Wed-Sat midnight, Sun 11 pm SW3 10.15 pm, Sun 9.45 pm; no Amex.

Strada £38 ❹❹❸
Branches throughout London
"A very good alternative to Pizza Express" (which it lags only narrowly in all survey-categories), this popular Italian chain is "pretty reliable", and "well geared up to cope with kids". / www.strada.co.uk; 10.30 pm-11 pm; some booking restrictions apply.

Stringray Café £27 ❹❹❹
36 Highbury Pk, N5 7354 9309 8–2D
Tufnell Pk, NW5 7482 4855 8–2B
109 Columbia Rd, E2 7613 1141 12–1C
"Oversized pizza and giant pastas" come at "very cheap" prices, at these "basic", "busy" and "cheerful" Italian stand-bys; E2 (near Columbia Road Market) scores best, while N5 (near the Arsenal ground) is best-known. / www.stringraycafe.co.uk; 11 pm; no Amex.

Sufi W12 £30 ❸❷④
70 Askew Rd 8834 4888 7–1B
*"A simple Persian café", in the depths of Shepherd's Bush; its "lovely"
staff serve up some "excellent" grills, and the bread to go with them
is "to die for". / www.sufirestaurant.com; 11 pm.*

Suk Saran SW19 £42 ❸④④
29 Wimbledon Rd 8947 9199 10–2B
*Looking for a "real taste of Thailand"? – the food at this high-street
operation, near Wimbledon station, is "surprisingly good".
/ www.sukhogroup.com; 11 pm; booking: max 20; set weekday L £30 (FP).*

Sukho Fine Thai Cuisine SW6 £40 ❶❷❸
855 Fulham Rd 7371 7600 10–1B
*"Dishes look like works of art, and taste like masterpieces too",
at this "obliging" and "reasonably-priced" Thai café; even though it's
"cramped" and rather "out of the way", in deepest Fulham,
"you must book". / www.sukhogroup.co.uk; 11 pm.*

The Summerhouse W9 £45 ④④❶
60 Blomfield Rd 7286 6752 8–4A
*"The food's nothing to shout about but, with that view of the canal,
who cares?" – that's the trade-off at this summer-only 'pop-up',
in Little Venice, which serves a "slightly overpriced menu, focussed
on fish". / www.summerhousebythewaterway.co.uk; 10.30 pm, Sun 10 pm;
Mon-Fri closed D, Sat & Sun open L & D; no Amex.*

Sumosan W1 £75 ❸❸❸
26b Albemarle St 7495 5999 3–3C
*"It doesn't pull in the crowds like some of its rivals", but this "high-
end" Mayfair haunt still serves some "mind-blowing" sushi and other
Japanese fusion fare that's on a par with the Nobus of the world –
it is likewise "priced for oligarchs", of course, but the style is relatively
low-key. / www.sumosan.com; 11.30 pm, Sun 10.30 pm; closed Sat L & Sun L.*

supperclub W10 £62 ④④❶
12 Acklam Rd 8964 6600 6–1A
*"Lounging on beds is a perfect way to spend a romantic evening with
someone", say fans of this decadent North Kensington nitespot,
where cabaret is a feature; "it's an interesting experience but, for the
quality of the food, an outrageously expensive one".
/ www.supperclub.com; 10.30 pm; D only.*

Le Suquet SW3 £65 ❸④④
104 Draycott Ave 7581 1785 5–2C
*A "very authentic French fish restaurant", on a quiet Chelsea corner
(where "sitting outdoors on a warm night evokes the Côte d'Azur");
the style may be "dated", but notably good fruits-de-mer are
a highlight of the "consistent" menu. / 11.30 pm.*

Sushi of Shiori NW1 £38 ❶❶④
144 Drummond St 7388 9962 8–4C
*A "tiny, Tokyo-style" joint, lost "amidst the curry houses of Drummond
Street", hailed by all who comment on it for "exquisite" sushi –
"authentic", "beautifully presented", and with "really unusual
flavours"; "best option is the Omakase – you set a price and leave
the selections to the chef". / www.sushiofshiori.co.uk; 10 pm; closed
Mon & Sun; no Amex; set always available £32 (FP).*

Sushisamba EC2 NEW
Heron Tower, 110 Bishopsgate awaiting tel 9–2D
*At the top of the City's Heron Tower – an offshoot of a trendy NYC
Japanese/South American fusion specialist, scheduled to open in late-
2011.*

Sushi-Say NW2 £41 **❶❶❸**
33b Walm Ln   8459 7512   1–1A
"The freshest sushi this side of Tokyo" and other "ethereal" Japanese dishes ("it's always worth asking about the day's specials") draw fans from far and wide to this "unlikely" – but "really outstanding" – family-run outfit, in deepest Willesden. / 10 pm, Sat 10.30 pm, Sun 9.30 pm; closed Mon, Tue-Fri D only, Sat & Sun open L & D; no Amex.

Sushinho SW3 £47 **④❸❷**
312-314 King's Rd   7349 7496   5–3C
Thanks to its "happy music" and "fantastic cocktails", this "elegant" Chelsea bar/restaurant certainly has a "good vibe"; Brazil meets Japan on its weird-looking fusion menu – there are some "delicious" outcomes, but results are "not consistent", and some of the prices are "eye-popping". www.sushinho.com; 10 pm; closed Mon L, Tue L & Sun L.

The Swan W4 £39 **❷❸❷**
119 Acton Ln   8994 8262   7–1A
"A really classy neighbourhood pub", "hidden-away" in a Chiswick backwater, and complete with "a lovely garden"; service is "charming", and the "earthy gastro-fare" offers some "first-rate value". / theswanchiswick.co.uk; 10 pm, Fri & Sat 10.30 pm, Sun 10 pm; closed weekday L.

Swan & Edgar NW1 £37 **④④❷**
43 Linhope St   7724 6268   2–1A
"A lovely, tiny place" that's making "a useful addition to the Baker Street area"; this somewhat eccentric gastropub offers "comforting", if slightly "hit-and-miss", cooking, plus "good wines by the glass". / www.swanandedgar.co.uk; 10 pm, Sun 9 pm; D only, ex Sun open L & D.

The Swan at the Globe SE1 £48 **④④❷**
21 New Globe Walk   7928 9444   9–3B
"Excellent views of the Thames and St Paul's" reward visitors to the first-floor dining room of the Bard's re-created South Bank theatre; the food – briefly bucked up after the arrival of Ramsay-protégé Mark Sargeant – has quickly reverted to its "unadventurous" old ways. / www.swanattheglobe.co.uk; 10.30 pm; closed Sun D.

Sweet & Spicy E1 £11 **❷❷⑤**
40 Brick Ln   7247 1081   12–2C
"Unbelievably cheap and authentic Indian/Pakistani food" wins praise for this "down-to-earth" caff – one of the best bets on Brick Lane; "good service" too. / www.sweetandspicylondon.co.uk; 11 pm, Fri & Sat midnight; no Amex.

Sweetings EC4 £58 **❸❸❸**
39 Queen Victoria St   7248 3062   9–3B
"Still Dickensian, still unique!"; "everyone should lunch at least once", at this "marvellous" City "throwback", which serves "very good" – and "very expensive" – seafood; NB: "get there early to avoid the pinstriped throngs!" / 3.30 pm; L only, closed Sat & Sun; no booking.

Taberna Etrusca EC4 £48 **④④④**
9 Bow Churchyard   7248 5552   9–2C
This "traditional" and ever-popular City Italian, with its sunny al fresco tables, remains "as good as it has been for years" – the less kind would say this means it is still "no great shakes". / www.etruscarestaurants.com; closed Sat & Sun.

The Table SE1 £40 ④❸❸
83 Southwark St 7401 2760 9–4B
A trendy communal canteen (part of an architects' practice), not far
from Southwark Bridge, where "fantastic" breakfasts are a highlight,
and which is good for lunch too; views (few) on the place's attractions
at dinner are rather mixed. / www.thetablecafe.com; 10.30 pm; closed
Mon D & Sun D.

Taiwan Village SW6 £32 ❶❶❸
85 Lillie Rd 7381 2900 5–3A
Given its "unpromising location" – just off the North End Road –
this sensational Chinese/Taiwanese outfit can seem like "a major
discovery"; choose the 'Leave It With Us' menu option for some
"amazing flavours", at "incredible-value" prices.
/ www.taiwanvillage.com; 11.30 pm; closed weekday L; booking: max 20.

Tajima Tei EC1 £32 ❶❷④
9-11 Leather Ln 7404 9665 9–2A
"Simple and unpretentious, but never failing to impress" –
this "very genuine" and "good-value" Japanese, off Hatton Garden,
is well worth seeking out for its "quality" cuisine. / www.tajima-tei.co.uk;
10 pm; closed Sat & Sun; no booking, L.

Talad Thai SW15 £28 ❸❸⑤
320 Upper Richmond Rd 8246 5791 10–2A
Not quite the 'rave' it once was, but this "functional" Putney Thai
retains an "authentic" quality that commends it to most reporters;
it's part 'n' parcel with the "handy oriental supermarket next door".
/ www.taladthai.co.uk; 10.30 pm, Sun 9.30 pm; no Amex.

Tamarai WC2 £52 ④④④
167 Drury Ln 7831 9399 4–1C
A "trendy"-looking Indian basement, in Covent Garden;
some reporters love its "darkly atmospheric" style, "clubby"
atmosphere, and "interesting" dishes – critics, however, "just do not
understand the fuss". / www.tamarai.co.uk; 11 pm; D only, closed Sun.

Tamarind W1 £68 ❸❸④
20 Queen St 7629 3561 3–3B
"Creative" Indian cooking and "attentive" service still win high praise
for this "sophisticated" Mayfair basement; critics fear, however,
that "the spark has gone", and the overall performance does indeed
risk becoming rather "middle-of-the-road".
/ www.tamarindrestaurant.com; 11 pm, Sun 10.30 pm; closed Sat L;
set weekday L £38 (FP).

Tandoori Nights SE22 £35 ❸❸❸
73 Lordship Ln 8299 4077 1–4D
The menu may be "due for an update", but this East Dulwich curry
house "continues to serve consistently tasty and freshly-spiced" North
Indian food. / www.tandoorinightsdulwich.co.uk; 11.30 pm; closed
weekday L & Sat L.

Tangawizi TW1 £41 ❸❸④
406 Richmond Rd 8891 3737 1–4A
"Some real hits, the odd miss" – that's what you should expect if you
visit this "very busy" Twickenham subcontinental. / www.tangawizi.co.uk;
11 pm, Sun 10.30 pm; D only.

Tapas Brindisa   £39   ❷❸❷

46 Broadwick St, W1   7534 1690   3–2D

18-20 Southwark St, SE1   7357 8880   9–4C

"Just like being in an upscale Madrid tapas place" – the *"chaotic"* Borough original has won an enormous following for its *"gutsy"* fare, and even if it's a tad *"pricey for what it is"*, you must *"arrive early"*; Soho (formerly Tierra Brindisa) is now a sibling – historically it's lagged SE1 in all areas but service. / 10.45 pm, Sun 10 pm; W1 booking: max 10.

Taqueria W11   £34   ❹❹❸

139-143 Westbourne Grove   7229 4734   6–1B

"Absolutely not Tex-Mex!" – this *"casual and buzzy"* Notting Hill Mexican actually delivers *"something akin to the real thing"*, with its fresh tacos and *"wonderful"* drinks; even so, it's really *"not cheap"* and a bit *"variable"* too, so *"best for a snack and a beer"*.
/ www.taqueria.co.uk; Mon-Thu 11 pm, Fri & Sat 11.30 pm, Sun 10.30 pm; no Amex; no booking Fri-Sun.

Taro   £28   ❸❸❸

10 Old Compton St, W1   7439 2275   4–2B

61 Brewer St, W1   7734 5826   3–2D

"Fast, cheerful and reliable" – these *"busy"* Japanese canteens, in Soho, offer an *"impressively wide"* menu of *"simple"* sushi, noodle and curry dishes, at *"cheap"* prices. / www.tarorestaurants.co.uk; 10.30 pm, Sun 9.30 pm; no Amex; Brewer St only small bookings.

Tartine SW3   £46   ❸❹❸

114 Draycott Ave   7589 4981   5–2C

"A nice place after a bit of Sloaney shopping" – and *"not overpriced by Chelsea standards"*, either – this superior Brompton Cross pit stop serves *"high-quality"* open sandwiches (pain Poilâne), and other light bites. / www.tartine.co.uk; Mon-Wed 11.30 pm, Thu-Sat 12pm, Sun 10.30 pm.

Tas   £32   ❹❸❸

22 Bloomsbury St, WC1   7637 4555   2–1C

33 The Cut, SE1   7928 2111   9–4A

72 Borough High St, SE1   7403 7200   9–4C

76 Borough High St, SE1   7403 8557   9–4C

37 Farringdon Rd, EC1   7430 9721   9–1A

"Affordable" and pretty *"reliable"* too, these ever-*"crowded"* Turkish restaurants are often hailed as an *"excellent stand-by"* (not least *"for big groups"*); critics, though, do feel the food *"has gone downhill"* in recent times. / www.tasrestaurant.com; 11.30 pm, Sun 10.30 pm; set always available £20 (FP).

Tas Pide SE1   £30   ❹❷❷

20-22 New Globe Walk   7928 3300   9–3B

A *"jolly"* Anatolian café, opposite Shakespeare's Globe, which is named after its Turkish 'pizza' speciality – a *"cheap"* and *"enjoyable"* snack, preferable to the *"rather ordinary"* mezze also available. / www.tasrestaurant.com/tas_pide; 11.30 pm, Sun 10.30 pm.

La Tasca   £30   ❺❸❸

Branches throughout London

"Staff who try hard can't make up for food that's very ordinary and tasteless", at these lively – but on occasion *"diabolical"* – tapas joints; perhaps the most eloquent commentary on the London outlets is the tiny number of reports they inspire. / www.latasca.co.uk; 11 pm; E14 10.45 pm; booking: min 8.

(Rex Whistler)
Tate Britain SW1   £51   ❸❸❷
Millbank   7887 8825   2–4C
The "beautiful" Whistler-muralled dining room of this Westminster gallery offers rather "old-fashioned" British food that's "always good"; even so, the scoff's "beside the point", compared to the "out-of-this-world" wine list (which is "fairly-priced" too). / www.tate.org.uk; L & afternoon tea only.

(Restaurant, Level 7)
Tate Modern SE1   £43   ④④❷
Bankside   7887 8888   9–3B
"Stunning views" – some of London's finest – are the draw to this South Bank gallery's "buzzy" 7th-floor café; fans say the "simple" fare is "enjoyable" too, but to critics it's just "basic" and "very ordinary". / www.tate.org.uk; 9.30 pm; Sun-Thu closed D, Fri & Sat open L & D.

(Café, Level 2)
Tate Modern SE1   £36   ❸④❸
Bankside   7401 5014   9–3B
The Tate's ground-floor café is sometimes "too busy", but foodwise it generally proves the more reliable of the two major options at this much-visited museum of modern art; it's a strikingly-designed and kid-friendly space, where the straightforward food usually satisfies. / www.tate.org.uk/modern/eatanddrink; Fri 9.30 pm; L & tea only, ex Fri open L & D.

Tatra W12   £35   ④④④
24 Goldhawk Rd   8749 8193   7–1C
On a corner near Goldhawk Road tube, this year-old venture goes largely un-noticed, but it's a "pleasant and efficient" spot offering "substantial portions of well-prepared Polish food". / www.tatrarestaurant.co.uk; 11 pm, Sun 10 pm.

Telegraph SW15   £36   ④④❸
Telegraph Rd   8788 2011   10–2A
"After a walk or bike ride on Wimbledon Common", this 'country pub in London' (their words) makes a "cosy" destination; there's "ample outdoor seating", but "it can get crowded" nonetheless. / www.thetelegraphputney.co.uk; 8.30 pm, Fri & Sat 9.30 pm.

Tempo W1 NEW   £58   ❸❷❸
54 Curzon St   7629 2742   3–3B
"Innovative" and "polished" cooking – from a Japanese chef! – has helped make Henry Togna's "friendly" Italian newcomer (on the site of Franks, RIP) a welcome addition to Mayfair; discreetly hidden-away upstairs, there's a "fabulous" bar. / www.tempomayfair.co.uk; 10.30 pm; closed Sat L & Sun; Table max 8.

Ten Ten Tei W1   £35   ❸❸⑤
56 Brewer St   7287 1738   3–2D
"Basic Japanese fare at very competitive prices" – the lure to this "grim"-looking Soho canteen; some regulars, though, fear that it has "slipped" of late. / 10 pm; closed Sun; no Amex; no booking Fri & Sat.

Tendido Cero SW5   £38   ❸❸❷
174 Old Brompton Rd   7370 3685   5–2B
With its "bubbly" style and "very dependable" cuisine, "Cambio de Tercio's fabulous, more tapas-y younger sibling" offers "a really fun night out"; this South Kensington dining room's "ruthless" two-sittings policy can be "annoying", though, and pricing can grate. / www.cambiodetercio.co.uk; 11 pm.

FSA

Tendido Cuatro SW6 £39 ❷❷❷
108-110 New King's Rd 7371 5147 10–1B
"Interesting tapas", "wonderful paella" and "fabulous red wine" create a more-than-local following for this Fulham outpost of the Cambio de Tercio empire. / www.cambiodetercio.co.uk; 11 pm.

Tentazioni SE1 £49 ❸❸❸
2 Mill St 7394 5248 11–2A
What's happening at this "quirky" and "stylish" Italian, "hidden-away down an alley near Tower Bridge"? – its "interesting" regional cooking "is not of the quality it was", and service (though often "lovely") has sometimes seemed "disinterested" of late. / www.tentazioni.co.uk; 10.45 pm; closed Sat L & Sun; set weekday L £21 (FP).

The Terrace in the Fields WC2 £39 ❸④❷
Lincoln's Inn Fields 7430 1234 2–2D
Leafy Lincoln's Inn Fields provides the "terrific", location ("really coming into its own in the summer") for this "rather hidden-away" modern shed, which serves "interesting" West Indian-influenced food. / www.theterrace.info; 9 pm; L only, closed Sat & Sun.

Terranostra EC4 £45 ❸❷④
27 Old Bailey 3201 0077 9–2A
Near the Old Bailey, a low-key spot worth seeking out for its "comparatively simple" Sardinian food, which is often "done really well". / www.terranostrafood.co.uk; 10 pm; closed Sat L & Sun.

TERROIRS WC2 £46 ❷❸❸
5 William IV St 7036 0660 4–4C
"Phenomenally innovative" ('biodynamique') wines twinned with a petits-plats-based menu of "rich" and "earthy" fare – including much charcuterie and cheese – have made a massive name for this "cramped" but "deservedly busy" and "convivial" spot, near Charing Cross. / www.terroirswinebar.com; 11 pm; closed Sun.

Texture W1 £79 ❷❶❸
34 Portman St 7224 0028 2–2A
A grand Marylebone dining room where Angar Sverrisson's "fascinating" cuisine – "subtle flavours, brilliantly juxtaposed" and with no butter or cream in the savoury dishes – comes "perfectly combined" with business partner Xavier Rousset's wine selection; if there's a niggle it's the setting – for some reporters it just "doesn't work". / www.texture-restaurant.co.uk; 10.30 pm; closed Mon & Sun; set weekday L £46 (FP).

Thai Corner Café SE22 £23 ❸❸❸
44 North Cross Rd 8299 4041 1–4D
"Delicious, authentic, casual, essential to book..." – this BYO East Dulwich café remains a "very dependable" local. / 10.30 pm; closed Mon L; no credit cards.

Thai Garden SW11 £30 ❸④④
58 Battersea Rise 7738 0380 10–2C
A "stalwart" Battersea Thai that "never lets you down" – the food is "not adventurous", but it is "tasty" and "fairly-priced". / www.thaigarden.co.uk; 11 pm; D only.

Thai on the River SW11 £42 ❸④❸
2 Lombard Rd 7924 6090 5–4B
Overlooking the Thames, this Battersea Thai survives on its all-round appeal, even if the cognoscenti may find the food a little 'safe'. / www.thaiontheriver.com; 10.30 pm.

Thai Pot WC2 £36 ❸❷❸
1 Bedfordbury 7379 4580 4–4C
"Very close to the Coliseum, and ideal for a group meal before a show", this "lively and cheerful" stand-by is "not unduly expensive", and it's "always popular". / www.thaipot.biz; 11.15 pm; closed Sun.

Thai Square £35 ④❸❸
21-24 Cockspur St, SW1 7839 4000 2–3C
27-28 St Annes Ct, W1 7287 2000 3–1D
5 Princess St, W1 7499 3333 3–1C
148 The Strand, WC2 7497 0904 2–2D
166-170 Shaftesbury Ave, WC2 7836 7600 4–1B
229-230 Strand, WC2 7353 6980 2–2D
19 Exhibition Rd, SW7 7584 8359 5–2C
347-349 Upper St, N1 7704 2000 8–3D
2-4 Lower Richmond Rd, SW15 8780 1811 10–1A
136-138 Minories, EC3 7680 1111 9–3D
1-7 Great St Thomas Apostle, EC4 7329 0001 9–3B
An Asian chain that's seen ratings ebb in recent years; fans still find it a "solid" performer, but sceptics say it "trades on its name and strong branch locations" – in particular, its striking SW15 site (by Putney Bridge) enjoys "fantastic Thames views". / www.thaisquare.net; 10 pm-11.30 pm; SW1 Fri & Sat 1 am; WC2, EC3, EC4 & St Annes Ct closed Sat & Sun.

Thali SW5 NEW £45 ❷❷④
166 Old Brompton Rd 7373 2626 5–2B
Still limited feedback on this oddly-configured (railway carriage-style) recent addition to South Kensington's 'Indian corner'; all reporters, however, have enjoyed the "flavoursome" cuisine. / www.thali.uk.com; 11.30 pm, Sun 10.30 pm; set weekday L £24 (FP).

Theo Randall
InterContinental Hotel W1 £80 ❷❸④
1 Hamilton Pl 7318 8747 3–4A
"Beautifully-married" flavours – including some "mouthwatering pasta"... and "even better fish!" – justify a trip to this celebrated chef's Mayfair Italian; well, it certainly can't be the "underwhelming" setting, or the sometimes "weak" service. / www.theorandall.com; 11.15 pm; closed Sat L & Sun; set always available £52 (FP).

34 Grosvenor Square W1 NEW
34 Grosvenor Sq awaiting tel 3–3A
Watch out Duke! – of Westminster, that is – as Richard Caring's take-over of Mayfair continues apace; the concept of the latest outpost, set to open in late-2011, is 'the grill version of Scott's' (itself two minutes' walk away).

The Thomas Cubitt SW1 £61 ❸❸❷
44 Elizabeth St 7730 6060 2–4A
"Ridiculously posh" for a pub, this "buzzy" Belgravian has become a linchpin of the area's social scene; "the bar food is very good" – above, there's a "terrific" dining room, where "roasts are a real highlight". / www.thethomascubitt.co.uk; 10 pm; closed Sat L & Sun D; booking only in restaurant.

tibits W1 £33 ❸④❸
12-14 Heddon St 7758 4110 3–2C
"It's not that it's the most amazing food ever, but the whole idea is fantastic" – this "pleasant" Swiss operation, just off Regent Street, dishes up some "delicious and very healthy" veggie fare, charged by weight. / www.tibits.co.uk; 11.30 pm, Sun 10 pm; no Amex; Only bookings for 8+.

Timo W8 £56 ❷❶④
343 Kensington High St   7603 3888   7–1D
"A warm and wonderful host welcomes you as if you were family",
at this somewhat anonymous-looking Kensington-fringe Italian;
"sometimes the food is very good, but at other times it's just good".
/ www.timorestaurant.net; 11 pm; closed Sun; set weekday L £32 (FP).

Tinello SW1 £39 ❷❶❷
87 Pimlico Rd   7730 3663   5–2D
Fresh "from the Locatelli stable", this "lovely" and "vibrant" Pimlico
Italian has been "packed ever since it opened"; the cooking
"combines comfort food with intensely-flavoured Tuscan invention",
but it is arguably eclipsed by the "perfect" service. / www.tinello.co.uk;
10.30 pm; closed Sun.

Toff's N10 £35 ❷❷④
38 Muswell Hill Broadway   8883 8656   1–1B
"Everything a chippy ought to be" – this "very busy" Muswell Hill
veteran dishes up "beautifully fresh fish" and "the best chips"; service
is "terrific" too; BYO. / www.toffsfish.co.uk; 10 pm; closed Sun.

Toku
Japan Center SW1 £35 ❸❸④
14-16 Regent St   3405 1246   3–3D
For a "no-fuss" bite in the heart of the West End, this "authentic"
Japanese café/canteen (part of a store, formerly in a different
location nearby) makes a handy find, serving "simple" fare
at "reasonable" prices (especially "if you print out the weekly voucher
on the website"). / 9 pm, Sun 8.45 pm; no Amex; no booking Sat.

Tokyo Diner WC2 £26 ④❷❸
2 Newport Pl   7287 8777   4–3B
A "cosy and traditional-looking" little stalwart, mislocated
in Chinatown; some dishes "rock", other's "less so", but "at the
prices, who's complaining?" / www.tokyodiner.com; midnight; no Amex;
no booking, Fri & Sat.

Tom Aikens SW3 £101
43 Elystan St   7584 2003   5–2C
This celebrity chef's Chelsea HQ re-opens in late-2011, after a major
refurbishment; in the prior year, ratings slumped, and some reporters
saw the place as a "rip-off"… so there's plenty of scope for
improvement. / www.tomaikens.co.uk; 11 pm; closed Sat L & Sun; jacket
and/or tie; booking: max 8.

Tom Ilic SW8 £46 ❷❷⑤
123 Queenstown Rd   7622 0555   10–1C
Tom Ilic is undoubtedly "a talent", and the "very porky menu"
he offers at this "great-value" Battersea fixture is "always exciting",
and service is "very welcoming and efficient" too; shame the setting
is so very "unexciting". / www.tomilic.com; 10.30 pm; closed Mon,
Tue L & Sun D.

Tom's Deli W11 £33 ❸④❸
226 Westbourne Grove   7221 8818   6–1B
Tom Conran's "friendly" deli, in the trendy heart of Notting Hill,
is primarily known for its "excellent breakfast/brunch" (for which it's
usually "difficult to get a seat"). / www.tomsdeli.co.uk; 5 pm; L only;
no Amex; no booking.

Tom's Kitchen SW3   £59   ④⑤④
27 Cale St   7349 0202   5–2C
Tom Aiken's once-oh-so-fashionable Chelsea hang-out seems ever more passé – it offers "overpriced and very average" gastropub fare, and service that's really "not great"; obvious solution? – announce a roll-out of six more branches… / www.tomskitchen.co.uk; 11 pm.

Tom's Terrace
Somerset House WC2   £52   ⑤④❸
150 Strand   7845 4646   2–2D
A spin-off of the rather ragged Tom Aikens empire, this clubby, tented Ibiza-style operation pops up on the wonderful terrace of Somerset House every summer – the little feedback it inspires suggests its location is the only undoubted plus.
/ www.tomskitchen.co.uk/somersethouse; 9.30 pm, Sun 4 pm; no booking.

The Tommyfield SE11   £46   ⑤⑤④
185 Kennington Ln   7735 1061   1–3C
Oh dear! – only a year or so in business, the relaunch of Kennington's former White Hart "has gone downhill really fast", with all-round standards too often seeming "distinctly average" nowadays.
/ www.thetommyfield.com; 10.15 pm.

Tompkins E14   £50   ⑤④④
3 Pan Peninsula Sq   8305 3080   11–2C
A "stark" modern yearling, seemingly designed for the business crowd, in a skyscraper, by South Quay; it can seems "cavernous and empty" – perhaps because the whole experience is rather "drab"?
/ www.tompkins.uk.com; 10.30 pm, Sun 8.30 pm.

Tortilla   £18   ❸❸④
6 Market Place, W1   7637 2800   3–1C
6a, King St, W6   8741 7959   7–2C **NEW**
13 Islington High St, N1   7833 3103   8–3D
106 Southwark St, SE1   7620 0285   9–4B
18 North Colonnade, E14   7719 9160   11–1C
28 Leadenhall Mkt, EC3   7929 7837   9–2D **NEW**
With their "healthy, delight-giving burritos", these Cal-Mex pit stops make a "fresh and exciting" refuelling option. / www.tortilla.co.uk; W1 & N1 11 pm, Sun 9 pm, SE1 & E14 9 pm, EC3 7 pm, E14 Sun 7 pm; SE1 & EC3 closed Sat &Sun; no Amex.

Tosa W6   £34   ❸④④
332 King St   8748 0002   7–2B
A Japanese café, near Stamford Brook, that's "a bit of a squash"; its "family-friendly" charms generally win people over, though, and the menu is "good all-round", with the yakitori "the real treat".
/ www.tosauk.com; 10.30 pm.

Toto's SW1   £67   ❸❸❸
Lennox Gardens Mews   7589 0075   5–2C
This "upscale" Italian, near Harrods, has a "lovely" interior, and the food's "reliable" too; the style that strikes fans as "refreshingly untrendy", however, is now at risk of seeming simply "dated", and while "the menu probably hasn't changed since the '80s, the prices certainly have!" / 11 pm, Sun 10.30 pm.

The Trafalgar Tavern SE10   £45   ⑤④❸
28 Park Row   8858 2909   1–3D
A majestic Thames-side location sets the scene at this historic and "lovely" Greenwich tavern; shame the food's so "lazy" though, and it can "take an age to be served" too. / www.trafalgartavern.co.uk; 10 pm; closed Sun D; no Amex.

The Tree House SW13 £38 ④❸❷
73 White Hart Ln 8392 1617 10–1A
"A nice outdoor terrace for a sunny day" is a highlight of this "welcoming" pub-conversion – nowadays more a wine bar/restaurant – on the fringes of Barnes; the food is a bit incidental.
/ www.treehousepeople.com; 11 pm, Fri & Sat midnight, Sun 10.30 pm.

TRINITY SW4 £56 ❶❶❷
4 The Polygon 7622 1199 10–2D
"The residents of Clapham are spoilt", says one of the fans of this dazzling neighbourhood blockbuster, where Adam Byatt's "carefully balanced" cuisine "just gets better and better"; it's a "stylish" place too, where "incredibly accommodating staff" contribute to the "convivial" ambience. / www.trinityrestaurant.co.uk; 10.30 pm; closed Mon L & Sun D.

Trishna W1 £51 ❶❷❸
15-17 Blandford St 7935 5624 2–1A
"Like going to India, but without the jet lag!"; "magical" dishes that are "light", "vibrant" and "perfectly spiced" win rave reviews for this Marylebone seafood-specialist – offshoot of a restaurant famous in Mumbai. / www.trishnalondon.com; Mon-Sat 10.45 pm, Sun 9.45 pm.

Les Trois Garçons E1 £67 ❸❸❶
1 Club Row 7613 1924 12–1C
"Don't be put off by all the stuffed animals!" – they form part of the "magical" setting you'll find at this fabulously "quirky" East End pub-conversion; as you'd expect, the Gallic cuisine rather plays second fiddle, but it's often been "better than expected" of late.
/ www.lestroisgarcons.com; Mon 9.30 pm, Tue-Thu 10 pm, Fri & Sat 10.30 pm; closed Sat L & Sun D; need credit card to book £25 deposit; set weekday L £39 (FP).

Trojka NW1 £29 ④④❸
101 Regent's Park Rd 7483 3765 8–2B
"An unusual atmosphere" adds interest to a trip to this crowded Russian café/bistro, in Primrose Hill; the scoff is often "tasty" too, but the entertainments – and the vodka selection – are arguably a greater attraction. / www.trojka.co.uk; 10.30 pm; no Amex.

LA TROMPETTE W4 £63 ❶❶❷
5-7 Devonshire Rd 8747 1836 7–2A
"Why go into town when this is on my doorstep?"; this sibling to Chez Bruce remains "the jewel in Chiswick's crown", twinning "faultless" cuisine with an "eclectic and fascinating" wine list; it's a "chic" but "unstuffy" place too (if a little on the "squashed" side).
/ www.latrompette.co.uk; 10.30 pm, Sun 10 pm.

Troubadour SW5 £36 ⑤❸❶
263-265 Old Brompton Rd 7370 1434 5–3A
Fans – some of decades' standing – still adore this wonderfully Bohemian Earls's Court fixture, for breakfast, for coffee, or even for a "romantic" bite; the food is not art, however, and prices are really pushing it nowadays. / www.troubadour.co.uk; 11 pm.

Truc Vert W1 £52 ❸④④
42 North Audley St 7491 9988 3–2A
"No frills, but very cute", this Mayfair deli/diner is "a little piece of France"; main meals here can sometimes seem "a bit hectic" to be truly enjoyable, but – for a "fabulous breakfast" – this is undoubtedly a top destination. / www.trucvert.co.uk; 10 pm; closed Sun D.

Trullo N1 £36 ❷❶❷
300-302 St Paul's Rd 7226 2733 8–2D
*"River Café-esque food at non-River Café prices" has instantly created
a "real buzz" around this "rustic" Islington newcomer… to the extent
that it's "often impossible to get a table"; critics may cry "hype",
but most reporters "absolutely love the place".*
/ www.trullorestaurant.com; 10.30 pm; closed weekday L & Sun D.

Tsunami £48 ❶❹❸
93 Charlotte St, W1 7637 0050 2–1C
5-7 Voltaire Rd, SW4 7978 1610 10–1D
*"Nobu-quality" fare, including "incredible sushi and sashimi" –
"at much lower prices", and "without the hype" – wins rave reviews
for these Japanese-fusion ventures; service can be "a let-down"
though (and the "unsexy" Fitzrovia spin-off is something of a
disappointment compared to the "buzzy" Clapham original).*
/ www.tsunamirestaurant.co.uk; SW4 10.30 pm, Fri & Sat 11 pm,
Sun 9.30 pm; W1 11 pm; SW4 Mon - Fri D only; W1 closed Sun, Sat D only;
no Amex.

Tsuru £28 ❸❹❹
201 Bishopsgate, EC2 7377 1166 12–2B
10 Queen St, EC4 7377 6367 9–2B **NEW**
4 Canvey St, SE1 7928 2228 9–4B
*These "bustling" Japanese "fast-food" operations – on the South
Bank, and in the City – serve "authentic dishes, which go beyond
simple sushi and noodles" ("excellent katsu curries", for example),
and at "reasonable prices" too!* / www.tsuru-sushi.co.uk; EC2 9 pm;
SE1 9 pm, Sat 7 pm, EC4 10; EC2 & EC4 closed Sat & Sun, SE1 closed Sun;
no booking L.

28-50 EC4 £49 ❸❷❸
140 Fetter Ln 7242 8877 9–2A
*"Once you get over the inauspicious office-block-basement location",
this City-fringe yearling is "the perfect modern wine bar" –
a "packed" but "cosy" place, where a "short but well-executed"
menu complements a range of 50 or so "incredible" wines by the
glass.* / www.2850.co.uk; 9.30 pm; closed Sat & Sun.

2 Amici SW1 £44 ❹❹❹
48a Rochester Rw 7976 5660 2–4C
*On most accounts, this "small and friendly" Westminster Italian is a
handy "cheap 'n' cheerful" local; it is not without critics, though,
for whom its whole approach reeks of the "lowest common
denominator".* / 11 pm; closed Sat L & Sun.

Two Brothers N3 £35 ❷❸❹
297-303 Regent's Park Rd 8346 0469 1–1B
*You get "really excellent fish" and "chunky chips", at this "basic and
often-crowded" Finchley institution – one of the capital's top chippies.*
/ www.twobrothers.co.uk; 10.15 pm; closed Mon & Sun; no booking at D.

202
Nicole Farhi W11 £50 ❹❸❸
202 Westbourne Grove 7727 2722 6–1B
*That quintessential "buzzy Notting Hill atmosphere" doesn't come
more concentrated than at this "hip" (and "pricey") brunch-and-lunch
spot (which is integrated into a fashion store); "reliable" food plays
rather a supporting role.* / 10 pm; closed Mon D & Sun D; only D.

2 Veneti W1 £47 ❸❷④
10 Wigmore St 7637 0789 3–1B
Near Wigmore Hall, this "calm and discreet oasis" is a "useful option
in a poorly-served area" – the Venetian-based cooking is "interesting"
and "reliable", and service is "warm" ("especially if they know you").
/ www.2veneti.com; 10.30 pm, Sat 11 pm; closed Sat L & Sun.

Uli W11 £38 ❸❶❸
16 All Saints Rd 7727 7511 6–1B
"Michael is an exceptional host", and his staff are "always smiling",
say fans of this "excellent, unassuming and well-priced" pan-Asian,
near Portobello Market; the food is usually "really inventive" and
"yummy" (although this year did see the odd "horror" too).
/ www.uli-oriental.co.uk; 11 pm; D only, closed Sun; no Amex.

Umu W1 £85 ❷❸❷
14-16 Bruton Pl 7499 8881 3–2C
"Beautiful" and "understated", this small Mayfair mews spot –
with its "divine sushi", and other "intricate and fabulously-presented"
"Kyoto-style" dishes – is sometimes tipped as "the best Japanese
in London"; for a few reporters, however, it's still a case of 'Emperor's
new clothes', and at "ludicrous" prices too. / www.umurestaurant.com;
11 pm; closed Sat L & Sun; no trainers; booking: max 14.

The Union Café W1 £54 ❸④④
96 Marylebone Ln 7486 4860 3–1A
Wine at (highish) "retail" prices adds to the "buzz" at John Brinkley's
"airy" neighbourhood stand-by, near trendy Marylebone High Street;
food-wise, it offers an "unadventurous" but "safe" mix, with "delicious
burgers" a speciality. / www.brinkleys.com; 11 pm; closed Sun D.

Union Street Café SE1 NEW
Harling Hs, Union St awaiting tel 9–4B
A 250-seater newcomer, scheduled to open near Borough Market
in late-2011; most of Gordon Ramsay's 'catering for the masses'
efforts so far have been pretty dismal – perhaps this place can mark
a change of course?

Uno SW1 £47 ④④④
1 Denbigh St 7834 1001 2–4B
On a prime Pimlico corner, a "closely-packed" (and sometimes very
noisy) neighbourhood Italian; despite its "reliable" cooking (including
pizza), it never seems to rise to more than stand-by status.
/ www.uno1.co.uk; 10 pm, Fri & Sun 10.30 pm.

Upstairs Bar SW2 £45 ❷❶❶
89b Acre Ln (door on Branksome Rd) 7733 8855 10–2D
"Like a supper-club, only better" – Brixton's "magnificently romantic"
secret "hide-away" ("ring a bell to enter") is a "small, but perfectly
formed" Gallic place whose overall "professionalism" would shame
many much bigger names, not least with its "outrageously good
value"! / www.upstairslondon.com; Tue-Thu 9.30 pm, Fri-Sat 10.30 pm;
D only, closed Mon & Sun.

Le Vacherin W4 £52 ❸❸❸
76-77 South Pde 8742 2121 7–1A
An "authentic slice of France", hidden-away "in the back of beyond"
(on the Acton/Chiswick borders); it's won a large and very "faithful"
clientele over the years, by offering "classic" cuisine ("good, without
being memorable") at "sensible prices". / www.levacherin.co.uk;
10.30 pm, Fri & Sat 11 pm, Sun 10 pm; closed weekday L.

iajante

he Wolseley

Lucca

Valentina £39 ❸❸❸
210 Up' Richmond Rd W, SW14 8392 9127 1–4A
75 Upper Richmond Rd, SW15 8877 9906 10–2B
Upmarket deli/diners in Sheen and Putney, which offer "lovely Italian food", and have quite a "feel-good factor" too – their "straightforward" style pleases all who comment on them. / SW15 10 pm, SW14 10.30 pm.

Vanilla W1 £50 ④④❸
131 Great Titchfield St 3008 7763 3–1C
Declining feedback on this style-conscious Fitzrovia basement, known for its striking (but now "slightly tatty") monochrome decor, romantic booths and punchy cocktails – "definitely worth a try... but maybe only once". / www.vanillalondon.com; 10 pm; closed Mon, Tue, Wed, Thu L, Fri L & Sun; no trainers; booking: max 6.

Vanilla Black EC4 £47 ❷❷④
17-18 Tooks Ct 7242 2622 9–2A
"Fine veggie dining is a rarity", and you find it at an unusually "imaginative" and "accomplished" level at this Chancery Lane two-year-old – pity the atmosphere doesn't have a bit more oomph. / www.vanillablack.co.uk; 10 pm; closed Sat L & Sun; Fri & Sat nights; 8 group max.

Vapiano W1 £30 ④④④
19-21 Great Portland St 7268 0080 3–1C
"Removed from the tourist/shopper crowds of Oxford Street", this large self-service food court strikes many reporters as a "decent" place for a quick meal, with a hint of Continental style thrown in; on the downside, it can seem "cavernous", "brash" and "noisy". / www.vapiano.co.uk; 11 pm, Sun 10 pm.

Vasco & Piero's Pavilion W1 £52 ❷❷❸
15 Poland St 7437 8774 3–1D
This "unassuming" Soho favourite "has been around for donkeys years", and offers "a tiny haven in a mad world"; "high-quality, fresh pasta" is the highlight of the "classic" Italian food, but it's the "very welcoming" service that really makes the experience. / www.vascosfood.com; 10.30 pm; closed Sat L & Sun.

Veeraswamy W1 £68 ❸❸❸
Victory Hs, 99-101 Regent St 7734 1401 3–3D
A "classic that keeps re-inventing itself"; London's oldest Indian – "terrifically-located", near Piccadilly Circus – is an all-round "winner", thanks to its "refined", "21st century" decor and its "contemporary cuisine"; ratings dipped a bit this year, though – "have they become too relaxed?" / www.realindianfood.com; 10.30 pm, Sun 10 pm; booking: max 12.

Venosi SW3 NEW £53 ④❷④
87 Sloane Ave 7998 5019 5–2C
"Deserving a larger clientele", says the – sole! – reporter to comment on this new Chelsea Italian; it's certainly a "friendly" place, useful for Brompton Cross shoppers, but we couldn't on our own visit see any reason actively to seek it out. / Rated on Editors' visit; www.venosi.co.uk; 10.45 pm; closed Sun; set weekday L £25 (FP).

El Vergel SE1 £29 ❷❷❷
132 Webber St 7401 2308 9–4B
"Amazingly, it's just as good in premises five times the size!" – this "incredible" Latino is going strong on its year-old new site, serving "some of the best Hispanic food in the UK", and at "ludicrously cheap" prices too. / www.elvergel.co.uk; 9.45 pm Sat; Mon-Fri closed D, Sat open L & D, closed Sun; no Amex.

Verru W1 NEW £51 ❷❸④
69 Marylebone Ln 7935 0858 2–1A

A "cosy" Marylebone newcomer that's so tiny "it's going to be tough to make it a success"; staff "try hard" though, and on most accounts its "eclectic", Scandinavian-influenced cuisine is "well-executed" and "convincing"; "excellent-value set lunch menu". / www.verru.co.uk; set weekday L £30 (FP).

Verta SW11 NEW £58 ④④④
Bridges Court Rd 7978 0875 10–1C

Aside from "good views over the Thames", the virtues of this "charmless" dining room by Battersea's helipad (opened as part of a Von Essen hotel, shortly before that group went bust) are quite hard to see; unless, of course, you're really desperate to arrive by helicopter... / www.hotelverta.com; 10.30 pm, Sun 10 pm; set weekday L £36 (FP).

Vertigo 42
Tower 42 EC2 £64 ④❸❶
25 Old Broad St 7877 7842 9–2C

"Amazing views" make this "well-spaced" 42nd-floor City eyrie just the place to woo a client or lover; stick to fizz and nibbles, though – the fare is decidedly "average". / www.vertigo42.co.uk; 10.45 pm; closed Sat L & Sun; no shorts; booking essential.

VIAJANTE E2 £90 ❷❷❸
Patriot Sq 7871 0461 1–2D

"Some dishes astound... some miss by quite a way", at Nuno Mendes's "experimental" open-kitchen yearling, in Bethnal Green; sceptics may find the cooking occasionally "over-engineered", but most reporters still feel it's "some of the most exciting food currently available in London". / www.viajante.co.uk; 9.30 pm; closed Mon L & Tue L; set weekday L £48 (FP).

Vicino SW6 £40 ❸❸❸
189 New King's Rd 7736 1145 10–1B

A "good neighbourhood Parson's Green Italian" that's a "solid performer", and which benefits from a "a great family atmosphere at weekends"; the menu, though, "could perhaps be a bit shorter". / www.vicinorestaurant.com; 11 pm; closed Sun D.

Il Vicolo SW1 £48 ④④④
3-4 Crown Passage 7839 3960 3–4D

Fans still say this St James's Sicilian, hidden-away down a cute alley, is a "predictable but dependable" favourite, albeit a "cramped" and "noisy" one; a couple of reports this year, however, suggest that standards are not being maintained. / 10 pm; closed Sat L & Sun.

The Victoria SW14 £41 ❸❸❷
10 West Temple 8876 4238 10–2A

"In a leafy street near Richmond Park", and with a "great garden for the kids to let off steam", Paul Merrett's large East Sheen gastropub has a particular name as a family destination (and can sometimes seem "overrun" at weekends); the food, though, is "consistently good". / www.thevictoria.net; 10 pm, Sat 10 pm; closed Sun D; no Amex.

Viet W1 £21 ❸④④
34 Greek St 7494 9888 4–3A

"You usually have to queue, and often end up sharing a table with strangers", at this "basic" Soho Vietnamese; no one minds, though – "for under a tenner", you can "stuff yourself" with "a good range of phos, and other tasty options"; BYO. / 10.30 pm, Fri 11 pm; closed Sun; no Amex; no booking.

Viet Garden N1 £35 ❸❸④
207 Liverpool Rd 7700 6040 8–2D
"Light and lovely" Vietnamese dishes, at "value-for-money" prices, have long made this "tired"-looking Angel veteran well worth seeking out; beware, though: "it does get very busy". / www.vietgarden.co.uk; 11 pm, Sat 11.30 pm; no Amex.

Viet Grill E2 £34 ❷④❷
58 Kingsland Rd 7739 6686 12–1B
"Stunningly fresh" and "fragrant" food – all at "incredibly cheap" prices – remains the hallmark of this "über-busy" and "vibrant" Shoreditch Vietnamese; service, though, "could be improved a lot". / www.vietnamesekitchen.co.uk; 11 pm, Fri & Sat 11.30 pm, Sun 10.30 pm.

Viet Hoa E2 £27 ❷④④
70-72 Kingsland Rd 7729 8293 12–1B
"Super food, very cheap" – that's the deal that's made this "authentic" Shoreditch Vietnamese quite a hit; "it's gone a bit upmarket after a revamp", though – "not necessarily what the place is about". / www.viethoarestaurant.co.uk; 11.30 pm.

Vijay NW6 £29 ❶❷④
49 Willesden Ln 7328 1087 1–1B
There's "no 'designer' packaging", at this rather "dilapidated"-looking Kilburn veteran – just "seriously delicious" south Indian dishes, including "divine dosas", at "great-value" prices. / www.vijayrestaurant.co.uk; 10.45 pm, Fri & Sat 11.45 pm.

Villa Bianca NW3 £56 ④❷❸
1 Perrins Ct 7435 3131 8–2A
Mega-cutely located in a little lane just off Hampstead High Street, this "traditional" Italian is a "pricey" sort of place, but reporters – more positive of late – see it as "dependable for good, slightly old-fashioned cooking". / www.villabiancanw3.com; 11.30 pm.

Village East SE1 £46 ❸❷❷
171-173 Bermondsey St 7357 6082 9–4D
A "laid-back" and "buzzy" brasserie, with a "very cool" location in a row of Bermondsey railway arches; the menu has "something for everyone" – particularly as a weekend brunch destination, this place "really hits the spot". / www.villageeast.co.uk; 10 pm, Sun 9.30 pm; closed Sat D & Sun D.

Villandry W1 £53 ④⑤④
170 Gt Portland St 7631 3131 2–1B
Smart Marylebone deli/diner that fans find a "reliable" stop that's "pleasant enough for lunch"; it's quite "cold" style-wise, though, and perennially "let down" by its "dreadful, dreadful" service; the offshoot 'Kitchens' were sold in mid-2011. / www.villandry.com; 10.30 pm; closed Sun.

The Vincent Rooms
Westminster Kingsway College SW1 £26 ❸④❸
76 Vincent Sq 7802 8391 2–4C
The "great value" of this Westminster catering-college restaurant "makes up for any lapses", such as the "inevitably patchy" service ("some students are really nervous"); if you hit a good day, though, the food from the trainee chefs can be "excellent" too. / www.thevincentrooms.com; 9 pm; times vary; only term times; closed Mon D, Wed D, Fri D, Sat & Sun; no Amex.

Vingt-Quatre SW10 £46 ④④④
325 Fulham Rd 7376 7224 5–3B
A 24/7 Chelsea veteran which fans say is "not just for night owls",
as it serves useful "hang-over food" and other "quick snacks" during
daylight hours too; for critics, though, it's just "one to avoid unless
you're desperate in the early hours". / www.vingtquatre.co.uk; open 24
hours; no booking.

Vinoteca £39 ❸②❶
15 Seymour Pl, W1 7724 7288 2–2A NEW
7 St John St, EC1 7253 8786 9–1B
"The clue is rather in the name", at this "bustling" wine bar duo
in Smithfield and now also Marylebone – yes, "there's some decent
fodder", but the main event is an "intriguing" selection of "incredible"
wines, delivered by "enthusiastic" and "professional" staff. / 10 pm,
W1 4 pm; EC1 Sun, W1 Sun D.

Vivat Bacchus £51 ④④⑤
4 Hay's Ln, SE1 7234 0891 9–4C
47 Farringdon St, EC4 7353 2648 9–2A
A "treasure" of a wine list ("leaning heavily to South Africa") and
a "fabulous" cheese selection – both chosen in walk-in cellars –
are stand-out features of these City-fringe and Southwark wine bars;
the food's "nothing special", though, and no one's wild about the
ambience either. / www.vivatbacchus.co.uk; 9.30 pm; EC4 closed Sat & Sun;
SE1 closed Sat L & Sun; set always available £32 (FP).

Vrisaki N22 £32 ④❸④
73 Middleton Rd 8889 8760 1–1C
"Much too much food" – the main problem when visiting this "jolly"
and "good-value" Bounds Green veteran, hidden-away behind
a kebab shop; "the mezze deal is the thing to go for". / 11.30 pm,
Sun 9 pm.

Wagamama £33 ④❸④
8 Norris St, SW1 7321 2755 4–4A
Harvey Nichols, Knightsbridge, SW1 7201 8000 5–1D
101a Wigmore St, W1 7409 0111 3–1A
10a Lexington St, W1 7292 0990 3–2D
4a Streatham St, WC1 7323 9223 2–1C
1 Tavistock St, WC2 7836 3330 4–3D
14a Irving St, WC2 7839 2323 4–4B
26a Kensington High St, W8 7376 1717 5–1A
N1 Centre, 37 Parkfield St, N1 7226 2664 8–3D
11 Jamestown Rd, NW1 7428 0800 8–3B
Royal Festival Hall, Southbank Centre, SE1 7021 0877 2–3D
50-54 Putney High St, SW15 8785 3636 10–2B
46-48 Wimbledon Hill Rd, SW19 8879 7280 10–2B
Jubilee Place, 45 Bank St, E14 7516 9009 11–1C
1a Ropemaker St, EC2 7588 2688 12–2A
22 Old Broad St, EC2 7256 9992 9–2C
Tower Pl, EC3 7283 5897 9–3D
109 Fleet St, EC4 7583 7889 9–2A
30 Queen St, EC4 7248 5766 9–3B
"A favourite oriental fix for a fast lunch" – this benchmark noodle-
chain still has a huge following for its "honest meals for
honest money" (and as "a great venue with kids" too); for critics,
though, the experience – perhaps inevitably – "doesn't seem as fresh
as once it did". / www.wagamama.com; no booking.

Wahaca £29 ④❸❸
80-82 Wardour St, W1 7734 0195 3–2D
66 Chandos Pl, WC2 7240 1883 4–4C
Westfield, Ariel Way, W12 8749 4517 7–1C
Unit 4, Park Pavilion, 40 Canada Sq, E14 7516 9145 11–1C
*"Wagamama a lo Mexicano"; they're "fun" and they're "festive",
and these "zoo-like" latinos still please fans with their "cheap" and
"tasty" bites; standards, though, aren't a patch on the early days.
/ www.wahaca.com; 11 pm; no booking.*

The Wallace
The Wallace Collection W1 £50 ④④❶
Hertford Hs, Manchester Sq 7563 9505 3–1A
*"A wonderful oasis"; this "spectacular" atrium of a Marylebone
palazzo is a "beautiful" space, where the food is "a bit pricey" for
what it is, but the service – if still sometimes "disinterested" –
has somewhat improved of late. / www.thewallacerestaurant.com; Fri & Sat
9.15 pm; Sun-Thu closed D; no Amex.*

The Walmer Castle W11 £36 ❸❷❷
58 Ledbury Rd 7229 4620 6–1B
*"Still as busy as ever"; "for tasty and good-value Thai fare",
this atmospheric Notting Hill pub remains "a destination venue".
/ www.walmercastle.co.uk; 11 pm.*

Walnut NW6 £39 ❸❷❷
280 West End Ln 7794 7772 1–1B
*"A West Hampstead gem" – this "friendly" fixture developed
"a strong environmental theme" long before it became fashionable,
and its "seasonal" dishes please all who comment on them; only real
downside? – "hard" seating. / www.walnutwalnut.com; 11 pm; D only,
closed Mon.*

Wapping Food E1 £48 ❸④❶
Wapping Power Station, Wapping Wall 7680 2080 11–1A
*With its "very cutting-edge" vibe, this former hydraulic power station
– now part art-space, part restaurant – provides a "fabulous,
industrial-chic" setting for weekend brunch, lunch or dinner;
the cooking is "good" too, if perhaps on the "pricey" side for what
it is. / www.thewappingproject.com; midnight; Mon-Fri D only, Sat open L & D,
closed Sun D.*

The Warrington W9 £56 ⑤⑤⑤
93 Warrington Cr 7592 7960 8–4A
*According to Gordon Ramsay's website, this huge Maida Vale boozer
offers an 'enchanting journey' and 'sophisticated' British cooking –
reporters, on the other hand, rate it like "a tired Torquay hotel",
where the food is "bland and incredibly expensive", and the service
simply "shocking". / www.gordonramsay.com; 10 pm, Fri & Sat 10.30 pm,
Sun 9 pm; Casual; set weekday L £36 (FP).*

Watatsumi
The Club Quarters Hotel WC2 NEW £55 ④❸④
7 Northumberland Ave 7036 8520 2–3C
*Handy for Trafalgar Square, a decent, if perhaps not inspired,
Japanese newcomer, housed in marbled Edwardian splendour;
its well-spaced tables are useful for business, and its set lunch menus
should also interest West End visitors generally. / Rated on Editors' visit;
www.watatsumi.co.uk; 11 pm.*

FSA

The Water Margin NW11   £28   ③②④
96 Golders Green Road   8458 5815   1–1B
The food comes "piping hot" and "bursting with flavour", at this stalwart Cantonese on Golder's Green's main drag, where "smiling" staff take the edge off a dining room that's rather "in need of a revamp". / www.the-water-margin.co.uk; 11 pm; no Amex.

Waterloo Bar & Kitchen SE1   £43   ④③④
131 Waterloo Rd   7928 5086   9–4A
"In an area badly served for decent food", this "bustling" brasserie, near the Old Vic, makes a reliably "useful" stand-by, and out-scores its similarly-named rival, the Waterloo Brasserie. / www.barandkitchen.co.uk; 10.30 pm.

Waterloo Brasserie SE1   £47   ⑤⑤④
119 Waterloo Rd   7960 0202   9–4A
Fans find it "perfect before the Old Vic", but this brilliantly-located brasserie (right by the railway station) is a terrible missed opportunity – critics say that its "unexciting" food and "slapdash" service make it "very much a restaurant of last resort". / www.waterloobrasserie.co.uk; 11 pm; closed Sun.

The Waterway W9   £47   ④⑤②
54 Formosa St   7266 3557   8–4A
"It's the setting you come for!"; this canal-side Maida Vale hang-out has a "delightful terrace", which makes it – just about – worth braving the "variable" food, and the sometimes "terrible" service. / www.thewaterway.co.uk; 10.30 pm, Sun 10 pm.

The Well EC1   £48   ③④③
180 St John St   7251 9363   9–1A
"Still a place to return to, despite the increasing competition in Clerkenwell", say fans of this long-established gastropub – they rate its cooking highly, but reports are far less numerous than once they were. / www.downthewell.com; 10.30 pm, Sun 9.30 pm.

The Wells NW3   £43   ③②②
30 Well Walk   7794 3785   8–1A
"Cosseted among the leafy gardens of Hampstead", this "very characterful" pub makes "an easy choice for all the family"; with "helpful" staff and "consistently good" food, it is also "perfect after a hearty walk on the Heath". / www.thewellshampstead.co.uk; 10 pm, Sun 9.30 pm.

The Westbourne W2   £40   ③④②
101 Westbourne Park Villas   7221 1332   6–1B
On a sunny Sunday, the terrace of this "absolute-favourite" local "hang-out" heaves with "hip Notting Hill types, and their kids"; the cooking is on the better side of what you might expect, but the "frosty" service "certainly leaves room for improvement". / www.thewestbourne.com; 10 pm, Sun 9.30 pm; closed Mon L.

The Wet Fish Cafe NW6   £40   ③②②
242 West End Ln   7443 9222   1–1B
An "excellent local café and brasserie", that's often – and especially for breakfast and brunch – "bustling" with West Hampstead types; NB: the name reflects the ex-fishmonger premises, not the menu. / www.thewetfishcafe.co.uk; 10 pm; closed Mon L; no Amex.

The Wharf TW11   £50   4️⃣2️⃣2️⃣
22 Manor Rd   8977 6333   1–4A
For "a leisurely meal watching the boats go by" ("ask for a window
seat"), the attractions of this "relaxed" Thames-side bar/restaurant
near Teddington Lock are self-evident; the brasserie fare can
sometimes "fall short", but it's mostly pretty "reliable".
/ www.thewharfteddington.com; 9.45 pm.

Wheeler's SW1   £58   5️⃣4️⃣5️⃣
72-73 St James's St   7408 1440   3–4D
"MPW should stick to making stock-cube adverts", says one of the
many critics of the celebrity-chef's "drab" and "disappointing" fish
restaurant, by St James's Palace – "simply don't bother!"
/ www.wheelersrestaurant.org; 11 pm; closed Sat L & Sun; set always available £39 (FP).

White Horse SW6   £43   3️⃣3️⃣3️⃣
1-3 Parsons Grn   7736 2115   10–1B
"The Sloaney Pony isn't as Sloaney as it used to be", but this Parson's
Green landmark still gets "exceedingly busy"; the food is "reliable",
both inside and out (there's a large terrace), and there is an
"excellent range of beers and wines" to go with it.
/ www.whitehorsesw6.com; 10.30 pm.

The White Swan EC4   £49   2️⃣3️⃣4️⃣
108 Fetter Ln   7242 9696   9–2A
"Surprising to find such good food in a pub"; "first-class" British
cooking and "interesting wine" make this "professionally run" City-
fringe dining room a handy business-lunch option.
/ www.thewhiteswanlondon.com; 10 pm; closed Sat & Sun.

Whitechapel Gallery Dining Room E1   £38
77-82 Whitechapel High St   7522 7896   12–2C
This elegant but tightly-packed, East End gallery dining room offers
a handy stand-by in a thin area; owing to various changes of régime
this year, we don't think a rating appropriate.
/ www.whitechapelgallery.org/dine; 9.30 pm; closed Mon, Tue D & Sun D.

Whits W8   £46   3️⃣1️⃣3️⃣
21 Abingdon Rd   7938 1122   5–1A
"Refreshingly genuine service" adds to the "congenial" charm of this
"personal" bistro, tucked-away off Kensington High Street; fans also
hail its "serious" Gallic cuisine, but doubters find it "rather average".
/ www.whits.co.uk; 10.30 pm; D only, closed Mon & Sun.

Wild Honey W1   £53   3️⃣3️⃣3️⃣
12 St George St   7758 9160   3–2C
"Inventive cooking, and one of London's most flexible wine lists" –
all at "very fair prices" – have made a formidable name for this
"lovely wood-panelled room" (a "former gents' outfitters"), in Mayfair;
sliding ratings, however, are grist to the mill of those who discern
"an over-riding feeling of complacency". / www.wildhoneyrestaurant.co.uk;
11 pm, Fri & Sat 11.30 pm, Sun 10 pm.

William Curley   £17   1️⃣3️⃣3️⃣
198 Ebury St, SW1   7730 5522   5–2D
10 Paved Ct, TW9   8332 3002   1–4A
The smart Belgravia café of "the best chocolatier in London" – worth
seeking out for its "stunning" puddings and cakes, and "luscious" hot
choc' too. / www.williamcurley.co.uk; 6.30 pm.

Wiltons SW1 £97 ④❷❷
55 Jermyn St   7629 9955   3–3C
"Quiet and dignified, as befits one's sole" (ho, ho) – this "convivial grande dame" of "timeless" St James's dining remains a top destination for "superb" fish, oysters and game; bills, however, are as "brutal" as the overall experience is "refined". / www.wiltons.co.uk; 10.30 pm; closed Sat & Sun; jacket required.

The Windmill W1 £36 ❷④❸
6-8 Mill St   7491 8050   3–2C
"Pies to die for" make it well worth seeking out this very traditional boozer, near Savile Row; it boasts a "nicely kept ale cellar" too. / www.windmillmayfair.co.uk; 9.30 pm, Sat 4 pm; closed Sat D & Sun; no Amex.

The Windsor Castle W8 £34 ④④❶
114 Campden Hill Rd   7243 8797   6–2B
"Like Alice in Wonderland, full of cubby holes and low doors", this "lovely" ancient tavern, near Notting Hill Gate, also has a gorgeous garden; its "normal pub fayre", however, tends to "unexceptional". / www.thewindsorcastlekensington.co.uk; 10 pm, Sun 9 pm; set always available £21 (FP).

Wine Gallery SW10 £50 ④❸❷
49 Hollywood Rd   7352 7572   5–3B
"If you're interested more in socialising than food", you "can't go wrong" at John Brinkley's age-old Chelsea wine bar – it's the good wine at reasonable prices, though, which is the real attractions, rather than the "simple" cuisine. / www.brinkleys.com; 11.30 pm; closed Sun D; booking: max 12; set weekday L £27 (FP).

The Wine Library EC3 £28 ⑤❸❶
43 Trinity Sq   7481 0415   9–3D
"A great concept for wine-lovers" – an ancient City cellar, selling "an amazing selection" at "fantastic" prices (scarcely higher than retail); the cheese and pâté buffet accompaniment is pretty "basic" but, say fans, "what more do you need?" / www.winelibrary.co.uk; 8 pm, Mon 6 pm; closed Mon D, Sat & Sun.

Wolfe's WC2 £43 ❸④④
30 Gt Queen St   7831 4442   4–1D
The '70s styling of this comfortable diner can seem distinctly passé, but this Covent Garden stalwart still has its (generally older) fans, who acclaim its "heavenly" burgers. / www.wolfes-grill.net; Fri & Sat 10.30 pm, Mon-Thu 10 pm, Sun 9 pm.

THE WOLSELEY W1 £57 ❸❷❶
160 Piccadilly   7499 6996   3–3C
Everyone who's anyone is to be found, throughout the day – from the "terrific" breakfast onward – at Corbin & King's "star-studded" grand café, by the Ritz; it can seem "crowded and noisy", though, and the brasserie fare is "competent, rather than dazzling". / www.thewolseley.com; midnight, Sun 11 pm.

Wong Kei W1 £26 ④⑤④
41-43 Wardour St   7437 8408   4–3A
"Nowadays, you can even buy a T-shirt!" celebrating the "legendarily rude" staff at this "massive" Chinatown institution; it's questionable whether they truly live up to that billing any more, but the "fast and furious" chow on offer is still "plentiful, cheap and edible". / 11.30 pm, Fri & Sat 11.45 pm, Sun 10.30 pm; no credit cards; no booking.

Woodlands £35 ❸❸④
37 Panton St, SW1   7839 7258   4–4A
77 Marylebone Ln, W1   7486 3862   2–1A
102 Heath St, NW3   7794 3080   8–1A
"An ideal place for a quick vegetarian fix" – a "consistently good"
(if "not very atmospheric") Indian mini-chain that's been around for
yonks. / www.woodlandsrestaurant.co.uk; 10 pm; NW3 no L Mon; set L £22 (FP).

Wright Brothers £51 ❷❸❸
12-13 Kingly St, W1   7434 3611   3–2D
11 Stoney St, SE1   7403 9554   9–4C
In "rough and ready" Borough Market – and now in more
"glamorous" and "restaurant-like" premises in Soho too – these
"bubbly" bars have won cult status for their "heavenly bivalves",
and other "awesome, fresh seafood"; the original branch is better.
/ 10.30 pm, Sun 9 pm; booking: max 8.

XO NW3 £47 ❸④❸
29 Belsize Ln   7433 0888   8–2A
Reports on this "trendy" Belsize Park outpost of Will ('E&O') Ricker's
empire are rather up-and-down, and even fans sometimes find its
pan-Asian tapas dishes "rather pricey" for what they are – "look out
for special offers!" / www.rickerrestaurants.com; 10.30 pm; set weekday L £29 (FP).

Yalla Yalla £31 ❸❸❷
1 Green's Ct, W1   7287 7663   3–2D
12 Winsley St, W1   7637 4748   3–1C **NEW**
"Like being in Beirut"; this "tiny" and "squished-in" Soho "hole in the
wall" has quickly made a name for "scrumptious" street food (spicy
wraps, mezze and kebabs) at "recession-busting" prices, and it's
"great fun" too; an offshoot recently opened near Oxford Circus.
/ Green's Court 11 pm; Winsley Street 11.30 pm; Winsley Street closed Sun.

Yashin W8 **NEW** £65 ❷④④
1a, Argyll Rd   7938 1536   5–1A
"A definite addition to London's dining scene" – this ambitious
Kensington newcomer serves "very creative" and exquisitely
presented sushi and sashimi, in a Manhattan-esque (and very un-
Japanese) setting; it's "too expensive" however, service is stilted,
and its dark-toned decor is a bit oppressive. / www.yashinsushi.com; 10 pm.

Yauatcha W1 £65 ❶④❷
Broadwick Hs, 15-17 Broadwick St   7494 8888   3–2D
"Mind-blowing", "new-wave" dim sum – "the best this side of HK" –
make a perennial hit of this "funky" Soho spot, with its "club-like"
(but "cramped") basement, and "sophisticated" (but less vibey)
ground-floor dining room; service, though, can be "supercilious".
/ www.yauatcha.com; 11.15 pm, Sun 10.30 pm.

The Yellow House SE16 £41 ❷❷④
126 Lower Rd   7231 8777   11–2A
The "best in SE16!" (not, admittedly, London's most hotly-contested
postcode) – this "fabulous local" is a "friendly" Surrey Quays spot,
where "slightly different" pizza and "yummy" puds are among the
culinary highlights. / www.theyellowhouse.eu; 10.30 pm, Sun 9.30 pm; closed
Mon, Tue–Sat closed L, Sun open L & D.

Yi-Ban E16 £42 ❸④④
Regatta Centre, Dockside Rd   7473 6699   11–1D
"It has a terrible location, is utterly impossible to get to, and hidden-
away in a concrete shed with views of London City Airport"… but,
fortunately, "superb dim sum" (and other "reliable" fare) reward
those who seek out this obscure dockside Chinese. / www.yi-ban.co.uk;
10.45 pm.

Yming W1 £40 ❷⓿❸
35-36 Greek St   7734 2721   4–2A
"Better than most of its neighbours in nearby Chinatown", Christine Lau's Soho Chinese remains a "long-term favourite"; the food is "really lovely", and staff – led by maître d' William – are "superbly welcoming" too. / www.yminglondon.com; 11.45 pm; set L & pre-th £21 (FP).

Yo Sushi £27 ⑤⑤⑤
Branches throughout London
A conveyor-chain whose "concept" has long seemed rather "stale"; "the food's at best OK, and at worst it can be vile" – "if that's sushi, I'm a Martian!". / www.yosushi.co.uk; 10.30 pm; no booking.

York & Albany NW1 £50 ④④④
127-129 Parkway   7388 3344   8–3B
"We loved it when it opened, but it's gone off in a big way..." – as is the case in many parts of the Gordon Ramsay empire, this "grand" (and potentially "chic") Regent's Park tavern serves up some "very mediocre" fare nowadays, and service can be "appalling" too. / www.gordonramsay.com; 10.30 pm, Sun 8 pm.

Yoshino W1 £37 ❷⓿❸
3 Piccadilly Pl   7287 6622   3–3D
"A little secret within 200 yards of Piccadilly Circus"; this minimalist Japanese café, off a small alleyway, offers "terrific" food – including "immaculate" sushi – and "very smiley" service too; it's even "reasonably priced"! / www.yoshino.net; 10.30 pm; closed Sun.

Yum Yum N16 £42 ❸❸❷
187 Stoke Newington High St   7254 6751   1–1D
This "massive" Stoke Newington Thai really "rocks!" – it's a "well-run" and "trusty" operation, that year-in, year-out churns out "reasonably-priced" fare, and "good cocktails" too. / www.yumyum.co.uk; 11 pm, Fri & Sat midnight.

Yuzu NW6 £38 ❷④⑤
102 Fortune Green Rd   7431 6602   1–1B
Ambience may be lacking, and the seating "too close for comfort", but this West Hampstead Japanese is, on most accounts, "an under-rated neighbourhood gem", which serves "interesting" dishes rather "in the style of Nobu"! / www.yuzu-restaurants.com; 10.30 pm; D only.

Zafferano SW1 £69 ❸④❸
15 Lowndes St   7235 5800   5–1D
Many reporters still find the cooking at this smart Belgravian "consistently very good", but the volume of complaints about "clumsy" service and "significant overpricing" are such nowadays that the oft-repeated claims that this is 'London's best Italian' are clearly no longer sustainable. / www.zafferanorestaurant.com; 11 pm.

Zaffrani N1 £41 ❸❸❸
47 Cross St   7226 5522   8–3D
"Still an excellent curry"; this Islington Indian wins praise for its "fresh" and "tasty" cuisine (with "a myriad of delicate flavours"); "distant" service, however, can take the edge off the experience. / www.zaffrani-islington.co.uk; 11 pm.

Zaika W8 £59 ⓿❷❸
1 Kensington High St   7795 6533   5–1A
"Under-appreciated" but "always a winner" – this "incredible" Indian offers really "imaginative" and "beautifully realised" cuisine, in "elegant" (but perhaps slightly "unatmospheric") former banking premises, opposite Kensington Gardens. / www.zaika-restaurant.co.uk; 10.45 pm, Sun 9.45 pm; closed Mon L; set pre theatre £36 (FP).

Zayna W1 £45 ❷④④
25 New Quebec St 7723 2229 2–2A
A "quality" Pakistani curry house, hidden-away near Marble Arch;
it may be "small in size", and offer "inconsistent" service, but the
food is "great". / www.zaynarestaurant.co.uk; 11.15 pm, Fri & Sat 11.45 pm;
set weekday L £29 (FP).

Zero Degrees SE3 £37 ❸④❷
29-31 Montpelier Vale 8852 5619 1–4D
"Offbeat pizzas" and "good home brews" – that's the deal that
keeps this chrome-decorated Blackheath microbrewery very busy;
only real problem? – "it can get a bit loud when it's full".
/ www.zerodegrees.co.uk; midnight, Sun 11.30 pm.

Ziani's SW3 £52 ❸❷❷
45 Radnor Walk 7351 5297 5–3C
"You can't beat this small and hidden-away trattoria", say Chelsea
locals; OK, it's "packed", "very noisy" and "a bit pricey", but it's
"never dull", and a "lovely venue for a family treat". / www.ziani.co.uk;
11 pm, Sun 10.30 pm.

Zilli Fish W1 £69 ④④④
36-40 Brewer St 7734 8649 3–2D
For "unfancy, but fresh and well-presented" fish dishes, this TV chef's
Soho corner spot still has many fans; those who remember its glory
days, however, feel it's "looking past its prime, and needs some TLC
at all levels". / www.zillirestaurants.co.uk/fish; 11 pm; closed Sun.

Zilli Green W1 £38
41 Dean St 7734 3924 4–2A
Aldo Zilli's "pleasant" enough veggie-Italian closed its doors
just before this guide went to press; we're told that they're actively
looking for a relaunch site, ideally in Soho.
/ www.zillirestaurants.co.uk/green; 11 pm; closed Mon L, Tue L & Sun D.

Zizzi £44 ④④④
Branches throughout London
"Branches vary greatly", perhaps explaining the up-and-down nature
of reports on this "rustic"-themed Italianate chain; fans say they're
"a welcome change from PizzaExpress", but their ratings lag their
rival (and by quite a margin). / www.zizzi.co.uk; 11 pm.

Zucca SE1 £40 ❶❶❷
184 Bermondsey St 7378 6809 9–4D
"Professionalism", "friendly hospitality" and "unfussy" but "uniformly
excellent" cooking (from an open kitchen), at "sensible prices" –
all the ingredients which have made a huge hit of this "relaxed"
Bermondsey Italian yearling; "the only snag? – getting a table!"
/ www.zuccalondon.com; 10 pm; closed Mon & Sun D; no Amex.

ZUMA SW7 £77 ❶❸❷
5 Raphael St 7584 1010 5–1C
"There's no sign of any recession" ("good luck getting a table!"),
at this "buzzy, brash and glitzy" Knightsbridge scene – London's No.
1 Japanese – which is as "exciting" as it is "seriously expensive";
"if your date turns out to be dull, there are lots of beautiful people
to watch". / www.zumarestaurant.com; 10.45 pm, Sun 10.15 pm; booking:
max 8.

BREAKFAST
(with opening times)

Central

Abokado:WC2 (7.30)
Adam Street (9)
Amaranto (6.30 am, Sat-Sun 7 am)
Apsleys (7)
aqua nueva (Sun brunch 12 pm)
Asia de Cuba (7)
Athenaeum (7)
Aubaine:W1 (8, Sat 10)
Automat (Mon-Fri 7)
Baker & Spice: SW1 (7)
Balans: all central branches (8)
Bar Boulud (6.30)
Bar Italia (6.30)
Benugo: all central branches (7.30)
Bistro 1: Beak St W1 (Sun 11)
Black & Blue: Berners St W1 (9)
The Botanist (8, Sat & Sun 9)
La Bottega: Eccleston St SW1 (8, Sat 9);
    Lower Sloane St SW1 (8, Sat 9, Sun 10)
Boyd's Brasserie (7.30, Sun 8)
Brasserie Roux (6.30, Sat & Sun 7)
Browns (Albemarle) (7, Sun 7.30)
The English Tea Rm (Browns) (8)
Browns:WC2 (9, 10 Sat & Sun)
Café Bohème (8, Sat & Sun 9)
Café in the Crypt (Mon-Sat 8)
Café Luc (Sat & Sun 9)
Caffè Vergnano:WC2 (8, Sun 11)
Canteen:W1 (8, Sat & Sun 9)
Cecconi's (7 am, Sat & Sun 8 am)
The Chelsea Brasserie (7)
Chez Gérard: Chancery Ln WC2 (8)
Chop'd:W1 (7)
Christopher's (Sat & Sun 11.30)
The Cinnamon Club (Mon-Fri 7.30)
City Café (6.30, Sat & Sun 7)
Cocorino:Thayer St W1 (7, Sat 8, Sun 9)
Comptoir Libanais:W1 (8.30)
Côte:W1 (8, Sat & Sun 10)
The Courtauld Gallery Café (10)
Daylesford Organic: SW1 (8, Sun 10)
Dean Street Townhouse (Mon-Fri
    7, Sat-Sun 8)
Diner:W1 (10, Sat & Sun 9)
Dishoom (8, Sat & Sun 10)
Dorchester Grill (7, Sat & Sun 8)
The Duke of Wellington (Sat 9.30)
Eagle Bar Diner (Sat 10.30)
The Ebury (Sat & Sun 11)
Fernandez & Wells: Beak St W1 (7.30,
    sat& sun 9); Lexington St W1 (7 am);
    St Anne's Ct W1 (8, sat 10)
Flat White (8, Sat & Sun 9)
The Fountain (Fortnum's) (7.30,
    Sun 11)
Franco's (7.30, Sat 8)
La Fromagerie Café (8, Sat 9, Sun 10)
Fuzzy's Grub: SW1 (7)
Gelupo (9, Sat & Sun 12)
Giraffe:W1 (7.45, Sat & Sun 9)
The Goring Hotel (7, Sun 7.30)
Guerilla Burgers (11)
Hélène Darroze (Sat 11)
Indigo (6.30)
Inn the Park (8, Sat & Sun 9)
Joe Allen (8)
JW Steakhouse (6.30 pm, Sat & Sun
    7 pm)
Kaffeine (7.30, Sat 9)
Kazan (Cafe):Wilton Rd SW1 (8 am,
    Sun 9 am)
Konditor & Cook:WC1 (9.30);W1 (9.30,

Sun 10.30)
Kopapa (8.30, Sat & Sun 10)
Ladurée:W1 (9);SW1 (Mon - Sat
    9, Sun noon - 1.30)
Lantana Cafe (8, Sat & Sun 9)
Leon:WC2 (7.30, Sat 9, Sun 10);
    Gt Marlborough St W1 (9.30, Sat & Sun
    10.30)
Maison Bertaux (8.30, Sun 9)
maze Grill (6.45)
Monmouth Coffee Company:WC2 (8)
Mount Street Deli (8, Sat 9)
Mrs Marengos (8, Sat noon)
Napket:Vigo St W1, Brook St W1 (7.30);
    Piccadilly W1 (8)
The National Dining Rooms (10)
National Gallery Café (8, Sat & Sun10)
Natural Kitchen:W1 (8, Sat 9, Sun 11)
Nopi (8, Sat 9, Sun 10)
Nordic Bakery: Golden Sq W1 (Mon-Fri
    8, Sat 9, Sun 11)
Noura:William St SW1 (8)
Number Twelve (7, Sat & Sun 7.30)
The Only Running Footman (7.30,
    Sat & Sun 9)
The Orange (8)
Oscar (7, Sun 12)
Ottolenghi: SW1 (8, Sun 9)
Ozer (8)
The Pantechnicon (Sat & Sun 8.30)
Paramount (8)
Paul:WC2 (7.30);W1 (7.30, Sat & Sun 8)
Pearl (6.30, Sat & Sun 7)
The Portrait (10)
Princi (7, Sun 9)
Providores (Tapa Room) (9, Sat
    & Sun 10)
Ranoush: SW1 (9)
Refuel (7, Sun 8)
Rib Room (7, Sun 8)
RIBA Café (8)
Riding House Café (8 am, Sat & Sun
    9 am)
Ritz (Palm Court) (7, Sun 8)
The Ritz Restaurant (7, Sun 8)
Roux At The Landau (7)
St John Hotel (7)
Savoy (River Rest') (7 am, Sun 7.30 am)
Scandinavian Kitchen (8, Sat & Sun 10)
Serafino (7)
Simpsons-in-the-Strand (Mon-Fri 7.30)
The Sketch (Parlour) (Mon-Fri 8, Sat 10)
Sophie's Steakhouse: all branches (Sat &
    Sun 11)
Sotheby's Café (9.30)
Spice Market (7, Sat & Sun 8)
Stock Pot: SW1 (9.30)
Tate Britain (Rex Whistler) (Sat-
    Sun 10)
The Terrace in the Fields (Mon-Fri 9)
tibits (9, Sun 11.30)
Tom's Terrace (10 Sat & Sun)
Truc Vert (7.30, Sat & Sun 9)
The Union Café (Sat & Sun 11)
The Wallace (10)
William Curley: all branches (9.30,
    Sun 10.30)
Wolfe's (9)
The Wolseley (7, Sat & Sun 8)
Yalla Yalla: Green's Ct W1 (Sat-Sun 9)

West

Adams Café (7.30 am)
Annie's:W4 (Tue - Thu 10, Fri & Sat 10.30,
    Sun 10)
Aubaine: SW3 (8, Sun 9);W8 (Mon-Sat

8 am, 9 am Sun)
Baker & Spice: *all west branches (7, Sun 8)*
Balans West: *SW5, W4, W8 (8)*
Bedlington Café *(8.30)*
Beirut Express: *W2 (7)*
Benugo: *W12 (9)*
Best Mangal: *SW6 (10-12)*
Bistro K *(9)*
Blakes *(7)*
Bluebird Café *(8, Sat & Sun 10)*
La Bottega: *Gloucester Rd SW7 (8, Sat 9, Sun 10)*
La Brasserie *(8)*
Bumpkin: *SW7 (11 am)*
The Cabin *(Sat & Sun 10)*
Café Laville *(10, Sat & Sun 9.30)*
Chelsea Bun Diner *(7, Sun 9)*
The Chelsea Kitchen *(Sat & Sun 8)*
Chiswick House Cafe *(9)*
Comptoir Libanais: *W12 (9.30)*
Daylesford Organic: *W11 (8, Sun 11)*
Del'Aziz: *W12 (8); SW6 (8 am)*
Electric Brasserie *(8)*
Fresco *(8, Sun 9)*
Gail's Bread: *W11 (7, Sat & Sun 8)*
Gallery Mess *(10)*
Geales Chelsea Green: *SW3 (9 am Sat & Sun)*
Giraffe: *W4, W8 (7.45, Sat & Sun 9); W11 (8, Sun 9)*
The Greedy Buddha *(Sat & Sun 10)*
The Henry Root *(Sat - Sun 9.30 am)*
High Road Brasserie *(7, Sat & Sun 8)*
Joe's Brasserie *(Sat & Sun 11)*
Julie's *(9, Sun 10.30)*
Kensington Square Kitchen *(8.30, Sun 9.30)*
Lisboa Pâtisserie *(7)*
Lola & Simón *(8, Sat & Sun 9.30)*
Lucky Seven *(Mon noon, Tue-Thu 10, Fri-Sun 9)*
Mona Lisa *(7)*
Napket: *SW3 (8)*
Nottingdale *(Mon-Fri 7)*
Ottolenghi: *W11 (8, Sun 8.30)*
Pappa Ciccia: *Fulham High St SW6 (7.30)*
Pissarro *(Sat & Sun 9)*
Ranoush: *W8 (10); W2 (9); SW3 (noon)*
Raoul's Café & Deli: *W11 (8.30); W9 (8.30 am)*
Sam's Brasserie *(9)*
Sophie's Steakhouse: *all branches (Sat & Sun 11)*
Stock Pot: *SW3 (8)*
Tartine *(11)*
Tom's Deli *(8, Sun 9)*
Tom's Kitchen *(8, Sat & Sun 10)*
Troubadour *(9)*
202 *(Mon & Sun 10, Tue-Sat 8.30)*
Vingt-Quatre *(24 hrs)*
The Waterway *(10 Sat & Sun)*
White Horse *(9.30)*

North

The Almeida *( )*
Banners *(9, Sat & Sun 10)*
Blue Legume *(9.30)*
Caponata *(9, Sun 10)*
Chamomile *(7, Sat & Sun 8)*
Chop'd: *NW1 (7)*
Del'Aziz: *NW3 (8)*
Diner: *N1, NW10 (sat, sun 9)*
The Engineer *(9)*
Euphorium Bakery *(7.30, Sun 9)*
Fifteen Trattoria *(7.30, Sun 8)*
Fine Burger Company: *NW1 (7 am);*

N1, NW3 *(midday, Sat & Sun 11 am)*
Gail's Bread: *NW3 (7, Sat & Sun 8)*
Gallipoli: *Upper St N1, Upper St N1 (10.30)*
Garufa *(10)*
Ginger & White *(7.30, Sat & Sun 8.30)*
Giraffe: *N1, Rosslyn Hill NW3 (7.45, Sat & Sun 9); Haverstock Hill NW3 (8, Sat & Sun 9)*
Harry Morgan's *(9)*
Homa *(Sun 10)*
Juniper Dining *(Sat & Sun 9)*
Kentish Canteen *(10)*
Kenwood (Brew House) *(9)*
Kipferl *(9, Sun 10)*
Landmark (Winter Gdn) *(7)*
The Lansdowne *(Sat & Sun 9.30)*
Ottolenghi: *N1 (8, Sun 9)*
Rugoletta *(9)*
S & M Café: *N1 (7.30)*
St Pancras Grand *(7, Sun 9)*
Stringray Café: *N5 (11); NW5 (Fri-Sun 11)*
Trojka *(Mon-Fri 8)*
The Wet Fish Cafe *(10)*
York & Albany *(7)*

South

Annie's: *SW13 (Tue-Sun 10)*
Archduke Wine Bar *(Sat & Sun10)*
The Bingham *(7, Sat-Sun 8)*
The Bolingbroke *(Sat & Sun 10)*
Brasserie James *(Sat & Sun 10 am)*
Browns: *SE1 (11 am)*
Buenos Aires Cafe: *SE10 (7.30 am)*
Butcher & Grill: *SW11 (8.30); SW19 (Sat & Sun 8.30)*
Caffè Vergnano: *SE1 (8, Sat & Sun 11)*
Canteen: *SE1 (8, Sat & Sun 9)*
Chapters *(8, Sun 9)*
Le Chardon: *SW4 (9); SE22 (Sat & Sun 9.30)*
Del'Aziz: *all south branches (8)*
The Depot *(Sat 9.30)*
Doukan *(9)*
Fat Boy's: *TW8 (Mon-Fri 11.30)*
fish! *(Thu-Fri 7, Sat 8, Sun 10)*
Franklins *(Sat 10)*
Frizzante Cafe *(10)*
Garrison *(8, Sat & Sun 9)*
Gastro *(8)*
Gazette: *SW12 (9); SW11 (8)*
Giraffe: *all south branches (7.45, Sat & Sun 9)*
Green & Blue *(9, Sun 11)*
Harrison's *(Sat & Sun 9)*
Hudsons *(9.30, Sat & Sun 9)*
Joanna's *(10)*
Konditor & Cook: *Cornwall Road SE1, Stoney St SE1 (7.30 am)*
Lola Rojo: *SW11 (Sat & Sun 11)*
Monmouth Coffee Company: *Park St SE1 (7.30); Maltby St SE1 (9)*
Orange Pekoe *(9)*
Le P'tit Normand *(Sun 9)*
Pantry *(8, Sat 8.30 & Sun 9.30)*
Petersham Hotel *(Mon-Fri 7, Sat & Sun 8)*
Plane Food *(5.30)*
Putney Station *(Sat & Sun 11)*
El Rincón Latino *(Sat & Sun 11)*
The Riverfront *(9.30)*
Rivington Grill: *SE10 (Thurs-Sun 10)*
Roast *(7, Sat 8)*
Scoffers *(10.30, Sun 9)*
Sonny's *(Sat & Sun 9.30)*
The Table *(7.30, Sat-Sun 9)*
Tapas Brindisa: *SE1 (Fri-Sat 9, Sun 11)*

BRUNCH MENUS

BUSINESS

Odin's
One-O-One
L'Oranger
Orrery
Oscar
The Palm
The Pantechnicon
Paramount
Patterson's
Pearl
Pétrus
Pied à Terre
Quilon
Quirinale
Quo Vadis
Refuel
Rhodes W1 Restaurant
Rib Room
Roka: *all branches*
Roussillon
Roux At Parliament Square
Roux At The Landau
Rules
Santini
Sartoria
Savoy Grill
Savoy (River Rest')
Scott's
J Sheekey
Shepherd's
Simpsons-in-the-Strand
The Square
Tamarind
Theo Randall
2 Veneti
Veeraswamy
Il Vicolo
The Wallace
Wheeler's
Wild Honey
Wiltons
The Wolseley
Zafferano

West
Bibendum
The Capital Restaurant
Gaucho: *SW3*
Gordon Ramsay
The Ledbury
Poissonnerie de l'Avenue
Racine
Tom Aikens
La Trompette
Zuma

North
Frederick's
Gaucho: *NW3*
Landmark (Winter Gdn)
Rotunda Bar & Restaurant
St Pancras Grand

South
Blueprint Café
Brasserie Joël
Butlers Wharf Chop House
Le Cassoulet
Chez Gérard: *all branches*
Delfina
Gaucho: *SE1,TW10*
The Glasshouse
Magdalen
Oxo Tower (Brass')
Oxo Tower (Rest')
Le Pont de la Tour

Roast
Skylon
Vivat Bacchus: *all branches*
Zucca

East
Alba
Amerigo Vespucci
L'Anima
Bevis Marks
Bleeding Heart
Boisdale of Bishopsgate
Bonds
Café du Marché
Caravaggio
Catch
Chamberlain's
The Chancery
Chez Gérard: *all branches*
Cinnamon Kitchen
City Miyama
Club Gascon
Coq d'Argent
Curve
Dockmaster's House
The Don
Eyre Brothers
Forman's
The Fox and Anchor
Galvin La Chapelle
Gaucho: *E14, EC2, EC3*
Goodman City : *all branches*
Gow's
Green's: *all branches*
High Timber
The Hoxton Grill
Imperial City
Luc's Brasserie
Lutyens
Malmaison Brasserie
The Mercer
Moro
1901
1 Lombard Street
Pacific Oriental
Paternoster Chop House
Plateau
Portal
Prism
Quadrato
Refettorio
Rhodes 24
Roka: *all branches*
The Royal Exchange Grand Café
St John
Sauterelle
Searcy's Brasserie
Smiths (Top Floor)
Smiths (Dining Rm)
Sweetings
Taberna Etrusca
Tompkins
Vertigo 42
Vivat Bacchus: *all branches*
The White Swan

BYO

*(Bring your own wine at no
or low – less than £3 – corkage.
Note for £5-£15 per bottle,
you can normally negotiate
to take your own wine to many,
if not most, places.)*

Central
Food for Thought
Fryer's Delight
Golden Hind
India Club
Paolina Café
Patogh
Ragam
Viet

West
Adams Café
Alounak: *all branches*
Bedlington Café
Café 209
Chelsea Bun Diner
Fitou's Thai Restaurant
Five Hot Chillies
Mirch Masala: *all branches*
Mohsen
Pappa Ciccia: *Munster Rd SW6*
Rôtisserie Bute Street

North
Ali Baba
Diwana Bhel-Poori House
Geeta
Huong-Viet
Rugoletta
Toff's
Vijay

South
Amaranth
Green & Blue
Hot Stuff
Lahore Karahi
Lahore Kebab House: *all branches*
Mien Tay: *all branches*
Mirch Masala: *all branches*
The Paddyfield
Simply Indian
Sree Krishna
Thai Corner Café

East
Lahore Kebab House: *all branches*
Little Georgia Café
Mangal 1
Mien Tay: *all branches*
Mirch Masala: *all branches*
New Tayyabs

CHILDREN

*(h – high or special chairs
m – children's menu
p – children's portions
e – weekend entertainments
o – other facilities)*

Central
Abeno: *WC2 (h); WC1 (hm)*
About Thyme *(hp)*
Acorn House *(h)*
Al Duca *(hp)*

Al Hamra *(hp)*
Al Sultan *(h)*
Albannach *(hmp)*
All Star Lanes: *all branches (hm)*
Alloro *(p)*
Apsleys *(hp)*
Arbutus *(hp)*
Asadal *(h)*
Asia de Cuba *(hp)*
L'Atelier de Joel Robuchon *(hp)*
Athenaeum *(m)*
Aubaine: *all branches (h)*
L'Autre Pied *(hp)*
Axis *(hm)*
Babbo *(hp)*
Back to Basics *(hp)*
Balans: *all central branches (hm)*
Bank Westminster *(hp)*
Bar Boulud *(hp)*
Bar Italia *(hp)*
Bar Trattoria Semplice *(hp)*
Il Baretto *(h)*
Barrica *(p)*
Bar Shu *(h)*
Beiteddine *(p)*
Belgo Centrale: *Earlham
  St WC2 (hm); Kingsway WC2 (m)*
Bellamy's *(h)*
Benares *(h)*
Benihana: *W1 (hm)*
Benito's Hat: *Goodge St W1 (hp)*
Benja *(h)*
Bentley's *(h)*
Bincho Yakitori *(hp)*
Bocca Di Lupo *(hp)*
Bodean's: *W1 (ehm)*
The Botanist *(h)*
Boudin Blanc *(hp)*
Boulevard *(hm)*
Boyd's Brasserie *(hp)*
Brasserie Roux *(hm)*
Browns (Albemarle) *(hmp)*
The English Tea Rm (Browns) *(h)*
Browns: *W1, WC2 (hm)*
Bumbles *(h)*
Byron: *Wellington St WC2 (hm)*
C London *(hp)*
Café Bohème *(h)*
Café des Amis *(h)*
Café Emm *(p)*
Café España *(h)*
Café in the Crypt *(hp)*
Café Luc *(hm)*
Café Pacifico *(hm)*
Caffè Caldesi *(hp)*
Caffè Vergnano: *WC2 (p)*
Cantina Laredo *(hm)*
Cape Town Fish Market *(hp)*
Le Caprice *(hp)*
Cecconi's *(hp)*
Le Cercle *(p)*
Chabrot Bistrot d'Amis *(p)*
The Chelsea Brasserie *(hm)*
Chez Gérard: *all central branches (em)*
China Tang *(h)*
Chipotle *(h)*
Chisou *(h)*
Chor Bizarre *(h)*
Christopher's *(hm)*
Chuen Cheng Ku *(h)*
Ciao Bella *(h)*
Cigala *(h)*
The Cinnamon Club *(h)*
City Café *(hm)*
Clos Maggiore *(hp)*
Colony *(hp)*
Como Lario *(hp)*

The Pig's Ear *(hp)*
El Pirata de Tapas *(hp)*
Pissarro *(hmp)*
PJ's Bar and Grill *(hm)*
Poissonnerie de l'Avenue *(h)*
Polish Club *(hp)*
Il Portico *(p)*
Portobello Ristorante *(hmp)*
Princess Victoria *(hp)*
Quantus *(h)*
Queen's Head *(hm)*
Racine *(hp)*
Randa *(h)*
Ranoush: *SW3,W8 (hp)*
Raoul's Café & Deli: *W11,W9 (hp)*
The Red Pepper *(hp)*
Riccardo's *(hp)*
The River Café *(hp)*
Rocca Di Papa: *SW7 (hp)*
Rodizio Rico: *W2 (h)*
The Roebuck *(hp)*
Rossopomodoro: *SW10 (hp);W11 (p)*
Rôtisserie Bute Street *(hm)*
Royal China: *all branches (h)*
Saf: *W8 (hm)*
Sagar: *W6 (hm)*
Saigon Saigon *(h)*
Sam's Brasserie *(hm)*
San Lorenzo *(hp)*
The Sands End *(hp)*
Santa Lucia *(hp)*
Santa Maria *(hp)*
Satay House *(h)*
Scalini *(hp)*
Seventeen *(p)*
La Sophia *(hp)*
Sophie's Steakhouse: *all branches (hm)*
Sticky Fingers *(ehm)*
Stock Pot: *SW3 (hm)*
Sufi *(hp)*
Sukho Fine Thai Cuisine *(hp)*
The Summerhouse *(hmp)*
The Swan *(h)*
Taiwan Village *(h)*
Taqueria *(hm)*
Tartine *(p)*
Tatra *(h)*
Tendido Cuatro *(hp)*
Thali *(p)*
Timo *(p)*
Tom's Deli *(h)*
Tom's Kitchen *(hp)*
La Trompette *(hp)*
Troubadour *(hp)*
202 *(p)*
Le Vacherin *(hp)*
Venosi *(hp)*
Vicino *(hp)*
Vingt-Quatre *(hp)*
Wagamama: *W8 (hm)*
Wahaca: *W12 (hp)*
The Walmer Castle *(hm)*
The Warrington *(hp)*
The Waterway *(hp)*
The Westbourne *(hp)*
White Horse *(hp)*
Wine Gallery *(hp)*
Yashin *(hp)*
Zaika *(hp)*
Zuma *(h)*

North
L'Absinthe *(hm)*
Afghan Kitchen *(h)*
The Albion *(hm)*
Ali Baba *(p)*

Alisan *(h)*
The Almeida *(hm)*
Anglo Asian Tandoori *(h)*
Artigiano *(hm)*
L'Artista *(hp)*
Les Associés *(hmp)*
Atari-Ya: *NW4 (p)*
L'Aventure *(hp)*
Il Bacio: *all branches (hmp)*
Bald Faced Stag *(hmp)*
The Banana Tree Canteen: *NW6 (ehm)*
Banners *(ehmp)*
The Barnsbury *(hp)*
Belgo Noord: *NW1 (hm)*
Beyoglu *(h)*
Bistro Aix *(p)*
Blue Legume *(hm)*
La Bota *(h)*
La Brocca *(hm)*
Browns: *N1 (hm)*
Bull & Last *(hmp)*
Byron: *Upper St N1 (hm)*
La Cage Imaginaire *(hp)*
Camden Brasserie *(hm)*
Camino *(hp)*
Canonbury Kitchen *(p)*
Caponata *(hp)*
Carob Tree *(h)*
Chamomile *(hm)*
Chez Liline *(hp)*
Chutneys *(p)*
The Clissold Arms *(hm)*
La Collina *(hp)*
The Compass *(h)*
Daphne *(hp)*
Del'Aziz: *NW3 (hmp)*
dim T: *all north branches (hmo)*
Don Pepe *(hp)*
Dotori *(p)*
The Drapers Arms *(hp)*
The Duke of Cambridge *(hp)*
The Engineer *(hp)*
The Fellow *(hp)*
Fifteen Dining Room *(hp)*
Fifteen Trattoria *(p)*
Fig *(h)*
Fine Burger Company: *N1 (hm)*
Fratelli la Bufala *(hp)*
Frederick's *(hm)*
Freemasons Arms *(hp)*
Furnace *(p)*
Gail's Bread: *NW3 (hmp)*
Gallipoli: *all branches (hp)*
Garufa *(hp)*
Gaucho: *NW3 (hp)*
Geeta *(hp)*
Gem *(hp)*
Gilgamesh *(hp)*
Ginger & White *(hm)*
Giraffe: *N1, Rosslyn Hill NW3 (ehm)*
La Giralda *(hp)*
Goldfish: *NW3 (hp)*
Good Earth: *NW7 (hp)*
Great Nepalese *(p)*
Green Cottage *(hp)*
Haché: *NW1 (h)*
Harry Morgan's *(hop)*
The Haven *(hp)*
Holly Bush *(hp)*
Homa *(hm)*
The Horseshoe *(hp)*
Hoxton Apprentice *(hp)*
Huong-Viet *(hp)*
Indian Rasoi *(hp)*
Izgara *(hp)*
Jin Kichi *(h)*
The Junction Tavern *(h)*

Yi-Ban *(h)*

ENTERTAINMENT
(Check times before you go)

Central
All Star Lanes: WC1
(bowling, DJ Sat)
Bentley's
(pianist, Wed-Sat)
Bincho Yakitori
(DJ, Mon; occasional live music, Wed)
Boisdale
(jazz, Mon-Sat)
The English Tea Rm (Browns)
(pianist, daily)
Café in the Crypt
(jazz, Wed night)
Le Caprice
(pianist, nightly)
Ciao Bella
(pianist, nightly)
Circus
(circus entertainment, nightly)
Criterion
(live music, Fri & Sat; jazz trio, Sun)
Eagle Bar Diner
(DJ, Thu-Sat)
Élysée
(live music, belly dancing, smashing plates Thurs, Fri, Sat)
Floridita
(live Cuban music, nightly)
Hakkasan: Hanway Pl W1
(DJ, nightly)
Hard Rock Café
(regular live music)
Harrods (Georgian Rest')
(pianist till 5.30 pm)
Imperial China
(pianist; private rooms with karaoke)
Ishtar
(live music, Tue-Sat; belly dancer, Fri & Sat)
Joe Allen
(pianist, Mon-Sat)
Kettners
(pianist Tue-Sat)
Langan's Brasserie
(jazz, Fri & Sat)
Levant
(belly dancer, nightly)
Little Italy
(DJ, Mon-Sat)
Maroush: W1
(music & dancing, nightly)
Mint Leaf: SW1
(DJ, Fri D)
Momo
(live world music, Tue)
Noura: W1
(belly dancer, Fri&Sat)
L'Oranger
(pianist, Fri & Sat)
Oscar
(film club, Sun)
Pearl
(pianist, Wed-Sat)
Quaglino's
(jazz, nightly)
Red Fort
(DJ, Fri & Sat)
Refuel
(film club, Sun 3.30 pm)
The Ritz Restaurant
(live music, Fri & Sat)
Roka: W1

(DJ, Thu-Sat)
Samarqand
(Karaoke and games consoles)
Sarastro
(opera, Sun & Mon D)
Savoy Grill
(pianist, nightly)
Savoy (River Rest')
(cabaret music)
Shanghai Blues
(live jazz, Fri & Sat)
Simpsons-in-the-Strand
(pianist, nightly)
Sketch (Gallery)
(DJ, Thu-Sat)
Tamarai
(club nights, Fri & Sat)
Thai Square: SW1
(DJ, Fri & Sat)
Tom's Terrace
(DJ, Thu-Fri)
Vanilla
(DJ's, Fri & Sat)
The Windmill
(live music, Mon)

West
All Star Lanes: W2
(bowling, DJ Thu-Sat)
Babylon
(nightclub, Fri & Sat; magician, Sun; jazz, Tue)
Beach Blanket Babylon: all branches
(DJ, Fri & Sat)
Belvedere
(pianist, nightly Sat & Sun all day)
Benugo: Cromwell Rd SW7
(jazz, Wed)
Big Easy
(live music, nightly)
Brompton Bar & Grill
(jazz, third Fri of the month)
Le Café Anglais
(magician, Sun L)
Chella
(live music, Sun)
Cheyne Walk Brasserie
(jazz, first Mon of month)
Del'Aziz: SW6
(belly dancer, Thu-Sat, live acoustic music);
W12
(live Jazz, Fri-Sat)
Formosa Dining Room
(quiz, Tue)
Frankie's Italian Bar & Grill: SW3
(magician, Sun)
Harwood Arms
(quiz night, Tue)
Maroush: I) 21 Edgware Rd W2
(music & dancing, nightly)
Mr Wing
(jazz, Thu-Sat)
Notting Hill Brasserie
(jazz, nightly, Sun L)
Nozomi
(DJ, every night)
Okawari
(karaoke)
Old Parr's Head
(quiz night, Mon; poker, Tue)
Il Pagliaccio
(Elvis impersonator, monthly)
Paradise by Way of Kensal Green
(burlesque, Mon; comedy nights, Wed; DJ, Fri-Sun)
Pasha

(belly dancer, weekends; tarot card reader, special occasions)

(Ciro's) Pizza Pomodoro
(live music, nightly)

Rôtisserie Bute Street
(live music)

Sam's Brasserie
(live music, first and third Sun of month)

Sticky Fingers
(face painter, Sun)

supperclub
(shows, nightly)

Troubadour
(live music, most nights)

The Waterway
(live music, Thu)

North

Bull & Last
(pub quiz, Sun)

Camino
(DJ, Thu-Sat)

Caponata
(live music, Tue-Sun)

Del'Aziz: NW3
(live Jazz, Fri & Sat)

The Fellow
(DJ, Thu-Fri)

Gilgamesh
(DJ, Fri & Sat)

The Haven
(jazz, Tue-Thu)

Isarn
(live music)

Landmark (Winter Gdn)
(pianist & musicians, daily)

Mestizo
(DJ, Thu)

The North London Tavern
(jazz, Sun; quiz night, Mon; open mic, Tue; Every third Thu comedy)

Prince Albert
(quiz, Sun D)

Rotunda Bar & Restaurant
(jazz, Fri)

Shaka Zulu
(music, bi-weekly)

Thai Square: N1
(DJ, Thu-Sat)

Trojka
(Russian music, Fri & Sat)

Villa Bianca
(guitarist, Mon-Thu; pianist, Sat & Sun)

The Wet Fish Cafe
(Spanish soul, occasionally)

York & Albany
(quiz night, Mon)

South

Al Forno: SW15
(live music, Sat)

Archduke Wine Bar
(jazz, Mon-Sun)

Avalon
(DJ, Fri & Sat)

Bayee Village
(pianist, Mon-Wed)

Bengal Clipper
(pianist, Tue-Sat)

Brasserie Toulouse-Lautrec
(live music, nightly)

Cantina Vinopolis
(singer, Fri)

Del'Aziz: Canvey St SE1
*(live balkan, gypsy and folk rhythms, wed live jazz, fri belly dancing); Bermondsey Sq SE1
(live Jazz Wed & Sat; belly-dancing Fri)*

Entrée
(jazz, Thu-Sat D)

The Fentiman Arms
(quiz night, Tue)

Florence
(play room)

The Gowlett
(DJ, Sun; Lucky 7s, Thu)

The Lighthouse
(live music)

The Little Bay: SW11
(opera, Thu-Sat; piano, Wed & Sun)

Meson don Felipe
(guitarist, nightly)

Oxo Tower (Brass')
(live jazz, Sat & Sun L, Sun-Mon D)

Le Pont de la Tour
(pianist, every evening; live jazz trio, Sun L)

The Prince Of Wales
(quiz night, Sun)

Roast
(jazz, Sun)

Santa Maria del Sur
(live music, Mon)

The Ship
(live music, Sun; quiz, Wed)

Tas: The Cut SE1, Borough High St SE1
(guitarist, nightly)

Tas Pide
(live music, daily D)

Thai Square: SW15
(DJ, Fri & Sat)

The Victoria
(Singer, one Wed a month)

The Wharf
(Salsa night, first Wed of month)

East

All Star Lanes: E1
(bowling)

Beach Blanket Babylon: all branches
(DJ, Fri & Sat)

Bistrotheque
(regular drag shows and cabarets, piano brunch)

Boisdale of Canary Wharf
(live music, daily)

Café du Marché
(pianist & bass, Mon-Thu, pianist, Fri & Sat)

Cinnamon Kitchen
(DJ, Wed-Fri)

Coq d'Argent
(jazz, Sun L)

Elephant Royale
(live music, Thu-Sat)

Frizzante at City Farm
(agriturismo night, Thu in summer)

Great Eastern Dining Room
(DJ, Fri & Sat)

The Hoxton Grill
(DJ, Thu-Sat)

Kenza
(belly dancers, Mon-Sat; tarot reader, Fri)

The Little Bay: EC1
(opera, Thu-Sat)

Mint Leaf: EC2
(Jazz, Fri D; DJ, weekends)

The Narrow
(quiz night, Mon; comedy, monthly; acoustic, Wed)

1901
(violinist or other live music, Wed-Thu)

Pizza East
(DJ, live music, quiz nights, Tue, Thu, Sat)

LATE

(open till midnight or later as shown; may be earlier Sunday)

253

Le Mercury *(1 am, not Sun)*
19 Numara Bos Cirrik
Pizzeria Pappagone
La Porchetta Pizzeria: *N4, NW1 (Sat & Sun midnight); N1 (weekends midnight)*
Rodizio Rico: *N1*
Sofra: *all branches*
Yum Yum *(Fri & Sat midnight)*

South
Archduke Wine Bar *(Fri & Sat 1 am)*
Basilico: *all south branches*
Belgo: *SW4 (midnight, Thu 1 am, Fri & Sat 2 am)*
Buona Sera: *all branches*
Caffè Vergnano: *SE1*
Cah-Chi: *SW18 (not Sat & Sun)*
Champor-Champor
Everest Inn
Firezza: *SW11 ; SW18 (Fri & Sat midnight)*
Fish in a Tie
Gastro
Green & Blue *(Fri & Sat midnight)*
Kennington Tandoori
Lahore Karahi
Lahore Kebab House: *all branches*
The Lighthouse *(Fri & Sat midnight)*
Mirch Masala: *all branches*
Nazmins
Putney Station
Scoffers *(Thu-Sat)*
Sree Krishna *(Fri & Sat midnight)*
The Tree House *(Fri & Sat midnight)*
Tsunami: *SW4 (Fri-Sun midnight)*
Zero Degrees

East
Brick Lane Beigel Bake *(24 hours)*
Cellar Gascon
Clifton
The Diner: *EC2 (not Sun & Mon)*
Elephant Royale *(Fri & Sat midnight)*
Giant Robot
Lahore Kebab House: *all branches*
Mangal 1 *(midnight, Sat-Sun 1 am)*
Mirch Masala: *all branches*
Pizza East *(Thu midnight, Fri & Sat 1 am)*
La Porchetta Pizzeria: *EC1 (Sat & Sun midnight)*
Redhook *(midnight, Thu-Sat 1 am)*
Rocket: *E14*
Sweet & Spicy *(Fri & Sat midnight)*
Wapping Food

OUTSIDE TABLES
(* particularly recommended)

Central
Abokado: *WC2*
Al Duca
Al Hamra
Al Sultan
Amaranto
Andrew Edmunds
Antidote
aqua kyoto*
aqua nueva
Archipelago
L'Artiste Musclé
Atari-Ya: *W1*
Aubaine: *W1*
Aurora
L'Autre Pied
Back to Basics
Baker & Spice: *SW1*

Balans: *Old Compton St W1*
Bam-Bou
Bank Westminster
Bar Italia
Bar Trattoria Semplice
Barrafina
Barrica
Benito's Hat: *Goodge St W1*
Bentley's
Benugo: *all central branches*
Bincho Yakitori
Bistro 1: *Frith St W1, WC2*
The Botanist
La Bottega: *Lower Sloane St SW1, Eccleston St SW1*
Boudin Blanc
The Bountiful Cow
Busaba Eathai: *WC1*
Café Bohème
Café des Amis
Café Luc
Caffè Caldesi
Cantina Laredo
Caraffini
Cecconi's
Cha Cha Moon
Chez Gérard: *all central branches*
Chisou
Ciao Bella
Cigala
City Café
Cocorino: *Thayer St W1*
Colony
Comptoir Libanais: *W1*
Côte: *WC2*
The Courtauld Gallery Café
Da Mario
Daylesford Organic: *all branches*
Dean Street Townhouse
Dehesa
Delfino
dim T: *W1*
Diner: *W1*
The Duke of Wellington
The Easton
Ed's Easy Diner: *Moor St W1*
Élysée
Fairuz
5 Pollen Street
Franco's
Giraffe: *W1*
Goodman: *W1*
Gordon's Wine Bar
Goya
Grazing Goat
Grumbles
Guerilla Burgers
Hard Rock Café
Hardy's Brasserie
Hellenic
Hush
Indali Lounge
Inn the Park
Ishbilia
Ishtar
Jenny Lo's Tea House
Kaffeine
Kazan: *all branches*
Kopapa
Kyashii
Ladurée: *SW1, W1*
Lantana Cafe
Leon: *Gt Marlborough St W1, WC2*
Levant
Little Italy
Lupita
Maison Bertaux

255

Hereford Road
High Road Brasserie
Hole in the Wall*
Indian Zing
The Jam Tree: W14
Joe's Brasserie
Julie's
Karma
Kateh
Kerbisher & Malt
Khan's
The Ladbroke Arms
The Ledbury
Lola & Simón
Made in Italy
Madsen
The Mall Tavern
Manicomio: all branches
Manson
The Meat & Wine Co
Mediterraneo
Medlar
Mohsen
Montpeliano
Noor Jahan: W2
Nottingdale
The Oak
Old Parr's Head
Osteria dell'Arancio
Otto Pizza
Il Pagliaccio
The Painted Heron
Pappa Ciccia: Fulham High St SW6
Paradise by Way of Kensal Green
Pellicano
The Phene
The Phoenix
Poissonnerie de l'Avenue
Polish Club
Il Portico
Portobello Ristorante*
Princess Victoria
Quantus
Queen's Head*
Raoul's Café & Deli: W11*; W9
The Real Greek: W12
The Red Pepper
Riccardo's
The River Café*
Rocca Di Papa: SW7
The Roebuck*
Rossopomodoro: W11
Rôtisserie Bute Street
Royal China: SW6
Saigon Saigon
The Sands End
Santa Lucia
Santa Maria
The Scarsdale
La Sophia
The Summerhouse*
Sushinho
The Swan
Tatra
Tendido Cero
Tendido Cuatro
Thali
Tom's Deli
Tosa
La Trompette
Troubadour
202
Uli
Wahaca: W12
The Walmer Castle
The Waterway*
The Westbourne*

White Horse
The Windsor Castle*
Wine Gallery

North
L'Absinthe
The Albion
Ali Baba
The Almeida
The Arches
Artigiano
Les Associés
L'Aventure
Bald Faced Stag
The Banana Tree Canteen: NW6
The Barnsbury
Blue Legume
Bull & Last
Café del Parc
La Cage Imaginaire
Camino
Caponata
Carob Tree
Chamomile
Charles Lamb
Chilango: N1
The Clissold Arms
La Collina
The Compass
Daphne
Del'Aziz: all branches
dim T: NW3
The Drapers Arms
The Duke of Cambridge
The Engineer*
The Fellow
Fig
Fine Burger Company: N1
The Flask
Fratelli la Bufala
Frederick's
Freemasons Arms*
Gail's Bread: all north branches
Gallipoli: all branches
Gaucho: NW3
Ginger & White
Giraffe: N1, Rosslyn Hill NW3
Haché: all branches
Harry Morgan's
The Haven
Homa
The Horseshoe
Hoxton Apprentice
Indian Rasoi
Isarn
The Junction Tavern
Kentish Canteen
Kenwood (Brew House)
The Lansdowne
Lemonia
Market
The Marquess Tavern
Masala Zone: N1
Mill Lane Bistro
Mosaica
The Northgate
Odette's
The Old Bull & Bush
The Orange Tree*
Ottolenghi: N1
El Parador
Petek
La Petite Auberge
Pizzeria Pappagone
La Porchetta Pizzeria: NW1
Prince Albert

257

William Curley: *all branches*
The Yellow House
Zero Degrees

East
Abokado: *EC4*
Al Volo*
Albion
Ambassador
Amerigo Vespucci*
Benugo: *all east branches*
Bevis Marks
Bistro du Vin: *EC1*
Bistrot Bruno Loubet
Bleeding Heart
Boisdale of Canary Wharf
Browns: *E14*
Buen Ayre
Café Below
Café Spice Namaste
Canteen: *E1*
Caravan
Chamberlain's
The Chancery
Chop'd: *EC3*
Cicada
Cinnamon Kitchen
Coach & Horses
Comptoir Gascon
Curve
$
The Eagle
Elephant Royale*
The Empress of India
The Farm Collective
La Figa
Fish Central
Forman's
The Fox
Frizzante at City Farm
Galvin La Chapelle
Gaucho: *E14*
Giant Robot
Gourmet Pizza Company: *all branches*
The Gun
Hazev
Hix Oyster & Chop House
The Hoxton Grill
Kolossi Grill
Leon: *E1, Ludgate Circus EC4*
The Little Bay: *EC1*
Little Georgia Café
LMNT
London Wall Bar & Kitchen
Lutyens
The Luxe
Manicomio: *all branches*
Memsaheb on Thames
The Modern Pantry
Morito
Moro
Namo
Napket: *EC3*
The Narrow
Northbank
Nusa Kitchen: *EC2*
Osteria Appennino
The Parlour Bar
Paternoster Chop House
The Peasant
E Pellicci
Plateau
Portal
Quadrato
Redhook
Relais de Venise L'Entrecôte: *all*

branches
Rochelle Canteen
Royal China: *E14*
S & M Café: *all branches*
Saf: *EC2*
Santore
Smiths (Top Floor)
Smiths (Ground Floor)
Spianata & Co: *E1, EC3*
Stringray Globe Café: *E2*
Taberna Etrusca
Terranostra
Vinoteca: *all branches*
The Well

PRIVATE ROOMS
**(for the most comprehensive
listing of venues for functions –
from palaces to pubs – visit
www.hardens.com/party, or buy
*Harden's London Party, Event
& Conference Guide*, available
in all good bookshops)
* particularly recommended**

Central
About Thyme *(40)*
Adam Street *(12,60,80,350)*
Al Hamra *(20)*
Alain Ducasse *(6,10,24)*
Albannach *(20)*
Alloro *(16)*
Amaranto *(8)*
Amaya *(14)*
Antidote *(30)*
Apsleys *(14,14)*
aqua kyoto *(8)*
aqua nueva *(16)*
L'Artiste Musclé *(25)*
Asadal *(14,14,14)*
Athenaeum *(12,60)*
Aurora *(20)*
L'Autre Pied *(16)*
The Avenue *(20)*
Axis *(18)*
Ba Shan *(10)*
Babbo *(14)*
Bam-Bou *(20,30,12,12,9)*
Bank Westminster *(20,20,10)*
Bar Boulud *(16,16)*
Bar Trattoria Semplice *(20)*
Bar Shu *(14)*
Belgo Centraal: *Earlham St WC2 (25,30)*
Benares *(16,36,7,8)*
Benihana: *all branches (10)*
Benja *(18)*
Bentley's *(14,60)*
Bincho Yakitori *(20)*
Bob Bob Ricard *(10)*
Bocca Di Lupo *(32)*
Bodean's: *W1 (10)*
Boisdale *(22)*
Boudin Blanc *(16)*
Boulevard *(35,50)*
The Bountiful Cow *(45)*
Boyd's Brasserie *(350)*
Brasserie St Jacques *(18)*
Browns: *WC2 (35,80,50)*
Bumbles *(40)*
Busaba Eathai: *WC1 (15)*
C London *(40)*
Café des Amis *(24)*
Café Emm *(60)*
Cantina Laredo *(20)*

259

261

The Peasant *(18)*
Piccolino: *EC2 (24)*
Pizza East *(18)*
Plateau *(24)*
Portal *(14)*
Prism *(30,55)*
The Punch Tavern *(50)*
Redhook *(15)*
Refettorio *(30)*
Le Rendezvous du Café *(30,60)*
Rhodes 24 *(8,20,30)*
Rivington Grill: *EC2 (25)*
Rocket: *EC2 (25)*
Rosa's: *E1 (40)*
Royal China: *E14 (12,12,12)*
The Royal Exchange Grand
    Café *(26)*
S & M Café: *E1 (40)*
Saf: *EC2 (25)*
St John *(18)*
Saki *(10)*
Sauterelle *(28)*
Searcy's Brasserie *(14)*
Shanghai *(40,50)*
Smithfield Bar & Grill *(10)*
Soseki *(12)*
Sweet & Spicy *(25)*
Tajima Tei *(16,6,4)*
Tas: *EC1 (50)*
Les Trois Garçons *(10)*
28-50 *(12,6)*
Viajante *(20)*
Viet Grill *(100)*
Vinoteca: *EC1 (30)*
Vivat Bacchus: *EC4 (45)*
The Well *(70)*
The White Swan *(52)*
Whitechapel Gallery *(14)*
Yi-Ban *(30)*

ROMANTIC

Central
Andrew Edmunds
Archipelago
L'Atelier de Joel Robuchon
Aurora
Bam-Bou
Boudin Blanc
Café Bohème
Le Caprice
Cecconi's
Le Cercle
Chor Bizarre
Clos Maggiore
Corrigan's Mayfair
Crazy Bear
Dean Street Townhouse
Les Deux Salons
Elena's L'Etoile
L'Escargot
Galvin at Windows
Gauthier Soho
Le Gavroche
Gay Hussar
Gordon Ramsay at Claridge's
Gordon's Wine Bar
Hakkasan: *Hanway Pl W1*
Hush
The Ivy
Kettners
Langan's Bistro
Langan's Brasserie
Levant
Locanda Locatelli
Marcus Wareing

Momo
Mon Plaisir
Odin's
L'Oranger
Orrery
La Petite Maison
Pied à Terre
Polpo
La Porte des Indes
La Poule au Pot
Refuel
The Ritz Restaurant
Roussillon
Roux At The Landau
Rules
St Moritz
Sarastro
Scott's
J Sheekey
J Sheekey Oyster Bar
Toto's
Vanilla
The Wolseley
Zafferano

West
Albertine
Angelus
Annie's: *W4*
The Ark
Assaggi
Babylon
Beach Blanket Babylon: *all branches*
Belvedere
Bibendum
Blakes
La Bouchée
Brinkley's
Café Laville
Charlotte's Place
Cheyne Walk Brasserie
Le Colombier
Daphne's
E&O
Eight Over Eight
La Famiglia
Ffiona's
First Floor
Julie's
Launceston Place
The Ledbury
Maggie Jones's
Mediterraneo
Mr Wing
Notting Hill Brasserie
Osteria Basilico
Paradise by Way of Kensal Green
Pasha
Patio
Pissarro
Polish Club
Portobello Ristorante
Racine
The River Café
Star of India
The Summerhouse
supperclub
Le Suquet
La Trompette
Troubadour
Le Vacherin
The Walmer Castle
Zuma

North
Anglo Asian Tandoori

Les Associés
L'Aventure
Bistro Aix
La Cage Imaginaire
The Engineer
Fig
The Flask
Frederick's
Mango Room
Le Mercury
Odette's
Oslo Court
Sardo Canale
Villa Bianca

South
A Cena
The Bingham
Brula
Cannizaro House
Le Cassoulet
Champor-Champor
Le Chardon: *SE22*
Chez Bruce
The Depot
Enoteca Turi
Four O Nine
Gastro
The Glasshouse
Joanna's
Lobster Pot
Oxo Tower (Brass')
Petersham Hotel
Petersham Nurseries
Le Pont de la Tour
Rock & Rose
Scoffers
The Spread Eagle
Thai on the River
The Tree House
Trinity
Upstairs Bar
The Wharf

East
Beach Blanket Babylon: *all branches*
Bleeding Heart
Café du Marché
Club Gascon
Comptoir Gascon
Galvin La Chapelle
LMNT
Moro
Pizza East
Soseki
Les Trois Garçons
Vertigo 42
Wapping Food

ROOMS WITH A VIEW

Central
Dinner
Fakhreldine
Galvin at Windows
The National Dining Rooms
Orrery
Paramount
The Portrait
Savoy (River Rest')
The Terrace in the Fields

West
Babylon
Belvedere

Café Laville
Min Jiang
Pissarro

North
Rotunda Bar & Restaurant

South
The Bingham
Blueprint Café
Butlers Wharf Chop House
The Depot
dim T: *SE1*
Gourmet Pizza Company: *SE1*
Oxo Tower (Brass')
Oxo Tower (Rest')
Petersham Hotel
Le Pont de la Tour
Roast
The Ship
Skylon
Stein's
The Swan at the Globe
Tate Modern (Level 7)
Tate Modern (Level 2)
Thai Square: *SW15*
The Trafalgar Tavern
Upstairs Bar

East
Barbecoa
Coq d'Argent
Curve
Elephant Royale
Forman's
The Grapes
The Gun
High Timber
Lotus Chinese Floating Restaurant
Memsaheb on Thames
The Narrow
Northbank
Plateau
Rhodes 24
Searcy's Brasserie
Smiths (Top Floor)
Vertigo 42
Yi-Ban

NOTABLE WINE LISTS

Central
Adam Street
Andrew Edmunds
Antidote
Arbutus
Barrica
Boisdale
Café des Amis
Le Cercle
Cigala
Clos Maggiore
Cork & Bottle
Dehesa
Ebury Wine Bar
L'Escargot
The Fifth Floor Restaurant
Fino
The Fountain (Fortnum's)
La Fromagerie Café
Galvin Bistrot de Luxe
Le Gavroche
Gordon Ramsay at Claridge's
Gordon's Wine Bar
The Greenhouse

An asterisk (*) after an entry indicates exceptional or very good cooking

AMERICAN
Central
All Star Lanes (WC1)
Automat (W1)
Bodean's (W1)
Christopher's (WC2)
Circus (WC2)
Guerilla Burgers (W1)
Hard Rock Café (W1)
Joe Allen (WC2)
Spuntino (W1)

West
All Star Lanes (W2)
Big Easy (SW3)
Bodean's (SW6)
Lucky Seven (W2)
Sticky Fingers (W8)

South
Bodean's (SW4)

East
All Star Lanes (E1)
Barbecoa (EC4)
Bodean's (EC3)
Giant Robot (EC1)
The Hoxton Grill (EC2)

AUSTRALIAN
Central
Lantana Cafe (W1)

BELGIAN
Central
Belgo Centraal (WC2)

North
Belgo Noord (NW1)

South
Belgo (SW4)
Brouge (TW2, TW9)

BRITISH, MODERN
Central
About Thyme (SW1)*
Acorn House (WC1)
Adam Street (WC2)
Alyn Williams (W1)
Andrew Edmunds (W1)
Arbutus (W1)*
Athenaeum (W1)*
Aurora (W1)
The Avenue (SW1)
Axis (WC2)
Balthazar (WC2)
Bank Westminster (SW1)
Bellamy's (W1)
Bob Bob Ricard (W1)
The Botanist (SW1)
Café Emm (W1)
Café Luc (W1)
Le Caprice (SW1)
Criterion (W1)
Daylesford Organic (SW1)
Dean Street Townhouse (W1)
Le Deuxième (WC2)
Dorchester Grill (W1)

The Duke of Wellington (W1)
The Easton (WC1)*
Ebury Wine Bar (SW1)
The Fifth Floor Restaurant (SW1)
Gordon's Wine Bar (WC2)
The Goring Hotel (SW1)
Grazing Goat (W1)
Hardy's Brasserie (W1)
Hix (W1)
Hush (W1)
Indigo (WC2)
Inn the Park (SW1)
The Ivy (WC2)
Kettners (W1)
Langan's Brasserie (W1)
Mews of Mayfair (W1)
The Norfolk Arms (WC1)
The Only Running Footman (W1)
The Orange (SW1)
Oscar (W1)
Ozer (W1)
The Pantechnicon (SW1)
Paramount (WC1)
Patterson's (W1)
Pollen Street Social (W1)*
The Portrait (WC2)
Quaglino's (SW1)
The Queens Arms (SW1)
Quo Vadis (W1)*
Refuel (W1)
Rhodes W1 Restaurant (W1)
RIBA Café (W1)
Roganic (W1)*
Roux At Parliament Square (SW1)
Roux At The Landau (W1)*
Rowley's (SW1)
Seven Park Place (SW1)*
Seven Stars (WC2)
1707 (W1)
Shampers (W1)
Smith Square (SW1)
Sotheby's Café (W1)*
Tate Britain (Rex Whistler) (SW1)
The Terrace in the Fields (WC2)
The Thomas Cubitt (SW1)
Tom's Terrace (WC2)
The Union Café (W1)
Vanilla (W1)
Villandry (W1)
The Vincent Rooms (SW1)
Vinoteca Seymour Place (W1)
Wild Honey (W1)
The Wolseley (W1)

West
The Abingdon (W8)
Admiral Codrington (SW3)
The Anglesea Arms (W6)*
The Anglesea Arms (SW7)
Babylon (W8)
Beach Blanket Babylon (W11)
Belvedere (W8)
Bluebird (SW3)
Brinkley's (SW10)
Brompton Bar & Grill (SW3)
The Builders Arms (SW3)
Butcher's Hook (SW6)
The Cadogan Arms (SW3)
The Carpenter's Arms (W6)
Clarke's (W8)*
The Cow (W2)
Daylesford Organic (W11)
The Dock Kitchen (W10)
Duke of Sussex (W4)
Ealing Park Tavern (W5)

Eighty-Six (SW3)
Electric Brasserie (W11)
The Enterprise (SW3)
First Floor (W11)
Formosa Dining Room (W9)
The Frontline Club (W2)
Harwood Arms (SW6)*
The Havelock Tavern (W14)*
Hedone (W4)*
The Henry Root (SW10)
High Road Brasserie (W4)
Hole in the Wall (W4)
Jam Tree (SW6,W14)
Joe's Brasserie (SW6)
Julie's (W11)
Kensington Place (W8)
Kensington Square Kitchen (W8)
Kitchen W8 (W8)*
The Ladbroke Arms (W11)*
Launceston Place (W8)*
The Ledbury (W11)*
Lots Road (SW10)
The Mall Tavern (W8)
Manson (SW6)*
Marco (SW6)
Notting Hill Brasserie (W11)
Paradise by Way of Kensal
   Green (W10)*
The Phene (SW3)
The Phoenix (SW3)
Pissarro (W4)
Princess Victoria (W12)*
Queen's Head (W6)
The Roebuck (W4)
Sam's Brasserie (W4)
The Sands End (SW6)*
supperclub (W10)
Tom Aikens (SW3)
Tom's Deli (W11)
Tom's Kitchen (SW3)
Vingt-Quatre (SW10)
The Warrington (W9)
The Waterway (W9)
The Westbourne (W2)
White Horse (SW6)
Whits (W8)

North

The Albion (N1)
Bald Faced Stag (N2)
The Barnsbury (N1)
Bradley's (NW3)
Charles Lamb (N1)
The Clissold Arms (N2)
The Compass (N1)
The Drapers Arms (N1)
The Duke of Cambridge (N1)
The Engineer (NW1)
The Fellow (N1)
Frederick's (N1)
Freemasons Arms (NW3)
The Haven (N20)
The Horseshoe (NW3)
Hoxton Apprentice (N1)
The Junction Tavern (NW5)
Juniper Dining (N5)*
Landmark (Winter Gdn) (NW1)
The Lansdowne (NW1)
Made In Camden (NW1)
Mango Room (NW1)
Market (NW1)
Mosaica (N22)
The North London Tavern (NW6)
The Northgate (N1)*
Odette's (NW1)*

The Old Bull & Bush (NW3)
Prince Albert (NW1)
Rising Sun (NW7)*
Roots At N1 (N1)*
The Rose & Crown (N6)
Rotunda Bar & Restaurant (N1)
St Pancras Grand (NW1)
Walnut (NW6)
The Wells (NW3)
The Wet Fish Cafe (NW6)

South

The Abbeville (SW4)
Alma (SW18)
Antelope (SW17)*
Avalon (SW12)
The Bingham (TW10)
Blueprint Café (SE1)
The Bolingbroke (SW11)
The Brown Dog (SW13)
Cannizaro House (SW19)
Cantina Vinopolis (SE1)
Chapters (SE3)
Chez Bruce (SW17)*
The Dartmouth Arms (SE23)
The Depot (SW14)
Earl Spencer (SW18)
The East Hill (SW18)
Emile's (SW15)*
Entrée (SW11)
The Fentiman Arms (SW8)
The Fire Stables (SW19)
Florence (SE24)
Four O Nine (SW9)
Franklins (SE22)
Garrison (SE1)
The Glasshouse (TW9)*
Harrison's (SW12)
Inside (SE10)*
Lamberts (SW12)*
The Lighthouse (SW11)
Magdalen (SE1)*
Menier Chocolate Factory (SE1)
Mezzanine (SE1)
The Old Brewery (SE10)
Oxo Tower (Rest') (SE1)
The Palmerston (SE22)*
Petersham Hotel (TW10)
Petersham Nurseries (TW10)*
Plane Food (TW6)
Le Pont de la Tour (SE1)
The Prince Albert (SW11)
The Prince Of Wales (SW15)
Ransome's Dock (SW11)
Rivington Grill (SE10)
Rock & Rose (TW9)
RSJ (SE1)
Scoffers (SW11)
Simplicity (SE16)
Skylon (SE1)
Sonny's (SW13)
The Swan at the Globe (SE1)
The Table (SE1)
Tom Ilic (SW8)*
The Tommyfield (SE11)
The Tree House (SW13)
Trinity (SW4)*
Union Street Café (SE1)
Verta (SW11)
The Victoria (SW14)
Waterloo Bar & Kitchen (SE1)
The Wharf (TW11)

East

Ambassador (EC1)

Beach Blanket Babylon *(E1)*
Bevis Marks *(EC3)*
Bistro du Vin *(EC1)*
Bistrotheque *(E2)*
The Boundary *(E2)*
Bread Street Kitchen *(EC4)*
Café Below *(EC2)*
Caravan *(EC1)**
The Chancery *(EC4)**
Chiswell Street Dining Rms *(EC1)*
Coach & Horses *(EC1)**
The Don *(EC4)*
The Empress of India *(E9)*
The Fox *(EC2)*
Gow's *(EC2)*
The Gun *(E14)**
High Timber *(EC4)*
Hilliard *(EC4)**
The Larder *(EC1)*
London Wall Bar & Kitchen *(EC2)*
Malmaison Brasserie *(EC1)*
The Mercer *(EC2)*
The Modern Pantry *(EC1)*
The Morgan Arms *(E3)*
The Narrow *(E14)*
North Road *(EC1)**
Northbank *(EC4)*
1 Lombard Street *(EC3)*
The Parlour Bar *(E14)*
The Peasant *(EC1)*
Princess of Shoreditch *(EC2)**
Prism *(EC3)*
The Restaurant at St Paul's *(EC4)*
Rhodes 24 *(EC2)*
Rivington Grill *(EC2)*
Rochelle Canteen *(E2)**
Searcy's Brasserie *(EC2)*
Smithfield Bar & Grill *(EC1)*
Smiths (Ground Floor) *(EC1)*
Tompkins *(E14)*
Vertigo 42 *(EC2)*
Vinoteca *(EC1)*
Wapping Food *(E1)*
The Well *(EC1)*
The White Swan *(EC4)**
Whitechapel Gallery *(E1)*

BRITISH, TRADITIONAL
Central
Boisdale *(SW1)*
The English Tea Rm (Browns) *(W1)*
Browns (Albemarle) *(W1)*
Canteen *(W1)*
Corrigan's Mayfair *(W1)*
Dinner *(SW1)**
The Fountain (Fortnum's) *(W1)*
Fuzzy's Grub *(SW1)*
Great Queen Street *(WC2)**
Green's *(SW1)**
The Guinea Grill *(W1)**
Hardy's Brasserie *(W1)*
Harrods (Georgian Rest') *(SW1)*
The National Dining Rooms *(WC2)*
Odin's *(W1)*
Porters English Restaurant *(WC2)*
Rib Room *(SW1)*
Rules *(WC2)*
St John Hotel *(WC2)*
Savoy Grill *(WC2)*
Scott's *(W1)**
Shepherd's *(SW1)*
Simpsons-in-the-Strand *(WC2)*
Wiltons *(SW1)*
The Windmill *(W1)**

West
Bumpkin *(SW7,W11)*
Ffiona's *(W8)*
Hereford Road *(W2)**
Maggie Jones's *(W8)*

North
Bull & Last *(NW5)**
Gilbert Scott *(NW1)*
Holly Bush *(NW3)*
Kentish Canteen *(NW5)*
The Marquess Tavern *(N1)*
S & M Café *(N1)*
St Johns *(N19)**

South
The Anchor & Hope *(SE1)**
Butlers Wharf Chop House *(SE1)*
Canteen *(SE1)*
Canton Arms *(SW8)**
Fox & Grapes *(SW19)*
Roast *(SE1)*

East
Albion *(E2)*
Boisdale of Bishopsgate *(EC2)*
Canteen *(E1, E14)*
Cock Tavern *(EC1)*
The English Pig *(EC1)**
The Farm Collective *(EC1)**
The Fox and Anchor *(EC1)*
Fuzzy's Grub *(EC4)*
George & Vulture *(EC3)*
Green's *(EC3)**
Hix Oyster & Chop House *(EC1)**
Ye Olde Cheshire Cheese *(EC4)*
Paternoster Chop House *(EC4)*
E Pellicci *(E2)*
S & M Café *(E1)*
St John *(EC1)**
St John Bread & Wine *(E1)**
Simpson's Tavern *(EC3)*
Sweetings *(EC4)*

EAST & CENT. EUROPEAN
Central
Gay Hussar *(W1)*
The Wolseley *(W1)*

West
Tatra *(W12)*

North
Kipferl *(N1)*
Trojka *(NW1)*

FISH & SEAFOOD
Central
Back to Basics *(W1)**
Belgo Centraal *(WC2)*
Bellamy's *(W1)*
Bentley's *(W1)**
Cape Town Fish Market *(W1)*
Fishworks *(W1)*
Green's *(SW1)**
Livebait *(WC2)*
Loch Fyne *(WC2)*
Olivomare *(SW1)**
One-O-One *(SW1)**
The Pantechnicon *(SW1)*
Pescatori *(W1)*
Quaglino's *(SW1)*
Randall & Aubin *(W1)*
Rasa Samudra *(W1)**

Rib Room *(SW1)*
Royal China Club *(W1)**
Scott's *(W1)**
J Sheekey *(WC2)**
J Sheekey Oyster Bar *(WC2)**
Wheeler's *(SW1)*
Wiltons *(SW1)*
Wright Brothers *(W1)**
Zilli Fish *(W1)*

West
Bibendum Oyster Bar *(SW3)*
Big Easy *(SW3)*
Le Café Anglais *(W2)*
Chez Patrick *(W8)*
The Cow *(W2)*
Geales *(W8)*
Geales Chelsea Green *(SW3)*
Mandarin Kitchen *(W2)**
Poissonnerie de l'Avenue *(SW3)*
The Summerhouse *(W9)*
Le Suquet *(SW3)*

North
Belgo Noord *(NW1)*
Bradley's *(NW3)*
Chez Liline *(N4)**
Olympus Fish *(N3)**
Sea Pebbles *(HA5)*
Toff's *(N10)**

South
Applebee's Cafe *(SE1)**
Bennett Oyster Bar *(SW11)*
Fish Place *(SW11)**
fish! *(SE1)*
Gastro *(SW4)*
Livebait *(SE1)*
Lobster Pot *(SE11)*
Wright Brothers *(SE1)**

East
Catch *(EC2)*
Chamberlain's *(EC3)*
Curve *(E14)*
Fish Central *(EC1)**
Forman's *(E3)**
Gow's *(EC2)*
The Grapes *(E14)*
Loch Fyne *(EC3)*
Redhook *(EC1)*
The Royal Exchange Grand
    Café *(EC3)*
Sweetings *(EC4)*

FRENCH
Central
Alain Ducasse *(W1)*
Antidote *(W1)*
L'Artiste Musclé *(W1)*
L'Atelier de Joel Robuchon *(WC2)**
L'Autre Pied *(W1)**
Bar Boulud *(SW1)**
Bellamy's *(W1)*
Bistro du Vin *(W1)*
Boudin Blanc *(W1)*
Boulevard *(WC2)*
Brasserie Roux *(SW1)*
Brasserie St Jacques *(SW1)*
Café Bohème *(W1)*
Café des Amis *(WC2)*
Le Cercle *(SW1)**
Chabrot Bistrot d'Amis *(SW1)*
The Chelsea Brasserie *(SW1)*
Chez Gérard *(W1,WC2)*

Le Cigalon *(WC2)**
Clos Maggiore *(WC2)**
Côte *(W1,WC2)*
Les Deux Salons *(WC2)*
The Ebury *(W1)*
Elena's L'Etoile *(W1)*
Élysée *(W1)*
L'Escargot *(W1)*
The Gallery *(W1)**
Galvin at Windows *(W1)*
Galvin Bistrot de Luxe *(W1)**
Gauthier Soho *(W1)**
Le Gavroche *(W1)**
The Giaconda Dining Room *(WC2)**
Gordon Ramsay at Claridge's *(W1)*
The Greenhouse *(W1)*
Hélène Darroze *(W1)*
Hibiscus *(W1)*
Incognico *(WC2)*
Koffmann's *(SW1)**
Langan's Bistro *(W1)*
Marcus Wareing *(SW1)**
maze *(W1)*
Mon Plaisir *(WC2)*
Odin's *(W1)*
L'Oranger *(SW1)*
Orrery *(W1)*
Pearl *(WC1)*
La Petite Maison *(W1)**
Pétrus *(SW1)*
Pied à Terre *(W1)**
La Poule au Pot *(SW1)*
Prix Fixe *(W1)*
Randall & Aubin *(W1)*
Le Relais de Venise
    L'Entrecôte *(W1)**
The Ritz Restaurant *(W1)*
Roussillon *(SW1)*
Savoir Faire *(WC1)*
Sketch (Lecture Rm) *(W1)*
Sketch (Gallery) *(W1)*
The Square *(W1)**
Terroirs *(WC2)**
Verru *(W1)**
Villandry *(W1)*
The Wallace *(W1)*

West
Albertine *(W12)*
Angelus *(W2)**
L'Art du Fromage *(SW10)*
Belvedere *(W8)*
Bibendum *(SW3)*
Bistro K *(SW7)*
La Bouchée *(SW7)*
La Brasserie *(SW3)*
Le Café Anglais *(W2)*
The Capital Restaurant *(SW3)*
Cassis Bistro *(SW3)*
Charlotte's Bistro *(W4)*
Charlotte's Place *(W5)*
Cheyne Walk Brasserie *(SW3)*
Chez Patrick *(W8)*
Le Colombier *(SW3)*
Côte *(SW6,W2,W4,W8)*
Electric Brasserie *(W11)*
L'Etranger *(SW7)*
Galoupet *(SW3)*
Gordon Ramsay *(SW3)*
Notting Hill Brasserie *(W11)*
The Pig's Ear *(SW3)*
Poissonnerie de l'Avenue *(SW3)*
Quantus *(W4)*
Racine *(SW3)*
Rôtisserie Bute Street *(SW7)*

271

La Sophia *(W10)**
Le Suquet *(SW3)*
Tartine *(SW3)*
La Trompette *(W4)**
Le Vacherin *(W4)*
Whits *(W8)*

North
L'Absinthe *(NW1)*
The Almeida *(N1)*
Les Associés *(N8)*
L'Aventure *(NW8)**
Bistro Aix *(N8)*
Blue Legume *(N16)*
Bradley's *(NW3)*
La Cage Imaginaire *(NW3)*
Charles Lamb *(N1)*
Cocotte *(NW3)*
Fig *(N1)**
Le Mercury *(N1)*
Mill Lane Bistro *(NW6)*
Morgan M *(N7)**
Oslo Court *(NW8)**
La Petite Auberge *(N1)*
Le Sacré-Coeur *(N1)*
St Johns *(N19)**
Somerstown Coffee House *(NW1)*
The Wells *(NW3)*

South
Bellevue Rendez-Vous *(SW17)**
Brasserie James *(SW12)*
Brasserie Joël *(SE1)**
Brasserie Toulouse-Lautrec *(SE11)*
Brula *(TW1)**
La Buvette *(TW9)*
Le Cassoulet *(CR2)*
Le Chardon *(SE22, SW4)*
Chez Gérard *(SE1)*
Chez Lindsay *(TW10)*
Côte *(SE1, SW19)*
Gastro *(SW4)*
Gazette *(SW11, SW12)*
Lobster Pot *(SE11)*
Ma Cuisine *(TW9)*
Le P'tit Normand *(SW18)*
The Spread Eagle *(SE10)*
Upstairs Bar *(SW2)**
Waterloo Brasserie *(SE1)*

East
Bistrot Bruno Loubet *(EC1)**
Bleeding Heart *(EC1)**
Le Bouchon Breton *(E1)*
Bar Battu *(EC2)*
Brasserie Blanc *(EC2)*
Brawn *(E2)**
Café du Marché *(EC1)**
Cellar Gascon *(EC1)*
Chez Gérard *(EC2, EC3, EC4)*
Club Gascon *(EC1)**
Comptoir Gascon *(EC1)**
Coq d'Argent *(EC2)*
Côte *(EC4)*
The Don *(EC4)*
Galvin La Chapelle *(E1)**
Luc's Brasserie *(EC3)*
Lutyens *(EC4)*
1901 *(EC2)*
Plateau *(E14)*
Relais de Venise L'Entrecôte *(EC2)**
Le Rendezvous du Café *(EC1)*
The Royal Exchange Grand
   Café *(EC3)*
Le Saint Julien *(EC1)*

Sauterelle *(EC3)*
Les Trois Garçons *(E1)*
28-50 *(EC4)*

FUSION
Central
Archipelago *(W1)*
Asia de Cuba *(WC2)*
Kopapa *(WC2)*
Providores (Tapa Room) *(W1)**

West
E&O *(W11)**
Eight Over Eight *(SW3)**
L'Étranger *(SW7)*
Sushinho *(SW3)*

North
XO *(NW3)*

South
Champor-Champor *(SE1)**
Tsunami *(SW4)*
Village East *(SE1)*

East
Caravan *(EC1)**
Viajante *(E2)**

GAME
Central
Boisdale *(SW1)*
Rules *(WC2)*
Wiltons *(SW1)*

West
Harwood Arms *(SW6)**

North
San Daniele del Friuli *(N5)*

East
Boisdale of Bishopsgate *(EC2)*

GERMAN
South
Stein's *(TW10)*

GREEK
Central
Élysée *(W1)*
Hellenic *(W1)*
Real Greek *(W1, WC2)*

West
Costa's Grill *(W8)*
Halepi *(W2)*
The Real Greek *(W12)*

North
Carob Tree *(NW5)*
Daphne *(NW1)*
Lemonia *(NW1)*
The Real Greek *(N1)*
Retsina *(NW3)*
Vrisaki *(N22)*

South
Real Greek *(SE1)*

East
Kolossi Grill *(EC1)*
Real Greek *(E1)*

HUNGARIAN
Central
Gay Hussar (W1)

South
Cafe Strudel (SW14)

INTERNATIONAL
Central
Balans (W1)
Boulevard (WC2)
Browns (SW1,W1,WC2)
Bumbles (SW1)
Café in the Crypt (WC2)
City Café (SW1)
Cork & Bottle (WC2)
The Forge (WC2)
Giraffe (SW1,W1,WC1)
Gordon's Wine Bar (WC2)
Govinda's (W1)
Grumbles (SW1)
Motcombs (SW1)
National Gallery Café (WC2)
Novikov (W1)
The Providores (W1)
Sarastro (WC2)
Savoy (River Rest') (WC2)
Stock Pot (SW1)
Terroirs (WC2)*

West
Annie's (W4)
Balans West (SW5,W12,W4,W8)
Blakes (SW7)
Café Laville (W2)
Chelsea Bun Diner (SW10)
The Chelsea Kitchen (SW10)
Foxtrot Oscar (SW3)
Gallery Mess (SW3)
The Gate (W6)*
Giraffe (W11,W4,W8)
The Kensington Wine Rooms (W8)
Lola & Simón (W6)
Medlar (SW10)*
Michael Nadra (W4)*
Mona Lisa (SW10)
The Scarsdale (W8)
Stock Pot (SW3)
202 (W11)
The Windsor Castle (W8)
Wine Gallery (SW10)

North
The Arches (NW6)
Banners (N8)
Browns (N1)
The Flask (N6)
Giraffe (N1, NW3)
The Haven (N20)
The Old Bull & Bush (NW3)
The Orange Tree (N20)
Petek (N4)*
Spaniard's Inn (NW3)
Swan & Edgar (NW1)

South
Annie's (SW13)
Brinkley's Kitchen (SW17)
Browns (SE1)
Delfina (SE1)
Giraffe (SE1, SW11)
Green & Blue (SE22)
Hudsons (SW15)
Joanna's (SE19)
The Light House (SW19)

The Riverfront (SE1)*
The Ship (SW18)
Tate Modern (Level 2) (SE1)
Tate Modern (Level 7) (SE1)
Telegraph (SW15)
The Trafalgar Tavern (SE10)
Vivat Bacchus (SE1)
The Wharf (TW11)
The Yellow House (SE16)*

East
Browns (E14, EC2)
Dans le Noir (EC1)
$ (EC1)
Giraffe (E1)
LMNT (E8)
The Luxe (E1)
The Punch Tavern (EC4)
Les Trois Garçons (E1)
Vivat Bacchus (EC4)
The Wine Library (EC3)

IRISH
East
Lutyens (EC4)

ITALIAN
Central
Al Duca (SW1)
Alloro (W1)
Amaranto (W1)
Apsleys (SW1)
Babbo (W1)
Bar Trattoria Semplice (W1)
Il Baretto (W1)*
Bertorelli (W1)
Bertorelli (WC2)
Bocca Di Lupo (W1)*
La Bottega (SW1)
C London (W1)
Caffè Caldesi (W1)
Caffè Vergnano (WC2)
Caraffini (SW1)
Cecconi's (W1)
Ciao Bella (WC1)
Cocorino (W1)*
Como Lario (SW1)
Il Convivio (SW1)
Da Mario (WC2)
da Polpo (WC2)
Dehesa (W1)*
Delfino (W1)*
Dolada (W1)
5 Pollen Street (W1)
Franco's (SW1)
La Genova (W1)
Gran Paradiso (SW1)
Incognico (WC2)
Jamie's Italian (WC2)
Latium (W1)*
Little Italy (W1)
Locanda Locatelli (W1)
Mennula (W1)*
Murano (W1)
Number Twelve (WC1)
Oliveto (SW1)*
Olivo (SW1)
Olivomare (SW1)*
Opera Tavern (WC2)*
Orso (WC2)
Osteria Dell'Angolo (SW1)
Ottolenghi (SW1)*
Pescatori (W1)
Piccolino (W1)
Polpetto (W1)*

Polpo *(WI)*
La Porchetta Pizzeria *(WCI)*
Princi *(WI)*
Quirinale *(SWI)**
Ristorante Semplice *(WI)**
Rossopomodoro *(WC2)*
Sale e Pepe *(SWI)*
Salt Yard *(WI)*
Santini *(SWI)*
Sapori *(WC2)*
Sardo *(WI)*
Sartoria *(WI)*
Serafino *(WI)*
Signor Sassi *(SWI)*
Tempo *(WI)*
Theo Randall *(WI)**
Tinello *(SWI)**
Toto's *(SWI)*
2 Amici *(SWI)*
2 Veneti *(WI)*
Uno *(SWI)*
Vapiano *(WI)*
Vasco & Piero's Pavilion *(WI)**
Il Vicolo *(SWI)*
Zafferano *(SWI)*
Zilli Fish *(WI)*
Zilli Green *(WI)*

West

L'Accento Italiano *(W2)*
Aglio e Olio *(SW10)*
The Ark *(W8)*
Assaggi *(W2)**
La Bottega *(SW7)*
Buona Sera *(SW3)*
Canta Napoli *(W4)*
Carvosso's *(W4)*
Cavallino *(SW3)*
Cibo *(W14)*
Da Mario *(SW7)*
Daphne's *(SW3)*
La Delizia Limbara *(SW3)*
Dragoncello *(W2)*
El leven Park Walk *(SW10)*
Edera *(W11)**
Essenza *(W11)*
Falconiere *(SW7)*
La Famiglia *(SW10)*
Frankie's Italian Bar & Grill *(SW3, SW6)*
Frantoio *(SW10)*
Ida *(W10)*
Ilia *(SW3)*
Jamie's Italian *(W12)*
Locanda Ottomezzo *(W8)*
Lucio *(SW3)*
Made in Italy *(SW3)**
Manicomio *(SW3)*
Mediterraneo *(W11)*
Montpeliano *(SW7)*
Napulé *(SW6)*
Nottingdale *(W11)**
Nuovi Sapori *(SW6)**
The Oak *(W2)**
Osteria Basilico *(W11)*
Osteria dell'Arancio *(SW10)*
Ottolenghi *(W11,W8)**
Il Pagliaccio *(SW6)*
Pappa Ciccia *(SW6)*
Pellicano *(SW3)*
Il Portico *(W8)*
Portobello Ristorante *(W11)*
The Red Pepper *(W9)**
Riccardo's *(SW3)*
The River Café *(W6)**

Rocca Di Papa *(SW7)*
Rossopomodoro *(SW10,W11)*
San Lorenzo *(SW3)*
Santa Lucia *(SW10)*
Scalini *(SW3)*
Timo *(W8)**
Venosi *(SW3)*
Vicino *(SW6)*
Ziani's *(SW3)*

North

Artigiano *(NW3)*
L'Artista *(NW11)*
Il Bacio *(N16, N5)*
La Brocca *(NW6)*
Canonbury Kitchen *(NI)*
Canta Napoli *(N12)*
Caponata *(NW1)*
La Collina *(NW1)*
Fifteen Dining Room *(NI)*
Fifteen Trattoria *(NI)*
500 *(N19)**
Fratelli la Bufala *(NW3)*
Marine Ices *(NW3)*
Ottolenghi *(NI)**
Pizzeria Oregano *(NI)*
Pizzeria Pappagone *(N4)*
La Porchetta Pizzeria *(NI, N4, NWI)*
Rugoletta *(N2)*
The Salt House *(NW8)*
The Salusbury *(NW6)*
San Daniele del Friuli *(N5)*
Sardo Canale *(NW1)*
Sarracino *(NW6)**
Trullo *(NI)**
Villa Bianca *(NW3)*
York & Albany *(NW1)*

South

A Cena *(TW1)**
Al Forno *(SW15, SW19)*
Antipasto & Pasta *(SW11)*
La Barca *(SE1)*
Buona Sera *(SW11)*
Cantina del Ponte *(SE1)*
Cantinetta *(SW15)*
La Delizia *(SW18)*
Donna Margherita *(SW11)**
Enoteca Turi *(SW15)**
Frizzante Cafe *(SE16)*
Isola del Sole *(SW15)*
La Lanterna *(SE1)*
Numero Uno *(SW11)*
Osteria Antica Bologna *(SW11)*
Piccolino *(SW19)*
Pizza Metro *(SW11)*
Le Querce *(SE23, SE3)**
Riva *(SW13)**
San Lorenzo Fuoriporta *(SW19)*
Scarpetta *(TW11)*
Tentazioni *(SE1)*
Valentina *(SW14, SW15)*
Zucca *(SE1)**

East

Al Volo *(E1)**
Alba *(EC1)*
Amerigo Vespucci *(E14)*
Amico Bio *(EC1)*
L'Anima *(EC2)*
Bertorelli *(EC3)*
Il Bordello *(E1)**
Caravaggio *(EC3)*
Fabrizio *(EC1)**
La Figa *(E14)*

Frizzante at City Farm *(E2)*
Giant Robot *(EC1)*
Jamie's Italian *(E14)*
Manicomio *(EC2)*
Osteria Appennino *(EC2)**
E Pellicci *(E2)*
Piccolino *(EC2)*
La Porchetta Pizzeria *(EC1)*
Quadrato *(E14)*
Refettorio *(EC4)*
Santore *(EC1)*
Taberna Etrusca *(EC4)*
Terranostra *(EC4)*

MEDITERRANEAN
Central
About Thyme *(SW1)**
Aurelia *(W1)*
Bistro 1 *(W1,WC2)*
Hummus Bros *(W1,WC1)**
Massimo *(SW1)*
Nopi *(W1)**
The Norfolk Arms *(WC1)*
Quince *(W1)*
Riding House Café *(W1)**
Rocket *(W1)*
Truc Vert *(W1)*

West
The Atlas *(SW6)**
Cochonnet *(W9)*
Cumberland Arms *(W14)*
Del'Aziz *(SW6,W12)*
Locanda Ottomezzo *(W8)*
Made in Italy *(SW3)**
Mediterraneo *(W11)*
Raoul's Café *(W9)*
Raoul's Café & Deli *(W11,W6)*
La Sophia *(W10)**
The Swan *(W4)**
Tom's Deli *(W11)*
Troubadour *(SW5)*

North
Camden Brasserie *(NW1)*
Del'Aziz *(NW3)*
Homa *(N16)*
The Little Bay *(NW6)*
Mem & Laz *(N1)*
Petek *(N4)**
Queen's Head & Artichoke *(NW1)*
Stringray Café *(N5, NW5)*

South
Cantina del Ponte *(SE1)*
Cantina Vinopolis *(SE1)*
Del'Aziz *(SE1)*
Fish in a Tie *(SW11)*
The Fox & Hounds *(SW11)**
The Little Bay *(SW11)*
Oxo Tower (Brass') *(SE1)*
Putney Station *(SW15)*
The Wharf *(TW11)*

East
Ambassador *(EC1)*
Bonds *(EC2)*
The Eagle *(EC1)*
Eyre Brothers *(EC2)*
Hummus Bros *(EC2)**
The Little Bay *(EC1)*
Portal *(EC1)**
Rocket *(EC2)*
Stringray Globe Café *(E2)*
Vinoteca *(EC1)*

ORGANIC
Central
Acorn House *(WC1)*
Daylesford Organic *(SW1)*

West
Daylesford Organic *(W11)*

North
The Duke of Cambridge *(N1)*
Holly Bush *(NW3)*
Walnut *(NW6)*

East
Saf *(EC2)**
Smiths (Dining Rm) *(EC1)*

POLISH
West
Gessler at Daquise *(SW7)*
Polish Club *(SW7)*
Patio *(W12)*

South
Baltic *(SE1)*

PORTUGUESE
West
Lisboa Pâtisserie *(W10)**

East
Corner Room *(E2)*
The Gun *(E14)**
Portal *(EC1)**

RUSSIAN
Central
Samarqand *(W1)*

North
Trojka *(NW1)*

SCANDINAVIAN
Central
Nordic Bakery *(W1)*
Scandinavian Kitchen *(W1)*
Texture *(W1)**
Verru *(W1)**

West
Madsen *(SW7)*

East
North Road *(EC1)**

SCOTTISH
Central
Albannach *(WC2)*
Boisdale *(SW1)*

East
Boisdale of Bishopsgate *(EC2)*
Boisdale of Canary Wharf *(E14)*

SPANISH
Central
aqua nueva *(W1)*
Barrafina *(W1)**
Barrica *(W1)*
Café España *(W1)*
Cigala *(WC1)*
Dehesa *(W1)**
Fino *(W1)**

Goya *(SW1)*
Ibérica *(W1)*
Mar I Terra *(W1)*
Navarro's *(W1)*
Opera Tavern *(WC2)**
El Pirata *(W1)*
Salt Yard *(W1)*
Tapas Brindisa Soho *(W1)**

West
Cambio de Tercio *(SW5)**
Capote Y Toros *(SW5)*
Casa Brindisa *(SW7)*
Duke of Sussex *(W4)*
Galicia *(W10)*
Lola Rojo *(SW6)**
El Pirata de Tapas *(W2)*
Tendido Cero *(SW5)*
Tendido Cuatro *(SW6)*

North
La Bota *(N8)*
Café del Parc *(N19)**
Camino *(N1)*
Don Pepe *(NW8)*
La Giralda *(HA5)*
El Parador *(NW1)**

South
Angels & Gypsies *(SE5)**
don Fernando's *(TW9)*
José *(SE1)*
Lola Rojo *(SW11)**
La Mancha *(SW15)*
Mar I Terra *(SE1)*
Meson don Felipe *(SE1)*
Pizarro *(SE1)*
Rebato's *(SW8)**
El Rincón Latino *(SW4)*
Tapas Brindisa *(SE1)**

East
Eyre Brothers *(EC2)*
Ibérica *(E14)*
Morito *(EC1)**
Moro *(EC1)**
Pinchito *(EC1)*

STEAKS & GRILLS
Central
Black & Blue *(W1)*
Bodean's *(W1)*
The Bountiful Cow *(WC1)*
Boyd's Brasserie *(WC2)*
Chez Gérard *(W1,WC2)*
Christopher's *(WC2)*
Cut *(W1)*
Gaucho *(W1,WC2)*
Goodman *(W1)**
The Guinea Grill *(W1)**
Hawksmoor *(WC2)**
JW Steakhouse *(W1)*
maze Grill *(W1)*
The Palm *(SW1)*
Rowley's *(SW1)*
Sophie's Steakhouse *(WC2)*
34 Grosvenor Square *(W1)*
Wolfe's *(WC2)*

West
Black & Blue *(SW3, SW7,W8)*
Bodean's *(SW6)*
The Cabin *(W4)*
Gaucho *(SW3)*
Haché *(SW10)*

Kings Road Steakhouse *(SW3)*
The Meat & Wine Co *(W12)*
PJ's Bar and Grill *(SW3)*
Popeseye *(W14)**
Sophie's Steakhouse *(SW10)*

North
Camden Brasserie *(NW1)*
Garufa *(N5)*
Gaucho *(NW3)*
Haché *(NW1)*
Rôtisserie *(HA5, N20, NW6, NW8)*

South
Archduke Wine Bar *(SE1)*
Black & Blue *(SE1)*
Bodean's *(SW4)*
Buenos Aires *(SE3)*
Butcher & Grill *(SW11, SW19)*
Cattle Grid *(SW11, SW12)*
Chez Gérard *(SE1)*
Constancia *(SE1)**
Gaucho *(SE1, SE10,TW10)*
Kew Grill *(TW9)*
Popeseye *(SW15)**

East
A La Cruz *(EC1)*
Buen Ayre *(E8)**
Chez Gérard *(EC2, EC3, EC4)*
Gaucho *(E14, EC1, EC2, EC3)*
Goodman City *(EC2)**
Hawksmoor *(E1, EC2)**
MPW Steakhouse & Grill *(E1)*
Redhook *(EC1)*
Simpson's Tavern *(EC3)*
Smithfield Bar & Grill *(EC1)*
Smiths (Top Floor) *(EC1)*
Smiths (Dining Rm) *(EC1)*
Smiths (Ground Floor) *(EC1)*

SWISS
Central
St Moritz *(W1)*

VEGETARIAN
Central
Chop'd *(W1)*
Food for Thought *(WC2)**
Govinda's *(W1)*
Hummus Bros *(W1,WC1)**
Malabar Junction *(WC1)*
Masala Zone *(W1)*
Mildreds *(W1)**
Ragam *(W1)**
Rasa *(W1)**
Rasa Maricham *(WC1)**
Roussillon *(SW1)*
Sagar *(W1)**
tibits *(W1)*
Woodlands *(SW1,W1)*
Zilli Green *(W1)*

West
The Gate *(W6)**
Masala Zone *(SW5, SW6,W2)*
Saf *(W8)**
Sagar *(W6)**

North
Chop'd *(NW1)*
Chutneys *(NW1)*
Diwana Bhel-Poori House *(NW1)*
Geeta *(NW6)*

Kovalam *(NW6)**
Manna *(NW3)*
Masala Zone *(N1)*
Rani *(N3)**
Rasa *(N16)**
Rasa Travancore *(N16)**
Sakonis *(HA0)*
Vijay *(NW6)**
Woodlands *(NW3)*

South
Ganapati *(SE15)**
Le Pont de la Tour *(SE1)*
Sree Krishna *(SW17)**

East
Amico Bio *(EC1)*
Carnevale *(EC1)*
Chop'd *(E1, E14, EC3)*
Hummus Bros *(EC2)**
Saf *(EC2)**
Vanilla Black *(EC4)**

AFTERNOON TEA
Central
Brasserie Roux *(SW1)*
The English Tea Rm (Browns) *(W1)*
The Fountain (Fortnum's) *(W1)*
La Fromagerie Café *(W1)**
Ladurée *(SW1, W1, WC2)*
Napket *(W1)*
Oscar *(W1)*
Ritz (Palm Court) *(W1)*
The Sketch (Parlour) *(W1)*
Villandry *(W1)*
William Curley *(SW1)**
The Wolseley *(W1)*
Yauatcha *(W1)**

West
Napket *(SW3)*

South
San Lorenzo Fuoriporta *(SW19)*

East
Napket *(EC3)*

BURGERS, ETC
Central
Automat *(W1)*
Black & Blue *(W1)*
Byron *(SW1, W1, WC2)*
Diner *(W1)*
Eagle Bar Diner *(W1)*
Ed's Easy Diner *(W1)*
Guerilla Burgers *(W1)*
Hard Rock Café *(W1)*
Joe Allen *(WC2)*
Wolfe's *(WC2)*

West
Big Easy *(SW3)*
Black & Blue *(SW3, SW7, W8)*
Byron *(SW3, SW5, SW7, W12, W8)*
Haché *(SW10)*
Lucky Seven *(W2)*
Sticky Fingers *(W8)*
Troubadour *(SW5)*

North
Byron *(N1)*
Diner *(N1, NW1, NW10)*
Fine Burger Company *(N1, NW1,*

NW3)
Haché *(NW1)*
Harry Morgan's *(NW8)**

South
Black & Blue *(SE1)*
Byron *(SW15)*

East
Byron *(E14, EC2)*
The Diner *(EC2)*
$ *(EC1)*
Smithfield Bar & Grill *(EC1)*
Smiths (Dining Rm) *(EC1)*

CRÊPES
South
Chez Lindsay *(TW10)*

FISH & CHIPS
Central
Fryer's Delight *(WC1)*
Golden Hind *(W1)*
North Sea Fish *(WC1)*
Rock & Sole Plaice *(WC2)*
Seafresh *(SW1)*

West
Geales *(W8)*
Kerbisher & Malt *(W6)**

North
Nautilus *(NW6)**
The Sea Shell *(NW1)*
Skipjacks *(HA3)**
Toff's *(N10)**
Two Brothers *(N3)**

South
Brady's *(SW18)*
Fish Club *(SW11, SW4)**
Masters Super Fish *(SE1)**
Olley's *(SE24)*
The Sea Cow *(SE22)*

East
Ark Fish *(E18)**
Faulkner's *(E8)**

ICE CREAM
Central
Gelupo *(W1)**

North
Marine Ices *(NW3)*

PIZZA
Central
Il Baretto *(W1)**
Delfino *(W1)**
Fire & Stone *(WC2)*
Oliveto *(SW1)**
Piccolino *(W1)*
Pizzeria Malletti *(W1)**
La Porchetta Pizzeria *(WC1)*
Rocket *(W1)*
Sapori *(WC2)*

West
Basilico *(SW6)**
Buona Sera *(SW3)*
Cochonnet *(W9)*
Da Mario *(SW7)*
La Delizia Limbara *(SW3)*

Fire & Stone *(W12)*
Firezza *(SW10,W11,W4)**
Franco Manca *(W4)**
Frankie's Italian Bar & Grill *(SW3)*
Made in Italy *(SW3)**
The Oak *(W2)**
Osteria Basilico *(W11)*
Otto Pizza *(W2)**
Pizza East Portobello *(W10)*
(Ciro's) Pizza Pomodoro *(SW3)*
The Red Pepper *(W9)**
Santa Maria *(W5)**

North
Il Bacio *(N16, N5)*
Basilico *(N1, N8, NW3)**
La Brocca *(NW6)*
Firezza *(N1)**
Furnace *(N1)*
Marine Ices *(NW3)*
Pizzeria Oregano *(N1)*
La Porchetta Pizzeria *(N1, N4, NW1)*

South
Al Forno *(SW15, SW19)*
Basilico *(SW11, SW14)**
Buona Sera *(SW11)*
Donna Margherita *(SW11)**
Eco *(SW4)*
Firezza *(SW11, SW18)**
Franco Manca *(SW9)**
Gourmet Pizza Company *(SE1)*
The Gowlett *(SE15)**
La Lanterna *(SE1)*
Piccolino *(SW19)*
Pizza Metro *(SW11)*
Rocca Di Papa *(SE21)*
Zero Degrees *(SE3)*

East
Il Bordello *(E1)**
Fire & Stone *(E1)*
Gourmet Pizza Company *(E14)*
Piccolino *(EC2)*
Pizza East *(E1)*
Pizzeria Malletti *(EC1)**
La Porchetta Pizzeria *(EC1)*
Rocket *(E14)*
Rocket *(EC2)*

SANDWICHES, CAKES, ETC
Central
Abokado *(W1)*
Aubaine *(W1)*
Baker & Spice *(SW1)*
Bar Italia *(W1)*
Benugo *(W1)*
The Courtauld Gallery Café *(WC2)*
Fernandez & Wells *(W1)**
Flat White *(W1)**
La Fromagerie Café *(W1)**
Fuzzy's Grub *(SW1)*
Kaffeine *(W1)**
Konditor & Cook *(W1,WC1)**
Ladurée *(SW1,W1)*
Leon *(W1,WC2)*
Maison Bertaux *(W1)**
Monmouth Coffee Company *(WC2)**
Mount Street Deli *(W1)*
Mrs Marengos *(W1)**
Napket *(W1)*
Natural Kitchen *(W1)*
Paul *(W1,WC2)*
Pod *(WC1)*
Scandinavian Kitchen *(W1)*

The Sketch (Parlour) *(W1)*

West
Aubaine *(SW3,W8)*
Baker & Spice *(SW3,W9)*
Benugo *(SW7,W12)*
Bluebird Café *(SW3)*
Chiswick House Cafe *(W4)*
Fulham Wine Rooms *(SW6)*
Gail's Bakery *(W4)*
Gail's Bread *(W11)*
Lisboa Pâtisserie *(W10)**
Napket *(SW3)*
Tom's Deli *(W11)*
Troubadour *(SW5)*

North
Benugo *(NW1)*
Chamomile *(NW3)*
Euphorium Bakery *(N1)*
Gail's Bread *(NW3, NW8)*
Ginger & White *(NW3)*
Kenwood (Brew House) *(NW3)*

South
Benugo *(SE1)*
Caffé Vergnano *(SE1)*
Gail's Bread *(SW11)*
Konditor & Cook *(SE1)**
Leon *(SE1)*
Monmouth Coffee Company *(SE1)**
Orange Pekoe *(SW13)*
Pantry *(SW18)*
Pod *(SE1)*
Spianata & Co *(SE1)**
William Curley *(TW9)**

East
Abokado *(EC1, EC4)*
Benugo *(EC1)*
Brick Lane Beigel Bake *(E1)**
Caffé Vergnano *(EC4)*
Dose *(EC1)**
Fuzzy's Grub *(EC4)*
Gail's Bakery *(EC1)*
Konditor & Cook *(EC3)**
Leon *(E1, E14, EC4)*
Natural Kitchen *(EC4)*
Nusa Kitchen *(EC1, EC2)**
Pod *(EC1, EC2, EC3, EC4)*
Spianata & Co *(E1, EC1, EC2, EC3, EC4)**

SALADS
Central
Chop'd *(W1)*
Kaffeine *(W1)**
Natural Kitchen *(W1)*

West
Beirut Express *(SW7,W2)**

North
Chop'd *(NW1)*

East
Chop'd *(E1, E14, EC3)*
Natural Kitchen *(EC4)*

ARGENTINIAN
Central
Gaucho *(W1,WC2)*

West
Casa Malevo *(W2)*

Gaucho *(SW3)*
Lola & Simón *(W6)*
Quantus *(W4)*

North
Garufa *(N5)*
Gaucho *(NW3)*

South
Buenos Aires Cafe *(SE10, SE3)*
Constancia *(SE1)**
Gaucho *(SE1, TW10)*
Santa Maria del Sur *(SW8)**

East
Buen Ayre *(E8)**
Gaucho *(E14, EC2, EC3)*

BRAZILIAN
West
Rodizio Rico *(SW6, W2)*
Sushinho *(SW3)*

North
Rodizio Rico *(N1)*

East
Sushisamba *(EC2)*

CUBAN
Central
Floridita *(W1)*

South
Angels & Gypsies *(SE5)**

MEXICAN/TEXMEX
Central
Benito's Hat *(W1, WC2)*
Café Pacifico *(WC2)*
Cantina Laredo *(WC2)*
Chilango *(WC2)**
Chipotle *(WC2)*
Lupita *(WC2)*
Tortilla *(W1)*
Wahaca *(W1, WC2)*

West
Crazy Homies *(W2)*
Taqueria *(W11)*
Tortilla *(W6)*
Wahaca *(W12)*

North
Chilango *(N1)**
Mestizo *(NW1)**
Tortilla *(N1)*

South
Tortilla *(SE1)*

East
Barbecoa *(EC4)*
Chilango *(EC4)**
Tortilla *(E14, EC3)*
Wahaca *(E14)*

PERUVIAN
East
Sushisamba *(EC2)*

SOUTH AMERICAN
West
Quantus *(W4)*

North
Sabor *(N1)*

South
El Vergel *(SE1)**

East
A La Cruz *(EC1)*

AFRO-CARIBBEAN
Central
The Terrace in the Fields *(WC2)*

North
Mango Room *(NW1)*

MOROCCAN
West
Adams Café *(W12)*
Pasha *(SW7)*

South
Doukan *(SW18)*

NORTH AFRICAN
Central
Momo *(W1)*

West
Azou *(W6)*
Del'Aziz *(SW6)*

East
Kenza *(EC2)*

SOUTH AFRICAN
North
Shaka Zulu *(NW1)*

TUNISIAN
West
Adams Café *(W12)*

EGYPTIAN
North
Ali Baba *(NW1)*

ISRAELI
Central
Gaby's *(WC2)*

North
Solly's *(NW11)*

KOSHER
Central
Reubens *(W1)*

North
Kaifeng *(NW4)**
Solly's *(NW11)*

East
Bevis Marks *(EC3)*
Brick Lane Beigel Bake *(E1)**

LEBANESE
Central
Al Hamra *(W1)*
Al Sultan *(W1)**
Beiteddine *(SW1)*
Comptoir Libanais *(W1)*
Fairuz *(W1)*
Fakhreldine *(W1)*
Ishbilia *(SW1)**
Levant *(W1)*
Maroush *(W1)**
Noura *(SW1, W1)*
Ranoush *(SW1)**
Yalla Yalla *(W1)*

West
Al-Waha *(W2)**
Beirut Express *(SW7, W2)**
Chez Marcelle *(W14)**
Comptoir Libanais *(W12)*
Fresco *(W2)*
Maroush *(SW3)**
Maroush *(W2)**
Pasha *(SW7)*
Randa *(W8)*
Ranoush *(SW3, W2, W8)**

South
Palmyra *(TW9)*

East
Kenza *(EC2)*

MIDDLE EASTERN
Central
Patogh *(W1)**

North
Solly's *(NW11)*

East
Morito *(EC1)**

PERSIAN
West
Alounak *(W14, W2)*
Chella *(W4)*
Faanoos *(W4)*
Kateh *(W9)*
Mohsen *(W14)**
Sufi *(W12)*

South
Faanoos *(SW14)*

SYRIAN
West
Abu Zaad *(W12)*

TURKISH
Central
Cyprus Mangal *(SW1)**
Ishtar *(W1)*
Kazan *(SW1)**
Quince *(W1)*
Sofra *(W1, WC2)*
Tas *(WC1)*

West
Best Mangal *(SW6, W14)*

North
Beyoglu *(NW3)*
Gallipoli *(N1)*

Gem *(N1)**
Izgara *(N3)*
Mangal II *(N16)*
19 Numara Bos Cirrik *(N16)*
Petek *(N4)**
Sofra *(NW8)*

South
Tas *(SE1)*
Tas Pide *(SE1)*

East
Haz *(E1, EC2, EC3)*
Hazev *(E14)*
Mangal I *(E8)**
Tas *(EC1)*

AFGHANI
North
Afghan Kitchen *(N1)**

BURMESE
West
Mandalay *(W2)*

CHINESE
Central
Ba Shan *(W1)**
Baozi Inn *(WC2)**
Bar Shu *(W1)**
Cha Cha Moon *(W1)*
Chilli Cool *(WC1)**
China Tang *(W1)*
Chuen Cheng Ku *(W1)*
Empress of Sichuan *(WC2)*
The Four Seasons *(W1)**
Golden Dragon *(W1)*
The Grand Imperial *(SW1)*
Hakkasan *(W1)**
Haozhan *(W1)*
Harbour City *(W1)**
Hunan *(SW1)**
Imperial China *(WC2)*
Jenny Lo's Tea House *(SW1)*
Joy King Lau *(WC2)*
Kai Mayfair *(W1)*
Ken Lo's Memories *(SW1)**
Made in China *(SW1)*
Mekong *(SW1)*
Mr Chow *(SW1)*
Mr Kong *(WC2)*
New Mayflower *(W1)**
New World *(W1)*
Plum Valley *(W1)*
Princess Garden *(W1)**
Royal China *(W1)**
Royal China Club *(W1)**
Shanghai Blues *(WC1)**
Wong Kei *(W1)*
Yauatcha *(W1)**
Yming *(W1)**

West
Choys *(SW3)*
Fortune Cookie *(W2)**
The Four Seasons *(W2)**
Good Earth *(SW3)*
Ken Lo's Memories of China *(W8)**
Magic Wok *(W2)*
Mandarin Kitchen *(W2)**
Maxim *(W13)*
Min Jiang *(W8)**
Mr Wing *(SW5)*
New Culture Revolution *(SW3, W11)*

North China (W3)*
Pearl Liang (W2)*
Royal China (SW6,W2)*
Seventeen (W11)*
Stick & Bowl (W8)
Taiwan Village (SW6)*

North
Alisan (HA9)*
Goldfish (NW3)*
Good Earth (NW7)
Green Cottage (NW3)*
Gung-Ho (NW6)
Kaifeng (NW4)*
New Culture Revolution (N1)
Phoenix Palace (NW1)*
Sakonis (HA0)
Singapore Garden (NW6)*
The Water Margin (NW11)

South
Bayee Village (SW19)
Dalchini (SW19)
Dragon Castle (SE17)*
Four Regions (TW9)
O'Zon (TW1)
Peninsular (SE10)*
Royal China (SW15)

East
Chinese Cricket Club (EC4)
Goldfish City (EC2)*
Gourmet San (E2)*
Imperial City (EC3)
Lotus Chinese Floating
   Restaurant (E14)
My Old Place (E1)*
Royal China (E14)*
Shanghai (E8)
Yi-Ban (E16)

CHINESE, DIM SUM
Central
Chuen Cheng Ku (W1)
dim T (W1)
Golden Dragon (W1)
Hakkasan (W1)*
Harbour City (W1)*
Imperial China (WC2)
Joy King Lau (WC2)
Leong's Legends (W1)
New World (W1)
ping pong (W1)
Princess Garden (W1)*
Royal China (W1)*
Royal China Club (W1)*
Shanghai Blues (WC1)*
Yauatcha (W1)*

West
Leong's Legends (W2)
Min Jiang (W8)*
Pearl Liang (W2)*
ping pong (W2)
Royal China (SW6,W2)*

North
Alisan (HA9)*
dim T (N6, NW3)
Phoenix Palace (NW1)*
ping pong (NW3)

South
dim T (SE1)

Dragon Castle (SE17)*
Peninsular (SE10)*
ping pong (SE1)
Royal China (SW15)

East
Lotus Chinese Floating
   Restaurant (E14)
ping pong (E1, EC2, EC4)
Royal China (E14)*
Shanghai (E8)
Yi-Ban (E16)

GEORGIAN
East
Little Georgia Café (E2)

INDIAN
Central
Amaya (SW1)*
Benares (W1)*
Chor Bizarre (W1)
The Cinnamon Club (SW1)*
Dishoom (WC2)
Gaylord (W1)
Gopal's of Soho (W1)
Imli (W1)
Indali Lounge (W1)
India Club (WC2)
Malabar Junction (WC1)
Masala Zone (W1,WC2)
Mela (WC2)
Mint Leaf (SW1)
Mooli's (W1)*
Moti Mahal (WC2)*
La Porte des Indes (W1)
Ragam (W1)*
Red Fort (W1)*
Sagar (W1,WC2)*
Salaam Namaste (WC1)*
Salloos (SW1)*
Tamarind (W1)
Trishna (W1)*
Veeraswamy (W1)
Woodlands (SW1,W1)
Zayna (W1)*

West
Anarkali (W6)
Bombay Bicycle Club (W11)
Bombay Brasserie (SW7)
Bombay Palace (W2)*
Brilliant (UB2)*
Chutney Mary (SW10)*
Five Hot Chillies (HA0)*
Gifto's (UB1)*
The Greedy Buddha (SW6)
Haandi (SW3)*
Indian Zing (W6)*
kare kare (SW5)
Karma (W14)*
Khan's (W2)
Khan's of Kensington (SW7)
Madhu's (UB1)*
Malabar (W8)*
Masala Zone (SW5, SW6,W2)
Memories of India (SW7)
Mirch Masala (UB1,W14)*
Monty's (SW6,W13,W5)
Noor Jahan (SW5,W2)*
The Painted Heron (SW10)*
Rasoi (SW3)
Sagar (W6)*
Star of India (SW5)*
Thali (SW5)*

281

Zaika (W8)*

North
Anglo Asian Tandoori (N16)*
Chutneys (NW1)
Diwana Bhel-Poori House (NW1)
Eriki (NW3)*
Geeta (NW6)
Great Nepalese (NW1)
Indian Rasoi (N2)*
Jai Krishna (N4)
Kovalam (NW6)*
Masala Zone (N1, NW1)
Rani (N3)*
Roots At N1 (N1)*
Sakonis (HA0)
Vijay (NW6)*
Woodlands (NW3)
Zaffrani (N1)

South
Babur (SE23)*
Bangalore Express (SE1)
Bengal Clipper (SE1)
Bombay Bicycle Club (SW12)
Chutney (SW18)*
Cochin Brasserie (SW15)*
Dalchini (SW19)
Everest Inn (SE3)*
Ganapati (SE15)*
Gandhi's (SE11)
Hot Stuff (SW8)*
Indian Moment (SW11)
Indian Ocean (SW17)*
Indian Zilla (SW13)*
Kennington Tandoori (SE11)
Lahore Karahi (SW17)*
Ma Goa (SW15)*
Mango & Silk (SW14)
Mango Tree (SE1)*
Mirch Masala (SW16, SW17)*
Mogul (SE10)
Nazmins (SW18)
Origin Asia (TW9)*
Simply Indian (SE1)
Sree Krishna (SW17)*
Tandoori Nights (SE22)
Tangawizi (TW1)

East
Anokha Restaurant (EC3, EC4)*
Bangalore Express (EC3)
Café Spice Namaste (E1)*
Cinnamon Kitchen (EC2)*
Clifton (E1)
Dockmaster's House (E14)
Lahore Kebab House (E1)*
Memsaheb on Thames (E14)
Mint Leaf (EC2)
Mirch Masala (E1)*
Needoo (E1)*
New Tayyabs (E1)*
Rasa Mudra (E11)*
Sweet & Spicy (E1)*

INDIAN, SOUTHERN
Central
India Club (WC2)
Malabar Junction (WC1)
Quilon (SW1)*
Ragam (W1)*
Rasa (W1)*
Rasa Maricham (WC1)*
Sagar (W1)*
Woodlands (SW1, W1)

West
Sagar (W6)*
Shilpa (W6)*

North
Chutneys (NW1)
Geeta (NW6)
Kovalam (NW6)*
Rani (N3)*
Rasa (N16)*
Rasa Travancore (N16)*
Vijay (NW6)*
Woodlands (NW3)

South
Cochin Brasserie (SW15)*
Cocum (SW20)
Ganapati (SE15)*
Sree Krishna (SW17)*

East
Rasa Mudra (E11)*

INDONESIAN
Central
Melati (W1)

West
Kiasu (W2)

JAPANESE
Central
Abeno (WC1, WC2)
Abokado (W1, WC2)
aqua kyoto (W1)
Atari-Ya (W1)*
Benihana (W1)
Bincho Yakitori (W1)
Chisou (W1)*
Defune (W1)*
Dinings (W1)*
Edokko (WC1)*
Hazuki (WC2)*
Ikeda (W1)*
Inamo (W1)
Kiku (W1)*
Koya (W1)*
Kulu Kulu (W1, WC2)
Kyashii (WC2)
Matsuri (SW1)*
Misato (W1)
Mitsukoshi (SW1)*
Miyama (W1)*
Nizuni (W1)*
Nobu (W1)*
Nobu (W1)
Roka (W1)*
Sake No Hana (SW1)
Sakura (W1)*
Satsuma (W1)
Soho Japan (W1)
Sumosan (W1)
Taro (W1)
Ten Ten Tei (W1)
Toku (SW1)
Tokyo Diner (WC2)
Tsunami (W1)*
Umu (W1)*
Wagamama (SW1, W1, WC1, WC2)
Watatsumi (WC2)
Yoshino (W1)*

West
Atari-Ya (W5)*

Benihana *(SW3)*
Inaho *(W2)**
Itsu *(SW3,W11)*
Kiraku *(W5)**
Kulu Kulu *(SW7)*
Nozomi *(SW3)*
Okawari *(W5)*
Sushinho *(SW3)*
Tosa *(W6)*
Wagamama *(W8)*
Yashin *(W8)**
Zuma *(SW7)**

North
Asakusa *(NW1)**
Atari-Ya *(NW4, NW6)**
Bento Cafe *(NW1)**
Café Japan *(NW11)**
Dotori *(N4)**
Jin Kichi *(NW3)**
Sushi of Shiori *(NW1)**
Sushi-Say *(NW2)**
Wagamama *(N1, NW1)*
Yuzu *(NW6)**

South
Cho-San *(SW15)**
Fujiyama *(SW9)*
Matsuba *(TW9)**
Slurp *(SW16, SW19)*
Tsunami *(SW4)**
Tsuru *(SE1)*
Wagamama *(SE1, SW15, SW19)*

East
Abokado *(EC1, EC4)*
City Miyama *(EC4)**
Itsu *(E14)*
K10 *(EC2)*
Kurumaya *(EC4)**
Mugen *(EC4)*
Pham Sushi *(EC1)**
Roka *(E14)**
Saki *(EC1)**
Soseki *(EC3)**
Sushisamba *(EC2)*
Tajima Tei *(EC1)**
Tsuru *(EC2, EC4)*
Wagamama *(E14, EC2, EC3, EC4)*

KAZAKHSTANI
Central
Samarqand *(W1)*

KOREAN
Central
Asadal *(WC1)*
Kimchee *(WC1)*
Koba *(W1)*

North
Dotori *(N4)**

South
Cah-Chi *(SW18, SW20)*

MALAYSIAN
Central
C&R Cafe *(W1)*
Jom Makan *(SW1)*
Melati *(W1)*
Spice Market *(W1)*

West
Awana *(SW3)*
Jom Makan *(W12)*
Kiasu *(W2)*
Satay House *(W2)*

North
Singapore Garden *(NW6)**

South
Champor-Champor *(SE1)**

East
54 Farringdon Road *(EC1)*
Sedap *(EC1)*

PAKISTANI
Central
Salloos *(SW1)**

West
Mirch Masala *(UB1,W14)**

South
Lahore Karahi *(SW17)**
Lahore Kebab House *(SW16)**
Mirch Masala *(SW16, SW17)**

East
Lahore Kebab House *(E1)**
Mirch Masala *(E1)**
Needoo *(E1)**
New Tayyabs *(E1)**

PAN-ASIAN
Central
Banana Tree Canteen *(W1)*
Colony *(W1)*
dim T *(SW1,W1)*
Haozhan *(W1)*
Hare & Tortoise *(WC1)*
Inamo *(SW1)*
Tamarai *(WC2)*

West
Banana Tree Canteen *(W2,W9)*
E&O *(W11)**
Eight Over Eight *(SW3)**
Hare & Tortoise *(W14,W5)*
Mao Tai *(SW6)*
Uli *(W11)*

North
The Banana Tree Canteen *(NW6)*
dim T *(N6, NW3)*
Gilgamesh *(NW1)*
XO *(NW3)*

South
The Banana Tree Canteen *(SW11)*
dim T *(SE1)*
Hare & Tortoise *(SW15)*
O'Zon *(TW1)*

East
Banana Tree Canteen *(EC1)*
Cicada *(EC1)**
Great Eastern Dining Room *(EC2)**
Hare & Tortoise *(EC4)*
Pacific Oriental *(EC2)*

THAI
Central
Benja *(W1)**

Blue Jade *(SW1)*
Busaba Eathai *(SW1,W1,WC1)*
C&R Cafe *(W1)*
Crazy Bear *(W1)*
Mango Tree *(SW1)*
Mekong *(SW1)*
Nahm *(SW1)*
Paolina Café *(WC1)*
Patara *(W1)**
Rosa's Soho *(W1)*
Siam Central *(W1)*
Spice Market *(W1)*
Thai Pot *(WC2)*
Thai Square *(SW1,W1,WC2)*

West
Addie's Thai Café *(SW5)**
Bangkok *(SW7)**
Bedlington Café *(W4)*
Busaba Eathai *(W12)*
C&R Cafe *(W2)*
Café 209 *(SW6)*
Charm *(W6)*
Churchill Arms *(W8)**
Esarn Kheaw *(W12)**
Fat Boy's *(W4,W5)*
Fitou's Thai Restaurant *(W10)**
Old Parr's Head *(W14)*
Patara *(SW3)**
Sukho Fine Thai Cuisine *(SW6)**
Thai Square *(SW7)*
The Walmer Castle *(W11)*

North
Isarn *(N1)**
Thai Square *(N1)*
Yum Yum *(N16)*

South
Amaranth *(SW18)**
Fat Boy's *(SW14,TW1,TW8)*
The Paddyfield *(SW12)**
The Pepper Tree *(SW4)*
Suk Saran *(SW19)*
Talad Thai *(SW15)*
Thai Corner Café *(SE22)*
Thai Garden *(SW11)*
Thai on the River *(SW11)*
Thai Square *(SW15)*

East
Busaba Eathai *(EC1)*
Elephant Royale *(E14)*
Rosa's *(E1)*
Thai Square *(EC4)*
Thai Square City *(EC3)*

UZBEKISTANI
Central
Samarqand *(W1)*

VIETNAMESE
Central
Bam-Bou *(W1)*
Cây Tre *(W1)**
Mekong *(SW1)*
Pho *(W1)**
Spice Market *(W1)*
Viet *(W1)*

West
Kiasu *(W2)*
Pho *(W12)**
Saigon Saigon *(W6)**

North
Huong-Viet *(N1)*
Khoai *(N8)*
Khoai Cafe *(N12)*
Viet Garden *(N1)*

South
Mien Tay *(SW11)**
The Paddyfield *(SW12)**

East
Cây Tre *(EC1)**
Green Papaya *(E8)**
Mien Tay *(E2)**
Namo *(E9)*
Pho *(EC1)**
Sông Quê *(E2)**
Viet Grill *(E2)**
Viet Hoa *(E2)**

CENTRAL

**Soho, Covent Garden & Bloomsbury
(Parts of W1, all WC2 and WC1)**

| £90+ | L'Atelier de Joel Robuchon | French | ② ③ ② |
| | Asia de Cuba | Fusion | ④ ⑤ ④ |

| £80+ | Pearl | French | ④ ④ ③ |
| | Savoy (River Rest') | International | ⑤ ⑤ ③ |

£70+	Rules	British, Traditional	④ ③ ②
	Savoy Grill	"	③ ② ③
	Simpsons-in-the-Strand	"	④ ⑤ ④
	Ladurée	Afternoon tea	④ ④ ③
	aqua kyoto	Japanese	③ ③ ①
	Spice Market	Vietnamese	④ ④ ④

£60+	Christopher's	American	④ ③ ③
	Adam Street	British, Modern	④ ④ ②
	Hix	"	③ ④ ③
	Indigo	"	④ ② ③
	The Ivy	"	④ ② ②
	Paramount	"	④ ④ ①
	St John Hotel	British, Traditional	③ ② ④
	J Sheekey	Fish & seafood	⓪ ⓪ ②
	Zilli Fish	"	④ ④ ④
	Gauthier Soho	French	⓪ ② ③
	Little Italy	Italian	④ ④ ③
	aqua nueva	Spanish	④ ④ ④
	Floridita	Cuban	④ ④ ④
	Shanghai Blues	Chinese	② ④ ②
	Yauatcha	"	⓪ ④ ②
	Red Fort	Indian	② ③ ③

£50+	Circus	American	④ ④ ②
	Joe Allen	"	④ ④ ②
	Arbutus	British, Modern	② ② ③
	Axis	"	④ ② ④
	Bob Bob Ricard	"	④ ② ②
	Dean Street Townhouse	"	④ ③ ②
	Le Deuxième	"	④ ③ ⑤
	Quo Vadis	"	② ② ②
	Refuel	"	③ ③ ②
	Tom's Terrace	"	⑤ ④ ③
	The National Dining Rms	British, Traditional	⑤ ⑤ ④
	Wright Brothers	Fish & seafood	② ③ ③
	Bistro du Vin	French	④ ⓪ ④
	Café des Amis	"	④ ④ ④
	Chez Gérard	"	⑤ ⑤ ⑤
	Le Cigalon	"	② ② ②
	Clos Maggiore	"	② ⓪ ⓪
	Les Deux Salons	"	③ ④ ③
	L'Escargot	"	③ ② ②
	Incognico	"	④ ④ ④
	Mon Plaisir	"	④ ④ ③
	The Forge	International	④ ④ ④
	National Gallery Café	"	④ ④ ④

		Rating		
Bocca Di Lupo	*Italian*	②	②	②
Number Twelve	*"*	③	④	④
Orso	*"*	③	③	④
Vasco & Piero's Pavilion	*"*	②	②	③
Nopi	*Mediterranean*	②	②	③
Albannach	*Scottish*	⑤	⑤	⑤
Gaucho	*Steaks & grills*	③	④	③
Hawksmoor	*"*	②	②	②
St Moritz	*Swiss*	③	④	③
Moti Mahal	*Indian*	②	③	④
Kyashii	*Japanese*	④	④	③
Watatsumi	*"*	④	③	④
Tamarai	*Pan-Asian*	④	④	④

£40+

All Star Lanes	*American*	④	⑤	③
Bodean's	*"*	④	⑤	④
Spuntino	*"*	③	②	②
Acorn House	*British, Modern*	④	④	⑤
Andrew Edmunds	*"*	③	②	❶
Aurora	*"*	③	③	②
The Easton	*"*	②	②	③
Kettners	*"*	④	③	③
The Portrait	*"*	④	②	❶
Shampers	*"*	③	②	②
Great Queen Street	*British, Traditional*	②	③	③
Cape Town Fish Market	*Fish & seafood*	③	④	④
Livebait	*"*	④	④	⑤
Loch Fyne	*"*	④	④	④
J Sheekey Oyster Bar	*"*	❷	❶	❶
Antidote	*French*	③	④	③
Café Bohème	*"*	④	②	❶
The Giaconda	*"*	②	②	④
Randall & Aubin	*"*	③	③	②
Terroirs	*"*	②	③	③
Kopapa	*Fusion*	③	③	④
Gay Hussar	*Hungarian*	⑤	③	②
Balans	*International*	④	③	③
Browns	*"*	⑤	④	④
Cork & Bottle	*"*	⑤	④	②
Giraffe	*"*	⑤	④	④
Sarastro	*"*	⑤	⑤	❶
Bertorelli	*Italian*	⑤	⑤	⑤
Ciao Bella	*"*	④	②	②
Dehesa	*"*	❶	❶	②
Jamie's Italian	*"*	④	③	④
Rossopomodoro	*"*	③	④	④
Sapori	*"*	④	③	④
Barrafina	*Spanish*	❶	❶	②
Cigala	*"*	③	③	④
Opera Tavern	*"*	②	③	③
The Bountiful Cow	*Steaks & grills*	③	④	④
Boyd's Brasserie	*"*	④	④	④
Sophie's Steakhouse	*"*	④	③	③
Mildreds	*Vegetarian*	②	④	④
Wolfe's	*Burgers, etc*	③	④	④
Café Pacifico	*Mexican/TexMex*	⑤	④	③
Cantina Laredo	*"*	③	④	⑤
Bar Shu	*Chinese*	②	④	③

	Empress of Sichuan	"	③③④
	Imperial China	"	③③④
	Yming	"	②①③
	Malabar Junction	Indian	③③③
	Edokko	Japanese	②①③
	Inamo	"	④④②
	Asadal	Korean	③④④
	Benja	Thai	②②③
	Patara	"	②③③
£35+	Belgo Centraal	Belgian	④④③
	Café Emm	British, Modern	④④③
	The Norfolk Arms	"	④④③
	The Terrace	"	③④②
	Porters	British, Traditional	④③③
	Côte	French	④③②
	Savoir Faire	"	③④③
	Real Greek	Greek	⑤⑤④
	Boulevard	International	⑤⑤④
	Da Mario	Italian	④②②
	Polpetto	"	②②①
	Zilli Green	"	– – –
	Tapas Brindisa Soho	Spanish	②③②
	Fire & Stone	Pizza	④③③
	Lupita	Mexican/TexMex	④④④
	Sofra	Turkish	④④④
	Dishoom	Indian	③③①
	Imli	"	④③④
	Mela	"	③③③
	Rasa Maricham	Indian, Southern	②②③
	Abeno	Japanese	③②④
	Hazuki	"	②②④
	Satsuma	"	– – –
	Ten Ten Tei	"	③③⑤
	Melati, Gt Windmill St	Malaysian	④③⑤
	Haozhan	Pan-Asian	③④⑤
	Busaba Eathai	Thai	③③②
	Thai Pot	"	③②③
	Thai Square	"	④③③
	Cây Tre	Vietnamese	②④④
£30+	Seven Stars	British, Modern	④④②
	da Polpo	Italian	③②④
	La Porchetta Pizzeria	"	③③③
	Byron	Burgers, etc	③③③
	Diner	"	⑤⑤③
	North Sea Fish	Fish & chips	③③③
	Rock & Sole Plaice	"	③④③
	Fernandez & Wells	Sandwiches, cakes, etc	②②②
	Paul	"	③④③
	Yalla Yalla	Lebanese	③③②
	Tas	Turkish	④③③
	Ba Shan	Chinese	②④③
	Chuen Cheng Ku	"	③④④
	Golden Dragon	"	③③③
	Harbour City	"	②④④
	Joy King Lau	"	③④④
	Mr Kong	"	③③④

	Name	Cuisine	Ratings
	New Mayflower	"	②③④
	New World	"	④④❸
	Plum Valley	"	❸②❸
	Leong's Legends	Chinese, Dim sum	④④❸
	ping pong	"	④④❸
	Gopal's of Soho	Indian	❸❸❸
	Masala Zone	"	❸❸❸
	Sagar	"	②②④
	Salaam Namaste	"	②❸④
	Bincho Yakitori	Japanese	❸④④
	Misato	"	④④⑤
	Wagamama	"	④❸④
	Kimchee	Korean	❸❸❸
	Banana Tree Canteen	Pan-Asian	❸②❸
	Rosa's Soho	Thai	❸④❸
	Pho	Vietnamese	②❸❸
£25+	Prix Fixe	French	④❸❸
	Café in the Crypt	International	④④❸
	Gordon's Wine Bar	"	⑤④❶
	Polpo	Italian	❸②❶
	Princi	"	❸④②
	Café España	Spanish	❸②②
	Mar I Terra	"	❸②❸
	Ed's Easy Diner	Burgers, etc	④❸②
	Bar Italia	Sandwiches, cakes, etc	❸④❶
	The Courtauld (Café)	"	④❸❸
	Wahaca	Mexican/TexMex	④❸❸
	Gaby's	Israeli	❸④⑤
	Cha Cha Moon	Chinese	④④❸
	Chilli Cool	"	②⑤④
	The Four Seasons	"	②④⑤
	Wong Kei	"	④⑤④
	India Club	Indian	④④④
	Kulu Kulu	Japanese	④④⑤
	Taro	"	❸❸❸
	Tokyo Diner	"	④②❸
	Hare & Tortoise	Pan-Asian	❸❸❸
£20+	Bistro 1	Mediterranean	④❸④
	Konditor & Cook	Sandwiches, cakes, etc	②❸❸
	Leon	"	❸❸❸
	Benito's Hat	Mexican/TexMex	❸②④
	Koya	Japanese	②②❸
	Paolina Café	Thai	❸④⑤
	Viet	Vietnamese	❸④④
£15+	Hummus Bros	Mediterranean	②②④
	Nordic Bakery	Scandinavian	❸❸②
	Food for Thought	Vegetarian	②④⑤
	Mrs Marengos	Sandwiches, cakes, etc	❶❸④
	Chipotle	Mexican/TexMex	❸④④
	Baozi Inn	Chinese	②⑤④
	Abokado	Japanese	④❸④
	C&R Cafe	Thai	❸④⑤
£10+	Govinda's	International	❸④④
	Caffé Vergnano	Italian	④❸❸

	Fryer's Delight	Fish & chips	③④④
	Flat White	Sandwiches, cakes, etc	②②③
	Maison Bertaux	"	②③①
	Monmouth Coffee Co	"	②②②
	Pod	"	③④④
	Chilango	Mexican/TexMex	①②④
	Mooli's	Indian	②②④
£5+	Gelupo	Ice cream	②②④
	Pizzeria Malletti	Pizza	②③③

Mayfair & St James's (Parts of W1 and SW1)

£110+	Alain Ducasse	French	④④④
	Le Gavroche	"	①①②
	Hibiscus	"	③④④
	The Ritz Restaurant	"	③②①
£100+	G Ramsay at Claridges	French	⑤④⑤
	Hélène Darroze	"	③④③
	Sketch (Lecture Rm)	"	⑤⑤③
	The Square	"	②②③
	Kai Mayfair	Chinese	③③④
£90+	Wiltons	British, Traditional	④②②
	The Greenhouse	French	③③②
	Murano	Italian	③②③
£80+	Dorchester Grill	British, Modern	④③④
	Galvin at Windows	French	③②②
	L'Oranger	"	③③②
	C London	Italian	⑤⑤④
	Theo Randall	"	②③④
	maze Grill	Steaks & grills	④④④
	Hakkasan	Chinese	②④②
	Ikeda	Japanese	②②⑤
	Matsuri	"	②②⑤
	Nobu, Park Ln	"	②④④
	Nobu, Berkeley St	"	③④③
	Umu	"	②③②
£70+	Bellamy's	British, Modern	③②③
	Patterson's	"	③③④
	Seven Park Place	"	①①②
	Browns (Albemarle)	British, Traditional	③②②
	Corrigan's Mayfair	"	③③③
	Scott's	Fish & seafood	②①①
	maze	French	④④④
	La Petite Maison	"	②②②
	Amaranto	Italian	– – –
	Babbo	"	④④⑤
	5 Pollen Street	"	④③③
	Ladurée	Afternoon tea	④④③
	Quince	Turkish	④③⑤
	China Tang	Chinese	④④③
	Benares	Indian	②②③
	Sumosan	Japanese	③③③

£60+					
	Athenaeum	*British, Modern*	②	②	③
	Le Caprice	"	③	⓪	②
	Criterion	"	④	④	②
	Langan's Brasserie	"	④	④	②
	Pollen Street Social	"	⓪	⓪	②
	Quaglino's	"	⑤	⑤	⑤
	The Fountain (Fortnum's)	*British, Traditional*	④	③	③
	Green's	"	②	②	②
	Bentley's	*Fish & seafood*	②	③	③
	Brasserie Roux	*French*	③	②	③
	The Gallery	"	②	⓪	④
	Sketch (Gallery)	"	⑤	⑤	④
	Cecconi's	*Italian*	③	②	⓪
	Franco's	"	④	④	④
	La Genova	"	③	②	③
	Ristorante Semplice	"	②	②	③
	Goodman	*Steaks & grills*	②	②	③
	The Guinea Grill	"	②	③	③
	JW Steakhouse	"	④	④	④
	Rowley's	"	⑤	⑤	⑤
	Momo	*North African*	④	⑤	③
	Mint Leaf	*Indian*	③	④	③
	Tamarind	"	③	③	④
	Veeraswamy	"	③	③	③
	Benihana	*Japanese*	④	③	③
	Kiku	"	②	②	④
	Miyama	"	②	④	⑤
	Sake No Hana	"	③	④	④
£50+	Automat	*American*	④	④	④
	The Avenue	*British, Modern*	④	③	③
	Hush	"	⑤	⑤	④
	Mews of Mayfair	"	④	③	③
	Sotheby's Café	"	②	②	②
	Wild Honey	"	③	③	③
	The Wolseley	"	③	②	⓪
	Pescatori	*Fish & seafood*	③	②	④
	Wheeler's	"	⑤	④	⑤
	Boudin Blanc	*French*	③	④	②
	Brasserie St Jacques	"	④	③	④
	Chez Gérard	"	⑤	⑤	⑤
	Alloro	*Italian*	③	③	③
	Dolada	"	③	③	④
	Sartoria	"	③	③	③
	Serafino	"	③	②	④
	Tempo	"	③	②	③
	Truc Vert	*Mediterranean*	③	④	④
	Gaucho	*Steaks & grills*	③	④	③
	Aubaine	*Sandwiches, cakes, etc*	④	④	④
	Fakhreldine	*Lebanese*	④	④	④
	Noura	"	③	④	④
	Princess Garden	*Chinese*	②	②	③
	Mitsukoshi	*Japanese*	②	②	⑤
£40+	Hard Rock Café	*American*	④	②	②
	Inn the Park	*British, Modern*	④	⑤	③
	The Only Running Footman	"	③	③	③
	1707	"	④	③	③

	Restaurant	Cuisine	Ratings
	Fishworks	Fish & seafood	❸❸④
	Browns	International	⑤④④
	Al Duca	Italian	④④⑤
	Bar Trattoria Semplice	"	④④⑤
	Piccolino	"	④④④
	Il Vicolo	"	④④④
	Rocket	Mediterranean	④④❸
	Ritz (Palm Court)	Afternoon tea	④❸❷
	Delfino	Pizza	❷④④
	The Sketch (Parlour)	Sandwiches, cakes, etc	④④❸
	Al Hamra	Lebanese	④⑤④
	Al Sultan	"	❷❸⑤
	Chor Bizarre	Indian	④④❷
	Chisou	Japanese	❷❸④
	Inamo	Pan-Asian	④④❷
	Patara	Thai	❷❸❸
£35+	The Windmill	British, Traditional	❷④❸
	L'Artiste Musclé	French	④❸❸
	El Pirata	Spanish	④❷❶
	Sofra	Turkish	④④④
	Woodlands	Indian	❸❸④
	Rasa	Indian, Southern	❷❷❸
	Toku	Japanese	❸❸④
	Yoshino	"	❷❶❸
	Busaba Eathai	Thai	❸❸❷
	Thai Square	"	④❸❸
£30+	tibits	Vegetarian	❸④❸
	Byron	Burgers, etc	❸❸❸
	Benugo	Sandwiches, cakes, etc	④⑤❸
	Sakura	Japanese	❷④④
	Wagamama	"	④❸④
£25+	English Tea Rm (Browns)	British, Traditional	❸❷❶
	Stock Pot	International	⑤④④
	Ed's Easy Diner	Burgers, etc	④❸❷
	Jom Makan	Malaysian	④⑤⑤
£20+	Napket	Afternoon tea	④④❸
	Mount Street Deli	Sandwiches, cakes, etc	④④④
£15+	La Bottega	Italian	❸❸❸
£10+	Fuzzy's Grub	Sandwiches, cakes, etc	④④④
	Chop'd	Salads	❸❸④

Fitzrovia & Marylebone (Part of W1)

	Restaurant	Cuisine	Ratings
£90+	Pied à Terre	French	❶❷❷
£80+	Roux At The Landau	British, Modern	❷❷❷
	Hakkasan	Chinese	❷④❷
£70+	Roganic	British, Modern	❶❷⑤
	Locanda Locatelli	Italian	❸❸❸
	Texture	Scandinavian	❷⓪❸
	Roka	Japanese	❶❸❷

Price	Name	Cuisine	Ratings
£60+	Oscar	British, Modern	④❸❷
	Rhodes W1 Restaurant	"	④❸⑤
	L'Autre Pied	French	❷❷❸
	Orrery	"	❸❷❷
	The Providores	International	❸④④
	La Porte des Indes	Indian	❸④❷
£50+	Café Luc	British, Modern	④④❷
	Grazing Goat	"	❸❷❷
	The Union Café	"	❸④④
	Vanilla	"	④④❸
	Odin's	British, Traditional	④❷❷
	Pescatori	Fish & seafood	❸❷④
	Elena's L'Etoile	French	⑤④④
	Galvin Bistrot de Luxe	"	❷⓪❷
	Villandry	"	④⑤④
	The Wallace	"	④④⓪
	Archipelago	Fusion	❸❸⓪
	Il Baretto	Italian	❷④④
	Caffè Caldesi	"	④❷❸
	Mennula	"	❷❸④
	Verru	Scandinavian	❷❸④
	Fino	Spanish	❷❷❷
	Gaucho	Steaks & grills	❸④❸
	Reubens	Kosher	④⑤⑤
	Levant	Lebanese	❸❸⓪
	Royal China Club	Chinese	❷❸④
	Trishna	Indian	⓪❷❸
	Colony	Pan-Asian	❸④⑤
	Crazy Bear	Thai	❸❸⓪
£40+	The Duke of Wellington	British, Modern	❸④❸
	Hardy's Brasserie	"	④④❸
	Ozer	"	④④④
	RIBA Café	"	④⑤❷
	Back to Basics	Fish & seafood	❷❷④
	Fishworks	"	❸❸④
	Langan's Bistro	French	❸❷❷
	Le Relais de Venise	"	❷❸❸
	Providores (Tapa Room)	Fusion	❷④④
	Élysée	Greek	④❸❷
	Hellenic	"	④❷❸
	Giraffe	International	⑤④④
	Latium	Italian	❷⓪❸
	Sardo	"	❸❸④
	2 Veneti	"	❸❷④
	Riding House Café	Mediterranean	❷❷⓪
	Ibérica	Spanish	❸❸❸
	Black & Blue	Steaks & grills	④④④
	Fairuz	Lebanese	❸❸④
	Maroush	"	❷④④
	Royal China	Chinese	❷④④
	Gaylord	Indian	❸④④
	Zayna	"	❷④④
	Defune	Japanese	❷⓪④
	Dinings	"	⓪❷⑤
	Soho Japan	"	❸❷④
	Tsunami	"	⓪④❸

	Koba	Korean	❸❸④
	Samarqand	Uzbekistani	④④❸
	Bam-Bou	Vietnamese	❸❸❷
£35+	Vinoteca Seymour Place	British, Modern	❸❷⓪
	Canteen	British, Traditional	④④④
	Real Greek	Greek	⑤⑤④
	Navarro's	Spanish	❸④❷
	Salt Yard	"	❸❷❷
	Eagle Bar Diner	Burgers, etc	❸❸❷
	La Fromagerie Café	Sandwiches, cakes, etc	❷❸❷
	Ishtar	Turkish	❸❷❸
	Sofra	"	④④④
	Woodlands	Indian	❸❸④
	Rasa Samudra	Indian, Southern	❷❷❸
	Nizuni	Japanese	❷❷❸
£30+	Guerilla Burgers	American	❸❷❷
	Lantana Cafe	Australian	❸❸❸
	Vapiano	Italian	④④④
	Barrica	Spanish	❸❸❷
	Benugo	Sandwiches, cakes, etc	④⑤❸
	Paul	"	❸④❸
	Natural Kitchen	Salads	❸❸❸
	Yalla Yalla	Lebanese	❸❸❷
	ping pong	Chinese, Dim sum	④④❸
	Indali Lounge	Indian	❸❸❸
	Sagar	"	❷❷④
	Wagamama	Japanese	④❸④
	dim T	Pan-Asian	⑤④❸
	Pho	Vietnamese	❷❸❸
£25+	Ragam	Indian	⓪❷⑤
	Atari-Ya	Japanese	⓪❷④
	Siam Central	Thai	❸④❸
£20+	Golden Hind	Fish & chips	⓪❷❸
	Leon	Sandwiches, cakes, etc	❸❸❸
	Benito's Hat	Mexican/TexMex	❸❷④
£15+	Cocorino	Italian	⓪⓪❸
	Nordic Bakery	Scandinavian	❸❸❷
	Tortilla	Mexican/TexMex	❸❸④
	Comptoir Libanais	Lebanese	④⑤④
	Abokado	Japanese	④❸④
£10+	Scandinavian Kitchen	Scandinavian	❸❷❷
	Kaffeine	Sandwiches, cakes, etc	❷⓪⓪
	Patogh	Middle Eastern	❷❸④

**Belgravia, Pimlico, Victoria & Westminster
(SW1, except St James's)**

Price	Restaurant	Cuisine	Rating
£110+	Marcus Wareing	*French*	❷❷❷
£100+	Rib Room	*British, Traditional*	– – –
£90+	Dinner	*British, Traditional*	❷❷❷
	One-O-One	*Fish & seafood*	❶❸❺
	Apsleys	*Italian*	❸❷❸
£80+	Roux At Parliament Square	*British, Modern*	❸❹❺
	Pétrus	*French*	❹❷❸
	Roussillon	*"*	❸❸❹
	The Palm	*Steaks & grills*	❹❹❺
	Nahm	*Thai*	❸❸❺
£70+	The Goring Hotel	*British, Modern*	❸❶❶
	Koffmann's	*French*	❷❷❹
	Massimo	*Mediterranean*	❹❷❷
	Ladurée	*Afternoon tea*	❹❹❸
	Mr Chow	*Chinese*	❹❹❹
£60+	The Fifth Floor Restaurant	*British, Modern*	❹❸❹
	The Thomas Cubitt	*"*	❸❸❷
	Harrods (Georgian Rest')	*British, Traditional*	❸❸❸
	Olivomare	*Fish & seafood*	❷❸❹
	Quirinale	*Italian*	❷❶❸
	Santini	*"*	❹❹❹
	Signor Sassi	*"*	❸❸❷
	Toto's	*"*	❸❸❸
	Zafferano	*"*	❸❹❸
	Boisdale	*Scottish*	❹❹❷
	Amaya	*Indian*	❶❷❷
	The Cinnamon Club	*"*	❷❸❷
£50+	Bank Westminster	*British, Modern*	❹❸❹
	The Botanist	*"*	❺❺❺
	The Pantechnicon	*"*	❸❸❷
	Tate Britain (Rex Whistler)	*"*	❸❸❷
	Shepherd's	*British, Traditional*	❹❸❸
	Bar Boulud	*French*	❷❷❸
	Chabrot Bistrot d'Amis	*"*	❸❶❸
	The Chelsea Brasserie	*"*	❹❹❹
	La Poule au Pot	*"*	❸❸❶
	Motcombs	*International*	❹❹❸
	Il Convivio	*Italian*	❸❸❹
	Olivo	*"*	❸❸❺
	Osteria Dell'Angolo	*"*	❸❸❺
	Sale e Pepe	*"*	❹❸❸
	Oliveto	*Pizza*	❶❸❹
	Ishbilia	*Lebanese*	❷❹❺
	Noura	*"*	❸❹❹
	Hunan	*Chinese*	❶❷❹
	Ken Lo's Memories	*"*	❷❸❸
	Quilon	*Indian, Southern*	❶❶❹
	Mango Tree	*Thai*	❸❹❹

£40+	Daylesford Organic	British, Modern	④⑤④
	Ebury Wine Bar	"	④❸❸
	The Orange	"	❸❸②
	The Queens Arms	"	❸❸❸
	Smith Square	"	– – –
	Le Cercle	French	❷❷❷
	The Ebury	"	④④❸
	Browns	International	⑤④④
	Bumbles	"	❸❷④
	City Café	"	④❸④
	Giraffe	"	⑤④④
	Grumbles	"	⑤④④
	Caraffini	Italian	❸⓿❷
	Como Lario	"	⑤④❸
	Gran Paradiso	"	④❸④
	Ottolenghi	"	⓿❸❸
	2 Amici	"	④④④
	Uno	"	④④④
	About Thyme	Mediterranean	❷⓿④
	Goya	Spanish	④④④
	Baker & Spice	Sandwiches, cakes, etc	❸❸❷
	Beiteddine	Lebanese	❸④⑤
	Ranoush	"	❷④④
	Kazan	Turkish	❷❷❸
	The Grand Imperial	Chinese	④❸④
	Made in China	"	④④④
	Salloos	Pakistani	❷❸④
£35+	Tinello	Italian	❷⓿❷
£30+	Seafresh	Fish & chips	❸④⑤
	Jenny Lo's	Chinese	❸⓿④
	Wagamama	Japanese	④❸④
	dim T	Pan-Asian	⑤④❸
	Blue Jade	Thai	❸⓿❸
	Mekong	Vietnamese	❸❷④
£25+	The Vincent Rooms	British, Modern	❸④❸
	Cyprus Mangal	Turkish	❷❸④
£15+	La Bottega	Italian	❸❸❸
	William Curley	Afternoon tea	⓿❸❸

WEST

Chelsea, South Kensington, Kensington, Earl's Court & Fulham (SW3, SW5, SW6, SW7, SW10 & W8)

£120+	Gordon Ramsay	*French*	④③④
£100+	Tom Aikens	*British, Modern*	– – –
£90+	The Capital Restaurant	*French*	③④④
	Rasoi	*Indian*	③④③
£80+	Blakes	*International*	④③②
£70+	Launceston Place	*British, Modern*	②②②
	Bibendum	*French*	③②②
	Cassis Bistro	*"*	④④④
	Nozomi	*Japanese*	④⑤④
	Zuma	*"*	①③②
£60+	Babylon	*British, Modern*	④④②
	Clarke's	*"*	②②③
	Maggie Jones's	*British, Traditional*	⑤④①
	Bibendum Oyster Bar	*Fish & seafood*	③②②
	Poissonnerie de l'Av.	*"*	③③④
	Le Suquet	*"*	③④④
	Belvedere	*French*	④③①
	Cheyne Walk Bras'	*"*	③④③
	L'Etranger	*"*	③②③
	Racine	*"*	③②③
	Ilia	*Italian*	③④④
	Lucio	*"*	③③③
	Montpeliano	*"*	④④④
	San Lorenzo	*"*	④④④
	Scalini	*"*	④④③
	Locanda Ottomezzo	*Mediterranean*	④②③
	Min Jiang	*Chinese*	①②①
	Bombay Brasserie	*Indian*	③③③
	Benihana	*Japanese*	④③③
	Yashin	*"*	②④④
	Mao Tai	*Pan-Asian*	③④③
£50+	Big Easy	*American*	④④②
	The Abingdon	*British, Modern*	③②②
	Bluebird	*"*	⑤④④
	Brinkley's	*"*	⑤④③
	The Enterprise	*"*	③③②
	Kensington Place	*"*	③③④
	Kitchen W8	*"*	①②②
	Manson	*"*	①④③
	Marco	*"*	④⑤⑤
	Tom's Kitchen	*"*	④⑤④
	Bistro K	*French*	④④④
	Le Colombier	*"*	③②②
	Galoupet	*"*	①②③
	Foxtrot Oscar	*International*	④③④
	Gallery Mess	*"*	④④④

Medlar	"	**1**	**2**	**3**
Wine Gallery	"	**4**	**3**	**2**
The Ark	Italian	**3**	**3**	**2**
Cavallino	"	–	–	–
Daphne's	"	**3**	**2**	**2**
El leven Park Walk	"	**3**	**4**	**4**
La Famiglia	"	**3**	**3**	**3**
Frantoio	"	**4**	**3**	**3**
Manicomio	"	**3**	**4**	**3**
Osteria dell'Arancio	"	**3**	**3**	**3**
Pellicano	"	**3**	**3**	**4**
Timo	"	**2**	**0**	**4**
Venosi	"	**4**	**2**	**4**
Ziani's	"	**3**	**2**	**2**
Cambio de Tercio	Spanish	**2**	**2**	**2**
Gaucho	Steaks & grills	**3**	**4**	**3**
Kings Road Steakhouse	"	**4**	**4**	**4**
PJ's Bar and Grill	"	**4**	**4**	**3**
Aubaine	Sandwiches, cakes, etc	**4**	**4**	**4**
Pasha	Moroccan	**5**	**4**	**2**
Good Earth	Chinese	**3**	**3**	**5**
Chutney Mary	Indian	**2**	**2**	**2**
The Painted Heron	"	**1**	**2**	**3**
Zaika	"	**1**	**2**	**3**
Awana	Malaysian	**4**	**4**	**4**
Eight Over Eight	Pan-Asian	**2**	**3**	**2**
£40+				
Bodean's	American	**4**	**5**	**4**
Sticky Fingers	"	**4**	**4**	**3**
Admiral Codrington	British, Modern	**3**	**4**	**3**
The Anglesea Arms	"	**3**	**4**	**2**
Brompton Bar & Grill	"	**4**	**3**	**3**
The Builders Arms	"	**3**	**3**	**2**
The Cadogan Arms	"	**3**	**4**	**3**
Eighty-Six	"	**4**	**5**	**3**
Harwood Arms	"	**2**	**2**	**2**
The Henry Root	"	**4**	**2**	**3**
Jam Tree	"	**4**	**2**	**3**
Joe's Brasserie	"	**3**	**3**	**3**
Lots Road	"	**3**	**2**	**4**
The Mall Tavern	"	**3**	**3**	**2**
The Phene	"	**4**	**4**	**2**
The Phoenix	"	**4**	**5**	**3**
The Sands End	"	**2**	**3**	**2**
Vingt-Quatre	"	**4**	**4**	**4**
White Horse	"	**3**	**3**	**3**
Whits	"	**3**	**0**	**3**
Bumpkin	British, Traditional	**5**	**4**	**3**
Ffiona's	"	**4**	**2**	**0**
Chez Patrick	Fish & seafood	**3**	**2**	**3**
Geales Chelsea Green	"	**3**	**3**	**4**
L'Art du Fromage	French	**3**	**2**	**4**
La Bouchée	"	**3**	**4**	**2**
La Brasserie	"	**5**	**4**	**3**
The Pig's Ear	"	**3**	**3**	**0**
Tartine	"	**3**	**4**	**3**
Sushinho	Fusion	**4**	**3**	**2**
Balans West	International	**4**	**3**	**3**

	Giraffe	"	⑤④④
	The Kensington Wine Rms	"	④❷❷
	Falconiere	Italian	④❸⑤
	Frankie's Italian Bar & Grill	"	⑤⑤④
	Nuovi Sapori	"	❷⓪④
	Ottolenghi	"	⓪❸❸
	Il Portico	"	❸⓪❷
	Riccardo's	"	④④④
	Rossopomodoro	"	❸④④
	Santa Lucia	"	❸④❸
	Vicino	"	❸❸❸
	The Atlas	Mediterranean	❷❸❸
	Del'Aziz	"	④⑤❷
	Polish Club	Polish	⑤④❸
	Madsen	Scandinavian	④④④
	Black & Blue	Steaks & grills	④④④
	Sophie's Steakhouse	"	④❸❸
	Saf	Vegetarian	❷④④
	Geales	Fish & chips	❸❸④
	(Ciro's) Pizza Pomodoro	Pizza	④④❷
	Baker & Spice	Sandwiches, cakes, etc	❸❸❷
	Fulham Wine Rooms	"	④❸❸
	Rodizio Rico	Brazilian	⑤④⑤
	Maroush	Lebanese	❷④④
	Randa	"	❸❸④
	Ranoush	"	❷④④
	Ken Lo's Memories	Chinese	⓪❷❸
	Mr Wing	"	❸④❷
	Royal China	"	❷④④
	Haandi	Indian	❷❷④
	kare kare	"	❸❸④
	Malabar	"	❷❷❸
	Star of India	"	❷④❸
	Thali	"	❷❷④
	Patara	Thai	❷❸❸
	Sukho Fine Thai Cuisine	"	⓪❷❸
£35+	Butcher's Hook	British, Modern	❸❸❸
	Côte	French	④❸❷
	Rôtisserie Bute Street	"	❸④④
	The Scarsdale	International	④❸❷
	Aglio e Olio	Italian	❸❸❸
	Buona Sera	"	❸⓪⓪
	Da Mario	"	④❷❸
	Made in Italy	"	❷❸❷
	Napulé	"	❸④❸
	Gessler at Daquise	Polish	④❷❸
	Capote Y Toros	Spanish	– – –
	Casa Brindisa	"	❸④❸
	Lola Rojo	"	❷❸❷
	Tendido Cero	"	❸❸❷
	Tendido Cuatro	"	❷❷❷
	Haché	Steaks & grills	❸❸❸
	Bluebird Café	Sandwiches, cakes, etc	⑤⑤④
	Troubadour	"	⑤❸⓪
	Beirut Express	Lebanese	❷④④
	Choys	Chinese	④④④
	Khan's of Kensington	Indian	❸❸❸

	Noor Jahan	"	❷❷④
	Bangkok	Thai	❷❷❸
	Thai Square	"	④❸❸
£30+	Kensington Square Kitchen	British, Modern	❸❷❸
	The Windsor Castle	International	④④❶
	Il Pagliaccio	Italian	④❸❶
	Pappa Ciccia	"	❸④④
	Rocca Di Papa	"	④❸❸
	Byron	Burgers, etc	❸❸❸
	Basilico	Pizza	❷❸④
	La Delizia Limbara	"	❸❸❸
	Firezza	"	❷❸④
	Benugo	Sandwiches, cakes, etc	④⑤❸
	Best Mangal	Turkish	❸❸❸
	New Culture Rev'n	Chinese	❸④④
	Taiwan Village	"	❶❶❸
	The Greedy Buddha	Indian	❸❷❸
	Masala Zone	"	❸❸❸
	Memories of India	"	❸④④
	Monty's	"	❸❸④
	Itsu	Japanese	④④④
	Wagamama	"	④❸④
	Addie's Thai Café	Thai	❷❷❸
£25+	Costa's Grill	Greek	④❸④
	Chelsea Bun Diner	International	❸❷❸
	The Chelsea Kitchen	"	④❸❸
	Mona Lisa	"	④❶❷
	Stock Pot	"	⑤④④
	Kulu Kulu	Japanese	④④⑤
	Churchill Arms	Thai	❷❸❷
£20+	Napket	Afternoon tea	④④❸
	Stick & Bowl	Chinese	❸❸❸
	Café 209	Thai	❸❷❷
£15+	La Bottega	Italian	❸❸❸

Notting Hill, Holland Park, Bayswater, North Kensington & Maida Vale (W2, W9, W10, W11)

£90+	The Ledbury	British, Modern	❶❶❷
£70+	Notting Hill Brasserie	British, Modern	❸④❸
	Angelus	French	❷❶❸
£60+	Beach Blanket Babylon	British, Modern	⑤⑤❶
	supperclub	"	④④❶
	Assaggi	Italian	❷❷❸
	Edera	"	❷❶❸
£50+	Julie's	British, Modern	④④❶
	The Warrington	"	⑤⑤⑤
	Le Café Anglais	French	❸❸❸
	202	International	④❸❸
	Dragoncello	Italian	④❷❸
	Essenza	"	❸❸④

	Mediterraneo	"	③③③
	Osteria Basilico	"	③③②
	E&O	Pan-Asian	②③②
£40+	All Star Lanes	American	④⑤③
	Lucky Seven	"	③③②
	The Cow	British, Modern	③④②
	Daylesford Organic	"	④⑤④
	The Dock Kitchen	"	③③❶
	First Floor	"	③②❶
	Formosa Dining Room	"	③④③
	The Frontline Club	"	③②②
	The Ladbroke Arms	"	②③②
	The Waterway	"	④⑤②
	The Westbourne	"	③④②
	Bumpkin	British, Traditional	⑤④③
	Hereford Road	"	②②④
	The Summerhouse	Fish & seafood	④④❶
	Electric Brasserie	French	④④②
	La Sophia	"	②②④
	Halepi	Greek	③❶③
	Giraffe	International	⑤④④
	L'Accento Italiano	Italian	③②③
	The Oak	"	②③❶
	Ottolenghi	"	❶③③
	Portobello Ristorante	"	③④④
	Rossopomodoro	"	③④④
	Cochonnet	Mediterranean	③②③
	The Red Pepper	Pizza	②③④
	Baker & Spice	Sandwiches, cakes, etc	③③②
	Casa Malevo	Argentinian	④④④
	Rodizio Rico	Brazilian	⑤④⑤
	Crazy Homies	Mexican/TexMex	③④❶
	Al-Waha	Lebanese	②③④
	Maroush	"	②④④
	Ranoush	"	②④④
	Royal China	Chinese	②④④
	Seventeen	"	②②③
	Bombay Bicycle Club	Indian	– – –
	Bombay Palace	"	②②⑤
	Inaho	Japanese	❶⑤⑤
£35+	Paradise, Kensal Green	British, Modern	②②❶
	Côte	French	④③②
	Café Laville	International	④④❶
	Ida	Italian	③②②
	Nottingdale	"	②④②
	Raoul's Café & Deli	Mediterranean	④⑤④
	Pizza East Portobello	Pizza	– – –
	Beirut Express	Lebanese	②④④
	Kateh	Persian	③②③
	Mandarin Kitchen	Chinese	②④⑤
	Pearl Liang	"	❶②②
	Noor Jahan	Indian	②②④
	Satay House	Malaysian	③③④
	Uli	Pan-Asian	③❶③
	The Walmer Castle	Thai	③②②

£30+	Galicia	Spanish	3 4 3
	El Pirata de Tapas	"	3 2 2
	Firezza	Pizza	2 3 4
	Tom's Deli	Sandwiches, cakes, etc	3 4 3
	Taqueria	Mexican/TexMex	4 4 3
	Magic Wok	Chinese	3 3 5
	New Culture Rev'n	"	3 4 4
	Leong's Legends	Chinese, Dim sum	4 4 3
	ping pong	"	4 4 3
	Masala Zone	Indian	3 3 3
	Itsu	Japanese	4 4 4
	Banana Tree Canteen	Pan-Asian	3 2 3
£25+	Otto Pizza	Pizza	2 2 3
	Gail's Bread	Sandwiches, cakes, etc	3 3 4
	Alounak	Persian	3 4 3
	Mandalay	Burmese	3 3 5
	Fortune Cookie	Chinese	2 4 5
	The Four Seasons	"	2 4 5
	Kiasu	Indonesian	3 4 4
£20+	Fresco	Lebanese	3 2 3
	Khan's	Indian	3 4 3
	Fitou's Thai Restaurant	Thai	2 3 4
£15+	C&R Cafe	Thai	3 4 5
£5+	Lisboa Pâtisserie	Sandwiches, cakes, etc	2 3 4

Hammersmith, Shepherd's Bush, Olympia, Chiswick, Brentford & Ealing (W4, W5, W6, W12, W13, W14, TW8)

£70+	Hedone	British, Modern	2 4 4
	The River Café	Italian	2 2 3
£60+	La Trompette	French	0 0 2
£50+	Charlotte's Bistro	French	4 4 4
	Le Vacherin	"	3 3 3
	The Meat & Wine Co	Steaks & grills	4 0 4
£40+	The Anglesea Arms	British, Modern	2 4 2
	The Carpenter's Arms	"	3 4 4
	Duke of Sussex	"	3 2 2
	Ealing Park Tavern	"	3 3 4
	The Havelock Tavern	"	2 4 2
	High Road Brasserie	"	4 4 2
	Hole in the Wall	"	3 4 3
	The Jam Tree	"	4 2 3
	Pissarro	"	4 4 3
	Princess Victoria	"	2 2 2
	The Roebuck	"	3 2 2
	Sam's Brasserie	"	4 3 3
	Charlotte's Place	French	3 3 3
	Annie's	International	4 2 2
	Balans	"	4 3 3
	Giraffe	"	5 4 4

			Rating
	Michael Nadra	"	①③④
	Carvosso's	Italian	⑤④③
	Cibo	"	③③④
	Jamie's Italian	"	④③④
	Cumberland Arms	Mediterranean	③③③
	Del'Aziz	"	④⑤②
	The Cabin	Steaks & grills	④④④
	Popeseye	"	①②③
	The Gate	Vegetarian	②③④
	Lola & Simón	Argentinian	③②③
	Quantus	South American	③②③
	Indian Zing	Indian	①②③
	Charm	Thai	③③②
	Saigon Saigon	Vietnamese	②②③
£35+	Queen's Head	British, Modern	④②②
	Tatra	East & Cent. European	④④④
	Côte	French	④③②
	The Real Greek	Greek	⑤④④
	Raoul's Café & Deli	Mediterranean	④⑤④
	The Swan	"	②③②
	Fire & Stone	Pizza	④③③
	Chella	Persian	③②③
	North China	Chinese	②②③
	Brilliant	Indian	①②③
	Karma	"	②①④
	Madhu's	"	③③③
	Busaba Eathai	Thai	③③②
£30+	Albertine	French	④②①
	Canta Napoli	Italian	③③④
	Patio	Polish	③②①
	Byron	Burgers, etc	③③③
	Firezza	Pizza	②③④
	Benugo	Sandwiches, cakes, etc	④⑤③
	Azou	North African	③③②
	Sufi	Persian	③②④
	Best Mangal	Turkish	③③③
	Maxim	Chinese	③④④
	Anarkali	Indian	③②③
	Monty's	"	③③④
	Sagar	"	②②④
	Shilpa	Indian, Southern	①③⑤
	Kiraku	Japanese	①②③
	Okawari	"	③③④
	Tosa	"	③④④
	Esarn Kheaw	Thai	①③④
	Fat Boy's	"	③④③
	Pho	Vietnamese	②③③
£25+	Santa Maria	Pizza	②②②
	Gail's Bakery	Sandwiches, cakes, etc	③③④
	Wahaca	Mexican/TexMex	④③③
	Adams Café	Moroccan	③⓪②
	Chez Marcelle	Lebanese	①⑤⑤
	Alounak	Persian	③④③
	Faanoos	"	③③③
	Mohsen	"	②③⑤

	Atari-Ya	*Japanese*	❶❷④
	Jom Makan	*Malaysian*	④⑤⑤
	Hare & Tortoise	*Pan-Asian*	❸❸❸
	Bedlington Café	*Thai*	④❷⑤
£20+	Franco Manca	*Pizza*	❶❸❸
	Chiswick House Cafe	*Sandwiches, cakes, etc*	④⑤❸
	Abu Zaad	*Syrian*	❸❸④
	Gifto's	*Indian*	❷❸④
	Mirch Masala	*Pakistani*	❷④④
	Old Parr's Head	*Thai*	④④❸
£15+	Tortilla	*Mexican/TexMex*	❸❸④
	Comptoir Libanais	*Lebanese*	④⑤④
£10+	Kerbisher & Malt	*Fish & chips*	❷❸④

NORTH

Hampstead, West Hampstead, St John's Wood, Regent's Park, Kilburn & Camden Town (NW postcodes)

£70+	Landmark (Winter Gdn)	British, Modern	④❸❷
£60+	Gilbert Scott	British, Traditional	④❷❷
	Shaka Zulu	South African	⑤④❷
	Kaifeng	Chinese	❷❷④
	Gilgamesh	Pan-Asian	❸④❷
£50+	Bradley's	British, Modern	④④❸
	Odette's	"	❷❷❷
	St Pancras Grand	"	⑤⑤④
	L'Aventure	French	❷❷❶
	Oslo Court	"	❷④❷
	Villa Bianca	Italian	④❷❸
	York & Albany	"	④④④
	Gaucho	Steaks & grills	❸④❸
	Rôtisserie	"	④❸④
	Manna	Vegetarian	⑤④④
	Good Earth	Chinese	❸❸⑤
£40+	The Engineer	British, Modern	④④❷
	Freemasons Arms	"	⑤④❷
	The Horseshoe	"	④❸❸
	The Lansdowne	"	❸❸❷
	Market	"	❸❸④
	The North London Tavern	"	❸④❸
	The Wells	"	❸❷❷
	The Wet Fish Cafe	"	❸❷❷
	Bull & Last	British, Traditional	❶❷❷
	Holly Bush	"	❸❸❶
	La Cage Imaginaire	French	④❷❸
	Cocotte	"	④④❸
	Mill Lane Bistro	"	❸❷④
	Lemonia	Greek	⑤❷❷
	Retsina	"	❸❷❸
	The Arches	International	④❸❷
	Giraffe	"	⑤④④
	Spaniard's Inn	"	❸❸❶
	Artigiano	Italian	④❸④
	Caponata	"	❸❷❷
	La Collina	"	– – –
	Fratelli la Bufala	"	❸④④
	The Salt House	"	❸❸❷
	The Salusbury	"	❸❸❸
	Sardo Canale	"	④④④
	Sarracino	"	❷❷④
	Camden Brasserie	Mediterranean	④❸④
	Del'Aziz	"	④⑤❷
	Queen's Head & Artichoke	"	④④❸
	The Sea Shell	Fish & chips	❸❸❸
	Mestizo	Mexican/TexMex	❷❷④
	Mango Room	Afro-Caribbean	❸❷❷
	Solly's	Israeli	④⑤⑤

	Goldfish	Chinese	②	③	④
	Phoenix Palace	"	②	③	③
	Jin Kichi	Japanese	①	②	④
	Sushi-Say	"	①	①	③
	Singapore Garden	Malaysian	②	②	③
	XO	Pan-Asian	③	④	③
£35+	Belgo Noord	Belgian	④	④	③
	The Junction Tavern	British, Modern	③	②	②
	The Old Bull & Bush	"	⑤	⑤	②
	Prince Albert	"	③	③	③
	Rising Sun	"	②	②	③
	Walnut	"	③	②	②
	Kentish Canteen	British, Traditional	③	②	③
	L'Absinthe	French	③	①	②
	Somerstown Coffee House	"	④	③	③
	Swan & Edgar	International	④	④	②
	L'Artista	Italian	④	④	③
	Marine Ices	"	③	②	②
	Haché	Steaks & grills	③	③	③
	Harry Morgan's	Burgers, etc	②	③	③
	Nautilus	Fish & chips	②	②	④
	Skipjacks	"	①	②	⑤
	La Brocca	Pizza	④	④	③
	Sofra	Turkish	④	④	④
	Alisan	Chinese	①	②	④
	Gung-Ho	"	③	②	③
	Eriki	Indian	②	①	③
	Woodlands	"	③	③	④
	Sushi of Shiori	Japanese	①	①	④
	Yuzu	"	②	④	⑤
£30+	Made In Camden	British, Modern	③	③	④
	Carob Tree	Greek	④	②	④
	Daphne	"	③	①	①
	La Porchetta Pizzeria	Italian	③	③	③
	The Little Bay	Mediterranean	④	②	①
	Don Pepe	Spanish	③	②	③
	El Parador	"	②	①	③
	The Diner	Burgers, etc	⑤	⑤	③
	Fine Burger Company	"	④	④	④
	Basilico	Pizza	②	③	④
	Benugo	Sandwiches, cakes, etc	④	⑤	③
	Beyoglu	Turkish	③	④	④
	ping pong	Chinese, Dim sum	④	④	③
	Masala Zone	Indian	③	③	③
	Asakusa	Japanese	①	④	④
	Bento Cafe	"	②	②	④
	Café Japan	"	①	②	④
	Wagamama	"	④	③	④
	The Banana Tree Canteen	Pan-Asian	③	②	③
	dim T	"	⑤	④	③
£25+	Sea Pebbles	Fish & seafood	③	③	④
	Stringray Café	Mediterranean	④	④	④
	Trojka	Russian	④	④	③
	La Giralda	Spanish	③	②	③
	Chamomile	Sandwiches, cakes, etc	③	②	③

	Gail's Bread	"	❸❸④
	Kenwood (Brew House)	"	④④❷
	Green Cottage	Chinese	❷④⑤
	The Water Margin	"	❸❷④
	Chutneys	Indian	❸❸❸
	Diwana B-P House	"	❸⑤⑤
	Five Hot Chillies	"	❷④⑤
	Great Nepalese	"	❸❷⑤
	Kovalam	"	❷④⑤
	Vijay	"	❶❷④
	Atari-Ya	Japanese	❶❷④
£15+	Ali Baba	Egyptian	❸❷❸
	Geeta	Indian	❸❶⑤
	Sakonis	"	❸④⑤
£10+	Chop'd	Salads	❸❸④
£5+	Ginger & White	Sandwiches, cakes, etc	❸❷❷

Hoxton, Islington, Highgate, Crouch End, Stoke Newington, Finsbury Park, Muswell Hill & Finchley (N postcodes)

£70+	Fifteen Restaurant	Italian	⑤⑤⑤
£60+	Morgan M	French	❶❶❸
£50+	Frederick's	British, Modern	④④❷
	The Almeida	French	④❸④
	Bistro Aix	"	❷❷❷
	Fifteen Trattoria	Italian	④⑤④
	Rôtisserie	Steaks & grills	④❸④
£40+	The Albion	British, Modern	④④❷
	Bald Faced Stag	"	❸❷❷
	The Barnsbury	"	❸④❸
	The Clissold Arms	"	④④④
	The Drapers Arms	"	④④❸
	The Duke of Cambridge	"	④④❸
	The Fellow	"	④④④
	The Haven	"	④④④
	Hoxton Apprentice	"	❸④❷
	Mosaica	"	❸❷❸
	The Rose & Crown	"	④④④
	Rotunda Bar & Restaurant	"	④❸❷
	The Marquess Tavern	British, Traditional	❸❸❸
	St Johns	"	❷❷❷
	Chez Liline	Fish & seafood	❶❷⑤
	Les Associés	French	④❷④
	Fig	"	❶❷❷
	Banners	International	④④❸
	Browns	"	⑤④④
	The Flask	"	❸❸❷
	Giraffe	"	⑤④④
	Canonbury Kitchen	Italian	❸❷④
	Ottolenghi	"	❶❸❸
	Homa	Mediterranean	❸❸❸

Camino	Spanish	④	⑤	❸
Garufa	Steaks & grills	❸	④	❸
Il Bacio	Pizza	❸	④	④
Rodizio Rico	Brazilian	⑤	④	⑤
Sabor	South American	❸	⓿	❸
Roots At N1	Indian	❷	❷	④
Zaffrani	"	❸	❸	❸
Isarn	Thai	❷	⓿	❸
Yum Yum	"	❸	❸	❷

£35+	Charles Lamb	British, Modern	❸	❸	❷
	The Compass	"	❸	④	❸
	Juniper Dining	"	❷	❸	❸
	The Northgate	"	❷	❷	❸
	La Petite Auberge	French	④	❸	❷
	Le Sacré-Coeur	"	④	❷	❸
	The Real Greek	Greek	⑤	⑤	④
	The Orange Tree	International	❸	❸	❷
	500	Italian	⓿	⓿	❷
	Pizzeria Oregano	"	❸	❷	❸
	Rugoletta	"	❸	❸	❸
	San Daniele	"	❸	❸	❷
	Trullo	"	❷	⓿	❷
	Toff's	Fish & chips	❷	❷	④
	Two Brothers	"	❷	❸	④
	Furnace	Pizza	❸	❸	❸
	Mangal II	Turkish	❸	❸	④
	Rasa Travancore	Indian, Southern	❷	❷	❸
	Thai Square	Thai	④	❸	❸
	Viet Garden	Vietnamese	❸	❸	④

£30+	S & M Café	British, Traditional	④	④	④
	Kipferl	East & Cent. European	❸	❷	❷
	Blue Legume	French	❸	④	❷
	Vrisaki	Greek	④	❸	④
	Canta Napoli	Italian	❸	❸	④
	Pizzeria Pappagone	"	❸	❷	❸
	La Porchetta Pizzeria	"	❸	❸	❸
	Byron	Burgers, etc	❸	❸	❸
	Diner	"	⑤	⑤	❸
	Fine Burger Company	"	④	④	④
	Basilico	Pizza	❷	❸	④
	Firezza	"	❷	❸	④
	Gallipoli	Turkish	❸	④	❸
	Izgara	"	❸	❷	❸
	Petek	"	❷	❷	❷
	New Culture Rev'n	Chinese	❸	④	④
	Anglo Asian Tandoori	Indian	❷	⓿	❷
	Indian Rasoi	"	⓿	❷	❷
	Masala Zone	"	❸	❸	❸
	Wagamama	Japanese	④	❸	④
	dim T	Pan-Asian	⑤	④	❸
	Khoai Cafe	Vietnamese	❸	❸	④

£25+	Olympus Fish	Fish & seafood	❷	❷	④
	Le Mercury	French	④	❸	❷
	Mem & Laz	Mediterranean	④	❷	❷
	Stringray Café	"	④	④	④

	La Bota	*Spanish*	❸❷❸
	Rani	*Indian*	❷❸④
	Rasa	*Indian, Southern*	❶❶❷
	Dotori	*Korean*	❷❸❸
	Huong-Viet	*Vietnamese*	④⑤⑤
£20+	Gem	*Turkish*	❷❶❷
	19 Numara Bos Cirrik	*"*	❸❸④
	Afghan Kitchen	*Afghani*	❷④④
	Jai Krishna	*Indian*	❸❷❸
£15+	Café del Parc	*Spanish*	❷❷❷
	Tortilla	*Mexican/TexMex*	❸❸④
£10+	Chilango	*Mexican/TexMex*	❶❷④
£5+	Euphorium Bakery	*Sandwiches, cakes, etc*	❸④❸

SOUTH

South Bank (SE1)

£80+	Oxo Tower (Rest')	British, Modern	⑤⑤④
£70+	Oxo Tower (Brass')	Mediterranean	⑤④❸
£60+	Le Pont de la Tour	British, Modern	④❸❷
	Butlers W'f Chop-house	British, Traditional	④④❸
	Roast	"	❸④❸
	Brasserie Joël	French	❷④⑤
£50+	Blueprint Café	British, Modern	❸❸❶
	Cantina Vinopolis	"	④④④
	Magdalen	"	❶❷❷
	Skylon	"	④④❷
	Wright Brothers	Fish & seafood	❷❸❸
	Chez Gérard	French	⑤⑤⑤
	Vivat Bacchus	International	④④⑤
	La Barca	Italian	④❸❷
	Gaucho	Steaks & grills	❸④❸
£40+	Garrison	British, Modern	❸❸❶
	Menier Chocolate Factory	"	⑤④❷
	Mezzanine	"	④❸④
	RSJ	"	❸❷⑤
	The Swan at the Globe	"	④④❷
	The Table	"	④❸❸
	Waterloo Bar & Kitchen	"	④❸④
	Applebee's Cafe	Fish & seafood	❷❸④
	fish!	"	④⑤⑤
	Livebait	"	④④⑤
	Waterloo Brasserie	French	⑤⑤④
	Champor-Champor	Fusion	❷❷❷
	Village East	"	❸❷❷
	Browns	International	⑤④④
	Delfina	"	❸❸❸
	Giraffe	"	⑤④④
	Tate Modern (Level 7)	"	④④❷
	Cantina del Ponte	Italian	⑤④④
	Tentazioni	"	❸❸❸
	Zucca	"	❶❷❷
	Del'Aziz	Mediterranean	④⑤❷
	Baltic	Polish	④④④
	José	Spanish	– – –
	Archduke Wine Bar	Steaks & grills	⑤④④
	Black & Blue	"	④④④
	Constancia	Argentinian	❷❶❷
	Mango Tree	Indian	❷❸④
£35+	The Anchor & Hope	British, Traditional	❶❸❷
	Canteen	"	④④④
	Côte	French	④❸❷
	Real Greek	Greek	⑤⑤④
	The Riverfront	International	❷❷❸
	Tate Modern (Level 2)	"	❸④❸
	La Lanterna	Italian	❸❶❸

	Meson don Felipe	Spanish	4 4 2
	Tapas Brindisa	"	2 3 2
	Bengal Clipper	Indian	3 4 3
£30+	Gourmet Pizza Co.	Pizza	3 3 3
	Benugo	Sandwiches, cakes, etc	4 5 3
	Tas	Turkish	4 3 3
	Tas Pide	"	4 2 2
	ping pong	Chinese, Dim sum	4 4 3
	Bangalore Express	Indian	4 3 2
	Wagamama	Japanese	4 3 4
	dim T	Pan-Asian	5 4 3
£25+	Mar I Terra	Spanish	3 2 3
	Masters Super Fish	Fish & chips	2 4 5
	El Vergel	South American	2 2 2
	Simply Indian	Indian	3 4 4
	Tsuru	Japanese	3 4 4
£20+	Konditor & Cook	Sandwiches, cakes, etc	2 3 3
	Leon	"	3 3 3
£15+	Tortilla	Mexican/TexMex	3 3 4
£10+	Caffé Vergnano	Sandwiches, cakes, etc	4 3 3
	Monmouth Coffee Co	"	2 2 2
	Pod	"	3 4 4
	Spianata & Co	"	2 3 4

Greenwich, Lewisham, Dulwich & Blackheath
(All SE postcodes, except SE1)

£50+	Rivington Grill	British, Modern	3 4 4
	Lobster Pot	Fish & seafood	3 3 3
	The Spread Eagle	French	4 4 3
	Buenos Aires	Steaks & grills	3 3 3
	Gaucho	"	3 4 3
	Buenos Aires Cafe	Argentinian	3 3 3
£40+	Chapters	British, Modern	4 3 4
	Franklins	"	3 4 3
	Inside	"	2 2 4
	Simplicity	"	4 3 3
	The Tommyfield	"	5 5 4
	Le Chardon	French	4 5 4
	Joanna's	International	3 2 2
	The Trafalgar Tavern	"	5 4 3
	The Yellow House	"	2 2 4
	Babur	Indian	0 0 2
£35+	The Dartmouth Arms	British, Modern	3 3 2
	Florence	"	4 3 3
	The Old Brewery	"	4 4 2
	The Palmerston	"	2 2 3
	Brasserie Toulouse-Lautrec	French	4 2 2
	Le Querce	Italian	0 2 2
	Olley's	Fish & chips	3 3 4
	The Gowlett	Pizza	2 4 2

	Zero Degrees	"	③④②
	Angels & Gypsies	Cuban	②③②
	Dragon Castle	Chinese	②④④
	Kennington Tandoori	Indian	③②②
	Tandoori Nights	"	③③③
£30+	Green & Blue	International	④②②
	Rocca Di Papa	Pizza	④③③
	Peninsular	Chinese	②④④
	Everest Inn	Indian	②③②
	Ganapati	"	①①②
	Mogul	"	③②③
£25+	The Sea Cow	Fish & chips	③③③
	Gandhi's	Indian	③②③
£20+	Frizzante Cafe	Italian	③④③
	Thai Corner Café	Thai	③③③

Battersea, Brixton, Clapham, Wandsworth
Barnes, Putney & Wimbledon
(All SW postcodes south of the river)

£60+	Cannizaro House	British, Modern	④④③
	Chez Bruce	"	①①②
£50+	The Fire Stables	British, Modern	④④②
	Four O Nine	"	③②②
	Ransome's Dock	"	④③④
	Trinity	"	①①②
	Verta	"	④④④
	Bennett Oyster Bar	Fish & seafood	④⑤④
	Fish Place	"	②②⑤
	Enoteca Turi	Italian	①①③
	Riva	"	②②④
	San Lorenzo Fuoriporta	"	④⑤④
£40+	Bodean's	American	④⑤④
	The Abbeville	British, Modern	④③②
	Avalon	"	④③②
	The Bolingbroke	"	③③③
	The Brown Dog	"	③②②
	The Depot	"	③②①
	Earl Spencer	"	③③③
	Emile's	"	②①③
	Entrée	"	③④③
	Harrison's	"	④④③
	Lamberts	"	①①②
	The Prince Albert	"	④③②
	The Prince Of Wales	"	③④③
	Sonny's	"	④②③
	Tom Ilic	"	②②⑤
	The Victoria	"	③③②
	Fox & Grapes	British, Traditional	③④③
	Bellevue Rendez-Vous	French	②②②
	Brasserie James	"	④③④
	Le Cassoulet	"	③④③

Name	Cuisine	Ratings
Le Chardon	"	④⑤④
Gastro	"	④⑤❸
Upstairs Bar	"	❷⓿❶
Cafe Strudel	Hungarian	❸④④
Annie's	International	④❷❷
Brinkley's Kitchen	"	④❸❸
Giraffe	"	⑤④④
The Light House	"	❸❸❸
The Ship	"	❸❸❶
Cantinetta	Italian	④⑤❸
Donna Margherita	"	❷❸❷
Isola del Sole	"	❸⓿❷
Numero Uno	"	❸❷❸
Piccolino	"	④④④
The Fox & Hounds	Mediterranean	❷❷❷
La Mancha	Spanish	❸❷❸
Butcher & Grill	Steaks & grills	④❸④
Cattle Grid	"	④④④
Popeseye	"	⓿❷❸
Santa Maria del Sur	Argentinian	❷④❸
Royal China	Chinese	④④④
Bombay Bicycle Club	Indian	– – –
Indian Zilla	"	❷⓿❸
Cho-San	Japanese	❷❸④
Tsunami	"	⓿④❸
Suk Saran	Thai	❸④④
Thai on the River	"	❸④❸
£35+ Belgo	Belgian	④④❸
Alma	British, Modern	④⑤❸
Antelope	"	❷❸❷
The East Hill	"	❸❸❷
The Fentiman Arms	"	❸❸❷
The Lighthouse	"	❸❷❷
Scoffers	"	④⓿❷
The Tree House	"	④❸❷
Canton Arms	British, Traditional	❷❷⓿
Côte	French	④❸❷
Gazette	"	④④❷
Le P'tit Normand	"	❸❷❸
Hudsons	International	④④❸
Telegraph	"	④④❸
Antipasto & Pasta	Italian	❸❷❸
Buona Sera	"	❸⓿⓿
Ost. Antica Bologna	"	❸❸❸
Pizza Metro	"	❸❸❷
Valentina	"	❸❸❸
Putney Station	Mediterranean	④④❸
Lola Rojo	Spanish	❷❸❷
Rebato's	"	❷⓿⓿
Fish Club	Fish & chips	❷❷④
Al Forno	Pizza	❸❷❷
Eco	"	❸④❸
Doukan	Moroccan	❸❷❷
Bayee Village	Chinese	❸❸❷
Dalchini	"	❸❸④
Ma Goa	Indian	❷⓿❸
Mango & Silk	"	④④❸

	Thai Square	*Thai*	4 3 3
£30+	La Delizia	*Italian*	3 3 3
	Fish in a Tie	*Mediterranean*	4 2 1
	The Little Bay	*"*	4 2 1
	El Rincón Latino	*Spanish*	4 2 2
	Byron	*Burgers, etc*	3 3 3
	Brady's	*Fish & chips*	3 3 3
	Basilico	*Pizza*	2 3 4
	Firezza	*"*	2 3 4
	Cochin Brasserie	*Indian*	2 4 4
	Indian Moment	*"*	3 3 4
	Nazmins	*"*	3 2 4
	Cocum	*Indian, Southern*	3 3 3
	Wagamama	*Japanese*	4 3 4
	Cah-Chi	*Korean*	3 1 3
	The Banana Tree Canteen	*Pan-Asian*	3 2 3
	Amaranth	*Thai*	2 2 3
	Fat Boy's	*"*	3 4 3
	Thai Garden	*"*	3 4 4
£25+	Gail's Bread	*Sandwiches, cakes, etc*	3 3 4
	Faanoos	*Persian*	3 3 3
	Chutney	*Indian*	2 2 3
	Indian Ocean	*"*	2 3 3
	Sree Krishna	*"*	1 2 3
	Fujiyama	*Japanese*	3 3 4
	Slurp	*"*	3 3 5
	Hare & Tortoise	*Pan-Asian*	3 3 3
	The Pepper Tree	*Thai*	3 3 3
	Talad Thai	*"*	3 3 5
	The Paddyfield	*Vietnamese*	2 4 3
£20+	Franco Manca	*Pizza*	1 3 3
	Hot Stuff	*Indian*	2 1 2
	Lahore Kebab House	*Pakistani*	1 5 4
	Mirch Masala SW16	*"*	2 4 4
	Mien Tay	*Vietnamese*	1 4 4
£15+	Orange Pekoe	*Sandwiches, cakes, etc*	3 2 2
	Pantry	*"*	3 3 3
	Lahore Karahi	*Pakistani*	1 4 4

Outer western suburbs
Kew, Richmond, Twickenham, Teddington

£80+	The Bingham	*British, Modern*	4 4 3
£60+	Petersham Hotel	*British, Modern*	3 2 2
£50+	The Glasshouse	*British, Modern*	1 1 3
	Petersham Nurseries	*"*	2 4 1
	Rock & Rose	*"*	4 3 1
	The Wharf	*"*	4 2 2
	Brula	*French*	2 1 1
	Gaucho	*Steaks & grills*	3 4 3
	Kew Grill	*"*	3 2 4

£40+	Plane Food	British, Modern	④❸④
	Chez Lindsay	French	④❸④
	Ma Cuisine	"	④❸④
	A Cena	Italian	❷❷❷
	Scarpetta	"	❸❸④
	don Fernando's	Spanish	❸❷❸
	Four Regions	Chinese	❸❷④
	Tangawizi	Indian	❸❸④
	Matsuba	Japanese	❷❸④
£35+	Brouge	Belgian	④❸❷
	La Buvette	French	❸❷❶
	Palmyra	Lebanese	❸❷④
	Origin Asia	Indian	❷❷❸
£30+	O'Zon	Chinese	❸④④
	Fat Boy's	Thai	❸④❸
£25+	Stein's	German	❸④❷
£15+	William Curley	Sandwiches, cakes, etc	❶❸❸

EAST

Smithfield & Farringdon (EC1)

Price	Name	Cuisine			
£70+	St John	British, Traditional	2	3	4
	Club Gascon	French	2	2	3
	Dans le Noir	International	5	4	1
£60+	Hix	British, Traditional	2	3	3
	Bleeding Heart	French	2	2	2
	Portal	Mediterranean	2	2	2
	Smiths (Top Floor)	Steaks & grills	4	4	3
£50+	Bistro du Vin	British, Modern	4	3	4
	Chiswell Street Dining Rms	"	3	2	3
	Malmaison Brasserie	"	4	3	3
	North Road	"	2	3	4
	Smithfield Bar & Grill	"	4	4	4
	Café du Marché	French	2	2	1
	Le Saint Julien	"	4	2	4
	Alba	Italian	3	2	4
	Gaucho	Steaks & grills	3	4	3
	Smiths (Dining Rm)	"	4	4	3
£40+	Ambassador	British, Modern	3	3	3
	Coach & Horses	"	2	2	3
	The Larder	"	4	3	4
	The Modern Pantry	"	3	3	3
	The Peasant	"	4	3	3
	The Well	"	3	4	3
	The English Pig	British, Traditional	2	2	4
	The Fox and Anchor	"	3	2	1
	Bistrot Bruno Loubet	French	2	2	3
	Comptoir Gascon	"	2	3	2
	Le Rendezvous du Café	"	3	2	2
	$	International	4	4	3
	Fabrizio	Italian	2	0	4
	Moro	Spanish	2	2	3
	A La Cruz	Steaks & grills	3	3	4
	Redhook	"	4	4	3
	Carnevale	Vegetarian	3	2	4
	Saki	Japanese	2	3	4
	54 Farringdon Road	Malaysian	3	3	4
	Cicada	Pan-Asian	2	2	3
£35+	Giant Robot	American	3	4	2
	Caravan	British, Modern	2	2	0
	Vinoteca	"	3	2	0
	Cellar Gascon	French	3	3	2
	Santore	Italian	3	2	3
	Amico Bio	Vegetarian	4	4	4
	Busaba Eathai	Thai	3	3	2
	Cây Tre	Vietnamese	2	4	4
£30+	La Porchetta Pizzeria	Italian	3	3	3
	The Little Bay	Mediterranean	4	2	0
	Pinchito	Spanish	4	3	0
	Benugo	Sandwiches, cakes, etc	4	5	3

			Rating
	Tas	*Turkish*	④❸❸
	Pham Sushi	*Japanese*	❶④④
	Tajima Tei	"	❶②④
	Banana Tree Canteen	*Pan-Asian*	❸②❸
	Pho	*Vietnamese*	❷❸❸
£25+	Smiths (Ground Floor)	*British, Modern*	④④❷
	Cock Tavern	*British, Traditional*	❸④④
	Fish Central	*Fish & seafood*	❷❷❸
	Kolossi Grill	*Greek*	④❷❷
	The Eagle	*Mediterranean*	❸④❶
	Gail's Bakery	*Sandwiches, cakes, etc*	❸❸④
£20+	Morito	*Spanish*	❷❷❷
	Sedap	*Malaysian*	❸④⑤
£15+	Abokado	*Japanese*	④❸④
£10+	Dose	*Sandwiches, cakes, etc*	❷❶④
	Nusa Kitchen	"	❷④④
	Pod	"	❸④④
	Spianata & Co	"	❷❸④
£5+	The Farm Collective	*British, Traditional*	❷❸❸
	Pizzeria Malletti	*Pizza*	❷❸❸

The City (EC2, EC3, EC4)

			Rating
£80+	Rhodes 24	*British, Modern*	❸❸❸
£60+	1 Lombard Street	*British, Modern*	④④④
	Prism	"	④④④
	Vertigo 42	"	④❸❶
	Green's	*British, Traditional*	❷❷❷
	Chamberlain's	*Fish & seafood*	❸❸④
	Coq d'Argent	*French*	④⑤④
	Lutyens	"	❸❸④
	1901	"	④❸❸
	L'Anima	*Italian*	❸❸❸
	Caravaggio	"	④④④
	Bonds	*Mediterranean*	④④④
	Goodman City	*Steaks & grills*	❷❷❸
	Bevis Marks	*Kosher*	❸❸❸
	Mint Leaf	*Indian*	❸④❸
£50+	Barbecoa	*American*	④④④
	The Chancery	*British, Modern*	❷❸④
	The Don	"	❸❷❸
	High Timber	"	❸❷❸
	The Mercer	"	❸❷❸
	Northbank	"	❸❸❷
	Rivington Grill	"	❸④④
	Searcy's Brasserie	"	④④❸
	Paternoster Chop House	*British, Traditional*	⑤⑤④
	Catch	*Fish & seafood*	④④④
	Sweetings	"	❸❸❸
	Chez Gérard	*French*	⑤⑤⑤

	Name	Cuisine			
	Sauterelle	"	④	❸	❸
	Vivat Bacchus	International	④	④	⑤
	Manicomio	Italian	❸	④	❸
	Refettorio	"	④	④	④
	Boisdale of Bishopsgate	Scottish	❸	❸	❸
	Eyre Brothers	Spanish	❸	❸	❸
	Gaucho	Steaks & grills	❸	④	❸
	Hawksmoor	"	❷	❷	❷
	Kenza	Lebanese	④	④	❸
	Cinnamon Kitchen	Indian	❷	❸	④
	City Miyama	Japanese	❷	④	⑤
	Soseki	"	❷	❷	❷
£40+	Bodean's	American	④	⑤	④
	The Hoxton Grill	"	❸	❸	❷
	Princess of Shoreditch	British, Modern	❷	❸	❸
	The White Swan	"	❷	❸	④
	George & Vulture	British, Traditional	⑤	④	❷
	Gow's	Fish & seafood	④	❸	❸
	Loch Fyne	"	④	④	④
	Bar Battu	French	❸	❸	❸
	Brasserie Blanc	"	❸	❸	❸
	Luc's Brasserie	"	④	❸	❷
	Relais de Venise L'Entrecôte	"	❷	❸	❸
	The Royal Exchange	"	④	④	❶
	28-50	"	❸	❷	❸
	Browns	International	⑤	④	④
	Bertorelli	Italian	⑤	⑤	⑤
	Osteria Appennino	"	❷	④	④
	Piccolino	"	④	④	④
	Taberna Etrusca	"	④	④	④
	Terranostra	"	❸	❷	④
	Rocket	Mediterranean	④	④	❸
	Saf	Vegetarian	❷	④	④
	Vanilla Black	"	❷	❷	④
	Goldfish City	Chinese	❷	❸	④
	Imperial City	"	④	❸	❸
	Anokha Restaurant	Indian	❷	❸	❸
	Mugen	Japanese	❸	❷	❸
	Gt Eastern Dining Room	Pan-Asian	❷	❸	❷
	Pacific Oriental	"	④	❸	❸
£35+	Café Below	British, Modern	❸	❸	❸
	The Fox	"	❸	④	❸
	London Wall Bar & Kitchen	"	④	④	❸
	The Restaurant at St Paul's	"	❸	④	❸
	Ye Olde Cheshire Cheese	British, Traditional	④	④	❶
	Simpson's Tavern	"	④	❸	❶
	Côte	French	④	❷	❷
	Haz	Turkish	❸	❸	❷
	Chinese Cricket Club	Chinese	❸	④	⑤
	K10	Japanese	❸	❸	④
	Kurumaya	"	❷	❷	④
	Thai Square City	Thai	④	❸	❸
£30+	Byron	Burgers, etc	❸	❸	❸
	The Diner	"	⑤	⑤	❸
	Natural Kitchen	Salads	❸	❸	❸

	ping pong	Chinese, Dim sum	④④❸
	Bangalore Express	Indian	④❸❷
	Wagamama	Japanese	④❸④
£25+	Hilliard	British, Modern	❷❷❸
	The Punch Tavern	International	❸④❸
	The Wine Library	"	⑤❸❶
	Tsuru	Japanese	❸④④
	Hare & Tortoise	Pan-Asian	❸❸❸
£20+	Napket	Afternoon tea	④④❸
	Konditor & Cook	Sandwiches, cakes, etc	❷❸❸
	Leon	"	❸❸❸
£15+	Hummus Bros	Mediterranean	❷❷④
	Tortilla	Mexican/TexMex	❸❸④
	Abokado	Japanese	④❸④
£10+	Caffè Vergnano	Sandwiches, cakes, etc	④❸❸
	Fuzzy's Grub	"	④④④
	Nusa Kitchen	"	❷④④
	Pod	"	❸④④
	Spianata & Co	"	❷❸④
	Chop'd	Salads	❸❸④
	Chilango	Mexican/TexMex	❶❷④

East End & Docklands (All E postcodes)

£90+	Viajante	Fusion	❷❷❸
£70+	Roka	Japanese	❶❸❷
£60+	Beach Blanket Babylon	British, Modern	⑤⑤❶
	The Boundary	"	❸❸❷
	Le Bouchon Breton	French	④⑤⑤
	Galvin La Chapelle	"	❷❶❶
	Plateau	"	⑤④④
	Les Trois Garçons	"	❸❸❶
	Quadrato	Italian	④④⑤
£50+	Bistrotheque	British, Modern	④④❶
	The Gun	"	❷④❷
	The Narrow	"	④④④
	Tompkins	"	⑤④④
	St John Bread & Wine	British, Traditional	❶❷❷
	Curve	Fish & seafood	❸④④
	Forman's	"	❷❷④
	Boisdale of Canary Wharf	Scottish	④④❸
	Gaucho	Steaks & grills	❸④❸
	Hawksmoor	"	❷❷❷
	MPW Steakhouse & Grill	"	④④⑤
	Café Spice Namaste	Indian	❶❶❸
	Dockmaster's House	"	④④❸
£40+	All Star Lanes	American	④⑤❸
	The Empress of India	British, Modern	❸❸❷
	The Morgan Arms	"	❸❷❷
	The Parlour Bar	"	⑤⑤⑤

Wapping Food	"	❸❹❶
Albion	British, Traditional	❸❸❷
The Grapes	Fish & seafood	❸❸❷
Brawn	French	❶❷❷
Browns	International	⑤④④
Giraffe	"	⑤④④
The Luxe	"	⑤⑤④
Amerigo Vespucci	Italian	④④❸
Il Bordello	"	❷⓿❷
Jamie's Italian	"	④❸④
Ibérica	Spanish	❸❸❸
Ark Fish	Fish & chips	⓿❷④
Pizza East	Pizza	❸❹❶
Rocket	"	④④❸
Buen Ayre	Argentinian	❶❸❸
Royal China	Chinese	❷④④
Yi-Ban	"	❸④④
Elephant Royale	Thai	④❸❸
£35+	Whitechapel Gallery	British, Modern	– – –
	Canteen	British, Traditional	④④④
	Real Greek	Greek	⑤⑤④
	LMNT	International	❸❷❶
	La Figa	Italian	❸❷❸
	Corner Room	Portuguese	– – –
	Fire & Stone	Pizza	④❸❸
	Haz	Turkish	❸❸❷
	Lotus	Chinese	④④❸
	Rasa Mudra	Indian	❷❷❸
£30+	Rochelle Canteen	British, Modern	❷⓿❷
	S & M Café	British, Traditional	④④④
	Al Volo	Italian	❷④❸
	Byron	Burgers, etc	❸❸❸
	Gourmet Pizza Co.	Pizza	❸❸❸
	Hazev	Turkish	④④④
	My Old Place	Chinese	❷⑤④
	Shanghai	"	❸❸❶
	ping pong	Chinese, Dim sum	④④❸
	Memsaheb on Thames	Indian	④❷❸
	Itsu	Japanese	④④④
	Wagamama	"	④❸④
	Rosa's	Thai	❸④❸
	Green Papaya	Vietnamese	❷❷❷
	Namo	"	❸❸❸
	Viet Grill	"	❷④❷
£25+	Frizzante at City Farm	Italian	❸❸❷
	Stringray Globe Café	Mediterranean	④④④
	Faulkner's	Fish & chips	❷❷❸
	Wahaca	Mexican/TexMex	④❸❸
	Mangal I	Turkish	⓿❷❸
	Little Georgia Café	Georgian	❸❸❸
	Clifton	Indian	❸❸❸
	Needoo	Pakistani	⓿❸④
	New Tayyabs	"	⓿④❸
	Sông Quê	Vietnamese	❷⑤⑤
	Viet Hoa	"	❷④④

£20+	Leon	Sandwiches, cakes, etc	❸❸❸
	Gourmet San	Chinese	❷④⑤
	Lahore Kebab House	Pakistani	❶⑤④
	Mirch Masala	"	❷④④
	Mien Tay	Vietnamese	❶④④
£15+	Tortilla	Mexican/TexMex	❸❸④
£10+	E Pellicci	Italian	❸❷❶
	Spianata & Co	Sandwiches, cakes, etc	❷❸④
	Chop'd	Salads	❸❸④
	Sweet & Spicy	Indian	❷❷⑤
£5+	Brick Lane Beigel Bake	Sandwiches, cakes, etc	❶④⑤

MAP 1 - LONDON OVERVIEW

A

Skipjacks

NORTH

- - - - - - - -

Brent

A5

B

Rising Sun
Atari-Ya, Good Earth
Kaifeng Olympus Fish
Rani Solly's
Water Margin

Toffs,
Orange Khoai C
Tree, Canta Nap

Haven
Two Brothers
Izgara

Indian Ra
Bald Face
Stag, Rug

L'Artista
Café Japan
Rôtisserie

Map 8

Hampstea

I

Giralda, Sea Pebbles

Rôtisserie

Five Hot Chillies
• Alisan

• Sakonis

Wembley

Basilico •
Nautilus, Yuzu •
Mill Lane Bistro
Brocca, Walnut,
Wet Fish Café, Rôtisserie

Gung-Ho

West
Hampstead

Sarracino
Banana Tree •

Sushi Say •

Vijay • • Geeta

North London Tavern •

The Salusbury •

Kovalam •

Little Bay •

Cochonnet •

Kilburn

Regen
Park

• Diner
Paradise • Ida •
Dock Kitchen •

2

North Circular Road A406

A40

Map 6

Acton

Notting Hill

Fat Boy's, Monty's

Hare & Tortoise

Monty's

WEST

- - - - - - -

Okawari

Kiraku,
Atari-Ya,
Charlotte's Place
Santa Maria

Map 7

Map 5

Chiswick

Chelsea

Madhu's, Mirch Masala,
Gifto's,
Brilliant
Ealing Park
Tavern

3 *M4*

← Maxim
← Plane Food

Map 10

Fat Boy's   Annie's

← Kew Grill

Palmyra •

Ma Cuisine,
Glasshouse,

Valentina,
Mango & Silk •

Battersea

Fulham

on
ernando's
• Four Regions,
Rock & Rose
William Curley
• Buvette
• Origin Asia
Brouge
• Matsuba
Chez Lindsay, Gaucho Grill, Bingham
Stein's
A Cena
Brula
Fat Boy's
← Petersham Hotel
O'Zon,
Tangawizi
Brouge
← Petersham Nurseries
← Wharf, Scarpetta

Fat Boy's, Faanoos, Cafe Strudel

Putney

Wandsworth

Richmond

Kew

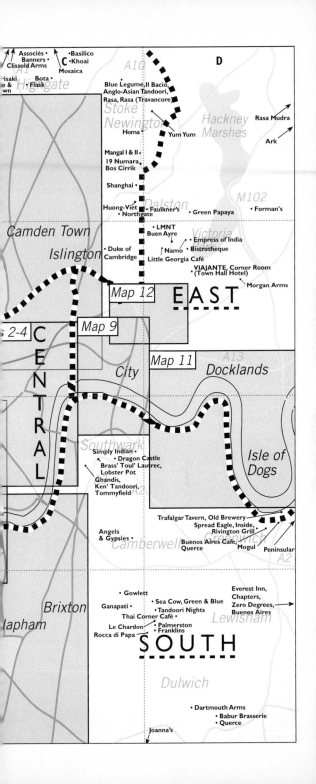

Associés •
Banners •
Clissold Arms
C •Khoai
•Basilico
Mosaica

•risaki
e &
wn

Bota •
• Flask

Highgate

A1

D

A10

Blue Legume, Il Bacio,
Anglo-Asian Tandoori,
Rasa, Rasa (Travancore)

Stoke
Newington

Hackney
Marshes

Rasa Mudra →

Homa •

Yum Yum

Ark →

Mangal I & II •
19 Numara,
Bos Cirrik

Shanghai •

Dalston

M102

Huong-Viet • • Faulkner's
• Northgate

• Green Papaya

• Forman's

Camden Town

• LMNT
Buen Ayre

Victoria

• Empress of India
↑ Namo • Bistrotheque

Islington

• Duke of
Cambridge

Little Georgia Café

• VIAJANTE, Corner Room
(Town Hall Hotel)

Morgan Arms

Map 12

E A S T

2-4

C

Map 9

**E
N
T
R
A
L**

City

Map 11

A13

Docklands

Southwark

Simply Indian •
• Dragon Castle
Brass' Toul' Lautrec,
Lobster Pot
Ghandis,
Ken' Tandoori,
Tommyfield

A2

**Isle of
Dogs**

Trafalgar Tavern, Old Brewery
Spread Eagle, Inside,
Rivington Grill
Buenos Aires Cafe,
Querce

Mogul

Peninsular

Angels
& Gypsies •

Camberwell

A2

Brixton

• Gowlett

• Sea Cow, Green & Blue

Everest Inn,
Chapters,
Zero Degrees,
Buenos Aires →

Ganapati •
• Tandoori Nights
Thai Corner Café •

Lewisham

lapham

Le Chardon •
Rocca di Papa •

• Palmerston
• Franklins

S O U T H

Dulwich

• Dartmouth Arms
• Babur Brasserie
• Querce

Joanna's ↓

MAP 2 - WEST END OVERVIEW

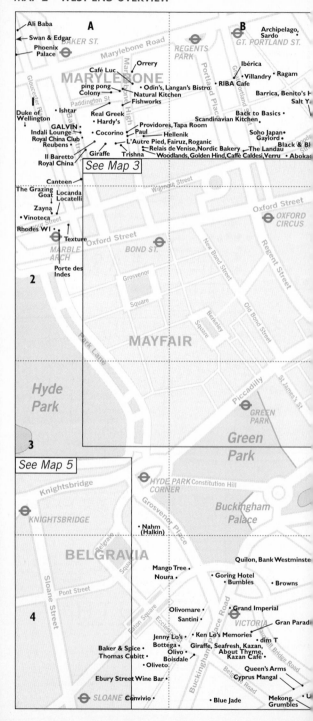

← Ali Baba

← Swan & Edgar

← Phoenix Palace

A

B

Archipelago, Sardo

GT. PORTLAND ST.

BAKER ST.

Marylebone Road

REGENTS PARK

Ibérica

Café Luc • Orrery

• Villandry • Ragam

MARYLEBONE

RIBA Cafe

ping pong • Odin's, Langan's Bistro

Colony • Natural Kitchen

Barrica, Benito's H

Paddington St • Fishworks

Salt Ya

• Ishtar

Real Greek

Back to Basics

Duke of Wellington

• Hardy's

Scandinavian Kitchen

GALVIN •

Providores, Tapa Room

Soho Japan •

Indali Lounge

• Cocorino Paul — Hellenik

Gaylord •

Royal China Club

L'Autre Pied, Fairuz, Roganic

Black & Bl

Reubens •

Relais de Venise, Nordic Bakery — The Landau

Il Baretto Giraffe Trishna

Woodlands, Golden Hind, Caffè Caldesi, Verru • Aboka

Royal China

See Map 3

Canteen

Wigmore Street

The Grazing Goat Locanda

Oxford Street

Zayna Locatelli

OXFORD CIRCUS

• Vinoteca

Rhodes W1 •

Texture Oxford Street

MARBLE ARCH

BOND ST.

New Bond Street

Regent Street

Grosvenor

2

Porte des Indes

Square

Old Bond Street

MAYFAIR

Berkeley

Park Lane

Square

Hyde Park

Piccadilly

St James's St.

GREEN PARK

3

Green Park

See Map 5

HYDE PARK CORNER Constitution Hill

Knightsbridge

Grosvenor Place

Buckingham Palace

KNIGHTSBRIDGE

Belgrave

• Nahm (Halkin)

BELGRAVIA

Quilon, Bank Westminste

Mango Tree •

• Goring Hotel

Noura •

• Bumbles • Browns

Sloane Street

Pont Street

Olivomare •

• Grand Imperial

Santini •

VICTORIA — Gran Parad

Eccleston

Eaton Square

Jenny Lo's • • Ken Lo's Memories • dim T

Bottega • Giraffe, Seafresh, Kazan,

Baker & Spice Olivo • About Thyme,

Thomas Cubitt • Boisdale Kazan Café

Buckingham Palace Road

• Oliveto

Queen's Arms

Ebury Street Wine Bar •

Cyprus Mangal

Belg

Road

SLOANE Convivio •

Mekong, Grumbles

• Blue Jade

• U

4

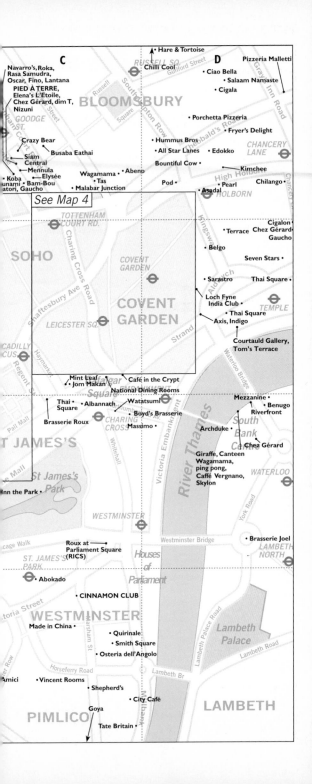

MAP 3 - MAYFAIR, ST JAMES'S & WEST SOHO

Defune •

• Fromagerie Café •

A

B

• Union Café

• Wallace   • Cocorino, Samarqand

2 Veneti •

Baker St

• Levant •

Wigmore Street

1

Black & Blue •

• Comptoir Libanais

Wagamama •

James Street

Guerilla Burgers

ping pong •   • Sofra

• Maroush

Atari-Ya •

Busaba Eathai •

Ed's Easy Diner

• Daylesford Organic

Bar Trattoria Semplice •

Rasa •

Oxford Street

Ristorante Semplice •

BOND
STREET

Napke

Ikeda •

North Audley Street

Petite Maison •

Hush, Rocket, Mews of Mayfair

2

Genova •

• Princess Garden

Maze, Maze Grill •

Brook Street

• Gordon Ramsay
at Claridge's

Saga

Truc Vert •

GAVROCHE •

*Grosvenor
Square*

Bellan

34 Grosvenor Square •

Grosvenor Street

C London •

Guinea •

Hélène Darroze (Connaught) •

• Serafino

Berkele Squ

← Corrigan's

Delfino •

Benares •

SCOTT'S •

Mount Street

← JW Steakhouse
(Grosvenor House)

• Mount Street Deli

3

South Audley Street

Kai •

Only Running Footm
•

Park Lane

Park Lane

• Greenhouse

• Dorchester
(Alain Ducasse,
China Tang, Grill Room)

Tamarind •
Murano •

Chop'd
Tempo •

Benugo, Noura •

Miyama •

Curzon Street

Boudin Blanc •

• Cut
(45 Park Lane)

Al Hamra •

• Artiste Mu
Kiko

Al Sultan •   • Sofra

*Hyde
Park*

4

• El Pirata

Galvin at Windows (Hilton) •

• Nobu
(Metropolitan)

Athenaeum •

Amaranto (Four Seasons) •

Piccadilly

Theo Randall (InterContinental) •

• Hard Rock Café

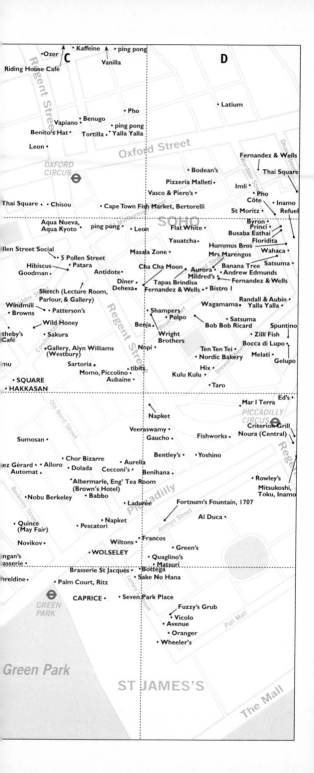

•Ozer • Kaffeine • ping pong
C **D**
Riding House Café Vanilla

•Latium

•Pho
Vapiano • Benugo
Benito's Hat • • ping pong
Tortilla • Yalla Yalla
Leon •

Oxford Street

OXFORD CIRCUS ⊖

Fernandez & Wells
Thai Square

•Bodean's
Pizzeria Malleti •
Imli •
Thai Square • • Chisou Vasco & Piero's • •Pho
Côte
•Cape Town Fish Market, Bertorelli St Moritz • •Inamo
Refuel

Aqua Nueva, Byron •
Aqua Kyoto ping pong •Leon Flat White • Princi
Busaba Eathai
Yauatcha • Floridita
llen Street Social Hummus Bros • Wahaca
•5 Pollen Street Masala Zone • Mrs Marengos
Hibiscus Cha Cha Moon • Banana Tree Satsuma
Goodman • •Patara Antidote • Aurora • •Andrew Edmunds
Diner • Tapas Brindisa Mildred's • Fernandez & Wells
Dehesa • Fernandez & Wells • Bistro 1
Sketch (Lecture Room,
Parlour, & Gallery) Wagamama • Randall & Aubin •
Windmill • Yalla Yalla •
•Browns •Patterson's Shampers •
Wild Honey •Polpo • Satsuma
theby's Benja • Bob Bob Ricard Spuntino •
Café •Sakura Wright • Zilli Fish
Brothers Bocca di Lupo •
•Gallery, Alyn Williams Nopi • Melati •
(Westbury) Ten Ten Tei • Gelupo
mu Sartoria • • tibits • Nordic Bakery
Momo, Piccolino • Hix •
•SQUARE Aubaine • Kulu Kulu •
•HAKKASAN •Taro

Ed's •
Mar I Terra • *PICCADILLY*
Napket *CIRCUS* ⊖
Criterion Grill
Veeraswamy • Noura (Central) •
Sumosan • Gaucho • Fishworks •

Bentley's • •Yoshino
ez Gérard • •Alloro •Chor Bizarre •Aurelia
Automat • •Dolada Cecconi's • Benihana •
•Albermarle, Eng' Tea Room •Rowley's
•Nobu Berkeley (Brown's Hotel) Mitsukoshi,
•Babbo Toku, Inamo

•Ladurée Fortnum's Fountain, 1707
•Quince •Napket
(May Fair) •Pescatori Al Duca •
Novikov • Wiltons • Francos
•WOLSELEY • Green's
ngan's •Quaglino's
asserie • Brasserie St Jacques • •Matsuri
•Bottega
hreldine • •Palm Court, Ritz Sake No Hana
⊖ CAPRICE • •Seven Park Place
GREEN PARK Fuzzy's Grub
• Vicolo
• Avenue
• Oranger
• Wheeler's

Green Park

ST JAMES'S

The Mall

MAP 4 - EAST SOHO, CHINATOWN & COVENT GARDEN

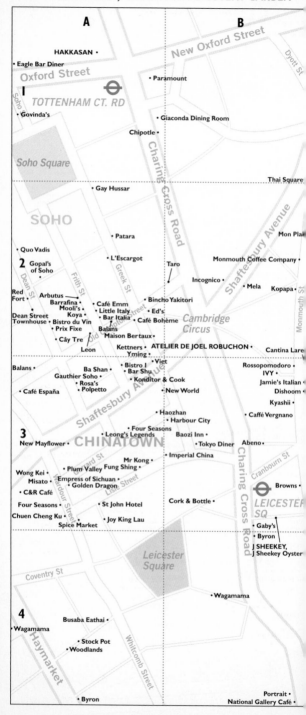

A   B

New Oxford Street

• HAKKASAN •

• Eagle Bar Diner

Oxford Street

Dyott St

• Paramount

TOTTENHAM CT. RD

• Govinda's

• Giaconda Dining Room

Chipotle •

Soho Square

Thai Square

• Gay Hussar

SOHO

Charing Cross Road

Shaftesbury Avenue

• Patara

• Mon Plai

2 • Quo Vadis

• Gopal's of Soho

• L'Escargot

Taro

Monmouth Coffee Company •

Incognico •

• Mela

Kopapa •

Red Fort •

Arbutus

Barrafina •
Mooli's •
Koya •

• Café Emm

• Bincho Yakitori

Dean Street Townhouse

• Bistro du Vin
• Prix Fixe

• Little Italy
• Bar Italia

• Ed's

Monmouth St

• Câv Tre

Balans
Maison Bertaux •

• Café Bohème

Cambridge Circus

Leon

Kettners •

Yming

ATELIER DE JOEL ROBUCHON •

Cantina Lare

Balans •

Ba Shan •

Gauthier Soho •
• Rosa's
• Polpetto

• Bistro 1
• Bar Shu

• Konditor & Cook

• Viet

Rossopomodoro •

IVY •

Jamie's Italian •

• Café España

Shaftesbury Avenue

• New World

Dishoom •

Kyashii •

• Haozhan

• Caffè Vergnano

• Harbour City

3 New Mayflower •

• Four Seasons

Leong's Legends •

CHINATOWN

Baozi Inn •

Four Seasons

• Tokyo Diner

Abeno •

Wong Kei •

Misato •

Mr Kong •

• Plum Valley Fung Shing •

Empress of Sichuan •
Golden Dragon •

• Imperial China

Charing Cross Road

Cranbourn St

• Browns •

LEICESTER SQ

• C&R Café

Four Seasons •

Chuen Cheng Ku •

• St John Hotel

• Joy King Lau

Cork & Bottle •

• Gaby's

• Byron

J SHEEKEY,

Spice Market •

J Sheekey Oyster

Leicester Square

Coventry St

• Wagamama

4 • Wagamama

Busaba Eathai •

Whitcomb Street

Haymarket

• Stock Pot

• Woodlands

• Byron

Portrait

National Gallery Café •

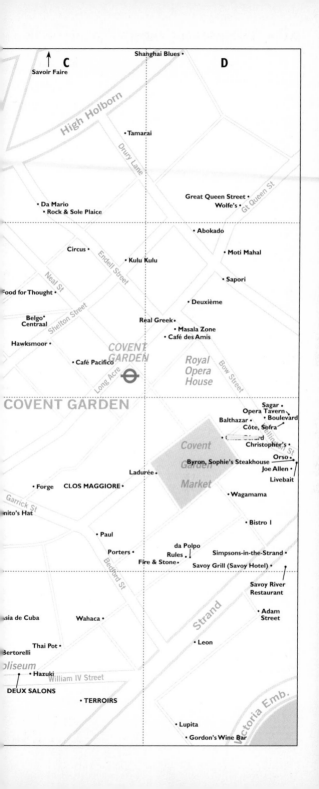

MAP 5 - KNIGHTSBRIDGE, CHELSEA & SOUTH KENSINGTON

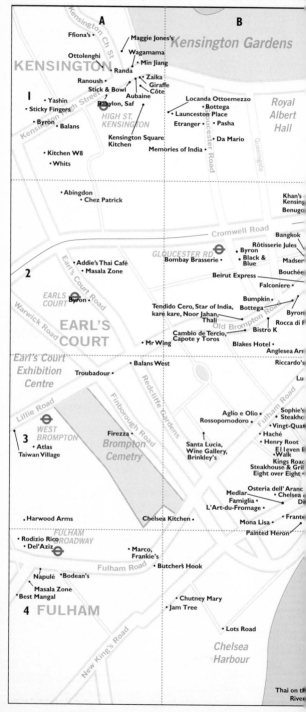

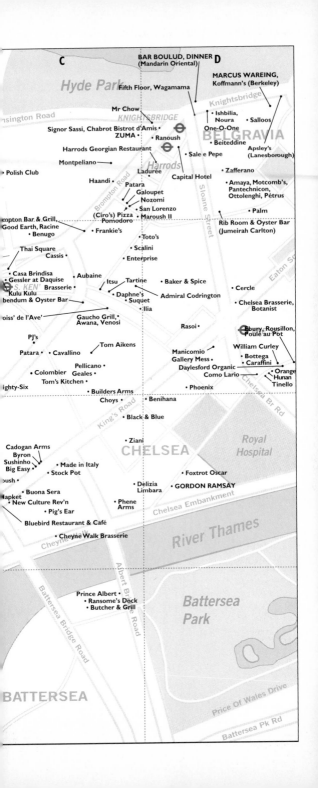

MAP 6 - NOTTING HILL & BAYSWATER

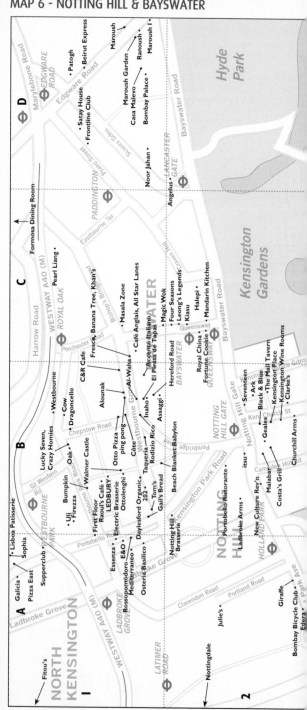

Hyde Park

Kensington Gardens

Maroush
Beirut Express
Patogh
Maroush Garden
Ranoush I
Casa Malevo
Bombay Palace
Satay House
Frontline Club
Noor Jahan

Angelus

Formosa Dining Room

Pearl Liang

WESTWAY A40 (M)

ROYAL OAK

Westbourne
Cow
Dragoncello
Oak

Fresco, Banana Tree, Khan's
Masala Zone
Café Anglais, All Star Lanes
Accento Italiano
El Pirata de Tapas

Magic Wok
Four Seasons
Leong's Legends, Kiasu
Halepi
Mandarin Kitchen

C&R Cafe
Al-Waha
Alounak
Inaho
Assaggi

Hereford Road
Royal China
Fortune Cookie

Lucky Seven,
Crazy Homies
Walmer Castle
Otto Pizza
ping pong
Côte
Taqueria
Rodizio Rico
Tom's
Gail's Bread

Beach Blanket Babylon

Seventeen
Ark
Black & Blue
The Mall Tavern
Kensington Place
Kensington Wine Rooms
Clarke's

Geales
itsu

Churchill Arms

Uli
Firezza
First Floor
Raoul's Café
Electric Brasserie
Ottolenghi
LEDBURY
Daylesford Organic
202
Notting Hill
Brasserie

Fitou's
Lisboa Patisserie
Sophia
Galicia
Pizza East
Supperclub
Esenza
Rossopomodoro E&O
Mediterraneo
Osteria Basilico

New Culture Rev'n
Malabar
Costa's Grill

Ladbroke Arms
Portobello Ristorante

Julie's

Bombay Bicycle Club
Edera
Giraffe

Nottingdale

NORTH
KENSINGTON

NOTTING
HILL

HOLLAND PARK

MAP 7 - HAMMERSMITH & CHISWICK

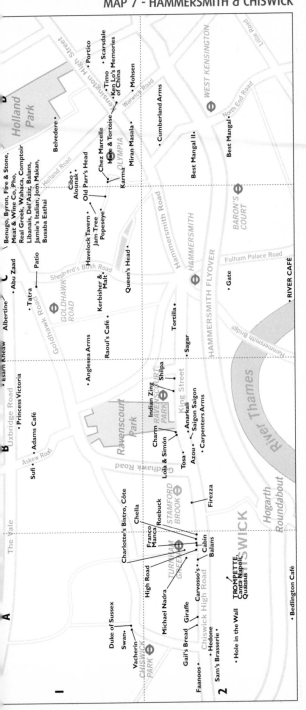

Holland Park

Benugo, Byron, Fire & Stone,
Meat & Wine Co, Pho,
Real Greek, Wahaca, Comptoir
Libanais, Del'Aziz, Balans,
Jamie's Italian, Jom Makan,
Busaba Eathai

Kensington High Street

Timo • Scarsdale
Portico
Ken Lo's Memories
of China
Mohsen

Belvedere •

WEST KENSINGTON

Cibo •
Alounak •
Old Parr's Head •
Havelock Tavern •
Jam Tree •
Popeseye •

Chez Marcelle
Hare & Tortoise •
OLYMPIA
Karma
Miran Masala •

Cumberland Arms •

Holland Road

Warwick Road

Abu Zaad
Patio

Albertine

• Tatra

Esarn Kheaw

Uxbridge Road

GOLDHAWK
ROAD

Shepherd's Bush Road

Kerbisher &
Malt

Queen's Head •

Hammersmith Road

HAMMERSMITH

Best Mangal II •

BARON'S
COURT

Best Mangal •

North End Road

Lillie Road

Princess Victoria •

Sufi • • Adams Café

Askew Road

The Vale

Raoul's Café •

Anglesea Arms •

Goldhawk Road

Ravenscourt
Park

Indian Zing
RAVENSCOURT
PARK
Charm
Lola & Simón •
Tosa •
Azou •

Shilpa

King Street

Anarkali •
Saigon Saigon •
Carpenters Arms •

Sagar •

Tortilla •

Fulham Palace Road

HAMMERSMITH FLYOVER

HAMMERSMITH BRIDGE

Gate •

RIVER CAFÉ •

River Thames

Charlotte's Bistro, Côte

Chella •

Franco
Manca
Roebuck •

STAMFORD
BROOK

Cabin •

Balans •

Firezza •

Hogarth
Roundabout

CHISWICK

High Road

Duke of Sussex •

Swan •

Vacherin •

CHISWICK
PARK

Michael Nadra •

Gail's Bread • Giraffe •

Faanoos •

Sam's Brasserie •

TURNHAM
GREEN

Chiswick High Road

Hedone •

Carvosso's •

TROMPETTE,
Canta Napoli,
Quantus

• Hole in the Wall

• Bedington Café

MAP 8 - HAMPSTEAD, CAMDEN TOWN & ISLINGTON

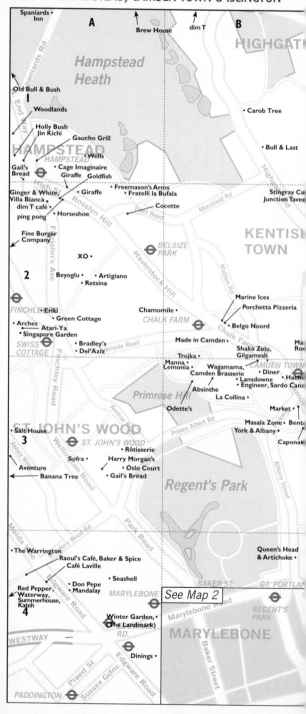

Spaniards • Inn

A

Brew House

dim T

B

HIGHGAT

Hampstead Heath

• Carob Tree

Old Bull & Bush

• Woodlands

• Bull & Last

Holly Bush • Jin Kichi

Gaucho Grill

HAMPSTEAD

• Wells

HAMPSTEAD

Stingray Ca Junction Taver

Gail's Bread

• Cage Imaginaire
Giraffe   Goldfish

Ginger & White, Villa Bianca
dim T café •
ping pong

• Giraffe

Freemason's Arms
• Fratelli la Bufala

• Cocotte

Mansfield Rd

KENTISH
TOWN

• Horseshoe

Rossiyn Hill

Fleet Road

Fine Burger Company

XO •

BELSIZE
PARK

Haverstock Hill

2

Beyoglu •   • Artigiano
• Retsina

Marine Ices

Porchetta Pizzeria

Maiden Rd

Ma
Roa

FINCHLEY

• Eriki

• Green Cottage

Chamomile •

CHALK FARM

• Belgo Noord

Chalk Far

• Arches
Atari-Ya •
• Singapore Garden

SWISS
COTTAGE

• Bradley's
• Del'Aziz

Adelaide Road

Made in Camden

Shaka Zulu,
Gilgamesh

CAMDEN TOWN

Trojka •
Manna •
Lemonia •   • Wagamama
Camden Brasserie

• Diner
• Lansdowne
• Engineer, Sardo Cana

Finchley Road

Primrose Hill

Absinthe

La Collina •

Camden

Odette's •

Market •

ST. JOHN'S WOOD

Avenue

Salt House •

Wellington Road

ST. JOHN'S WOOD

Prince Albert Rd

Masala Zone • • Bent
York & Albany •

Caponat

Albany Street

3

• Rôtisserie

Sofra •

Harry Morgan's

Abbot Road

Aventure
Banana Tree

• Oslo Court
• Gail's Bread

Regent's Park

Queen's Head
& Artichoke •

• The Warrington

Raoul's Café, Baker & Spice
Café Laville

Park Road

Maida

St John's Wood Rd

Edgware Road

• Seashell

• Don Pepe
• Mandalay

BAKER ST.

GT. PORTLAN

Red Pepper, Waterway,
Summerhouse,
Kateh

MARYLEBONE

See Map 2

REGENT'S
PARK

4

Winter Garden, •
(the Landmark)

Marylebone Road

MARYLEBONE

WESTWAY

RD.

• Dinings

Baker Street

PADDINGTON

Praed St

Sussex Gdns

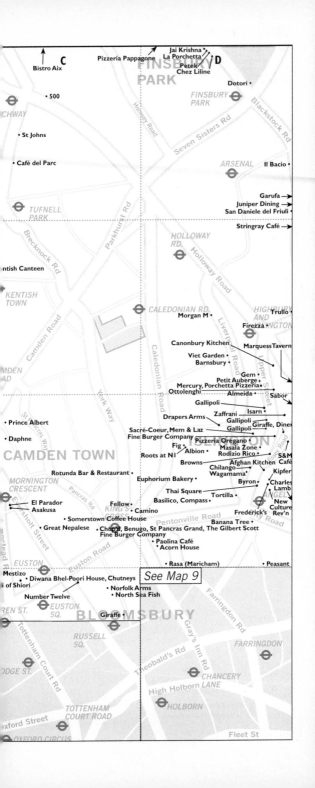

C
Bistro Aix

Pizzeria Pappagone

Jai Krishna •
La Porchetta •
Petek •
Chez Liline

D

FINSBURY
PARK

Dotori •

• 500

CHWAY

FINSBURY
PARK

• St Johns

Seven Sisters Rd

• Café del Parc

ARSENAL

Il Bacio •

TUFNELL
PARK

Garufa →
Juniper Dining →
San Daniele del Friuli •

Breacknock Rd

Parkhurst Rd

Stringray Café →

HOLLOWAY
RD.

ntish Canteen

KENTISH
TOWN

Holloway Road

CALEDONIAN RD.

HIGHBURY
AND

Morgan M •

Trullo •

Firezza •

NGTON

Camden Road

Canonbury Kitchen

Marquess Tavern

Caledonian Road

Liverpool Road

Viet Garden •
Barnsbury •

York Way

Upper Street

MDEN
AD

Gem •
Petit Auberge •
Mercury, Porchetta Pizzeria •
Ottolenghi •

Masala Zone •
Almeida •

Sabor

• Prince Albert

Gallipoli •

Zaffrani •

Isarn

Drapers Arms •

Gallipoli
Giraffe, Diner

• Daphne

Sacré-Coeur, Mem & Laz
Fine Burger Company

Gallipoli

CAMDEN TOWN

Fig •
Roots at N1 •

Pizzeria Oregano •
Albion •
Rodizio Rico •

Browns •

S&M Café

Afghan Kitchen •

Kipfer

• Prince Albert

Rotunda Bar & Restaurant •

Chilango
Wagamama •

Byron •

Charles
Lamb

MORNINGTON
CRESCENT

Euphorium Bakery •

New
Culture
Rev'n

ANGEL

• El Parador
Asakusa

Fellow •

Thai Square •
Basilico, Compass •

Tortilla •

Frederick's •

Pancras Rd

Eversholt Street

• Camino

Pentonville Road

• Somerstown Coffee House

Banana Tree •

• Great Nepalese

Chop'd, Benugo, St Pancras Grand, The Gilbert Scott
Fine Burger Company

Euston Road

EUSTON

Mestizo •
i of Shiori

• Paolina Café
• Acorn House

• Diwana Bhel-Poori House, Chutneys

Number Twelve

REN ST.

EUSTON
SQ.

• Norfolk Arms
• North Sea Fish

Giraffe •

• Rasa (Maricham)

See Map 9

• Peasant

Farringdon Rd

BLOOMSBURY

Gray's Inn Rd

RUSSELL
SQ.

FARRINGDON

Tottenham Court Road

Theobald's Rd

DGE ST.

CHANCERY
LANE

High Holborn

HOLBORN

TOTTENHAM
COURT ROAD

xford Street

OXFORD CIRCUS

Fleet St

MAP 9 - THE CITY

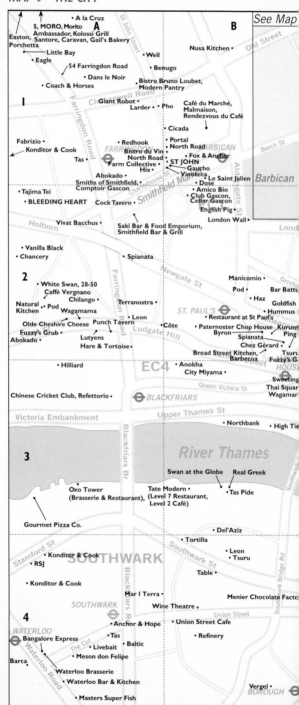

See Map

A

B

• A la Cruz

$, MORO, Morito
Ambassador, Kolossi Grill
Santore, Caravan, Gail's Bakery

Easton,
Porchetta

Nusa Kitchen •

Old Street

• Little Bay

• Well

• Eagle

• 54 Farringdon Road

• Benugo

• Dans le Noir

Bistro Bruno Loubet,
Modern Pantry

• Coach & Horses

Giant Robot •

Larder • Pho

Café du Marché,
Malmaison,
Rendezvous du Café

Fabrizio •

Cicada •

Konditor & Cook

• Portal

North Road •

Beech St

Barbican

Fox & Anchor •

• Redhook

Bistro du Vin

North Road

ST JOHN

Gaucho

Le Saint Julien

Farm Collective •

Vinoteca •

Tas •

Hix •

Dose •

Smiths of Smithfield,
Comptoir Gascon

Amico Bio •
Club Gascon,
Cellar Gascon

• Tajima Tei

Abokado •

• BLEEDING HEART

English Pig •

Cock Tavern •

London Wall •

Holborn

Lond

Saki Bar & Food Emporium,
Smithfield Bar & Grill

Vivat Bacchus •

• Vanilla Black

• Chancery

• Spianata

Newgate St

Manicomio •

Gresh

• White Swan, 28-50

Pod •

Bar Battu

Caffè Vergnano

• Haz

Chilango

Goldfish

Natural
Kitchen

• Pod

ST. PAUL'S

Hummus

Wagamama

Terranostra •

• Restaurant at St Paul's

Kurum
Ping

Olde Cheshire Cheese

Punch Tavern •

• Leon

• Paternoster Chop House

• Côte

Byron

Spianata

Fuzzy's Grub •

Tsuru

Abokado •

Lutyens

Chez Gérard •

Fuzzy's G

Hare & Tortoise •

Bread Street Kitchen,
Barbecoa

• Hilliard

• Anokha

City Miyama •

HOUS

• Hilliard

EC4

Sweeting

Chinese Cricket Club, Refettorio •

Queen Victoria St

Thai Squar

BLACKFRIARS

Wagamar

Victoria Embankment

Upper Thames St

• Northbank

• High Ti

3

River Thames

Oxo Tower
(Brasserie & Restaurant),

Tate Modern •
(Level 7 Restaurant,
Level 2 Café)

Swan at the Globe

Real Greek

• Tas Pide

Gourmet Pizza Co.

• Del'Aziz

• Tortilla

• Konditor & Cook

SOUTHWARK

Southwark St

• Leon

• RSJ

• Tsuru

• Konditor & Cook

Table •

Mar I Terra •

Menier Chocolate Facto

Wine Theatre •

SOUTHWARK

Union Street

4

WATERLOO

Bangalore Express

• Tas

• Anchor & Hope

• Union Street Cafe

• Refinery

• Livebait

• Baltic

Barca •

• Meson don Felipe

Waterloo Brasserie

• Waterloo Bar & Kitchen

Vergel •

• Masters Super Fish

BOROUGH

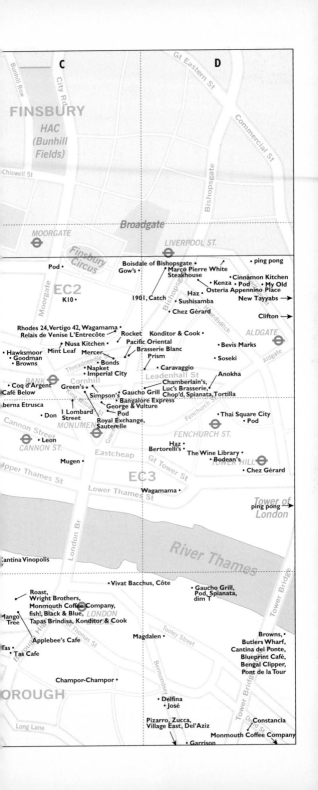

MAP 10 - SOUTH LONDON (& FULHAM)

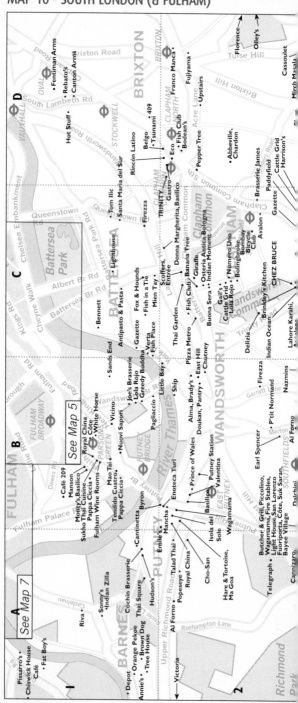

MAP 11 - EAST END & DOCKLANDS

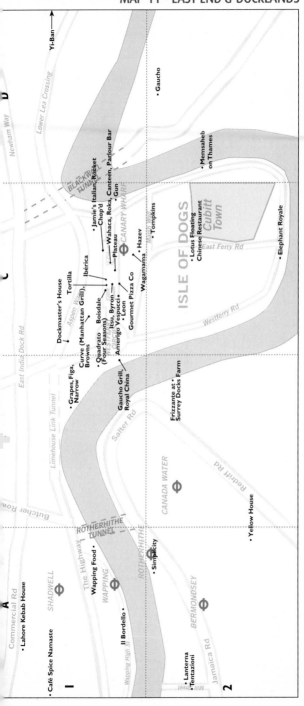

Yi-Ban →

Newham Way

Lower Lea Crossing

• Guacho

BLACKWALL TUNNEL

• Jamie's Italian
Rocket
Chop'd •
Wahaca, Roka, Canteen, Parlour Bar
• Gun
Plateau •

• Memsaheb
on Thames

CANARY WHARF

• Hazev
• Tompkins

Iberica

Dockmaster's House •
Tortilla

Aspen Way

Curve (Manhattan Grill), •
Browns
Quadrato •
Boisdale •
(Four Seasons) • Itsu, Byron
• Amerigo Vespucci
Gourmet Pizza Co
• Leon
Wagamama

• Lotus Floating
Chinese Restaurant

Cubitt
Town

ISLE OF DOGS

East Ferry Rd

East India Dock Rd

Westferry Rd

• Elephant Royale

Limehouse Link Tunnel

• Grapes, Figa,
Narrow

Gaucho Grill, •
Royal China

Salter Rd

Frizzante at •
Surrey Docks Farm

Butcher Row

The Highway

ROTHERHITHE
TUNNEL

CANADA WATER

Redriff Rd

• Yellow House

Commercial Rd

SHADWELL

• Lahore Kebab House

Wapping Food •
WAPPING

ROTHERHITHE

• Simplicity

• Café Spice Namaste

Wapping High St

Il Bordello •

BERMONDSEY

Jamaica Rd

Mill Street

• Lanterna
Tentazioni

1

2

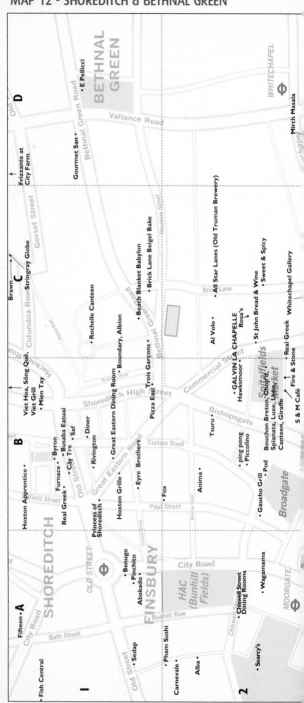

MAP 12 - SHOREDITCH & BETHNAL GREEN

BETHNAL GREEN

SHOREDITCH

FINSBURY

MOORGATE

WHITECHAPEL

Broadgate

Spitalfields

HAC (Bunhill Fields)

A · B · C · D

1 · 2

Bath Street
City Road
Old Street
Bunhill Row
City Road
Chiswell Street
Bishopsgate
Curtain Road
Paul Street
Great Eastern Road
Old Street
Hackney Road
Columbia Road
Gosset Street
Bethnal Green Road
Vallance Road
Old
Commercial Street
Brick Lane
Bethnal Green Road

Fish Central
Fifteen
Hoxton Apprentice
Real Greek
Furnace
Byron
Cây Tre
Saf
Diner
Rivington
Great Eastern Dining Room
Hoxton Grille
Eyre Brothers
Princess of Shoreditch
Benugo
Pinchito
Abokado
Fox
Anima
Pham Sushi
Sedap
Carnevale
Alba
Searcy's
Chiswell Street Dining Rooms
Wagamama
Gaucho Grill
Pod
ping pong
Piccolino
Tsuru
Bouchon Breton, Chop'd, Spianata, Luxe, Leon, Canteen, Giraffe
S & M Cafe
Fire & Stone
Real Greek
Whitechapel Gallery
Sweet & Spicy
St John Bread & Wine
GALVIN LA CHAPELLE
Hawksmoor
Rosa's
Al Volo
All Star Lanes (Old Truman Brewery)
Mirch Masala
Viet Hoa, Sông Quê, Viet Grill
Mien Tay
Busaba Eatuai
Rochelle Canteen
Pizza East
Trois Garçons
Boundary, Albion
Beach Blanket Babylon
Brick Lane Beigel Bake
Stringray Globe
Brawn
Frizzante at City Farm
Gourmet San
E Pellicci
Shoreditch High Street
Bethnal Green Road

PLACES PEOPLE TALK ABOUT

These are the restaurants outside London that were mentioned most frequently by reporters (last year's position is shown in brackets). For the list of London's most mentioned restaurants, see page 29.

1   Fat Duck (1)
    Bray, Berks
2   Manoir aux Quat' Saisons (2)
    Great Milton, Oxon
3   Waterside Inn (3)
    Bray, Berks
4   Seafood Restaurant (5)
    Padstow, Cornwall
5   Northcote (6)
    Langho, Lancs

6   Hind's Head (5)
    Bray, Berk
7   Gidleigh Park (14=)
    Chagford, Devon
8= Kitchin (16=)
    Edinburgh
8= Chapter One (12)
    Locksbottom, Kent
10 Hand & Flowers (-)
    Marlow, Bucks

11 Vineyard at Stockcross (13=
    Stockcross, Berkshire
12 Hix Oyster & Fish House (11)
    Lyme Regis, Dorset
13= Walnut Tree (10)
    Llandewi Skirrid, Monmouthshire
13= Star Inn (7=)
    Harome, N Yorks
13= Yang Sing (8=)
    Manchester

16 Sportsman (-)
    Whitstable, Kent
17= Magpie (8=)
    Whitby, N Yorks
17= L'Enclude (-)
    Cartmel, Cumbria
19 Yorke Arms (-)
    Ramsgill-in-Nidderdale, N Yorks
20 Hambleton Hall (16=)
    Hambleton, Rutland

TOP SCORERS

All restaurants whose food rating is ❶; plus restaurants whose price is £50+ with a food rating of ❷.

£210+	The Fat Duck (Bray)	❷❷❸
£140+	Le Manoir aux Quat' Saisons *(Great Milton)*	❶❷❶
£120+	Gidleigh Park *(Chagford)*	❶❷❶
	Waterside Inn *(Bray)*	❶❷❶
£110+	Andrew Fairlie *(Auchterarder)*	❶❶❸
£100+	Midsummer House *(Cambridge)*	❶❸❸
	Restaurant Nathan Outlaw *(Rock)*	❶❸❸
	John Campbell *(Ascot)*	❷❷❶
	Lucknam Park *(Colerne)*	❷❷❷
	Restaurant Sat Bains *(Nottingham)*	❷❸④
£90+	L'Enclume *(Cartmel)*	❶❶❷
	Restaurant Martin Wishart *(Edinburgh)*	❶❷❸
	Sharrow Bay *(Ullswater)*	❷❸❶
	21212 *(Edinburgh)*	❷❷❷
	Martin Wishart *(Loch Lomond)*	❷❷❷
	The Latymer *(Bagshot)*	❷❸❷
	Dining Room *(Easton Gray)*	❷❷④
	Paris House *(Woburn)*	❷❷④
	Simon Radley *(Chester)*	❷❷④
£80+	Hambleton Hall *(Hambleton)*	❶❷❶
	The Three Chimneys *(Dunvegan)*	❶❷❶
	La Bécasse *(Ludlow)*	❶❶❷
	The Kitchin *(Edinburgh)*	❶❶❷
	Yorke Arms *(Ramsgill-in-Nidderdale)*	❶❶❷
	Bybrook Restaurant *(Castle Combe)*	❶❷❸
	Mallory Court *(Bishops Tachbrook)*	❷❷❷
	Summer Lodge *(Evershot)*	❷❷❷
	Morston Hall *(Morston)*	❷④❷
	Number One *(Edinburgh)*	❷❷❸
	Ocean Restaurant *(Jersey)*	❷❸❸
	Holbeck Ghyll *(Windermere)*	❷④❸
	Harry's Place *(Great Gonerby)*	❷❶④
	Turners *(Birmingham)*	❷❸④
£70+	Mr Underhill's *(Ludlow)*	❶❶❷
	Simpsons *(Birmingham)*	❶❶❷
	The Albannach *(Lochinver)*	❶❶❷
	Airds Hotel *(Port Appin)*	❶❷❷
	Bohemia *(Jersey)*	❶❷❷

TOP SCORERS

£70+		
Plumed Horse *(Edinburgh)*		❶❷❷
Seafood Restaurant *(Padstow)*		❶❷❷
Summer Isles Hotel *(Achiltibuie)*		❶❷❷
The Box Tree *(Ilkley)*		❶❷❷
Tyddyn Llan *(Llandrillo)*		❶❷❷
The Hambrough *(Ventnor)*		❶❷❸
Northcote *(Langho)*		❶❸❸
Drakes *(Ripley)*		❶❶④
Kinloch Lodge *(Sleat)*		❷⓿❷
Bailiffscourt Hotel *(Climping)*		❷❷❷
Ockenden Manor *(Cuckfield)*		❷❷❷
Read's *(Faversham)*		❷❷❷
The French Horn *(Sonning-on-Thames)*		❷❷❷
Kinloch House *(Blairgowrie)*		❷⓿❸
Harrow at Little Bedwyn *(Marlborough)*		❷❷❸
36 on the Quay *(Emsworth)*		❷❸❸
The Olive Tree *(Bath)*		❷❸❸
Michael Caines *(Manchester)*		❷④④

£60+		
Artichoke *(Amersham)*		⓿⓿❷
Braidwoods *(Dalry)*		⓿⓿❷
The Castle Terrace *(Edinburgh)*		⓿⓿❷
Fischers at Baslow Hall *(Baslow)*		⓿❷❷
Lumière *(Cheltenham)*		⓿❷❷
Purnells *(Birmingham)*		⓿❷❷
The Peat Inn *(Cupar)*		⓿❷❷
The Seahorse *(Dartmouth)*		⓿❷❷
The Star Inn *(Harome)*		⓿❷❷
Caldesi in Campagna *(Bray)*		⓿❷❸
Fraiche *(Oxton)*		⓿❷❸
Little Barwick House *(Barwick)*		⓿❷❸
The Vanilla Pod *(Marlow)*		⓿❷❸
The Fish House *(Chilgrove)*		⓿④❸
Le Champignon Sauvage *(Cheltenham)*		⓿❷④
Ramsons *(Ramsbottom)*		⓿❷④
Sienna *(Dorchester)*		⓿❷⑤
Combe House *(Honiton)*		❷❷⓿
Driftwood Hotel *(Rosevine)*		❷❷⓿
McCoys at the Tontine *(Northallerton)*		❷❷⓿
Seafood Restaurant *(St Andrews)*		❷❷⓿
The Oak Room *(Egham)*		❷❷⓿
Monachyle Mhor *(Balquhidder)*		❷❸⓿
Plas Bodegroes *(Pwllheli)*		❷⓿❷
Feversham Arms *(Helmsley)*		❷❷❷
Green Inn *(Ballater)*		❷❷❷
Hand & Flowers *(Marlow)*		❷❷❷
Hipping Hall *(Kirkby Lonsdale)*		❷❷❷
Horn of Plenty *(Gulworthy)*		❷❷❷
Hotel Endsleigh *(Tavistock)*		❷❷❷

TOP SCORERS

Restaurant	Score
Lavender House *(Brundall)*	❷❷❷
Michael Caines *(Chester)*	❷❷❷
Samuel's *(Masham)*	❷❷❷
The Neptune *(Old Hunstanton)*	❷❷❷
Casamia *(Bristol)*	❷❸❷
Van Zeller *(Harrogate)*	❷❸❷
The Merchant Hotel *(Belfast)*	❷④❷
Allium *(Fairford)*	❷❷❸
Edmunds *(Birmingham)*	❷❷❸
The Crown at Whitebrook *(Whitebrook)*	❷❷❸
The Royal Oak *(Maidenhead)*	❷❷❸
Orwells *(Shiplake)*	❷❸❸
Thackeray's *(Tunbridge Wells)*	❷❸❸
Fishmore Hall *(Ludlow)*	❷❷④
JSW *(Petersfield)*	❷❷④
Alimentum *(Cambridge)*	❷❸④
Darroch Learg *(Ballater)*	❷❸④
Elephant Restaurant & Brasserie *(Torquay)*	❷❸④

£50+	Restaurant	Score
	The Pipe & Glass Inn *(Beverley)*	⓿❷⓿
	Paul Ainsworth at Number 6 *(Padstow)*	⓿⓿❷
	Pebble Beach *(Barton-on-Sea)*	⓿⓿❷
	Sportsman *(Whitstable)*	⓿⓿❷
	The Old Passage Inn *(Arlingham)*	⓿⓿❷
	The Wensleydale Heifer *(West Witton)*	⓿⓿❷
	Chapter One *(Locksbottom)*	⓿❷❷
	Craig Millar @ 16 West End *(St Monans)*	⓿❷❷
	Rockfish *(Bristol)*	⓿❷❷
	Tanners Restaurant *(Plymouth)*	⓿❷❷
	Jeremy's at Borde Hill *(Haywards Heath)*	⓿❸❷
	Pierhouse Hotel *(Port Appin)*	⓿❸❷
	Apicius *(Cranbrook)*	⓿❷❸
	Lasan *(Birmingham)*	⓿❷❸
	Ondine *(Edinburgh)*	⓿❷❸
	Ostlers Close *(Cupar)*	⓿❷❸
	The Bildeston Crown *(Bildeston)*	⓿❷❸
	The Dining Room *(Ashbourne)*	⓿❷❸
	The Oyster Shack *(Bigbury-on-Sea)*	⓿❷❸
	The Walnut Tree *(Llandewi Skirrid)*	⓿❷❸
	Black Swan *(Oldstead)*	⓿❸❸
	The Hardwick *(Abergavenny)*	⓿❸❸
	The French Table *(Surbiton)*	⓿❶④
	Aumbry *(Manchester)*	⓿❷④
	Goodfellows *(Wells)*	⓿❷④
	The West House *(Biddenden)*	⓿❷④
	Jerichos *(Windermere)*	⓿❸④
	No 7 Fish Bistro *(Torquay)*	⓿❸④
	Babington House *(Babington)*	❷❷⓿
	Hotel Tresanton *(St Mawes)*	❷❷⓿

TOP SCORERS

£50+ La Chouette (Dinton) — 2 2 1
The Sir Charles Napier (Chinnor) — 2 3 1
Lido (Bristol) — 2 4 1
Café 21 (Newcastle upon Tyne) — 2 2 2
Crab & Lobster (Asenby) — 2 2 2
Estbek House (Sandsend) — 2 2 2
Firenze (Kibworth Beauchamp) — 2 2 2
Nutter's (Norden) — 2 2 2
Pecks (Congleton) — 2 2 2
Portmeirion Hotel (Portmeirion) — 2 2 2
Silver Darling (Aberdeen) — 2 2 2
Smith's Brasserie (Ongar) — 2 2 2
The Black Rat (Winchester) — 2 2 2
The Hind's Head (Bray) — 2 2 2
The King John Inn (Tollard Royal) — 2 2 2
Two Fat Ladies at The Buttery (Glasgow) — 2 2 2
Grain Store (Edinburgh) — 2 3 2
Restaurant Tristan (Horsham) — 2 3 2
The Sun at Northaw (Northaw) — 2 3 2
The Wheatsheaf (Bath) — 2 3 2
Yew Tree Inn (Newbury) — 2 3 2
Hix Oyster and Fish House (Lyme Regis) — 2 4 2
Terravina (Woodlands) — 2 0 3
Arundell Arms (Lifton) — 2 2 3
Bell's Diner (Bristol) — 2 2 3
Bluebells (Sunningdale) — 2 2 3
Cotto (Cambridge) — 2 2 3
Gamba (Glasgow) — 2 2 3
Horseshoe Inn (Peebles) — 2 2 3
Tanroagan Seafood Restaurant (Douglas) — 2 2 3
The Mason's Arms (Knowstone) — 2 2 3
Agaric (Ashburton) — 2 3 3
Black Bull (Moulton) — 2 3 3
Moat House (Acton Trussell) — 2 3 3
Ode (Shaldon) — 2 3 3
Riverside (Bridport) — 2 3 3
Second Floor Restaurant (Manchester) — 2 3 3
St Petroc's Hotel & Bistro (Padstow) — 2 3 3
The Foxhunter (Nant-y-Derry) — 2 3 3
The Marquis (Alkham) — 2 3 3
The Restaurant at Drakes (Brighton) — 2 3 3
Three Acres (Shelley) — 2 3 3
The Bell at Sapperton (Sapperton) — 2 4 3
5 North Street (Winchcombe) — 2 2 4
James Street South (Belfast) — 2 2 4
Sangster's (Elie) — 2 2 4
Tony Tobin @ The Dining Room (Reigate) — 2 2 4
Wedgwood (Edinburgh) — 2 2 4

TOP SCORERS

		Score
	Chino Latino *(Nottingham)*	❷❸④
	The Crab at Chieveley *(Newbury)*	❷❸④
	Three Lions *(Stuckton)*	❷❸④
	Froggies at The Timber Batts *(Bodsham)*	❷④④
	La Potinière *(Gullane)*	❷④④
£40+	Porthminster Café *(St Ives)*	❶②❶
	Fat Olives *(Emsworth)*	❶❶②
	The Malt Shovel *(Brearton)*	❶❶②
	Cafe Fish *(Torbermory)*	❶②②
	El Gato Negro Tapas *(Ripponden)*	❶②②
	Gingerman *(Brighton)*	❶②②
	Great House *(Lavenham)*	❶②②
	Les Mirabelles *(Nomansland)*	❶②②
	Wheelers Oyster Bar *(Whitstable)*	❶②②
	Tuscan Kitchen *(Rye)*	❶③②
	Vujon *(Newcastle upon Tyne)*	❶❶③
	Anokaa *(Salisbury)*	❶②③
	Bilash *(Wolverhampton)*	❶②③
	Indian Summer *(Brighton)*	❶②③
	Lanterna *(Scarborough)*	❶②③
	Maliks *(Cookham)*	❶②③
	Samphire *(Whitstable)*	❶②③
	The Ambrette *(Margate)*	❶②③
	Le Langhe *(York)*	❶④③
	J Baker's Bistro Moderne *(York)*	❶②④
	The Westerly *(Reigate)*	❶②④
	The Feathers Inn *(Hedley On The Hill)*	❶③④
	Maliks *(Gerrards Cross)*	❶④④
	Culinaria *(Bristol)*	❶②⑤
£30+	Mother India *(Glasgow)*	❶②②
	The Chilli Pickle *(Brighton)*	❶②②
	Cafe Maitreya *(Bristol)*	❶②③
	Sea Dogs *(Edinburgh)*	❶②③
	The Art Kitchen *(Warwick)*	❶②③
	Riverford Field Kitchen *(Buckfastleigh)*	❶③③
	Magpie Café *(Whitby)*	❶②④
	Colmans *(South Shields)*	❶③④
	Kalpna *(Edinburgh)*	❶④④
£30+	Rainbow Café *(Cambridge)*	❶③③
	Anstruther Fish Bar *(Anstruther)*	❶④④
	The Company Shed *(West Mersea)*	❶④③
£20+	This & That *(Manchester)*	❶③⑤

Gidleigh Park

Harbourmaster   £ 46   ④❸❸
Quay Pde SA46 0BT (01545) 570755
"A fantastic location on the waterfront" underpins the appeal of this
"long-time favourite" harbour-side inn, where the fish specials are a
highlight; even fans can find its performance *"very variable"*, though.
/ **Details:** www.harbour-master.com; 9 pm; no Amex. **Accommodation:** 13
rooms, from £110.

The Hive On The Quay   £ 41   🅣
Cadwgan Pl SA46 5DQ (01545) 570445
This *"above-average"* waterside café is a top tip locally for a
"wonderful sandwich lunch", even if it can be *"crowded and
somewhat chaotic"*. / **Details:** www.thehiveaberaeron.com; 9 pm; closed
Mon & Sun D; no Amex.

Silver Darling   £ 57   ❷❷❷
Pocra Quay, North Pier AB11 5DQ (01224) 576229
It may be a tad *"expensive"*, but the *"city's best restaurant"*, in the
former harbour control building – *"ships enter and leave at eye
level"* – invariably hits the spot; house speciality, *"very good fish"*.
/ **Details:** www.silverdarlingrestaurant.co.uk; beside harbourmaster's tower;
9 pm; closed Sat L & Sun; children: +16 after 8 pm.

The Angel Hotel   £ 43   ❷❸❸
15 Cross St NP7 5EN (01873) 857121
This *"busy"* town-centre hotel is claimed by fans to be *"better than
the Walnut Tree!"* (with which it has a proprietor in common); that's
overdoing it a bit, but its cuisine is certainly accomplished, and its
afternoon tea is *"outstanding"*.
/ **Details:** www.angelhotelabergavenny.com; 10 pm. **Accommodation:** 35
rooms, from £96.

The Hardwick   £ 57   ❶❸❸
Old Raglan Rd NP7 9AA (01873) 854220
Settling down after its recent *"major expansion"*, Stephen Terry's
"beautifully-located" inn is reinforcing its position as one of Wales's
top destinations; *"fine, unfussy cooking using the best local produce"*
is on offer, and with *"no airs or graces"*.
/ **Details:** www.thehardwick.co.uk; 10 pm; no Amex. **Accommodation:** 8
rooms, from £150.

Summer Isles Hotel   £ 74   ❶❷❷
IV26 2YG (01854) 622282
"The journey's worth it!"; this celebrated hotel – *"at the end of one
of Scotland's most exciting single-track roads"* – *"fully meets
expectations"*; it serves *"superb food using local ingredients
according to the season"*, plus a huge selection of wine that's *"strong
on classics"*, but with *"interesting"* New World options too.
/ **Details:** www.summerisleshotel.com; 25m N of Ullapool on A835; 8 pm;
Closed from 1st Nov - 27 Mar; no Amex; children: 8+. **Accommodation:** 13
rooms, from £155.

Moat House   £ 54   ❷❸❸
Lower Penkridge Rd ST17 0RJ   (01785) 712217
*"An attractive restaurant in the conservatory of an old farmhouse
overlooking the canal, just off J13 of the M6"; all reports confirm this
is "an exceptional stop-off for the motorway traveller", offering food
that's surprisingly good for the location.*
/ **Details:** www.thelewispartnership.co.uk; J13 off the M6, follow signs for
A449; 9.30 pm. **Accommodation:** 41 rooms, from £155.

Planet Spice   £ 37   ⓣ
88 Selsdon Park Rd CR2 8JT   (020) 8651 3300
*The low ceiling may inject a rather "claustrophobic" air, but this
suburban subcontinental is nonetheless resoundingly tipped for its
"flavoursome" cuisine.* / **Details:** www.planet-spice.com; 11.30 pm.

The Ginger Fox   £ 47   ❷❷❷
Muddleswood Road BN6 9EA   (01273) 857 888
*"Improved" of late, this "top-quality" gastropub (in a former petrol
station!) is now beginning to live up to the standards of the locally
pre-eminent Gingerman Group, of which it is a member; for
particularly good value, "seek out the lunch and early-evening
menus".* / **Details:** www.gingermanrestaurants.com; 10 pm, Sun 9 pm.

Aldeburgh Fish And Chips   £ 15   ❷❸⑤
225 High St IP16 4BZ   (01728) 454685
*"Long queues" advertise the location of this celebrated seaside
chippy – "however good it is, though", says the occasional critic, "it's
not worth waiting over an hour for!"* / **Details:** 8 pm; no credit cards.

The Brudenell   £ 46   ⓣ
The Pde IP15 5BU   (01728) 452071
*Tipped for its "lovely beach location", a seafront hotel whose dining
room enjoys fine views; the cooking is usually "competent" or better
– sometimes, though, it's "let down by the service".*
/ **Details:** www.brudenellhotel.co.uk; 9.30 pm. **Accommodation:** 44 rooms,
from £190.

The Lighthouse   £ 45   ❸❷④
77 High St IP15 5AU   (01728) 453377
*"Gets it right every time", says one of the many fans of this
"deservedly successful" seaside fish-and-seafood bistro – an
"informal", "café-style" sort of place where "families are welcome".*
/ **Details:** www.lighthouserestaurant.co.uk; 10 pm.

152   £ 37   ④④④
152 High St IP15 5AX   (01728) 454594
*This popular seaside restaurant is "a reliably good and efficient
place, right by the beach"; a regular's tip – "go out of season when
they have more time to look after the food and the guests".*
/ **Details:** www.152aldeburgh.com; 10 pm.

Regatta   £ 41   ❷❷❸
171-173 High St IP15 5AN   (01728) 452011
*This "delightful family restaurant" is "always full of people enjoying
themselves" and remains one of the town's hot spots, thanks to its
"buzzy" style and fish dishes which are "always fresh and delicious".*
/ **Details:** www.regattaaldeburgh.com; 10 pm.

The Wentworth Hotel   £ 37   ④❸❸
Wentworth Rd IP15 5BD   (01728) 452312
"Better than a typical seaside hotel experience" – this family-run
hotel (run by the Pritt family since the '20s) is an *"unpretentious"*
place with *"old-fashioned"* service, a *"comfortable"* interior and
"surprisingly good" (if *"simply executed"*) food.
/ **Details:** www.wentworth-aldeburgh.com; 9 pm. **Accommodation:** 35
rooms, from £122.

ALDFORD, CHESHIRE   5–3A

The Grosvenor Arms   £ 43   ❸❷❶
Chester Rd CH3 6HJ   (01244) 620228
*Perhaps the best member of an usually solid gastropub group
(Brunning & Price), this "comfortable and very characterful" inn, in a
quiet village, offers "a very extensive, well-priced menu, with
imaginative dishes mainly based on local produce" and "good beers
and wines".* / **Details:** www.grosvenorarms-aldford.co.uk; 6m S of Chester on
B5130; 9.30 pm, Fri & Sat 10 pm, Sun 9 pm.

ALKHAM, KENT   3–3D

The Marquis   £ 59   ❷❸❸
Alkham Valley Rd CT15 7DF   (01304) 873410
"An outstanding destination in the desert of South East Kent!"; this
restaurant-with-rooms – a former pub with *"a really warm and lively
feel"* and *"lovely views"* – is highly praised for its *"first-class local
food"* and its *"intelligent"* service.
/ **Details:** www.themarquisatalkham.co.uk; 9.30 pm, Sun 8.30 pm; closed
Mon L; children: 8+ D. **Accommodation:** 10 rooms, from £95.

ALNWICK, NORTHUMBERLAND   8–1B

The Tree House
The Alnwick Garden   £ 42   ⓣ
Denwick Ln NE66 1YU   (01665) 511852
A "fabulous fairy-tale setting" – imagine a real tree house with a bit
of help from Disney! – helps make this adjunct to the Duchess of
Northumberland's contemporary-style garden a *"perfect venue for a
meal to please all the family"*; the scoff's *"reasonably good"* too.
/ **Details:** www.alnwickgarden.com; 9.15 pm; closed Sun-Wed D; no Amex.

ALTRINCHAM, CHESHIRE   5–2B

Dilli   £ 34   ④❷④
60 Stamford New Rd WA14 1EE   (0161) 929 7484
"A cut above" – this *"innovative"* and *"friendly"* Altrincham spot is
still hailed by fans for *"the best Indian food in the area"*; on the
downside it's *"not so far ahead as when it opened"* (seven years-
ago). / **Details:** www.dilli.co.uk; on A538; 11 pm, Sun 10 pm.

ALVESTON, WARWICKSHIRE   2–1C

Baraset Barn   £ 44   ⓣ
1 Pimlico Lane CV37 7RJ   (01789) 295510
*An "open" and "airy" modern operation in a "great rural setting" (a
converted tithe barn), tipped for its "interesting variations on your
standard gastropub fare".* / **Details:** www.barasetbarn.co.uk; 9.30 pm;
closed Sun D; no Amex.

AMBERLEY, WEST SUSSEX

Amberley Castle £ 85

BN18 9LT (01798) 831992

As this guide was going to press, this fairytale castle, complete with portcullis, was bought by the ABode Hotels people; in the circumstances, no rating is appropriate.
/ Details: www.amberleycastle.co.uk; N of Arundel on B2139; 9 pm; no jeans or trainers; booking: max 8; children: 12+. **Accommodation:** *19 rooms, from £230.*

AMBLESIDE, CUMBRIA

Doi Intanon £ 33 🅣

Market Place LA22 9BU (01539) 432119

Chris and Busara Knight's "Thai restaurant in the sticks" is tipped as a "very pleasant surprise"; its all-round appeal includes cooking with "just the right balance of spiciness and subtlety".

Drunken Duck £ 47 ❸❷⓿

Barngates LA22 0NG (01539) 436347

"Still a favourite after many years" – this acclaimed Lakeland inn-cum-microbrewery won all-round praise this year, thanks to its "unbeatable location", "very accomplished" food, and interesting home brews. / Details: www.drunkenduckinn.co.uk; 3m from Ambleside, towards Hawkshead; 11 pm, Sun 10.30 pm; no Amex; no trainers; booking: max 6 (D only). **Accommodation:** *17 rooms, from £95.*

DONE £ 35 ❷❷⓿

Compston Rd LA22 9AD (01539) 433845

A "popular port of call when in the Lakes", linked to a three-screen cinema; the ambience is "very good" and the food – especially the "good range of pasta and pizza" – "shows that vegetarian doesn't have to be boring"! / Details: www.zeffirellis.com; 10 pm; no Amex.

AMERSHAM, BUCKINGHAMSHIRE

Artichoke £ 64 ⓿⓿❷

9 Market Sq HP7 0DF (01494) 726611

"Better than ever since they re-opened after their fire" – Laurie Gear's "intense" ("shades of Noma") cuisine wins rave reviews for this "cosy" and "unpretentious" neighbourhood spot in Old Amersham. / Details: www.theartichokerestaurant.co.uk; 10 pm; closed Mon & Sun; no shorts.

Gilbey's £ 48 ❸❸❸

1 Market Sq HP7 0DF (01494) 727242

"Friendly but cramped", this stalwart bistro benefits from being located in a "beautifully restored" school building in Old Amersham, and most reporters find its cuisine "consistent" and relatively "affordable" too; wines include a selection from the patron's own vineyard. / Details: www.gilbeygroup.com; in Old Amersham; 9.30 pm, Sat 9.45 pm, Sun 8.45 pm.

ANSTRUTHER, FIFE

Anstruther Fish Bar £ 25 ⓿④④

42-44 Shore St KY10 3AQ (01333) 310518

"One of the country's best chippies" – the fish is "so fresh it wriggles", at this famous institution which occupies "a nice spot across from the harbour". / Details: www.anstrutherfishbar.co.uk; 10 pm; no Amex; no booking.

The Cellar £ 58 🅣

24 East Grn KY10 3AA (01333) 310378

*Limited feedback of late on Peter & Susan Jukes's long-acclaimed fish and seafood basement near the harbour, which turns 30 this year; such feedback as there is, however, remains adulatory – "it's quite expensive, but has no equal!" / **Details:** www.cellaranstruther.co.uk; in the harbour area; 9 pm; closed Mon & Sun.*

APPLECROSS, HIGHLAND 9–2B

Applecross Inn £ 36 ❷❸❸

Shore St IV54 8LT (01520) 744262

*"A total experience!" – "the finest seafood in sublime scenery" makes this remote but famous inn ("at the end of a long and winding road") a surprisingly "busy" destination. / **Details:** www.applecross.uk.com; off A896, S of Shieldaig; 9 pm; no Amex; need 6+ to book. **Accommodation:** 7 rooms, from £90.*

ARGYLL, ARGYLL AND BUTE 9–3B

Kilberry Inn £ 49 ❷❷❷

Nr Tarbert PA29 6YD (01880) 770223

*"Cyclists, well-dressed types, dogs… all are welcomed with equal warmth" at this "miles-from-anywhere" inn, which is reached "down a long single-track road" through "fabulous" scenery – "a lovely place to eat and stay". / **Details:** www.kilberryinn.com; 9 pm; closed Mon; no Amex. **Accommodation:** 5 rooms, from £195.*

ARLINGHAM, GLOUCESTERSHIRE 2–2B

The Old Passage Inn £ 57 ❶❶❷

Passage Rd GL2 7JR (01452) 740547

*"Sophisticated dining in an unlikely but picturesque setting on the banks of The Severn" – that's the deal at that this "trustworthy" spot, which is "worth seeking out" for its "fabulous seafood, impeccably cooked and presented"; or book ahead for a "Bore Breakfast"! / **Details:** www.theoldpassage.com; 9 pm; closed Mon & Sun D. **Accommodation:** 3 rooms, from £80.*

ARUNDEL, WEST SUSSEX 3–4A

The Town House £ 43 ❷❸❷

65 High St BN18 9AJ (01903) 883847

*The "fantastic ceiling" – from 16th century Florence no less! – is a feature of the dining room at this small restaurant-with-rooms overlooking Arundel Castle, praised by all-comers for its "great local and seasonal food"; "unbeatable deal for residents". / **Details:** www.thetownhouse.co.uk; 9.30 pm; closed Mon & Sun. **Accommodation:** 4 rooms, from £85.*

ASCOT, BERKSHIRE 3–3A

Ascot Oriental £ 47 ❷❷❸

London Rd SL5 0PU (01344) 621877

*Konrad Liu's "much-loved" Chinese venture is acclaimed by its strong local fan club as a "perennial favourite" – even a critic who found the food "run-of-the-mill" praised its "lovely setting and very friendly staff". / **Details:** www.ascotoriental.com; 2m E of Ascot on A329; 10.30 pm.*

John Campbell
Coworth Park £102 ❷❷❶
Blacknest Rd SL5 7SE   (01344) 876 600
*Thanks not least to its "fairytale" interior and "wonderful setting in
the wilds of rural Berkshire", this country house yearling is a major
hit; John Campbell (ex-Vineyard at Stockcross) delivers "refined
interpretations" of classic dishes, while service manages to be both
"enthusiastic" and "discreet". / Details: www.coworthpark.com.*

The Thatched Tavern £ 41 ❸❷❷
Cheapside Rd SL5 7QG   (01344) 620874
*This pretty-looking inn on the high street offers a "varied" menu of
"enjoyable" dishes; "it's dog-friendly too, which is a nice bonus".
/ Details: www.thethatchedtavern.co.uk; 2m from Ascot, signed to Cheapside
village; 9.30 pm.*

ASENBY, NORTH YORKSHIRE 8–4C

Crab & Lobster £ 59 ❷❷❷
Dishforth Rd YO7 3QL   (01845) 577286
*"The eccentric surroundings do not detract from the quality of the
food", says one of the many fans of this "romantic" thatched pub
whose interior is packed with bric-à-brac; culinary highlight –
"fabulous" fish. / Details: www.crabandlobster.co.uk; at junction of Asenby
Rd & Topcliffe Rd; 9 pm, 9.30 pm Sat. Accommodation: 14 rooms,
from £150.*

ASHBOURNE, DERBYSHIRE 5–3C

The Dining Room £ 59 ❶❷❸
33 St. John's St DE6 1GP   (01335) 300666
*"A real delight"; Peter and Laura Dale's six-table restaurant in an
ancient building in the heart of the town inspires fabulous feedback
– the "absolutely amazing" food "far exceeds the setting or the
price". / Details: www.thediningroomashbourne.co.uk; 7 pm; D only, closed
Mon & Sun; no Amex; booking essential; children: 12+. Accommodation: 1
room, at about £100.*

ASHBURTON, DEVON 1–3D

Agaric £ 56 ❷❸❸
30 North St TQ13 7QD   (01364) 654478
*Not many reports, but all feedback tips this "friendly" village-
restaurant as a real all-rounder, where the menu – "which ranges
from the usual to the less usual" – is consistently well done.
/ Details: www.agaricrestaurant.co.uk; 9.30 pm; closed Mon, Tue, Sat L &
Sun; no Amex. Accommodation: 5 rooms, from £110.*

ASTON TIRROLD, OXFORDSHIRE 2–2D

Sweet Olive £ 48 ❷❷❸
Baker St OX11 9DD   (01235) 851272
*"A great place for a fine Gallic meal in a charming pub-like
atmosphere"; this "always-welcoming" inn – where the "ever-
changing" menu displays some "global influences" too – inspires
much commentary, all of it upbeat. / Details: www.sweet-olive.com; half
a mile off the A417 between Streatley & Wantage; 9 pm; closed Feb.*

Andrew Fairlie
Gleneagles Hotel £117 **❶❶❸**
PH3 1NF (01764) 694267
"The best restaurant in Scotland by a country mile", say fans of
Andrew Fairlie's "unmissable" venue in the bowels of this famous
Edwardian hotel – a moodily decorated room where the
"inspirational" cuisine is delivered by staff who, though ultra-
professional, "could not be friendlier". / Details: www.andrewfairlie.com;
10 pm; L only, closed Sun; children: 12+. **Accommodation:** 273 rooms,
from £320.

Jon & Fernanda's £ 45 **T**
34 High St PH3 1DB (01764) 662442
"A hidden gem on the high street"; this ten-year-old operation by the
church is run by a former Gleneagles head chef together with a
former head waitress – all the (limited) feedback it inspires applauds
its "excellent" value. / Details: www.jonandfernandas.co.uk.

Mountain Cafe £ 32 **T**
111 Grampian Rd PH22 1RH (01479) 812473
"An amazing find in a bit of a foodie desert!" – this "superb" café
over a sports shop is tipped for its "wholesome and plentiful" cuisine
("fabulous" breakfasts a speciality) and "stunning views over the
Cairngorms". / Details: www.mountaincafe-aviemore.co.uk; village centre;
L only; no Amex.

River Cottage Canteen £ 39 **❷❹❹**
Trinity Sq EX13 5AN (01297) 631715
"Wholesome" and "delicious", the "reasonably-priced" food served
in the "crowded" annex to Hugh Fearnley-Whittingstall's food store
impresses all who comment on it; just occasionally, though, portion
control can seem unduly zealous. / Details: www.rivercottage.net; 9 pm;
closed Mon D & Sun D.

Hartwell House £ 74 **❸❶❷**
Oxford Rd HP17 8NR (01296) 747444
"True country house atmosphere" doesn't come much more refined
than at Louis XVIII's one-time refuge in exile (nowadays run by the
NT); Daniel Richardson's cuisine is "a treat" too – top tip is "go for
lunch" so you can enjoy "delightful views of the grounds" (plus a
"romantic stroll afterwards"). / Details: www.hartwell-house.com; 2m W
of Aylesbury on A418; 9.45 pm; no jeans or trainers; children: 4+.
Accommodation: 49 rooms, from £260.

Hengist £ 48 **❷❷❷**
7-9 High St ME20 7AX (01622) 719273
A "novel" modern interior within an "historic" (Tudor) shell adds
interest to a visit to this "relaxed" Gallic restaurant, which offers
"good and well-presented food using local ingredients"; lunch in
particular, offers "astonishingly good value".
/ Details: www.hengistrestaurant.co.uk; 10 pm; closed Mon & Sun D.

BABINGTON, SOMERSET

2–3B

Babington House

£ 55   ❷❷❶

BA11 3RW   (01373) 812266

This achingly hip, urbs-in-rure outpost of the Soho House group does what it does very well, offering "well-cooked straightforward food" in a "truly relaxed" country house environment; if you're not a member you need to stay to eat. / **Details:** www.babingtonhouse.co.uk; 11 pm; open to residents & members only; children: 16+ in the Orangery. **Accommodation:** 32 rooms, from £260.

BAGSHOT, SURREY

3–3A

The Latymer
Pennyhill Park Hotel

£ 92   ❷❸❷

London Rd GU19 5EU   (01276) 471774

With its "gorgeous" décor and "attentive" service, not to mention Michael Wignall's "fantastic" cuisine, this luxurious country house hotel's "impressive" standards can come as "a complete surprise" to first-time reporters; critics, though, can still find the style "a bit pretentious". / **Details:** www.exclusivehotels.co.uk; 9.15 pm, Fri & Sat 9.30 pm; closed Mon, Sat L & Sun; booking: max 8; children: 11. **Accommodation:** 123 rooms, from £315.

BAKEWELL, DERBYSHIRE

5–2C

The Monsal Head Hotel

£ 40   🅣

DE45 1NL   (01629) 640250

Tipped for its particularly "beautiful" Peak District location (overlooking a huge railway viaduct) and its "excellent range of beers", this former coaching inn inspires more mixed opinions food-wise – the fare, though, is generally at least "serviceable". / **Details:** www.monsalhead.com; just up from Ashford in the Water on the B6465; 9.30 pm, Sat & Sun 9 pm; no Amex. **Accommodation:** 7 rooms, from £90.

Piedaniels

£ 43   🅣

Bath St DE45 1BX   (01629) 812687

The Piedaniels are "very nice people" and all visitors tip this "hidden-away" restaurant in a beautiful village for its overall "good value for money". / **Details:** www.piedaniels-restaurant.com; 10.15 pm; closed Mon.

BALLANTRAE, SOUTH AYRSHIRE

7–2A

Glenapp Castle

£ 85   🅣

KA26 0NZ   (01465) 831212

This storybook castle attracts very limited feedback, but it's all to the effect that Adam Stokes's "beautiful" cuisine and the "amazing" surroundings are "up there with the best". / **Details:** www.glenappcastle.com; 9.30 pm; D only; children: 5+ after 7PM. **Accommodation:** 17 rooms, from £445.

BALLATER, ABERDEENSHIRE

9–3C

Darroch Learg

£ 61   ❷❸④

Braemar Rd AB35 5UX   (01339) 755443

"The best of everything!"; this Baronial-style country house hotel offers "surprisingly good" cooking, and the wine list to go with it is "thoughtful". / **Details:** www.darrochlearg.co.uk; on A93 W of Ballater; 9 pm; D only, ex Sun open L & D; no Amex. **Accommodation:** 12 rooms, from £130.

Green Inn   £ 62   ❷❷❷
9 Victoria Rd AB35 5QQ   (01339) 755701
With its "superb" cuisine and wonderfully warm service too, the
conservatory dining room of the O'Halloran family's restaurant-with-
*rooms "never fails to please"! / **Details:** www.green-inn.com; in centre of*
village, on the green; 9 pm; D only, closed Mon & Sun; no Amex; no shorts.
***Accommodation:** 3 rooms, from £60.*

BALQUHIDDER, PERTH AND KINROSS   9–3C

Monachyle Mhor   £ 64   ❷❸❶
FK19 8PQ   (01877) 384622
It certainly has a "magical" setting, and the Lewis family's homely
restaurant-with-rooms in the Trossachs National Park, wins high
acclaim for its "inventive" cuisine; service can be a bit "ragged",
though, and the odd critic finds the food "unexceptional".
*/ **Details:** www.mhor.net; take the Kings House turning off the A84; 8.45 pm;*
*children: 12+ at D. **Accommodation:** 14 rooms, from £128.*

BARNET, HERTFORDSHIRE   3–2B

Savoro   £ 39   ❷❷④
206 High St EN5 5SZ   (020) 8449 9888
"Nothing's challenging, but that's OK as you know what you're going
to get!", say fans of this low-key modern restaurant-with-rooms in the
town centre, which attracts praise for a menu that's "all home-
*made" and "amazing value". / **Details:** www.savoro.co.uk; 9.45 pm;*
*closed Sun D. **Accommodation:** 11 rooms, from £75.*

BARRASFORD, NORTHUMBERLAND   8–2A

Barrasford Arms   £ 39   ❷❷④
NE48 4AA   (01434) 681237
Tony Binks's "plain pub in an isolated village" is "worth a bit of a
trek" – its "robust" gastropub cuisine is some of the best of its type
*to be found in the North East. / **Details:** www.barrasfordarms.co.uk;*
9 pm; closed Mon L & Sun D; no Amex; children: 18 + in bar after 9.30pm.
***Accommodation:** 7 rooms, from £85.*

BARTON-ON-SEA, HAMPSHIRE   2–4C

Pebble Beach   £ 51   ❶❶❷
Marine Drive BH25 7DZ   (01425) 627777
"Atop the cliffs with amazing vistas towards the Isle of Wight", this
"spectacularly-located" venue sweeps practically all reporters away,
thanks not least to Pierre Chevillard's "expert" cuisine; fish, in
*particular, is "fabulous". / **Details:** www.pebblebeach-uk.com; 9 pm, Fri &*
*Sat 9.30 pm; booking advisable. **Accommodation:** 4 rooms, from £90.*

BARWICK, SOMERSET   2–3B

Little Barwick House   £ 63   ❶❷❸
BA22 9TD   (01935) 423902
A "real dining experience" rewards visitors to Tim & Emma Ford's
"lovely" Georgian dower house – a place where "staff work hard",
and the "dishes feature beautiful combinations of flavours".
*/ **Details:** www.littlebarwick.co.uk; take the A37 Yeovil to Dorchester road, turn*
left at the brown sign for Little Barwick House; Tue-Fri 9 pm, Sat 9.30 pm;
*closed Mon, Tue L & Sun D; no Amex; children: 5+ . **Accommodation:** 6*
rooms, from £69 pp.

The Cavendish   £ 54   🅣
Church Ln DE45 1SP   (01246) 582311
*On the Chatsworth Estate, a hotel in country-house style; it's
primarily tipped for its "comfortable" charms rather than food of
any particular note.* / *Details:* www.cavendish-hotel.net; J29 of the M1,
follow tourist signs to Chatsworth; 10 pm; no jeans or shorts.
Accommodation: 24 rooms, from £163.

Fischers at Baslow Hall   £ 69   ❶❷❷
Calver Rd DE45 1RR   (01246) 583259
*"A real class act"; this lovely Peak District restaurant-with-rooms has
gone from strength to strength in recent times, thanks not least to
Rupert Rowley's "locally-sourced food with a modern twist", often
realised to an "outstanding" level.*
/ *Details:* www.fischers-baslowhall.co.uk; on the A623; Sun-Fri 8.30 pm, Sat
9 pm; no jeans or trainers; children: 8+ at D, L (except Sun).
Accommodation: 11 rooms, from £155.

Bath Priory Hotel   £ 93   ❸❷❷
Weston Rd BA1 2XT   (01225) 331922
*For a "dignified" meal in "tranquil" surroundings, this "lovely"
country house hotel remains a highly-rated destination, thanks not
least to the "imaginative" cuisine from Michael Caines protégé Sam
Moody.* / *Details:* www.thebathpriory.co.uk; 1m W of city centre, past
Victoria Park; 9.30 pm; no jeans or trainers; children: 8+ D.
Accommodation: 31 rooms, from £260.

Beaujolais Bistro Bar   £ 42   ❹❸❸
5 Chapel Row, Queen Sq BA1 1HN   (01225) 423417
*The "longest-running restaurant in Bath" is a "pleasant" ("if hardly
earth-shattering") destination where lunch, in particular, can be
"excellent value".* / *Details:* next to Francis Hotel; 9.30 pm, Fri & Sat
10.30 pm; closed Mon L & Sun.

Casanis   £ 48   ❷❷❷
4 Saville Row BA1 2QP   (01225) 780055
*"A no-nonsense bistro, better than most I've found in France!" – a
"cramped" but "personable" and "good-value" spot, "tucked-away in
a narrow lane".* / *Details:* www.casanis.co.uk; 10 pm; closed Mon & Sun;
no Amex.

The Circus   £ 43   ❷❷❸
34 Brock St BA1 2LN   (01225) 466020
*This "convivial if cramped" spot near the Royal Crescent is "really
worth seeking out"; numerous reports attest to its "special" staff,
but also its "consistently good" food... and in "large portions" too!*
/ *Details:* www.thecircuscafeandrestaurant.co.uk; 10 pm; closed Sun; children:
7+ at D.

Demuths   £ 41   ❷❸❹
2 North Parade Pas BA1 1NX   (01225) 446059
*Back on form, the city's "best vegetarian" is a "small" and "slightly
basic" outfit on a cute pedestrian alley, offering "simple" but
"succulent" dishes; it's always "busy", though, and service can be
"slow".* / *Details:* www.demuths.co.uk; 9.30 pm; no Amex; booking: max 12.

The Dower House
Royal Crescent Hotel £ 85
16 Royal Cr BA1 2LS (01225) 823333

"A fantastic patio for summer eating" is a highlight at this secluded venue in the garden of this famous hotel; it has often seemed a *"grossly overpriced"* venue – whether this will change after its re-sale following the collapse of owners, Von Essen, remains to be seen (so we've left it un-rated). / **Details:** www.royalcrescent.co.uk; 9.30 pm; no jeans or trainers; booking: max 8. **Accommodation:** 45 rooms, from £199.

The Eastern Eye £ 35 ❷❷❷
8a Quiet St BA1 2JS (01225) 422323

An *"awe-inspiring"* Georgian room provides the somewhat unlikely setting for this *"huge"* Indian; the culinary style may be *"old-fashioned"*, but *"quality never wavers"*. / **Details:** www.easterneye.co.uk; 11.30 pm.

The Garrick's Head £ 46 ❹❹❸
7-8 St. John's Pl BA1 1ET (01225) 318368

"A compact dining room adjoining a busy town-centre pub" where *"well-sourced steaks are the star feature"*; a couple of disappointing reports this year tend to confirm suspicions of slippage *"downhill"*. / **Details:** www.garricksheadpub.com; 9 pm.

Hall & Woodhouse £ 43 ❷
1 Old King St BA1 2JW (01225) 469 259

This *"spectacular"* conversion of Bonham's old auction rooms features a *"magnificent staircase leading to a stunning roof terrace"*; *"always buzzing"*, it's tipped as *"a good place to meet up"*, even if the food can be *"unexciting"*. / **Details:** www.hall-woodhouse.co.uk; 9 pm; no Amex.

The Hole in the Wall £ 46 ❸❸❷
16 George St BA1 2EN (01225) 425242

Has the corner finally been turned?; most reports suggest that the quirky basement site – which, in the '50s, housed one of Britain's seminal post-war restaurants – is *"in the ascendant again"*; lunch and pre-theatre menus come particularly recommended. / **Details:** www.theholeinthewall.co.uk; 10 pm; closed Mon & Sun D.

The Hudson Bar & Grill £ 51 ❷
14 London St BA1 5BU (01225) 332323

"As an expat New Yorker, I was stunned to find the best steak in the world is in Bath!" – more reports please on this *"stylish restaurant above a bar"* which attracts few, but remarkably positive, reports. / **Details:** www.hudsonbars.co.uk; 10.30 pm; D only, closed Sun.

Jamie's Italian £ 41 ❹❹❸
10 Milsom Pl BA1 1BZ (01225) 432340

"Decent" food and *"accommodating"* staff – and of course the Jamie-branding – have made a hit of this *"pricey"* chain-outlet; as the group grows, though, there's a growing feeling that the food is *"not as good as it used to be"*. / **Details:** www.jamieoliver.com; 11 pm, Sun 10.30 pm; Booking 6+.

King William £ 45 ❸❸❹
36 Thomas Street BA1 5NN (01225) 428096

Is popularity leading to uneven standards at this *"charming, if somewhat crowded"* gastropub? – ratings dipped a little this year, but those praising its locally-sourced fare still outnumber disappointments by about two to one. / **Details:** www.kingwilliampub.com; 10 pm; closed Mon L & Tue L.

Marlborough Tavern £ 44 🅣
35 Marlborough Buildings BA1 2LY (01225) 423731
Just off the Royal Crescent – a gastropub tipped for its "inventive" cuisine and "nice beer garden" ("well, courtyard"); more reports please! / Details: www.marlborough-tavern.com; 9.30 pm, Fri & Sat 10 pm, Sun 9 pm; no Amex.

The Olive Tree
Queensberry Hotel £ 70 ❷❸❸
Russell St BA1 2QF (01225) 447928
*"Never lets you down", say fans of this "intimate" basement, who applaud a "long-standing favourite" with "beautifully-presented" cuisine; there are still sceptics, though, who feel the place is "not as good as it thinks it is", and who gripe at the "not insignificant" prices. / Details: www.thequeensberry.co.uk; 9.45 pm; closed Mon L.
Accommodation: 29 rooms, from £125.*

The Pump Room £ 46 🅣
Stall St BA1 1LZ (01225) 444477
Who cares if the service is sometimes "pretty useless", or the fare somewhat "pricey"? – this famous refreshment spot is still tipped for its "gorgeous" Georgian interior. / Details: www.searcys.co.uk; by the Abbey; L only; no booking, Sat & Sun.

Rajpoot £ 37 🅣
4 Argyle St BA2 4BA (01225) 466833
In an impressive Georgian cellar, an Indian restaurant whose all-round charms – including a handy location – make it a popular stand-by. / Details: www.rajpoot.com; 11 pm.

Raphael £ 39 🅣
Upper Borough Walls BA1 1RN (01225) 480042
"Very handy for the Theatre Royal", a city-centre stand-by "rather like an upmarket Café Rouge", especially tipped for its "reasonably-priced pre-performance meals". / Details: www.raphaelrestaurant.co.uk; 10.15 pm.

The Wheatsheaf £ 51 ❷❸❷
Combe Hay BA2 7EG (01225) 833504
*"A great find!" – this country inn has a "lovely setting", just 10 minutes outside the city, and is known for "bistro-style cooking of excellent quality"; this year's ratings, though, were knocked by the occasional "disappointing" report.
/ Details: www.wheatsheafcombehay.com; 9.30 pm; closed Mon & Sun D; no Amex. **Accommodation:** 4 rooms, from £120.*

The White Hart Inn £ 39 🅣
Widcombe Hill BA2 6AA (01225) 338053
*In a pleasant back street behind the railway station, a "cheery" pub tipped for food that's not only "affordable" but "consistently good".
/ Details: www.whitehartbath.co.uk; 10 pm; closed Sun D; no Amex.
Accommodation: 4 private, 24 dormitory beds rooms, from £25.*

Yen Sushi £ 33 🅣
11 Bartlett St BA1 2QZ (01225) 333313
Looking for "the best sushi in Bath"? – this cheap 'n' cheerful conveyor-café is the top tip locally. / Details: www.yensushi.co.uk; 10.30 pm.

The Wellington Arms £ 44 ❷❷❷
Baughurst Rd RG26 5LP (0118) 982 0110
"Run with real heart" – "with ambition and cooking skills to match" – this "small", "intimate" and "professional" inn ("more restaurant than pub") is widely hailed by reporters as a "gem"; "much of the produce is home-grown or very local".
/ **Details:** www.thewellingtonarms.com; 9.30 pm; closed Sun D; no Amex.

China Rose £ 38 ❷❷❸
16 South Pde DN10 6JH (01302) 710461
"Best Chinese in the area"; this rural Cantonese remains "very popular", thanks to its "unfailing standard of cuisine".
/ **Details:** www.chinarose-bawtry.co.uk; 10 pm, Fri & Sat 10.30 pm; D only.

Crazy Bear £ 61 ④④❷
HP9 1LX (01494) 673086
"If there was a rating for bling it would be off the charts!" – this "stunning" and "quirky" restaurant-with-rooms comes as "a big shock in the Home Counties"; but while the bar is "wonderful", the fare (both Thai and British in separate rooms) seems ever-more "average" and "vastly overpriced".
/ **Details:** www.crazybeargroup.co.uk/beaconsfield; 10 pm; children: Bar, not after 6pm. **Accommodation:** 10 rooms, from £345.

The Royal Standard Of England £ 40 Ⓣ
Brindle Ln HP9 1XS (01494) 673382
Tipped for its "good traditional pub food" and "agreeable country setting", this ancient boozer has been noted for "variability" of late; the recipe for success seems to be to "avoid Sunday lunch" – "the quality of food and service decline dramatically".
/ **Details:** www.rsoe.co.uk; 10.45 pm; no Amex.

Spice Merchant £ 45 ❷❸❸
33 London End HP9 2HW (01494) 675474
This "sophisticated" Indian hides a "luxurious" interior "behind a dull shop front" and maintains its reputation for "top-quality, fresh cuisine"; weather permitting, you can dine outside in "wonderful Bollywood style"! / **Details:** www.spicemerchantgroup.com; opp Beaconsfield wine cellar; 11 pm, Sun 9.30 pm.

The Wild Garlic £ 50 ④⑤④
4 The Sq DT8 3AS (01308) 861446
On a good day you can get a "very, very good" meal at the restaurant of Masterchef-winner Matt Follas; it's an "unexciting" sort of place, though, and there are quite a few critics who complain of "very average" food and in particular of "disappointing" service.
/ **Details:** www.thewildgarlic.co.uk; 9 pm; closed Mon D, Tue D & Sun D; no Amex. **Accommodation:** 1 room, at about £120.

Fish On The Green £ 53 ❸❷❸
Church Ln ME14 4EJ (01622) 738 300
"Just what Maidstone needs!" – this former coaching inn attracts consistent praise for its "delicious" food and its "bubbly service"; "very good-value set lunch" too. / **Details:** www.fishonthegreen.com.

The Loft Restaurant
Ye Olde Bull's Head   £ 67   🌸

Castle St LL58 8AP   (01248) 810329

The dining room (plus more modern brasserie) of this wonderful ancient inn inspires only limited feedback; such as it is, however, reporters tip its food as "of high quality" – "perhaps not the most ambitious, but well cooked". / Details: www.bullsheadinn.co.uk; on the High Street, opposite the Spar shop; 9.30 pm; D only, closed Sun; no jeans; children: 7+ at D. Accommodation: 26 rooms, from £110.

Devonshire Arms   £ 40   🌸

Devonshire Sq DE4 2NR   (01629) 733259

Tipped as a "romantic" all-rounder – a "charming" Chatsworth Estate inn where you can eat at the bar or in the "modern bistro". / Details: www.devonshirebeeley.co.uk; 9.30 pm; bookings for breakfast. Accommodation: 8 rooms, from £120.

Aldens   £ 40   ❷❷❸

229 Upper Newtownards Rd BT4 3JF   (028) 9065 0079

"Still a special night out"; in a scene without many long-term stars, this contemporarily-styled operation just outside the city-centre remains a "consistently good" performer – even a reporter who discerns the "occasional slip" confirms that standards are "generally excellent". / Details: www.aldensrestaurant.com; 2m from Stormont Buildings; 10 pm, Fri & Sat 10.30 pm; closed Sun D.

Cayenne   £ 45   ❷❷❸

7 Ascot Hs, Shaftesbury Sq BT2 7DB   (028) 9033 1532

"Paul Rankin is now back at the stoves" of this city-centre venture – hailed by almost all reporters for the "reliable quality" of its "interesting" (but "no-nonsense") fusion-based cuisine. / Details: www.cayenne-restaurant.co.uk; near Botanic Railway Station; 10 pm, Fri & Sat 11 pm; closed Tue & Sat L.

Deanes   £ 59   ❹❹❸

36-40 Howard St BT1 6PF   (028) 9056 0000

This "Belfast big-hitter" doesn't really impress reporters; there are views both strongly positive and negative, but the middle-course view is that it's "a bit pretentious all-round" (and "overpriced" too). / Details: www.michaeldeane.co.uk; near Grand Opera House; 10 pm; closed Sun.

Ginger   £ 44   🌸

7-8 Hope St BT2 5EE   (0871) 426 7885

All feedback, limited as it is, confirms that Simon McCance's sometimes "noisy" bistro makes a very superior lunch or dinner destination. / Details: www.gingerbistro.com; 9.30 pm, Mon 9 pm, Fri & Sat 10 pm; closed Mon L & Sun; no Amex.

James Street South   £ 50   ❷❷❹

21 James Street South BT2 7GA   (028) 9043 4310

Niall McKenna's "buzzy city-centre brasserie" has "high standards all-round"; it's an "efficient" sort of place, with "nicely spaced tables", and is particularly handy as a business rendezvous. / Details: www.jamesstreetsouth.co.uk; behind the City Hall, off Bedford Street; 10.45 pm, Sun 9 pm; closed Sun L.

The Merchant Hotel £ 66 ❷④❷
16 Skipper Street BT1 2DZ (028) 90234888
"'Seeming to be THE place to eat in Belfast at the moment" – this dining room in a former bank may inspire fewer reports than we'd like, but practically all of them confirm it as a "dazzling" space, with food that's good, "bordering on excellent".
/ **Details:** www.themerchanthotel.com; 9.45 pm, Sun 8.30 pm.
Accommodation: 62 rooms, from £220.

Mourne Seafood Bar £ 38 ❷❸❸
34-36 Bank St BT1 1HL (028) 9024 8544
"Superb fish and seafood at reasonable prices" wins very consistent support for this no-nonsense city-centre five-year-old – "a top tip for any visitor", according to one local; it also has a sibling in Dundrum.
/ **Details:** www.mourneseafood.com; beside Kelly Cellars; Tue & Wed 9.30 pm, Thu, Fri & Sat 10.30 pm, Sun 6 pm, Mon 5 pm; closed Mon D & Sun D.

Tedfords Restaurant £ 47 🅣
5 Donegall Quay BT1 3EA (028) 90434000
Especially tipped as a pre-theatre destination, this ambitious three-floor operation near the Waterfront Hall also attracts impressive feedback at other times – more reports please!
/ **Details:** www.tedfordsrestaurant.com; 9.30 pm; closed Mon, Tue L, Sat L & Sun; children: "not a family restaurant".

BENDERLOCH, ARGYLL AND BUTE	9–3B

Isle of Eriska £ 57 🅣
PA37 1SD (01631) 720371
On its own island, one of Scotland's top hotels, where "locally-sourced" cuisine is "always prepared to a very high standard".
/ **Details:** www.eriska-hotel.co.uk; 9 pm; D only; no jeans or trainers; children: 6pm; high tea for resident's chldren. **Accommodation:** 25 rooms, from £325.

BEVERLEY, EAST YORKSHIRE	6–2A

The Pipe & Glass Inn £ 52 ❶❷❶
West End HU17 7PN (01430) 810246
"Hallelujah!" – the "brilliant" food at James & Kate Mackenzie's "professional" but still "pubby" operation in a "pretty village" has rightly won acclaim; this all-purpose place is equally at home "for a ploughman's lunch outside on a sunny day, or a special dinner".
/ **Details:** www.pipeandglass.co.uk; 9.30 pm; closed Mon & Sun D; no Amex.

Whites £ 45 ❸❸❸
12-12a North Bar Without HU17 7AB (01482) 866121
The award of one of Michelin's bibs has won a flurry of attention for John Robinson's town-centre restaurant-with-rooms; most reporters do indeed profess themselves "well-pleased" with the ambitious cuisine – critics, though, can find it a bit "dull".
/ **Details:** www.whitesrestaurant.co.uk; 9 pm; closed Mon & Sun; no Amex; Booking essential. **Accommodation:** 4 rooms, from £85.

BIBURY, GLOUCESTERSHIRE	2–2C

Bibury Court
Bibury Court Hotel £ 61 🅣
GL7 5NT (01285) 740337
"A lovely house in a wonderful setting" – this Jacobean manor house is just the place for a "romantic" meal; its food has traditionally been highly rated – fingers crossed new chef, Nigel Godwin maintains standards. / **Details:** www.biburycourt.co.uk; 9 pm. **Accommodation:** 18 rooms, from £170.

Cayenne

nes Street South

lens

BIDDENDEN, KENT 3–4C

The Three Chimneys £ 47 **❷❷❸**
Hareplain Rd TN27 8LW (01580) 291472
In a "lovely rural setting", an inn whose "wide range of imaginative, contemporary dishes" is commended by almost all who comment on it; "book ahead". / Details: www.thethreechimneys.co.uk; A262 between Biddenden and Sissinghurst; 9.30 pm; no Amex.

The West House £ 52 **❶❷④**
28 High St TN27 8AH (01580) 291341
*Remarkably consistent feedback on Graham Garrett's "petite" restaurant in a "quaint" village – the food is "technically brilliant, with taste and imagination", but it rather eclipses the ambience, which is sometimes "very quiet".
/ Details: www.thewesthouserestaurant.co.uk; 8.45 pm; closed Mon, Sat L & Sun D; no Amex.*

BIGBURY-ON-SEA, DEVON 1–4C

Burgh Island Hotel £ 78 **④❷❶**
TQ7 4BG (01548) 810514
*"A fantastic hotel frozen in '20s style"; the food may be "just part of the experience", but all reporters confirm that a visit to this "romantic" Art Deco fantasy is "pure magic"!
/ Details: www.burghisland.com; 8.30 pm; D only, ex Sun open L & D; no Amex; jacket & tie; children: 12+ at D. Accommodation: 25 rooms, from £390.*

The Oyster Shack £ 52 **❶❷❸**
Millburn Orchard Farm, Stakes Hills TQ7 4BE
(01548) 810876
*"Absolutely fantastic seafood served by friendly people in a quirky setting" – that's the deal that draws an enthusiastic fan club for this "slightly shabby", but also "fun and happening", seaside spot.
/ Details: www.oystershack.co.uk; 9 pm.*

BILDESTON, SUFFOLK 3–1C

The Bildeston Crown
The Crown Hotel £ 56 **❶❷❸**
High St IP7 7EB (01449) 740510
*"London-style standards in a quiet Suffolk village" – most reporters find "truly impressive" quality all-round at this "smart" inn.
/ Details: www.thebildestoncrown.com; from the A14, take the B115 to Bildeston; 9.45 pm, Sun 9.30 pm. Accommodation: 12 rooms, from £150.*

BIRCHANGER, ESSEX 3–2B

The Three Willows £ 28 **❸❸④**
Birchanger Ln CM23 5QR (01279) 815913
"The only decent pub food for miles around" – with fish "cooked to perfection" the highlight – draws many admirers to this "welcoming" spot; it enjoys a location that's "surprisingly quiet, given its proximity to the M11". / Details: one mile from Birchanger Green service station on M11; 9 pm; closed Sun D; no Amex; children: 14.

BIRMINGHAM, WEST MIDLANDS 5–4C

Asha's Indian Bar and Restaurant £ 39 **❷④❷**
12-22 Newhall St B3 3LX (0121) 200 2767
You get "excellent" curries ("even if the prices do reflect it!") at this "first-class" city-centre spot, universally praised for its "very good" and "consistent" cuisine; it's "comfortable" too – "ideal for a birthday, or an anniversary". / Details: www.ashauk.co.uk; 10.30 pm; closed Sat L & Sun L.

Chung Ying Garden £ 35 ❷④④

17 Thorp St B5 4AT (0121) 666 6622
*"A veritable Chinatown bastion of Cantonese consistency for so
many years" – a "buzzy" sort of place where the "overwhelming"
menu, which includes some "great dim sum", "always delivers".*
/ Details: www.chungying.co.uk; 11 pm, Sun 10 pm.

Cielo £ 46 ④❸④

6 Oozells Sq B1 2JB (0121) 632 6882
*This "buzzy" Brindleyplace Italian "may be fairly conventional", but
it's a consistent and "convenient" spot (including for those with kids
in tow); set deals are particularly worth seeking out.*
*/ Details: www.cielobirmingham.com; 11 pm, 10 pm Sun; Max booking: 20,
Sat & Sun D.*

Edmunds £ 60 ❷❷❸

6 Central Sq B1 2JB (0121) 633 4944
*"Secure", "safe", "convenient" – the sort of adjectives often used to
describe this much commented-on Brindleyplace all-rounder, where
the cuisine is almost invariably "of high quality".*
/ Details: www.edmundsbirmingham.com; 10 pm; closed Mon, Sat L & Sun.

Henry Wong £ 34 ❸④④

283 High St B17 9QH (0121) 427 9799
*"Better than the Brum average" – this Harborne institution is
praised for its "top-end" Chinese cuisine. / Details: close to Bengal Hall;
11 pm; closed Sun.*

Hotel du Vin et Bistro £ 51 ④④④

25 Church St B3 2NR (0121) 200 0600
*Handily located in the city centre, a "reliable" – some would say
"pedestrian" – outpost of the wine-led hotel-bistro chain; typically for
the group, it's the "unusual" and "interesting" wine list which is the
safest attraction. / Details: www.hotelduvin.co.uk; 10 pm, Fri & Sat
10.30 pm; booking: max 12. Accommodation: 66 rooms, from £160.*

Itihaas £ 42 ❷⑤④

18 Fleet St B3 1JL (0121) 212 3383
*At its best, this "opulent" city-centre spot offers a "refreshing" take
on Indian food and a "lovely" experience overall; performance varies,
though – "we went after they'd just finished filming for a show which,
on our experience, should have been called Michel Roux's
Abominable Service!" / Details: www.itihaas.co.uk; 10 pm; closed Sat L &
Sun L.*

Jyoti £ 20 ⓣ

105 Stratford Rd B28 8AS (0121) 77855501
*A well-maintained city-centre spot, tipped for "good-quality" Gujarati
(veggie) fare at "ridiculously low" prices. / Details: www.jyotis.co.uk;
10 pm; closed Mon, Tue-Thu D only; no Amex.*

Lasan £ 53 ❶❷❸

3-4 Dakota Buildings, James St B3 1SD (0121) 212 3664
*In the city-centre, this "special-occasion Indian" has made a big
name for its "subtle", "light" and "inventive" cuisine and
"considerate" service too. / Details: www.lasan.co.uk; 11 pm; closed Sat L.*

Opus Restaurant £ 48 ❷❷❸

54 Cornwall St B3 2DE (0121) 200 2323
*"Very good food", "attentive" service and some "interesting" and
"affordable" wines – all help maintain the appeal of this well-spaced
city-centre spot as a "perfect" business rendezvous.*
/ Details: www.opusrestaurant.co.uk; 9.30 pm; closed Sat L & Sun.

Purnells £ 69 ❶❷❷
55 Cornwall St B3 2DH (0121) 212 9799
"Exciting and imaginative cooking of the highest standard" makes
Glynn Purnell's contemporary venture the jewel in the crown of
Brum's city-centre options; *"reasonable weekday lunch prices"* add to
its appeal as a business rendezvous.
/ **Details:** www.purnellsrestaurant.com; 9.15 pm; closed Mon, Sat L & Sun;
children: 6+.

San Carlo £ 44 ❹❹❸
4 Temple St B2 5BN (0121) 633 0251
"It could be Italy", says one of the fans of this *"buzzy"* city-centre
spot of long standing, to whom the *"authentic"* waiting staff (*"easily
distracted by a pretty face"*) add *"plenty of atmosphere"*; in terms of
both fame and overall quality, however, it now lags its Manchester
spin-off by some margin. / **Details:** www.sancarlo.co.uk; near St Philips
Cathedral; 11 pm.

Shimla Pinks £ 46 🆃
255 Broad St B15 1AY (0121) 633 0366
*Now in a new location, this once-famous Indian is still sometimes
tipped for its "high-quality" cuisine, though more sceptical reporters
feel it's "not bad" but "not cheap" either.*
/ **Details:** www.shimlapinks.com; 11 pm; closed Sat L & Sun L.

Simpsons £ 72 ❶❶❷
20 Highfield Rd B15 3DU (0121) 454 3434
"The best restaurant in the West Midlands!"; Andreas Antona's
gracious Georgian villa in leafy Edgbaston wows reporters with the
sheer all-round quality of the experience, not least his
"craftsmanlike" contemporary cuisine.
/ **Details:** www.simpsonsrestaurant.co.uk; 9 pm, Fri & Sat 9.30 pm; closed
Sun D. **Accommodation:** 4 rooms, from £160.

Turners £ 80 ❷❸❹
69 High St B17 9NS (0121) 426 4440
*It may occupy "a nondescript bit of high street" but Richard Turner's
"unlikely" Harborne venture has won deserved renown, thanks to
the "superb" seasonal cuisine that's amongst the best in the
Midlands; even fans, though, can baulk at the ambitious prices.*
/ **Details:** www.turnersofharborne.com; 9.30 pm; closed Mon & Sun; no Amex.

BISHOPS STORTFORD, HERTFORDSHIRE 3–2B

Baan Thitiya £ 37 ❷❷❸
102 London Rd CM23 3DS (01279) 658575
"Good food in Bishops Stortford, who would have thought it?" – this
Thai restaurant in a former pub is praised by almost all reporters for
its *"freshly prepared"* cuisine and its *"friendly and attentive"* service.
/ **Details:** www.baan-thitiya.com; 11 pm.

BISHOPS TACHBROOK, WARWICKSHIRE 5–4C

Mallory Court £ 84 ❷❷❷
Harbury Ln CV33 9QB (01926) 330214
*This Lutyens-designed country house hotel pleases most reporters all
round, especially as a destination for a "memorable" celebration
meal, even if its style – in the new brasserie as much as in the
"romantic" main dining room – can sometimes seem a touch
"formal".* / **Details:** www.mallory.co.uk; 2m S of Leamington Spa, off B4087;
8.30 pm; closed Sat L. **Accommodation:** 30 rooms, from £139.

Eagle & Child £ 37 🕔

Maltkiln Ln L40 3SG (01257) 462297

"A reliable English pub without pretensions"; it's consistently tipped by reporters for its "good, traditional fare".

/ **Details:** www.ainscoughs.co.uk; M6, J27; 8.30 pm; no Amex.

BLACKPOOL, LANCASHIRE 5–1A

Kwizeen £ 37 ②②④

47-49 King St FY1 3EJ (01253) 290045

"A good find in Blackpool amongst the takeaways and burger bars"; this well-established back street operation attracts consistent praise for cooking that's "all home-made" and makes "great use of local ingredients" – don't miss the "utterly delicious ice cream".

/ **Details:** www.kwizeenrestaurant.co.uk; 100 yards inland from the Winter Gardens; 9 pm; closed Sun; no Amex; no shorts.

BLAIRGOWRIE, PERTH AND KINROSS 9–3C

Kinloch House £ 73 ②②③

PH10 6SG (01250) 884237

"A wonderful experience"; this "very smart and very professional" Georgian country house hotel boasts "exceptional" service, and chef Steve MacCallum (who joined in 2009) has "taken the food up a further notch" in recent times. / **Details:** www.kinlochhouse.com; past the Cottage Hospital, turn L, procede 3m along A923, (signposted Dunkeld Road); 8.30 pm; jacket required. **Accommodation:** 18 rooms, from £230.

BODIAM, EAST SUSSEX 3–4C

The Curlew £ 48 ②③③

Junction Rd TN32 5UY (01580) 861 394

"Many locals were surprised by the award of a Michelin star", but this "modern restaurant in an old pub" seems, if anything, to have gone backwards since being blessed by the tyre men; service has had notable 'downs' as well as 'ups', and the food is "good… but not that good". / **Details:** www.thecurlewrestaurant.co.uk; 9.30 pm; closed Mon & Tue; no Amex.

BODSHAM, KENT 3–3C

Froggies at The Timber Batts £ 55 ②④④

School Ln TN25 5JQ (01233) 750237

Joel Gros's "beautiful pub, with a decent French restaurant" makes "an excellent local choice" and it continues to impress most (if not quite all) of the reporters who comment on it; "they take dogs too!" / **Details:** www.thetimberbatts.co.uk; come through Wye, then Hastingsleigh and Bodsham is the next village; 9 pm; closed Mon & Sun D; booking essential.

BOLNHURST, BEDFORDSHIRE 3–1A

The Plough at Bolnhurst £ 40 ②③③

MK44 2EX (01234) 376274

"A bit of an oasis in this part of the world", this "inventive" gastropub has made quite a name for fare that's "tasty, seasonal and hearty"; it benefits from a "lovely rural location" too. / **Details:** www.bolnhurst.com; 9.30 pm; closed Mon & Sun D; no Amex.

Burlington
The Devonshire Arms £ 95 ④❷❷
BD23 6AJ (01756) 718 111
The "lovely location lifts the experience" of a visit to this grand,
ducally-owned Dales inn whose main restaurant is a renowned foodie
Mecca, complete with "biblical wine list"; "it all feels a little Michelin-
reverential", though, and critics feel that "the food could be better,
given the reputation". / **Details:** www.thedevonshirearms.co.uk.

The Devonshire Brasserie
The Devonshire Arms £ 46 ⓣ
BD23 6AJ (01756) 710710
Some reporters "deliberately opt for the brasserie over the over-
formal main restaurant" at this upmarket Dales hotel, which is
tipped as "a great alternative to the main restaurant".
/ **Details:** www.devonshirehotels.co.uk; on A59, 5m NE of Skipton; 9 pm, Fri &
Sat 9.30 pm. **Accommodation:** 40 rooms, from £200.

The Manor Restaurant
Eastwell Manor £ 55 ④❸❷
Eastwell Pk TN25 4HR (01233) 213000
"A glorious Elizabethan manor house in a beautiful setting" – the
odd critic finds its rather "traditional" cuisine merely "average", but
the dining experience as a whole is generally hailed as being
"altogether memorable". / **Details:** www.eastwellmanor.co.uk; 3m N of
Ashford on A251; 9.30 pm; no jeans or shorts; booking: max 8.
Accommodation: 62 rooms, from £180.

The Mulberry Tree
 £ 36 ❸④❸
Hermitage Ln ME17 4DA (01622) 749082
Reviews on this "off-the-beaten-track" restaurant (with courtyard
garden) remain a little mixed, but there's some evidence that the
new chef is tightening up standards – supporters insist it's now a real
"value for money" destination that's "well worth seeking out".
/ **Details:** www.themulberrytreekent.co.uk; 9 pm, Fri & Sat 9.30 pm; closed
Mon & Sun D; no Amex.

Chez Fred
 £ 21 ❷④④
10 Seamoor Rd BH4 9AN (01202) 761023
Over 30 years in business, the Capel family's chippy continues to
please all reporters with its "lovely fish 'n' chips"; it's "crowded",
though, and don't be surprised if there's a queue.
/ **Details:** www.chezfred.co.uk; 1m W of town centre; 9.45 pm, 9 Sun; closed
Sun L; no Amex; no booking.

Edge
 £ 53 ⓣ
2 Studland Rd BH4 8JA (01202) 757 007
"On the top floor of a new development overlooking the beach at
Durley Chine", this relative newcomer is tipped for its "superb view"
(and it has a "striking" interior too); the food can be "excellent", but
it can also be "rather ordinary". / **Details:** www.edgerestaurant.co.uk;
9.30 pm.

Ocean Palace £ 33 Ⓣ
8 Priory Rd BH2 5DG (01202) 559127
A very busy Chinese of long standing, still tipped for its "huge" menu, realised to a "good" standard (and offering particular value at lunch); arguably, however, "it could do with a serious facelift".
/ Details: www.oceanpalace.co.uk; 11 pm.

WestBeach £ 48 ❸❸❷
Pier Approach BH2 5AA (01202) 587785
"A great position overlooking the sea" ensure that this "professional" operation inspires a good number of reports; but while that's its key strength, most reporters say its fish and seafood are "always delicious" too. / Details: www.west-beach.co.uk; 10 pm.

BOURTON ON HILL, GLOUCESTERSHIRE 2–1C

Horse & Groom £ 39 ❷❷❷
GL56 9AQ (01386) 700413
Will and Tom Greenstock's well-acclaimed, stone-clad Cotswold inn – a fine listed Georgian building – is an all-round crowd-pleaser; "helpful" staff serve a "very-interesting, locally-sourced menu" and achieve "first-class" results. / Details: www.horseandgroom.info.

BRADFORD, WEST YORKSHIRE 5–1C

Aagrah £ 37 ❷❸④
Thornbury BD3 7AY (01274) 668818
A large outpost of the famous NE subcontinental chain; fans insist it's still "better than the other superstar Bradford curry houses", but its ratings were a shade less stellar this year.
/ Details: www.aagrah.com; 11.30 pm; closed Mon-Thu L & Sat L.

Akbar's £ 27 ❷❷❸
1276 Leeds Rd BD3 8LF (01274) 773311
Reports on "the best curry house for miles around" are difficult to disentangle from those on its "often crowded" unlicensed café offshoot (at 524 Leeds Road, 01274 737458); fortunately, the food at both is usually "wonderful". / Details: www.akbars.co.uk; midnight, Sun 11.30 pm; D only; l.

Karachi £ 15 ❷❷⑤
15-17 Neal St BD5 0BX (01274) 732015
"So plain, but so right"; this Formica-tabled veteran – the city's oldest subcontinental – wins praise for "the best curry ever", and at a keen price too. / Details: l am, 2 am Fri & Sat; no credit cards.

Mumtaz £ 27 ❷❸④
Great Horton Rd BD7 3HS (01274) 571861
Many reports confirm it's "a good all-round experience" to visit this "buzzy" ("Bollywood-style") curry house which is nowadays decked out in very contemporary idiom; culinarily speaking, though, it's no longer quite the stand-out it once was. / Details: www.mumtaz.com; midnight.

Prashad £ 24 ❷❷❸
86 Horton Grange Rd BD7 2DW (01274) 575893
"Zingy" South Indian veggie food that fans say is "exquisite" (plus a spot of publicity, courtesy of Gordon Ramsay) is making quite a name for this "inventive" spot; be warned, though – "alcohol is not allowed". / Details: www.prashad.co.uk; 10.30 pm; closed Mon; no Amex.

Zouk £ 34 🅣

1312 Leeds Rd BD3 8LF (01274) 258 025

We don't yet have enough reports for a full listing, but this two-year-old establishment is tipped by its small fan club as offering 'new-generation' Indian food that's "as good as you'll find anywhere"; "shame about the ambience", though. / **Details:** www.zoukteabar.co.uk; midnight; no Amex; no shorts.

BRAMPTON, CUMBRIA 7–2D

Farlam Hall £ 59 ❸❷❸

CA8 2NG (01697) 746234

"Not adventurous, but reliable", this family-run country house hotel really pleases most reporters with its "'70s time-warped" style; for one (74-year-old) reporter, however, the approach feels a little too "formal and proper"! / **Details:** www.farlamhall.co.uk; 2.5m S.E of Brampton on A689, not in Farlam Village; 8.30 pm; D only; no shorts; children: 5+. **Accommodation:** 12 rooms, from £200.

BRAMPTON, DERBYSHIRE 5–2C

Nonsolovino £ 42 ❷❷❸

417 Chatsworth Rd S40 3AD (01246) 276760

This "ambitious" small venue – "a light and airy space, attached to an Italian wine merchant" – "marries an upmarket wine bar with a high-end restaurant"; it can seem an "unlikely" format, but its "good value" dishes (and "fine selection" of vintages) makes it popular with all who comment on it. / **Details:** www.nonsolovino.co.uk; 9.30 pm; closed Mon.

BRANCASTER STAITHE, NORFOLK 6–3B

The White Horse £ 43 ④④❷

Main Rd PE31 8BY (01485) 210262

"After a morning striding over the marshes", fans say you get "great food" and "lovely views of the North Norfolk coast" at this well-known fish-specialist gastropub; there's quite a feeling, though, that its cuisine has become a touch "uneven" of late.
/ **Details:** www.whitehorsebrancaster.co.uk; 9 pm; no Amex.
Accommodation: 15 rooms, from £134.

BRANSCOMBE, DEVON 2–4A

Masons Arms £ 41 🅣

Main St EX12 3DJ (01297) 680300

An idyllic boozer, tipped for its "very good food and delightful setting" (and "the best staff" too). / **Details:** www.masonsarms.co.uk; 9 pm; no Amex; children: 14+ in restaurant. **Accommodation:** 21 rooms, from £85.

BRAY, BERKSHIRE 3–3A

Caldesi in Campagna £ 61 ❶❷❸

Old Mill Ln SL6 2BG (01628) 788500

"Lunch was a triumph, what more can I say?"; with its "true Italian family welcome" and "excellent cuisine", Giancarlo Caldesi's two-year-old Tuscan is a destination with which no one finds any real fault. / **Details:** www.caldesi.com; 9.30 pm; closed Mon & Sun D.

Crown Inn
£ 47 ④④❸

High St SL6 2AH (01628) 621936

Divided views on the "lovely" old inn recently added to Heston's burgeoning portfolio; fans insist it "still feels like a local pub", and that the food is "tasty" and "reasonably-priced" – almost as many critics, though, find the product rather "sanitised".
/ **Details:** www.crownatbray.co.uk; opposite the village hall; 9.30 pm, Fri & Sat 10.30 pm; booking essential.

The Fat Duck
£215 ❷❷❸

High St SL6 2AQ (01628) 580333

"The most wonderful gastronomic experience of my life!" – Heston Blumenthal's world-famous shrine to "theatrical" molecular gastronomy ("like a journey through Alice in Wonderland!") still bedazzles most reporters; the utterly "astronomical" prices seem ever-more "gouging", however… and are still rising.
/ **Details:** www.thefatduck.co.uk; 9 pm; closed Mon & Sun D.

The Hind's Head
£ 51 ❷❷❷

High St SL6 2AB (01628) 626151

"Simple genius comes at sensible prices" at this "Heston-lite" village inn – "a benchmark among gastropubs" serving "superb old British dishes, better than mother used to make" in a "lovely relaxed setting"; gripes? – service is sometimes "tardy".
/ **Details:** www.hindsheadbray.com; from the M4 take exit to Maidenhead Central, then go to Bray village; 9.30 pm; closed Sun D.

Riverside Brasserie
£ 63 🅣

Monkey Island Ln, Bray Marina SL6 2EB (01628) 780553

"Al freso dining at its best, and romantic too!" – perhaps because it's hard-to-find and open in summer only, there are only a few reports on this outfit in Bray Marina, where "the setting makes for a lovely meal". / **Details:** www.riversidebrasserie.co.uk; follow signs for Bray Marina off A308; 9.30 pm.

Waterside Inn
£126 ❶❷❶

Ferry Rd SL6 2AT (01628) 620691

"Everything I hoped and expected!" – the Roux family's "blissful" Thames-sider may be turning 40 this year, but remains "perfect in every way" – not least its "superlative, traditional Gallic cuisine"; prices are "ludicrous", naturally… but the odd thing is that hardly any reporters actually seem to begrudge paying 'em!
/ **Details:** www.waterside-inn.co.uk; off A308 between Windsor & Maidenhead; 10 pm; closed Mon & Tue; no jeans or trainers; booking: max 10; children: 14+ D. **Accommodation:** 13 rooms, from £200.

BREARTON, NORTH YORKSHIRE
8–4B

The Malt Shovel
£ 46 ❶❶❷

HG3 3BX (01423) 862929

This "beautiful" pub "nestles in an amazing chocolate box village" and serves up "delicious" food… but "it's the friendliness of the owners, the Bleiker family, which makes it special".
/ **Details:** www.themaltshovelbrearton.co.uk; off A61, 6m N of Harrogate; 9.30 pm; closed Mon, Tue & Sun D; no Amex; need 8+ to book.

BRECON, POWYS
2–1A

The Felin Fach Griffin
£ 46 ❷❷❸

Felin Fach LD3 0UB (01874) 620111

"Everything a country gastropub should be" – the gist of practically all of the many and enthusiastic reports on this "beautiful inn set at the foot of the Brecon Beacons", which rightly remains "very popular". / **Details:** www.eatdrinksleep.ltd.uk; 20 mins NW of Abergavenny on A470; 9 pm; no Amex. **Accommodation:** 7 rooms, from £115.

Pappadums
£ 36   ❷❷❸

Ferry Quays, Ferry Ln TW8 0BT   (020) 8847 1123
*"Assured and interesting" cooking, and "lovely, friendly staff" help make this popular Indian one of Brentford's prime claims to culinary fame; it also has a "delightful" location – "near a little marina at the side of the Thames". / **Details:** www.pappadums.co.uk; 9 pm, Sat 11 pm, Sun 10.30 pm.*

The Bull Hotel
£ 43   🅣

34 East St DT6 3LF   (01308) 422878
*An old coaching inn tipped for food that's often "surprisingly good" nowadays; critics, however, feel that "service needs a shift up". / **Details:** www.thebullhotel.co.uk; 9.30 pm. **Accommodation:** 19 rooms, from £85.*

Hive Beach Cafe
£ 39   ❸④❷

Beach Rd DT6 4RF   (01308) 897070
*This "bustling" seaside café, "beautifully situated" right on the beach, is much praised for its "unfussy style" and "wonderfully fresh fish and seafood"; critics like the concept, but find the place "too busy" and pricey. / **Details:** www.hivebeachcafe.co.uk; refer to website, changes all year; no bookings. **Accommodation:** 2 rooms, from £95.*

Riverside
£ 55   ❷❸❸

West Bay DT6 4EZ   (01308) 422011
*"Slightly old-fashioned, but none the worse for that", this "homely" survivor from the '60s retains a massive following among reporters for its "well-cooked and extremely fresh fish", and the puddings are "a delight". / **Details:** www.thefishrestaurant-westbay.co.uk; 9 pm; closed Mon & Sun D; no Amex.*

The Stable
£ 33   🅣

34 East St DT6 3LF   (01308) 422878
*"Great food, good for kids, and a lovely building too" – this "cider house, pizza and pies" operation is a top tip as a destination for all the family. / **Details:** www.thestabledorset.co.uk.*

Brook's
£ 41   🅣

6 Bradford Rd HD6 1RW   (01484) 715284
*"Always a pleasant experience" – a popular Pennines eatery not far from the M62, tipped by a number of reporters for its all-round quality. / **Details:** www.brooks-restaurant.co.uk; 11 pm; D only, closed Sun; no Amex.*

Basketmakers Arms
£ 28   🅣

12 Gloucester Rd BN1 4AD   (01273) 689006
*For "genuine pub food", this small boozer in North Laine offers "many tasty specials", and it's often "very crowded". / **Details:** 8.30 pm; no booking.*

Bill's at the Depot £ 36 ❷❸❷
100 North Rd, The Depot BN1 1YE (01273) 692894
"Don't be put off by the healthy exterior!" – this *"very lively"*, *"barn-style canteen"* in North Laine is especially well known for its *"scrummy"* breakfasts, *"fabulous"* brunches and *"grandiose cakes"*; *"get there early, or face the queues"*.
/ **Details:** www.billsproducestore.co.uk; 10 pm; no Amex.

Casa Don Carlos £ 30 ❷❷❷
5 Union St BN1 1HA (01273) 327177
"Fun and frantic but always efficient", this *"friendly"* tapas bar in the Lanes is an *"authentic"* sort of place whose *"tasty"* dishes impress all who comment on it. / **Details:** 10.30 pm.

The Chilli Pickle £ 39 ❶❷❷
17 Jubilee St BN1 1GE (01273) 900 383
"Much bigger in the new location but still maintaining excellent standards" – this *"friendly"* operation is, say fans, *"by far the best Indian in town"*, attracting universal praise for its *"terrific"* cooking.
/ **Details:** www.thechillipickle.com; 10.30pm, Sun 10.15pm; closed Tue.

China Garden £ 36 ❷❷❸
88-91 Preston St BN1 2HG (01273) 325124
"Very good and dependable" at any time, this Hove/Brighton-border Chinese is of particular note for *"the best dim sum"* – visit at weekends, and there's a *"great atmosphere"* too.
/ **Details:** www.chinagarden.name; opp West Pier; 11.30 pm.

The Restaurant at Drakes
Drakes Hotel £ 56 ❷❸❸
44 Marine Pde BN2 1PE (01273) 696934
"One of Brighton's few fine dining experiences", this *"good but pricey"* Kemp Town spot impresses almost all who comment on it; *"the only real drawback is the basement setting"*.
/ **Details:** www.therestaurantatdrakes.co.uk; 9.45 pm. **Accommodation:** 20 rooms, from £105.

Due South £ 41 ❷❷❷
139 King's Road Arches BN1 2FN (01273) 821218
No wonder this *"lovely seafront restaurant"* inspires so many upbeat reports – it combines a *"stunning location"* with a *"well-balanced menu"* (using *"very fresh produce"*) and an *"excellent wine list"*; *"friendly and attentive"* service does nothing to let the side down either. / **Details:** www.duesouth.co.uk; Brighton Beach, below the Odeon cinema; 9.45 pm.

English's £ 44 ④④④
29-31 East St BN1 1HL (01273) 327980
This *"historic"* Lanes seafood *"icon"* (of over 150 years' standing) again inspired mixed feedback this year; the safest bet is to go for oysters al fresco – otherwise, this very *"traditional"* operation can seem rather too much *"in need of a refurb"*.
/ **Details:** www.englishs.co.uk; 10 pm, Sun 9.30 pm.

Fishy Fishy £ 45 ❸❷❸
36 East St BN1 1HL (01273) 723750
"Good sustainable fish at good prices" – that's the mantra that wins very consistent support for this *"friendly"* seafood bistro in a townhouse in the Lanes. / **Details:** www.fishyfishy.co.uk; the Pavillion end of East Street; 9.30 pm, Fri & Sat 10 pm.

Food for Friends £ 37 ❷❷❸
17-18 Prince Albert St BN1 1HF (01273) 202310
A "small and friendly" café in the Lanes that's won a good following
for its "interesting and different" veggie fare; perhaps surprisingly,
"great cocktails" too. / *Details: www.foodforfriends.com; in the Lanes,
South end; 10 pm, Fri & Sat 10.30 pm; no booking, Sat L & Sun L.*

The Ginger Dog £ 41 ❷❸❸
12 College Pl BN2 1HN (01273) 620 990
"A worthy addition to the Gingerman empire", this Kemp Town
corner boozer is a "fun" and "bustling" sort of place, offering
gastropub food "of London quality".
/ *Details: www.gingermanrestaurants.com; off Eastern Road near Brighton
College; 10 pm.*

The Ginger Pig £ 41 ❷❶❷
3 Hove St BN3 2TR (01273) 736123
A "buzzy" Hove hang-out, offering "interesting" gastropub dishes
that are "always of good quality", plus "top-quality wines at fair
prices"; this is, say fans, "the most consistently reliable eatery in
Brighton" – "hard to get into, but worth it".
/ *Details: www.gingermanrestaurant.com; 10 pm; no trainers.*

Gingerman £ 47 ❶❷❷
21a Norfolk Sq BN1 2PD (01273) 326688
"The original, and by far the best"; the cradle of Ben McKellar's
'Ginger' empire may be a "very small" and "intimate" operation, but
its "terrific" (if "not cutting-edge") cooking maintains its position as
"the top restaurant in Brighton".
/ *Details: www.gingermanrestaurants.com; off Norfolk Square; 9.45 pm;
closed Mon.*

Graze £ 48 ❷❷❸
42 Western Rd BN3 1JD (01273) 823707
In Hove, this "delightful" neighbourhood spot (part of the Bath Ales
group) has won quite a following for its small-plates grazing formula,
and fans say its "intimate" style makes it a romantic choice too.
/ *Details: www.graze-restaurant.co.uk; 9.30 pm.*

Hotel du Vin et Bistro £ 49 ❺❹❸
Ship St BN1 1AD (01273) 718588
"Quality slides, but prices remain high" at this potentially "beautiful"
dining room which is poorly-served by its "complacent" approach; for
consolation, look to the "extensive" wine list.
/ *Details: www.hotelduvin.com; 9.45 pm; booking: max 10.*
Accommodation: 49 rooms, from £210.

Indian Summer £ 40 ❶❷❸
69 East St BN1 1HQ (01273) 711001
"You thought you had eaten Indian food before? – try it here!";
"every dish has distinct and beautifully-balanced spicing" says one of
the many fans of the cuisine at this "creative" Lanes spot.
/ *Details: www.indian-summer.org.uk; 10.30 pm; closed Mon L.*

Jamie's Italian £ 41 ❸❸❸
11 Black Lion St BN1 1ND (01273) 915480
Jamie O's "large" and "buzzy" ("loud") chain-outlet in the Lanes still
strikes most reporters as a "fun" sort of place; the food is generally
held to be "pretty authentic" too, but – as at other members of the
group – ratings are on the wane. / *Details: www.jamieoliver.com; 11 pm,
Sun 10.30 pm; need 6+ to book.*

The Meadow Restaurant £ 45 ❸❷❸
64 Western Rd BN3 2JQ   (01273) 721182
*In a former Hove banking hall, "an open and spacious modern restaurant" whose "good, locally-sourced menu" pleases most reporters; it's the "impeccable" service, though, which particularly impresses. / **Details:** www.themeadowrestaurant.co.uk; 9.30 pm; closed Mon & Sun D; no Amex; no shorts.*

Pub du Vin
Hotel du Vin £ 49 ⓣ
7 Ship St BN1 1AD   (01273) 718588
*A pub version of the Hotel du Vin brand, which has a handy location just off the seafront, and is (mostly) tipped for "first-class", "traditional-with-a-twist" scoff. / **Details:** www.hotelduvin.co.uk/pub-du-vin; 10 pm; no shorts. **Accommodation:** 49 rooms, from £220.*

The Regency £ 29 ❸❸❸
131 Kings Rd BN1 2HH   (01273) 325014
*"Very busy at times, and you can see why!" – this "old-style", tiled seafront spot (complete with "bright lighting and Formica tables") is best known for its "very good fish 'n' chips", but its range of (mainly fishy) fare is in fact quite extensive. / **Details:** www.theregencyrestaurant.co.uk; opp West Pier; 11 pm. **Accommodation:** 30 rooms, from £60.*

Riddle & Finns £ 47 ❷❷❸
12a Meeting House Ln BN1 1HB   (01273) 323008
*In the Lanes, a "quirky", "friendly" and "lively" fish and oyster bar where candelabra adorn each of the high marble counters (be prepared to share); the food is "always of high quality" and the wine (and Champagne) list is pretty good too; no bookings. / **Details:** www.riddleandfinns.co.uk; 10 pm, Sat & Sun late; No reservations; waiting list policy.*

Sam's Of Brighton £ 42 ❷❸❸
1 Paston Pl BN2 1HA   (01273) 676222
*"Improved" in its second full year of operation, Sam Metcalfe's "unpretentious" Kemp Town bistro is a "reliable" and "enjoyable" sort of place offering a "very good choice" of "confident" dishes; at peak times, though, it can feel "cramped" and "noisy". / **Details:** www.samsofbrighton.co.uk; directly opposite County Hospital; 10 pm, Sun 8 pm.*

Terre à Terre £ 47 ❷❷❸
71 East St BN1 1HQ   (01273) 729051
*"Brilliant" dishes "brimming with flavour" have won renown for this "inventive" Lanes fixture as "the UK's best veggie restaurant"; a number of former fans have found the experience "more frenetic" of late, however, and the cooking a touch "hit-and-miss". / **Details:** www.terreaterre.co.uk; 10.30 pm; booking: max 8 at weekends.*

BRINKWORTH, WILTSHIRE   2–2C

The Three Crowns £ 41 ⓣ
The St SN15 5AF   (01666) 510366
*"A favourite haunt for Swindonians" – this favourite gastropub shows "no sign of complacency despite no competition hereabouts"; it also "offers easy access from the M4 to break a journey". / **Details:** www.threecrowns.co.uk; opposite church in middle of village; 9.30 pm, Sun 9 pm.*

A Cappella   £ 25   🅣
184c, Wells Rd, Lower Knowle BS4 2AL   (0117) 9713377
*A small café between Totterdown and Knowle where "the star of the
show is the evening pizza" – "beautiful thin and crispy bases with
lovely fresh toppings"; you can BYO too (corkage £1).*
/ **Details:** www.acappellas.co.uk.

The Albion   £ 47   ❷❹❷
Boyces Ave BS8 4AA   (0117) 973 3522
*"Hearty, quality gastropub fare in a delightful setting in Clifton
Village" – that's the appeal that keeps this busy 'public house &
dining rooms' "chugging along" as a top destination locally.*
/ **Details:** www.thealbionclifton.co.uk; 10 pm; closed Mon & Sun D.

Bell's Diner   £ 54   ❷❷❸
1 York Rd BS6 5QB   (0117) 924 0357
*"Serious foodies head here!"; "Chris Wicks's original restaurant" – in
"a wonderfully-converted former shop" in "edgy" Montpelier –
"continues to delight"; its "delicious" and original cuisine is produced
"with love and care".* / **Details:** www.bellsdiner.co.uk; 10 pm; closed Mon L,
Sat L & Sun.

Berwick Lodge   £ 61   🅣
Berwick Drive BS10 7TD   (0117) 9581590
*Few reports on this country house hotel yearling overseen by 'local
hero' Chris Wicks (of Bell's Diner fame) – fans claim "it's clearly
Bristol's best place to eat!", but not everyone is convinced.*
/ **Details:** www.berwicklodge.co.uk; no Amex. **Accommodation:** 10 rooms,
from £90.

Bordeaux Quay   £ 47   ❹❹❸
Canons Way BS1 5UH   (0117) 943 1200
*With its "interesting" interior and "fantastic views of the docks", this
"barn-like" waterfront eco-brasserie (with 'fine dining' room above)
has established itself as Bristol's best-known destination; reports are
mixed – a fair mid-point would be that "it's all a bit haphazard, but
the food's fine".* / **Details:** www.bordeaux-quay.co.uk; in the V Shed; 10 pm;
closed Mon, Tue–Sat D only, closed Sun D.

Boston Tea Party   £ 27   ❷❸❹
75 Park St BS1 5PF   (0117) 929 8601
*Lots of reports, and not a single negative one, on the excellent West
Country café/bistro chain of which this is a leading outlet; it's of
particular note for "the best coffee in town", and the cakes are
"pretty good" too.* / **Details:** www.bostonteaparty.co.uk; very near Bristol
University; 8 pm; no Amex; no booking.

Brasserie Blanc   £ 36   🅣
The Friary Building BS1 3DF   (0117) 910 2410
*"Particularly handy as a lunchtime destination", this city-centre
outpost of Raymond B's brasserie chain is tipped for its "well
thought-out" dishes, and the surroundings are surprisingly
"atmospheric" too.* / **Details:** www.brasserieblanc.com; Mon-Fri 10 pm, Sat
10.30 pm, Sun 9 pm.

Cafe Maitreya   £ 36   ❶❷❸
89 St Marks Rd BS5 6HY   (0117) 951 0100
*"Outstanding" veggie fare which is "light", "tasty" and "beautifully
presented" is making a big name for this basic café – "the best
veggie in the South West".* / **Details:** www.cafemaitreya.co.uk; 9.45pm;
closed Mon & Sun; no Amex.

ulinaria

erwick Lodge

PRIMROSE CAFE
Mon - Sat 10am - 5pm
Sunday 10.30am - 2.30pm

BISTR

Tue - Sat 7.30

imrose Cafe

Casamia £ 66 ❷❸❷
38 High St BS9 3DZ (0117) 959 2884
This family-owned spot offers "adventurous" and "stunningly presented" dishes of Italian inspiration; service can be prone to "long pauses", though, with dishes sometimes taking "as long to describe as to eat". / Details: www.casamiarestaurant.co.uk; midnight; closed Mon, Tue L, Wed L, Thu L, Fri L & Sun; no Amex.

The Cowshed £ 44 🅣
46 Whiteladies Rd BS8 2NH
Decked-out in rustic style, this new Clifton grill-restaurant is already tipped as a "pleasant" and "efficient" sort of place, offering "the best steaks for miles around", and a "good-value lunchtime deal". / Details: www.thecowshedbristol.com.

Culinaria £ 46 ❶❷⑤
1 Chandos Rd BS6 6PG (0117) 973 7999
"Classic Elizabeth David, with occasional 21st-century hints" – how one reporter evokes the "consistently wonderful" food at Stephen Markwick's Redland dining room, which many people think offers "Bristol's finest cuisine"; disappointing "IKEA-style" decor, though. / Details: www.culinariabristol.co.uk; 9.30 pm; closed Sun-Wed; no Amex.

Dynasty £ 34 🅣
16a St. Thomas St BS1 6JJ (0117) 925 0888
"Not inspiring, but utterly professional", this city-centre spot offers "good, solid Cantonese cooking" and is tipped for its "pretty good dim sum". / Details: www.dynasty-bristol.co.uk; 11 pm, 10 pm.

Fishers £ 43 ④④④
35 Princess Victoria St BS8 4BX (0117) 974 7044
This "good, basic fish restaurant" is "a consistently satisfactory performer" in a "lovely Clifton location"; it's "well-priced" and "always busy", although "the food, while reliable enough, is never better than 'absolutely fine'". / Details: www.fishers-restaurant.com; 10.30 pm, Sun 10 pm.

Flinty Red £ 42 ❷❷❸
34 Cotham HIll BS6 6LA (0117) 923 8755
"Zingy small plates matched up with a brilliantly interesting wine list" – that's the formula that quickly won a big following for this "bustling" Franco-Spanish tapas two-year-old in Cotham. / Details: www.flintyred.co.uk; 10.15 pm; closed Mon L & Sun; booking essential.

Greens' Dining Room £ 40 ❷❸❸
25 Zetland Rd BS6 7AH (0117) 924 6437
It has an "unprepossessing exterior and inexpensive caff interior", but Redland locals say this is a "brilliant" neighbourhood favourite where the food is simply "stunning". / Details: www.greensdiningroom.com; 10 pm; closed Mon & Sun; no Amex.

Hotel du Vin et Bistro £ 47 ④❸❸
Sugar Hs, Narrow Lewins Mead BS1 2NU (0117) 925 5577
Especially "for a romantic retreat", this warehouse-conversion (part of the wine-led boutique hotel chain) still wins praise; not all reports are positive, though, and there's quite a feeling that "as its prices go up, its quality goes down". / Details: www.hotelduvin.com; 9.45 pm; booking: max 10. Accommodation: 40 rooms, from £145.

The Kensington Arms £ 42 🅣
35-37 Stanley Rd BS6 6NP (0117) 944 6444
A "relaxed" Redland gastropub, which, for its strong local fan club, "always hits the spot". / Details: www.thekensingtonarms.co.uk; near Redland Railway station; 10 pm; closed Sun D.

Lido £ 52 ❷④❶
Oakfield Pl BS8 2BJ   (0117) 933 9533
This "cool" Victorian lido (which is "wonderfully lit" by night) makes such a "beautiful" and "unusual" setting that it's surprising just how "good and interesting" the "North African-influenced" food is; service, though, can be "haphazard". / Details: www.lidobristol.com; on the edge of Clifton; 10 pm; closed Sun D; no Amex.

Loch Fyne £ 38 ❼
51 Queen Charlotte St BS1 4HQ   (0117) 930 7160
*"Packed and noisy", this branch of the national fish and seafood chain attracts a surprisingly high number of reports, and is generally tipped for its "consistent" culinary standards.
/ Details: www.lochfyne.com; near Bristol Temple Meads station, next to Queen's Square; 10 pm, Sat 10.30 pm.*

Mud Dock Café CycleWorks £ 36 ❼
40 The Grove BS1 4RB   (0117) 934 9734
For a bite or brunch on a sunny day, seek out this terrace above a bike store, overlooking the quay, which offers "a good, informal, café experience". / Details: www.mud-dock.com; close to the Industrial Museum & Arnolfini Gallery; 10 pm; closed Mon D & Sun D.

Primrose Café £ 43 ❼
1 Clifton Arcade, 6 Boyces Ave BS8 4AA   (0117) 946 6577
"A very pleasant café with a lovely community feel"; it's tipped both as "very popular for breakfast" and as "very good" for more substantial meals too – "the catch of the day is particularly reliable". / Details: www.primrosecafe.co.uk; 10 pm; Sun D; no booking at L.

Prosecco £ 40 ④④④
25 The Mall BS8 4JG   (0117) 973 4499
In Clifton, a "neighbourhood Italian" which generates a good volume of feedback; many reports laud its "genuine" food at "reasonable prices" – it also seems to have "off-days", though, when the food is "ordinary". / Details: www.proseccoclifton.com; 11 pm; closed Mon & Sun, Tue-Thu L ; no Amex.

riverstation £ 41 ❸❷❷
The Grove BS1 4RB   (0117) 914 4434
*"Good views over the old dockside" and an "interesting and attractive" building (a former river-police station) lend instant appeal to this bar/café plus first-floor restaurant; in recent times, it has also been notable for its "reliably good food and interesting wine".
/ Details: www.riverstation.co.uk; 10.30 pm, Fri & Sat 11 pm; closed Sun D; no Amex.*

Rockfish £ 54 ❶❷❷
128-130 Whiteladies Road BS8 2RS   (0117) 9737384
*"Pricey, but excellent" – the gist of most reports on Mitch Tonks's take-over of a former FishWorks outlet, which offers "outstanding seafood" and a "great wine list to go with it".
/ Details: www.rockfishgrill.co.uk; 10 pm, Fri & Sat 10.30 pm; closed Mon & Sun D.*

San Carlo £ 47 ❼
44 Corn St BS1 1HQ   (0117) 922 6586
Not many reports compared to branches in Manchester and so on, but this city-centre Italian of 15 years' standing is still tipped by one or two reporters as "the best restaurant in town", thanks to the "reliability of its quality and welcome". / Details: www.sancarlo.co.uk; 11 pm.

The Thali Café £ 26 ❷❸❷
12 York Rd BS6 5QE (0117) 942 6687
For "veggie Indian food with a difference", this "fun" and "reliable"
spot – part of a small local chain – continues to please, with a menu
that's "limited, but great value". / **Details:** www.thethalicafe.co.uk; 10 pm;
D only, closed Mon; no Amex.

BRIXHAM, DEVON 1–3D

Poopdeck £ 45 ❷❸❸
14 The Quay TQ5 8AW (01803) 858 681
"A superb range of great-value fish dishes and local wines too" –
part of the formula that helps ensure this "very unstuffy and down-
to-earth" bistro is "very popular".
/ **Details:** www.poopdeckrestaurant.com.

BROAD HAVEN, PEMBROKESHIRE 4–4B

Druidstone Hotel £ 44 ❶
SA62 3NE (01437) 781221
"Still my favourite hotel in the whole world, and I've seen a few!" –
this "eccentric" family-friendly cliff-top destination inspires raves from
its tiny fan club, especially as "a paradise for families"; its organic
fare is "very variable but can be sublime".
/ **Details:** www.druidstone.co.uk; from B4341 at Broad Haven turn right, then
left after 1.5m; 9.30 pm. **Accommodation:** 11 rooms, from £75.

BROADWAY, WORCESTERSHIRE 2–1C

Buckland Manor £ 72
WR12 7LY (01386) 852626
In the twilight of the Von Essen régime the dining room of this grand
country house hotel became "deservedly very popular locally"; let's
hope new owners, the backers of ABode Hotels, can keep up
standards – no rating, however, is appropriate.
/ **Details:** www.bucklandmanor.co.uk; 2m SW of Broadway on B4632; 9 pm;
jacket & tie at D; booking: max 8; children: 12+. **Accommodation:** 13
rooms, from £280.

Russell's £ 47 ❸❷❷
20 High St WR12 7DT (01386) 853555
Right at the heart of this famously pretty Cotswold village, a
restaurant-with-rooms ("beautifully appointed") that's particularly
worth seeking out for its "great-value" lunch menu; by night, it's
generally "buzzing" too. / **Details:** www.russellsofbroadway.co.uk; 9.30 pm.
Accommodation: 7 rooms, from £98.

BROCKHAM, SURREY 3–3A

The Grumpy Mole £ 37 ❶
RH3 7JS (01737) 845 101
In a roadside inn that's had an up-and-down history in recent years,
an informal new restaurant that's already tipped as quite a "find"
locally. / **Details:** www.thegrumpymole.co.uk.

BROMESWELL, SUFFOLK 3–1D

British Larder £ 48 ❷❷❸
Oxford Rd IP12 2PU (01394) 460 310
"London-style quality, but with rural charm"; this recently-converted
pub uses ingredients which are "almost entirely locally-sourced" to
"imaginative" – and often "outstanding" – effect.
/ **Details:** www.britishlarder.co.uk; 9 pm, Fri-Sat 9.30 pm; no Amex.

BROMLEY, KENT
3–3B

Tamasha £ 45 ❸❸❸
131 Widmore Rd BR1 3AX (020) 8460 3240
*"A 'jewel in the crown' for Bromley!" – this out-of-town Raj-style
subcontinental, wins praise not just for "fantastic" food but an overall
"experience to savour" too. / Details: www.tamasha.co.uk; 10.30 pm;
no shorts. Accommodation: 7 rooms, from £75.*

BROUGHTON, NORTH YORKSHIRE
8–4B

Bull at Broughton £ 40 ❷❷❸
BD23 3AE (01756) 792065
*"You get Northcote quality at everyday prices", at this "well-
modernised pub", says a fan of this outpost of the (Lancastrian)
Ribble Valley Inns chain – a competent all-rounder with "courteous
staff" and "skilful cooking". / Details: www.thebullatbroughton.com;
8.30 pm, Fri & Sat 9 pm, Sun 8 pm.*

BRUNDALL, NORFOLK
6–4D

Lavender House £ 62 ❷❷❷
39 The St NR13 5AA (01603) 712215
*"Wonderful for a special occasion", Richard Hughes's village-
restaurant occupies an attractive thatched building, and its all-round
charms impress all who comment on it.
/ Details: www.thelavenderhouse.co.uk; 9.30 pm; D only, closed Sun & Mon;
no Amex.*

BRUTON, SOMERSET
2–3B

At The Chapel £ 43 ❸❷❷
28 High St BA10 0AE (01749) 814070
*A "beautiful" former chapel provides the setting for this "busy" all-
day café/bakery/pizzeria, where "helpful" staff "do their best to
keep up with demand". / Details: www.atthechapel.co.uk; 9.30 pm; closed
Sun D.*

BUCKFASTLEIGH, DEVON
1–3D

Riverford Field Kitchen £ 39 ❶❸❸
Wash Barn, Buckfast Leigh TQ11 0JU (01803) 762074
*As you might hope at a farm, it's the "excellent fresh produce"
(especially "unbeatable" vegetables) which is the real highlight of a
meal at this communal-tables dining room, and the puddings are
"memorable" too; its off-beat style is somewhere between "austere",
and "really enjoyable". / Details: www.riverford.co.uk; 8 pm; closed
Mon D & Sun D; no Amex.*

BUCKHORN WESTON, DORSET
2–3B

The Stapleton Arms £ 40 ❶
Church Hill SP8 5HS (01963) 370396
*A "really excellent country pub" unanimously tipped by reporters as
a "find", offering "good food and real ales, in nice surroundings, and
at reasonable prices". / Details: www.thestapletonarms.com; 10 pm,
9.30 pm Sun. Accommodation: 4 rooms, from £90.*

BUCKINGHAM, BUCKINGHAMSHIRE
2–1D

The Halibut £ 38 ❷❷❸
15 Cornwall Pl, High St MK18 1SB (01280) 817 141
*"A funky little restaurant above a fishmonger/traiteur", where, say
fans, the fish is "always excellent"; the desserts are "interesting" too.
/ Details: www.thehalibut.co.uk; 10 pm; closed Mon & Sun.*

BUCKLAND MARSH, OXFORDSHIRE 2–2C

The Trout Inn £ 44 🆃
Tadpole Bridge SN7 8RF (01367) 870382
In a "pleasant" riverside setting, an inn tipped for grub that's "much
better than your usual pub grub"; "the other dishes are good too,
but it's the fish people talk about". / Details: www.trout-inn.co.uk; 11 pm;
closed Sun D; no Mastercard. Accommodation: 6 rooms, from £120.

BUNBURY, CHESHIRE 5–3B

The Dysart Arms £ 34 🆃
Bowes Gate Rd CW6 9PH (01829) 260183
"A lovely pub near the church"; part of the Brunning & Price empire,
it's tipped for its "good choice" of "above-average" grub.
/ Details: www.dysartarms-bunbury.co.uk; 9.30 pm, Sun 9 pm.

BUNNY, NOTTINGHAMSHIRE 5–3D

Rancliffe Arms £ 37 🆃
139 Loughborough Rd NG11 6QT (0115) 98447276
"No wonder it's so popular"; this pretty old inn is tipped for "the best
carvery ever" – even the veg are "beautiful"!
/ Details: www.rancliffearms.co.uk; 9 pm.

BURFORD, OXFORDSHIRE 2–2C

The Swan Inn £ 43 🆃
Swinbrook OX18 4DY (01993) 823339
"Perfect for devotees of the Mitford sisters!"; Debo Devonshire's very
own Cotswold inn is tipped by all reporters as a "reliable" and
"good-value" all-rounder. / Details: www.theswanswinbrook.co.uk; 9 pm,
Fri & Sat 9.30 pm. Accommodation: 6 rooms, from £120.

BURNLEY, LANCASHIRE 5–1B

The Sparrowhawk £ 39 🆃
Wheatley Lane Rd, Fence BB12 9QG (01282) 603 034
Attracting only a modest level of commentary, but all very positive,
this pretty Pendle Forest inn – "even better after its recent refurb" –
is tipped for its "good and honest seasonal food" and "relaxed" all-
round charm. / Details: www.thesparrowhawk.co.uk; 9.30 pm.

BURNSALL VILLAGE, NORTH YORKSHIRE 8–4B

Devonshire Fell £ 52 🆃
BD23 6BT (01756) 729000
A nicely-located restaurant-with-rooms tipped for its "excellent" food
from the "good range" offered by its prix-fixe menu.
/ Details: www.devonshirefell.co.uk. Accommodation: 12 rooms, from £138.

BURY ST EDMUNDS, SUFFOLK 3–1C

Maison Bleue £ 46 ❷❷❷
30-31 Churchgate St IP33 1RG (01284) 760623
"A beacon in East Anglia", this "marvellous French fish and seafood
specialist" is an "outstanding" member of the estimable Crépy family
collection – a "pleasantly busy" sort of place hailed by many
reporters as "thoroughly enjoyable" all-round.
/ Details: www.maisonbleue.co.uk; near the Cathedral; 9.30 pm; closed
Mon & Sun; no Amex.

Pea Porridge £ 42 ❷❷❷

28-29 Cannon St IP33 IJR (01284) 700200

"A real find"; with its "interesting and reasonably-priced food" and a good dose of "rustic charm" too, this "quirky backstreet restaurant" has been a "most welcome" arrival; it serves a hearty British menu "with lots of interesting 'nose-to-tail' dishes".

/ Details: www.peaporridge.co.uk; 10 pm; closed Mon & Sun; no Amex.

BUSHEY HEATH, HERTFORDSHIRE 3–2A

The Alpine £ 50 ④④④

135 High Rd WD23 IJA (020) 8950 2024

An enthusiastic fan club "of a certain age" rave about this veteran '70s Italian which is "the place to impress locally" – "those in the know sit downstairs at the back"; critics, though, find the place "overpriced and uninspiring". / Details: www.thealpinerestaurant.co.uk; 10.30 pm; closed Mon.

BUSHEY, HERTFORDSHIRE 3–2A

St James £ 45 ④❷④

30 High St WD23 3HL (020) 8950 2480

"A star in the culinary desert of Metroland!" say fans of this "absolute stalwart"; it's "always busy", but critics just don't 'get it' – "either the locals don't get about much or they are too easily pleased!" / Details: www.stjamesrestaurant.co.uk; opp St James Church; 9.30 pm; closed Sun D; booking essential.

CAMBER, EAST SUSSEX 3–4C

The Gallivant £ 43 ❷④❸

New Lydd Rd TN31 7RB (01797) 225 057

Recently relaunched in New England style, this "well-located" hotel – "across the dunes at Camber Beach" – is just the job as a "family-friendly" destination, and all early reports place the cuisine somewhere between "good" and "exceptional"; "locally-caught fish" is a highlight. / Details: www.thegallivanthotel.com; 9 pm, Fri-Sat 9.30 pm.

CAMBRIDGE, CAMBRIDGESHIRE 3–1B

Alimentum £ 65 ❷❸④

152-154 Hills Rd CB2 8PB (01223) 413000

On most accounts, Mark Poynton's "outstanding" cooking makes this minimalist spot "a real star"; the "bizarre" location by a main road doesn't do much for the ambience, though, and critics find the cuisine "over-titivated" and "over-hyped".

/ Details: www.restaurantalimentum.co.uk; 10 pm; closed Sun D; booking essential.

The Cambridge Chop House £ 41 ❸❸❸

I Kings Pde CB2 ISJ (01223) 359506

"A glorious location on King's Parade" adds lustre to this "lively" grill-restaurant (and its less central 'St John's' sibling too at 21-24 Northampton St, 01223 353110); critics feel it "could be better", but most reports applaud its "reliable, locally-sourced British fare". / Details: www.cambridgechophouse.co.uk; 10.30 pm, Sat 11 pm, Sun 9.30 pm.

Cotto £ 57 ❷❷❸

183 East Rd CBI IBG (01223) 302010

"Inauspiciously-located, but a real find" – this is on some accounts "the best mid-range restaurant in Cambridge" (and, on others, "the only one"!); in particular, it's "very good for a simple lunch". / Details: www.cottocambridge.co.uk; 8.45 pm; opening times vary seasonally; children: 5+ in the evenings.

d'Arry's £ 41 **T**
2-4 King St CB1 1LN (01223) 505015
Still tipped for its "interesting" and "hearty" Antipodean grub, this "reliable" gastropub is perhaps of most note for its extensive choice of d'Arenberg wines. / **Details:** www.darrys.co.uk; 10 pm; no Amex; need 8+ to book.

Dojo £ 29 **T**
1-2 Millers Yd, Mill Ln CB2 1RQ (01223) 363471
"A reliable non-chain fore-runner of Wagamama", this "great little noodle place" is tipped for its "outstandingly fresh Asian fusion fare"; "a romantic destination, however, this is not".
/ **Details:** www.dojonoodlebar.co.uk; off Trumpington St; 11 pm; no Amex; no booking.

Graffiti
Hotel Felix £ 44 ④④❸
Whitehouse Ln CB3 0LX (01223) 277977
This "sophisticated" dining room pleases most reporters with ambitious food that, at best, is "superb"; service, though "can be a bit Fawlty Towers", and the odd reporter finds the cooking "not quite as good as they think it is". / **Details:** www.hotelfelix.co.uk; 10 pm, Fri & Sat 10.30 pm, Sun 9.30 pm. **Accommodation:** 52 rooms, from £190.

Jamie's Italian £ 41 ④❷❸
The Old Library, Wheeler St CB2 3QJ (01223) 654094
Contrasting views on this recent addition to the Jamie O franchise; fans report "uniformly positive" experiences in a "funky" refurbishment of an "amazing" city-centre building – for critics, though, it's just "over-rated", "overpriced" and "over-enthusiastic".
/ **Details:** www.jamieoliver.com; 11 pm, Sun 10.30 pm.

Loch Fyne £ 44 ④④④
37 Trumpington St CB2 1QY (01223) 362433
OK, this is just a branch of the well-known seafood chain (actually, one of the first), but it has a large fan club among reporters, seduced by its generally "dependable" charms.
/ **Details:** www.lochfyne.com; opp Fitzwilliam Museum; 10 pm.

Midsummer House £108 ❶❸❸
Midsummer Common CB4 1HA (01223) 369299
"An amazing experience"; Daniel Clifford's "highly creative" cuisine – "superbly inventive without losing its delicious flavour" – makes this swanky spot by the River Cam (no view) not just "the best restaurant in the Fens", but one of the UK's best too; critics still find the place "overpriced", but they're less vocal than they were.
/ **Details:** www.midsummerhouse.co.uk; on the river Cam, near Mitchams Corner and the boat sheds; 9.30 pm; closed Mon, Tue L & Sun.

Oak Bistro £ 42 ❷❷❷
6 Lensfield Rd CB2 1EG (01223) 323361
All reports extol the "top-class food, wonderful service, and good atmosphere, all at reasonable prices", at this "gem" of a little place, on the way to the station. / **Details:** www.theoakbistro.co.uk; 10 pm; closed Sun.

Peking Restaurant £ 34 ❷❷⑤
Unit 3, The Belvedere, Homerton St CB2 8NX
(01223) 245457
It's worth putting up with the "off-putting" building! – this "friendly" local institution offers the best Chinese food in town ("… provided you like chillies"), and in "enormous portions" too.
/ **Details:** 10.30 pm; closed Mon L; no Amex.

Oak Bistro

limentum

idsummer House

Rainbow Café £ 28 ❶❸❸
9a King's Pde CB2 1SJ (01223) 321551
"Ambrosial" cooking from an "imaginative" and "varied" menu, including a "fantastic" range of puddings, and "friendly" service – this cellar-café's only possible drawback is that its menu includes no meat dishes; handy location by King's College too.
/ **Details:** www.rainbowcafe.co.uk; 9 pm; closed Mon & Sun D; no Amex; no booking.

Sea Tree £ 31 ⬤
13 The Broadway CB1 3AH (01223) 414349
"A new favourite"; this chippy is the top tip for those in search of "fresh fish, traditionally served". / **Details:** 9 pm sun; closed Thu L, Fri L & Sat L.

Restaurant 22 £ 48 ❷④❷
22 Chesterton Rd CB4 3AX (01223) 351880
"It feels rather like dining in someone's front room", when you visit the Tommaso family's genteel villa near Victoria Avenue Bridge; the menu offers "good value for money", but some reporters do feel the service "lacks any sense of urgency". / **Details:** www.restaurant22.co.uk; 9.30 pm; closed Tue-Sat L ; children: 12+.

CANTERBURY, KENT   3–3D

Café des Amis £ 36 ④④❷
95 St Dunstan's St CT2 8AD (01227) 464390
"Maintaining cheap 'n' cheerful standards", this long-established Mexican "institution" by Westgate Towers has a big name locally for its "tasty" cuisine, "lively" atmosphere and "friendly" service.
/ **Details:** www.cafedez.com; by Westgate Towers; 10 pm, Fri & Sat 10.30 pm, Sun 9.30 pm; booking: max 6 at D Fri-Sat.

Cafe Mauresque £ 37 ❷❷❷
8 Butchery Ln CT1 2JR (01227) 464300
In the heart of the city, a "truly inspired little restaurant"; at first sight it seems like a trendy hang-out rather than anything more, but reporters consistently praise its "really tasty" Moroccan cuisine – "stick to the mezze and you are in grazing heaven!"
/ **Details:** www.cafemauresque.com; 10 pm, Fri & Sat 10.30 pm.

Goods Shed £ 43 ❷④④
Station Road West CT2 8AN (01227) 459153
"The theatre of a busy farmers' market" (a co-occupant of this former goods shed near Canterbury West) peps up daytime visits to this "relaxed" and "pleasant" restaurant; even fans can find it "a bit pricey", but the "interesting" cuisine generally satisfies.
/ **Details:** www.thegoodsshed.net; 9.30 pm; closed Mon & Sun D.

Michael Caines
ABode Canterbury £ 59 ❸④④
High St CT1 2RX (01227) 766266
This potentially "slick" city-centre dining room put in a stronger showing this year, winning praise for its "comfortable" style and food that's "a class above anything else locally"; there are still gripes, though, about "anorexic portions", "lack of ambience" and "high prices". / **Details:** www.abodehotels.co.uk; 10 pm; closed Sun D; booking max 7. **Accommodation:** 72 rooms, from £105.

Casanova £ 39 ❷❸④
13 Quay St CF10 1EA (029) 2034 4044
"A good place that's getting better"; this "friendly" city-centre spot is sometimes – in default of much competition, admittedly – hailed as the top Italian in town. / Details: www.casanovacardiff.com.

Happy Gathering £ 32 ❸❸④
233 Cowbridge Road East CF11 9AL (029) 2039 7531
"The decor's way past its best", but this city-centre behemoth's "vast menu" still offers "the best Chinese food in Cardiff"; "take a Chinese friend to taste the hidden menu". / Details: www.happygathering.co.uk; 10.30 pm, Sun 9 pm.

Mint and Mustard £ 41 ❷❷④
134 Whitchurch Rd CF14 3LZ (02920) 620333
"In a city with a thousand identical Bangladeshi taste-alikes, this stands out" – a "modern and eclectic" Gabalfa three-year-old that impresses all who comment on it with its Keralan and Goan cuisine. / Details: www.mintandmustard.com; 11 pm; no shorts.

Le Monde £ 41 ❿
62 St Mary St CF10 1FE (029) 2038 7376
Tipped as the city-centre venue of choice for those "in the know" – a sawdust-on-the-floor, first-floor operation, where you choose your steak or fish (with some emphasis on the latter) from the chiller-cabinets. / Details: www.le-monde.co.uk; 11 pm; closed Sun; need 10+ to book.

Patagonia £ 45 ❿
11 Kings Rd CF11 9BZ (029) 2019 0265
Surprisingly few reports on this Spanish-run riverside restaurant, but it's still tipped for "the best all-round cuisine and value in town" from its "eclectic" menu. / Details: www.patagonia-restaurant.co.uk; 10.30 pm, Sat 11 pm; D only, closed Mon & Sun; no Amex.

Woods Brasserie £ 46 ❿
Pilotage Building, Stuart St CF10 5BW (029) 2049 2400
A Cardiff Bay spot which inspires oddly little commentary given that it's such a long-standing fixture; it is tipped for "friendly" service and cuisine that makes "skilful use of local ingredients". / Details: www.woods-brasserie.com; next to the Mermaid Quay Complex; 10 pm; closed Sun D.

The Masons Arms £ 39 ❿
Strawberry Bank LA11 6NW (01539) 568486
A fell-side inn tipped for "lots of outdoor dining space" and "glorious views"; the food is always "more than adequate". / Details: www.strawberrybank.com; W from Bowland Bridge, off A5074; 9 pm. Accommodation: 7 rooms, from £75.

L'Enclume £ 90 ❶❶❷
Cavendish St LA11 6PZ (01539) 536362
"Pure theatre, a feast for all the senses"; Simon Rogan's "breathtaking" dishes – "playful, without being silly" – win a hymn of praise for his "wonderful" conversion of an old Lakeland smithy; the downside? – it's "very expensive". / Details: www.lenclume.co.uk; J36 from M6, down A590 towards Cartmel; 9 pm; closed Mon L & Tue L; children: no children at D. Accommodation: 12 rooms, from £99.

Mint and Mustard

woods
bar & brasserie

Woods Brasserie

Rogan & Co £ 42 🅣

Devonshire Sq LA11 6QD (01539) 535917

*Given the fame of the chef, this town-centre bistro inspires surprisingly little feedback; praise is muted too, but fans still tip the place for its "innovative" ideas. / **Details:** www.roganandcompany.co.uk; 9 pm; no Amex.*

CASTLE COMBE, WILTSHIRE 2–2B

Bybrook Restaurant
Manor House Hotel £ 87 ❶❷❸

SN14 7HR (01249) 782206

*"Stunningly located", this "lovely old country house" offers a wonderful and "romantic" experience, with "attentive" service and "exceptionally good" food; the dining room itself, however, can seem "just a little lacking in ambience". / **Details:** www.exclusivehotels.co.uk; 9.30 pm; closed Mon L; no trainers; children: 11+. **Accommodation:** 48 rooms, from £245.*

CHADDESLEY CORBETT, WORCESTERSHIRE 5–4B

Brockencote Hall £ 57 ❸❸❷

DY10 4PY (01562) 777876

*"So good it's too popular!", says a fan of the Petitjeans' country-house hotel set in 70 acres of parkland; most accounts applaud its all-round "faultless attention to detail", but a minority of reporters suffered from "painfully slow" or "unconcerned" service. / **Details:** www.brockencotehall.com; on A448, just outside village; 9 pm; no trainers. **Accommodation:** 17 rooms, from £120.*

CHAGFORD, DEVON 1–3C

Gidleigh Park £125 ❶❷❶

TQ13 8HH (01647) 432367

*"So artistic it's scary" – Michael Caines's "outstanding" cuisine comes twinned with some "truly special" wines (listed in "an astonishing tome"), at this "delightful" Tudorbethan mansion, "beautifully located" "down tiny lanes" on the edge of Dartmoor – a destination practically all reporters find "perfect in every way". / **Details:** www.gidleigh.com; from village, right at Lloyds TSB, take right fork to end of lane; 9.30 pm; no jeans or trainers; children: 8+ at D. **Accommodation:** 24 rooms, from £310.*

CHANDLER'S CROSS, HERTFORDSHIRE 3–2A

The Clarendon £ 50 ❸❸❸

Redhall Ln WD3 4LU (01923) 270009

*Despite the odd whiff of "hype", this smart bar and restaurant in a former pub has an impressive following locally; the set lunch in particular is often said to offer "exceptionally good value". / **Details:** www.theclarendon.co.uk; 10 pm.*

The Glasshouse
The Grove £ 60 ❸❹❸

WD3 4TG (01923) 296015

*The buffet-restaurant at this "groovy-grand" country house hotel is sometimes dismissed "a glorified carvery"; supporters say the food is "fabulous", and even critics concede that "you certainly never leave hungry". / **Details:** www.thegrove.co.uk; 9.30 pm, Sat 10.30 pm. **Accommodation:** 227 rooms, from £310.*

Brasserie Blanc
The Queen's Hotel £ 34 ❶
The Promenade GL50 1NN (01242) 266800
"Improved a lot", this "buzzing" chain-outlet is especially tipped as a "good-value" lunch or pre-theatre destination.
/ **Details:** www.brasserieblanc.com; 10.30 pm, Sat 11 pm, Sun 10 pm.

Le Champignon Sauvage £ 60 ❶❷④
24-28 Suffolk Rd GL50 2AQ (01242) 573449
David & Helen Everitt-Mathias's "assured" city-centre fixture – 25 this year – continues to thrill with cuisine that's not only "superbly creative" but "good value" too; the room can be "a bit of a let-down", though, and the occasional reporter leaves unconvinced.
/ **Details:** www.lechampignonsauvage.co.uk; near Cheltenham Boys College; 9 pm; closed Mon & Sun.

The Daffodil £ 44 ④❸❷
18-20 Suffolk Pde GL50 2AE (01242) 700055
With its "fabulous setting in a former Art Deco cinema" – and "jazz nights" too – this city-centre bar/restaurant has obvious advantages as a party venue (and they "deal with large groups very effectively"); the food is a bit incidental, but it generally seems to please.
/ **Details:** www.thedaffodil.com; just off Suffolk Square; 10 pm, Sat 10.30 pm; closed Sun.

Lumière £ 61 ❶❷❷
Clarence Pde GL50 3PA (01242) 222200
Under Jon Howe and Helen Aubrey's two-year reign, this "intimate" town-centre operation has become an "outstanding" destination, thanks to its "personalised" service, and its "innovative" and "artistically presented" cuisine (which features some "unusual ingredients"). / **Details:** www.lumiere.cc; off the Promenade on the Inner Ring; 9 pm; closed Mon & Sun, Tue L; booking: max 10; children: 8+ D.

The Royal Well Tavern £ 44 ④❷❸
5 Royal Well Pl GL50 3DN (01242) 221212
"A bustling city-centre gastropub" of three years' standing, which pleases all reporters with its "unfussy" but well-realised cooking, and its "casual" style. / **Details:** www.theroyalwelltavern.com; by the main bus station; 10 pm, Sat 10.30 pm; closed Sun D.

Storyteller £ 40 ④❸❸
11 North Pl GL50 4DW (01242) 250343
"The intriguing way of choosing your wines" (you select your own in the cellar) has long been a feature at this town-centre fixture; its "really interesting" menu of "well-executed" dishes mostly wins praise too, although this year also saw a couple of less enthusiastic reports. / **Details:** www.storyteller.co.uk; near the cinema; 10 pm.

La Brasserie
Chester Grosvenor £ 55 ❸❷❷
Eastgate CH1 1LT (01244) 324024
A London-based reporter was "hugely surprised and impressed" by this grandly fitted-out brasserie by the iconic Eastgate clock, whose standards would hold their own in the metropolis; it makes a "lovely" lunch venue in particular. / **Details:** www.chestergrosvenor.com; 10 pm.
Accommodation: 80 rooms, from £240.88.

1539   **£ 53**   🆃

The Racecourse CH1 2LY (01244) 304 611

"Buzzing on race days, but quiet and romantic at other times", this
"promising" spot is tipped for its views of "the racecourse, and the
Welsh hills beyond"; the food is rather better than you might expect
too. / **Details:** www.restaurant1539.co.uk; 9.30 pm.

Michael Caines
ABode Hotels   **£ 63**   ❷❷❷

Grosvener Rd CH1 2DJ (01244) 347 000

It had a bit of a rocky start, but this "plush" restaurant on the top
floor of a major new building by the Castle, is settling in well – most
reports speak in terms of "superb food in classy surroundings" (and
"great views of the racecourse" too). / **Details:** www.abodehotels.co.uk;
10 pm; no Amex; no jeans or trainers.

Moules A Go Go   **£ 38**   🆃

39 Watergate Row CH1 2LE (01244) 348818

"Still a winner after all these years", this informal mussels-specialist
on the 'rows' is often tipped as the sort of "reliable" place that
makes "a good lunchtime option". / **Details:** www.moulesagogo.co.uk;
10 pm, Sun 9 pm.

Oddfellows   **£ 50**   🆃

20 Lower Bridge St CH1 1RS (01244) 400001

Still attracting surprisingly little commentary, this elegant restaurant-
with-rooms is tipped for "the best value food in town"; it is presided
over from afar by Kentish chef Richard Phillips, which presumably
explains the presence of some "excellent English wines" on the list.
/ **Details:** www.oddfellows.biz.

Simon Radley
The Chester Grosvenor   **£ 92**   ❷❷④

Eastgate CH1 1LT (01244) 324024

"Top-notch" innovative cuisine is matched by a "superb cellar" (over
1000 bins) at Simon Radley's supremely comfortable dining room in
the heart of this unusually luxurious city-centre hotel; but even fans
can find it "very expensive". / **Details:** www.chestergrosvenor.com; 9 pm;
D only, closed Mon & Sun; no trainers; children: 12+. **Accommodation:** 82
rooms, from £180.

CHETTLE, DORSET   2–3C

Castleman Hotel   **£ 38**   🆃

DT11 8DB (01258) 830096

This traditional manor house hotel doesn't attract a great number of
reports, but fans insist that, "for the price", it's "outstanding".
/ **Details:** www.castlemanhotel.co.uk; 1m off the A354, signposted; 9 pm;
D only, ex Wed & Sun open L & D; no Amex. **Accommodation:** 8 rooms,
from £80.

CHICHESTER, WEST SUSSEX   3–4A

Brasserie Blanc   **£ 37**   🆃

Richmond Hs, The Square PO19 7SJ (01243) 534200

A new outpost of the generally creditable Raymond Blanc-branded
brasserie chain – "slow service" is a bit of a bugbear, but otherwise
it's a pretty good all-rounder. / **Details:** www.brasserieblanc.com; 10 pm,
Fri & Sat 10.30 pm, Sun 9 pm.

Cassons Restaurant & Bar £ 52 🅣

Arundel Road, Tangmere PO18 0DU (01243) 773294

A family-run restaurant praised for its all-round standards, but tipped particularly for its wine list – "for a country restaurant, hard to beat". / Details: www.cassonsrestaurant.co.uk.

Comme Ça £ 47 ❷❷❷

67 Broyle Rd PO19 6BD (01243) 788724

Michel Navet's "always-welcoming" restaurant (of 25 years' standing) offers "the best French cooking for miles around" and at "reasonable prices"; highlights – "super pre-theatre meals" and "an impressive and wide ranging wine list". / Details: www.commeca.co.uk; 0.5m N of city-centre; 9.30 pm, Fri & Sat 10.30 pm; closed Mon, Tue L & Sun D.

Field & Fork
Pallant House Gallery £ 44 ❷❸❸

9 North Pallant PO19 1TJ (01243) 770 827

"Much better food than you'd expect in the café of a small art gallery!" – this "attractive" spot has a major following for its "well thought-out" cuisine (even if it does come in rather "over-delicate portions"). / Details: www.fieldandfork.co.uk; 8.45 pm; closed Mon, Tue D & Sun D.

CHIDDINGFOLD, SURREY 3–3A

The Mulberry Inn £ 46 ❸❷❸

Petworth Rd GU8 4SS (01428) 644 460

"It possibly trades a bit too much on being owned by Chris Evans", but this "good-quality" restaurant in a former pub pleases pretty much all reporters with its "consistent" charms. / Details: www.evanspubs.co.uk; 10 pm, Sun 9 pm.

The Swan Inn £ 45 ❷❷❷

Petworth Rd GU8 4TY (01428) 684 688

New owners are making a great success of this "great local pub/restaurant-with-rooms", praised for its "lovely welcome" and its "really good food" too. / Details: www.theswaninnchiddingfold.com; 10 pm, Sun 9 pm. Accommodation: 10 rooms, from £100.

CHILGROVE, WEST SUSSEX 3–4A

The Fish House £ 60 ❶❹❸

High St PO18 9HX (01243) 519444

"The fish can't be faulted", at this well-named restaurant in a former pub on the edge of the South Downs – pretty much all reports confirm it offers "excellent" cooking and a "very good wine list" to go with it. / Details: www.thefishhouse.co.uk; 9.30 pm, Fri & Sat 10 pm, Sun 9 pm; no Amex. Accommodation: 15 rooms, from £150.

CHINNOR, OXFORDSHIRE 2–2D

The Sir Charles Napier £ 50 ❷❸❶

Spriggs Alley OX39 4BX (01494) 483011

"Stunning gardens" help set the scene at Julie Griffiths's "cosy" and "beautiful" Chilterns inn, known since the '70s as a "reliable" and classy day out for townies; prices are "premium" and service can occasionally be "snooty", but the cooking goes from strength to strength. / Details: www.sircharlesnapier.co.uk; M40, J6 into Chinnor, turn right at roundabout, carry on straight up hill for 2 miles; Tue-Fri 9.30 pm, Sat 10 pm; closed Mon & Sun D.

CHIPPING CAMPDEN, GLOUCESTERSHIRE   2–1C

The Ebrington Arms   £ 44   ❷④❸
GL55 6NH (01386) 593 223
In a "perfect Cotswolds location", a "cosy" small pub hailed as "a real treat", thanks to its "very good" food; it offers "an excellent range of beers" too. / **Details:** www.theebringtonarms.co.uk; 9 pm.

CHIPSTEAD, KENT   3–3B

The George & Dragon   £ 41   ❷❸❸
39 High St TN13 2RW (01732) 779 019
Recently revamped, an ancient inn worth seeking out for its "inventive and tasty" food… and it has some great lake-views too. / **Details:** www.georgeanddragonchipstead.com.

CHRISTCHURCH, DORSET   2–4C

The Jetty   £ 52   ❸❸❸
95 Mudeford BH23 3NT (01202) 400950
Mixed feedback on this waterside dining room where Gary Rhodes used to have his name over the door; supporters praise "great views over the harbour" – "a great place now Alex Aitken, formerly of the Poussin empire, has taken over" – but critics say it's "still stuffy and boring!" / **Details:** www.thejetty.co.uk; 9.45 pm, Sun 7.45 pm; closed Sun D.

CHURCH STRETTON, SHROPSHIRE   5–4A

Berry's   £ 29   ⓣ
17 High St SY6 6BU (01694) 724452
"A little treasure of a café, hidden-away down a side street"; it's tipped as "the best place around for coffee and cakes", and other "good wholesome fare" too. / **Details:** www.berryscoffeehouse.co.uk; 7 pm; closed for D Mon-Thu & Sun D; no credit cards; no bookings.

CLACHAN, ARGYLL AND BUTE   9–3B

Loch Fyne Oyster Bar   £ 49   ❷❸❸
PA26 8BL (01499) 600236
"Both the location and the freshness of the seafood are hard to beat" at this lochside smokehouse, which is run independently of the nationwide chain it spawned. / **Details:** www.loch-fyne.com; 10m E of Inveraray on A83; 8 pm.

CLAVERING, ESSEX   3–2B

The Cricketers   £ 44   ❸④❸
Wicken Rd CB11 4QT (01799) 550442
"Better known as Jamie's Mum & Dad's Place", this "competent" village green-side boozer "doesn't content itself with getting by on the family name" but offers a "wide-ranging" menu of "unfussy food" that's "surprisingly good, and not at silly prices". / **Details:** www.thecricketers.co.uk; on B1038 between Newport & Buntingford; 9.00 pm. **Accommodation:** 14 rooms, from £95.

CLIFTON, CUMBRIA   8–3A

George & Dragon   £ 44   ⓣ
CA10 2ER (01768) 865381
Fans insist that this "lovely" boozer, just off the M6, is a great place that "never disappoints"; its ratings waned a bit this year, though – particularly for service. / **Details:** www.georgeanddragonclifton.co.uk; on the A6 in the village of Clifton, just 5 mins drive from Penrith and junction 40 of the M6.; 9 pm. **Accommodation:** 12 rooms, from £92.

Bailiffscourt Hotel £ 71 ❷❷❷
BN17 5RW (01903) 723511

In "romantic" 1920s/medieval style (complete with "mullioned windows, tapestries and beamed ceilings"), this "charming" country house hotel inspires a small but very enthusiastic fan club, who acclaim Russell Williams's cuisine as "superb".
/ **Details:** www.hshotels.co.uk; 9.30 pm; booking: max 8; children: 7+.
Accommodation: 39 rooms, from £205.

The Olive Branch £ 47 ❸❷❷
Main St LE15 7SH (01780) 410355

Just off the A1, this "lovely country pub", in a small village, has become one of the best-known in the country; most reporters still see it as "a template for how any gastropub should be", but even ardent fans sometimes feel it's getting a bit "pricey" and "predictable". / **Details:** www.theolivebranchpub.com; 2m E from A1 on B664; 9.30 pm, Sun 9 pm; no Amex. **Accommodation:** 6 rooms, from £135.

Inn at Whitewell £ 46 ❷❷❷
Forest of Bowland BB7 3AT (01200) 448222

This "historic", ultra-"romantic" inn "in the beautiful trough of Bowland" ("with spectacular views up the Hodder and Hareden rivers") has long been one of Lancashire's top destinations, and it's "always busy"; the cooking is of a "high standard" too, and is complemented by "an impressive wine list".
/ **Details:** www.innatwhitewell.com; 9.30 pm; bar open L & D, restaurant D only; no Amex. **Accommodation:** 23 rooms, from £113.

Clytha Arms £ 46 ❶
NP7 9BW (01873) 840206

An inn tipped for its "interesting and well prepared" meals by chef of 20 years' standing Andrew Canning; it's decidedly "not a place to eat if you're in a hurry" (but then why would you be in Monmouthshire if you were?). / **Details:** www.clytha-arms.com; on Old Abergavenny to Raglan road; 9.30 pm; closed Mon L & Sun D. **Accommodation:** 4 rooms, from £80.

La Capanna £ 60 ❶
48 High St KT11 3EF (01932) 862121

"21st-century food in a 16th-century building!"; that's the deal at this "special-occasion" Italian – "the best restaurant in the area".
/ **Details:** www.lacapanna.co.uk; 11 pm.

Kirkstile Inn £ 39 ❶
Loweswater CA13 0RU (01900) 85219

Not many reports, but this "gloriously-located" inn is strongly tipped as "just what you need after a day climbing the fells", thanks to its "simply glorious" location, "very good and hearty" cuisine, and "own-brew ales". / **Details:** www.kirkstile.com; 9 pm; no Amex.
Accommodation: 10 rooms, from £46.50.

COGGESHALL, ESSEX   3–2C

Baumann's Brasserie   £ 43   ④⑤④
4-6 Stoneham St CO6 1TT   (01376) 561453
*A long-established brasserie which inspires a good volume of reports;
fans praise its "inventive" menu as "a safe choice in this part of
Essex", but, there's also some feeling that "they could do better" –
service in particular is "hit-and-miss".*
/ **Details:** www.baumannsbrasserie.co.uk; 9.30 pm, Fri & Sat 10 pm, Sun
9 pm; closed Mon & Tue.

COLERNE, WILTSHIRE   2–2B

Lucknam Park   £103   ❷❷❷
SN14 8AZ   (01225) 742777
*"Hywel Jones doesn't get enough recognition", say fans of this
generally "faultless" country house dining room; the atmosphere of
the "beautiful" brasserie, however, is sometimes preferred to that of
the relatively "bland" main dining room.*
/ **Details:** www.lucknampark.co.uk; 6m NE of Bath; 9.30 pm; jacket and/or
tie; children: 5+ D & Sun L. **Accommodation:** 42 rooms, from £315.

COLNE, LANCASHIRE   5–1B

Banny's Restaurant   £ 28   ❷❷④
1 Vivary Way BB8 9NW   (01282) 856220
*At the end of the M65, a "bright and spotless" modern chippy on a
scale of which Cecil B DeMille would have approved – it's "always
busy", and it's "easy to see, and taste, why!"*
/ **Details:** www.bannys.co.uk.

COMPTON, SURREY   3–3A

The Withies Inn   £ 47   ④❸❷
Withies Ln GU3 1JA   (01483) 421158
*Tipped for its "atmospheric" charms, this Surrey Hills inn "hasn't
changed much in 30 years"; it may be true that the menu, in
keeping, "never changes", but at least "you know what you are going
to get!"* / **Details:** www.thewithiesinn.com; off A3 near Guildford, signposted
on B3000; 9.30 pm, Sun 4 pm; closed Sun D.

CONGLETON, CHESHIRE   5–2B

Pecks   £ 53   ❷❷❷
Newcastle Rd CW12 4SB   (01260) 275161
*"Theatrical presentation" has helped make a name locally for this
"elegant" restaurant where "innovative" no-choice dinners – on
which puddings are a particular highlight – are served at 8pm
nightly; "they also do a good-value lunch".*
/ **Details:** www.pecksrest.co.uk; off A34; 8 pm; closed Mon & Sun D; booking
essential.

COOKHAM, BERKSHIRE   3–3A

Maliks   £ 40   ❶❷❸
High St SL6 9SF   (01628) 520085
*"Sensational" cuisine – quite "unlike your normal Indian" – again
wins rave write-ups for this "busy" former boozer: "the only better
Indian food I have ever had was just outside Udaipur!"*
/ **Details:** www.maliks.co.uk; from the M4, Junction 7 for A4 for Maidenhead;
11.30 pm, Sun 10.30 pm.

The White Oak £ 41 ❸④❸
The Pound SL6 9QE (01628) 523043
This "stripped-down" gastroboozer is on most accounts a "top-notch" and "good-value" destination and it has established itself as a "popular" all-rounder; the occasional reporter, though, does find quality a touch "inconsistent". / Details: www.thewhiteoak.co.uk; 9.30 pm; closed Sun D.

COPSTER GREEN, LANCASHIRE 5–1B

Yu And You £ 45 ❶
500 Longsight Rd BB1 9EU (01254) 247111
A family-run restaurant, tipped by a number of locals for Chinese food "of the highest quality". / Details: www.yuandyou.com; off the A59 7 miles towards Clitheroe; 11 pm, Fri & Sat 2 am; D only, closed Mon.

CORTON DENHAM, SOMERSET 2–3B

The Queen's Arms £ 38 ❶
DT9 4LR (01963) 220317
"Wellies and dogs are welcome, says the sign on the door" – if you're looking for a "day-out destination", this out-of-the-way boozer is a top tip; the bar, though, is to be preferred to the restaurant. / Details: www.thequeensarms.com; 10 pm, Sun 9.30 pm.
Accommodation: 5 rooms, from £85.

CRANBROOK, KENT 3–4C

Apicius £ 53 ❶❷❸
23 Stone St TN17 3HF (01580) 714666
"One of the best restaurants in the South East and deserving wider recognition!"; thanks to Tim Johnson's "imaginative" and "beautifully-presented" cooking, this small and "beautifully calm" ("slightly rarified") high street restaurant inspires consistently enthusiastic reports. / Details: www.restaurant-apicius.co.uk; take the A21, turn left through Goudhurst, take the 3rd exit left on the roundabout; 9 pm; closed Mon, Tue, Sat L & Sun D; no Amex; Recommended / max group 6; children: 8+.

CRAYKE, NORTH YORKSHIRE 5–1D

Durham Ox £ 47 ❷❸❷
Westway YO61 4TE (01347) 821506
For a "proper country pub experience", this "really cosy and atmospheric" inn – with its "good food", "huge portions" and "roaring fire" – is very hard to beat. / Details: www.thedurhamox.com; 9.30 pm, Sat 10 pm, Sun 8.30 pm. **Accommodation:** 5 rooms, from £100.

CREIGIAU, CARDIFF 2–2A

Caesars Arms £ 46 ❷❷❸
Cardiff Rd CF15 9NN (029) 2089 0486
*"A brasserie-style eatery I would claim as the best restaurant in Wales… and I've eaten there over 100 times!" – this very busy rural inn has long been a well-known destination, thanks to its "good-value" formula whereby "you choose your meat or fish from the display cabinet and it's cooked to order".
/ Details: www.caesarsarms.co.uk; beyond Creigiau, past golf club; 10 pm; closed Sun D.*

The Bear £ 36 🆃

High St NP8 1BW (01873) 810408

A "charming old coaching inn", tipped for its thoroughly "traditional" style... and, of course, the famous bread 'n' butter pudding – "of rare quality, and lightness of touch". / Details: www.bearhotel.co.uk; 9.30 pm; D only, ex Sun open L only, closed Mon; children: 7+.
Accommodation: 34 rooms, from £90.

The Punch Bowl £ 44 ❷❷❷

LA8 8HR (01539) 568237

"A must after a hard days walking in the Lakes"; this "classy" but "very relaxed and friendly" inn is "everything a gastropub should be" – it serves "super food in proper Northern portions", and "excellent" ales too. / Details: www.the-punchbowl.co.uk; off A5074 towards Bowness, turn right after Lyth Hotel; 9.30 pm. **Accommodation:** 9 rooms, from £120.

Albert's Table £ 45 ❷❸④

49c South End CR0 1BF (020) 8680 2010

"You forget you are in grotty Croydon", when you visit Joby Wells's three-year-old "gem", which – on many reports – is "just what the area had needed", thanks to its "cleverly constructed but not over-fussy food"; at times, though, service "needs sharpening up". / Details: www.albertstable.co.uk; 10.30 pm; closed Mon & Sun D; no Amex.

Fish & Grill £ 50 ④④❸

48-50 South End CR0 1DP (020) 8774 4060

Malcolm John's helpfully-named neighbourhood venture inspires a good number of reviews; unfortunately they are very mixed – from: "mad if you go anywhere else"... to: "an expensive disaster". / Details: www.fishandgrill.co.uk; 11.30 pm.

McDermotts Fish & Chips £ 25 ❷❶❷

5-7 The Forestdale Shopping Centre Featherbed Ln CR0 9AS (020) 8651 1440

"A really welcoming family restaurant", recommended by a number of fans for "the best fish 'n' chips in South London". / Details: www.mcdermottsfishandchips.co.uk; 9.30 pm, Sat 9 pm; closed Mon & Sun; no Amex.

The Potting Shed £ 43 ❸❸❷

The St SN16 9EW (01666) 577833

"An idyllic pub in an idyllic Cotswolds setting", where the food is "nothing OTT or overly fancy" – it is "varied", though, and includes some "great stalwart dishes". / Details: www.thepottingshedpub.com; 9.30 pm, Sun 9 pm; no Amex. **Accommodation:** 12 rooms, from £95.

Ockenden Manor £ 76 ❷❷❷

Ockenden Ln RH17 5LD (01444) 416111

"Over a hundred visits in a decade, and never disappointed!" – this country house hotel makes a "superb" destination, thanks not least to Stephen Crane's "excellent" cuisine; the dining room has recently been re-sited, which, says a fan, "should lay to rest any past concerns about the slightly gloomy former setting". / Details: www.hshotels.co.uk; 9 pm; no jeans or trainers.
Accommodation: 28 rooms, from £183.

CUPAR, FIFE

Ostlers Close £ 53 ❶❷❸
25 Bonnygate KY15 4BU (01334) 655574
*Over 30 years in business, a "pricey" town-centre spot with a "cosy"
and "romantic" charm that equips it well as a "special occasion"
destination; feedback remains impressively consistent.*
/ **Details:** www.ostlersclose.co.uk; *centrally situated in the Howe of Fife;
9.30 pm; closed Sun & Mon, Tue-Fri D only, Sat L & D; children: 5+.*

The Peat Inn £ 60 ❶❷❷
KY15 5LH (01334) 840206
*This famous country inn is an "adorable little place" run by the
Smeddle family for the past half-decade; if anything, they've boosted
its high renown as a destination for "good food, cooked extremely
well, and presented with a smile from people who truly want their
guests to enjoy".* / **Details:** www.thepeatinn.co.uk; *at junction of B940 &
B941, SW of St Andrews; 9 pm; closed Mon & Sun.* **Accommodation:** *8
rooms, from £180.*

DALRY, NORTH AYRSHIRE
9–4B

Braidwoods £ 64 ❶❶❷
Drumastle Mill Cottage KA24 4LN (01294) 833544
*"Still one of the best in Scotland"; at their "beautifully-located" croft,
Keith & Nicola Braidwood "use the best ingredients to create honest
and satisfying dishes which are also exciting and refined".*
/ **Details:** www.braidwoods.co.uk; *9 pm; closed Mon, Tue L & Sun D; children:
12+ at D.*

DARTMOUTH, DEVON
1–4D

Angelique £ 55 ④④④
2 South Embankment TQ6 9BH (01803) 839425
*"Alan Murchison can do much better than this!"; the few reports on
the new occupant of the site once famous as the 'Carved Angel'
(now an outpost of the Ortolan, Shinfield empire) are few and
notably mixed.* / **Details:** www.angeliquedartmouth.co.uk; *9 pm, Fri-Sat
9.30 pm; closed Mon, Tue L & Sun D.* **Accommodation:** *6 rooms, from £95.*

The Seahorse £ 63 ❶❷❷
5 South Embankment TQ6 9BH (01803) 835147
*"Awesome" fish dishes served by "friendly" staff in a "vibrant"
setting win a major thumbs-up for Mitch Tonks's "charming" three-
year-old, near the river.* / **Details:** www.seahorserestaurant.co.uk; *10 pm;
closed Mon, Tue L & Sun D.*

DEDHAM, ESSEX
3–2C

The Sun Inn £ 37 ❶
High St CO7 6DF (01206) 323351
*Sometimes tipped for "memorable" Italian fare (and "interesting"
wines), a beautiful old pub that's also of some notes as a key
Constable Country destination... "if you can find somewhere to
park", that is.* / **Details:** www.thesuninndedham.com; *opp church on the
high street; Fri & Sat 10 pm, 9.30 pm.* **Accommodation:** *5 rooms, from £75.*

Le Talbooth £ 61 ④❸❷
Gun Hill CO7 6HP (01206) 323150
*"Getting better of late!" — perhaps in preparation for its 60th
birthday — this "wonderfully-located" riverside spot seems to have
bucked its ideas up a bit; even so, there's still something of a feeling
that "the surroundings are not quite matched by the food".*
/ **Details:** www.milsomhotels.com; *5m N of Colchester on A12, take B1029;
9 pm; closed Sun D; no jeans or trainers.*

Swan Inn £ 42 ❷❷❷
Village Rd UB9 5BH (01895) 832085
"Fun, good value and lively" – this village inn (part of a small local chain) is a *"busy"* all-rounder that never seems to disappoint; it has a *"pleasant"* garden too, but parking is *"a pain"*.
/ **Details:** www.swaninndenham.co.uk; 9.30 pm, Fri & Sat 10 pm.

Anoki £ 46 ❷❷❷
First Floor, 129 London Rd DE1 2QN (01332) 292888
It's not just the "extraordinary" Art Deco setting of this converted cinema ("watch Bollywood dancing on the big screen while you eat") which makes this *"upmarket"* Indian worth seeking out – the food is *"always impressive"* too. / **Details:** www.anoki.co.uk; 2m from town centre, opposite hospital; 11.30 pm; D only, closed Sun.

Darleys £ 53 ❸❷❷
Darley Abbey Mill DE22 1DZ (01332) 364987
The *"stunning"* setting (and terrace) helps make it an *"all-round experience"* to visit this riverside operation; the food is *"always of a high standard"* too, say fans – for critics, however, *"the prices manage to make it disappointing!"* / **Details:** www.darleys.com; 2m N of city centre by River Derwent; 9 pm; closed Sun D; no Amex.

Ebi Sushi £ 35 ❷❸④
Abbey St DE22 3SJ (01332) 265656
How to explain this *"town-centre gem"* where *"very good sushi"* is a highlight of *"some of the best Japanese cuisine ever"*? – the presence of a Toyota plant nearby may help… / **Details:** 10.30 pm; D only, closed Mon & Sun; no Amex.

La Chouette £ 54 ❷❷❶
Westlington Grn HP17 8UW (01296) 747422
"The chef/patron is barking mad, but the food is very good", at this low-ceilinged, beamed venue; presided over by 'The Belligerent Belgian', Frederic Desmette, it offers *"an experience every time"* that most reporters feel is simply *"brilliant"*. / **Details:** off A418 between Aylesbury & Thame; 9 pm; closed Sat L & Sun; no Amex.

The NoBody Inn £ 39 ④❸❷
EX6 7PS (01647) 252394
A *"lovely ancient inn"* that's of particular note for its *"wonderful cheese"*, *"great whisky list"* and *"huge selection of good wines"*… rather than for the cooking per se; it now has a *"pretty new garden area"* too. / **Details:** www.nobodyinn.co.uk; off A38 at Haldon Hill (signed Dunchidrock); 9 pm, Fri & Sat 9.30 pm; no Amex. **Accommodation:** 5 rooms, from £60.

The Forester £ 37 ❷❸❸
Lower St SP7 9EE (01747) 828038
"The food is always delicious", says one of the many fans of this *"excellent local gastropub"* which – with its *"irresistible menu, fair prices and brilliant execution"* – is hailed as a *"hidden gem"*.
/ **Details:** www.theforesterdonheadstandrew.co.uk; off A30; 9 pm; closed Sun D.

Sienna
£ 61   **❶❷⑤**

36 High West St DT1 1UP   (01305) 250022

"Fabulous food, but be prepared to bring your own atmosphere…";
Russell and Elaina Brown's shop-conversion premises are "not much
to look at", but all reporters agree "the food is so good that they
deserve to succeed" nonetheless. / **Details:** www.siennarestaurant.co.uk;
9 pm; closed Mon & Sun; no Amex; children: 12+.

Yalbury Cottage
£ 49   **T**

DT2 8PZ   (01305) 262382

In a "pretty village", a "cosy cottage-style hotel" tipped for its
"amazing" food at "tremendous-value" prices; more reports please!
/ **Details:** www.yalburycottage.com; 9 pm; D only, closed Mon & Sun.
Accommodation: 8 rooms, from £110.

DORKING, SURREY
3–3A

Little Dudley House
£ 50   **T**

77 South St RH2 2JU   (01306) 885550

"Filling the gap between chain eating and fine dining", a "friendly"
and "stylish" bar/restaurant tipped for its range of "good-value"
dishes. / **Details:** www.littledudleyhouse.co.uk; 10 pm, Sun 6 pm; closed
Sun D.

Restaurant Two To Four
£ 45   **❷❷❸**

2-4 West St RH4 1BL   (01306) 889923

"A funny little restaurant on three floors" in a "beautiful timbered
building", recommended by the locals for its "good-quality" food at
"reasonable prices" and its "friendly" and "efficient" style.
/ **Details:** www.2to4.co.uk; 10 pm; closed Mon & Sun; no Amex.

DOUGLAS, ISLE OF MAN
7–4B

Tanroagan Seafood Restaurant
£ 51   **❷❷❸**

9 Ridgeway St IM1 1EW   (01624) 612 355

"The choice of stars of stage and screen… when in the Isle of Man",
an "always-enjoyable", if "tightly packed", ten-year-old, where fish is
the speciality. / **Details:** www.tanroagan.co.uk.

DOVER, KENT
3–4D

The Allotment
£ 36   **T**

9 High St CT16 1DP   (01304) 214467

"The only place worth eating in Dover" – an informal
café/restaurant, opposite the Town Hall, serving a "varied" menu.
/ **Details:** www.theallotmentdover.co.uk; 10 pm; closed Mon & Sun; no Amex.

DUNVEGAN, HIGHLAND
9–2A

The Three Chimneys
£ 81   **❶❷❶**

Colbost IV55 8ZT   (01470) 511258

"Worth a trip to the back of beyond", this "unbelievably remote"
former crofter's cottage by Loch Dunvegan offers an absolutely
"stunning experience"; culinarily speaking, "they let the quality of the
seafood do the talking" – for best results try the "amazing 'Taste of
Skye' tasting menu". / **Details:** www.threechimneys.co.uk; 5m from
Dunvegan Castle on B884 to Glendale; 9.45 pm; closed Sun L; children: 8+.
Accommodation: 6 rooms, from £295.

Bistro 21   £ 45   ❸❷❷
Aykley Heads Hs DH1 5TS   (0191) 384 4354
Fans acclaim the "simple, fresh fare" at Terry Laybourne's
"charming" spot – long known as a "hidden gem", just outside the
city-centre; some regulars, however, sense "creeping complacency",
with more "predictable" cooking nowadays.
/ Details: www.bistrotwentyone.co.uk; near Durham Trinity School; 10 pm;
closed Sun.

Gourmet Spot
Farnley Tower Hotel   £ 56   ❼
The Ave DH1 4DX   (0191) 384 6655
"A relatively unknown restaurant offering some of Durham's finest
food" – this 'small, intimate, and a little bit funky' (their words)
venue is tipped for surprisingly ambitious cuisine "of very high
quality". / Details: www.gourmet-spot.co.uk; 9.30 pm; D only, closed Mon &
Sun. Accommodation: 13 rooms, from £80.

Oldfields   £ 43   ❹❹❸
18 Claypath DH1 1RH   (0191) 370 9595
Lots of reports feature this all-day brasserie where fans find
"excellent locally-sourced regional food" and "great-value set menus
for lunch and dinner"; there are quite a number of disgruntled
accounts, though, lending credence to those who say standards are
"slipping away". / Details: www.oldfieldsrealfood.co.uk; 10 pm, Sun 9 pm.

Jolly Sportsman   £ 47   ❸❸❷
Chapel Ln BN7 3BA   (01273) 890400
Bruce Wass's "very rural" inn by the South Downs, is "increasingly a
restaurant rather than a pub nowadays (although it still has all the
facilities a pub would provide" including a "super play area for kids"
in the "charming garden"); whatever you call it, it's "worth tracking
down". / Details: www.thejollysportsman.com; NW of Lewes; 9.15 pm, Sat
10 pm; no Amex.

The Star & Garter   £ 44   ❼
PO18 0JG   (01243) 811318
"A lovely brick and flint pub at the foot of the South Downs", tipped
in most (if not quite all) reports for its "great seafood" (and a "basic
menu of non-fish items"). / Details: www.thestarandgarter.co.uk; 10 pm,
Sun 9.30 pm; no Amex. Accommodation: 6 rooms, from £90.

Gravetye Manor   £ 77   ❹❸❶
Vowels Ln RH19 4LJ   (01342) 810567
Under Jeremy Hosking's year-old régime, this "delightful English
country house", famous for its "beautiful gardens", seems to be
reviving; the odd critic still notes a "tired" experience, but – for long
term fans in particular – it's "absolutely lovely".
/ Details: www.gravetyemanor.co.uk; 2m outside Turner's Hill; 9.30 pm, Sun
9 pm; booking: max 8; children: 7+. Accommodation: 17 rooms, from £200.

EAST HENDRED, OXFORDSHIRE 2–2D

The Eyston Arms £ 44 ❷❷❷
High St OX12 8JY (01235) 833320
"Miles from anywhere, but worth the journey" – this charming
Oxfordshire pub continues to inspire impressively consistent praise
for its "lively" style and its "very good food".
/ **Details:** www.eystons.co.uk; 9 pm; closed Sun D.

EAST LAVANT, WEST SUSSEX 2–4D

The Royal Oak £ 50 ❸❸❷
Pook Ln PO18 0AX (01243) 527 434
"A lovely country pub, with a very friendly landlord, offering well-
priced dishes from local produce" – with its "superb wine list" too, it
manages to appear "sophisticated" and "rustic" all at the same
time! / **Details:** www.royaloakeastlavant.co.uk; 9.30 pm; no shorts.
Accommodation: 8 rooms, from £110.

EAST LOOE, CORNWALL 1–4C

Squid Ink £ 46 ⓣ
Lower Chapel St PL13 1AT (01503) 262 674
"Worth a detour"; this "small, contemporary-style restaurant in the
heart of one of Cornwall's best-kept-secret villages", is tipped for
"innovative" food that fans say is "just wonderful"; more reports
please! / **Details:** www.squid-ink.biz.

EAST WITTON, NORTH YORKSHIRE 8–4B

Blue Lion £ 46 ❷❷❷
DL8 4SN (01969) 624273
"You can't go wrong here", say the many fans of this "beautifully-
located" Dales inn which offers "great locally-sourced food" in
"quirky" surroundings; "with its dark interiors and game-led menu,
it's particularly great in winter". / **Details:** www.thebluelion.co.uk; between
Masham & Leyburn on A6108; 9.15 pm; D only, ex Sun open L & D; no Amex.
Accommodation: 15 rooms, from £94.

EASTBOURNE, EAST SUSSEX 3–4B

The Mirabelle
The Grand Hotel £ 63 ④④④
King Edwards Pde BN21 4EQ (01323) 412345
Views divide on this old-fashioned and unusually grand seaside dining
room, which inspires only quite limited feedback; to fans its "an all-
round superb experience", but most reports are more middling,
finding the ambience a trifle "dull", and the food "OK but
unremarkable for the price". / **Details:** www.grandeastbourne.com;
9.45 pm; closed Mon & Sun; jacket or tie required at D.
Accommodation: 152 rooms, from £190.

EASTON GRAY, WILTSHIRE 2–2C

Dining Room
Whatley Manor £ 98 ❷❷④
SN16 0RB (01666) 822888
Martin Bruge's "remarkably inventive and creative" French cuisine –
"with extraordinary levels of presentation and service" – win rave
reviews for this contemporary country house hotel; although the
setting may be "fabulous", the ambience in the dining room can still
seem lacking. / **Details:** www.whatleymanor.com; 8 miles from J17 on the
M4, follow A429 towards Cirencester to Malmesbury on the B4040; 10 pm;
D only, closed Mon-Tue; children: 12+. **Accommodation:** 23 rooms,
from £305.

Café Marlayne £ 37 ❷❸④
1 Thistle St EH2 1EN (0131) 226 2230
*In the New Town, a "very handy, cheap 'n' cheerful French-style bistro", invariably praised by reporters for its "good value"; it now has a "less cramped" offshoot in Antigua Street, just off Leith Walk. / **Details:** www.cafemarlayne.com; 10 pm; no Amex.*

Café Royal Oyster Bar £ 42 ④❷❷
19 West Register St EH2 2AA (0131) 556 4124
*"The Edwardian decor is still a winner" at this popular New Town veteran; most reporters feel it's "just the place for oysters and champagne, without undue pomp", but there's no denying that the cooking can disappoint. / **Details:** www.thespiritgroup.com; opp Balmoral Hotel; 10 pm.*

Le Café St-Honoré £ 47 ❸❷❶
34 NW Thistle Street Ln EH2 1EA (0131) 226 2211
*"An unexpected gem" hidden away in an "unprepossessing" back street in the New Town – "you could think you were in Paris" at this "classic" operation – a place with a "real bistro feel", and where the cooking is almost invariably "reliable". / **Details:** www.cafesthonore.com; 10 pm.*

Calistoga Central £ 38 ❷❷❸
70 Rose St EH2 3DX (01312) 251233
*This New Town bistro offers "clean-flavoured" California-style cooking with "nothing really to fault" – it's the "friendly" service and "excellent low-mark-up US wine list", however, which make it particularly worth seeking out. / **Details:** www.calistoga.co.uk; 10 pm; closed Sun.*

The Castle Terrace £ 68 ❶❶❷
33/35 Castle Ter EH1 2EL (0131) 229 1222
*"Possibly even better than The Kitchin"!; all reporters salute Tom K's instantly "very busy" new operation at the base of the castle, where Dominic Jack's "very confident and innovative" cuisine achieves some "exquisite" results; lunch in particular is "unbelievable value", but the tasting menu is "fantastic" too. / **Details:** www.castleterracerestaurant.com; 9.30 pm; closed Mon & Sun.*

Centotre £ 48 ⑤⑤④
103 George St EH2 3ES (0131) 225 1550
*"A busy Italian in a grand ex-bank which has had a funky make-over"; even fans, though, can find "the show let down by careless cooking and lacklustre service"; and harsher critics say it's simply "not worth a visit". / **Details:** www.centotre.com; 10 pm, Fri & Sat 11 pm, Sun 8 pm.*

Chop Chop £ 29 ❸❸④
248 Morrison St EH3 8DT (0131) 221 1155
*"Like an upmarket version of a lorry drivers' caff", this "family-style" Haymarket (and Leith) Chinese generally impresses reporters with its "un-Anglicised" – shouldn't that be 'un-Caledonianified'? – cuisine. / **Details:** www.chop-chop.co.uk; 10 pm; closed Mon.*

Creelers £ 46 ❸❸④
3 Hunter Sq EH1 1QW (0131) 220 4447
*A small fish restaurant just off the Royal Mile that's "recently been refreshed"; reports of late have been a little up-and-down, but the more general view is that the shellfish, in particular, is "superb". / **Details:** www.creelers.co.uk; 10.30 pm.*

David Bann
£ 36 ❷❸❸

56-58 St Marys St EH1 1SX (0131) 556 5888

"Among the best vegetarians in the UK" say fans, this "surprisingly inventive" Old Town operation offers some "stunning" cuisine; the occasional visitor this year, however, found the experience rather "boring". / Details: www.davidbann.com; 10 pm, Fri & Sat 10.30 pm.

The Dogs
£ 35 ❷❷❸

110 Hanover St EH2 1DR (0131) 220 1208

This "cheap-and-cheerful bistro-style place" has made a big hit with its "good food" with a "seasonal/local twist", its "handy location" (in the heart of the New Town) and its "relaxed" style; it has two offshoots — Sea Dogs (see also), and the less impressive Amore. / Details: www.thedogsonline.co.uk; 10 pm.

Dusit
£ 44 ❷❷④

49a Thistle St EH2 1DY (0131) 220 6846

It may be "functional" (and "noisy" too), but this New Town Thai "maintains high standards", and its "lovely" food inspires almost unanimous praise from reporters; lunchtimes, in particular, offer "excellent value". / Details: www.dusit.co.uk; 11 pm.

L'Escargot Bleu
£ 37 ❷❸❸

56 Broughton St EH1 3SA (0131) 557 1600

"Et voilà…" – if you're looking for a good, if stereotypical, Gallic bistro, you won't do much better than this "authentic" operation (which is especially worth seeking out for the "terrific-value early-evening menu"); at the other end of the New Town, L'Escargot Blanc is a paler imitation. / Details: www.lescargotblanc.co.uk.

Favorita
£ 32 ❷❸④

325 Leith Walk EH6 8JA (0131) 554 2430

"A long-established Leith Walk pizzeria, which deserves its reputation for some of the best pizzas in Edinburgh". / Details: www.la-favorita.com; 11 pm; no Amex.

Fishers Bistro
£ 41 ❷❷❷

1 The Shore EH6 6QW (0131) 554 5666

"A Leith fish place that's well worth a visit" – a "popular" and "buzzy" bistro that's ideal for a straightforward meal near the waterfront. / Details: www.fishersbistros.co.uk; 10.30 pm.

Fishers in the City
£ 44 ❸❸❸

58 Thistle St EH2 1EN (0131) 225 5109

A "reliable" New Town fish specialist where the food is "not exactly 'gourmet' but properly done"; it's a "pleasant" place, too, even if its "cramped" interior can sometimes get rather "busy" for some tastes. / Details: www.fishersbistros.co.uk; 10.30 pm.

Forth Floor
Harvey Nichols
£ 48 ④❸❸

30-34 St Andrew Sq EH2 2AD (0131) 524 8350

"The food is not really the main event here, but a sunny-day seat on the terrace, with a bird's eye view of St Andrew's Square, makes up for a lot…" – one reporter neatly sums up the pros and cons of a lunchtime treat at this "swish" store café. / Details: www.harveynichols.com; 10 pm; closed Mon D & Sun D.

La Garrigue
£ 43 ❸❷④

31 Jeffrey St EH1 1DH (0131) 557 3032

Jean-Michelle Gauffre's "rustic", "cramped" and "busy" Old Town veteran is, on most accounts, a "good-value" sort of place, serving "first-class food from SW France"; the odd refusnik, however, does leave feeling a little "underwhelmed". / Details: www.lagarrigue.co.uk; 9.30 pm.

The Kitchin

David Bann

Grain Store £ 56 ❷❸❷

30 Victoria St EH1 2JW (0131) 225 7635

"Creaky wooden floors and candlelight" help set the "pleasant" tone of this former New Town warehouse; with its "quirky" vibe and "authentically Scottish" cuisine, it offers a "good all-round package". / Details: www.grainstore-restaurant.co.uk; 10 pm.

The Honours £ 48

58a North Castle Street EH2 3LU (0131) 220 2513

From The City's leading chef – Martin Wishart – this newcomer opened in early summer 2011, too late for feedback from the survey; the format is that of a swish modern brasserie, and early press reports are encouraging. / Details: www.thehonours.co.uk.

Kalpna £ 35 ❶④④

2-3 St Patrick Sq EH8 9EZ (0131) 667 9890

"A favourite when visiting Auld Reekie!"; this "consistently excellent" but inexpensive canteen veteran, near the university, has a dedicated following for its "great Indian food" – "so good, you forget it's veggie!" / Details: www.kalpnarestaurant.com; 10.30 pm; closed Sun; no Amex; no booking at L.

The Kitchin £ 80 ❶❶❷

78 Commercial Quay EH6 6LX (0131) 555 1755

"Worth a 300 mile trip!"; Tom Kitchin's "passionate and honest" cuisine – "seasonal classics with a modern twist" – wins many fans for this "tastefully minimalist" Leith warehouse-conversion; "incredibly knowledgeable" service (especially of wine) plays an honourable supporting role. / Details: www.thekitchin.com; opposite the Scottish Executive in Leith; 10 pm; closed Mon & Sun.

Mother India's Cafe £ 33 ❷❸❷

3-5 Infirmary St EH1 1LT (0131) 524 9801

"Great, authentic and tasty Indian food" (served tapas-style) continues to make quite a success of this "buzzy" Old Town offshoot of the famous 'Weegie' Indian; even fans, though, can find it "hit-and-miss". / Details: www.motherindiaglasgow.co.uk; Sun 10 pm, 10.30 pm, Fri & Sat 11 pm; no Amex.

Mussel Inn £ 41 ❸❸❸

61-65 Rose St EH2 2NH (0131) 225 5979

"The name does not lie!"; it may not be much to look at, but this "cheap", "buzzy" and "cheerful" New Town stand-by – with its "fresh and quick mussels" – remains as popular as ever. / Details: www.mussel-inn.com; 10 pm.

Number One
Balmoral Hotel £ 87 ❷❷❸

1 Princes St EH2 2EQ (0131) 557 6727

"I go back time after time, and have yet to be disappointed" – thanks to Jeff Bland's "interesting" cuisine, the "elegant" fine dining basement of the city's grandest hotel continues to impress locals and visitors alike; this year, however, a few reports were surprisingly "average" – hopefully just a blip. / Details: www.roccofortehotels.com; 10 pm; D only; no jeans or trainers. Accommodation: 188 rooms, from £360.

Oloroso £ 58 ④❺❸

33 Castle St EH2 3DN (0131) 226 7614

"Sitting on the terrace" of this once-fashionable operation – with its "transformative views of the beautiful Edinburgh skyline" – "one could forgive almost anything"; unfortunately there's quite a list, including "overpricing", service that "leaves a lot to be desired" and food that's "a bit pretentious". / Details: www.oloroso.co.uk; 10.30 pm, Sun 10 pm.

Ondine
£ 54   ❶❷❸

2 George IV Bridge EH1 1AD   (0131) 2261888
It has an "odd office-block location" near the Royal Mile, but Roy
Brett's first-floor two-year-old is making quite a name as a "classy"
all-rounder – fish and seafood a speciality.
/ **Details:** www.ondinerestaurant.co.uk; 10 pm; booking: max 8.

The Outsider
£ 41   ❸❷❷

15-16 George IV Bridge EH1 1EE   (0131) 226 3131
"Worth it for the view at lunch" – this busy bistro's top feature is its
spectacular view of the castle; "the food is good too, if quite plain".
/ **Details:** 11 pm; no Amex; booking: max 12.

Papoli
£ 23   ❿

244a Morrison St EH3 8DT   (0131) 4777047
Near Haymarket station, an "unassuming Italian-style restaurant"
(with a bit of a Middle Eastern influence) tipped for its "outstanding"
value; "shame they don't change the menu a bit more…"
/ **Details:** www.papoli.co.uk; 10.30 pm; closed Sun.

Plumed Horse
£ 70   ❶❷❷

50-54 Henderson St EH6 6DE   (0131) 554 5556
"Very different in style from the other Leith powerhouses" it may be,
but Tony Borthwick's "beautiful" but "homely" pub-conversion fully
lives up to its long-term reputation for "wonderful and innovative"
cuisine. / **Details:** www.plumedhorse.co.uk; 9 pm; closed Mon & Sun;
children: 5+.

Restaurant Martin Wishart
£ 92   ❶❷❸

54 The Shore EH6 6RA   (0131) 553 3557
"The best restaurant in Edinburgh, and better than most in
London…" – Martin Wishart's "exceptional" Leith dining room is
often recommended as "a special venue for a special meal", thanks
to its "highly professional" attitude and its "perfect" cuisine that's
"refined, yet full of flavour". / **Details:** www.martin-wishart.co.uk; near
Royal Yacht Britannia; 9.30 pm; closed Mon & Sun; no trainers.

Rhubarb
Prestonfield Hotel
£ 67   ❸❷❶

Priestfield Rd EH16 5UT   (0131) 225 1333
"Opulent", "theatrical", "fun" – the "dark" but "beautiful" dining
room of this country house on the fringe of the city "sets a tone few
other restaurants can match"; for most reporters, it lives up to the
"great gastronomic experience" which it offers, but critics say it's too
"uneven". / **Details:** www.prestonfield.com; 10 pm, Fri & Sat 11 pm;
children: 12+ at D, none after 7pm. **Accommodation:** 23 rooms, from £295.

Sea Dogs
£ 33   ❶❷❸

43 Rose St EH2 2NH   (0131) 225 8028
"David Ramsen provides Edinburgh citizens with another brilliant
and cheap selection of dishes" – in particular "surprisingly inventive
seafood" – at this "quirky" and "bustling" café.
/ **Details:** www.seadogsonline.co.uk; 10 pm.

The Stockbridge
£ 47   ❿

54 St Stephen's St EH3 5AL   (0131) 226 6766
This "small Scottish-French restaurant" occupies a "Baroque
basement setting" in the New Town; tipped as "stylish without being
overpowering", it offers "good wholesome food" and is "popular with
couples of all ages and budgets, from students to silver surfers".
/ **Details:** www.thestockbridgerestaurant.co.uk; 9.30 pm; closed Mon,
Tue-Fri D only, Sat & Sun open L & D; children: 18+ after 8 pm.

Sweet Melindas £ 42 ❷❸❸
11 Roseneath St EH9 1JH (0131) 229 7953
"Good seafood at a reasonable price in a cosy atmosphere" – that's
the deal that inspires unanimously positive feedback on this
Marchmont neighbourhood spot. / **Details:** www.sweetmelindas.co.uk;
10 pm; closed Mon L & Sun; children: Not allowed .

**The Tower
Museum of Scotland** £ 56 ❹❸❷
Chambers St EH1 1JF (0131) 225 3003
*Surprisingly few reports this year on this elevated dining room, which
benefits from impressive Castle-views – such as they are, though,
tend to support the view that the panorama is the main reason to
seek it out.* / **Details:** www.tower-restaurant.com; 11 pm.

21212 £ 95 ❷❷❷
3 Royal Ter EH7 5AB (0845) 222 1212
"Weird food, great fun!"; in the *"incredible open kitchen"* of this
"chic" Calton townhouse, Paul Kitching orchestrates an *"intricate
dance"* to produce some *"beautiful"* dishes (which seem to benefit
from being *"less outlandish"* than in his Manchester days); the odd
reporter may feel he's *"trying too hard"*, but feedback overall is
upbeat. / **Details:** www.21212restaurant.co.uk; 9.30 pm; closed Mon & Sun;
children: 5 +. **Accommodation:** 4 rooms, from £250.

Valvona & Crolla £ 37 ❹❹❸
19 Elm Row EH7 4AA (0131) 556 6066
*Not much excitement is expressed in reviews of the café annex of
this famous (and "expensive") Italian deli/restaurant of long standing
– hard to avoid the conclusion that it's long been "resting on its
laurels".* / **Details:** www.valvonacrolla.com; at top of Leith Walk, near
Playhouse Theatre; L only.

Vintners Rooms £ 62 ❹❷❷
87a Giles St EH6 6BZ (0131) 554 6767
*This ancient, candlelit whisky wareh CLOSED ith, offers a
"stunning" ng r a ca, nice ns s sonal" as
ever; its od rati is o he s e, th gh st that prices
"have be u uch for cuisine that can seem
"unimaginative".* / **Details:** www.vintnersrooms.com; 10 pm; closed Mon &
Sun.

Wedgwood £ 56 ❷❷❹
267 Canongate EH8 8BQ (0131) 558 8737
*Paul Wedgwood's food is "imaginative, without being quirky" and his
small, Old Town "gourmet gem" widely impresses, thanks to his
"artistically-presented" fare; one or two reporters, though, "question
the decor", or find the tables a bit "crammed in".*
/ **Details:** www.wedgwoodtherestaurant.co.uk; 10 pm.

Witchery by the Castle £ 61 ❸❷❶
Castlehill, The Royal Mile EH1 2NF (0131) 225 5613
"Simply the most romantic restaurant in the world!" – this
medieval/Gothic establishment *"stunningly located"* by the castle has
a *"dramatic"* and *"enchanting"* atmosphere, and offers a
"wonderful" wine list; sometimes, only, the food is *"fabulous"* too.
/ **Details:** www.thewitchery.com; 11.30 pm. **Accommodation:** 7 rooms,
from £325.

The Oak Room
Great Fosters Hotel £ 62 ❷❷❶
Stroude Rd TW20 9UR (01784) 433822
"An Elizabethan mansion in superb gardens" provides the *"refined"* setting for this *"elegant"* – if *"expensive"* – dining room; the cooking is *"more exciting than your classic 'country house'"*, and the wine list is *"very attractive"*. / **Details:** www.greatfosters.co.uk; 9.15 pm; closed Sat L; no jeans or trainers; booking: max 12. **Accommodation:** 44 rooms, from £155.

Sangster's £ 57 ❷❷④
51 High St KY9 1BZ (01333) 331001
"Always a joy" – this *"small and intimate"* restaurant is *"run by a very welcoming husband-and-wife team"* and offers a *"limited but varied menu"* that's invariably cooked *"to the very highest standard"*. / **Details:** www.sangsters.co.uk; 8.30 pm; no Amex; no jeans or shorts; children: 12+ at D.

La Cachette £ 41 ❶
31 Huddersfield Rd HX5 9AW (01422) 378833
"Always reliable", this Gallic restaurant and wine bar continues to impress with its *"solid"* and *"consistent"* cuisine, and its *"great"* wine list. / **Details:** www.lacachette-elland.com; 9.30 pm, Fri & Sat 10 pm; closed Sun; no Amex.

The Tempest Arms £ 37 ❷❷❷
BD23 3AY (01282) 842 450
"A very busy eating house" serving *"varied"* and *"substantial"* British fare; winter visitors are met with *"roaring log fires"*. / **Details:** www.tempestarms.co.uk.

The Boathouse £ 41 ❶
5-5A, Annesdale CB7 4BN (01353) 664388
An unpretentious tip for visitors to this beautiful city – a riverside restaurant with a *"lovely riverbank location, good food, and all within an easy walk of the cathedral too"*. / **Details:** www.cambscuisine.com/theboathouse; 9 pm, Fri-Sat 9.30 pm.

Old Fire Engine House £ 42 ❶
25 St Mary's St CB7 4ER (01353) 662582
Michael & Ann Jarman's *"very pleasant"* old-timer of over 40 years' standing near the cathedral is again tipped for its *"delightfully old-fashioned, proper cooking"* (*"no fancy flourishes or cheffy touches"*), and its *"personal"* and *"attentive"* service. / **Details:** www.theoldfireenginehouse.co.uk; 9 pm; closed Sun D; no Amex.

Fat Olives £ 45 ❶❶❷
30 South St PO10 7EH (01243) 377914
Not far up the hill from the waterfront, Julia & Lawrence Murphy's pocket-size gem wins enthusiastic endorsements – it offers *"meticulous"* service of *"consistently good and imaginative cooking"* in a *"delightful"* setting. / **Details:** www.fatolives.co.uk; 9.15 pm; closed Mon & Sun; no Amex; children: 8+, unless Sat L.

36 on the Quay £ 74 ❷❸❸
47 South St PO10 7EG (01243) 375592
Ramon Farthing's "special-occasion restaurant", "well located on the harbour", thrills most reporters with its "exciting" cuisine; "very, very slow" service can take the edge off the experience, though, and the occasional critics finds the whole approach "a little out-of-date".
/ Details: www.36onthequay.co.uk; off A27 between Portsmouth & Chichester; 9 pm; closed Mon & Sun; no Amex. Accommodation: 5 (plus cottage) rooms, from £100.

EPSOM, SURREY 3–3B

Le Raj £ 48 ❸④④
211 Fir Tree Rd KT17 3LB (01737) 371371
Attracting an impressive number of reports, this well-known suburban subcontinental is generally still hailed as a "cut above the norm"; service, though, can be "hit-and-miss", and there's something of a feeling in some quarters that it "could do better" generally.
/ Details: www.lerajrestaurant.co.uk; next to Derby race course; 11 pm; no jeans or trainers.

ESHER, SURREY 3–3A

Good Earth £ 49 ❷❷❸
14-18 High St KT10 9RT (01372) 462489
"Expensive, but worth it" – with its "high standard" of cuisine, this suburban Chinese proves a notably "reliable" destination for all of the good number of reporters who comment on it.
/ Details: www.goodearthgroup.co.uk; 11.15 pm, Sun 10.45 pm; booking: max 12, Fri & Sat.

ETON, BERKSHIRE 3–3A

Gilbey's £ 47 ❶
82-83 High St SL4 6AF (01753) 854921
A "great little bistro" (actually, not that little once you've found the rear conservatory) that's been in business for over three decades; "charming" staff and excellent wine are the prime draws, though the fare is certainly "decent". / Details: www.gilbeygroup.com; 5 min walk from Windsor Castle; 9.45 pm, Fri & Sat 10 pm.

EVERSHOT, DORSET 2–4B

Summer Lodge £ 86 ❷❷❷
DT2 0JR (01935) 482000
"Listening to sommelier Eric explain the wines is a true delight", at this grand and "romantic" Hardy Country manor house hotel; most (if not quite all) reporters acclaim its "welcoming" style and overall "wonderful" experience too. / Details: www.summerlodgehotel.co.uk; 12m NW of Dorchester on A37; 9.30 pm; no jeans or trainers. Accommodation: 24 rooms, from £295.

EVESHAM, WORCESTERSHIRE 2–1C

Evesham Hotel £ 43 ④❷❸
Coopers Ln WR11 1DA (01386) 765566
"If you are on the same wavelength as the eccentric owner, John Jenkinson", this "really fun" Cotswold-fringe hotel can offer an "uplifting and quirky" experience; true, its eclectic food can seem "ill thought out", but most reports focus on the "highly idiosyncratic wine list" – nothing French or German here!
/ Details: www.eveshamhotel.com; off Waterside, which runs parallel to the river; 9.30 pm; Max 16. Accommodation: 40 rooms, from £123.

Michael Caines
Royal Clarence Hotel £ 68 ❸❸④
Cathedral Yd EX1 1HD (01392) 223 638
Overseen by Michael Caines of nearby Gidleigh Park, this dining room "opposite the cathedral" is a solid all-rounder; some reporters find it "a little too formal to be properly relaxing", but it's well-rated, especially if you go for the "excellent-value set lunch".
/ **Details:** *www.abodehotels.co.uk; 9.45 pm; closed Sun; booking essential.*
Accommodation: *53 rooms, from £79.*

Allium £ 62 ❷❷❸
1 London St GL7 4AH (01285) 712200
"Deserving to be much better known", James & Erica Graham's accomplished town-centre restaurant is worth seeking out for its "superb" and "imaginative" cuisine, and its "charming" service.
/ **Details:** *www.alliumfood.co.uk/restaurant.html; 9 pm; closed Mon, Tue L, Sun D; booking: max 10.*

Bistro de la Mer £ 46 🅣
28 Arwenack St TR11 3JB (01326) 316509
"In a town not famous for its cuisine", this tiny bistro is – despite an interior that can seem disappointing – worth remembering for its "tasty, if not particularly cheap, seafood".
/ **Details:** *www.bistrodelamer.com; 9.30 pm, Fri & Sat 10 pm; closed Mon L & Sun L; no Amex.*

Indaba On The Beach £ 44 🅣
Swanpool TR11 5BG (01326) 311886
"The ambience suggests London more than Cornwall" at this beach-side venture (formerly The Three Mackerel), tipped for its "very relaxed" style and "very good fish". / **Details:** *www.indabafish.co.uk.*

Rick Stein's Fish & Chips £ 39 ❷④④
Discovery Quay TR11 3XA (01841) 532700
"Perfectly cooked fish 'n' chips" are (say most reports) to be found at this year-old invader from Padstow, although here the style is "more restaurant than chippy"; not everyone's impressed, though, and the odd reporter suggests that the less obvious dishes are the better choice. / **Details:** *www.rickstein.com; 9 pm; no Amex; no booking.*

The Museum Inn £ 53 ❸❷❸
DT11 8DE (01725) 516261
"A lovely village pub" consistently praised for its "excellent welcome" and "wide choice of food, served with finesse".
/ **Details:** *www.museuminn.co.uk; off the A354, signposted to Farnham; 9.30 pm, 9 pm Sun; no Amex.* **Accommodation:** *8 rooms, from £110.*

Read's £ 76 ❷❷❷
Macknade Manor, Canterbury Rd ME13 8XE (01795) 535344
Rona & David Pitchford's "lovely" operation (of over 30 years' standing) – in a "beautifully renovated" Georgian manor house – offers a "consistently brilliant" mix of "charming" service and "top-notch", "modern-classical" cuisine, plus "quality wines at modest prices". / **Details:** *www.reads.com; 9.30 pm; closed Mon & Sun.*
Accommodation: *6 rooms, from £165.*

Fence Gate Inn   £ 43   ⓣ
Wheatley Lane Rd BB12 9EE   (01282) 618101
"Never a bad meal", say fans of this large brasserie attached to a conference centre, tipped as a top-value destination in a part of the world without a huge number of other options.
/ **Details:** www.fencegate.co.uk; 9 pm, Fri 9.30 pm, Sat 10 pm, Sun 8 pm.

General Tarleton   £ 46   ❷❷❷
Boroughbridge Rd HG5 0PZ   (01423) 340284
"High-quality cooking of locally-sourced ingredients" and "friendly" staff make it an all-round "pleasant" experience to visit this popular inn, not far from the A1. / **Details:** www.generaltarleton.co.uk; 2m from A1, J48 towards Knaresborough; 9.15 pm. **Accommodation:** 14 rooms, from £129.

The Bricklayers Arms   £ 50   ❸❸❸
Hogpits Bottom HP3 0PH   (01442) 833322
The style is a little "old school" for some tastes, but this "scenically-located" pub is the type that makes "a great destination for Sunday lunch", and it has a strong fan club for its "consistently good" fare.
/ **Details:** www.bricklayersarms.com; J18 off the M25, past Chorleywood; 9.30 pm, Sun 8.30 pm.

The Griffin Inn   £ 43   ❷❸❷
TN22 3SS   (01825) 722890
"You leave with a feeling of well-being", say one of the many fans of this "warm and cheering" village pub where highlights include a "great barbecue" and a wine list that's "excellent by pub standards".
/ **Details:** www.thegriffininn.co.uk; off A272; 9.30 pm. **Accommodation:** 13 rooms, from £85.

The Parrot Inn   £ 39   ❸❸❷
RH5 5RZ   (01306) 621339
In the heart of the Surrey Hills, a "lovely old pub" which inspires many reports; the food may have no highfalutin aspirations, but dishes – often using meat from the owner's farm – are typically "simply cooked and simply delicious". / **Details:** www.theparrot.co.uk; 10 pm; closed Sun D; no Amex.

Anderida Restaurant
Ashdown Park Hotel   £ 67   ⓣ
Wych Cross RH18 5JR   (01342) 824988
A country house resort-hotel whose dining room is tipped as "a good environment for a high-quality meal", and with a "great wine list" too; sceptics say it's "perfectly nice but overpriced for what you get".
/ **Details:** www.ashdownpark.com; 9.30 pm, Fri - Sun 10 pm; jacket and/or tie. **Accommodation:** 106 rooms, from £199.

Roochi   £ 29   ❷❸❸
9 Hartfield Rd RH18 5DN   (01342) 825 251
"A great Indian where they use spices to give flavour, not to add heat" – this "friendly" recent arrival is approved by all who comment on it. / **Details:** www.roochi.co.uk.

Crannog   £ 48   🆃
Town Pier PH33 6DB   (01397) 705589
On the pier (and with "beautiful loch views"), this seafood restaurant of over 20 years' standing is tipped for "fish as it should be" – "simple and without too many enhancements"!
/ **Details:** www.crannog.net; 9.30 pm; no Amex.

Inverlochy Castle   £ 93   🆃
Torlundy PH33 6SN   (01397) 702177
There are few places in the Highlands as grand as this imposing, loch-side castle; even reporters who find it "old-fashioned, stodgy and pompous" tip it as a high-quality all-round experience!
/ **Details:** www.inverlochycastlehotel.com; off A82, 4 m N of Ft. William; 10 pm; jacket & tie required at D; children: 8+ at D. **Accommodation:** 17 & gate lodge rooms, from £300.

Sam's   £ 43   ④❸❷
20 Fore St PL23 1AQ   (01726) 832273
"You know you're on holiday when you come here", say fans of this "very friendly" and "happy" seaside bistro where simple dishes (of the seafood and burger variety) are realised to a "surprisingly good" standard. / **Details:** www.samsfowey.co.uk; 10 pm; no Amex; no booking.

The Fox & Goose   £ 45   ❷❶❷
Church Rd IP21 5PB   (01379) 586247
"A bit of out of the way, but well worth the journey", this "traditional" country pub is a "very cosy" sort of place, but with a "contemporary sensibility" when it comes to its "excellent" cooking; "exceptionally friendly" service too. / **Details:** www.foxandgoose.net; off A143; 8.45 pm, Fri & Sat 9 pm, Sun 8.15 pm; closed Mon; no Amex; children: 9+ for D.

The Pot Kiln   £ 47   ❷❷❸
RG18 0XX   (01635) 201366
"Well cooked and presented local game" is the menu highlight at this "hard-to-find" inn; perhaps surprisingly, though, "veggies are well catered for" too. / **Details:** www.potkiln.org; between J12 and J13 of the M4; 9 pm, Sun 8.30 pm; closed Tue.

The Alford Arms   £ 42   ❷❸❸
HP1 3DD   (01442) 864480
This mega-popular country inn achieves an impressive volume of praise for its "quaint" and "cosy" style, lovely terrace and "laid-back" atmosphere; harsher critics feel the food is "nothing special", but most reporters love the fact that it's so "very consistent".
/ **Details:** www.alfordarmsfrithsden.co.uk; near Ashridge College and vineyard; 9.30 pm, Fri & Sat 10 pm; booking: max 12.

The Palm £ 35   **T**
Bath Rd SN8 3HT (01672) 871 818
*A top tip for those looking for an "oasis" on the A4 (twixt
Marlborough and Hungerford); this lavish Indian newcomer "may not
look much from the outside", but it inspires only positive
commentary; "book ahead at weekends".*
*/ **Details:** www.thepalmindian.com.*

Apple Tree £ 40   **T**
Oxford Rd SL9 7AH (01753) 887335
*A "favourite local gastropub", tipped by a number of reporters for its
"tasty food" and "good value for money".*
*/ **Details:** www.appletreegerrardscross.co.uk; 10 pm.*

Indigo Bar And Grill £ 34   **T**
Indigo Hs, Oxford Rd SL9 7AL (01753) 883100
*A "very pleasant" all-rounder, tipped for Indian food that's not only
cooked "from scratch", but "to perfection" too.*

Maliks £ 45   **❶④④**
14 Oak End Way SL9 8BR (01753) 880888
*"Comfortably the best Indian in the area" – this "efficient" spin-off
from the acclaimed Cookham original can sometimes "give a
disappointing first impression" – soon dispelled, though, thanks to
the "tastiest" dishes, which demonstrate some "superb" spicing.*
*/ **Details:** www.maliks.co.uk; 10.45 pm.*

Brian Maule at Chardon D'Or £ 54   **❸❸④**
176 West Regent St G2 4RL (0141) 248 3801
*Views on this ex-Gavroche chef's grand and quite 'corporate'
restaurant remain rather mixed; its "sophisticated" cuisine generally,
pleases, though – go pre-theatre, and it can even be it can even be
relatively "affordable". / **Details:** www.brianmaule.com; 10 pm; closed Sun.*

Gamba £ 58   **❷❷❸**
225a West George St G2 2ND (0141) 572 0899
*"Thoughtful and very skilfully-prepared" fish dishes and
"knowledgeable" service have made a big name for David Marshall's
"highly recommended" and "reliable" city-centre basement – "some
of the best fine dining in town". / **Details:** www.gamba.co.uk; 10 pm;
closed Sun L.*

Hotel du Vin et Bistro £ 45   **④❸❸**
1 Devonshire Gdns G12 0UX (0141) 339 2001
*This potentially "lovely" hotel dining room once found fame as 'One
Devonshire Gardens' – it offers the group's trademark "huge" wine
list, of course, but ratings slipped across the board this year.
/ **Details:** 9.45 pm, Sat 10 pm; closed Sat L. **Accommodation:** 49 rooms,
from £140.*

biquitous Chip

vo Fat Ladies at (The Buttery)

amba

Mother India £ 36 ❶❷❷

28 Westminster Ter G3 7RU (0141) 221 1663

"The best Indian food in Glasgow, and possibly all of Scotland too!" – "freshly made" and "richly flavoursome", it comes in "huge portions" ("order half what you think"); this "rather basic" spot near Kelvingrove Park is a "welcoming" place too, if rather "cramped and noisy". / **Details:** www.motherindiaglasgow.co.uk; beside Kelvingrove Hotel; Mon-Thu 10.30 pm, Fri & Sat 11 pm, Sun 10.30 pm; Mon-Thu D only, Fri-Sun open L & D.

Rogano £ 62 ❸❷❷

11 Exchange Pl G1 3AN (0141) 248 4055

"A bit pricey, but worth it for the décor!" – this "sumptuous" Art Deco institution has "stabilised after its ups and downs of recent years"; the food (with fish the speciality) may not be remarkable, but at least it's now "predictable" (and "the early-evening menu offers exceptional value"). / **Details:** www.roganoglasgow.com; 10.30 pm.

Stravaigin £ 44 ❷❷❷

28 Gibson St G12 8NX (0141) 334 2665

"A very special place for pub-food or proper food"; Colin Clydesdale's "eclectic" West End bar/restaurant is "always buzzing", thanks to its "chatty" service and "sophisticated" cooking (including some "heavenly breakfasts"). / **Details:** www.stravaigin.com; 11 pm; closed weekday L.

Two Fat Ladies £ 48 ❷❷❸

118a, Blythswood St G2 4EG (0141) 847 0088

This city-centre spin-off from the original 'Two Fat Ladies' (at 88 Dumbarton Road, G11 – tel 0141 339 1944) is a "deservedly popular venue", highly rated for its "excellent" and "well-presented" fish dishes. / **Details:** www.twofatladiesrestaurant.com; 10 pm, Fri & Sat 11 pm, Sun 9 pm.

Two Fat Ladies at The Buttery £ 50 ❸❷❷

652 Argyle St G3 8UF (0141) 221 8188

Ornate and "lovely", this restaurant housed in a Victorian building near the SECC is "the best of the three 'Fat Lady' establishments"; serving a modern Scottish menu leading on seafood, it makes a notably consistent job of "keeping up standards". / **Details:** www.twofatladiesrestaurant.com; 10 pm, Sun 9 pm.

Ubiquitous Chip £ 57 ❸❷❷

12 Ashton Ln G12 8SJ (0141) 334 5007

"Still one of Glasgow's most popular and fun restaurants"; the famous 'Chip' inspires surprisingly few reports nowadays – almost all, however, praise it for its "romantic" setting (based around a "fantastic plant-fringed courtyard"), its "distinctly Scottish" cuisine, "huge" wine list and "relaxed" style. / **Details:** www.ubiquitouschip.co.uk; behind Hillhead station; 11 pm.

GODALMING, SURREY 3–3A

Bel & The Dragon £ 44 🅣

Bridge St GU7 1BY (01483) 527333

"Attractive and fun", this former church trades as a "restaurant with piano bar" nowadays; the food is "not that interesting", but the overall experience can be "spectacular".

/ **Details:** www.belandthedragon-godalming.co.uk; at the bottom of Godalming High St, directly opposite Waitrose; 10 pm, Sun 9 pm; no Amex.

La Luna　　　　　　　　　　　　£ 48　　❷❷❷
10-14 Wharf St GU7 1NN　(01483) 414155
"A lovely place for a treat"; "creative" cooking and "first-class" wines
have made quite a name for this "high-quality" Italian; "it has leaned
more towards a brasserie style in recent times, which has certainly
improved the ambience". / **Details:** www.lalunarestaurant.co.uk; between
the High Street and Flambard Way; 10 pm.

GODSHILL, ISLE OF WIGHT　　　　　　　　2–4D

The Taverners　　　　　　　　　£ 37　　❷❸❸
High St PO38 3HZ　(01983) 840 707
Not just in its "touristy" village setting is this "homely and welcoming
pub" particularly worth seeking out – all reporters praise its
"delicious" and "innovative" fare.
/ **Details:** www.thetavernersgodshill.co.uk.

GOLDSBOROUGH, NORTH YORKSHIRE　　　　8–3D

The Fox And Hounds Inn　　　　　£ 48　　🅣
YO21 3RX　(01947) 893372
Why so few reports? – such as there are unanimously tip the all-
round standards of this small inn, not least its "simple dishes,
beautifully cooked". / **Details:** www.foxandhoundsgoldsborough.co.uk;
8.30 pm; D only, closed Sun-Tue; no Amex.

GORING-ON-THAMES, BERKSHIRE　　　　　2–2D

Leatherne Bottel　　　　　　　£ 60　　❸❷❶
Bridleway RG8 0HS　(01491) 872667
The "dreamy" riverside location on the banks of the Thames helps
make this "pretty" spot a "favourite" for some reporters (and the
wine list is surprisingly impressive); the whole set-up, though, can
sometimes seem "a bit pricey" and "pretentious".
/ **Details:** www.leathernebottel.co.uk; 0.5m outside Goring on B4009; 9 pm;
closed Sun D; children: 10+ for D.

Pierreponts　　　　　　　　　£ 32　　🅣
High St RG8 9AB　(01491) 874 464
"A really lovely café in a pretty village"; what's not to like, especially
when it's tipped as an "excellent" destination offering "a lovely
selection of cheap eats and cakes"?

GRASMERE, CUMBRIA　　　　　　　　　7–3D

The Jumble Room　　　　　　　£ 46　　❷❷❶
Langdale Rd LA22 9SU　(01539) 435188
"A lovely find"; the "cosy", "relaxed" and "quirky" style of this first-
floor "Lakeland favourite" wins universal praise, as does its
"unusual" food (from a "tiny kitchen") and "friendly" service.
/ **Details:** www.thejumbleroom.co.uk; half way along the Langdale road,
between two hotels; 10 pm; closed Mon, Tue, Wed L & Thu L; no Amex.
Accommodation: 3 rooms, from £180.

GREAT DUNMOW, ESSEX　　　　　　　　3–2C

The Starr　　　　　　　　　　£ 52　　⑤④④
Market Pl CM6 1AX　(01371) 874321
"Oh dear, what has happened?" – this large town-centre inn-
conversion of nearly three decades' standing still inspires a lot of
reports, but it's hard to avoid the conclusion that it's "living on past
glories" nowadays. / **Details:** www.the-starr.co.uk; 8m E of M11, J8 on
A120; 9.30 pm; closed Mon & Sun D; no jeans or trainers.
Accommodation: 8 rooms, from £95.

Harry's Place £ 80 **②①④**
17 High St NG31 8JS (01476) 561780
*"Food from Harry and personal service from Caroline" – you don't get an experience much more "like eating in someone's home" than at the Hallams' celebrated 10-seater; although the odd critic feels its high renown is "a lot of fuss about nothing", most reporters find this "a superb experience in every way". / **Details:** on B1174 1m N of Grantham; 9.30 pm; closed Mon & Sun; no Amex; booking essential; children: 5+.*

GREAT MILTON, OXFORDSHIRE 2–2D

Le Manoir aux Quat' Saisons £148 **①②①**
Church Rd OX44 7PD (01844) 278881
*"Utterly perfect"; Raymond Blanc's "mind-blowing" manor house hotel is – with its "beautiful gardens" and "unrivalled accommodation" – "the real deal" (especially for a "romantic getaway"); the food – "classic cuisine with a vibrant twist" – is "out of this world" too (as, sadly, are the "heart-stopping" prices). / **Details:** www.manoir.com; from M40, J7 take A329 towards Wallingford; 9.30 pm; booking: max 8. **Accommodation:** 32 rooms, from £460.*

GREAT MISSENDEN, BUCKINGHAMSHIRE 3–2A

The Nags Head £ 48 **②④③**
London Rd HP16 0DG (01494) 862200
*More "reliable" of late, this popular country inn attracts plaudits for its "interesting and well-cooked" – sometimes "fantastic" – food, and a "great beer garden" too. / **Details:** www.nagsheadbucks.com; off the A413; 9.30 pm, Sun 8.30 pm. **Accommodation:** 5 rooms, from £95.*

GRINDLETON, LANCASHIRE 5–1B

The Duke Of York Inn £ 40 **②③④**
Brow Top BB7 4QR (01200) 441266
*"A real find"; this "emerging star of the Ribble Valley" attracts much praise for its "superb" food; early-bird and lunch menus offer particular value. / **Details:** www.dukeofyorkgrindleton.com; 9 pm, Sun 8 pm; closed Mon.*

GRINSHILL, SHROPSHIRE 5–3A

The Inn at Grinshill £ 45 **②③③**
The High St SY4 3BL (01939) 220410
*In a "delightful village", a "hard-to-find" gastropub which – under its new chef – "is beginning to make quite a name for its high-quality food". / **Details:** www.theinnatgrinshill.co.uk; 9.30 pm; closed Mon & Sun D; no Amex. **Accommodation:** 6 rooms, from £90.*

GUERNSEY, CHANNEL ISLANDS

Da Nello £ 43 **②①②**
46 Lower Pollet St GY1 1WF (01481) 721552
*In the same hands for over 30 years, this "wonderful family-fun Italian", in St Peter Port, continues to please almost all reporters with its "lovely" food and its "kind and efficient" service. / **Details:** www.danello.gg; 10 pm.*

Rumwong   £ 41   ❷❷❷
18-20 London Rd GU1 2AF (01483) 536092
It was established as far back as 1978, but this "very authentic" spot continues to impress a large local fan club with its "stimulating and imaginative" cuisine. / **Details:** www.rumwong.co.uk; 10.30 pm; closed Mon; no Amex.

The Thai Terrace   £ 37   ❷❸❷
Castle Car Pk, Sydenham Rd GU1 3RT (01483) 503350
"Ignore the fact that it's above a multi-storey car park" – "you soon forget" anyway, thanks to the "superb" Thai food and "stunning views" of this "always-packed" destination; "the only grumble is that the service is a little too efficient!" / **Details:** opposite Guildford Castle in town centre; 10.30 pm; closed Sun.

La Potinière   £ 54   ❷④④
Main St EH31 2AA (01620) 843214
Keith Marley and Mary Runciman's ambitious, if simply decorated, small restaurant is "invariably full", thanks to the "exceptional" quality of its cuisine ("albeit from a fairly restricted menu"); service, though, can show the strain. / **Details:** www.la-potiniere.co.uk; 20m E of Edinburgh, off A198; 8.30 pm; closed Mon, Tue & Sun D; no jeans or trainers; booking essential.

Horn of Plenty   £ 67   ❷❷❷
PL19 8JD (01822) 832528
"Not easy to find, but worth the effort"; this long-established restaurant-with-rooms – with "lovely views" over the Tamar Valley – continues to thrive since Peter Gorton left in 2010; there's the odd dud meal, but most reports speak of "pampering" service and deft handling of "honest local produce". / **Details:** www.thehornofplenty.co.uk; 3m W of Tavistock on A390; 8.45 pm; no jeans or trainers; children: 10+ at D. **Accommodation:** 10 rooms, from £125.

Tom Browns Brasserie   £ 47   ❸⑤④
The Old School Hs NG14 7FB (0115) 966 3642
A "modern and welcoming" brasserie on the River Trent of note for its "consistent" cuisine; "slow" service, though, can sometimes be an issue. / **Details:** www.tombrowns.co.uk; 10 pm.

Earle   £ 43   ④❷❸
4 Cecil Rd WA15 9PA (0161) 929 8869
Backing by footie players has helped boost the "celebrity factor" of this suburban venture, run by Simon Rimmer of Green's fame; on the food front, though, it's "good for a simple local meal rather than being any sort of 'destination' restaurant".
/ **Details:** www.earlerestaurant.co.uk; 10 pm, Sun 8 pm; closed Mon L.

Shibden Mill Inn £ 44 ❸❷❶
Shibden Mill Fold HX3 7UL (01422) 365840
"Deep in the heart of the valley", this "real, traditional inn" is a
"comforting" place that's "particularly cosy in winter"; its "reliable"
cuisine is of the "posh pub grub" variety.
/ **Details:** www.shibdenmillinn.com; off the A58, Leeds/Bradford road;
9.15 pm, Sun 7.30 pm. **Accommodation:** 11 rooms, from £100.

The Bugle £ 40 ❸❸❷
High St SO31 4HA (023) 8045 3051
A "really good gastropub" that pleases all who comment on it with
its "fresh and enjoyable" food at "good prices" and its "excellent
location overlooking the River Hamble".
/ **Details:** www.buglehamble.co.uk.

Finch's Arms £ 37 ❸④❷
Oakham Rd LE15 8TL (01572) 756575
"Lots of smart cars in the car-park" confirm the big local reputation
of this "lovely" inn which "mixes an old bar with a sophisticated
dining room" and has a "wonderful garden terrace overlooking
Rutland Water"; cooking quality can suffer at busy times, though,
and service is notably "patchy". / **Details:** www.finchsarms.co.uk;
9.30 pm, Sun 8 pm. **Accommodation:** 6 rooms, from £95.

Hambleton Hall £ 87 ❶❷❶
LE15 8TH (01572) 756991
"Dining heaven!"; Tim Hart's "very smart" country house hotel in a
"delightful" location overlooking Rutland Water, remains a "top-
class" traditional bastion, thanks to Aaron Patterson's "elegant" and
highly "accomplished" cuisine; if there is a criticism, it's that the
ambience can seem a trifle "pompous".
/ **Details:** www.hambletonhall.com; near Rutland Water; 9.30 pm.
Accommodation: 17 rooms, from £265.

The Pheasant Hotel £ 56 ❸❷❷
YO62 5JG (01439) 771241
This small hotel overlooking the village duck pond is "more austere
than the Star" (same owner) but a "pleasant" destination
nonetheless; the "well-presented, locally-sourced food" can be
"lovely" too, but is not as highly-rated as its stablemate's.
/ **Details:** www.thepheasanthotel.com; 9 pm; no Amex; Essential for weekends.
Accommodation: 14 rooms, from £150.

The Star Inn £ 60 ❶❷❷
YO62 5JE (01439) 770397
Andrew & Jacquie Pern's "cosseting" thatched inn (with "beautiful"
rooms) is back on top form; a few critics may find it "very pricey"
(and not everyone likes the recent extension), but its "robust" and
"intensely flavoured" cooking again won full marks this year.
/ **Details:** www.thestaratharome.co.uk; 3m SE of Helmsley off A170; 9.30 pm,
Sun 6 pm; closed Mon L & Sun D; no Amex. **Accommodation:** 14 rooms,
from £140.

Bettys   **£ 37**   ❷❷❷
1 Parliament St HG1 2QU   (01423) 814070
"Perhaps the poshest of all the Betties", this "perfect café from a
past age" is still "always busy" and yet – as a huge volume of
reports attest – it remains "consistently good in every way",
especially for "an indulgent tea" or "very civilised brunch".
/ Details: www.bettysandtaylors.co.uk; 9 pm; no Amex; no booking.

The Boar's Head   **£ 41**   ❼
Ripley Castle Estate HG3 3AY   (01423) 771888
A grand village inn with both a restaurant and (inspiring more
feedback) brasserie – both tipped for their "reliable" quality.
/ Details: www.boarsheadripley.co.uk; off A61 between Ripon & Harrogate;
9 pm. Accommodation: 25 rooms, from £125.

Brio   **£ 33**   ❼
Hornbeam Pk HG2 8RE   (01423) 870005
"Don't let the location put you off" – this office-block Italian is
tipped for "the best pizza in town" (as well as a wide range of other
dishes) which helps make it a particularly good weekend destination
for those with families in tow. / Details: www.brios.co.uk; 10 pm; closed
Sun; no Amex.

Clocktower Restaurant
Rudding Park Hotel   **£ 59**   ④④❷
Rudding Ln HG3 1JH   (01423) 871350
A country house hotel brasserie which benefits from "good views
over wonderful gardens" and inspires lots of feedback; reports are,
however, rather up-and-down – "it's a beautiful setting", says one of
the critics, "but at these prices the food should be rather more
inspirational". / Details: www.ruddingpark.co.uk; Exit A1 at J47; onto the
A59 signed to Harrogate; 9 pm. Accommodation: 90 rooms, from £126.

Drum & Monkey   **£ 45**   ❸❸❸
5 Montpellier Gdns HG1 2TF   (01423) 502650
A "firm Harrogate favourite" which attracts legions of reports; to
fans it's "quirky and old-fashioned, but the seafood is still super" –
there's a voluble band of critics for whom it's "trading on its former
reputation". / Details: www.drumandmonkey.co.uk; 10 pm; closed Sun D;
no Amex; booking: max 10.

Graveley's Fish & Chip Restaurant   **£ 38**   ❷❷❸
8-12 Cheltenham Pde HG1 1DB   (01423) 507093
"Been coming here for over twenty years, and it's still just as good" –
this "top chippy" may be "moving a little away from its chip shop
roots", but the quality of its fare continues to impress all who
comment on it. / Details: www.graveleysofharrogate.com; 9 pm, Fri & Sat
10 pm, Sun 8 pm.

Hotel du Vin et Bistro   **£ 49**   ④④④
Prospect Pl HG1 1LB   (01423) 856800
This outpost of the Gallic hotel and bistro chain again inspired erratic
feedback this year – those who say it's "always excellent" are almost
equally matched by those who find it "very disappointing"!
/ Details: www.hotelduvin.com; 9.45 pm, Fri & Sat 10 pm.
Accommodation: 48 rooms, from £110.

Orchid
£ 44 ❷❷❸

28 Swan Rd HG1 2SE (01423) 560425

"Consistently high-quality SE Asian food and a bustling atmosphere"
– that's the deal that wins unanimous praise for this "first-class" all-rounder; "book ahead", especially for the "amazing Sunday brunch"
*– it's a "local legend"! / **Details:** www.orchidrestaurant.co.uk; 10 pm;*
*closed Sat L. **Accommodation:** 28 rooms, from £115.*

Quantro
£ 45 ❷❷❸

3 Royal Pde HG1 2SZ (01423) 503034

*"As good as anywhere in London, and half the price!" – it doesn't have a huge following among reporters, but all feedback on this town-centre restaurant is notably positive and consistent across the board. / **Details:** www.quantro.co.uk; 10 pm, Sat 10.30 pm; closed Sun; children: no under 4's in evening.*

Sukhothai
£ 34 ❷❹❸

17-19 Cheltenham Pde HG1 1DD (01423) 500 869

"Every bit as good as the Leeds original", this "vast palace" of a restaurant is "by far the best of the many local Thais" – even the harshest report says it offers "good value"!
*/ **Details:** www.thaifood4u.co.uk.*

The Timble Inn
£ 43 ⓣ

Timble LS21 2NN (01943) 880530

"Best to book" – this "very consistent" gastropub is tipped for its "really nice Dales location" and its "great food and ales".
*/ **Details:** www.thetimbleinn.com; 9.30 pm; closed Mon & Tue; no shorts.*

Van Zeller
£ 64 ❷❸❷

8 Montpellier St HG1 2TQ (01423) 508762

Local lad Tom van Z serves up some "gorgeous" dishes at this "coolly decorated" but "intimate" town-centre two-year-old; service can be a tad "hit 'n' miss", though (which is ironic as his main backer is Pied à Terre's famed front-of-house, David Moore).
*/ **Details:** www.vanzellerrestaurants.co.uk; 9.30 pm; closed Mon & Sun D.*

William & Victoria
£ 40 ❸❸❷

6 Cold Bath Rd HG2 0NA (01423) 521510

"The best wine bar in town", of over 20 years' standing, offers a "varied" menu of dishes in "hearty" portions and in a "friendly" atmosphere; reporters like the restaurant upstairs too.
*/ **Details:** www.williamandvictoria.com; 10 pm; no Amex.*

HARTSHEAD, WEST YORKSHIRE
5–1C

The Gray Ox Inn
£ 38 ❷❷❸

15 Hartshead Ln WF15 8AL (01274) 872845

"A stunning local" – this Georgian inn offers "inventive, locally-produced food, and a 'steal' of an early-bird menu".
*/ **Details:** www.grayoxinn.co.uk/.*

HARWICH, ESSEX
3–2D

The Pier at Harwich
£ 53 ⓣ

The Quay CO12 3HH (01255) 241212

*A handy waterside bistro/restaurant where you go "downstairs for good fish 'n' chips, upstairs for good sea views and well-cooked but pricier fish" – most reporters go with the "straightforward" ground-floor option. / **Details:** www.milsomhotels.com; 9.30 pm, Sat 10 pm; no jeans. **Accommodation:** 14 rooms, from £130.*

Hassop Hall   £ 49   ❷⓿❷
DE45 1NS   (01629) 640488
For "traditional food in a beautiful setting", the Chapman family's
"popular" country house hotel "never fails to deliver"; it helps that
prices are fair, and that, for the staff, "nothing is too much trouble".
/ *Details:* www.hassophall.co.uk; on the B6001 Bakewell - Hathersage Road,
Junction 29 of M1; 9 pm; closed Mon L, Sat L & Sun D.
Accommodation: 13 rooms, from £95.

Maggie's   £ 23   🅣
Rock-a-Nore Rd TN34 3DW   (01424) 430 205
A "proper" fish 'n' chip place right on the beach, tipped for fish that
"leaps off the trawlers on to your plate".

Webbe's Rock-a-Nore   £ 40   ④④④
1 Rock-a-Nore Rd TN34 3DW   (01424) 721650
In its second full year, reports on this harbour-side restaurant have
become more mixed; even its worse critic applauds its "brilliantly
fresh" fish and seafood, but the dishes can seem "a bit standard and
safe" and not everyone likes the "dark" interior.
/ *Details:* www.webbesrestaurants.co.uk; 9.30 pm.

The Blue Strawberry   £ 41   ❷❷❸
The St CM3 2DW   (01245) 381333
"Very popular" (and sometimes "crowded"), this village-restaurant
now has nearly two decades behind it; ratings are not as stellar as
they once were, but most reporters feel it "fully deserves its
continuing success" even so. / *Details:* www.bluestrawberrybistro.co.uk;
3m E of Chelmsford; 10 pm; closed Sat L & Sun D.

The Plough Inn   £ 40   🅣
Leadmill Bridge S32 1BA   (01433) 650319
A "welcoming" inn on the banks of the River Derwent, tipped for the
"very good standard" of its food; even fans, however, may observe
that it's "not cheap". / *Details:* www.theploughinn-hathersage.co.uk; 9 pm,
Sat 9.30 pm; no Amex; booking: max 10. **Accommodation:** 9 rooms,
from £95.

The Great House   £ 42   ❷❸❷
Gills Grn TN18 5EJ   (01580) 753119
"Upscale" and "well run", this "very good" hostelry – teetering in
feel between pub and restaurant – impresses all who comment on it,
not least with its quality Gallic fare.
/ *Details:* www.elitepubs.com/the_greathouse; 9.30 pm; no Amex.

Weaver's   £ 41   🅣
15 West Ln BD22 8DU   (01535) 643822
Tipped for its "real atmosphere" and "good use of local produce" –
the Rushworth family's restaurant-with-rooms, by the Bronte
Parsonage Museum, continues to please.
/ *Details:* www.weaverssmallhotel.co.uk; 1.5m W on B6142 from A629, near
Parsonage; 9 pm; closed Mon, Sat L & Sun D; children: 5+ on Sat.
Accommodation: 3 rooms, from £110.

HAYWARDS HEATH, WEST SUSSEX
3–4B

Jeremy's at Borde Hill
£ 50 ❶❸❷

Balcombe Rd RH16 1XP (01444) 441102

"Jeremy Ashpool continues to set very high standards" at this "much-loved" county destination which again inspires rave reviews for his "beautifully prepared and presented" dishes; "there's a wonderful terrace for summer dining overlooking a lovely garden".
/ **Details:** www.jeremysrestaurant.com; Exit 10A from the A23; 10 pm; closed Mon & Sun D.

HEBDEN BRIDGE, WEST YORKSHIRE
5–1C

Rim Nam Thai Restaurant
£ 30 ❷❷❸

New road HX7 8AD (0871) 9624351

Fans applaud the "outstanding" Northern Thai cooking and super location overlooking the canal of this "friendly" operation; "the only drawback is that it's always busy, and comfort is not improved by some hideous seating!" / **Details:** midnight; closed Mon.

HEDDON ON THE WALL, TYNE AND WEAR
8–2B

Close House
£ 52 ❶

NE15 0HT (01661) 852255

A grand country house (golfing) hotel – recently lavishly revamped – tipped for its "excellent food and service".
/ **Details:** www.closehouse.co.uk; St Andrews Church; 9 pm.
Accommodation: 19 rooms, from £130.

HEDLEY ON THE HILL, NORTHUMBERLAND
8–2B

The Feathers Inn
£ 41 ❶❸④

Hedley-on-the-Hill NE43 7SW (01661) 843607

"Hard to beat for the variety of dishes and quality of cooking, and always good value-for-money" – no wonder this "lovely old pub in a hilltop village" can sometimes get "a bit crowded".
/ **Details:** www.thefeathers.net; 8.30 pm; closed Mon L; no Amex.

HELMSLEY, NORTH YORKSHIRE
8–4C

Black Swan
£ 38 ❶

Market Pl YO62 5BJ (01439) 770466

No one holds it up as a great foodie hotspot, but this ancient and pretty hotel is tipped for its "excellent lunches" and its "wonderful afternoon teas" too. / **Details:** www.blackswan-helmsley.co.uk; 9.30 pm.
Accommodation: 45 rooms, from £130.

Feversham Arms
£ 66 ❷❷❷

1-8 High St YO62 5AG (01439) 770766

"Hidden-away in deepest Yorkshire" this is the sort of hotel where "your car is whisked away and you go and have a glass of Champagne by the pool"; even those who say the cuisine "doesn't always quite hit the mark" note its "real ingenuity".
/ **Details:** www.fevershamarmshotel.com; 9.30 pm; no trainers; children: 12+ after 8 pm. **Accommodation:** 33 rooms, from £225.

HEMINGFORD GREY, CAMBRIDGESHIRE
3–1B

The Cock
£ 43 ❸❸❸

47 High St PE28 9BJ (01480) 463609

"A great family-friendly pub close to the A1"; its "very varied menu" of pub grub is "a cut above", and it has a "pretty setting" by the River Ouse. / **Details:** www.thecockhemingford.co.uk; just off the A14; follow signs to the river; 9 pm, Fri & Sat 9.30 pm, Sun 8.30 pm; 10+ Fri & Sat D; children: 5+ at D.

Hotel du Vin et Bistro £ 49 ⑤④❸
New St RG9 2BP (01491) 848400
*One of the weaker members of a hotel group that's been
inconsistent in recent times – this converted brewery by the Thames
is potentially a great venue (and still the most commented-on place
in the town) but is simply "not up to scratch" at present.*
/ Details: www.hotelduvin.com; 10 pm, Fri & Sat 10.30 pm.
Accommodation: 43 rooms, from £110.

Luscombes at the Golden Ball £ 56 ④④❸
Lower Assendon RG9 6AH (01491) 574157
*"More restaurant than pub, but retaining a lovely pub atmosphere"
– this "rustic" inn continues to impress most reporters with its
"consistent" culinary standards; its ratings are undercut, however, by
a minority who see the place as "overpriced and over-hyped".*
/ Details: www.luscombes.co.uk; 10.30 pm, Sun 9 pm; no Amex.

The Butchers Arms £ 50 ④④④
38 Towngate HD9 1TE (01484) 682361
*Tim Bilton's picturesquely-located Pennines gastropub drew a mixed
bag of reports this year; the middle view is that it's "rather pricey"
and "sometimes brilliant, sometimes not…"*
/ Details: www.thebutchersarmshepworth.co.uk; 10 pm, Sun 9 pm; no Amex.

Café at All Saints £ 24 ❶
All Saints Church, High St HR4 9AA (01432) 370415
*This church café "at the heart of its community" is tipped as an
"excellent lunch stop" and as a place for "scrummy cakes".*
*/ Details: www.cafeatallsaints.co.uk; near Cathedral; L only; closed Sun;
no Amex; no booking; children: 6+ upstairs.*

Le Petit Poisson £ 38 ❸②④
Pier Approach, Central Parade CT6 5JN (01227) 361199
*"Great seafood overlooking the sea" wins praise for this "superb little
place", which, if anything has been "improved by the recent
expansion"; "it's just as good as Whitstable", say fans, "but without
the Whitstable prices". / Details: www.lepetitpoisson.co.uk; 9.30 pm;
closed Mon & Sun D; no Amex.*

The Angel Inn £ 45 ❷❷❶
BD23 6LT (01756) 730263
*"A wonderful gem in beautiful countryside" – most reporters find
little to fault at this famous inn which offers "imaginative" cooking,
an "excellent choice of wine" and "friendly service"… and all in a
"lovely, busy traditional pub atmosphere".*
*/ Details: www.angelhetton.co.uk; 5m N of Skipton off B6265 at Rylstone;
9 pm, Sat 9.45 pm; D only, ex Sun open L only. Accommodation: 9 rooms,
from £140.*

Bouchon Bistrot £ 41 ④❸❸
4-6 Gilesgate NE46 3NJ (01434) 609943
Gallic fare that's "well cooked and precisely timed" has made quite a name for this bistro at the centre of a "fabulous market town"; critics, though, can find the approach a touch "routine".
/ **Details:** www.bouchonbistrot.co.uk; 9.30 pm; closed Mon & Sun.

The Old Queens Head £ 42 ❸④❷
Hammersley Ln HP10 8EY (01494) 813371
With its "high beams and barn-like interior", this gastropub in a "lovely" Tudor building is a "steady" local favourite with "above-average" fare; the main bugbear is its sometimes "chaotic" service – "only the bill came quickly!" / **Details:** www.oldqueensheadpenn.co.uk; 9.30 pm, Fri & Sat 10 pm.

Barnacles £ 43 ❷❸④
Watling St LE10 3JA (01455) 633220
"Strange to see a high-quality seafood restaurant in a location as far from the sea as you can get" (and "just off the M69" too); Martin Pegg's well-established venture overlooking a private lake wins consistently high ratings – even so, "the simplest dishes are often best". / **Details:** www.barnaclesrestaurant.co.uk; 9.30 pm; closed Mon L, Sat L & Sun D; no Amex.

Lord Poulett Arms £ 44 ❷❸❷
TA17 8SE (01460) 73149
This "truly quaint" pub is – on most accounts – "a really good find" which "never fails" to offer pub grub that's "more interesting than normal" and "very well made" too. / **Details:** www.lordpoulettarms.com; 9 pm; no Amex. **Accommodation:** 4 rooms, from £85.

Victoria at Holkham £ 35 🆃
Park Rd NR23 1RG (01328) 711008
"Possibly the nicest spot in England for a post-lunch walk!" – this inn near Holkham Beach is tipped for its "wholesome" food, and it's "always buzzing". / **Details:** www.victoriaatholkham.co.uk; on the main coast road, between Wells-next-the Sea and Burnham Overy Staithe; 9 pm; no Amex; booking essential. **Accommodation:** 10 rooms, from £125.

Byfords £ 37 🆃
1-3 Shirehall Plain NR25 6BG (01263) 711400
This very busy all-day café/restaurant inspires a good volume of reports and is strongly tipped for its "brilliant breakfast menu" and "good cakes and sarnies" ("be prepared to queue"); critics, though, can find it "a bit of a food factory". / **Details:** www.byfords.org.uk; 9.30 pm. **Accommodation:** 16 rooms, from £140.

The Pigs £ 42 ❸④④
Norwich Rd NR24 2RL (01263) 587634
*They sure have a gift for marketing at the home of the 'Pudding Club' (and also of Norfolk 'Iffits', or tapas as most people call them) – this relaxed boozer is "certainly different"; while the menu is seemingly "purpose-designed for kids", not all grown-ups are convinced by it. / **Details:** www.thepigs.org.uk; 9 pm. **Accommodation:** 3 rooms, from £110.*

HONITON, DEVON 2–4A

Combe House £ 65 ❷❷❶
Gittisham EX14 3AD (01404) 540400
*No disrespect to the "lovely" food, but it's the atmosphere of the "beautiful" and "interesting" (and also quite "pricey") dining room of this privately-owned Elizabethan manor house hotel that most excites reporters. / **Details:** www.combehousedevon.com; on the outskirts of Honiton; not far from the A30, A375, 303; 9.30 pm. **Accommodation:** 15 rooms, from £199.*

The Holt £ 41 🅃
178 High St EX14 1LA (01404) 47707
*A "consistent" boozer tipped for "good food and great beer" (and an "intelligent" wine list too); "when full, though, which is to say usually, it can get very noisy". / **Details:** www.theholt-honiton.com; 9 pm, Fri & Sat 9.30 pm; closed Mon & Sun.*

HOOK, HAMPSHIRE 2–3D

Old House at Home £ 47 🅃
Newham Grn RG27 9AH (01256) 762222
A traditional country boozer, tipped in all reports as "consistently good" (and "excellent for Sunday lunch" in particular).

HORNDON ON THE HILL, ESSEX 3–3C

The Bell Inn £ 44 ❷❷❷
High Rd SS17 8LD (01375) 642463
*Over four decades in the same ownership, this ever-popular coaching inn still has an impressive following, thanks to an "ever-changing menu" that "strikes the perfect balance between pubiness and foodiness"; (Sunday lunch, though, seems to be a bit of an Achilles' heel). / **Details:** www.bell-inn.co.uk; signposted off B1007, off A13; 9.45 pm; booking: max 12. **Accommodation:** 15 rooms, from £50.*

HORSHAM, WEST SUSSEX 3–4B

**Camellia Restaurant
South Lodge Hotel** £ 56 ❸❷❷
Brighton Rd RH13 6PS (01403) 891711
A "beautifully-located" country house hotel, which – as well as the more uncompromising Pass restaurant (complete with open kitchen) – also offers this "lovely" traditional dining option; on a food (but not ambience) front, Pass has the edge.
*/ **Details:** www.southlodgehotel.co.uk; opp Crabtree pub 1 mile up road from Leonards Lee gardens; 9.30 pm. **Accommodation:** 89 rooms, from £230.*

Restaurant Tristan £ 54 ❷❸❷
3 Stans Way, East St RH12 1HU (01403) 255688
*"Best in the region" say fans of Tristan Mason's "very friendly" beamed restaurant – his "superb" and "really interesting" cuisine features "surprising, expertly blended flavours", at "very reasonable prices". / **Details:** www.restauranttristan.co.uk; 9.30 pm; closed Mon & Sun.*

Brownlow Arms £ 46 🅣

High Rd NG32 2AZ (01400) 250234

*Tipped for "very good food" ("if at a price") – a "rural boozer" that's "worth the drive". / **Details:** www.brownlowarms.com; 9.15 pm; closed Mon, Tue–Sat D only, closed Sun D; no Amex; children: 12+.*
Accommodation: 5 rooms, from £96 in.

Lino's £ 35 🅣

122 Market St CH47 3BH (0151) 632 1408

Almost three decades in business, this family-owned establishment is still applauded in most reports for its "consistently high standards", but the occasional off-day is not unknown.
*/ **Details:** www.linosrestaurant.co.uk; 3m from M53, J2; 10 pm; closed Sun, Mon and Sat L; no Amex.*

Bradley's £ 35 🅣

84 Fitzwilliam St HD1 5BB (01484) 516773

A bistro tipped as "the best of the bunch" locally and of particular note for its "outstanding" lunchtime value.
*/ **Details:** www.bradleyscatering.co.uk; 10 pm; closed Sat L & Sun; no Amex.*

The Fox And Hounds £ 40 ❷❷❷

2 High St SG12 8NH (01279) 843999

*"Every visit is a joy", say fans of this country boozer which offers "superbly-prepared" food from an "imaginative" menu in a "lovely traditional setting". / **Details:** www.foxandhounds-hunsdon.co.uk; situated just off the A414, 10 min from Hertford; 10 pm.*

Old Bridge Hotel £ 52 ❸❷❷

1 High St PE29 3TQ (01480) 424300

This "well-appointed" riverside restaurant has "efficient" staff and food that's "hard to fault", but it's the "impressive" quality of the "quirky but mature" wine list (overseen by owner, John Hoskin MW) which comes as "a real surprise" to first-time visitors.
*/ **Details:** www.huntsbridge.com; off A1, off A14; 10 pm.*
Accommodation: 24 rooms, from £150.

Black Boys Inn £ 46 ❷❷❸

Henley Rd SL6 5NQ (01628) 824212

*"A homely rustic country restaurant-with-rooms that doesn't much feel like the roadside inn it once was"; it's a "friendly" sort of place whose "unfussy and well-presented" French cuisine is generally hailed as "good value". / **Details:** www.blackboysinn.co.uk; 9 pm; closed Sun D; no Amex.* **Accommodation:** 8 rooms, from £85.

The Olde Bell £ 57 ❹❹❷

High St SL6 5LX (01628) 825881

"Britain's second-oldest inn", in a "pretty village", is a "relaxed" place that makes a "lovely" destination; its "21st century menu", however, divides opinion – fans say it's "superb", but critics feel that "if the food were better, it would be interesting…"
*/ **Details:** www.theoldebell.co.uk; 9.45 pm; closed Sun D.*
Accommodation: 48 rooms, from £119.

The Bay Horse £ 49 ❷❷❸
45 The Grn DL2 2AA (01325) 720 663
A "great country pub" hailed in all reports for its "superb" (and "well presented") cuisine and its "welcoming and efficient" service. / **Details:** www.thebayhorsehuworth.com; 9.30 pm, Sun 8.30 pm; no Amex.

Everest Inn £ 32 🅣
32-34 High St CT21 5AT (01303) 269 898
"A restaurant of 'London' standard in a forgotten high street by the sea" – this sibling to the popular Blackheath establishment is tipped for its "precise, mainly Indian cuisine" (complemented by "a handful of Nepalese specialities"). / **Details:** www.everestinn.co.uk.

Bettys £ 40 ❷❷❷
32-34 The Grove LS29 9EE (01943) 608029
"The closest thing to a 'dead cert'"; especially "if Edwardian grandeur is your thing", a visit to these "always busy" tea rooms is hard to beat for an "expensive-but-worth-it" breakfast, lunch or tea. / **Details:** www.bettysandtaylors.com; 5.30 pm; no Amex; no booking.

The Box Tree £ 77 ❶❷❷
35-37 Church St LS29 9DR (01943) 608484
Under the ownership of Simon & Rena Gueller, this "delightful cosy" fine-dining veteran (originally established in 1962) seems to be "getting better every year", and the cooking – "light and delicious" – is "exemplary". / **Details:** www.theboxtree.co.uk; on A65 near town centre; 9 pm; closed Mon & Sun D; no Amex; children: 10+ at D.

The Far Syde £ 31 ❷❷❷
1-3 New Brook St LS29 8DQ (01943) 602030
"Modern British cuisine done exceptionally well for this sort of price bracket" wins consistent praise for this local favourite – a "friendly, bistro-style restaurant" in the town-centre. / **Details:** www.thefarsyde.co.uk; 10 pm; closed Mon & Sun; no Amex.

Ilkley Moor Vaults £ 34 🅣
Stockeld Rd LS29 9HD (01943) 607012
"Good-quality, locally-sourced food" in decent portions wins praise for this homely local, tipped as "a real find". / **Details:** www.ilkleymoorvaults.co.uk; 9 pm, 9.30 pm Fri & Sat; closed Mon & Sun D.

The Howard Arms £ 42 🅣
Lower Grn CV36 4LT (01608) 682226
"A lovely old stone inn", tipped for its "romantic" setting in an "idyllic Cotswold village"; it's undoubtedly a "very pleasant" destination, but the food has sometimes seemed a "little ordinary" of late – let's hope it's just a "blip". / **Details:** www.howardarms.com; 8m SW of Stratford-upon-Avon off A4300; 9.30 pm; no Amex. **Accommodation:** 8 rooms, from £145.

Chez Roux
Rocpool Reserve   £ 50   🕐
Culduthel Rd IV2 4AG   (01463) 240089
*"Le Gavroche, it is not", but Albert Roux is the executive chef of this
small and luxurious riverside dining room (which comes complete
with "ubiquitous photos" of the maestro); service is "warm and
friendly" and – notwithstanding the odd quibble – a visit here is
tipped as a "classy" overall experience. / Details: www.rocpool.com;
9.30 pm. Accommodation: 11 rooms, from £210.*

The Mustard Seed   £ 39   ❸❷❷
16 Fraser St IV1 1DW   (01463) 220220
*Occupying "a lovely building by the river", this venture in a converted
Georgian church is "part of the staggering improvement in Inverness
in recent years"; the top tip is its "exceptional value" lunch menu.
/ Details: www.themustardseedrestaurant.co.uk; on the bank of the Ness river,
30 yards from steeple; 9.45 pm.*

Rocpool   £ 49   ❷❷❸
1 Ness Walk IV3 5NE   (01463) 717274
*From a menu "dominated by seafood", "lovely" dishes are served –
"with a smile" – at this "impressive" and "busy" city-centre spot by
the river; there's an "extensive" wine list too.
/ Details: www.rocpoolrestaurant.com; 10 pm; closed Sun L , open Sun
evenings June-Sept only.; no Amex.*

Baipo   £ 36   ❷④⑤
63 Upper Orwell St IP4 1HP   (01473) 218402
*For its diehard local fans, this veteran outfit is not merely "the best
restaurant in town", but "the best Thai in the world"; a couple of
reporters this year, though, found results disappointingly "mundane".
/ Details: www.baipo.co.uk; 10.45 pm; closed Mon L & Sun; no Amex.*

Bistro on the Quay   £ 35   🕐
3 Wherry Quay IP4 1AS   (01473) 286677
*For "reasonably-priced food in a pleasant location", this spacious
waterfront ten-year-old in a converted warehouse, never seems to
disappoint. / Details: www.bistroonthequay.co.uk; 9.30 pm; closed Sun D.*

Mariners at Il Punto   £ 41   ④❸❷
Neptune Quay IP4 1AX   (01473) 289748
*This restaurant on a "beautifully restored" naval vessel, moored in
the marina, is still "not quite up to the usual Crépy family standards"
– those are high, though, and, for most reporters, this still makes a
"good-value" all-rounder. / Details: www.marinersipswich.co.uk; 9.30 pm;
closed Mon & Sun; no Amex.*

Salthouse Harbour Hotel   £ 47   ④④❸
1 Neptune Quay IP4 1AS   (01473) 226789
*This "light" room – "overlooking the crowded marina" from a
trendily revamped warehouse – makes an "attractive" destination; it
offers a "simple" menu featuring steak, which attracts consistently
positive reports. / Details: www.salthouseharbour.co.uk; 9.30 pm.
Accommodation: 70 rooms, from £130.*

Trongs   £ 33   ❷❸❸
23 St Nicholas St IP1 1TW   (01473) 256833
*"A family-run restaurant that goes from strength to strength", thanks
to its "wonderfully fresh and well presented" Vietnamese/Chinese
cooking; service is "first class" too. / Details: 10.30 pm; closed Sun;
booking essential.*

Black Horse at Ireland   £ 43   ❷❸❸
SG17 5QL   (01462) 811398
"A great pub serving great food!" – the gist of all commentary on
this *"consistently good"* inn, where the *"interesting"* menu includes
"a good range of specials". / **Details:** www.blackhorseireland.com;
9.30 pm, Fri & Sat 10 pm; closed Sun D. **Accommodation:** 2 rooms,
from £55.

JERSEY, CHANNEL ISLANDS

Bohemia
The Club Hotel & Spa   £ 70   ❶❷❷
Green St, St Helier JE2 4UH   (01534) 872 809
"My wife said it was one of her best meals ever!" – a report typical
of the enthusiasm for this *"calm"* operation, in a small
contemporary-style hotel near the commercial heart of St Helier;
Shaun Rankin's *"brilliant"* food is matched by some *"very
professional"* service. / **Details:** www.bohemiajersey.com; 10 pm; closed
Sun; no trainers. **Accommodation:** 46 rooms, from £185.

Longueville Manor   £ 85   ❸❸❸
Longueville Rd, St Saviour JE2 7WF   (01534) 725501
*A grand country house hotel, just outside St Helier, that can still
serve up some "superbly cooked and presented dishes"; to enjoy it
properly, though, it may help to be in the mood for "a very
traditional and old-school experience".*
/ **Details:** www.longuevillemanor.com; head from St. Helier on the A3 towards
Gorey; less than 1 mile from St. Helier; 10 pm; no jeans or trainers.
Accommodation: 31 rooms, from £220.

Ocean Restaurant
Atlantic Hotel   £ 83   ❷❸❸
Le Mont de la Pulente, St Brelade JE3 8HE   (01534) 744101
*A liner-style dining room, in which some tables benefit from a direct
ocean-view through palm trees; it's Mark Jordan's "very beautiful"
cuisine, though, which can often make a visit "a truly amazing
experience".* / **Details:** www.theatlantichotel.com; 10 pm.
Accommodation: 50 rooms, from £150 - 250.

Oyster Box   £ 41   ❷❷❷
St Brelade's Bay JE3 8EF   (01534) 743311
"Stunningly-located" in St Brelade's Bay and with *"fantastic views"*,
this beach bar/restaurant just *"gets better and better"* – its *"friendly
and attentive staff"* serve up some *"superb"* fish and seafood.
/ **Details:** www.oysterbox.co.uk; 9.30 pm, Fri & Sat 10 pm, Sun 9 pm; closed
Mon L.

Bosquet   £ 53   ❸❷④
97a, Warwick Rd CV8 1HP   (01926) 852463
*Bernard Lignier may have been cooking at this local landmark for
over 30 years, but his Gallic cuisine still draws a dedicated local
following who say it's been "on top form" of late.*
/ **Details:** www.restaurantbosquet.co.uk; on the main road through Kenilworth;
9 pm; closed Mon, Sat L & Sun; closed Aug.

Blue Ginger   £ 35   ❸④❸
383 Kenton Rd HA3 0XS   (020) 8909 0100
*An 'Indo-Oriental' restaurant that's strongly tipped for its "great",
mainly Indian food, served in a "modern" environment; it makes a
good destination for "family get-togethers".*

Lakeland Pedlar Wholefood Café £ 29 🅣

Hendersons Yard, Bell Close CA12 5JD (01768) 774492

A destination that lives up to its name, and a top tip for a "hearty and good-value vegetarian lunch". / Details: www.lakelandpedlar.co.uk; off the Bell Close car park; 5 pm, 9 pm; D closing times, summer 9 pm, winter 4 pm; no Amex; book only at D.

Lyzzick Hall Country House Hotel £ 44 ❷❷❸

CA12 4PY (017687) 72277

The Spanish owner of this small hotel "takes pride in a fascinating Iberian wine list", but the food is of interest too – it has been "consistently good over many years". / Details: www.lyzzickhall.co.uk.

The Swan Inn £ 44 🅣

Macclesfield Rd SK23 7QU (01663) 732943

"Set in stunning Peak District countryside", this "small country pub" is tipped as "the best eating place in the area"; "delicious fresh fish" is a highlight. / Details: www.swankettleshulme.com; 8.30 pm, Thu-Fri 7 pm, Sat 9 pm, Sun 4 pm; closed Mon L; no Amex.

The Pheasant at Keyston £ 48 ❷❸❸

Loop Rd PE28 0RE (01832) 710241

"Put on the map by a Ramsay TV programme", this "warm and friendly" inn seems to have survived mercifully unscathed by the experience – in fact, it might even have improved! / Details: www.thepheasant-keyston.co.uk; 1m S of A14 between Huntingdon & Kettering, J15; 9.30 pm.

Firenze £ 50 ❷❷❷

9 Station St LE8 0LN (0116) 279 6260

"A little piece of Italy in the Leicestershire countryside" – the Poli family's "stylish" and "buzzy" fixture pleases most reporters with its "seasonally-changing" cuisine and "very good wine list"; it is rather "expensive", though – "it might up its game if there was more local competition". / Details: www.firenze.co.uk; 10 pm; closed Mon & Sun; no Amex.

Daylesford Café £ 46 ❸❸❸

GL56 0YG (01608) 731700

Especially on days when you can sit in the courtyard, Lady Bamford's "symphony-of-good-taste" food store/café can be a "fantastic place for lunch" (or brunch) – even a reporter who found the service "terrible" notes a visit here as "a nice change from all those Cotswold pubs!" / Details: www.daylesfordorganic.com; Mon-Wed 5 pm, Thu-Sat 6 pm, Sun 4pm; L only.

The Kingham Plough
£ 45   ❸④④

The Grn OX7 6YD (01608) 658327

Even critics of Emily Watkins's "lovely country pub" acknowledge the "high-quality technique and sourcing" of her "creative" cooking, and to most reporters the place is "a gem in every way"; to a few, though, it's "less than the sum of its parts", not helped by "amateurish" service and a crowd that can seem rather "up itself".
/ **Details:** www.thekinghamplough.co.uk; 8.45 pm, Sun 8 pm; no Amex.
Accommodation: 7 rooms, from £85.

The Canbury Arms
£ 42   ❷❷❸

49 Canbury Park Rd KT2 6LQ (020) 8255 9129

Very much a pub in style, but serving "fantastic" dishes of "restaurant quality" – this "friendly" spot inspires only positive reviews; "eat in the pub, though, not the shed!"
/ **Details:** www.thecanburyarms.com; 9 pm, Fri & Sat 10 pm.

Frère Jacques
£ 44   🅣

10-12 Riverside Walk KT1 1QN (020) 8546 1332

"A splendid setting on the Thames" is a high point at this "staple" Gallic brasserie, by Kingston Bridge; it's "simple" bistro fare is best enjoyed at the "remarkably good, cheap set lunch".
/ **Details:** www.frerejacques.co.uk; next to Kingston Bridge and market place; 10 pm; no Amex.

Riverside Vegetaria
£ 37   ❸❸❸

64 High St KT1 1HN (020) 8546 7992

"A wide range of well-prepared vegetarian food" – in "enormous portions" and with "super service" – again inspires plaudits for this "cramped" but "good-value" café by the river.
/ **Details:** www.rsveg.plus.com; 10 mins walk from Kingston BR; 11 pm, Sun 10.30 pm; children: 18+ ex L.

Roz ana
£ 40   ❷❸❸

4-8 Kingston Hill KT2 7NH (020) 8546 6388

"An Indian with a difference!" – with its "fusion" fare and its "wicked selection of cocktails", this "stylish" Norbiton spot impresses all who comment on it. / **Details:** www.roz-ana.com; 10.30 pm, Fri & Sat 11 pm, Sun 10 pm.

The Woodman Inn
£ 33   🅣

Thunderbridge HD8 0PX (01484) 605778

A "great local pub" tipped for its "healthy portions of decent quality 'gastropub' fare"; for more of a sense of occasion, there's a dining room upstairs. / **Details:** www.woodman-inn.co.uk.

Hipping Hall
£ 68   ❷❷❷

Cowan Bridge LA6 2JJ (01524) 271187

One reporter found the lighting level in the 15th-century hall a little sepulchral, but that's one of the few reservations about this "great getaway" on the fringe of the Dales – a "romantic" destination where the cooking can be "very good". / **Details:** www.hippinghall.com; 9.15 pm; closed weekday L; no Amex; no trainers; booking essential; children: 10+.* **Accommodation:** 9 rooms, from £200.

The Mason's Arms   £ 55   ❷❷❸
EX36 4RY   (01398) 341231
"Head and shoulders above the country pubs norm", Mark Dodson's thatched Exmoor inn is certainly "worth a detour", with almost all reports saying it offers "innovative but not OTT" food in "glorious surroundings". / **Details:** www.masonsarmsdevon.co.uk; 9 pm; closed Mon & Sun D; children: 5+ after 6pm.

Belle Époque   £ 54   ❸④❶
60 King St WA16 6DT   (01565) 633060
Few English restaurants match the "romantic" interior of this "beautiful" Art Nouveau landmark; its food has varied in recent years – while fans insist "it continues to improve", critics still say it's "over-rated and over-expensive". / **Details:** www.thebelleepoque.com; 1.5m from M6, J19; 9.30 pm; closed Sat L & Sun D; booking: max 6, Sat. **Accommodation:** 7 rooms, from £100.

The Bay Horse   £ 44   ❸④④
Bay Horse Ln LA2 0HR   (01524) 791204
"Straightforward but delicious cooking" makes Craig Wilkinson's long-established inn a popular stop-off from the M6 (and handy for visitors to the university too); it can seem "expensive for what it is", though, and the occasional visit of late has been spoilt by "ungracious" service. / **Details:** www.bayhorseinn.com; 0.75m S of A6, J33 M6; 9 pm; closed Mon & Sun D. **Accommodation:** 2 rooms, from £89.

Pizza Margherita   £ 33   ❸❷❷
2 Moor Ln LA1 1QD   (01524) 36333
"Well up to PizzaExpress standard" – this "buzzy" pizzeria run for over thirty years by the sister of that chain's founder remains on top form. / **Details:** www.pizza-margherita.co.uk; 10.30 pm.

Simply French   £ 35   ❷❸❸
27a St Georges Quay LA1 1RD   (01524) 843199
"As close as you'll get in Lancashire to being in France" – a city-centre bistro which consistently "does what it says on the can". / **Details:** www.quitesimplyfrench.co.uk; 9.30 pm, Sun & Mon 9 pm; D only, ex Sun open L & D; no Amex.

Langar Hall   £ 53   ❸❷❷
Church Ln NG13 9HG   (01949) 860559
The venue for Ed Milliband's May 2011 nuptials! – Imogen Skirving's "really charming" and endearingly "eccentric" country house boasts "big rooms and a warm welcome"; most reports also acclaim its "beautiful cooking", but there's the occasional fear that it's seemed "a bit ordinary" of late. / **Details:** www.langarhall.com; off A52 between Nottingham & Grantham; 9.30 pm; no Amex; no trainers. **Accommodation:** 14 rooms, from £100.

LANGHO, LANCASHIRE   5–1B

Northcote   £ 75   ❶❸❸
Northcote Rd BB6 8BE   (01254) 240555
*This "imposing" (perhaps slightly "stiff") manor house remains one
of the North West's best-known destinations, thanks not least to Lisa
Allen's "unfussy and fully flavoured" food, which is founded on
"outstanding local ingredients"; occasionally, service can be "slow".
/ **Details:** www.northcote.com; M6, J31 then A59; 9.30 pm.
Accommodation: 14 rooms, from £210.*

LAVANT, WEST SUSSEX   3–4A

The Earl Of March   £ 47   ❷④❸
Lavant Rd PO18 0BQ   (01243) 533993
*"A hugely popular dining pub" where, all reporters agree, the
"above-average" cuisine "makes good use of local produce"; sit
outdoors and you get "lovely views" too.
/ **Details:** www.theearlofmarch.com; 9.30 pm; closed Sun D.*

LAVENHAM, SUFFOLK   3–1C

Great House   £ 48   ❶❷❷
Market Pl CO10 9QZ   (01787) 247431
*"What a treat to have a French restaurant of this quality in an
English village!"; 25 years in business, 'Chez Crépy' sits in an
"ancient but comfortable" building in a "serene and picturesque"
square... and remains pretty much "faultless".
/ **Details:** www.greathouse.co.uk; follow directions to Guildhall; 9.30 pm; closed
Mon & Sun D; closed Jan; no Amex. **Accommodation:** 5 rooms, from £95.*

LEAMINGTON SPA, WARWICKSHIRE   5–4C

La Coppola   £ 28   ❷❷❷
86 Regent St CV32 4NS   (01926) 888 873
*"A little bit of Italy rather nearer to home!" – this "busy" city-centre
spot wins praise for its "fresh and tasty" cuisine, "great" wine list
and "attentive" service; "you need to book ahead, even for lunch!"
/ **Details:** www.lacoppola.co.uk.*

LEEDS, WEST YORKSHIRE   5–1C

Aagrah   £ 33   ❷❷❸
Aberford Rd LS25 2HF   (0113) 287 6606
*"Great Indian food" from "a large menu that offers plenty of choice"
– that's the unchanging formula at this "reliably good" outpost of the
eminent NE subcontinental chain; this year's ratings, though, were
not quite as good as usual. / **Details:** www.aagrah.com; from A1 take
A642 Aberford Rd to Garforth; 11.30 pm, Sun 10.30 pm; D only.*

Akbar's   £ 30   ❷❸❸
16 Greek St LS1 5RU   (0113) 242 5426
*The atmosphere of this "huge", "busy" and "noisy" Indian may tend
to "Soviet", but – with the "best naans around", "delicious lamb"
and a range of other "reliable and interesting" dishes – this is
undoubtedly a "quality curry house". / **Details:** www.akbars.co.uk;
midnight; D only.*

Anthony's   £ 63   ❸❷④
19 Boar Ln LS1 6EA   (0113) 245 5922
*For fans, Anthony Flynn's "incredibly inventive" molecular gastronomy
still makes this basement restaurant "the best restaurant in Leeds";
it's difficult not to feel it's losing its way, though – sceptics fear that in
"striving to be different" the style seems ever more "pretentious".
/ **Details:** www.anthonysrestaurant.co.uk; 9.30 pm; closed Mon & Sun;
no Amex.*

Art's £ 36 ❸④❷
42 Call Ln LS1 6DT (0113) 243 8243
"Overlook the bare floors and uncomfy chairs", this long-established "bistro-style restaurant" is "convenient, unfussy and a good place to talk"; just the spot then for a "relaxed" and "reasonably-priced" bite. / Details: www.artscafebar.com; near Corn Exchange; 10 pm, 2 am Sat; no booking, Sat L.

Bibis Italianissimo £ 40 ⑤⑤④
Criterion Pl, Swingate LS1 4AG (0113) 243 0905
This "spectacular" Big Night Out destination – an Art Deco-style Italian near the city-centre – certainly "has the wow-factor", say its fans; but critics find it a "woeful cornucopia of chavdom", which – with its "dire" food – "epitomises everything that's wrong with 'Italian' restaurants in the UK"! / Details: www.bibisrestaurant.com; 11.30 pm; no shorts; no booking, Sat.

Brasserie Forty 4 £ 42 ❶
44 The Calls LS2 7EW (0113) 234 3232
"Good value, generous portions and a nice buzz, but nothing exactly outstanding" – one reporter fairly sums up the virtues of this "quietly efficient" bistro veteran. / Details: www.brasserie44.com; 10 pm, Sat 10.30 pm; closed Sun. Accommodation: 41 rooms, from £140.

Casa Mia Millenium £ 39 ❶
Millenium Sq, Great George St LS2 3AD (0845) 688 3030
This city-centre Italian (part of a local mini-empire) is tipped for Italian food of "consistently high" quality (with "lovely fish" a highlight); further attractions include a "huge" wine list and "consistently welcoming" service. / Details: www.casamiaonline.com; 10.30 pm, Thu-Sat 11.30 pm, Sun 11 pm.

Chaophraya £ 42 ❷❸❸
20a, First Floor, Blayds Ct LS2 4AG (0113) 244 9339
"Faultless" Thai food – from a "wide menu" and in "generous portions" – makes it well worth seeking out this "reliable" outpost of a small Northern chain; no wonder it's "always busy"; "good for groups" too. / Details: www.chaophraya.co.uk; in Swingate; 10.30 pm.

The Cross Keys £ 39 ❸❷❸
107 Water Ln LS11 5WD (0113) 243 3711
"Good, honest fresh food" makes this inner-city boozer a good all-purpose stand-by for almost all who comment on it, not least as a destination for "the best Sunday lunch in town". / Details: www.the-crosskeys.com; 10 pm.

Fourth Floor Café
Harvey Nichols £ 40 ❶
107-111 Briggate LS1 6AZ (0113) 204 8000
"More style than substance" the performance may be, but this handily-located department store dining room is nonetheless tipped for its "fairly-priced set lunch menu". / Details: www.harveynichols.com; 10 pm; L only, ex Thu-Sat open L & D.

Fuji Hiro £ 24 ❷❸④
45 Wade Ln LS2 8NJ (0113) 243 9184
"Noodle bars proliferate, but this is still the best"; don't be put off by the "Formica table tops" of this city-centre "gem" which "just carries on doing what it does best" – "fantastic noodles". / Details: 10 pm, Fri & Sat 11 pm; no Amex; need 5+ to book.

Anthonys

Salvos

Casa Mia Grande

La Grillade £ 37 ❸❷❸
Wellington St LS1 4HJ (0113) 245 9707
There's "no finer place for steak/frites and an authentically French bistro experience", say fans of this "long-standing Leeds favourite" in the "whitewashed basement of an old hotel"; "it's great for business, with lots of small alcoves for hushed conversations and – even better – no mobile signal!" / Details: www.lagrillade.co.uk; 10 pm, Sat 10.30 pm; closed Sat L & Sun.

Hansa's £ 31 ❷❷❸
72-74 North St LS2 7PN (0113) 244 4408
"The only veggie food my husband will eat!"; the "delicious fresh-tasting" cuisine of Mrs Hansa Dabhi's "delightful" veggie Gujarati in the city-centre maintains its position as the city's best-known Indian; this year, though, ratings were hit by a couple of disappointing reports. / Details: www.hansasrestaurant.com; 10 pm, Fri & Sat 11 pm; D only, ex Sun L only.

Kendells Bistro £ 44 ❷❷❷
St Peters square LS9 8AH (0113) 243 6553
This "really buzzy" city-centre spot "has succeeded in creating a real bistro atmosphere" and on quite a scale too; it helps that the Gallic dishes from the blackboard menu are "often excellent" and that the staff are notably "welcoming" too; handy pre-theatre. / Details: www.kendellsbistro.co.uk; 9 pm, Fri & Sat 10 pm; D only, closed Mon & Sun; no Amex; booking essential.

Little Tokyo £ 42 🅣
24 Central Rd LS1 6DE (0113) 243 9090
A "basic" but "good-value" spot behind Debenhams where "gorgeous" Bento boxes are a highlight. / Details: 10 pm, Fri & Sat 11 pm; need 8+ to book.

Livebait £ 42 ❹❸❹
The Calls LS2 7EY (0113) 2444144
"It may be a chain, but I've yet to have a disappointing meal" – this "buzzing" offshoot of the small national group usually satisfies, especially given the absence of much in the way of local fishy competition. / Details: www.livebaitrestaurant.co.uk; 10.30 pm; closed Sun.

The Piazza By Anthony
The Corn Exchange £ 39 ❹❺❸
Corn Exchange, Call Ln LS1 7BR (0113) 247 0995
The immensity of this "cavernous" Victorian edifice is daunting, and rather overshadows the spin-off operation of leading local chef, Anthony Flinn; service can seem "disinterested" too, and the "modern, bistro-type fare" is sometimes "poorly prepared". / Details: www.anthonysrestaurant.co.uk; 10 pm, Sun 9 pm, Fri & Sat 10.30 pm; no Amex.

Pickles & Potter £ 19 🅣
18 -20 Queens Arc LS1 6LF (0113) 242 7702
This small café wins numerous tips for its "amazingly tasty" selection of freshly-made sandwiches, soups, salads and hot dishes – "you'll be lucky to get a seat"; "the Headingley branch is just as good" too. / Details: www.picklesandpotter.co.uk; Sat 7 pm; L and Sat D only; no credit cards.

Rajas £ 26 🅣
186 Roundhay Rd LS8 5PL (0113) 248 0411
A small and "basic" Indian tipped for "fresh, well spiced, beautifully cooked and plentiful" dishes, and at "more than fair" prices. / Details: www.rajasleeds.co.uk; close to Roundhay Park; 10.30 pm; no Amex.

Red Chilli £ 38 ❷④❸
6 Great George St LS1 3DW (01132) 429688
"That'll blow out the cobwebs on a cold day!" – the *"terrifying"*
Sichuan food at this city-centre basement makes it, for fans, *"the*
city's pre-eminent Chinese"; the odd sceptic, though, does fret that
the menu has been dumbed down in recent times.
/ **Details:** www.redchillirestaurant.co.uk; 10.30 pm, Fri & Sat 11.30 pm.

The Reliance £ 37 ❸❸❷
76-78 North St LS2 7PN (0113) 295 6060
It's almost "self-consciously scruffy", but this "wonderfully informal",
boho-chic brasserie in the city-centre draws praise for its *"friendly*
and efficient" style and modern bistro fare that's *"spot on"*.
/ **Details:** www.the-reliance.co.uk; 10 pm, Thu-Sat 10.30 pm, Sun 9.30 pm;
no booking.

Salvo's £ 41 ❸❸❸
115 Otley Rd LS6 3PX (0113) 275 5017
"The gold standard for pizza, but don't expect a relaxing
experience" – this *"noisy"* and *"hard-surfaced"* Headingley spot is a
local *"institution"* of 35 years' standing, and still *"always busy"*.
/ **Details:** www.salvos.co.uk; 2m N of University on A660; 10.30 pm, Fri & Sat
11 pm, Sun 9 pm; no booking at D.

San Carlo £ 42 ❸❸❸
6-7 South Pde LS1 5QX (0113) 246 1500
"Huge and slightly impersonal, but the product is fine"; this *"glitzy"*
outpost of the Birmingham (and so on) Italian chain is a *"buzzy"*
sort of place, with impressively *"consistent"* standards across the
board; in particular it *"hits the spot for business lunches"*.
/ **Details:** www.sancarlo.co.uk/leeds; 11 pm.

Sous le Nez en Ville £ 41 ❷❷❸
Quebec Hs, Quebec St LS1 2HA (0113) 244 0108
"A long-established basement eatery which never fails to satisfy"; this
"buzzy" Gallic joint has a name not just for its *"excellent wine list"*
but also for *"unpretentious"* cooking that invariably hits the spot –
for *"exceptional value"* seek out the pre-theatre menu.
/ **Details:** www.souslenez.com; 10 pm, Sat 11 pm; closed Sun.

Sukhothai £ 34 ❷❶❸
8 Regent St LS7 4PE (0113) 237 0141
"Gorgeous" Thai food and *"wonderful"* service makes this Chapel
Allerton Thai restaurant a 'rave' for almost all who comment on it,
with the Sunday buffet offering particularly *"great value"*; also in
Headingley. / **Details:** www.thaifood4u.co.uk; 11 pm; closed Mon L;
no Amex.

LEICESTER, LEICESTERSHIRE 5–4D

Bobby's £ 25 ❷❸⑤
154-156 Belgrave Rd LE4 5AT (0116) 266 0106
Even if its "ambience is not the best", this "excellent" and super
"cheap" Indian veggie is worth seeking out; top section for visual
appeal – *"the excellent sweet counter"*.
/ **Details:** www.eatatbobbys.com; 10 pm; no Amex.

The Case £ 41 ⑤④❷
4-6 Hotel St LE1 5AW (0116) 251 7675
No-one disputes the "atmospheric" appeal of this factory-conversion
in St Martin's, which *"used to be regarded as Leicester's best"*;
nowadays, though, critics feel it badly *"needs to up its game"* – *"we*
used to be regulars, but now we travel to Nottingham!"
/ **Details:** www.thecase.co.uk; near the Cathedral, and St Martins Square;
9.45 pm; closed Sun.

Kayal   £ 35   ❷❷④

153 Granby St LE1 6FE   (0116) 255 4667

"Delicious and unusual Southern Indian food at wallet-friendly prices" – served by "people who care" – makes this "friendly" Keralan popular with all who comment on it.
/ **Details:** www.kayalrestaurant.com; 11 pm, Sun 10 pm.

The Tiffin   £ 36   ④❸❸

1 De Montfort St LE1 7GE   (0116) 247 0420

"Ideally placed for a curry before a concert at the De Montfort Hall", this civilised subcontinental is a popular stalwart with a "charming" owner; fans hail its "top quality" food too, but sceptics say it's "average for a city where the food can be such a highlight".
/ **Details:** www.the-tiffin.co.uk; near railway station; 10.45 pm; closed Sat L & Sun.

LEIGH-ON-SEA, ESSEX   3–3C

Simply Seafood   £ 46   ❷④④

High St SS9 2ER   (01702) 716645

"Generous" use of "top-quality" ingredients ensures that dishes at this seaside restaurant live up to its name; however, the location – "between a railway line and the sea" – is sometimes felt to "lack charm". / **Details:** www.simplyseafood.co.uk; 9 pm; closed Mon.

LEIGHTON BUZZARD, BEDFORDSHIRE   3–2A

The Kings Head   £ 52   🅣

Ivinghoe LU7 9EB   (01296) 668388

A grand traditional inn whose all-round charms seduce most of those who comment on it; it's tipped not only for its "excellent traditional duck" (the house speciality), but for "bargain" lunchtime menus too.
/ **Details:** www.kingsheadivinghoe.co.uk; 3m N of Tring on B489 to Dunstable; 9.30 pm; closed Sun D; jacket & tie required at D.

LEINTWARDINE, SHROPSHIRE   5–4A

Jolly Frog   £ 48   ❷❷❷

The Todden SY7 0LX   (01547) 540298

"A real surprise in the Shropshire countryside" – a gastropub well worth knowing about for its "super-fresh fish and seafood", served in "an authentic French bistro environment"; at quieter times, "kids get to make their own pizza" too! / **Details:** www.jollyfrogpub.co.uk; 9.30 pm; closed Mon.

LEVINGTON, SUFFOLK   3–1D

The Ship Inn   £ 39   ❷④❸

Church Ln IP10 0LQ   (01473) 659573

"It's worth being patient" ("space is limited", so "arrive early") at this "lovely" country pub, where "everything food-wise is of a high standard". / **Details:** 9.30 pm, Sun 9 pm; no Amex; children: 14+.

LEWDOWN, DEVON   1–3C

Lewtrenchard Manor   £ 73

EX20 4PN   (01566) 783256

"A wonderful Jacobean mansion" tipped as a "great destination for a romantic get-away"; with food that can be "sensational"; thanks to the demise of the parent Von Essen empire, however, we've left it un-rated. / **Details:** www.lewtrenchard.co.uk; off A30 between Okehampton & Launceston; 9 pm; no jeans or trainers; children: 8+ at D.
Accommodation: 16 rooms, from £220.

Bill's Produce Store £ 35 ❸❹❷
56 Cliffe High St BN7 2AN (01273) 476918
"Always full and fun", the home base of the growing café/deli chain
serves *"good wholesome nosh and great breakfasts too"*; service,
though, can go *"awry"* at busy times.
/ **Details:** www.billsproducestore.co.uk; over the bridge on the High Street;
9.30 pm; closed Mon D, Tue D, Wed D & Sun D; no Amex.

Arundell Arms £ 59 ❷❷❸
Fore St PL16 0AA (01566) 784666
Back on top form, this grand rural inn – a popular destination for
fishermen – offers visitors an *"uplifting"* overall experience; for non-
residents, the place is particularly popular as a lunch destination.
/ **Details:** www.arundellarms.com; 0.5m off A30, Lifton Down exit; 9.30 pm;
no jeans or shorts. **Accommodation:** 21 rooms, from £170.

Browns Pie Shop £ 39 🅣
33 Steep Hill LN2 1LU (01522) 527330
"The ambience carries the experience", at this cosy spot in an old
building near the cathedral; perhaps its menu of pies *"lacks finesse"*,
but portions are *"substantial"* and *"good value"*, and the place is
"great on a cold winter's evening". / **Details:** www.brownspieshop.co.uk;
near the Cathedral; 10 pm, Sun 8 pm; no Amex.

Fourteen £ 35 🅣
14 Bailgate LN1 3AE (01522) 576556
"A real find!" – this city-centre restaurant is tipped by a number of
reporters for its all-round high standards; more reports please!
/ **Details:** www.fourteenrestaurant.co.uk; 10 pm.

The Wig & Mitre £ 38 ④④❸
30-32 Steep Hill LN2 1TL (01522) 535190
"Returning to form", insist fans, this *"lovely, comfortable old pub"*
near the cathedral is a *"snug"* sort of place where the food offers
"good value"; for critics, though, *"indifference rules"*.
/ **Details:** www.wigandmitre.com; between Cathedral & Castle; 10.30 pm.

Champany Inn £ 89 🅣
EH49 7LU (01506) 834532
"Opulence abounds, but at a price!"; this famous inn is renowned for
its *"wonderfully cooked steaks in big portions"*, and its *"interesting"*
wines. / **Details:** www.champany.com; 2m NE of Linlithgow on junction of
A904 & A803; 10 pm; closed Sat L & Sun; no jeans or trainers; children: 8+.
Accommodation: 16 rooms, from £125.

Cabbage Hall £ 48 ❷❸④
Forest Rd CW6 9ES (01829) 760292
*Robert Kisby is a "highly acclaimed chef" locally, and he seems to
have found a happy perch at this "out-of-the-way" gastropub, which
is "as good for a bar snack as it is à la carte".*
/ **Details:** www.cabbagehallrestaurant.com; 9.30 pm, Sun 8 pm; no Amex.

The Cartford Inn £ 35 ❸❸❸
Cartford Ln PR3 0YP (01995) 670 166
By the Carford toll bridge, "a boutique gastropub" offering
"good and reasonably-priced" food, "helpful" service and
"regional ales from its own microbrewery"; "fish pie is the
stand-out dish". / Details: www.thecartfordinn.co.uk; 11 pm.

East Beach Cafe £ 46 ❹❹❷
Sea Rd, The Promenade BN17 5GB (01903) 731903
"An extraordinary structure that's worth a detour" and which offers
an "invigorating sea view too" – a good choice for a "winning
brunch" perhaps. / **Details:** www.eastbeachcafe.co.uk; 8.30 pm.

Alma De Cuba
St Peter's Church £ 42 ❺❹❷
Seel St L1 4BH (0151) 702 7394
"Unforgettable!" – it's the "spectacular" setting in a former church
("enjoy your aperitif by the newly-mirrored pulpit") that makes this
city-centre South American so "breathtaking"; "the food doesn't
quite measure up, but the place is always very busy".
/ **Details:** www.alma-de-cuba.com; 10 pm, Fri & Sat 11 pm; no shorts;
children: 18+ in bar.

Chaophraya £ 42 ❸❹❹
5-6 Kenyon Steps L1 3DF (0151) 7076323
A Thai operation in the Liverpool One development; the set-up can
feel "a bit cold and corporate" but it generally satisfies on the food
front. / **Details:** www.chaophraya.co.uk.

Delifonseca £ 39 ❷❷❸
12 Stanley St L1 6AF (0151) 255 0808
"By far the best places to eat in Liverpool" – these no-nonsense
deli/dining rooms are "friendly" places attracting consistent praise for
"good, wholesome food" (with "interesting mains from the
blackboard") and "knowledgeably-chosen" wines; the newer branch
is at Brunswick Dock L3 (booked via Stanley Street).
/ **Details:** www.delifonseca.co.uk; 9 pm, Fri & Sat 9.30 pm; closed Sun.

Host £ 35 ❸❷❸
31 Hope St L1 9XH (0151) 708 5831
"Fun, young and lively" – this offshoot of the 60 Hope Street empire
is a "bright" sort of place, praised for its "good, standard Asian-
fusion fare"; reporters often compare it with Wagamama, which
they generally say it "outclasses by far". / **Details:** www.ho-st.co.uk;
11 pm.

The Italian Club Fish £ 40 ❷❷❷
128 Bold St L1 4JA (0151) 707 2110
Arguably the city's top all-rounder – this "lovely, buzzy
café/restaurant" (related to Edinburgh's Valvona & Crolla) offers
"great fish and seafood" ("plus a couple of dishes for carnivores and
veggies"), and in a "lovely, warm atmosphere" too.
/ **Details:** www.theitalianclubfish.co.uk; 10 pm, Sun 9 pm; closed Mon L;
no Amex.

0 Hope Street

Delifonseca

pire

The London Carriage Works
Hope Street Hotel   £ 49   ④④④
40 Hope St L1 9DA   (0151) 705 2222
This über-trendy design-hotel put in another 'curate's egg' performance this year; to fans, it's still an outstanding all-rounder and one of the city's best venues, but to critics "amateurish" staff and "nothing special" cooking create a "joyless" ambience. / Details: www.tlcw.co.uk; opp Philharmonic Hall; 10 pm, Sun 9 pm; no shorts. Accommodation: 89 rooms, from £150.

Lunya   £ 39   🇹
18-20 College Ln L1 3DS   (0151) 706 9770
"Lovely Catalan staff" add joy to Peter Kinsella's new café/deli; it's sometimes tipped for "Spanish food at its best", although the occasional inconsistency is not unknown. / Details: www.lunya.co.uk; 11 pm, Sun 10 pm.

Malmaison   £ 56   🇹
William Jessop Way, Princes Dock L3 1QW   (0151) 229 5000
Tipped for its "warm and friendly" service, a "relaxed" and, some say "romantic" hotel dining room; the food, though, is no particular attraction. / Details: www.malmaison-liverpool.com; 10.30 pm. Accommodation: 130 rooms, from £99.

The Monro   £ 43   ❸④❸
92-94 Duke St L1 5AG   (0151) 707 9933
"A foodie pub in an up-and-coming location" that's "handy for Liverpool One", and offers "sound cooking at fair prices"; "set lunch and early-evening menus offer very good value". / Details: www.themonro.com; 9.45 pm, Sun 7.30 pm; no trainers.

Panoramic
Beetham West Tower   £ 54   ④❸❶
Brook St L3 9PJ   (0151) 236 5534
The views from this 34th-floor eyrie are undoubtedly "stunning", and fans say the food is "excellent" too; sceptics, though, find their enjoyment limited by "daft" prices. / Details: www.panoramicliverpool.com; 9.30 pm, Sun 5 pm; no trainers.

Puschka   £ 48   🇹
16 Rodney St L1 2TE   (0151) 708 8698
Oddly few reports this year on this "reliable" local ten-year-old tipped for its "high-quality food and service" and a "good wine list" too. / Details: www.puschka.co.uk; 10 pm, Sun 9 pm; D only, closed Mon.

The Quarter   £ 34   ④④❷
7-11 Falkner St L8 7PU   (0151) 707 1965
"A lively and popular pizza and pasta place, that's part of 60 Hope Street empire" – "lively" and "popular" (and convenient for the Phil too), it attracts "an eclectic clientele"; also open for breakfast. / Details: www.thequarteruk.com; 11 pm, Sun 10.30 pm.

Salt House   £ 35   ❷❷❸
Hanover Sq L1 3DW   (0151) 706 0092
"Amazingly good tapas" ("some classics, and some more inventive dishes") win praise for this new city-centre operation. / Details: www.salthousetapas.co.uk; 10.30 pm.

San Carlo   £ 45   ❷❸❷
41 Castle St L2 9SH   (0151) 236 0073
"Flashy, busy and bustling" – this relatively recent addition to the San Carlo family has all the brand's usual features; these include surprisingly good fish and seafood dishes, and service that's "better if you're a footballer or a WAG..." / Details: www.sancarlo.co.uk; 11 pm.

The Side Door
£ 43   ❸❷❷

29a, Hope St L1 9BQ   (0151) 7077888

Food that's "always of a good standard" wins strong support for this "friendly" and "relaxed" townhouse "gem"; pre-theatre dining is a bit of a speciality. / **Details:** www.thesidedoor.co.uk; 10 pm; closed Sun; no Amex.

60 Hope Street
£ 50   ❹❸❹

60 Hope St L1 9BZ   (0151) 707 6060

"It's a class above the rest", say fans of the city's original modern fine dining restaurant (with brasserie below) – still the most reported-on place in town; critics can find its approach rather "bland", though, and not everyone is convinced that the prices are justified. / **Details:** www.60hopestreet.com; 10.30 pm; closed Sat L.

Spire
£ 42   ⓣ

1 Church Rd L15 9EA   (0151) 734 5040

Not a huge volume of feedback unfortunately, but this Wavertree restaurant is tipped for "amazing" food and service that "treats you like a long-lost friend"; more reports please! / **Details:** www.spirerestaurant.co.uk; Mon-Thu 9 pm, Fri & Sat 9.30 pm; closed Mon L, Sat L & Sun.

Tai Pan
£ 29   ❷❹❹

WH Lung Bdg., Great Howard St L5 9TZ   (0151) 207 3888

"Yes it's above a warehouse, and yes, the staff can be curt, but it's the food you're here for" – this "canteen-like" Chinese continues to please reporters, not least for the "great value-for-money dim sum". / **Details:** 11.30 pm, Sun 9.30 pm.

LLANDEWI SKIRRID, MONMOUTHSHIRE   2–1A

The Walnut Tree
£ 58   ❶❷❸

NP7 8AW   (01873) 852797

Shaun Hill's "back-to-basics" cooking (with "no pretentious fuss") at this "simple"-looking rural pub-conversion is "second to none" – under his three-year reign, it has "re-established its reputation" as the best-known place in Wales. / **Details:** www.thewalnuttreeinn.com; 3m NE of Abergavenny on B4521; 10 pm; closed Mon & Sun.
Accommodation: 2 rooms, from £160.

LLANDRILLO, DENBIGHSHIRE   4–2D

Tyddyn Llan
£ 71   ❶❷❷

LL21 0ST   (01490) 440264

You get "the best food in Wales" (and an "outstanding-value wine list" too) at Bryan & Susan Webb's "beautiful" and "secluded" country house hotel on the edge of Snowdonia where "lots of fresh, local produce" is superbly presented. / **Details:** www.tyddynllan.co.uk; on B4401 between Corwen and Bala; 9 pm; closed Mon (Tue-Thu L by prior arrangement only); no Amex; booking essential Tue L-Thu L.
Accommodation: 13 rooms, from £150.

LLANDUDNO, CONWY   4–1D

Bodysgallen Hall
£ 58   ❹❸❸

LL30 1RS   (01492) 584466

Up-and-down reports on this "superbly-located Elizabethan mansion" – fans say "the food is finally living up to the surroundings", but critics still find this an "overpriced" and "pretentious" place which "trades on its past". / **Details:** www.bodysgallen.com; 2m off A55 on A470; 9.15 pm, Fri & Sat 9.30 pm; closed Mon; no jeans or trainers; children: 6+.
Accommodation: 31 rooms, from £255.

Jaya £ 42 ⓣ

36 Church Walks LL30 2HN   (01492) 818 198

Part of a "very upmarket B&B", this new dining room is tipped as "one of the few interesting restaurants in North Wales to have opened in the past decade!"… in a style which, rather improbably, "blends North Indian and East Africa"; more reports please!
/ **Details:** www.jayarestaurant.co.uk.

St Tudno Hotel £ 43 ⓣ

Promenade LL30 2LP   (01492) 874411

Near the Pier, a Victorian-style townhouse hotel consistently tipped as a bastion of "old-fashioned excellence" – a "pampering" place, whose proprietor of 40 years' standing is "the perfect host"; let's hope the new chef is maintaining culinary standards to match!
/ **Details:** www.st-tudno.co.uk; 9.30 pm; no shorts; children: 6+ after 6.30 pm.
Accommodation: 18 rooms, from £100.

LLANFRYNACH, POWYS 2–1A

White Swan £ 45 ⓣ

Brecon LD3 7BZ   (01874) 665276

"Just what you want to see in a country restaurant", this rural inn is tipped for its consistently "interesting" and "well cooked" cuisine.
/ **Details:** www.the-white-swan.co.uk; 9 pm; closed Mon & Tue; no Amex; booking essential.

LLANGOLLEN, DENBIGHSHIRE 5–3A

Corn Mill £ 38 ❸❸❶

Dee Ln LL20 8PN   (01978) 869555

"Overhanging the rapids of the River Dee", this "wonderfully situated" Brunning & Price group gastropub "couldn't have a better location"; food and service have traditionally played second fiddle, but a good number of reports confirm "improved standards" of late.
/ **Details:** www.cornmill-llangollen.co.uk; 9.30 pm, Sun 9 pm.

LLANWRTYD WELLS, POWYS 4–4D

Carlton Riverside £ 54 ❸❸④

Irfon Cr LD5 4SP   (01591) 610248

"Terrific gourmet food" still features in most feedback on this "slightly dated" riverside restaurant-with-rooms; the odd "ordinary" dish has been reported this year, but fans suggest the cooking has "stepped up" of late. / **Details:** www.carltonriverside.com; 8.30 pm; D only, closed Sun; no Amex.* **Accommodation:** 5 rooms, from £75.

LOCH LOMOND, DUNBARTONSHIRE 9–4B

Martin Wishart
Cameron House £ 92 ❷❷❷

G83 8QZ   (01389) 722504

"Combining tradition and modernity in both cuisine and ambience"; Martin Wishart's "pricey" outpost "on the bonnie banks of Loch Lomond" pleases almost all reporters with its "superb" standards.
/ **Details:** www.martinwishartlochlomond.co.uk; over Erskine Bridge to A82, follow signs to Loch Lomond; 9.45 pm; D only, closed Sun & Mon.
Accommodation: 129 rooms, from £215.

The Albannach £ 74 ❶❷❷
IV27 4LP (01571) 844407
With its "sourcing of the best local produce", "flair in the conception of dishes", "precision of the cooking itself" and "exquisite presentation" – not to mention "charming" service – the dining room at Colin Craig & Lesley Crosfield's remote hotel is nothing less than "a triumph". / Details: www.thealbannach.co.uk; one sitting; D only, closed Mon; no Amex; children: 12+. Accommodation: 5 rooms, from £260.

Chapter One £ 53 ❶❷❷
Farnborough Common BR6 8NF (01689) 854848
"West End-quality food well below West End prices", from chef Andrew McLeish, has carved out a huge reputation for this "superb" stalwart – an unusually notable destination by suburban standards. / Details: www.chaptersrestaurants.com; just before Princess Royal Hospital; Sun-Thu 9.15 pm, Fri & Sat 9.45 pm; booking: max 12.

The Mole & Chicken £ 41 ❷❷❷
Easington HP18 9EY (01844) 208387
"You'll need your sat nav" to find this "lovely old pub" in "the middle of nowhere"; worth seeking out, though, as it serves up "delicious unfancy food" at "value-for-money" prices; "great bedrooms too". / Details: www.themoleandchicken.co.uk; follow signs from B4011 at Long Crendon; 9.30 pm, Sun 9 pm. Accommodation: 5 rooms, from £95.

The Vine and Spice £ 41 ❷❷④
High St OX14 4QH (01865) 409 900
"An old pub that's been pleasantly refurbished, modernised, and turned into a new-style Indian restaurant"; it offers a "rather different experience", with the focus on "light, fresh dishes with some very delicious flavours". / Details: www.thevineandspice.co.uk; 10.30 pm.

The Longridge Restaurant £ 61 ❸❷❸
104-106 Higher Rd PR3 3SY (01772) 784969
Chris Bell is a "master chef" and many "beautifully crafted" meals are reported from the cottage-restaurant where leading North Western light, Paul Heathcote originally came to fame; off-days, however, are not unknown, and the kitchen can give the impression of "trying too hard". / Details: www.heathcotes.co.uk; follow signs for Jeffrey Hill; 9.30 pm, Sun 7.45 pm; closed Mon & Tue.

The Hammer and Pincers £ 50 ❶
5 East Rd LE12 6ST (01509) 880735
A "passionate" family-run rural restaurant, tipped for its "constantly changing menus that make the best of local produce" and its "friendly" welcome too. / Details: www.hammerandpincers.co.uk; 9.30 pm, Sun 6 pm; closed Sun D; no Amex.

The Anchor Inn £ 42 ❸❸❷
GU34 4NA (01420) 23261
"A very friendly and enjoyable country pub with a decent chef who knows what he's doing"; his highly "competent" cuisine contributes to a "delightful" all-round experience.
/ **Details:** www.anchorinnatlowerfroyle.co.uk; 9.30 pm. **Accommodation:** 5 rooms, from £120.

The Fox Inn £ 40 ❷❷❷
GL56 0UR (01451) 870555
"Lots of very pleasant dining areas and a lovely garden on warm days" add much to the charm of a visit to this "olde-worlde" inn "in a delightful, small, sleepy Cotswold village"; its "charming and professional" staff serve up food characterised by "good-quality ingredients and sensible prices". / **Details:** www.foxinn.net; on A436 near Stow-on-the-Wold; 10 pm, Sun 9.30 pm; no Amex. **Accommodation:** 3 rooms, from £75.

Lower Slaughter Manor
Von Essen £ 97
GL54 2HP (01451) 820456
Bought by the ABode Hotels people as this guide was going to press, this charming hotel cannot be rated for this year; we imagine, however, that its "fabulous surroundings inside and out" will survive the transition. / **Details:** www.lowerslaughter.co.uk; 2m from Burton-on-the-Water on A429; 9 pm; no jeans or trainers. **Accommodation:** 19 rooms, from £310.

La Bécasse £ 83 ❶❶❷
17 Corve St SY8 1DA (01584) 872325
"A sheer joy" – the general reaction to this panelled dining room (a stablemate to L'Ortolan at Shinfield), where Will Holland's "faultless" food benefits from both "creativity" and "local sourcing"; it's a shame, though, that all that Michelin-striving creates as atmosphere some reporters find "pompous". / **Details:** www.labecasse.co.uk; 9 pm, 9.30 pm; closed Mon, Tue L & Sun D; no Amex.

Fishmore Hall £ 64 ❷❷④
Fishmore Rd SY8 3DP (01584) 875148
"Attention to detail" helps underpin overall satisfaction with this Georgian country house hotel; the occasional reporter, though, does find the decor of the dining room a touch "sterile".
/ **Details:** www.fishmorehall.co.uk; 9.30 pm; booking essential. **Accommodation:** 15 rooms, from £140.

Green Café
Ludlow Mill On The Green £ 33 ❶
Dinham Millennium Grn SY8 1EG (01584) 879872
"A hidden gem of a café, nestled by the River Teme", tipped as a "delightful" spot for an "excellent" lunch or a "splendid" afternoon tea. / **Details:** www.ludlowmillonthegreen.co.uk.

Mr Underhill's £ 75 **❶❶❷**
Dinham Weir SY8 1EH (01584) 874443
Chris & Judy Bradley's "informal" and "efficient" restaurant-with-
rooms, "fabulously-located" by the River Teme, is a "magical" all-
rounder, offering a "locally-sourced" cuisine that's "splendidly cooked,
beautifully presented, and original"; interesting wine list too.
/ **Details:** www.mr-underhills.co.uk; 8.15 pm; D only, closed Mon & Tue;
no Amex; children: 8+. **Accommodation:** 6 rooms, from £140.

LYDDINGTON, RUTLAND   5–4D

Marquess Of Exeter £ 42 **❸❷❸**
52 Main St LE15 9LT (01572) 822 477
"A good gastropub, with some real high points"; Brian Baker's
"relaxing and always-welcoming" two-year-old can seem "a bit barn-
like", but wins very consistent praise for its "cheerful" service and
"competently executed" cooking. / **Details:** www.marquessexeter.co.uk;
9.30 pm, Sun 9 pm; no Amex.

LYDFORD, DEVON   1–3C

The Dartmoor Inn £ 46 **❶**
Moorside EX20 4AY (01822) 820221
An old coaching inn that's "more a restaurant with a bar attached"
nowadays, and tipped for its "interesting" cuisine – "plus some more
standard choices for the unadventurous"!
/ **Details:** www.dartmoorinn.com; on the A386 Tavistock to Okehampton road;
9.30 pm; closed Mon L & Sun D. **Accommodation:** 3 rooms, from £110.

LYDGATE, GREATER MANCHESTER   5–2B

The White Hart £ 39 **❶**
51 Stockport Rd OL4 4JJ (01457) 872566
On the edge of the Pennines, an inn tipped for its consistent overall
standards; for top value, visit for the Monday two-for-one offer!
/ **Details:** www.thewhitehart.co.uk; 2m E of Oldham on A669, then A6050;
9.30 pm. **Accommodation:** 12 rooms, from £120.

LYME REGIS, DORSET   2–4A

Harbour Inn £ 41 **❸❸❸**
Marine Pde DT7 3JF (01297) 442299
"Totally reliable for a dependably good meal, including some
delicious fish", this "popular and buzzy" beach-side inn pleases all
who comment on it. / **Details:** 9 pm.

Hix Oyster and Fish House £ 57 **❷❹❷**
Cobb Rd DT7 3JP (01297) 446910
"The view rivals the best in the world", at this cliff-top three-year-old,
where chef Phil Eagle produces "delicious" oysters and "wonderful"
fish – "so fresh and beautifully cooked"; not for the first time,
though, a Mark Hix establishment is "sometimes let down by
indifferent service". / **Details:** www.restaurantsetcltd.co.uk; 10 pm.

LYMINGTON, HAMPSHIRE   2–4C

Egan's £ 45 **❸❷❸**
24 Gosport St SO41 9BE (01590) 676165
"Always welcoming", this "great family-run restaurant" inspires only
positive reviews, not least for its "first-class cooking" (and in
particular its "excellent lunchtime value"). / **Details:** 10 pm; closed
Mon & Sun; no Amex; booking: max 6, Sat.

The Mill at Gordleton £ 49 ❷❷❷
Silver St SO41 6DJ (01590) 682219
In "beautiful surroundings" and offering a menu with "a wide range of dishes to suit all tastes", this "slightly old-fashioned" waterside favourite is proclaimed "a real treat" by almost all who comment on it. / Details: www.themillatgordleton.co.uk; on the A337, off the M27; 9.15 pm, Sun 8.15 pm. Accommodation: 8 rooms, from £140.

LYMM, CHESHIRE 5–2B

The Church Green £ 52 ④④❸
Higher Ln WA13 0AP (01925) 752068
"Refined cooking" wins praise for this fashionably revamped inn where a former Dorchester Grill chef is at the stoves; it can seem "over-hyped" and "overpriced" too – one of the reasons the bar is sometimes preferred to the main restaurant.
/ Details: www.thechurchgreen.co.uk; 9.30 pm, Fri & Sat 10 pm, Sun 7.45 pm.

LYNDHURST, HAMPSHIRE 2–4C

Lime Wood £ 70 ④④❸
Beaulieu Rd SO43 7FZ (02380) 287168
This "stylish" country house hotel certainly has a "beautiful" New Forest location, but reports have become very mixed – fans proclaim "great food in a magical setting", but numerous critics now find standards "disappointing, considering the prices".
/ Details: www.limewoodhotel.co.uk; 9.30 pm; no shorts.
Accommodation: 30 rooms, from £295.

LYTHAM, LANCASHIRE 5–1A

Hastings £ 41 ❷❸④
26 Hastings Pl FY8 5LZ (01253) 732400
Thanks to Warwick Dodds's "exceptional" cooking, this "modern, split-level bar/restaurant" is, for fans, "simply the best place to eat on the Fylde Coast"; reactions to its "smart but bland and beige" decor are, however, quite mixed. / Details: www.hastingslytham.com; round the corner from railway station; 10.30 pm; closed Mon & Sun D.

MADINGLEY, CAMBRIDGESHIRE 3–1B

Three Horseshoes £ 57 ④❸❸
CB23 8AB (01954) 210221
"Good-value, reliable, and convenient to Cambridge" – this classic day-out-from-the-Varsity destination strikes many reporters as a "gem", thanks to its "interesting" ("Italian-influenced") cuisine, "friendly" service and "nice conservatory".
/ Details: www.threehorseshoesmadingley.co.uk; 2m W of Cambridge, off A14 or M11; 9 pm, Fri & Sat 9.30 pm, Sun 8.30 pm.

MAIDENHEAD, BERKSHIRE 3–3A

Boulters Riverside Brasserie £ 52 ④④❷
Boulters Island SL6 8PE (01628) 621291
A "beautifully-located" venue with large picture windows perched over the Thames – "the setting is superb, but food and service quality are just average and prices a bit steep"; for a lower-cost recce, try a snack in the upstairs Terrace Bar.
/ Details: www.boultersrestaurant.co.uk; 9.30 pm; closed Mon & Sun D; no Amex.

The Royal Oak £ 63 ❷❷❸

Paley St SL6 3JN (01628) 620541

*The "un-flashy" charms of "Parkie's pub" – including all-round "attention to detail" – still impress most reporters; until recently it had notably avoided all the snares inherent in celeb-ownership, but it drew some flak this year for not being "quite as good as it thinks it is". / **Details:** www.theroyaloakpaleystreet.com; 9.30 pm, Fri & Sat 10 pm; closed Sun D; children: 3+ .*

MAIDENSGROVE, OXFORDSHIRE 2–2D

Five Horseshoes £ 45 🅣

RG9 6EX (01491) 641282

*A characterful pub with a big garden, beautifully-located in the heart of the Chilterns; it's tipped for its above-average pub grub, but can sometimes be "let down by poor service". / **Details:** www.thefivehorseshoes.co.uk; off B481 between Nettlebed & Watlington; 9.30 pm, Sun 8.30 pm; no Amex; booking essential.*

MALMESBURY, WILTSHIRE 2–2C

The Old Bell Hotel £ 52 ❹❸❷

Abbey Row SN16 0BW (01666) 822344

*England's oldest hotel is also "a beautiful place in a beautiful location" – the sort of place you can have a "wonderful Sunday lunch" too; more ambitious options, however, should be approached with care – "simpler would be so much better!" / **Details:** www.oldbellhotel.com; next to Abbey; 9 pm, Fri & Sat 9.30 pm.* **Accommodation:** *33 rooms, from £125.*

MALVERN WELLS, WORCESTERSHIRE 2–1B

Outlook
The Cottage in the Wood £ 48 🅣

Holywell Rd WR14 4LG (01684) 588860

*"Get a window table to enjoy the terrific views" (of the Malvern Hills), at this small, family-run hotel where ambitious cooking is always achieved to a standard that's at least "respectable"; there's also an "extensive and well-considered wine list". / **Details:** www.cottageinthewood.co.uk; 9.30 pm, Sun 9 pm.* **Accommodation:** *30 rooms, from £99.*

MANCHESTER, GREATER MANCHESTER 5–2B

Akbar's £ 29 ❷❷❸

73-83 Liverpool Rd M3 4NQ (0161) 834 8444

*"Heaving" crowds attest to the "all-round" appeal of this "very affordable", "fast" and "upbeat" Pakistani restaurant in Castlefield – "given the number of covers, the quality is unbelievable". / **Details:** www.akbars.co.uk; 11 pm, Fri & Sat 11.30 pm; D only; need 10+ to book.*

Albert's £ 44 ❷❸❸

120-122 Barlow Moor Rd M20 2PU (0161) 434 8289

*"A colourful addition to the South Manchester scene"; this "lively young venue" is already tipped for its "wide choice of good staples" (with "one or two innovative dishes" too). / **Details:** www.albertsdidsbury.com.*

Albert's Shed　　　　　　　　　　£ 44　　❸❷❷
20 Castle St M3 4LZ   (0161) 839 9818
*Bearing little obvious relationship to the workman's shed this once
was, this canal-side Castlefield spot makes a "pleasant" place to
hang out on a sunny day, and it's certainly "very popular"; the food,
if not the main point, can come as a "nice surprise" too.*
/ **Details:** www.albertsshed.com; 10 pm, Fri 10.30 pm, Sat 11 pm, Sun
9.30 pm; no Amex.

Armenian Taverna　　　　　　　£ 35　　　🆃
3-5 Princess St M2 4DF   (0161) 834 9025
*"Forty years on and still a different and authentic meal every time",
says a fan of this city-centre basement stalwart; it may win "no
prizes for decor", but the "consistent" mezze are "cheap and
satisfying".* / **Details:** www.armeniantaverna.co.uk; 11 pm; closed Mon,
Sat L & Sun L; children: 3+.

Aumbry　　　　　　　　　　　£ 51　　❶❷④
2 Church Ln M25 1AJ   (0161) 7985841
*"At last Manchester has a truly excellent restaurant"; the Prestwich
premises may be "small" and "crowded", but chefs Lawrence
Totingham and Mary-Ellen McTague "work miracles" there, offering
a cuisine that is both "sophisticated" and "refined".*
/ **Details:** www.aumbryrestaurant.co.uk; 10.30 pm; closed Mon, Tue & Sun D;
no Amex.

Chaophraya Thai Restaurant & Bar　£ 43　　❷❷❷
Chapel Walks M2 1HN   (0161) 832 8342
*Back on top form, this "consistently fine" city-centre spot can once
again confidently be proclaimed "the best Thai in Manchester";
some reporters find the food "faultless", and even the least
enthusiastic say it's "robust" and "'reliable".*
/ **Details:** www.chaophraya.co.uk; 10.30 pm.

Choice　　　　　　　　　　　£ 44　　❷❷❸
Castle Quay M15 4NT   (0161) 833 3400
*Living up to its name, an under-appreciated Castlefield gem praised
not only for its "lovely" canal-side setting and its "friendly" service,
but also its "great" (if not hugely innovative) cuisine.*
/ **Details:** www.choicebarandrestaurant.co.uk; 9.30 pm, Fri & Sat 10 pm.

Croma　　　　　　　　　　　£ 31　　④❷❷
1-3 Clarence St M2 4DE   (0161) 237 9799
*"The best place to avoid city-centre chain ubiquity"; this "classy"
pizzeria near the Town Hall – in fact run by former franchisees of
PizzaExpress! – remains a mega-popular and "buzzing" central
rendezvous.* / **Details:** www.croma.biz; off Albert Square; 10 pm, Fri & Sat
11 pm.

Croma　　　　　　　　　　　£ 30　　❸❷❸
500 Wilbraham Rd M21 9AP   (0161) 881 1117
*"A place for children of all ages"; this "consistently good" Chorlton
pizzeria is a "relaxed" and "friendly" all-rounder, and it always has
"a real buzz about it" too.* / **Details:** www.cromapizza.com; 10 pm,
Thu-Sat 11 pm; Bookings for 6+ only.

Dimitri's　　　　　　　　　　£ 41　　　🆃
1 Campfield Arc M3 4FN   (0161) 839 3319
*"A Manchester mainstay", this "buzzing" semi al fresco Greek
fixture in a Victorian arcade is still tipped as a destination for a
"good night out", especially in a group; but even some fans concede
that the food is "not exceptional".* / **Details:** www.dimitris.co.uk; near
Museum of Science & Industry and Hilton hotel; 11.30 pm.

Dough
£ 28 ❷❷❸
75-77 High St M4 1FS
"Better than Croma!", say some reporters, this light and bright Northern Quarter pizzeria if of note for offering some "really interesting" combinations. / Details: www.doughpizzakitchen.co.uk.

East Z East
Hotel Ibis
£ 35 ❷④④
Charles St M1 7DG (0161) 244 5353
In the basement of a budget hotel, "an above-average" Punjabi restaurant serving well cooked traditional dishes ("particularly good fish and seafood") of a type you don't often see, plus more standard fare; there's also a branch by the Irwell. / Details: www.eastzeast.com; 11.15 pm, Fri & Sat 11.45 pm, Sun 10.45 pm; D only.

Evuna
£ 41 ❷❸④
Deansgate M3 4EW (0161) 819 2752
"The best tapas in Manchester", and some "fantastic" vinos too make it well worth seeking out this 'Spanish Wine House' in the city-centre. / Details: www.evuna.com; 11 pm, Sun 9 pm.

The French Restaurant
Midland Hotel
£ 68 ❺
Peter St M60 2DS (0161) 236 3333
Vanishingly few reports on the city's grandest dining room (which is rather like a scaled-down, no-view version of that at London's Ritz); reporters tip a "lovely" room (suited to business and old-style romance), whose all-round appeal includes "an extensive wine list". / Details: www.qhotels.co.uk; 10.30 pm, Fri & Sat 11 pm; D only, closed Mon & Sun; no jeans or trainers; children: no children .
Accommodation: *312 rooms, from £145.*

Gaucho
£ 64 ❸❸❷
2a St Mary's St M3 2LB (0161) 833 4333
"Peter Stringfellow meets Texas-bordello", at this "blingy" former chapel by House of Fraser; on the one hand it's often said to offer "an amazing steak experience" (with good wines too), but there's also a feeling that it's "massively overpriced". / Details: www.gauchorestaurants.com; 10.30 pm, Fri & Sat 11 pm.

Glamorous
£ 27 ❷④④
Wing Yip Bus' Centre, Oldham Rd M4 5HU (0161) 839 3312
It's "like being in Hong Kong" to visit this "excellent establishment above the Wing Yip cash-and-carry"; "constantly replenished dim sum trolleys" helps ensure it's "especially busy with Asian customers at lunchtime". / Details: www.glamorous-restaurant.co.uk.

Great Kathmandu
£ 27 ❷❸④
140 Burton Rd M20 1JQ (0161) 434 6413
"Still reliable, despite expansion"; this long-established West Didsbury subcontinental has annexed two neighbouring premises over the years; it remains very highly-rated for "delicious" traditional Indian food and Nepalese specialities "as good as anything on the curry mile". / Details: www.greatkathmandu.com; near Withington hospital; midnight.

Green's
£ 37 ❷❸❷
43 Lapwing Ln M20 2NT (0161) 434 4259
"Delicious veggie food in leafy Didsbury" – that's the deal that makes an ongoing success of a "very busy" stalwart which is "good enough for meat-eaters too!" / Details: www.greensdidsbury.co.uk; 4m S of city centre; 10.30 pm; closed Mon L; no Amex.

Grill on the Alley £ 47 ❷❷❷
5 Ridgefield M2 6EG (0161) 833 3465
*"A place to suit all ages" – this "very buzzy" and "slick" city-centre
surf 'n' turf outfit has a "great location" (just off King Street) and
pleases almost all who comment on it; "amazing steaks" a highlight.
/ Details: www.blackhouse.uk.com; 11 pm.*

Gurkha Grill £ 31 ❷❹❹
194-198 Burton Rd M20 1LH (0161) 445 3461
*"Beats Rusholme every time!"; it's the "great curries" that win a
particular following for this West Didsbury Nepalese, but the service
and decor are "fine" too. / Details: www.gurkhagrill.com; midnight, Fri &
Sat 1 pm; D only.*

Gusto Restaurant & Bar £ 46 ❚❚
756 Wilmslow Road M20 2DW (0161) 445 8209
*A Didsbury Italian – part of a Northern chain – tipped as a pretty
consistent stand-by for a "cheap 'n' cheerful" bite.
/ Details: www.gustorestaurants.uk.com; 10.30 pm; no Amex.*

Jem & I £ 42 ❷❸❸
1c, School Ln M20 6RD (0161) 445 3996
*Reporters often assess Jem O'Sullivan's "friendly" Didsbury venture
by reference to nearby legend the Lime Tree (where he formerly
worked) – "it's a good alternative, with excellent food… but the
parking's just as bad". / Details: www.jemandirestaurant.co.uk; 10 pm,
Fri & Sat 10.30 pm.*

Katsouris Deli £ 10 ❷❷❸
113 Deansgate M3 2BQ (0161) 819 1260
*"The best cheap eat!" – fans are not shy in their praise of the
"ridiculously yummy" scoff at this city-centre café, most notably "the
best hot and cold sandwiches in the city" – no wonder it's always
"full to bursting"; also in Bury. / Details: L only; no Amex.*

The Lime Tree £ 40 ❷❚❷
8 Lapwing Ln M20 2WS (0161) 445 1217
*"Book weeks in advance" if you want a peak-time table at West
Didsbury's "all-round favourite": a "relaxed" brasserie, with "top
quality" fare, which – for over 20 years – has proved "remarkable in
its consistency". / Details: www.thelimetreerestaurant.co.uk; 10 pm; closed
Mon L & Sat L.*

Little Yang Sing £ 37 ❸❸❹
17 George St M1 4HE (0161) 228 7722
*The Chinatown basement, where the Yang Sing legend began, again
got mixed reports this year; on most accounts, it's still "superior for
Chinatown", but even some fans encounter the odd dish that's "not
special". / Details: www.littleyangsing.co.uk; 11.30 pm, Sat midnight, Sun
10.45 pm.*

Livebait £ 45 ❚❚
22 Lloyd St M2 5WA (0161) 817 4110
*"Snobs may sneer, but the quality of the food here is really good";
this city-centre outpost of the nowadays MOR national fish chain has
quite a few fans locally, and even critical reporters concede that
standards here are at worst "adequate".
/ Details: www.livebaitrestaurants.co.uk/manchester; 10.30 pm, Sat 11 pm,
Sun 9 pm.*

Lounge 10
£ 53   ❸❸❶

10 Tib Ln M2 4JB   (0161) 834 1331

With its "dramatic decor" and its "louche" and "sexy" vibe – not to mention its magicians and other "great entertainment" – this "quirky" city-centre spot has traditionally been seen as an 'atmosphere' destination; the "sophisticated" cuisine, however, generally hits the spot. / **Details:** www.loungetenmanchester.com; 10.30 pm, Fri & Sat 11 pm; closed Sat L & Sun.

The Mark Addy
£ 41   ❸④⑤

Stanley St M5 5EJ   (0161) 832 4080

A "very popular" Salford gastropub (whose chef, Robert Owen-Brown, is hailed as "a bit of a northern Fergus Henderson"); fans say his "unusual" food is "excellent", but critics sense "hype", and the location – "below a car-park, on the banks of an urban river" – is no particular attraction. / **Details:** www.markaddy.co.uk; 9.30 pm, hot food 7 pm; closed Sun D; no Amex.

The Market
£ 50   ❸❸❷

104 High St M4 1HQ   (0161) 834 3743

The "front-room-friendly" atmosphere of this "cosy" and "unique" Northern Quarter "institution" has survived its 'new' ownership (of three years' standing); after an unsettled patch, reporters are becoming more enthusiastic about its "fresh" (and "locally-sourced") cuisine too. / **Details:** www.market-restaurant.com; 9.30 pm, Sat 10.30 pm; closed Mon & Sun.

Michael Caines
ABode Hotel
£ 70   ❷④④

107 Piccadilly M1 2DB   (0161) 200 5678

"Interesting" dishes come in "blissful, small portions" at this trendy basement dining room, near Piccadilly Station; its "bargain" lunch menus help win it high popularity – dining à la carte, the slightly "soulless" ambience, and occasionally "chaotic" service are more evident. / **Details:** www.michaelcaines.com; 10 pm; closed Sun; no shorts; 8+ to go through Events. **Accommodation:** 61 rooms, from £79.

Mr Thomas's Chop House
£ 38   ❸❸❷

52 Cross St M2 7AR   (0161) 832 2245

Occupying "a classic, Victorian tiled room", this "reliable city-centre stand-by" has quite a name for its "wholesome, traditional Lancastrian fare", not least "the best steak 'n' kidney pud' you'll find" – "you deserve a medal if you finish it!" / **Details:** www.tomschophouse.com; 9.30 pm, Sun 8 pm.

The Northern Quarter
£ 45   ④④❸

108 High St M4 1HQ   (0161) 832 7115

"Doing exactly what you want of such an institution", this "neighbourhood restaurant" has achieved "stalwart" status in this trendy part of town; it serves "hearty" staples realised to a "solid" standard. / **Details:** www.tnq.co.uk; 10.30 pm, sun 7 pm.

Pacific
£ 40   ❶

58-60 George St M1 4HF   (0161) 228 6668

"Perhaps not as good as it was, but still a good stand-by" – this large Thai (upstairs) near Piccadilly Station seems to be "finding its feet again"; "at dinner, off-menu is definitely the way to go". / **Details:** www.pacificrestaurant.co.uk; midnight, Sun 10.30 pm.

Piccolino   £ 45   ④❸❸
8 Clarence St M2 4DW   (0161) 835 9860
Handily-located near the Town Hall, this "buzzy" outpost of a
"slightly superior" NW-based Italian chain makes a "reliable" and
"friendly" rendezvous that's very popular with most reporters; "pity
it's so noisy". / Details: www.piccolinorestaurants.co.uk/manchester; 11 pm,
Sun 10 pm.

Punjab Tandoori   £ 24   ❷④⑤
177 Wilmslow Rd M14 5AP   (0161) 225 2960
It can seem "tatty and old-fashioned", with iffy service and food
that's "bordering on too hot to enjoy", but this Curry Mile veteran
continues to thrill most reporters with its "great dosas" and its other
"authentic" fare. / Details: midnight; closed Mon L.

Red Chilli   £ 38   ❷④④
70-72 Portland St M1 4GU   (0161) 236 2888
A "wide menu" of "authentic Northern Chinese food" has carved a
big name for this Sichuanese spot in Chinatown, and most (if not
quite all) reporters remain "thrilled" with its "spicy" fare; there's a
branch near the university at 403-419 Oxford Road, tel 0161 273
1288. / Details: www.redchillirestaurant.co.uk; 11 pm; need 6+ to book.

El Rincon   £ 30   ④④❷
Longworth St, off St John's St M3 4BQ   (0161) 839 8819
"You could be in Spain!" at "the best tapas bar in the North West"
– a "hard-to-find" stalwart, just off Deansgate; most accounts
applaud its "top-class" fare, but the occasional meal was spoilt by
"borderline rude" service. / Details: off Deansgate; 11 pm.

Room   £ 50   ❸❸❷
81 King St M2 4AH   (0161) 8392005
The "buzzy" first-floor dining room of a wonderful Victorian club,
made over in contemporary style, provides the "amazing" setting for
this "unique" dining experience; the "modern take on traditional
British dishes" may not be bad, but prices are "way OTT".
/ Details: www.roomrestaurants.com; 10 pm, Sat 11 pm; closed Sun.

Rosso   £ 47   ⑤④❸
43 Spring Gdns M2 2BG   (0161) 8321400
"A let-down, after all the hype"; in the "grandiose" ex-bank premises
of the former Establishment (RIP), the city-centre spot co-owned by
Rio Ferdinand is slated by most reporters for its "bland" food,
"slapdash" service and "scary" celeb-centric clientele!
/ Details: www.rossorestaurants.com; 11 pm.

Sam's Chop House   £ 40   ❷❷❷
Back Pool Fold, Chapel Walks M2 1HN   (0161) 834 3210
In the heart of the city, a pub-like basement with "plenty of
atmosphere" which is popular for business; it offers "gut-busting"
traditional British "staples" and an "excellent" wine list.
/ Details: www.samschophouse.com; 9.30 pm, Sun 7 pm.

San Carlo   £ 38   ❷❷❷
40 King Street West M3 2WY   (0161) 834 6226
"The heart of Manchester's dining scene"; "cramped" and "raucous"
it may be, but the city's most famous Italian is always "busy",
"buzzing" and "great fun" ("assuming you can get a
reservation..."); across the road the new cicchetti (Italian tapas)
offshoot is going down well too. / Details: www.sancarlo.co.uk; 11 pm.

Wings

ams Chop House

Choice

Second Floor Restaurant
Harvey Nichols £ 59 **②③③**
21 New Cathedral St M1 1AD (0161) 828 8898
"Greatly improved" in recent times, the *"light-filled"* dining room of
this Knightsbridge-comes-to-the-North department store is now one
of the best city-centre options – even reports from those who say the
food's *"not entirely memorable"* are essentially upbeat.
/ Details: www.harveynichols.com; 9.30 pm; closed Mon D & Sun D.

Stock £ 51 **③③②**
4 Norfolk St M2 1DW (0161) 839 6644
*Impressively housed in the former (Victorian) stock exchange, a
"stylish" venue whose vibe is *"conducive to business"*; indeed, for
some reporters this is *"possibly Manchester's best all-rounder"* –
sadly, though, feedback on the Italian cuisine hits every note from
"excellent" to *"disappointing"*. / Details: www.stockrestaurant.co.uk;
10 pm; closed Sun.*

Tai Pan £ 33 **②④⑤**
81-97 Upper Brook St M13 9TX (0161) 273 2798
*Handy for the university, a *"functional"* Chinese above a Longsight
cash-and-carry, of particular note as *"a top spot for dim sum"*.
/ Details: 11 pm, Sun 9.30 pm.*

Tai Wu £ 32 **④④④**
44 Oxford Rd M1 5EJ (0161) 236 6557
*A vast and *"thriving"* city-centre Chinese of particular note for *"good
dim sum"* (served from trolleys) – most reports still acclaim it as a
"brilliant" experience, but this year's feedback included accounts of a
couple of dud meals. / Details: www.tai-wu.co.uk; 2.45 am.*

Tampopo £ 28 **③②③**
16 Albert Sq M2 5PF (0161) 819 1966
*For *"a great Oriental fast bite"* that's *"fresh, tasty and inexpensive"*
(so *"ideal pre-theatre"* or for lunch), check out the *"reliable"*
branches of this pan-Asian noodle chain. / Details: www.tampopo.co.uk;
11 pm, Sun 10 pm; need 7+ to book.*

This & That £ 11 **❶③⑤**
3 Soap St M4 1EW (0161) 832 4971
"Home-style curries with fabulous depth of flavour" have made this
"very basic" but *"cheerful"* caff a famously *"popular"* Northern
Quarter destination for those seeking a lunchtime *"bargain"*; the
(relatively) *"posh"* new offshoot near House of Fraser, has also gone
down well. / Details: www.thisandthatcafe.co.uk; 4 pm, Fri & Sat 8 pm;
no credit cards.*

Try Thai £ 35 **Ⓣ**
52-54 Faulkner St M1 4FH (0161) 228 1822
"In Chinatown, but offering some of the best Thai food around!" –
this *"authentic"* and *"great-value"* spot just *"keeps getting better"*,
says its small but dedicated local fan club. / Details: www.try-thai.co.uk.*

Vermilion £ 44 **Ⓣ**
Lord North St M40 8AD (0161) 202 0055
*Bereft of the super-casino which was supposed to be built next door,
this grandiose Thai/Indian bar/restaurant somehow manages not only
to survive but seemingly even to prosper – it's tipped for its top-value
lunch menu and also its *"ultra-modern"* surroundings.
/ Details: www.vermilioncinnabar.com; 10 pm, Sat 11 pm; no trainers.*

Wing's £ 46 ❷❷❷
1 Lincoln Sq M2 5LN (0161) 834 9000

"Head and shoulders above the other Chinese restaurants in town" say fans of this smart city-centre operation; though "not cheap", it typically offers "a truly excellent experience" all-round – on the rare occasions reports are bad though, they're really bad!
/ **Details:** www.wingsrestaurant.co.uk; midnight, Sun 11 pm; closed Sat L; no trainers; children: 11+ after 8 pm Mon-Fri, 21+ D.

Yang Sing £ 43 ❷❸❸
34 Princess St M1 4JY (0161) 236 2200

The North of England's most famous Chinese is "still the best" for its many fans, who applaud its "excellent" – and, "if they don't fob you off", "challenging" – cuisine, and in particular "the best dim sum"; no avoiding the fact, though, that about one reporter in five feels it's "living on its reputation". / **Details:** www.yang-sing.com; 11.30 pm, Sun 10.30 pm.

MANNINGTREE, ESSEX 3–2C

Lucca Enoteca £ 36 ❓
39-43 High St CO11 1AH (01206) 390044

"Cooked in front of you in a wooden oven", the pizza at this rural Italian is the best to be found for many miles around.
/ **Details:** www.luccafoods.co.uk; 9.30 pm, Fri & Sat 10 pm; no Amex.

MARGATE, KENT 3–3D

The Ambrette £ 40 ❶❷❸
44 King St CT9 1QE (01843) 231 504

"Some of the best fine Indian dining anywhere in the UK!"; Dev Biswal's "inventive" Old Town restaurant is "putting Margate back on the map" – its "well-conceived" and "brilliantly executed" dishes take subcontinental cuisine "to a whole new level".
/ **Details:** www.theambrette.co.uk; 9.30 pm, Fri & Sat 10 pm; closed Mon.

MARLBOROUGH, WILTSHIRE 2–2C

The Harrow at Little Bedwyn £ 73 ❷❷❸
Little Bedwyn SN8 3JP (01672) 870871

"A treasure trove of well-selected wines at fair prices" has helped put Roger & Sue Jones's "welcoming" inn on the map, and many reporters feel the food is "fabulous" too; there's a disgruntled minority, though, who feel standards have "gone off the boil".
/ **Details:** www.theharrowatlittlebedwyn.co.uk; 9 pm; closed Mon, Tue & Sun; no Amex; no trainers.

MARLOW, BUCKINGHAMSHIRE 3–3A

Adam Simmons
Danesfield House Hotel £ 86 ❹❹❸
Henley Rd SL7 2EY (01628) 891010

Everyone agrees the location is "superb", but this wedding cake-like country house hotel otherwise inspires a mixed bag of views; fans say Andrew Simmonds's food is "unforgettable", but sceptics opine that it's "lacking wow-factor" and "not worth the huge outlay".
/ **Details:** www.danesfieldhouse.co.uk; 3m outside Marlow on the A4155; 9.30 pm; closed Mon, Tue L, Wed L & Sun; no trainers. **Accommodation:** 86 rooms, from £134.

Aubergine
Compleat Angler £ 75 ④④④
Marlow Bridge SL7 1RG (01628) 405405
Overlooking the weir, the dining room of this famous riverside hotel makes "a great venue for a romance" and its ambitious cuisine is often "faultless" too; it's also "very expensive", though, and – "given the prices" – some reporters "expected more".
/ **Details:** www.atozrestaurants.com; from M4 Junction 89 then A404; 10.30 pm; closed Mon & Tue; no shorts. **Accommodation:** 64 rooms, from £150.

Hand & Flowers £ 62 ❷❷❷
West St SL7 2BP (01628) 482277
Aided by its "easy-going" style, the Kerridges' acclaimed gastropub has made quite a name; its "sophisticated pub food" is "superb" too, although reporters drawn by its Michelin star sometimes "missed the expected wow-factor" (… which makes the subsequent award of a second star hard to fathom). / **Details:** www.thehandandflowers.co.uk; 9.30 pm; closed Sun D. **Accommodation:** 4 rooms, from £140.

The Royal Oak £ 43 ❷❸④
Frieth Rd, Bovingdon Grn SL7 2JF (01628) 488611
A "fantastic" find for first-timers – this "cosy" half-timbered inn just outside the town has a massive reputation for its "excellent and imaginative" cuisine (and it's a "child-" and "dog-friendly" place); there's a fair minority of reporters, however, for whom this is a "useful choice, but not a top one". / **Details:** www.royaloakmarlow.co.uk; half mile up from Marlow High Street; 9.30 pm, Fri & Sat 10 pm.

The Vanilla Pod £ 64 ❶❷❸
31 West St SL7 2LS (01628) 898101
Michael Macdonald's "first class" Gallic cuisine makes this "lovely little place" a "must" so far as most reporters are concerned – an "intimate venue offering understated style and comfort"; just occasionally the service hits the wrong note, but generally it's "pleasant", "efficient" and "unobtrusive".
/ **Details:** www.thevanillapod.co.uk; 10 pm; closed Mon & Sun.

MASHAM, NORTH YORKSHIRE 8–4B

Black Sheep Brewery Bistro £ 35 ❸❷❸
Wellgarth HG4 4EN (01765) 680101
"Competent, simple food in pleasant surroundings, (sometimes complete with the smell of brewing)" – that's the deal at this large café within the brewery, which is "an always enjoyable place to meet up"; lovely beer too. / **Details:** www.blacksheep.co.uk; 9 pm; Sun-Wed L only, Thu-Sat L & D; no Amex.

Samuel's
Swinton Park Hotel & Spa £ 68 ❷❷❷
HG4 4JH (01765) 680900
This castellated country house is, on most accounts, a "wonderful experience", hailed for its "fabulous" interior and for Simon Crannage's "superb" cuisine; there are critics, though, who find it "quite pretentious". / **Details:** www.swintonpark.com; 9.30 pm, Fri & Sat 10 pm; no jeans or trainers; booking: max 8; children: 8+ at D. **Accommodation:** 30 rooms, from £175.

The Grill On The Hill (formerly Cassis)
Stanley House Hotel £ 43 🅣
Off Preston New Rd BB2 7NP (01254) 769200
*Reports are few, but they again recommend this smart country
house hotel for its "sumptuous" and "romantic" surroundings and its
"artistic" cuisine. / Details: www.stanleyhouse.co.uk; 9.30 pm, Fri & Sat
9.45 pm; closed Mon, Tue, Sat L & Sun D; no trainers. Accommodation: 12
rooms, from £185.*

The Running Horses £ 49 🅣
Old London Rd RH5 6DU (01372) 372279
*This 16th-century freehouse is tipped as a "a faultless pub dining
room" offering "first-rate" service, dependable traditional fare and
good beers and wines. / Details: www.therunninghorses.co.uk; off A24 near
Dorking or Leatherhead; 9.30 pm, Sun 9 pm. Accommodation: 5 rooms,
from £110.*

Brasserie Blanc £ 43 ❷❷❷
Chelsea Hs, 301 Avebury Boulevard MK9 2GA
(01908) 546590
*The "utterly reliable" charms of this outlet of the Raymond Blanc
bistro chain make it a very popular destination locally; "great for
children" too. / Details: www.brasserieblanc.com; 9.45, Sun 9 pm.*

Jaipur £ 39 ❷❸❸
599 Grafton Gate East MK9 1AT (01908) 669796
*This massive Indian palace near the railway station brings a hint of
Vegas to MK; it's not just its scale which makes it stand out, either –
"the food is well above-average". / Details: www.jaipur.co.uk; near the
train station roundabout; they are the big white building; 11.30 pm, Sun
10.30 pm; no shorts.*

The Mistley Thorn Hotel £ 39 ❸❹④
High St CO11 1HE (01206) 392 821
*"A gastropub/hotel" consistently praised for cooking of "metropolitan
standards" (although, "as far as possible it's locally sourced"); some
find its riverside location "romantic" too.
/ Details: www.mistleythorn.com; 9.30 pm; no Amex. Accommodation: 8
rooms, from £80.*

Glasfryn £ 38 🅣
Raikes Ln CH7 6LR (01352) 750500
*A classic member of the Brunning & Price gastropub chain – a
"busy" place with a "good range of food and beers", and tipped as
"ideal pre-Theatr Clwyd". / Details: www.glasfryn-mold.co.uk; 9.30 pm,
Sun 9 pm.*

The Swan Inn £ 35 🅣
The St IP7 7AU (01449) 741391
Limited reports suggest that the interior of this rural gastropub does it no favours; the food, however, is tipped as being "of a very high standard". / **Details:** www.monkseleigh.com; 9 pm; closed Mon & Sun D; no Amex.

Midland Hotel £ 46 🅣
Marine Road central LA4 4BU (08458) 501240
"The food's fine", but it's "the view" that makes this "stylish" Art Deco hotel dining room particularly worth seeking out. / **Details:** www.elh.co.uk; 9.30 pm, Fri & Sat 10 pm; booking essential.
Accommodation: 44 rooms, from £94.

Horse & Groom £ 40 ❸❸❸
Upper Oddington GL56 0XH (01451) 830584
A "stripped-down" Cotswolds gastropub, with "friendly" staff and a fine selection of real ales; it serves a "consistently good" menu, which mixes pub classics with fancier fare, all at "reasonable prices". / **Details:** www.horseandgroom.uk.com; right in the centre of the village; 9.00 pm; no Amex. **Accommodation:** 7 rooms, from £89.

Morston Hall £ 80 ❷④❷
Main Coast Rd NR25 7AA (01263) 741041
"Norfolk's finest!"; Galton Blackiston's acclaimed country house hotel "on the windswept coast" put in a more consistent showing this year, and his "faultless" cuisine may now be ranked "with the best in London"; some meals, though, are still diminished by "slack" or "pompous" service. / **Details:** www.morstonhall.com; between Blakeney & Wells on A149; 8 pm; D only, ex Sun open L & D. **Accommodation:** 13 rooms, from £145 pp.

The Beetle & Wedge Boathouse £ 47 ④④❷
Ferry Ln OX10 9JF (01491) 651381
It's the "stunning location by the river" – on one of the Thames's most picturesque stretches – which makes this former boathouse worth seeking out; the food is "mostly good", but it's "nothing exceptional". / **Details:** www.beetleandwedge.co.uk; on A329 between Streatley & Wallingford, take Ferry Lane at crossroads; 9.45 pm.
Accommodation: 3 rooms, from £90.

Black Bull £ 51 ❷❸❸
DL10 6QJ (01325) 377289
"A hidden treasure just a stone's throw from the A1"; this popular pub not only has "lots of character", but also its very own Pullman railway carriage, which makes a "romantic" venue for a meal; the "honest" cooking is "better than standard" too, with the fish dishes "particularly good". / **Details:** www.blackbullmoulton.com; 1m S of Scotch Corner; 9.30 pm, Fri & Sat 10 pm; closed Sun D.

Cornish Range   £ 44   ❷❸❸
6 Chapel St TR19 6SB   (01736) 731488
*"Good fresh fish" is a highlight of the "well-presented" cuisine at this
pleasant restaurant-with-rooms in a backstreet near the harbour
(complete with courtyard garden); take the kids early on and you can
enjoy a "fantastic-value early-bird dinner menu".*
/ **Details:** www.cornishrange.co.uk; on coast road between Penzance & Lands
End; 9.30 pm, 9 pm in Winter; no Amex. **Accommodation:** 3 rooms,
from £80.

2 Fore Street Restaurant   £ 43   ❷❸❸
2 Fore St TR19 6PF   (01736) 731164
*"Super fresh seafood cooked with creativity", with perhaps "a touch
more sophistication than you might expect", draws a good number
of reporters to this "cute" little bistro, near the harbour.*
/ **Details:** www.2forestreet.co.uk; 9.30 pm. **Accommodation:** 2 rooms,
from £250 pw.

The Nut Tree Inn   £ 46   ❷❷❷
Main St OX5 2RE   (01865) 331253
*"In the middle of nowhere, but well worth the journey", this "much
better-than-average pub-restaurant" – in an attractive thatched
building – continues to win very high acclaim for its "stunningly
good" traditional fare.* / **Details:** www.nuttreeinn.co.uk; 9 pm.

Barley Bree   £ 45   ❷❸❸
6 Willoughby St PH5 2AB   (01764) 681451
*"Lovely in every way", the "imaginative" and "consistently good"
dining room of this "rustic" hotel is all the more worth knowing
about in a "sparse" area.* / **Details:** www.barleybree.com; 9 pm Wed-Sat,
7.30pm Sun; closed Mon & Tue; no Amex. **Accommodation:** 6 rooms,
from £100.

Wild Garlic   £ 46   ❷❸❸
3 Cossack Sq GL6 0BD   (01453) 832615
*Matthew Birdshall's small restaurant-with-rooms offers "high-end
cooking" ("beautiful dishes, well prepared and presented"), which its
small fan club proclaims "the best in the area".*
/ **Details:** www.wild-garlic.co.uk.

The Foxhunter   £ 53   ❷❸❸
NP7 9DN   (01873) 881101
*"The trick is to make sure that Matt Tebbutt is in the kitchen", if you
visit his "quiet" pub, in a former stationmaster's house, consistently
praised for its "interesting and reliable cooking, using excellent local
ingredients".* / **Details:** www.thefoxhunter.com; 9.30 pm; closed Mon &
Sun D. **Accommodation:** 2 cottages rooms, from £145.

NANTGAREDIG, CARMARTHENSHIRE 4–4C

Y Polyn £ 43 ❷❷❷
SA32 7LH (01267) 290000
*"Great food, but don't forget your compass!" – this "shabby-chic"
gastropub, in "deepest West Wales", "never fails to deliver"; run by
a pair of husband-and-wife teams, it delivers "robust food of terrific
quality" in a "friendly, informal and efficient" manner.
/ Details: www.ypolyn.co.uk; 9 pm; closed Mon & Sun D.*

NETHER BURROW, CUMBRIA 7–4D

The Highwayman £ 41 ❸❸❸
LA6 2RJ (01524) 273338
*Most reporters find it "a real treat" to visit this extremely popular
outpost of the Ribble Valley Inns chain; even those who find the food
"lovely", though, can find it very "expensive", and the odd sceptic
leaves distinctly unimpressed. / Details: www.highwaymaninn.co.uk;
8.30 pm, Fri & Sat 9 pm, Sun 8 pm.*

NEW MILTON, HAMPSHIRE 2–4C

Chewton Glen £ 87 ❹❸❸
Christchurch Rd BH25 6QS (01425) 275341
*With its "stunning surroundings" and "very attentive" service, this
"wonderful" country house hotel is one of the most luxurious in the
country; fans (most reporters) extol its "delightful" cuisine, although
– as ever – there are sceptics to whom it seems "average, for the
money". / Details: www.chewtonglen.com; on A337 between New Milton &
Highcliffe; 10 pm; no jeans; children: 5+ at D. Accommodation: 58 rooms,
from £299.*

NEWARK, NOTTINGHAMSHIRE 5–3D

Café Bleu £ 45 ❹❹❷
14 Castle Gate NG24 1BG (01636) 610141
*This "fabulous" restaurant offers "good food in an attractive
location" (near the castle) and remains, for some reporters, a "long-
standing favourite"; it does have its critics, though, and even
supporters can complain of "quite high prices" for a menu that can
seem on the "static" side. / Details: www.cafebleu.co.uk; 9.30 pm; closed
Sun D; no Amex.*

NEWBURY, BERKSHIRE 2–2D

The Crab at Chieveley £ 58 ❷❸❹
Wantage Rd RG20 8UE (01635) 247550
*This popular thatched country restaurant receives high praise for its
"consistently good" fish-heavy cuisine, and it has "a lovely location"
(though the interior can seem "a bit business-like"); for "particular
value", seek out the lunch menu. / Details: www.crabatchieveley.com; M4
J13 to B4494 – 0.5 mile on right; 9 pm, Sat 9.30 pm. Accommodation: 13
rooms, from £80.*

Yew Tree Inn £ 56 ❷❸❷
Hollington Cross, Andover Rd RG20 9SE (01635) 253360
*"Heart-warming, traditional dishes" in "hearty" portions again win
plenty of praise for Marco Pierre White's "very rural-feeling" inn,
which benefits from a "lovely" location and "relaxed" style.
/ Details: www.yewtree.net; off the A343, near Highclere Castle; 9 pm;
booking essential. Accommodation: 7 rooms, from £120.*

Blackfriars Restaurant   £ 45   ⑤④❷
Friars St NE1 4XN   (0191) 261 5945
It's the "interesting and atmospheric" setting – "one of the oldest
dining rooms in England" – that makes this city-centre operation of
note; fans insist the "traditional" British is "well-prepared" too, but
there were also a couple of very 'down' reports this year.
/ **Details:** www.blackfriarsrestaurant.co.uk; 10 pm; closed Sun D.

Café 21   £ 55   ❷❷❷
Trinity Gdns NE1 2HH   (0191) 222 0755
"Laybourne's first, and Laybourne's best!" – this "stylish",
"welcoming" and "professional" joint, just off the Quayside, is "still
the Newcastle benchmark" and "still the best place in town for a
foodie night out". / **Details:** www.cafetwentyone.co.uk; 10.30 pm, Sun
8 pm.

Café 21
Fenwick   £ 32   ④❸④
39 Northumberland St, First Floor NE1 7DE   (0191) 260 3373
This "very busy" ("be prepared to queue") in-store spin-off from the
famous Café 21 won nothing but praise this year for its "high-
quality" salads and snacks; it's most popular for its "great brunch"
(and "unlike the rest of Newcastle, it's even open on Sunday
mornings"). / **Details:** www.cafetwentyone.co.uk; 0; L only.

Café Royal   £ 39   ❷❸❸
8 Nelson St NE1 5AW   (0191) 231 3000
For "the best coffee and cakes in the North East" or "a long lazy
lunch" whilst out shopping, this grand café by Grainger Market has
been "on top form" of late; "the downside is that it's always busy".
/ **Details:** www.sjf.co.uk; 6 pm; L only, ex Thu open L & D; no booking, Sat.

Caffè Vivo   £ 37   ❸❸❸
29 Broad Chare NE1 3DQ   (0191) 232 1331
"Creeping" prices and a "noisy" and "unrelaxing" vibe risk
undercutting support for the popular Italian offshoot of Café 21, just
off the Quayside; for most reporters, though, it still makes a handy
stand-by. / **Details:** www.caffevivo.co.uk; 9.30 pm; closed Mon & Sun.

Francesca's   £ 33   ④❸❶
Manor House Rd NE2 2NE   (0191) 281 6586
"Fabulous value" helps "draw the hungry hordes" to this Jesmond
pizzeria; the food, though, is only OK – it's the "always-superb
waiters" who help create the brilliant "casual" atmosphere.
/ **Details:** 9.30 pm; closed Sun; no Amex; no booking.

Hotel du Vin et Bistro   £ 43   ❷❷❷
Allan Hs, City Rd NE1 2BE   (0191) 229 2200
"Looking down on the Quayside", this is "one of the best outposts"
of the wine-led brasserie/hotel chain – it offers some "very tasty and
well-presented dishes", complemented by a "superb" wine list and
"attentive" service too. / **Details:** www.hotelduvin.com; 10 pm, Sun
9.45 pm. **Accommodation:** 42 rooms, from £150.

Jesmond Dene House   £ 65   ❸❸❸
Jesmond Dene Rd NE2 2EY   (0191) 212 6066
Local hero Terry Laybourne's country house hotel in an Arts & Crafts
house, inspires a lot of praise for food that's "fabulous, imaginative
and served with flair"; its ratings are undercut, however, by the
number of reporters who also feel it's "hugely overpriced".
/ **Details:** www.jesmonddenehouse.co.uk; out of the city centre, towards
Jesmond, which is clearly signposted; 10 pm. **Accommodation:** 43 rooms,
from £144.

Pan Haggerty
£ 47 ❷❷❷
21 Queen St NE1 3UG (0191) 221 0904
This "very accommodating" bistro, in the former Café 21 premises, offers "locally-sourced" cuisine of "high quality" in "Northumberland-modern" style, and at "really reasonable prices" too.
/ Details: www.panhaggerty.com; 9.30 pm; closed Sun D.

Pani's
£ 31 ❸❷❷
61-65 High Bridge NE1 6BX (0191) 232 4366
"A long-standing local legend that's still doing the business!"; this "loud and jolly" Sardinian is arguably "the best cheap eat in town" – consequently there's "often a queue". / Details: www.paniscafe.co.uk; off Gray Street; 10 pm; closed Sun; no Amex; no booking at L.

Paradiso
£ 33 ❸❸❷
1 Market Ln NE1 6QQ (0191) 221 1240
"Tucked-away down a quiet back lane", this Mediterranean spot is a "friendly" sort of place, well worth seeking out for its "eclectic" (and perhaps slightly "variable") cuisine; "for the summer, there's a great deck" too. / Details: www.paradiso.co.uk; opp fire station; 10.30 pm, Fri & Sat 10.45 pm; closed Sun.

Rasa
£ 31 ❷❷❷
27 Queen St NE1 3UG (0191) 232 7799
"Like no Indian meal ever tasted!"; this outpost of the well-loved London chain offers many of the aspects – "delicious" flavours, "delicate" spicing and "gorgeous" aromas – that have made the original operation so noteworthy. / Details: www.rasarestaurants.com; 11 pm; closed Sun L.

Sachins
£ 39 ❼
Forth Banks NE1 3SG (0191) 261 9035
Not far from Central station, a "busy" Indian restaurant of long standing, tipped for its "always-high standards".
/ Details: www.sachins.co.uk; behind Central Station; 11.15 pm; closed Sun.

Six
Baltic Centre
£ 52 ❸❸❶
Gateshead Quays, South Shore Rd NE8 3BA (0191) 440 4948
"Tremendous views" (especially from the loos) reward visitors to the "slick" and "lovely" space atop the impressive Gateshead art complex; fans say the food's "fantastic" too, but ratings are held down by the sizeable minority who proclaim it something of a "let-down". / Details: www.sixbaltic.com; 9.30 pm, Fri & Sat 10 pm; closed Sun D; no Amex.

A Taste of Persia
£ 25 ❷❶❸
14 Marlborough Cr NE1 4EE (0191) 221 0088
"A real find", this "small family-run restaurant" offers some "excellent" and "authentic" Middle Eastern dishes and "very friendly" service – in short, "very good value for money".
/ Details: www.atasteofpersia.com; 10 pm; closed Sun.

Tyneside Coffee Rooms
Tyneside Cinema
£ 23 ❼
10 Pilgrim St NE1 6QG (0191) 227 5520
In an Art Deco cinema, a "time warp" restaurant tipped for those in search of "a unique experience of times past"; it's "always busy" thanks not least to its "wholesome" menu of "British comfort food".
/ Details: www.tynecine.org; 9 pm; no Amex.

Jesmond Dene House

Panis

Vujon £ 40 ❶❶❸

29 Queen St NE1 3UG (0191) 221 0601

"Still the best place for a posh Indian dinner"; this Quayside fixture continues to inspire impressively consistent commentary on its "outstanding food and service". / **Details:** www.vujon.com; 11.30 pm; closed Sun L.

NEWPORT, PEMBROKESHIRE 4–4B

Llys Meddyg £ 49 ❷❸❷

East St SA42 0SY (01239) 820008

"Excellent for a romantic meal or for a family lunch", this "elegant" restaurant-with-rooms pleases most reporters with its "very good" food; for critics, though, "inflated" prices can take the edge off the experience. / **Details:** www.llysmeddyg.com; 9 pm; D only, closed Mon & Sun; no Amex. **Accommodation:** 8 rooms, from £100.

NEWTON LONGVILLE, BUCKINGHAMSHIRE 3–2A

Crooked Billet £ 42 ❷❷❸

2 Westbrook End MK17 0DF (01908) 373936

"Incongruously sited on the edge of Milton Keynes", this "attractive" inn boasts a wine list that includes "no fewer than 200 choices by the glass"; on the food front, it "continues to deliver consistency and quality year after year". / **Details:** www.thebillet.co.uk; 9.30 pm, Fri & Sat 10 pm; D only, ex Sun open L only.

NEWTON ON OUSE, NORTH YORKSHIRE 8–4C

The Dawnay Arms £ 44 ❶

YO30 2BR (01347) 848345

This Georgian gastropub, with a large garden by the River Ouse, inspires only relatively limited feedback – ratings, though, are consistently high. / **Details:** www.thedawnayatnewton.co.uk.

NEWTON-ON-THE-MOOR, NORTHUMBERLAND 8–2B

Cook & Barker £ 39 ❶

NE65 9JY (01665) 575234

A top tip for A1 travellers – no foodie destination, but a popular boozer in a "lovely country setting" which makes an effort to keep the kids happy; the food is generally good, but it "can vary". / **Details:** www.cookandbarkerinn.co.uk; 12m N of Morpeth, just off A1; 9 pm. **Accommodation:** 19 rooms, from £80.

NOMANSLAND, WILTSHIRE 2–3C

Les Mirabelles £ 43 ❶❷❷

Forest Edge Rd SP5 2BN (01794) 390205

"A lovely place on the edge of the New Forest" – this "wonderful all-rounder" continues to offer "high-class cooking and incredible value", all provided by a largely French team who manage to be "friendly without being over-friendly". / **Details:** www.lesmirabelles.co.uk; off A36 between Southampton & Salisbury; 9.30 pm; closed Mon & Sun.

NORDEN, LANCASHIRE 5–1B

Nutter's £ 51 ❷❷❷

Edenfield Rd OL12 7TT (01706) 650167

"One of the best venues in the North West", the Nutter family's "classy conversion of an old manor" overlooking the moors is a "relaxed" sort of place whose all-round standards – including "excellent" food and a "fantastic wine list" – are a "wow!" / **Details:** www.nuttersrestaurant.com; between Edenfield & Norden on A680; 9 pm; closed Mon.

Betty's £ 41 ❷❷❷
189a High St DL7 8LF (01609) 775154
For an "unparalleled tea shop experience" – a famous "Northern institution" that's "not cheap, but very good".
/ **Details:** www.bettys.co.uk; 5.30 pm; no Amex.

McCoys at the Tontine £ 60 ❷❷❶
DL6 3JB (01609) 882 671
"A great place for a night out with friends", this "crazily-furnished" country house hotel has "a lovely air of faded glory, especially in the conservatory"; moreover, its kitchen has delivered some very good meals of late, and there's an "amazing" wine list.
/ **Details:** www.mccoystontine.co.uk; junction of A19 & A172; 9 pm, Fri & Sat 9.45 pm, Sun 8.30 pm; bistro L & D every day, restaurant Sat D only.
Accommodation: 7 rooms, from £130.

NORTHAW, HERTFORDSHIRE 3–2B

The Sun at Northaw £ 52 ❷❸❷
1 Judges Hill EN6 4NL (01707) 655507
"Locally-sourced" ingredients take centre stage in some "exciting" dishes on offer at this "really good gastropub" – a "family-friendly" sort of place where "enthusiastic staff add to the atmosphere".
/ **Details:** www.thesunatnorthaw.co.uk; 10 pm, Sun 4 pm; closed Mon & Sun D; no Amex.

NORTHLEACH, GLOUCESTERSHIRE 2–1C

Wheatsheaf Inn £ 41 ❓
GL54 3EZ (01451) 860244
"Good food and friendly service in this very attractive small Cotswolds town" – this "great gastropub" is tipped by a number of reporters for its all-round charms. / **Accommodation:** 9 rooms, from £.

NORTON, WILTSHIRE 2–2B

The Vine Tree £ 41 ❸❸❷
Foxley Rd SN16 0JP (01666) 837654
"The epitome of an excellent village gastropub", albeit one "in the middle of nowhere" – a "very friendly" place serving "better-than average" fare. / **Details:** www.thevinetree.co.uk; 9.30 pm, Fri & Sat 9.45 pm.

NORWICH, NORFOLK 6–4C

Waffle House £ 28 ❓
39 St Giles St NR2 1JN (01603) 612790
"THE Norwich culinary institution", tipped for its "tasty and interesting food to suit all tastes"; breakfast is "a bargain" – at other times "you'd never know there were so many possible recipes till you read the specials board!" / **Details:** www.wafflehouse.co.uk; 10 pm; no Amex; need 6+ to book.

NOSS MAYO, DEVON 1–4C

The Ship Inn £ 41 ❸❸❷
PL8 1EW (01752) 872387
In "one of Devon's most picturesque villages", "a very buzzy pub, with a great river outlook, much loved by the local sailing community"; with its "seasonal" and "reliable" fare, it makes "quite a beacon in what's otherwise a thin area".
/ **Details:** www.nossmayo.com; 9.30 pm, Sun 9 pm.

Anoki   £ 45   ❷❸❷
Barker Gate NG1 1JU   (01159) 483888
"Authentic", "quiet" and "intimate" – this "beautifully designed"
Indian, opposite the National Ice Centre, offers a "wonderful setting"
in which to enjoy some "truly delicious" dishes.
/ **Details:** www.anoki.co.uk.

Atlas   £ 22   ❷❸❸
9 Pelham St NG1 2EH   (0115) 950 1295
"Supercharged sandwiches" make this the perfect pit stop – a
"hidden gem" of a café near the Council House, which does "great
*coffee" too. / **Details:** www.atlasdeli.co.uk; 4 pm, Sat 5 pm; L only.*

Chino Latino
Park Plaza Hotel   £ 59   ❷❸④
41 Maid Marian Way NG1 6GD   (0115) 947 7444
"Consistent quality for over half a decade" makes this Asian-fusion
hang-out rather an unusual venue to find off the foyer of an
ordinary-looking city-centre hotel; prices are "steep", though,
especially as the clubby decor "may have seen better days".
/ **Details:** www.chinolatino.co.uk; 10.30 pm; closed Sun.

Crème   £ 32   ❸❸❸
12 Toton Ln NG9 7HA   (0115) 939 7422
A "very popular" restaurant in the suburb of Stapleford offering
some "delicious traditional cooking"; even a reporter who finds the
food rather hit-and-miss says: "in an area badly in need of a decent
restaurant, this is a place worth supporting".
/ **Details:** www.cremerestaurant.co.uk; 9.30 pm; closed Mon, Sat L & Sun D;
children: 10+.

Delilahs   £ 25   ⓣ
15 Middle Pavement NG1 7DX   (0115) 948 4461
A "fantastic little deli/café" which generates an extraordinary
amount of feedback considering it has only seven seats (at a
counter); it's tipped for its "fresh and generous" bites.
/ **Details:** www.delilahfinefoods.co.uk; 7 pm, Sun 5 pm; no Amex.

French Living   £ 36   ❸❷❶
27 King St NG1 2AY   (0115) 958 5885
"French country cooking as you remember it" draws many fans to
this "unshakably Gallic (well, Corsican)" and recently expanded city-
centre restaurant, often praised for its "authenticity".
/ **Details:** www.frenchliving.co.uk; near Market Square; 10 pm; closed Sun;
no Amex.

Hart's   £ 49   ❸❷❸
Standard Ct, Park Row NG1 6GN   (0115) 988 1900
"Complete confidence you will have a good experience" has long
been a hallmark of Tim Hart's "upmarket but not OTT" brasserie
near the castle – the city-centre's best-known place; it's drawing
increasing complaints, though, about "bland" food and "inattentive"
*service. / **Details:** www.hartsnottingham.co.uk; near Castle; 10 pm, Sun*
9 pm. **Accommodation:** 32 rooms, from £120.

Iberico   £ 33   ❷❸❷
The Shire Hall, High Pavement NG1 1HN   (01159) 410410
It's not just the "intimate cellar environment" which makes this
"lively" Lace Market bar worth seeking out – the "authentic" tapas
are "beltingly good" (as is the "authentic prix-fixe lunch").
/ **Details:** www.ibericotapas.com; 10 pm, Fri & Sat 10.30 pm; closed Sun;
no Amex; children: 16+ D.

Kayal
£ 29 ❷❷❸

8 Broad St NG1 3AL (0115) 941 4733

*"Perfectly authentic Southern Indian cuisine" and notably "friendly" and "personal" service come together to make this restaurant, near the Victoria Centre, well worth seeking out; it's "good value" too! / **Details:** www.kayalrestaurant.com; 11 pm, Sun 10 pm.*

The Library Bar Kitchen
£ 29 ❸④❸

Beeston NG9 2NG (0115) 922 2268

*As "a good place for an inexpensive lunch" this Beeston tapas operation has its fans, and – although the odd "bland" choice is noted – most of its "hotch potch" of (not-very-Spanish) dishes are "very tasty". / **Details:** www.thelibrarybarkitchen.co.uk; 9.30 pm; closed Sun.*

MemSaab
£ 38 ❷❷❷

12-14 Maid Marian Way NG1 6HS (0115) 957 0009

*"Fine dining, Indian-style", with "imaginative" cuisine (inspired by London chef Atul Kochar) and supremely "welcoming and friendly" service have made this city-centre fixture one of the city's most "popular" destinations; it's a "big" and "busy" place, though – "often you can't hear your neighbour speak". / **Details:** www.mem-saab.co.uk; near Castle, opposite Park Plaza Hotel; 10.30 pm, Fri & Sat 11 pm, Sun 10 pm; D only; no shorts.*

Petit Paris
£ 32 ④❸❸

2 Kings Walk NG1 2AE (0115) 947 3767

*"Vive la France!", say fans of this "basic" city-centre spot, which is of particular note for its "excellent pre-theatre menu"; it can get "very, very busy". / **Details:** www.petitparisrestaurant.co.uk; near Theatre Royal; 10.15 pm; closed Sun.*

Restaurant Sat Bains
£107 ❷❸④

Old Lenton Ln NG7 2SA (0115) 986 6566

*"Surrounded by pylons and busy roads", Sat Bain's city-fringe restaurant-with-rooms makes for a decidedly "unexpected" foodie Mecca; fortunately, his food is often "utter bliss" – service can be "haughty", though, and there are a few critics who complain of "London prices" for a meal that's "nothing to shout about". / **Details:** www.restaurantsatbains.com; 8.30 pm; closed Mon & Sun; children: 12+. **Accommodation:** 8 rooms, from £129.*

Tarn Thai
£ 36 ❕

9 George St NG1 1BU (0115) 959 9454

*An "exotic" and "peaceful" Thai restaurant off the Lace Market, tipped by locals for its "amazing" decor and its "bargain express lunch". / **Details:** www.tarnthai.co.uk; 10.30 pm, Fri & Sat 11 pm.*

Tonic
£ 43 ❸❷❸

6 Chapel Quarter, Chapel Bar NG1 6JS (0115) 941 4770

*"A great night out without breaking the bank"; this "trendy bar-restaurant" – "with music at weekends" – doesn't aim for culinary fireworks, but most reporters take to its "consistently pleasing" style. / **Details:** www.tonic-online.co.uk; 10 pm; closed Sun D.*

Victoria Hotel
£ 34 ❸❸❸

Dovecote Ln NG9 1JG (0115) 925 4049

*"An old-fashioned boozer" by Beeston station which offers an "interesting" menu including "a good range of meat and veggie dishes"; "great beers" and "an amazing selection of whiskies". / **Details:** www.victoriabeeston.co.uk; by Beeston railway station; 9.30 pm, Sun-Tue 8.45 pm; no Amex; children: 18+ after 8 pm.*

The Wollaton　　　　　　　　**£ 40**　　**T**
Lambourne Drive　NG8 1GR　(0115) 9288610
'Nottingham's Premier Gastropub' (well, that's what their website
says) has a small but enthusiastic fan base amongst reporters, who
hail its "reliably good" food and "family-friendly" style.
/ **Details:** www.thewollaton.co.uk.

World Service　　　　　　　**£ 53**　　**❸❷❷**
Newdigate Hs, Castlegate　NG1 6AF　(0115) 847 5587
For fans, this "professional" city-centre spot – entered through a
"lovely garden for pre-prandials" – is "still the best restaurant in
Nottingham", with "slick" service and "outstanding" cuisine; for a
minority, though, it's "gone off the boil" and is "always expensive" for
food that "sounds more exciting than it tastes".
/ **Details:** www.worldservicerestaurant.com; 10 pm; closed Sun D; children:
12+ at D.

OAKMERE, CHESHIRE　　　　　　　　5–2B

Nunsmere Hall　　　　　　　**£ 54**　　**T**
Tarporley Rd　CW8 2ES　(01606) 889100
We wish we had more reports on this "historic house, with a
beautiful setting in lovely grounds" – a number of tips as a
"romantic" or "top gastronomic experience" support its reputation
as a major North Western destination.
/ **Details:** www.primahotels.co.uk/nunsmere; off A49, 4m SW of Northwich;
10 pm; no jeans or trainers. **Accommodation:** 36 rooms, from £135.

OARE, KENT　　　　　　　　3–3C

The Three Mariners　　　　　**£ 37**　　**❷❸④**
2 Church Rd　ME13 0QA　(01795) 533633
"A cheap and cheerful pub" serving "good and honest grub" that's
"worth a trip"; the interior's unremarkable, but the place has an
"interesting village location" near the water.
/ **Details:** www.thethreemarinersoare.co.uk; 8.30 pm, Fri & Sat 9 pm;
no Amex.

OBAN, ARGYLL AND BUTE　　　　　　　　9–3B

Ee-Usk (Seafood Restaurant)　　**£ 46**　　**❷❸❷**
North Pier　PA35 5QD　(01631) 565666
"A good range of simple fish dishes" in a "stunning pier head
location" and with "fantastic views" too – that's the formula that
wins a resounding cheer for this "buzzy" waterside joint.
/ **Details:** www.eeusk.com; 9 pm; no Amex; children: 12+ at L, not welcome at
D.

OCKLEY, SURREY　　　　　　　　3–4A

Bryce's at the Old School House　　**£ 49**　　**❷❷❸**
Stane St　RH5 5TH　(01306) 627430
Bill & Elizabeth Bryce's "extraordinarily good food pub specialising in
fish" is just entering its 20th year; it inspires a huge number of
reports, applauding it as "a very well managed operation" with
"standards that are very reliable and very high".
/ **Details:** www.bryces.co.uk; 8m S of Dorking on A29; 9 pm; no Amex.

The Neptune £ 65 ❷❷❷
85 Old Hunstanton Rd PE36 6HZ (01485) 532122
"A fine dining restaurant in an unlikely setting"; Kevin & Jacki
Mangeolles's small restaurant-with-rooms impresses all reporters
with its "seasonal and innovative" cooking, as well as its "very
friendly and personal service". / **Details:** www.theneptune.co.uk; 9 pm;
closed Mon, Tue-Sat D only, Sun open L & D; children: 10.
Accommodation: 6 rooms, from £110.

Black Swan £ 57 ❶❸❸
YO61 4BL (01347) 868 387
"In a beautiful location near Byland Abbey", this "hidden delight" of
a pub comes highly recommended, thanks not least to Adam
Jackson's cuisine – "excellent both in the quality of its ingredients
and its execution". / **Details:** www.blackswanoldstead.co.uk; 9 pm;
no Amex.

Smith's Brasserie £ 57 ❷❷❷
Fyfield Rd CM5 0AL (01277) 365578
"Where the Essex in-crowd goes!" – this "slick" operation offers
some "excellent fresh fish", and the service is usually "efficient" too;
there are critics too, though – they don't dispute that it's a "good
place", but just find it "overpriced and over-hyped".
/ **Details:** www.smithsbrasserie.com; left off A414 towards Fyfield; 10 pm,
Fri & Sat 10.30 pm; closed Mon L; no Amex; children: 12+.

Loch Leven Seafood Café £ 46 ❶
PH33 6SR (01855) 821048
No doubting the "beautiful view" at this simple waterside café; fans
applaud its "beautiful food at a very reasonable price", but we've
made it a tip only due to a gripe that it's "sitting on recent laurels".
/ **Details:** www.lochlevenseafoodcafe.co.uk; no Amex.

Butley Orford Oysterage £ 37 ❷❷④
Market Hill IP12 2LH (01394) 450277
"Never changing over the decades" (nearly five of 'em!), this "basic"
dining room serves "some of the freshest seafood you will ever find";
"it may feel like a school dining room, but the food makes up for it".
/ **Details:** www.butleyorfordoysterage.co.uk; on the B1078, off the A12 from
Ipswich; 9 pm; no Amex.

The Crown & Castle £ 45 ④❸④
IP12 2LJ (01394) 450205
Very mixed views on the 'Hotel Inspector's' very own property; most
reports do praise the "great value" offered by the menu of this
"really lovely" inn, but critics – citing "mean" portions and "ordinary"
standards – say it's "a shadow of its one-time self".
/ **Details:** www.crownandcastle.co.uk; on main road to Orford; 9.15 pm; closed
Sun D in winter; no Amex; booking: max 8; children: 8+ at D.
Accommodation: 19 rooms, from £125.

Jolly Sailor £ 37 🪪

Quay St IP12 2NU (01394) 450243

"An atmospheric old seaport pub in a characterful village", with "a pleasant but cramped interior" and "a large terrace at the back that's good for kids"; the food (stone-baked pizza and so on) isn't art, but it's "dependable and reasonably priced".
/ **Details:** www.thejollysailor.net; 9.45 pm; no Amex.

ORMSKIRK, LANCASHIRE 5–2A

Marco Pierre White's The Swan Inn £ 45 ❸❷❸

Springfield Rd, Aughton L39 6ST (01695) 421450

"Genuinely warm" service is a particular highlight of this celebrity-branded inn (which advertises its aim as 'affordable glamour'); it also achieves consistent ratings for its "well-executed and professional" cooking (which includes a set lunch which is "very good value").
/ **Details:** www.mpwtheswan.co.uk.

ORPINGTON, KENT 3–3B

Xian £ 31 ❷❶❸

324 High St BR6 0NG (01689) 871881

"A gem in the gloom of a fading high street" that's "still turning out top-notch Chinese food at sensible prices" and still impressing all who comment on it; "tables are shoe-horned in, but curiously it doesn't seem to matter". / **Details:** near the war memorial; 11 pm; closed Mon & Sun L.

OSWESTRY, SHROPSHIRE 5–3A

The Walls £ 36 🪪

Welsh Walls SY11 1AW (01691) 670970

In a notably thin area, an impressive former school building where reporters (few) tip "great food and service every time".
/ **Details:** www.the-walls.co.uk; from town centre, take Cross Street, fork right then first left; 9.30 pm; closed Sun D.

OVINGTON, HAMPSHIRE 2–3D

The Bush Inn £ 45 ❷❷❷

SO24 0RE (01962) 732764

"Excellent in all categories" – this notably attractive inn produces "consistently good" results (from a menu which offers "a good choice of light and hearty bites"). / **Details:** www.thebushinn.co.uk; just off A31 between Winchester & Alresford; 9 pm, Sun 8.30 pm.

OXFORD, OXFORDSHIRE 2–2D

Al-Shami £ 28 ❸❹❹

25 Walton Cr OX1 2JG (01865) 310066

"Is it an insult to call this brilliant restaurant cheap 'n' cheerful?"; with its "authentic" and "great-value" mezze, the city's oldest ("and still best") Lebanese venture, in Jericho, "never lets you down", and "Château Musar at affordable prices clinches it as a top place!"
/ **Details:** www.al-shami.co.uk; 11.30 pm. **Accommodation:** 12 rooms, from £50.

Anchor £ 43 🪪

2 Hayfield Rd OX2 6TT (01865) 510282

Tipped for its "consistent" gastropub cuisine, twinned with a "changing choice of real ales", this "good, reliable local" is a haunt – apparently – of "quiet academics and their families".
/ **Details:** www.theanchoroxford.com; 9 pm; no Amex.

Ashmolean Dining Room   £ 43   ④④❷
Beaumont St OX1 2PH (01865) 553 823
With its "fantastic location overlooking the rooftops of Oxford", the
airy top-floor dining room of this famous museum still sometimes
seems a "welcome addition to the city's appalling dining scene"; its
ratings slipped even further this year, though, and critics now find it
"mediocre in every way". / **Details:** www.ashmoleandiningroom.com;
10 pm, Sun 6pm; closed Mon; no Maestro.

Atomic Burger   £ 27   ❷❷❸
96 Cowley Rd OX4 1JE (01865) 790 855
This "super-funky" diner pleases all reporters, not least with its
"generous" and "freshly-cooked" burgers; "the queues are proof that
this is one of the few decent joints in Oxford!"
/ **Details:** www.atomicburger.co.uk.

Aziz   £ 34   ⓣ
228-230 Cowley Rd OX4 1UH (01865) 794945
OK, it never sets the world on fire, but this East Oxford Indian of
long standing rarely disappoints, and fans tip it for its "first-rate"
food and service. / **Details:** www.aziz.uk.com; 11.30 pm, Sat midnight;
closed Fri L.

Bombay   £ 23   ❷❷❸
82 Walton St OX2 6EA (01865) 511188
"The best Indian restaurant in Oxford, and it's BYO too which makes
it even more attractive!" – this "reasonably-priced" Jericho institution
remains a top choice for (almost) all who comment on it.
/ **Details:** 11 pm; closed Fri L; no Amex.

Branca   £ 39   ④❷❸
111 Walton St OX2 6AJ (01865) 556111
"Good-value lunch deals" provide the particular reason to seek out a
Jericho Italian that remains popular, even if the food is "nothing out
of the ordinary"; evenings can be "very noisy".
/ **Details:** www.branca-restaurants.com; 11 pm.

Brasserie Blanc   £ 43   ❸❷❸
71-72 Walton St OX2 6AG (01865) 510999
This "reliable mid-range brasserie" is the original of the fast-
expanding chain; it has become an "all-round solid performer"
offering "good quality at a fair price"… in which respect the group
is, sadly, still quite unusual! / **Details:** www.brasserieblanc.com; 10 pm,
Sat 10.30 pm, Sun 9.30 pm.

Browns   £ 39   ④④❸
5-11 Woodstock Rd OX2 6HA (01865) 511995
Critics say it offers "nothing special apart from its history", but this
once-famous and still "great-looking" British-brasserie institution put
in a stronger showing this year, even if the food is still "fairly
mediocre". / **Details:** www.browns-restaurants.com; 11 pm, Fri & Sat
11.30 pm, Sun 10.30 pm.

Cherwell Boathouse   £ 44   ④❸❷
Bardwell Rd OX2 6ST (01865) 552746
"Overlooking people messing about in punts", this charming
veteran's riverside setting makes it "an unbeatable venue on a sunny
evening", and the wine is "fantastic" too; the food? – "a great deal
better than it used to be". / **Details:** www.cherwellboathouse.co.uk; 9 pm,
Fri & Sat 9.30 pm.

Chiang Mai
£ 37   ❷❸❷

Kemp Hall Pas, 130a High St OX1 4DH   (01865) 202233
"Still one of Oxford's top restaurants", this *"buzzy"* Thai – located,
somewhat bizarrely in a Tudor building just off the High Street –
continues to enchant its many fans with its *"imaginative"* and
"subtly-spiced" cuisine; overall, however, reports are a little less
gushing than they once were. / **Details:** www.chiangmaikitchen.co.uk;
10.30 pm.

La Cucina
£ 34   🅣

39-40 St Clements OX4 1AB   (01865) 793811
A *"buzzy"* St Clement's Italian that's *"always full"*; it's tipped for food
that's *"uniformly good"* and *"good value"* too, and for its *"helpful
and knowledgeable"* staff. / **Details:** www.lacucinaoxford.co.uk; 10.30 pm.

The Fishes
£ 42   ❸④❷

North Hinksey OX2 0NA   (01865) 249796
"Beautifully-located" by a stream, and with a large garden (picnics
available), this *"lovely"*, if often *"busy"* boozer has a strong following
among reporters, even though the quality of its cuisine *"varies
widely"*. / **Details:** www.fishesoxford.co.uk; just off the A34; 9.45 pm;
no Amex.

Gee's
£ 55   ④❷❶

61 Banbury Rd OX2 6PE   (01865) 553540
The food tends to be *"unspectacular"*, but it's the *"magical"* setting
of this Victorian conservatory that's long made it the city's
"romantic" rendezvous par excellence; and you don't have to be
starry-eyed to find the venue *"useful for lunch"* too.
/ **Details:** www.gees-restaurant.co.uk; 10 pm, Fri & Sat 10.30 pm.

Jamie's Italian
£ 41   ④❸④

24-26 George St OX1 2AE   (01865) 838383
Admittedly it still attracts more reviews than anywhere else in town,
but the ever-present queues at this city-centre Italian seem to have
"more to do with Jamie's name than the food" – the latter strikes
rather too many reporters as *"boring"* and *"unimaginative"*.
/ **Details:** www.jamieoliver.com; 11 pm, Sun 10.30 pm; Booking 6+.

The Magdalen Arms
£ 40   ❷④❸

243 Iffley Rd OX4 1SJ   (01865) 243 159
"Another winner from the Anchor & Hope stable", say fans of this
"buzzy" gastropub which inspires many reports of *"fabulous"*
cooking; they're *"finding it hard to cope with the popularity"*, though,
and a rather worrying number of critics found standards *"poor all
round"*. / **Details:** www.magdalenarms.com; 10 pm; closed Mon, Tue L &
Sun D; no Amex.

Malmaison
£ 50   ❸❷❷

3 Oxford Circle OX1 1AY   (01865) 268400
Contrary to what you might fear, the location in the former gaol
proves to be a *"great gimmick"* for this *"high-class"* hotel restaurant;
surprisingly, the food is *"reliably good"* too.
/ **Details:** www.malmaison.com; situated down long driveway after "The Living
Room" restaurant; 10 pm; 6+ need to book. **Accommodation:** 95 rooms,
from £160.

My Sichuan
£ 30   ❷❸❸

The Old School, Gloucester Grn OX1 2DA   (01865) 236 899
"An all-round taste sensation!" – the *"interesting"* setting in an old
school house gives no hint of the *"large and authentically
flavoursome"* Sichuan menu on offer at this *"well located"* city-centre
spot. / **Details:** www.mysichuan.co.uk.

Gees

Cherwell Boathouse

CHIANG MAI

Chiang Mai

The Nosebag £ 28 ⓣ
6-8 St Michael's St OX1 2DU (01865) 721033
"A find!"; there aren't many of those in the centre of Oxford, so this
"healthy pit stop" where much of the menu is vegetarian, is all the
more worth knowing about; "imaginative" salads a highlight.
/ **Details:** www.nosebagoxford.co.uk; 9.30 pm, Fri & Sat 10 pm, Sun 8.30 pm.

The Old Parsonage £ 59 ⓣ
1 Banbury Rd OX2 6NN (01865) 292305
This "beautifully restored former parsonage", just north of the city-
centre, is tipped as a "pretty" destination for meeting-the-parents –
"always safe", "moderately expensive", with "interesting wines" and
"traditional" fare; "super breakfasts" too.
/ **Details:** www.oldparsonage-hotel.co.uk; 0.5m N of city centre; 10.30 pm.
Accommodation: 30 rooms, from £200.

Pierre Victoire £ 43 ❸❷❸
Little Clarendon St OX1 2HP (01865) 316616
"Consistently churning out homely but well-presented French food at
very reasonable prices", this remnant of a once-national chain of
bistros has quite a fan club; the pre-theatre menu offers "particular
value". / **Details:** www.pierrevictoire.co.uk; 11 pm, 10 pm Sun; no Amex.

Quod
Old Bank Hotel £ 45 ⑤④④
92-94 High St OX1 4BN (01865) 799599
"An attractive place, so it's a shame the food is inferior and the
service indifferent" – only in Oxford, it seems to us, could such a
large and mediocre Italian restaurant have so prominently thrived for
so many years. / **Details:** www.oldbank-hotel.co.uk; opp All Souls College;
11 pm, Sun 10.30 pm; no booking at D. **Accommodation:** 42 rooms,
from £175.

Randolph £ 60 ❸❸❸
Beaumont St OX1 2LN (01865) 256 400
The "old-fashioned" dining room of this prominent hotel has bucked
up its ideas in recent years – the cuisine may be "relatively simple",
but it's consistently "well cooked". / **Details:** www.macdonaldhotels.com;
opp Ashmolean Museum; 10 pm; Mon-Thu D only, Fri-Sun open L & D.
Accommodation: 151 rooms, from £140.

Shanghai 30s £ 36 ④❸❸
82 St Aldates OX1 1RA (01865) 242230
Near Christ Church, this "lovely oak-panelled dining room" – once
the celebrated 'Elizabeth' restaurant – has served a Chinese menu
for five years now; most reports are of "standards maintained" and
"delicious fare with a spicy kick", but there were also a couple of
"horror stories" this year. / **Details:** www.shanghai30s.com; 10.30 pm;
closed Mon L.

Sojo £ 39 ❷❷④
8-9 Hythe Bridge St OX1 2EW (01865) 202888
"Something special" – especially for Oxford! – this "efficient"
Chinese venture has quite a fan club for its "fragrant and spicy"
Sichuan cuisine, not least "absolutely outstanding dim sum"; service
is "surprisingly warm" too! / **Details:** www.sojo-oxford.co.uk; 10.30 pm,
Sun 9.30 pm.

OXTED, SURREY 3–3B

The Gurkha Kitchen £ 32 ❷❷❸
111 Station Road East RH8 0AX (01883) 722621
"Brilliant food every time" ensures this "brilliant" subcontinental –
"consistent over many years" – again impresses all who comment on
it. / **Details:** www.moolirestaurant.co.uk; 11 pm, Sun 10 pm; no Amex.

Fraiche
£ 62 ❶❷❸

11 Rose Mount CH43 5SG   (0151) 652 2914
Mark Wilkinson's "innovative" and "immaculately presented"
modern cuisine continues to win congratulatory reviews for this very
personal operation, on the fringes of Birkenhead.
/ **Details:** www.restaurantfraiche.com; 8.30 pm, Sun 7 pm; closed Mon, Tue,
Wed L, Thu L & Sun L; no Amex.

Margot's
£ 43 ❷❷❶

11 Duke St PL28 8AB   (01841) 533441
"A fantastic rival to Rick Stein!" – Adrian Oliver's "cosy little back
street bistro" is a "friendly", "no-fuss" sort of place, where the "well
cooked seasonal and local produce" pleases all who comment on it.
/ **Details:** www.margots.co.uk; 9 pm; D only, closed Mon & Sun.

Paul Ainsworth at Number 6
£ 53 ❶❶❷

6 Middle St PL28 8AP   (01841) 532093
"Paul Ainsworth is going from strength to strength" at this "pretty"
townhouse-restaurant, whose "stunning" ratings rival those of its
more famous neighbour – "the freshest local produce cooked with
immense care" is served by "exceptional" staff.
/ **Details:** www.number6inpadstow.co.uk; 10 pm; closed Mon & Sun; no Amex.

Rick Stein's Café
£ 42 ❷❷❸

10 Middle St PL28 8AP   (01841) 532700
"You can experience Rick Stein, without the hefty bill of the main
restaurant" at this "bustling" all-day bistro, whose "high-quality" fish
and "fun" style mostly wins a thumbs-up, despite gripes about
"London prices". / **Details:** www.rickstein.com; 9.30 pm; no Amex; Only for
D. **Accommodation:** 3 rooms, from £97.

St Petroc's Hotel & Bistro
£ 54 ❷❸❸

4 New St PL28 8EA   (01841) 532700
The Stein empire has "taken the bistro title to heart with simple yet
tasty dishes", at this "fun" boutique hotel dining room; it pleases
reporters, even if it is rather "Spartan" and "packed".
/ **Details:** www.rickstein.com; 10 pm; no Amex. **Accommodation:** 10 rooms,
from £145.

Seafood Restaurant
£ 76 ❶❷❷

Riverside PL28 8BY   (01841) 532700
Currently on cracking form, Rick Stein's famous quayside fixture (in
fact, largely run by ex-wife, Jill) receives numerous bouquets for its
"unfussy and excellent" fish and "fruits-de-mer par excellence" –
"seriously expensive", yes, but most reporters seem to think it's
worth it. / **Details:** www.rickstein.com; opp harbourmaster's car park; 10 pm;
; no Amex; booking: max 14; children: 3+. **Accommodation:** 16 rooms,
from £145.

Stein's Fish & Chips
£ 37 ❷④④

South Quay PL28 8BL   (01841) 532700
"Precisely cooked fish, crunchy batter and dripping-cooked chips" –
all at "good-value" prices – win acclaim for "the cheapest option in
Rick's empire"; "ambience? – we sit on the quayside, and it's always
a joy". / **Details:** www.rickstein.com; 10 pm; no Amex.

PARKGATE, CHESHIRE

5–2A

Marsh Cat £ 39 🅣
1 Mostyn Sq CH64 6SL (0151) 336 1963
Tipped for its "pleasant views over the Dee estuary", this
"consistently good" local continues to please all who comment on it.
/ **Details:** www.marshcat.com; 10 pm, Tue-Sun 9 pm.

PEEBLES, SCOTTISH BORDERS

9–4C

Horseshoe Inn £ 50 ❷❷❸
EH45 8QP (01721) 730225
This rather grand restaurant (cum bistro) with-rooms attracts praise
from almost all reporters for its "wonderful" food and
"knowledgeable" service. / **Details:** www.horseshoeinn.co.uk; Tue-Thu &
Sun 9 pm, Fri & Sat 9.30 pm; closed Mon & Sun D; no Amex.
Accommodation: 8 rooms, from £100.

PENSHURST, KENT

3–3B

Spotted Dog £ 33 🅣
Smarts Hill TN11 8EE (01892) 870253
"A nice and atmospheric old pub", tipped – in the early days of its
new ownership – for "well-executed" traditional fare, and a setting
that's "as lovely as ever". / **Details:** www.spotteddogpub.co.uk; near
Penshurst Place; 9 pm, Fri & Sat 9.30 pm, Sun 7 pm.

PENZANCE, CORNWALL

1–4A

The Honey Pot £ 23 🅣
5 Parade St TR18 4BU (01736) 368686
"The dishes are delicious and filling, and the cakes are scrummy" at
this "comfy and fun" café, tipped for its simple fare and excellent
coffee. / **Details:** L only, closed Sun; no credit cards.

PERTH, PERTH AND KINROSS

9–3C

Cafe Tabou £ 45 ❷❷❷
4 St John's Pl PH1 5SZ (01738) 446698
"A little gem of a restaurant that could have been picked up in Paris
and put down in Perth"; it's "always busy and bustling", which is
testament to its "fair prices". / **Details:** www.cafetabou.com; 9 pm,
Wed & Thu 9.30 pm, Fri & Sat 10 pm; closed Mon D & Sun; no Amex.

PETERSFIELD, HAMPSHIRE

2–3D

JSW £ 64 ❷❷④
20 Dragon St GU31 4JJ (01730) 262030
Jake Saul Watkins's offers "imaginative" – to fans, "amazing" –
cuisine at this former coaching inn, making it one of the county's
best-known foodie destinations; the downside? – the "subdued" room
can feel "a bit morgue-like". / **Details:** www.jswrestaurant.com; on the old
A3; 8 min walk from the railway station; 9.30 pm; closed Mon & Sun;
no Amex; children: 5+ D. **Accommodation:** 3 rooms, from £110.

PETWORTH, WEST SUSSEX

3–4A

The Noahs Ark Inn £ 42 ❷❷❷
Lurgashall GU28 9ET (01428) 707346
"Very good news all round"; this "lovely" boozer-by-the-village-green
is "always busy", thanks to its "charming" style and "freshly
produced" dishes. / **Details:** www.noahsarkinn.co.uk; 9.30 pm; closed
Sun D.

PICKERING, NORTH YORKSHIRE
8–4C

The White Swan £ 47 ❷❷❷
Market Pl YO18 7AA (01751) 472288
*"Everything is first-class", says one of the fans of the "simply-prepared" fare on offer at this former coaching inn, in a "charming" village; you can eat in the candlelit bar or the dining room.
/ **Details:** www.white-swan.co.uk; 9 pm.* **Accommodation:** *21 rooms, from £150.*

PILSLEY, DERBYSHIRE
5–2C

Devonshire Arms at Pilsley £ 35 🅣
DE45 1UL (01246) 583258
Looking for a "value-for-money sibling to the Devonshire Arms, Beeley"? – this establishment is tipped as having the same designer (the Duchess) and the same chef patron (Alan Hill), plus "plenty of dishes for less than a tenner". / **Details:** *www.devonshirepilsley.co.uk.*

PLEASINGTON, LANCASHIRE
5–1B

Clog And Billycock £ 39 ❷❷❷
Billinge End Rd BB2 6QB (01254) 201163
*Part of the Ribble Valley Inns ('Northcote') empire – this "great family-friendly pub" impresses most, if not quite all, reporters with its "consistently good" and of course, "locally-sourced" cuisine.
/ **Details:** www.theclogandbillycock.com; follow the brown signs to The Clog and Billycock; 8.30 pm Mon-Thu, Fri & Sat 9 pm, Sun 8 pm.*

PLOCKTON, HIGHLAND
9–2B

Plockton Inn £ 32 ❷❸❸
Innes St IV52 8TW (01599) 544222
*Seafood "so fresh, it's an absolute joy" – and at "reasonable prices" too – consistently wins high acclaim for this small hotel, whose kitchen "is about 10 yards from Loch Carron".
/ **Details:** www.plocktoninn.co.uk; 9 pm, Winter 8.30 pm; no Amex.*
Accommodation: *14 rooms, from £94.*

PLUMTREE, NOTTINGHAMSHIRE
5–3D

Perkins £ 39 ❷❷❷
Old Railway Station NG12 5NA (0115) 937 3695
*A number of reporters noted "improved" standards at this refurbished ("now more modern") family-run restaurant in a former railway station – the cooking is fairly simple ("brasserie-style"), but the attention to details stands out.
/ **Details:** www.perkinsrestaurant.co.uk; off A606 between Nottingham & Melton Mowbray; 9.30 pm; closed Sun D.*

PLUSH, DORSET
2–4B

Brace of Pheasants £ 36 ❷❷❷
DT2 7RT (01300) 348357
"Obscurely located down winding lanes, but well worth seeking out for its brilliant menu", this "great little village inn" attracts only rave reviews, not least for the "quality of ingredients" and its "attention to detail" generally. / **Details:** *www.braceofpheasants.co.uk; 9.30 pm.*
Accommodation: *4 rooms, from £95.*

The Barbican Kitchen Brasserie   £ 41   **T**
60 Southside St, The Barbican PL1 2LQ   (01752) 604448
*In the former Plymouth Gin Distillery, a brasserie run by local heros
the Tanner brothers, and tipped as "reliable" and "great-value".*
/ **Details:** www.barbicankitchen.com; 10 pm.

Chloe's
Gill Akaster House   £ 56   **T**
Princess St PL1 2EX   (01752) 201523
*Didier & Jo Franchet's Gallic restaurant is tipped as a a "good-value"
destination, especially "worth a visit", given the "dearth of
competition locally".* / **Details:** www.chloesrestaurant.co.uk; 10 pm; closed
Mon & Sun.

Tanners Restaurant   £ 55   **❶❷❷**
Prysten Hs, Finewell St PL1 2AE   (01752) 252001
*"The best place in Plymouth by a long chalk!" – the Tanner brothers'
"chic" little restaurant has won very consistently high ratings of late
for its "really imaginative" and "flawlessly-executed" cuisine.*
/ **Details:** www.tannersrestaurant.com; 9.30 pm; closed Mon & Sun.

Sams on the Beach   £ 41   **❷❷❸**
PL24 2TL   (01726) 812255
*In a former lifeboat station on a picturesque beach, this offshoot of
the popular Fowey restaurant of the same name serves "a range of
food, but the pizzas are especially good"; the acoustics, though, can
be "jarring", and the parking is "way up the hill!"*
/ **Details:** www.samsfowey.co.uk; 9 pm.

Guildhall Tavern   £ 43   **❷❶❷**
15 Market St BH15 1NB   (01202) 671717
*This "converted pub in the old town" is nowadays a "delightfully
French" and "well-run" fish restaurant where "brilliant fresh fish
dishes" are served "with plenty of Gallic charm".*
/ **Details:** www.guildhalltavern.co.uk; 10 pm; closed Mon & Sun; no Amex.

Storm   £ 49   **❷❸❸**
16 High St BH15 1BP   (01202) 674970
*"A very competent fish restaurant in an under-served port"; it's an
"informal" ("basic") and "lively" sort of place where the oftentimes
"great" cuisine can come as "a real surprise".*
/ **Details:** www.stormfish.co.uk; 9.30 pm, Fri & Sat 10 pm; closed Mon L,
Tue L & Sun L.

Airds Hotel   £ 70   **❶❷❷**
PA38 4DF   (01631) 730236
*Feedback was thin this year, but all of it confirmed the "extremely
good" ongoing standards at this hotel besides Loch Linnhe; it's the
fish and seafood, of course, that's "particularly delicious".*
/ **Details:** www.airds-hotel.com; 20m N of Oban; 9.30 pm; no jeans or
trainers; children: 8+ at D. **Accommodation:** 11 rooms, from £245.

Pierhouse Hotel £ 51 ❶❸❷
PA38 4DE   (01631) 730302
"An amazing setting and some seriously good seafood" continue to
justify the trip to this *"very special"* and remote spot – next to the
pier, it enjoys *"fabulous views"* over Loch Linhe.
/ **Details:** www.pierhousehotel.co.uk; just off A828, follow signs for Port
Appin & Lismore Ferry; 9.30 pm. **Accommodation:** 12 rooms, from £100.

PORTHGAIN, PEMBROKESHIRE 4–4B

The Shed £ 42 ❸❸❷
SA62 5BN   (01348) 831518
*The location by the sea is "so romantic", and this "eccentric" spot
pleases most reporters with its "fantastic fresh fish" – 'off-days' are
also reported, though, including the odd "terrible disappointment".*
/ **Details:** www.theshedporthgain.co.uk; 9 pm; closed Sun D; no Amex.

PORTHLEVEN, CORNWALL 1–4A

Kota £ 44 ❷❷❷
Harbour Head TR13 9JA   (01326) 562407
"Such good value for a lovely meal in a beautiful location" – that's
the gist of all the impressive feedback on this harbour-side
restaurant, noted for its *"flavourful"*, *"Maori-influenced"* fish cuisine,
and its *"thoughtful"* wine list too. / **Details:** www.kotarestaurant.co.uk;
9 pm; closed Mon L, Tue L, Wed L, Thu L & Sun; no Amex.
Accommodation: 2 rooms, from £65.

PORTMAHOMACK, HIGHLAND 9–2C

The Oystercatcher £ 57 🅣
Main St IV20 1YB   (01862) 871560
*A small beach-side restaurant-with-rooms; it doesn't generate a huge
amount of feedback, but is tipped for fish "cooked with passion,
straight off the boat".* / **Details:** www.the-oystercatcher.co.uk; 11 pm;
closed Mon & Tue; no Amex. **Accommodation:** 3 rooms, from £70.

PORTMEIRION, GWYNEDD 4–2C

Portmeirion Hotel £ 58 ❷❷❷
LL48 6ET   (01766) 772440
"A perfect retreat by the romantic and exotic Welsh seaside!" – the
dining room of the hotel of Sir Clough Williams-Ellis's fantasy-
Italianate village continues to offer *"excellent"* cuisine in a *"stunning"*
setting, and at pretty reasonable prices too.
/ **Details:** www.portmeirion-village.com; off A487 at Minffordd; 9 pm.
Accommodation: 14 rooms, from £185.

PORTSMOUTH, HAMPSHIRE 2–4D

abarbistro £ 36 ❷❸④
58 White Hart Rd PO1 2JA   (02392) 811585
*Celebrating a decade in business, a bright dining room in a building
that was once a pub; "it's very close to the fish market and you get
good fish", and on the wine front there are "interesting weekly
picks".* / **Details:** www.abarbistro.co.uk; 2 min walk from Portsmouth
Cathedral; midnight, Sun 10.30 pm.

Brasserie Blanc £ 42 🅣
1 Gunwharf Quays PO1 3FR   (02392) 891 320
*An "oasis" hereabouts – this "professional" chain outlet is tipped for
its "wholesome" dishes, and at "very good-value" prices too.*
/ **Details:** www.brasserieblanc.com; 10 pm. 10.30 Sat, 9 pm Sun.

Le Café Parisien £ 28   **T**
1 Lord Montgomery Way PO1 2AH (023) 9283 1234
*In the University Quarter, "a vibrant cafe popular with locals, international students and creative types"; tipped for "fantastic pannini", "fresh juices" and the like. / **Details:** www.lecafeparisien.com; 8 pm; closed Sun; no Amex.*

Loch Fyne £ 38   ❷❸④
Unit 2 Vulcan Buildings PO1 3TY (023) 9277 8060
*"A really pleasant, spacious, relaxed branch of this reliable chain" in a 'designer' harbour-side development, whose "tasty fresh fish" makes it a top tip locally. / **Details:** www.lochfyne.com; 10 pm.*

Relentless Steak & Lobster House £ 44   ❷❸❸
85 Elm Grove PO5 1JF (02392) 822888
"Best for fresh lobster" – this recently-opened surf 'n' turf joint is acclaimed in all reports as a "good-value" destination, and it has "plenty of buzz" too.

Restaurant 27 £ 34   ❷❷❸
27a, Southsea Pde PO5 2JF (023) 9287 6272
*"The best thing to happen to Portsmouth for a long time", this "elegant" restaurant, near the Southsea seafront is – say fans – now "the town's best fine dining restaurant by a long stretch".
/ **Details:** www.restaurant27.com.*

PRESTON BAGOT, WARWICKSHIRE   5–4C

The Crabmill £ 44   ④④④
B95 5EE (01926) 843342
*Fans insist this is a top gastropub offering "good food and service and a wonderful ambience too"; sceptics, though, are less convinced – "I'm not sure if it lives up to the hype, but it's certainly very popular". / **Details:** www.thecrabmill.co.uk; on main road between Warwick & Henley-in-Arden; 9.30 pm; closed Sun D; no Amex; booking essential.*

PRIORS HARDWICK, WARWICKSHIRE   2–1D

The Butchers Arms £ 50   ❸❷❸
Church End CV47 7SN (01327) 260504
*Long run by a Portuguese family, this ancient inn offers a rather 'period' dining experience (complete with "that sweet trolley"), with a bit of an international slant, and a "brilliant" welcome too.
/ **Details:** www.thebutchersarms.com; off J11/12 of the M40; 9.30 pm; closed Sat L & Sun D.*

PWLLHELI, GWYNEDD   4–2C

Plas Bodegroes £ 61   ❷❶❷
Nefyn Rd LL53 5TH (01758) 612363
*"A beautiful, romantic setting with lovely rooms and glorious gardens" helps inspire praise for Chris & Gunna Chown's attractive restaurant-with-rooms; the odd reporter speaks of "inconsistent" cooking, but on most accounts it "just seems to get better and better". / **Details:** www.bodegroes.co.uk; on A497 1m W of Pwllheli; 9.30 pm; closed Mon, Tue-Sat D only, closed Sun D; no Amex; children: not at D. **Accommodation:** 10 rooms, from £130.*

Dakota Forth Bridge £ 45 ❸❸❷

Ferrimuir Retail Pk EH30 9QZ (0870) 423 4293

"Bizarrely-located in a Tesco car park at the South end of the Forth Road Bridge", this nightclubby ("Hakkasan-look") and "very professional" hotel dining room certainly makes an unlikely find; there is the occasional report of "slipping standards", but more reporters still find this a "really enjoyable" all-rounder.
/ **Details:** www.dakotaforthbridge.co.uk; 10 pm; booking essential.
Accommodation: 132 rooms, from £99.

Ramsons £ 62 ❶❷④

18 Market Pl BL0 9HT (01706) 825070

A "true enthusiast" (Chris Johnson) presides over this "small and well-run establishment of 25 years' standing" – "a hidden gem of the North West"; the "divine" Italian food shows "genuine star quality" and is matched by a "tremendous range" of Italian wine.
/ **Details:** www.ramsons-restaurant.com; 9.30 pm; closed Mon, Tue L & Sun D; no Amex.

Age & Sons £ 36 ⓣ

Charlotte Ct CT11 8HE (01843) 851515

"Hard to see what it's doing in Ramsgate!" – this quirky "oasis" is tipped as "always worth a punt", thanks to Toby Leigh's "interesting and well-executed" fare; shame about the "shambolic" service, though – it can be "very slow indeed". / **Details:** www.ageandsons.com; 10 pm; closed Mon & Sun D.

Eddie Gilbert's £ 42 ❷❷❸

32 King St CT11 8NT (01843) 852 123

"The daily catch is landed just yards from this excellent fishmonger/chippy/seafood restaurant" – the last particularly impresses all reporters with its "tasteful" decor and, in particular, "beautiful" dishes from a "wide-ranging and innovative" menu.
/ **Details:** www.eddiegilberts.com; off the Main Street; 9.30pm; closed Sun D; no Amex.

Yorke Arms £ 83 ❶❶❷

HG3 5RL (01423) 755243

"The jewel in the crown of the Yorkshire Dales" – Frances & Gerald Atkins's "perfect country inn" is set in a really lovely village and offers an "outstanding" and "truly romantic" all-round experience, not least the "freshest of local ingredients", "superbly cooked and stylishly served". / **Details:** www.yorke-arms.co.uk; 4m W of Pateley Bridge; 8.45 pm; no Amex. **Accommodation:** 12 rooms, from £150.

Forbury's Restaurant & Wine Bar £ 50 ⓣ

1 Forbury Sq RG1 3BB (0118) 957 4044

Feedback on this Gallic venture in the city-centre is limited nowadays; however, it did once look as if it might be destined for the Premier League, and – with Gavin Young's cuisine still showing "great attention to detail" – fans still tip the place as "the best in town".
/ **Details:** www.forburys.co.uk; 10 pm; closed Sun.

London Street Brasserie £ 47 ❸❸❸
2-4 London St RG1 4PN (0118) 950 5036
With its "great riverside location" and "reasonably-priced" lunch
menu, this town-centre fixture makes a very useful midday
destination; service can be "rather slow", though, and there's a
feeling in some quarters that the evening performance is "only good
in parts". / Details: www.londonstbrasserie.co.uk; on the corner of the Oracle
shoping centre; 10.30 pm.

REIGATE, SURREY 3–3B

La Barbe £ 48 ❸❸④
71 Bell St RH2 7AN (01737) 241966
"Authentic", "popular", "reliable" – the sort of words that keep
cropping up in reviews of the Gallic staples served at this "classic
bistro" of over a quarter of a century's standing.
/ Details: www.labarbe.co.uk; 9.30 pm; closed Sat L & Sun D.

Tony Tobin @ The Dining Room £ 59 ❷❷④
59a High St RH2 9AE (01737) 226650
The dining room which is the HQ of TV chef Tony Tobin has "a cosy
living-room feel"; both tasting and vegetarian menus are an option,
and all reports say his cuisine's "always reliable" and "still evolving".
/ Details: www.tonytobinrestaurants.co.uk; 10 pm; closed Sat L & Sun D.

The Westerly £ 45 ❶❷④
2-4 London Rd RH2 9AN (01737) 222733
John Coombe delivers "bistro-type food with real panache and a
different edge" while service (under wife, Cynthia) is "efficient and
very friendly" at this town-centre venture; some investment in the
room, though – "still no carpet!" – might yield a good return?
/ Details: www.thewesterly.co.uk; 10 pm; closed Mon, Tue L, Sat L & Sun.

REYNOLDSTON, SWANSEA 1–1C

Fairyhill £ 65 ④④❸
SA3 1BS (01792) 390139
Fans say it's "a delightful experience from start to finish" to visit this
Gower Peninsula country house hotel; critics, however, find the food
"bland and pretentious" – ratings are certainly not a patch on the
glory days. / Details: www.fairyhill.net; 20 mins from M4, J47 off B4295;
9 pm; no Amex; children: 8+ at D. **Accommodation:** *8 rooms, from £180.*

RIPLEY, SURREY 3–3A

Drakes £ 72 ❶❶④
The Clock Hs, High St GU23 6AQ (01483) 224777
"Still Surrey's best!" – Steve Drake's "peaceful" village-restaurant
wows reporters with "amazing combinations of flavour" (that "lack
excessive weirdness"); stubbornly, however, the atmosphere can
seem "somewhat stilted". / Details: www.drakesrestaurant.co.uk; just
beyond the intersection of A3 and M25 (J10) heading towards Guildford;
9.30 pm; closed Mon, Tue L, Sat L & Sun; no Amex; booking: max 12; children:
12+.

RIPON, NORTH YORKSHIRE 8–4B

The Old Deanery £ 44 ❸❺❷
Minster Rd HG4 1QS (01765) 600003
"In the heart of the city", a "comfortable" restaurant-with-rooms in
an "interesting" old building, where the food is "tasty" and "well-
presented"; service, though, could do with tightening up.
/ Details: www.theolddeanery.co.uk; 9 pm, Fri & Sat 9.30 pm; closed Sun D;
no Amex. **Accommodation:** *11 rooms, from £125.*

El Gato Negro Tapas   £ 42   ❶❷❷

1 Oldham Rd HX6 4DN   (01422) 823070

With its "brilliant tapas" – and offering "value for money too" – Simon Shaw's "affable" and "consistently buzzy" rural tapas bar (in a converted pub) is an ongoing success story that continues to impress all who comment on it. / Details: www.elgatonegrotapas.com; 9.30 pm, Fri & Sat 10 pm, Sun 7.30 pm; closed Mon, Tue, Wed L, Thu L, Fri L & Sun D.

Old Bore   £ 40   ❷❷❸

Oldham Rd HX6 4QU   (01422) 822291

An "individual" village-restaurant, praised by all who comment on it for its "impressive consistency" and "charming service". / Details: www.oldbore.co.uk; on the main Oldham road; 9.30 pm; closed Mon, Tue & Sun D; no Amex.

Restaurant Nathan Outlaw
The St Enodoc Hotel   £104   ❶❸❸

PL27 6LA   (01208) 863394

Nathan Outlaw's "genius" cuisine ("almost entirely fish and seafood") continues to make a smash hit of this "small and very intimate" (if, perhaps slightly "bland") dining room, which boasts "gorgeous views" across the Camel Estuary. / Details: www.nathan-outlaw.co.uk; 9 pm; D only, closed Mon & Sun; no Amex; no shorts; Essential; children: 12+ D. Accommodation: 20 rooms, from £130.

Jack in the Green Inn   £ 46   ④④❸

London Rd EX5 2EE   (01404) 822240

Critics may find it "over-popular because it's so convenient for those heading for Cornwall", but this "friendly" inn nonetheless pleases most reporters with its "huge portions" of dependable fare. / Details: www.jackinthegreen.uk.com; 2 miles from Exeter airport on the old A30; 9.30 pm; no Amex.

The Rose & Crown   £ 43   ❸④④

DL12 9EB   (01833) 650213

In its "picturesque setting by the village green", this family-owned inn has a good name for its "excellent" food; service is often highly rated too, but it has also sometimes seemed "under par" of late. / Details: www.rose-and-crown.co.uk; 6m NW of Barnard Castle on B6277; 9 pm; no Amex; children: 6+ in restaurant. Accommodation: 12 rooms, from £140.

Driftwood Hotel   £ 63   ❷❷❶

TR2 5EW   (01872) 580644

"A lovely location, with high-class food"; the "subtle" and "tasteful" dining room of this modern seaside hotel pleases all reporters with its "well-executed" cuisine; "wonderful views" too. / Details: www.driftwoodhotel.co.uk; off the A30 to Truro, towards St Mawes; 9.30 pm; D only; booking: max 6; children: 8+. Accommodation: 15 rooms, from £195.

The George & Dragon £ 43 ❷❸❸
High St SN10 2PN (01380) 723053
"A country pub specialising in Cornish fish"; it's a "welcoming",
"lively" and "reliable" sort of place, which all reporters agree is
"something of an oasis in a culinary desert".
/ **Details:** www.thegeorgeanddragonrowde.co.uk; on A342 between Devizes &
Chippenham; 10 pm; closed Sun D. **Accommodation:** 3 rooms, from £55
week 105 wkend.

Chequers Inn £ 44 ⓣ
RH12 3PY (01403) 790480
Surprisingly few reports on this "excellent village pub"; it's still tipped,
though, for "the best food on the Surrey/Sussex borders".
/ **Details:** www.chequersrowhook.com; 9 pm; closed Sun D; no Amex.

Landgate Bistro £ 36 ❷❷❸
5-6 Landgate TN31 7LH (01797) 222829
"Nothing changes" at this long-established coastal bistro, whose
"lovely, fresh and local" food "could easily compete with many pricier
establishments" – the occasional critic, though, does find it rather
"hyped". / **Details:** www.landgatebistro.co.uk; below Landgate Arch; 9.15 pm;
closed Mon, Tue, Wed L, Thu L, Fri L & Sun D.

Tuscan Kitchen £ 40 ❶❸❷
8 Lion St TN31 7LB (01797) 223269
"Hospitable, if slightly eccentric" service "adds to the charm" of this
family-run spot where "beautiful, rustic Tuscan food created by a
genuine Tuscan chef" again inspires incredibly enthusiastic reports.
/ **Details:** www.tuscankitchenrye.co.uk; 10 pm; closed Mon, Tue L, Wed L,
Thu L & Sat L.

Webbe's at The Fish Cafe £ 43 ❸❸④
17 Tower St TN31 7AT (01797) 222226
"Fabulous freshly-caught fish" provides the backbone of the menu at
this town-centre café whose all-round standards please most, if not
quite all, of the reporters who comment on it.
/ **Details:** www.thefishcafe.com; 9.30 pm.

Table 10 £ 36 ⓣ
10 Northenden Rd M33 3BR (0161) 282 2212
"An excellent family-run bistro in unfashionable Sale!" – this new kid
on the block is tipped for "fantastic" food in a "friendly"
atmosphere; more reports please!

Anokaa £ 43 ❶❷❸
60 Fisherton St SP2 7RB (01722) 414142
"One of the best Indians I've ever been to!" – "Salisbury's top
restaurant" inspires a hymn of praise for its "refined" cuisine –
"fresh-tasting, creative and beautiful dishes" that "make your taste
buds crave for more!" / **Details:** www.anokaa.com; 10.30 pm; no shorts.

Hox Brasserie £ 34 ❷❸④
155 Fisherton St SP2 7RP (01722) 341600
"A magnet for lovers of subcontinental food", the city's largest
restaurant pleases all reporters with its *"different"* (South Indian)
cuisine; *"if you like peace and quiet, it's best to go early in the
week".* / **Details:** www.hoxbrasserie.co.uk.

Jade £ 35 ❷❸④
109a Exeter St SP1 2SF (01722) 333355
*"Dig beneath the surface of this ordinary looking Chinese restaurant
and you'll find some superb cooking"*, with seafood the highlight –
"for a special meal, let Joe choose for you".
/ **Details:** www.jaderestaurant.co.uk; near the Cathedral; 11.30 pm; closed
Sun; no Amex.

SALTAIRE, WEST YORKSHIRE 5–1C

Salts Diner £ 35 ❸❸❷
Salts Mill, Victoria Rd BD18 3LA (01274) 531163
*A former mill – now an arts/retail centre – provides a "bright and
airy" space for this artsy diner ("napkins illustrated by Hockney!")
whose "family-friendly bistro-style dishes" (plus pizza, cakes, etc)
invariably hit the spot; "arrive early for the daily specials".*
/ **Details:** www.saltsmill.org.uk; 2m from Bradford on A650; L & afternoon tea
only; no Amex.

SALTHOUSE, NORFOLK 6–3C

Cookies Crab Shop £ 21 ❶
The Grn, Coast Rd NR25 7AJ (01263) 740352
*"Bizarre, ridiculous, chaotic, fantastic, honest, charming,
enterprising, timeless…"* – fans tip this self-explanatory *"shack"* as
"the sort of place everyone should go at least once!"
/ **Details:** www.salthouse.org.uk; on A149; 7.30 pm; no credit cards.

SANDSEND, NORTH YORKSHIRE 8–3D

Estbek House £ 58 ❷❷❷
East Row YO21 3SU (01947) 893424
"Fresh and well-prepared fish dishes" are a highlight at this
restaurant-with-rooms near the beach, which also features an
"excellent" wine list; it's a place *"where you can really feel at home"*
too. / **Details:** www.estbekhouse.co.uk; 9 pm; D only; no Amex.
Accommodation: 4 rooms, from £125.

SANQUHAR, DUMFRIES AND GALLOWAY 7–1B

Blackaddie Country House Hotel £ 63 ❶
DG4 6JJ (01659) 502 70
*This "beautifully grand yet comfortable 16th-century country house
hotel"* is tipped for its *"excellent local fare".*
/ **Details:** www.blackaddiehotel.co.uk.

SAPPERTON, GLOUCESTERSHIRE 2–2C

The Bell at Sapperton £ 50 ❷④❸
GL7 6LE (01285) 760298
*A "civilised" and very popular Cotswold gastropub offering "great
food in a wonderful village location"*; just occasionally its staff seem
"a bit snooty", but generally it's a *"lovely"* experience.
/ **Details:** www.foodatthebell.co.uk; from Cirencester take the A419 towards
Stroud, turn right to Sapperton; 9.30 pm, Sun 9 pm; no Amex; children: 10+ at
D.

SAWLEY, LANCASHIRE 5–1B

The Spread Eagle £ 38 ❸❸❷
BB7 4NH (01200) 441202
*This is "another great Lancashire pub-with-rooms", serving up
"fashionable but well put-together" dishes using "excellent local
produce"; it has "a great location on the River Ribble" too.
/ Details: www.spreadeaglesawley.co.uk; 9.15 pm, Sun 7.15 pm.*
Accommodation: *7 rooms, from £80.*

SAWSTON, CAMBRIDGESHIRE 3–1B

Jade Fountain £ 27 ❷❷④
42-46 High St CB2 4BG (01223) 836100
*Fans say it offers "the best Chinese food in East Anglia", and this
"family-favourite" spot remains well rated for its "excellent value for
money" (and its accommodating service too). / Details: 1m from M11,
J10; 11 pm; closed Mon.*

SCARBOROUGH, NORTH YORKSHIRE 8–4D

Lanterna £ 46 ❶❷❸
33 Queen St YO11 1HQ (01723) 363616
*"Like stepping back 40 years", this "friendly but slightly worn"
trattoria is prized by all who comment on it for its "homely" style
and its "gutsy and traditional" cuisine – not least "first-class pasta"
and "the best Lobster Thermidor in the world!"
/ Details: www.giorgioalessio.co.uk; near the Old Town; 9.30 pm; D only,
closed Sun; no Amex.*

SEAHAM, COUNTY DURHAM 8–3C

**The White Room
Seaham Hall** £ 77
Lord Byron's Walk SR7 7AG (0191) 516 1400
*Part of the (disintegrating) Von Essen empire – this country house
hotel is one of the North East's grandest destinations; during this
unsettled period, it attracted very mixed views (from "perfect and
exciting" to "average and disappointing") so – while the dust settles
– we've left it un-rated. / Details: www.seaham-hall.co.uk; 9.45 pm; D only,
ex Sun open L & D; no trainers; booking: max 8.* **Accommodation:** *20
rooms, from £300.*

SEER GREEN, BUCKINGHAMSHIRE 3–3A

The Jolly Cricketers £ 47 ❷❷❷
24 Chalfont Rd HP9 2YG (01494) 676308
*A "gem" of a "little pub-restaurant", acclaimed by all who comment
on it; "judged by the buzz and constant crowds", this "fairly recent
addition to the local scene" seems "to be making its mark".
/ Details: www.thejollycricketers.co.uk; 9 pm; closed Mon & Sun D.*

SEVENOAKS, KENT 3–3B

The Vine £ 55 ④④❸
11 Pound Ln TN13 3TB (01732) 469510
*"It may lack spark, but as a stalwart it's a good 'un" – this "solid
local performer" with views over England's oldest cricket ground,
wins all-round praise for its "attractive interior" and "pleasant" fare;
"it can be noisy when full". / Details: www.vinerestaurant.co.uk; 11 pm;
closed Sun D; no Amex.*

Ode £ 54 ❷❸❸
Fore St TQ14 0DE (01626) 873977
"A small and romantic restaurant in a little, seaside village" – for
most reporters, the ambition and freshness of its cuisine make it *"a
real find"*. / **Details:** www.odetruefood.co.uk; 9.30 pm; closed Mon, Tue L,
Wed L, Sat L & Sun; no Amex; booking essential.

The Seahorse £ 54 🅣
52-54 The St GU4 8BU (01483) 514 351
"More a restaurant than a pub nowadays", this recently launched
gastroboozer is tipped for *"good food"* generally (and, in particular,
some *"excellent fish"*). / **Details:** www.theseahorseguildford.co.uk; 10 pm,
Fri & Sat 10.30 pm, Sun 9 pm.

Aagrah £ 32 ❷❹❸
Unit 1 Leopold Sq, Leopold St S1 2JG (0114) 279 5577
A large outpost of Yorkshire's celebrated chain of curry houses that's
often *"very very busy"*, thanks not least to food that's (almost)
"always good". / **Details:** www.aagrah.com; Mon-Thu 11 pm, Fri & Sat
midnight; D only.

The Cricket Inn £ 38 🅣
Penny Ln S17 3AZ (0114) 236 5256
A *"lovely"* rural pub, run by Sheffield bigwig Richard Smith and
tipped for its *"good and hearty food"*; it's also *"excellent with
children and family groups"*. / **Details:** www.relaxeatanddrink.com;
Mon-Sat 9.30 pm, Sun 8 pm; no Amex.

Kitchen £ 38 ❷❷❹
762 Ecclesall Rd S11 9TB (0114) 267 1351
Sometimes *"amazing"* food – particularly in the light of the *"dearth
of fine dining"* locally – is the theme of much of the commentary on
this new add-on to a wine-and-food store… even if the interior is
perhaps a bit *"uninspiring"*. / **Details:** www.sheffieldkitchen.com.

The Milestone £ 41 ❸❹❸
84 Green Lane At Ball St S3 8SE (0114) 272 8327
"Fast becoming a Sheffield legend", this *"lively"* gastropub – *"tucked-
away in an old industrial corner of the city"* – attracts masses of
(generally) very positive feedback; for a few critics, though, it
"doesn't live up to the hype". / **Details:** www.the-milestone.co.uk; 9 pm,
Sun 8.30 pm.

Moran's £ 44 ❷❸❹
289 Abbeydale Road South S17 3LB (01142) 350101
"A busy little restaurant, and justifiably so"; with its *"good food"* and
"charming service", this *"classy"* but *"well-priced"* operation – a few
miles to the SW of the city-centre – wows all who comment on it.
/ **Details:** www.moranssheffield.co.uk; 9 pm, Fri & Sat 9.30 pm; closed Mon,
Tue L & Sun D; no Amex.

Nonna's £ 42 ❸❷❷
539-541 Eccleshall Rd S11 8PR (0114) 268 6166
Thanks not least to its positively *"Mediterranean"* atmosphere, this
"popular" and *"very friendly"* Eccleshall spot is often hailed as the
"best Italian" locally. / **Details:** www.nonnas.co.uk; M1, J33 towards
Bakewell; 9.45 pm; no Amex.

The Old Vicarage £ 83 ④⑤⑤
Ridgeway Moor, Ridgeway S12 3XW (0114) 247 5814
As it nears its 25th year, Tessa Bramley's (Michelin-starred) operation in a "beautiful old building" stirs up a mixed bag of emotions; even critics concede the food can be "technically great", but prices are "astronomical", service can be "bumbling", and the overall experience is sometimes simply "dismal".
/ **Details:** www.theoldvicarage.co.uk; 10 mins SE of city centre; 9.30 pm; closed Mon, Sat L & Sun; no Amex.

Piccolino £ 43 ⓣ
4 Millennium Sq S1 2JL (01142) 752698
In a city still quite thinly-provided, a branch of the Italian national chain tipped for its notably consistent all-round performance.
/ **Details:** www.piccolinorestaurants.co.uk.

Rafters £ 52 ⓣ
220 Oakbrook Rd, Nether Grn S11 7ED (0114) 230 4819
Looking for "top-quality cooking in a quiet Sheffield suburb" (Ranmoor)? – this "great local restaurant", over a decade in business, comes strongly tipped. / **Details:** www.raftersrestaurant.co.uk; 10 pm; D only, closed Tue & Sun.

Silversmiths £ 31 ❷❸❸
111 Arundel St S1 2NT (0114) 270 6160
This three-year-old establishment in the 'Cultural Quarter' attracts impressively consistent ratings, not least for its "excellent-value early-evening menu". / **Details:** www.silversmiths-restaurant.com; 11.30 pm, Fri & Sat midnight; D only, closed Sun; no Amex.

Wasabisabi £ 32 ⓣ
227A, London Rd S2 4NF (0114) 258 5838
A large Japanese restaurant tipped not only for "excellent" sushi but an "entertaining teppan-yaki" too – more reports please!
/ **Details:** www.wasabisabi.co.uk; 11 pm; no Amex.

SHELLEY, WEST YORKSHIRE 5–2C

Three Acres £ 57 ❷❸❸
Roydhouse HD8 8LR (01484) 602606
This bleakly-located inn (more a "rural bistro") on Emley Moor has long been a top destination for "wonderful, hearty Yorkshire cuisine from a great menu including seafood"; reports nowadays, however, often come with just a hint of qualification, in particular that it's "pricey"; even so "booking is essential". / **Details:** www.3acres.com; near Emley Moor TV tower; 9.30 pm; no Amex. **Accommodation:** 16 rooms, from £125.

SHERBORNE, DORSET 2–3B

The Green £ 44 ❷❷❸
The Green DT9 3HY (01935) 813821
Fans of this "helpful" town-centre spot say it's "the best in the area by a country mile" – "there's not much choice on its simple menu, but it's always very good". / **Details:** www.greenrestaurant.co.uk; 9 pm; closed Mon & Sun; no Amex.

King's Arms £ 45 ❸❷❷
Charlton Horethorne DT9 4NL (01963) 220281
"In a lovely village just outside Sherborne", this "classy refurb of an old pub" has a "lovely" location (with outdoor seating), and offers "great food from local producers". / **Details:** www.thekingsarms.co.uk; ?; no Amex. **Accommodation:** 10 rooms, from £105.

Kinghams　　　　　　　　　　　£ 50　　④❸❷
Gomshall Ln GU5 9HE　(01483) 202168
*The "olde-worlde" and "romantic" charms of this beamed cottage
restaurant help it attract a good volume of feedback; its cuisine can
seem "reliable but not exciting", but most reporters still feel this is
"a welcome oasis in a bare patch of the county".*
/ **Details:** www.kinghams-restaurant.co.uk; off A25 between Dorking &
Guildford; 9 pm; closed Mon & Sun D.

The William Bray　　　　　　　£ 48　　❸④❸
Shere Ln GU5 9HS　(01483) 202 044
*In a "very pretty village", a "a posh pub with restaurant attached"
which is proving "a fantastic addition to the drab local scene"; the
proprietor was formerly Top Gear's Stig.*
/ **Details:** www.thewilliambray.co.uk; 10 pm; no Amex.

L'Ortolan　　　　　　　　　　　£ 92　　❸❷❸
Church Ln RG2 9BY　(0118) 988 8500
*"Excellent classic French dishes" and "discreet" service again win
many plaudits for Alan Murchison's swish former rectory, a short
drive from the M4; it might be even better, though, if its ambition for
you-know-whats wasn't quite so "palpable".*
/ **Details:** www.alanmurchisonrestaurants.co.uk; J11, take first exit left on all
three roundabouts, then follow sign posts; 9 pm, Sat 9.30 pm; closed Mon &
Sun.

The Chaser Inn　　　　　　　　£ 43　　❷④❸
Stumble Hill TN11 9PE　(01732) 810360
*A quality gastropub offering much to like, including "consistent good
quality", "reasonable prices" and a "lovely garden".*
/ **Details:** www.thechaserinn.co.uk; 9.30 pm, Sun 9 pm.

Orwells　　　　　　　　　　　　£ 64　　❷❸❸
Shiplake Row RG9 4DP　(0118) 940 3673
*"Great gourmet food and service" is winning many fans for Ryan
Simpson's "innovative" new restaurant in a former pub; in these
early days, however, the odd 'bad trip' has not been unknown.*
/ **Details:** www.orwellsatshiplake.co.uk; 9.30 pm; closed Mon & Sun D;
no Amex.

Aagrah　　　　　　　　　　　　£ 30　　❷❷❸
4 Saltaire Rd BD18 3HN　(01274) 530880
*A popular member of the impressive Indian Yorkshire chain – here
you eat choose between the 'A la carte Restaurant' or the 'Grill &
Carvery'; though ratings slipped a tad this year, all reports still praise
"a winning formula that's great value".* / **Details:** www.aagrah.com;
11.30 pm; closed Sat L.

The Saracen's Head　　　　　　£ 37　　🆃
Church Ln DE6 3AS　(01335) 360 330
*"Always reliable", this "well refurbished" inn is hailed by all reporters
for "very good food" served in "enormous portions"; it has a "great
rural setting" too.* / **Details:** www.saracens-head-shirley.co.uk.

SKENFRITH, MONMOUTHSHIRE

The Bell at Skenfrith　　　**£ 49**　　④④④
NP7 8UH　(01600) 750235
Lots of reports mention this "remote" but "busy" inn, which has built quite a name for its "interesting" cooking and "exceptional" wine; not all reporters are swept away, though, with some complaining of "a triumph of style over substance". / **Details:** www.skenfrith.co.uk; on B4521, 10m E of Abergavenny; 9.30 pm, Sun 9 pm; no Amex; children: 8+ at D. **Accommodation:** 11 rooms, from £110.

SLEAT, HIGHLAND

Kinloch Lodge　　　**£ 76**　　❷❶❷
IV43 8QY　(01471) 833333
It's not just the "very romantic location" on the Isle of Skye that makes it worth seeking out the ancestral home of the Macdonald of Macdonald – Marcello Tully's cooking is "really first-class", and "beautifully presented" too. / **Details:** www.kinloch-lodge.co.uk; 9 pm; no Amex. **Accommodation:** 14 rooms, from £150.

SMALL HYTHE, KENT

Richard Phillips at Chapel Down　　**£ 49**　　❷❸❷
Tenterden Vineyard　TN30 7NG　(01580) 761616
"Charmingly-located" above the wine shop of one of England's leading vineyards, this "busy and buzzy" dining room offers seasonal food cooked "with flair" to a standard that's "sometimes exceptional"; are the portions becoming a little small, though? / **Details:** www.richardphillipsatchapeldown.co.uk; 9.30 pm; closed Mon, Tue D, Wed D & Sun D.

SONNING-ON-THAMES, BERKSHIRE

The Bull Inn　　　**£ 45**　　🅣
High St　RG4 6UP　(0118) 969 3901
A "charming old building" with a "lovely" interior and setting near the river help to ensure this olde-worlde pub is "always busy"; no culinary fireworks – just "good, home-cooked fare". / **Details:** www.fullershotels.com; off A4, J10 between Oxford & Windsor; 9.30 pm; no booking. **Accommodation:** 7 rooms, from £85.

The French Horn　　　**£ 77**　　❷❷❷
RG4 6TN　(0118) 969 2204
In the same ownership for over 40 years, this "beautifully-located" Thames-sider can perhaps seem a little "dated"; traditionalists, though, say it's "hard to beat for all-round quality" – not least "simple food done very well" (most famously spit-roast duck), and a "novel" of a wine list (albeit at "eye-watering" prices). / **Details:** www.thefrenchhorn.co.uk; M4, J8 or J9, then A4; 9.30 pm; booking: max 10. **Accommodation:** 21 rooms, from £160.

SOUTH SHIELDS, TYNE AND WEAR

Colmans　　　**£ 34**　　❶❸④
182-186 Ocean Rd　NE33 2JQ　(0191) 456 1202
"Approved by the Queen" apparently, this "superb" chippy – established in 1926 and nowadays an institution on quite a scale – inspires only the most positive reports from loyal subjects for its "top-quality fish and outstanding non-greasy chips". / **Details:** www.colmansfishandchips.com; L only; no Amex.

Kuti's £ 32 🆃
37-39 Oxford St SO14 3DP (023) 8022 1585
A good all-rounder ("by Southampton standards"); this Indian brasserie again attracts consistent praise for the quality of its cuisine (and its "unfailingly friendly" staff too); the lunchtime buffet offers "excellent value". / **Details:** *www.kutis.co.uk; near Stanley Casino; 11 pm.*

White Star £ 46 🆃
28 Oxford St SO14 3DJ (023) 8082 1990
"A popular dining pub" particularly tipped for its "very good fish and chips", and at "very reasonable prices" too. / **Details:** *www.whitestartavern.co.uk; 9.45 pm.* **Accommodation:** *13 rooms, from £85.*

Gusto Trattoria £ 35 🆃
58-62 Lord St PR8 1QB (01704) 544 255
Nowadays the top tip in this rather thinly provided part of the world – a "small and intimate Italian restaurant" where the "generous" cuisine includes some "excellent home-made pizzas" and some "good reasonably-priced wines". / **Details:** *www.gustotrattoria.co.uk.*

Michael's £ 38 ❸❷❸
47 Liverpool Rd PR8 4AG (01704) 550886
Rather unsettled reports of late on Michael Wichmann's small and very personal restaurant; for fans it "never fails to excel, offering "wonderful food, friendly staff and cosy" surroundings"; critics, however, fear it's "gone off". / **Details:** *www.michaelsbirkdale.co.uk; 2 minutes walk from Birkdale train station; 10 pm; D only, closed Mon & Sun.*

The Swan at Southrop £ 42 ❷❷❷
GL7 3NU (01367) 850205
"A great example of how good pub-restaurants can be", say fans; this "beautiful" Cotswold "find" has a huge following for its "delicious" food, "warm" ambience and "lovely village location". / **Details:** *www.theswanatsouthrop.co.uk; 10 pm; closed Sun D; no Amex.*

Coasters £ 42 🆃
Queen St IP18 6EQ (01502) 724734
"Best meal we had in Southwold last year" – this small restaurant (with courtyard) doesn't get many reports, but all applaud its "great food and good value-for-money"; "they need a bigger place so more people can enjoy it!" / **Details:** *www.coastersofsouthwold.co.uk; 2 min walk from seafront and Market square; 9 pm; closed Mon & Sun D; no Amex; booking essential.*

The Crown
Adnams Hotel £ 50 ❸❷❷
High St IP18 6DP (01502) 722275
"Wonderfully relaxed and convivial" – this "characterful" Adnams-owned inn is a "buzzing" sort of place offering not just "freshly-brewed beer" but also a "comprehensive wine list by the glass"; the food, in comparison, can seem a tad "staid", but it's generally reckoned to be pretty "consistent". / **Details:** *www.adnamshotels.co.uk; 9 pm, Fri & Sat 9.30 pm.* **Accommodation:** *14 rooms, from £145.*

Sole Bay Fish Company £ 27 ⊤

22e Blackshore IP18 6ND   (01502) 724241
Tipped for "great fresh fish", a harbour-front café where you bring not only your own wine, but also your own bread.
/ **Details:** www.solebayfish.co.uk; closed Mon.

The Swan £ 50 ④❷❷

The Market Pl IP18 6EG   (01502) 722186
Fans of this Adnams-owned hotel – with its "vast" traditional dining room – still find it a "special experience" with "formal but helpful" staff and quality cuisine; others, though, feel it's still stuck "in a mediocre phase" and that the food tends to "unimaginative".
/ **Details:** www.adnams.co.uk; 9 pm; children: 5+ at D.
Accommodation: 42 rooms, from £150.

SOWERBY BRIDGE, WEST YORKSHIRE 5–1C

Gimbals £ 38 ⊤

76 Wharf St HX6 2AF   (01422) 839329
A "cosy","friendly" and "popular" bistro, tipped as "a good venue for a night out with friends or family". / **Details:** www.gimbals.co.uk; 9.15 pm; D only, closed Sun; no Amex.

SPARSHOLT, HAMPSHIRE 2–3D

The Plough Inn £ 44 ⊤

SO21 2NW   (01962) 776353
"Great venue, great pub food, great beer" – this "reliably good" inn ("more a restaurant, really") is tipped by a number of reporters for its all-round standards. / **Details:** www.theploughsparsholt.co.uk; 9 pm, Sun & Mon 8.30 pm, Fri & Sat 9.30 pm; no Amex.

SPELDHURST, KENT 3–4B

George & Dragon £ 42 ❷❷❷

Speldhurst Hill TN3 0NN   (01892) 863125
"A bustling pub in a lovely village setting" that "lives up to its claim to serve high-quality, locally-sourced food"; "great outdoor area" too.
/ **Details:** www.speldhurst.com; 9.30 pm; closed Sun D; no Amex.

ST ALBANS, HERTFORDSHIRE 3–2A

Barissimo £ 14 ⊤

28 St Peters St AL1 3NA   (01727) 869999
It may just be an "excellent coffee bar", but this "family-run cheap 'n' cheerful spot" is tipped by a number of reporters for its all-round quality; "try the panini". / **Details:** L only; no credit cards.

The Blue Anchor £ 46 ⊤

145 Fishpool St AL3 4RY   (01727) 855 038
"A great family venue"; this "good local gastropub" is tipped for its "consistently good" and "imaginative" cuisine.
/ **Details:** www.theblueanchorstalbans.co.uk; Tue-Fri, Sun 6pm; closed Mon.

La Cosa Nostra £ 39 ⊤

62 Lattimore Rd AL1 3XR   (01727) 832658
It has "no pretensions", but this long-established family-run Italian is still tipped by some reporters as "one of the town's top cheap 'n' cheerful destinations". / **Details:** www.lacosanostraltd.co.uk; near railway station; 10.30 pm; closed Sat L & Sun; no Amex.

Darcy's   £ 48   ❷❷❸
2 Hatfield Rd AL1 3RP   (01727) 730777
*"The best of the bunch locally", this city-centre ten-year-old offers an
"interesting" Pan-Asian slanted menu (of a type "without direct
competition locally") its "reliability" helps please all the numerous
reporters who comment on it. /* **Details:** *www.darcysrestaurant.co.uk;
9 pm, Fri & Sat 10 pm.*

Mumtaj   £ 30   ❷❸④
115 London Rd AL1 1LR   (01727) 843691
*"Forget the posh London Indians, this is the real deal", say fans of
this "old-school curry house" whose "fantastic" standards impress
almost all who comment on it; its offshoot, Chez Mumtaj, offers a
more evolved formula – a hit with most reporters, even if the service
can be "desperately slow". /* **Details:** *midnight.*

St Michael's Manor   £ 50   🅣
Fishpool St AL3 4RY   (01727) 864444
*"Lovely gardens" beside a river set an upscale and romantic tone at
this country house hotel, which is sometimes tipped as offering "the
best dining in St Albans". /* **Details:** *www.stmichaelsmanor.com; near the
Cathedral; 9 pm.* **Accommodation:** *30 rooms, from £130.*

Zaza   £ 33   🅣
5a High St AL3 4ED   (01727) 812683
*A "busy" Italian that's a top tip locally for those in search of
somewhere "reliable, convenient and welcoming".
/* **Details:** *www.sazio.co.uk; 10.30 pm.*

The Waffle House
Kingsbury Water Mill   £ 20   🅣
St Michael's St AL3 4SJ   (01727) 853502
*Got kids in tow? – that's the top reason to know about this "packed-
out" snackery in a pretty old mill, a destination to please all the
family for over three decades. /* **Details:** *www.wafflehouse.co.uk; near
Roman Museum; 6 pm; L only; no Amex; no booking.*

ST ANDREWS, FIFE   9–3D

Seafood Restaurant   £ 61   ❷❷❶
The Scores, Bruce Embankment KY16 9AB   (01334) 479475
*"This glass box perched on the dunes on the edge of the North Sea
would be worth sitting in for the view alone"... but, with its
"stupendous" food (in particular "brimming seafood platters") and
"helpful" service, it's a "sheer joy" all round.
/* **Details:** *www.theseafoodrestaurant.com; 10 pm; ; children: 12+ at D.*

Vine Leaf   £ 46   ❷❶❸
131 South St KY16 9UN   (01334) 477497
*"Hidden-away in the old part of the town", this quarter-centenarian
(and perhaps now slightly "dated") bistro is a "lovely" place which
impresses all reporters with its "perfect" service and "good and
varied" cuisine. /* **Details:** *www.vineleafstandrews.co.uk; 9.30 pm; D only,
closed Mon & Sun.* **Accommodation:** *3 guest apartments rooms, from £80.*

ST DAVIDS, PEMBROKESHIRE   4–4A

Cwtch   £ 38   ❷❷❷
22 High St SA62 6SD   (01437) 720491
*Simple but carefully-prepared cuisine and "friendly service"
contribute to the "comfortable" experience of visiting this "friendly"
small operation in the heart of the town.
/* **Details:** *www.cwtchrestaurant.co.uk; 9.30 pm; D only.*

Alba Restaurant   £ 41   ❷❷❸
The Old Life Boat Hs, Wharf Rd TR26 ILF (01736) 797222
*"With beautiful views from window tables upstairs", this "simply
decorated" harbourside café is still, on most accounts, a "lovely"
destination, with "inventive but reliable" fish-based cuisine; recent
reports, however, have been a tad less consistent than usual.*
/ **Details:** *www.thealbarestaurant.com; 9.30 pm.*

Porthgwidden Beach Café   £ 40   ❷❷❶
Porthgwidden Beach TR26 ISL (01736) 796791
*"The least-known of the three beach cafés in St Ives"; fans say it's
"slightly more relaxed" than the others, but has a "similarly
spectacular view" and is still "a fantastic place to eat", either for a
"chill out breakfast" or other "hearty" fare.*
/ **Details:** *www.porthgwiddencafe.co.uk; 10 pm; no Amex; booking: max 10.*

Porthminster Café   £ 48   ❶❷❶
Porthminster Beach TR26 2EB (01736) 795352
*"Outstanding" Asian-influenced fish dishes, "glorious setting
overlooking white sand" and "cheerfully breezy" style – hardly
surprising this is the most "popular" beach-side restaurant in the
UK.* / **Details:** *www.porthminstercafe.co.uk; near railway station; 10 pm;
no Amex.*

The Seafood Café   £ 39   ❸❷❸
45 Fore St TR26 IHE (01736) 794004
*This "brightly-lit café restaurant" has won popularity for its order-at-
the-bar fishy formula – given the venue's simple style, results can
seem "better than you might expect".* / **Details:** *www.seafoodcafe.co.uk;
map on website; 10.30 pm; no Amex.*

Tate Cafe
Tate Gallery   £ 33   ❶
Porthmeor Beach TR26 ITG (01736) 796226
*Tipped for "one of the best views in town" and a "fantastic fresh fish
sandwich" too, this cultural facility café otherwise inspires mixed
reviews.* / **Details:** *www.tate.org.uk; L only; no Amex.*

St Clement's   £ 44   ❶
3 Mercatoria TN38 0EB (01424) 200355
*Not everyone likes the "café-ish" interior, but this "small and tucked-
away" fish bistro is tipped by numerous reporters for "fresh local fish
at good prices".* / **Details:** *www.stclementsrestaurant.co.uk; 10 pm; closed
Mon & Sun D; no Amex.*

Hotel Tresanton   £ 58   ❷❷❶
27 Lower Castle Rd TR2 5DR (01326) 270055
*"An idyllic place with an equally beautiful restaurant… but it is
expensive" – Olga Pollizzi's fashionable sea-view hotel has "a
location to die for", and many al fresco tables on its cascading
terraces; its "quality" food somewhat plays second fiddle, though.*
/ **Details:** *www.tresanton.com; near Castle; 9.30 pm; booking: max 10;
children: 6+ at dinner.* **Accommodation:** *29 rooms, from £240.*

ST MERRYN, CORNWALL   1–3B

The Cornish Arms   £ 32   ④④❸
Churchtown PL28 8ND   (01841) 520288
*Mixed views on this pub offshoot of the Rick Stein empire, a short
drive from Padstow; most reviews speak of "basic pub food done
really well" in a "no-nonsense" setting – to a minority, however, it's a
"cavernous, barren place, not up to his usual standard".*

ST MONANS, FIFE   9–4D

Craig Millar @ 16 West End   £ 58   ❶❷❷
16 West End KY10 2BX   (01333) 730327
*Now under Craig Millar's personal branding, the former 'Seafood
Restaurant' still offers "perfectly cooked, very fresh fish" in an
elegant seaside dining room with lovely views over the harbour; it's
"relatively inexpensive" too. / Details: www.16westend.com; 9.30 pm;
closed Mon & Tue; children: 5+.*

STAMFORD, LINCOLNSHIRE   6–4A

The George Hotel   £ 68   ④❸❶
71 St Martins PE9 2LB   (01780) 750750
*"A genuine slice of English tradition" – this monumental inn at the
heart of this gorgeous town is a "glorious" place (especially if you get
a table in the "charming oak-panelled main restaurant"); reviews are
decidedly up-and-down, though, with critics finding the fare "a bit
'70s" and "expensive". / Details: www.georgehotelofstamford.com; off A1,
14m N of Peterborough, onto B1081; 10 pm; jacket and/or tie; children: 8+ at
D. Accommodation: 47 rooms, from £150.*

Jim's Yard   £ 42   ❸❷❷
3 Ironmonger St PE9 1PL   (01780) 756080
*Particularly worth seeking out for its "terrific-value lunch menus",
this "bistro-cum-conservatory" is consistently praised for its "good
food" ("a rarity in Stamford") and "attentive" service.
/ Details: www.jimsyard.biz; 9.30 pm; closed Mon & Sun; no Amex.*

STANTON, SUFFOLK   3–1C

Leaping Hare Vineyard   £ 39   ❷❸❷
Wyken Vineyards IP31 2DW   (01359) 250287
*A "delightful barn-conversion" that's "worth travelling to the middle
of nowhere for" – it makes "a wonderful setting for lunch or dinner",
offering a "straightforward" menu that's "appealing" and
"reasonably-priced" too, plus "interesting" wines (mostly their own,
of course!) / Details: www.wykenvineyards.co.uk; 9m NE of Bury St
Edmunds; follow tourist signs off A143; 6 pm, Fri & Sat 9 pm; L only, ex Fri &
Sat open L & D; no Amex.*

STATHERN, LEICESTERSHIRE   5–3D

Red Lion Inn   £ 36   ❷❸❷
2 Red Lion St LE14 4HS   (01949) 860868
*Though less well-known than its famous Clipsham sibling, the Olive
Branch, this "cosy and characterful dining room", in an "agreeably
rustic" pub near Belvoir Castle, currently enjoys higher ratings,
including for its "tried and trusted" traditional dishes, "cooked very
well". / Details: www.theredlioninn.co.uk; 9.30 pm; closed Sun D; no Amex.*

STOCKBRIDGE, HAMPSHIRE 2–3D

Clos du Marquis £ 48 ❷❷❷
London Rd SO20 6DE (01264) 810738
"A taste of real French cooking in the depths of Hampshire"; with its "accurate" cuisine and a "wonderful welcome" too, Germain Marquis's "unassuming"-looking 'auberge' lives up to its "local-favourite" status. / Details: www.closdumarquis.co.uk; 2m E on A30 from Stockbridge; 9 pm; closed Mon & Sun D.

Greyhound £ 47 ❸❸❸
31 High St SO20 6EY (01264) 810833
*Less enthusiastic reviews this year on this rural gastropub; fans again hail a welcoming place with a "varied and consistently delicious" menu – of late, however, there have been almost as many sceptics for whom it was "not as good as hoped".
/ Details: www.thegreyhound.info; 9 pm, Fri & Sat 9.30 pm; closed Sun D; no Amex; booking: max 12. Accommodation: 7 rooms, from £95.*

STOCKCROSS, BERKSHIRE 2–2D

The Vineyard at Stockcross £ 98 ❸❹❸
RG20 8JU (01635) 528770
*Sir Peter Michael's California-style country house hotel still divides views; fans proclaim the "slick" combination of Daniel Galmiche's "sinful" cooking with a "magnificent" New World wine list ("you need two hours just to read it!"); the occasional critic, though, still finds the whole experience rather "sterile". / Details: from M4, J13 take A34 towards Hungerford; 9.30 pm; no jeans or trainers.
Accommodation: 49 rooms, from £125.*

STOCKPORT, LANCASHIRE 5–2B

Damson £ 46 ❷❷❸
113 Heaton Moor Rd SK4 4HY (0161) 4324666
An "excellent neighbourhood restaurant", in Heaton Moor, whose "well-executed dishes" would be welcome anywhere – around Manchester, the "inventive and unusual" approach makes this "one of the best places around". / Details: www.damsonrestaurant.co.uk; take the A6 until the Royal Bank of Scotland on left;all the way down the High Street and then turn left; 9.30 pm, Fri & Sat 10 pm; closed Sun D.

STOKE ROW, OXFORDSHIRE 2–2D

The Crooked Billet £ 47 ❷❷❷
Newlands Ln RG9 5PU (01491) 681048
"Down a long and winding country lane", this "delightful olde-worlde pub" is a popular destination that's "full of character" and with "friendly" and "efficient" service too; on the food front, "classics are done very well". / Details: www.thecrookedbillet.co.uk; off the A4130; 10 pm.

STOKE-BY-NAYLAND, SUFFOLK 3–2C

The Crown £ 43 ❸❹❸
Park St CO6 4SE (01206) 262346
*"Not adventurous, but the sort of place anyone can find something to enjoy" – this "buzzy gastropub" (with a "glorious courtyard") is often hailed as quite a "find" even if prices can seem "a little high for this part of the world"; service doesn't always measure up.
/ Details: www.crowninn.net; on B1068; 9.30 pm, Fri & Sat 10 pm, Sun 9 pm. Accommodation: 11 rooms, from £80.*

Howards   £ 41   ❷④④
30 College Sq TS9 5DN   (01642) 713391
*For a superior "cheap 'n' cheerful meal", this smart village diner – offering "imaginative" menu and "good selection of wines" – comes unanimously recommended. / **Details**: www.howards-eatery.co.uk; Mon-Weds 8 pm, Thu-Sun 9 pm; closed Sun D.*

The Old Butchers   £ 42   ❷❶❷
Park St GL54 1AQ   (01451) 831700
*"Superb" and "imaginative" food that "bursts with flavour" makes this surprisingly "affordable" town-centre brasserie a "gem"; its standards of late have been particularly impressive. / **Details**: www.theoldbutchers.com; on the main road heading out of Stow on the Wold towards Oddington; 9.30 pm, Sat 10 pm; Max 12.*

Inver Cottage Restaurant   £ 37   ❶
Stracthlachlan PA27 8BU   (01369) 860537
*"Heaven on Earth", exclaim fans of this waterside croft on the shore of Lachlan Bay tipped for its "brilliant, locally sourced and original" food, as well as its "excellent" service and "breath-taking" location. / **Details**: www.invercottage.com; 8.30 pm; closed Mon & Tue; no Amex.*

Lambs   £ 45   ④❷❸
12 Sheep St CV37 6EF   (01789) 292554
*This olde-worlde Tudor building has long housed one of the town's better eating options, including pre-theatre; reports were a bit up-and-down this year, but still suggest it's an "efficient" spot which offers "a good choice of dishes". / **Details**: www.lambsrestaurant.co.uk; 9.30 pm; closed Mon L; no Amex.*

Rooftop Restaurant
Royal Shakespeare Theatre   £ 50   ⑤⑤❸
Waterside CV37 6BB   (01789) 403449
*"A great opportunity lost"; it may have "the best view in town", but otherwise the restaurant on top of the rejuvenated theatre delivers a "disappointing" performance. / **Details**: www.rsc.org.uk/eat; 9.45 pm; no Amex.*

The Vintner   £ 39   ❶
4-5 Sheep St CV37 6EF   (01789) 297259
*"Always a good meal, like at the sister restaurant, Lamb's" – this popular destination is particularly tipped for its "good-value pre-theatre menu". / **Details**: www.the-vintner.co.uk; 9.30 pm, Fri & Sat 10 pm, Sun 8.30 pm; no Amex.*

Kishorn Seafood Bar   £ 32   ❶
Kishorn IV54 8XA   (01520) 733240
*"Don't be fooled by the unprepossessing appearance!" – this "Little Chef-style roadside hut" is tipped as "a paradise for seafood-lovers". / **Details**: www.kishornseafoodbar.co.uk.*

STUCKTON, WILTSHIRE 2–3C

Three Lions £ 52 ❷❸④
Stuckton Rd SP6 2HF (01425) 652489
"The highest cooking standards in the area" make it worth seeking
out the Womersley family's *"friendly"*, perhaps rather *"old-
fashioned"* New Forest restaurant, which continues to impress all
reporters with its *"consistently delicious"* (if *"slightly pricey"*) dishes.
/ **Details:** www.thethreelionsrestaurant.co.uk; 1m E of Fordingbridge off
B3078; 9 pm, Fri & Sat 9.30 pm; closed Mon & Sun D; no Amex.
Accommodation: 7 rooms, from £80.

STUDLAND, DORSET 2–4C

Shell Bay Seafood £ 38 ❸④❶
Ferry Rd BH19 3BA (01929) 450363
"Standards can fluctuate a bit... but the view doesn't!" – *"arrive
early for a front-row seat"* best to enjoy the panorama at this
"brilliantly-located" watersider where the fish 'n' chips are usually
"very good", and the *"reasonably-priced"* seafood is often great too.
/ **Details:** www.shellbay.net; just near the Sandbanks to Swanage ferry; 9 pm.

SUNBURY ON THAMES, SURREY 3–3A

Indian Zest £ 31 ❷❷❷
21 Thames St TW16 5QF (01932) 765 000
"Rapidly established as the best Indian in the area", this rambling
three-year-old sibling to the well-known Hammersmith star, Indian
Zing, likewise serves notably *"good and 'different'"* cuisine.
/ **Details:** www.indianzest.co.uk; 12.00 pm.

SUNNINGDALE, BERKSHIRE 3–3A

Bluebells £ 59 ❷❷❸
Shrubs Hill SL5 0LE (01344) 622 722
"Fine cooking at incredible prices" (*"we have clients who will visit us
just so they can go to lunch!"*) makes the lunch menu at this
intimate rural restaurant particularly worth seeking out – *"dinner is
pricier, but worth it too"*. / **Details:** www.bluebells-restaurant.com;
9.45 pm; closed Mon & Sun D.

SURBITON, SURREY 3–3A

The French Table £ 51 ❶❶④
85 Maple Rd KT6 4AW (020) 8399 2365
"It would hold its own in the 7ème!"; *"absolutely authentic Gallic
bistro-style grub"* makes an ongoing hit of Eric & Sarah Guignard's
"treasure of suburbia" – a *"lovely"*, if *"noisy"* spot, that invariably
impresses; can its new café-offshoot really be called the French
Tarte? / **Details:** www.thefrenchtable.co.uk; 10.30 pm; closed Mon & Sun D.

Joy £ 31 ❸④④
37 Brighton Rd KT6 5LR (020) 8390 3988
"A better-than-average Indian" in a *"pleasant modern room with
well spaced tables"*, consistently praised by a big local fan club for
"enjoyable" dishes that are a bit *"out of the ordinary"*.
/ **Details:** www.joy-restaurant.co.uk; 11.30 pm.

Red Rose £ 27 ❼
38 Brighton Rd KT6 5PQ (020) 8399 9647
*"I'd go back, despite the competition from other well-reputed Indians
nearby!"* – this suburban subcontinental is again tipped for its
"willing" staff and *"tasty"* fare. / **Details:** www.redroseofsurbiton.com;
11.30 pm.

The Anchor £ 40 🆃
Bury Ln CB6 2BD (01353) 778537
Not many reports of late, but this atmospheric inn beside the Ouse wash is still tipped as an "always-dependable" destination.
/ **Details:** www.anchorsuttongault.co.uk; 7m W of Ely, signposted off B1381 in Sutton; 9 pm, Sat 9.30 pm, Sun 8.30 pm. **Accommodation:** 4 rooms, from £79.5.

Olive Tree £ 43 ④④❸
Sutton Green Rd GU4 7QD (01483) 729999
"Out in the sticks", a gastropub with a reputation for "pretty decent fare" (especially fish and seafood); standards have of late sometimes seemed rather "variable", though, and some reporters fear the place is "resting on its laurels". / **Details:** 9.30 pm; closed Mon D & Sun D; no Amex.

Morgans
Morgans Hotel £ 34 🆃
Somerset Pl SA1 1RR (01792) 484848
At Swansea's top hotel, "the impressive board room of this early 20th century building forms a great setting for dining"; we only incude it as a tip, though, as reports are few, and (like last year) tell tales of highs and lows. / **Details:** www.morganshotel.co.uk; 9.45 pm; children: 12+. **Accommodation:** 42 rooms, from £100.

The Wheatsheaf at Swinton £ 43 ❸❸❸
Main St TD11 3JJ (01890) 860257
Handy (and well commented-on) in a thinly-provided part of the world – a "great restaurant with rooms" offering a "thoroughly enjoyable, pub-like experience". / **Details:** www.wheatsheaf-swinton.co.uk; between Kelso & Berwick-upon-Tweed, by village green; 9 pm, 8.30 pm; Closed Sun D Jan & Feb; no Amex; children: 8+. **Accommodation:** 10 rooms, from £112.

The Terrace
Cliveden House £ 87
Cliveden Rd SL6 0JF (01628) 668561
The Astors' palazzo near the Thames – in recent times a Von Essen property – will move into new ownership in late 2011; it's been known in recent times for its "amazing" surroundings and "daylight robbery" prices – perhaps under the new régime the cuisine will begin to live up to the house's history, architecture and view?
/ **Details:** www.clivedenhouse.co.uk; 9.30 pm; no trainers.
Accommodation: 38 + cottage rooms, from £240.

Waldo's
Cliveden House £ 97
Clivedon Rd SL6 0JF   (01628) 668561
*As ever, there's little and very mixed feedback on the fine dining
room at this incredible palazzo, with fans hailing its "old-fashioned
glamour and outstanding food" and critics just dismissing it as "really
poor"; as at other Von Essen properties, we've left it un-rated as the
dust settles on the group's fortunes. / Details: www.clivedenhouse.co.uk;
M4, J7 then follow National Trust signs; 9.30 pm; D only, closed Mon & Sun;
no trainers; booking: max 6; children: 12+. Accommodation: 38 + Spring
Cottage rooms, from £195.*

TAUNTON, SOMERSET 2–3A

Augustus £ 36 ❸❷❷
3 The Courtyard, St James St TA1 1JR   (01823) 324 354
*From a team who met at the (now defunct) dining room of the
Castle Hotel, this "neighbourhood bistro" is hailed as a "welcome
newcomer", and its charm and overall "good value" commend it to
all early-days reporters. / Details: www.augustustaunton.co.uk; 9.30 pm;
closed Mon & Sun; no Amex.*

Brazz
Castle Hotel £ 44 🅣
Castle Bow TA1 1NF   (01823) 252000
*The "well furnished" brasserie offshoot of the Castle Hotel (for many
years a culinary destination of note) is tipped as a "great lunch
venue"; service, though, is "not always the fastest", and prices à la
carte can seem "high". / Details: www.brazz.co.uk; 10 pm.
Accommodation: 44 rooms, from £230.*

The Willow Tree £ 42 ❷❸❷
3 Tower Ln TA1 4AR   (01823) 352835
*"Wow, who knew you could find food this good in Somerset!" – this
"small but beautifully formed restaurant" (ten years old this year) is
a "reliable" and "friendly" spot hailed as offering "the best food for
miles around!" / Details: www.thewillowtreerestaurant.com; 9.15 pm;
D only, closed Sun & Mon; no Amex; Essential.*

TAVISTOCK, DEVON 1–3C

Hotel Endsleigh £ 60 ❷❷❷
PL19 0PQ   (01822) 870 000
*Olga & Alex Polizzi's "very refined" country house hotel has a
"stunning" bucolic location and a dining room offering food that's
always "good" and sometimes "unforgettable"; service is "of the
highest standard" too. / Details: www.hotelendsleigh.com; 9.30 pm.
Accommodation: 16 rooms, from £180.*

TEDDINGTON, SURREY 3–3A

Imperial China £ 39 🅣
196-198 Stanley Rd TW11 8UE   (020) 8977 8679
*"A very superior Chinese in an out-of-the-way location" – tipped as
"a local favourite for dim sum, and understandably so".
/ Details: www.imperialchinalondon.co.uk; 11 sun 10 pm.*

TENDRING, ESSEX 3–2D

The Fat Goose £ 38 ❸❸❸
Heath Rd CO16 0BX   (01255) 870060
*This "excellent" gastropub of recent vintage inspires only positive
reports, not least on the food front – it serves "a good selection of
old, hearty favourites, yet with enough real flair to make a meal of
interest". / Details: www.fat-goose.co.uk.*

Calcot Manor £ 61 T
GL8 8YJ (01666) 890391
"Much improved" of late – the conservatory dining room of this famously child-friendly Cotswold hotel may still not offer great gastronomic excitement, but it's undoubtedly "pleasant", and almost all reports confirm its impressive all-round consistency.
/ **Details:** www.calcotmanor.co.uk; junction of A46 & A4135; 9.30 pm, Sun 9 pm. **Accommodation:** 35 rooms, from £260.

Gumstool Inn
Calcot Manor £ 44 ❷④❸
GL8 8YJ (01666) 890391
Not quite as good as the main restaurant but more reasonably priced; this "classy" pub-styled brasserie is kitted out in Olde-English style and much recommended as a "convivial" and "reliable" operation. / **Details:** www.calcotmanor.co.uk; cross roads of a46 & A41345; 9.30 pm, Sun 9 pm; no jeans or trainers; children: 12+ at dinner in Conservatory. **Accommodation:** 35 rooms, from £240.

Trouble House Inn £ 44 ❷❸④
Cirencester Rd GL8 8SG (01666) 502206
"Honest, unpretentious and just very good" – this "welcoming" gastropub is "a handy stop-off when motoring through the Cotswolds", thanks to its "consistently tasty scoff"; "with all the hard surfaces", though, it "can get a bit noisy" at busy times.
/ **Details:** www.troublehouse.co.uk; 1.5m from Tetbury on A433 towards Cirencester; 9.30 pm; closed Mon; closed 2 weeks in Jan; booking: max 8; children: 14+ in bar.

Ronnie's £ 41 T
11 St Mary St BS35 2AR (01454) 411137
Ron Faulkner's four-year-old venture in a former 17th century barn is "not the most ergonomic" set-up, but is tipped for its "exemplary" food and "professional" (if "sometimes over-stretched") service.
/ **Details:** www.ronnies-restaurant.co.uk; 930 tue thur 1030 thur -sat; closed Mon & Sun D; no Amex.

Thornbury Castle £ 69
Castle St BS35 1HH (01454) 281182
The survey recorded some "superb" cooking at this fairytale castle in its own vineyard; with ownership of all properties in the Von Essen group being "in flux", however, we don't think a rating is appropriate. / **Details:** www.thornburycastle.co.uk; near intersection of M4 & M5; 9 pm; no jeans or trainers. **Accommodation:** 27 rooms, from £175.

Bakers Arms £ 39 T
Main St LE16 7TS (01858) 545201
"A great local favourite gastropub", tipped for its "super-homely food" and "great service". / **Details:** www.thebakersarms.co.uk; near Market Harborough off A6; 9.30 pm; D only, ex Sat open L & D & Sun open L only, closed Mon; no Amex; children: 12+.

TITLEY, HEREFORDSHIRE   2–1A

Stagg Inn   £ 47   ❷❷❷
HR5 3RL   (01544) 230221
"Still doing a great job in the middle of nowhere" – this *"fantastic"*
inn *"can have the odd blip"*, but the huge volume of positive
feedback it inspires is impressive; good accommodation at their
"quirky" B&B down the road too. / **Details:** www.thestagg.co.uk; on
B4355, NE of Kington; 9 pm; closed Mon & Sun D. **Accommodation:** 6
rooms, from £85.

TOLLARD ROYAL, WILTSHIRE   2–3C

The King John Inn   £ 51   ❷❷❷
SP5 5PS   (01725) 516 207
"Great pub food" is hailed by all reporters of this *"fantastic"* inn
whose attractions also run to *"an excellent selection of wines"*.
/ **Details:** www.kingjohninn.co.uk.

TOPSHAM, DEVON   1–3D

Darts Farm Café   £ 32   ❷❸④
Clyst St George EX3 0QH   (01392) 878201
This scale of this rural operation makes it a 'farm café' rather in the
sense that Harrods is a 'corner shop'; it still makes *"a great place for
brunch or lunch"*, though, the best bet being the *"upmarket fish 'n'
chips"*. / **Details:** www.dartsfarm.co.uk; M5 Junction 30, A376 towards
Exmouth; L only; no Amex.

The Galley   £ 46   ❷❷❸
41 Fore St EX3 0HU   (01392) 876078
"The new owners should be congratulated" says a fan of this
"quirky" fish restaurant where the new régime is *"trying hard"* and –
on all accounts – invariably succeeding.
/ **Details:** www.galleyrestaurant.co.uk; 9.30 pm; closed Mon & Sun; booking
essential; children: 12+.

La Petite Maison   £ 51   ⓣ
35 Fore St EX3 0HR   (01392) 873660
"A bit of an oasis in a desert", this cute little spot is tipped for its
"charming hosts" and cooking that's *"great value"* too.
/ **Details:** www.lapetitemaison.co.uk; next to The Globe Hotel; 10 pm; closed
Mon & Sun; no Amex; booking essential at L.

TORBERMORY, ARGYLL AND BUTE   9–3A

Cafe Fish   £ 40   ❶❷❷
The Pier PA75 6NU   (01688) 301253
"Never eaten fish this good, even at Rick Stein's!" – this *"lovely"*
waterside shack serves *"outstanding"* dishes *"straight-from-boat-to-
table"*; *"there's a great terrace where birds come and go, and if
you're lucky dolphins too"*. / **Details:** www.thecafefish.com; 30-40 min
drive north from the ferry pier at Criagnure; 9 pm; no Amex.

TORCROSS, DEVON   1–4D

Start Bay Inn   £ 30   ❷❸❷
TQ7 2TQ   (01548) 580553
"Right on Slapton Sands" this beach-side boozer is *"always crowded"*
(*"finding a table can be difficult"*), thanks to its *"delicious, fresh-
caught fish"* ('n' chips) and other *"very good seafood"* – *"the owner
dives for the scallops!"* / **Details:** www.startbayinn.co.uk; on beach front
(take A379 coastal road to Dartmouth); 10 pm; no Amex; no booking.

The Cary Arms £ 44 ❷❸❷
Babbacombe Beach TQ1 3LX (01803) 327 110
It's not just the "stunning location, right on the bay" that recommends this "idyllic" beach-side inn to reporters – its "locally-sourced and freshly cooked cuisine" conveys "a real sense of quality"; "good letting rooms" too – many "with private cliff-top terraces!" / **Details:** www.caryarms.co.uk; 9 pm.

Elephant Restaurant & Brasserie £ 64 ❷❸④
3-4 Beacon Ter, Harbourside TQ1 2BH (01803) 200044
"Best meal of the year", "never fails to impress", "superb"… – most reporters are very impressed by this first floor town-centre gem (with bistro below), noted particularly for its seafood. / **Details:** www.elephantrestaurant.co.uk; 9.30 pm; closed Mon & Sun; children: 14+ at bar.

No 7 Fish Bistro £ 50 ❶❸④
7 Beacon Ter TQ1 2BH (01803) 295055
Beware "lots of tables jammed into a smallish space", at this "noisy", "no-frills" bistro; it justifies the squash, though, with its "super-fresh fish, beautifully cooked". / **Details:** www.no7-fish.com; 9.45 pm; D only Sun-Tue.

Gurnards Head £ 43 ④④❷
TR26 3DE (01736) 796928
"Right at the tip of Cornwall", this "shabby chic" coastal gastropub is, say fans, a "fabulous all-seasons destination" offering a "delicious" fish-centric menu; sceptics, though, feel it "thinks far too much of itself" and say that – though "everyone raves" – the food is "only just OK". / **Details:** www.gurnardshead.co.uk; on coastal road between Land's End & St Ives, near Zennor B3306; 9.30 pm; no Amex. **Accommodation:** 7 rooms, from £90.

Olive Limes £ 36 ❷❸❸
60 High St HP23 5AG (01442) 828283
The occasional critic does find the style "annoyingly pompous", but this Indian overlooking Tring Park pleases most reporters with its "good and interesting" cuisine. / **Details:** www.olivelimes.co.uk; 11 pm, fri & sat 11.30 pm.

Queen's Head £ 42 ❶
Townhead LA23 1PW (01539) 432174
"A Lakeland favourite" – this atmospheric pub is tipped for the "hearty fare" from its "daily-changing menu". / **Details:** www.queensheadhotel.com; A592 on Kirkstone Pass; 9 pm; no Amex. **Accommodation:** 15 rooms, from £120.

Indaba £ 44 ❷❷❸
Tabernacle St TR1 2EJ (01872) 274 700
"The new chef has much improved the quality of the food", says a fan of this airy fish-specialist, which some reporters now claim to be "quite simply the best restaurant in Truro"! / **Details:** www.indabafish.co.uk.

Saffron £ 38 ❷❸④
5 Quay St TR1 2HB (01872) 263771
"You're almost guaranteed a high-quality meal" says a fan of this
"great little bistro" – the menu may be *"small"*, but it's *"interesting"*
and *"ever-changing".* / **Details:** www.saffronrestauranttruro.co.uk; 10 pm;
closed Sun.

TUNBRIDGE WELLS, KENT 3–4B

Hotel du Vin et Bistro £ 42 **T**
Crescent Rd TN1 2LY (01892) 526455
*An outpost of the boutique hotel chain tipped for "a relaxed
atmosphere that always feels special" – there's also, of course, the
group's famous wine list; the food is rather incidental.*
/ **Details:** www.hotelduvin.com; opp Assembly Hall; 10 pm, Fri & Sat
10.30 pm; booking: max 10. **Accommodation:** 34 rooms, from £120.

Thackeray's £ 64 ❷❸❸
85 London Rd TN1 1EA (01892) 511921
It's the "stonkingly good-value set lunch" which inspires waves of
upbeat reports for Richard Phillips's *"classy"* ten-year-old in a *"lovely"*
Regency villa; the dinnertime experience inspires much less
feedback. / **Details:** www.thackerays-restaurant.co.uk; near Kent and Sussex
hospital; 10.30 pm; closed Mon & Sun D.

TURNERS HILL, WEST SUSSEX 3–4B

Tarana £ 30 ❷❷❷
Selsfield Rd RH10 4PP (01342) 716 363
*With its "imaginative" menu, "well above-average" food and
"friendly" service, this "really pleasant" village Indian inspires only
the most positive reports.* / **Details:** www.taranarestaurant.co.uk;
10.45 pm; no Amex.

TUXFORD, NOTTINGHAMSHIRE 5–2D

Mussel and Crab £ 43 **T**
Sibthorpe Hill NG22 0PJ (01777) 870 491
"Almost like being at the seaside" (no mean feat in a land-locked
county!) – this *"friendly"* operation of over 20 years' standing is a
top tip for those in search of good fish and seafood.
/ **Details:** www.musselandcrab.com.

TWICKENHAM, SURREY 3–3A

Pallavi £ 27 ❷❸④
Unit 3, Cross Deep Ct, Heath Rd, TW1 4QJ (020) 8892
2345
*Ignore the surroundings – it's the "genuine" south Indian cooking
that makes this somewhat "uninspiring" looking spot worth seeking
out.*

ULLSWATER, CUMBRIA 7–3D

Sharrow Bay £ 94 ❷❸❶
CA10 2LZ (01768) 486301
*The "incomparable" lake-view setting of this "historic temple of
gastronomy" – often regarded as the UK's original country house
hotel – will survive the ongoing disintegration of its owner, the Von
Essen group; fingers crossed the "superb" traditional British food
holds up too!* / **Details:** www.sharrowbay.co.uk; on Pooley Bridge Rd towards
Howtown; 8 pm; children: 10+. **Accommodation:** 24 rooms, from £175.

UPPER SLAUGHTER, GLOUCESTERSHIRE 2–1C

Lords of the Manor £ 82 ④④❸
GL54 2JD (01451) 820243
*"You are made to feel like 21st-century Lords of the Manor", say
fans of this Cotswold country house, which they acclaim as a
"romantic" destination with "adventurous" British food; too many
reporters feel it's disappointing, though, saying the "value's not
great" and the food's "trying to be too flash".
/ **Details:** www.lordsofthemanor.com; 4m W of Stow on the Wold; 9.30 pm;
D only, ex Sun open L & D; no jeans or trainers; children: 7+ at D in
restaurant. **Accommodation:** 26 rooms, from £195.*

UPPINGHAM, RUTLAND 5–4D

The Lake Isle £ 46 ⓣ
16 High Street East LE15 9PZ (01572) 822951
*A small restaurant-with-rooms – cutely-located at the heart of an
attractive small town – tipped for its "short" but "imaginative" menu
and "seriously good wine". / **Details:** www.lakeisle.co.uk; past the Market
place, down the High Street; 9 pm, Fri & Sat 9.30 pm; closed Mon L & Sun D.
Accommodation: 12 rooms, from £75.*

UTTOXETER, STAFFORDSHIRE 5–3C

Restaurant Gilmore £ 48 ⓣ
Strine's Farm ST14 5DZ (01889) 507100
*Few reports sadly, but all confirm the quality of this "unpretentious"
farmhouse-restaurant, tipped for its "good food in generous
portions"; more reports please! / **Details:** www.restaurantgilmore.com;
9 pm; closed Mon, Tue, Wed L, Sat L & Sun D; no Amex; booking essential.*

VENTNOR, ISLE OF WIGHT 2–4D

The Hambrough £ 76 ❶❷❸
Hambrough Road PO38 1SQ (01983) 856333
*"Food in a different league from anywhere else on the island" –
indeed, from most places! – is carving a big reputation for Richard
Thompson's "sophisticated" operation, where a "small but very
interesting" menu is "beautifully cooked and served"; "book a table
at the front for the enchanting sea views!"
/ **Details:** www.robert-thompson.com; 9.30 pm; closed Mon & Sun; no Amex.
Accommodation: 7 rooms, from £170.*

VERYAN-IN-ROSELAND, CORNWALL 1–4B

**Dining Room
The Nare Hotel** £ 61 ⓣ
Carne Beach TR2 5PF (01872) 501111
*The very traditional dining room of this luxurious country-house style
hotel by the sea is tipped for "quality cooking with local ingredients";
there is also a more informal brasserie, which is some people's
preferred option. / **Details:** www.narehotel.co.uk; 9.30 pm; D only; jacket &
tie; Booking essential; children: 7+. **Accommodation:** 40 rooms, from £328.*

WADEBRIDGE, CORNWALL 1–3B

Relish £ 32 ⓣ
Foundry Ct PL27 7QN (01208) 814214
*Looking for a place where "coffee is a passion as well as an art", or
just for a light lunch with a glass of wine? – this café/deli (with
courtyard) is "the place to go". / **Details:** www.relishwadebridge.co.uk;
closed Mon & Sun; no Amex.*

WAKEFIELD, WEST YORKSHIRE 5–1C

Aagrah £ 32 ❸❷❸
Barnsley Rd WF1 5NX (01924) 242222
"Excellent service" helps distinguish this "long-standing and reliable" branch of the excellent Yorkshire Indian chain.
/ **Details:** www.aagrah.com; from M1, J39 follow Barnsely Rd to A61; 11.30 pm, Sun 11 pm; D only. **Accommodation:** 10 rooms, from £35.

WALBERSWICK, SUFFOLK 3–1D

The Anchor £ 43 ❸❹❸
Main St IP18 6UA (01502) 722112
Rather erratic reports of late from this well-known coastal gastropub; on a good day you can hope to find "good, precise cooking", "professional service" and "reasonable prices" – at busy times, though, the kitchen can seem "unable to cope".
/ **Details:** www.anchoratwalberswick.com; 9 pm. **Accommodation:** 10 rooms, from £100.

WARNINGLID, WEST SUSSEX 3–4B

The Half Moon £ 43 🅣
The Street RH17 5TR (01444) 461227
"An attractive pub with garden in a pretty village", tipped for its "really reliable" food that's "well above average".
/ **Details:** www.thehalfmoonwarninglid.co.uk; 9.30 pm; closed Sun D; no Amex; children: 14+.

WARWICK, WARWICKSHIRE 5–4C

The Art Kitchen £ 37 ❶❷❸
7 Swan St CV34 4BJ (01926) 494303
"Jolts you out of any formulaic expectations" you might have been harbouring – "very classy food at reasonable prices", "genuinely complementary wine" and "friendly" staff make it "always a pleasure" to dine at this town-centre Thai.
/ **Details:** www.theartkitchen.com; 10 pm.

The Saxon Mill £ 40 🅣
Coventry Rd, Guys Cliffe CV34 5YN (01926) 492255
"Sit on the terrace, overlooking the rushing river" to get the best out of this "busy" and "airy" riverside pub, which is primarily tipped for its location. / **Details:** www.saxonmill.co.uk; 9.30 pm, Sun 9 pm.

WATERGATE BAY, CORNWALL 1–3B

The Beach Hut
Watergate Bay Hotel £ 43 ❹❹❷
On The Beach TR8 4AA (01637) 860543
"A great place to chill after a day on the beach"; this surfers' café does "amazing" burgers and "lovely fresh seafood" too, but it's the "truly great location" that really sets it apart.
/ **Details:** www.watergatebay.co.uk; 9 pm; no Amex. **Accommodation:** 69 rooms, from £105.

Fifteen Cornwall
Watergate Bay Hotel £ 62 ❸❷❶
TR8 4AA (01637) 861000
"Stunning sea views" and a "well-designed" interior help inspire enthusiasm for Jamie O's "bright and airy" beach-side chef-training operation; fans find the food "great" too, but critics find it "super-expensive" and "lacking in oomph". / **Details:** www.fifteencornwall.co.uk; on the Atlantic coast between Padstow and Newquay; 9.15 pm.

The Bell Inn   £ 39   ❸❸❸
Binton Rd CV37 8EB   (01789) 750 353
"Enlivened by a recent change of ownership", this small inn offers an "interesting" menu which features some "very good grazing dishes"; it has a "very nice garden" too, and it's "always busy".
/ **Details:** www.thebellald.co.uk; 9.30 pm. **Accommodation:** 6 rooms, from £42.

Goodfellows   £ 52   ❶❷④
5 Sadler St BA5 2RR   (01749) 673866
Adam Fellows's "odd L-shaped restaurant next door to a café", in the town-centre, is a notably "accomplished" spot; perhaps the interior is "a little dull", but his cooking (majoring in fish) is "consistently brilliant" (and his desserts are "divine")".
/ **Details:** www.goodfellowswells.co.uk; near the Cathedral and the Market Square; 9.30 pm; closed Mon, Tue D & Sun. **Accommodation:** 0 rooms, from £0.

Old Spot   £ 44   ❸❸❸
12 Sadler St BA5 2SE   (01749) 689099
It's not just the "amazing" views of the cathedral that makes Ian Bates's restaurant worth seeking out – all reports confirm the food is "delicious" too. / **Details:** www.theoldspot.co.uk; 10.30 pm; closed Mon, Tue L & Sun D.

Auberge du Lac
Brocket Hall   £ 84   ❸❷❷
AL8 7XG   (01707) 368888
"A beautiful setting for any occasion"; this "romantic" lakeside destination, with terrace, makes an especially good lunch destination, especially when the bargain menu is "second only to Le Gavroche for value!" – the occasional visit this year, however, was upset by "inattentive" service. / **Details:** www.brocket-hall.co.uk; on B653 towards Harpenden; 9.30 pm; closed Mon & Sun; no jeans or trainers.
Accommodation: 16 rooms, from £175.

Brocket Arms   £ 37   ❸④❸
Ayot St Lawrence AL6 9BT   (01438) 820250
A hard-to-find gastropub praised by most reporters as "worth the drive down windy lanes" for its "lovely" atmosphere and "well-executed and presented" dishes; no denying, though, that the occasional critic finds it "overpriced" or "average".
/ **Details:** www.brocketarms.com; 9 pm; closed Sun D; no Amex.
Accommodation: 6 rooms, from £85 b&b.

The Wellington   £ 44   ④④❸
1 High St AL6 9LZ   (01438) 714036
"Recovered from the fire", this "buzzy" boozer is of note for its range of "unusual" Oz (d'Arenberg) wines, and a "well chosen" menu; more sceptical reporters, however, find it "formulaic".
/ **Details:** www.wellingtonatwelwyn.co.uk; 10 pm. **Accommodation:** 6 rooms, from £100.

Chu Chin Chow £ 35 **T**
63 Old Woking Rd KT14 6LF (01932) 349581
Top tip for those in search of a "great local Chinese", offering "quality food in a nice setting, and at a reasonable price".
/ Details: www.chuchinchow.com; 11 pm.

The Cat Inn £ 44 **❸❸❸**
Queen's Sq RH19 4PP (01342) 810369
"A lively pub with good food prepared by former Gravetye Manor chef"; its "friendly" and "reliable" charms commend it to all who comment on it; the rear room – "with a view of the churchyard" – is the one to seek out. / Details: www.catinn.co.uk; 9 pm, Fri-Sun 9.30 pm; closed Sun D; no Amex; children: 7+. Accommodation: 4 rooms, from £100.

The Swan £ 49 **❹❹❸**
35 Swan St ME19 6JU (01732) 521910
Up-and-down reports again on this "stylish" brasserie in a former coaching inn – fans still say it offers "gorgeous food in a gorgeous setting", but critics speak of a "overpriced food and falling standards". / Details: www.theswanwestmalling.co.uk; 11 pm, Sun 8 pm.

The Thomas Lord £ 44 **❷❸❸**
High St GU32 1LN (01730) 829244
"A real jewel in the new South Downs National Park"; "fabulous fresh produce" is transformed into "refined dishes that really taste of the surrounding landscape" at this shabby-chic village inn.
/ Details: www.thethomaslord.co.uk; 9 pm, Sat 9.30 pm; no Amex.

The Company Shed £ 24 **❶❹❸**
129 Coast Rd CO5 8PA (01206) 382700
"Simply fantastic seafood" (with "no frills") underpins the phenomenal popularity of this "fun" seaside "rough diamond" – a waterside shed where you "BYO wine, bread and mayo"; it's horribly over-subscribed, though – "arrive either early or late".
/ Details: www.the-company-shed.co.uk; 4 pm; L only, closed Mon; no credit cards; no booking.

West Mersea Oyster Bar £ 35 **❷❸❹**
Coast Rd CO5 8LT (01206) 381600
"A little gem just along the road from the more famous 'Shed'" – this "bright and IKEA-esque" small outfit is often "heaving"; it majors in "brilliant fish 'n' chips", "cheap" oysters and "reasonable wine" (local!); certainly "an easier choice if you can't be bothered to BYO half your meal…" / Details: www.westmerseaoysterbar.co.uk; 8.30 pm; Sun-Thu closed D; no Amex; no shorts.

The Wensleydale Heifer £ 53 **❶❶❷**
Main St DL8 4LS (01969) 622322
"One of the best pub restaurants around with especially good fish" and "brilliant" service – this "incongruously land-locked" Dales inn wins hearty endorsements from practically all of the many people who report on it. / Details: www.wensleydaleheifer.co.uk; 9.30 pm; booking required. Accommodation: 13 rooms, from £130.

Perry's
£ 44 ④④❸

4 Trinity Rd, The Old Harbour DT4 8TJ   (01305) 785799

*A harbour-view fish restaurant which inspires a wide range of opinions – the middle view is that it's a "consistent" place, with a handy location, where the fish and seafood are generally dependable.
/ **Details:** www.perrysrestaurant.co.uk; 9.30 pm; no Amex; children: 7+.*

Food by Breda Murphy
£ 37 ❷❸❸

41 Station Rd BB9 9RH   (01254) 823446

*"A café-style restaurant-cum-deli" that's usually only open during the day; the food, though, is "excellent and just that little bit different", and includes some "very interesting" vegetarian choices.
/ **Details:** www.foodbybredamurphy.com; 5 pm; closed Mon & Sun, Tue-Sat D; no Amex.*

Three Fishes
£ 39 ❸❸❷

Mitton Rd BB7 9PQ   (01254) 826888

*The first of the 'son-of-Northcote' Ribble Valley Inns maintains a gigantic following for its "first-class 'local' food" (plus "decent beer and wine"); reports have included the odd "disappointment" of late, however, and critics say it's "over-rated".
/ **Details:** www.thethreefishes.com; 9 pm, Sun 8.30 pm.*

L'Olivo
£ 39 ❶

135 Marford Rd AL4 8NH   (01582) 834 145

*In a former boozer, an Italian restaurant that's "seemingly sprung up from nowhere"; service can be "over-enthusiastic", but the place is tipped for its "reliable" cooking and "lively" style.
/ **Details:** www.lolivo-restaurant.com; 9.30 pm; D only, closed Sun.*

The White Horse
£ 42 ❷❷❸

Rede Rd IP29 4SS   (01284) 735 760

*"Unfussy, freshly-cooked, always-enjoyable" – the fare at this "pleasant", "relaxed" and "reasonably-priced" inn, recently elegantly revamped, pleases almost all who comment on it.
/ **Details:** www.whitehorsewhepstead.co.uk.*

Greens
£ 45 ❷④④

13 Bridge St YO22 4BG   (01947) 600284

*"A nice alternative to the host of chip shops" – this admittedly "rather pricier" alternative attracts consistent praise for its "high-end" cuisine; the setting, though, can seem a bit "crammed-in".
/ **Details:** www.greensofwhitby.com; 9.30 pm, Fri & Sat 10 pm.*

Magpie Café
£ 38 ❶❷④

14 Pier Rd YO21 3PU   (01947) 602058

*"The most amazing fish 'n' chips you will ever eat!" win ongoing fame and adulation for this "friendly" harbour-side "institution" – the UK's best-known chippy; even the queues ("ridiculous") do nothing to dim enthusiasm. / **Details:** www.magpiecafe.co.uk; opp Fish Market; 9 pm; no Amex; no booking at L.*

Trenchers £ 39 ❸❷④
New Quay Rd YO21 1DH (01947) 603212
A "posh" but "pricey" chippy "tucked-away near the harbour",
tipped by its fans as "a serious competitor to the Magpie".
/ **Details:** www.trenchersrestaurant.co.uk; opp railway station, near marina;
8.30 pm; need 7+ to book.

WHITEBROOK, MONMOUTHSHIRE 2–2B

The Crown at Whitebrook £ 67 ❷❷❸
NP25 4TX (01600) 860254
"In a romantic setting on the Borders", this "hidden jewel" of a
restaurant-with rooms is a "must-try for foodies", thanks to James
Sommerin's ambitious cuisine; even fans, though, can feel the food
"occasionally suffers from over-complication".
/ **Details:** www.crownatwhitebrook.co.uk; 2m W of A466, 5m S of Monmouth;
9 pm; children: 12+ for D. **Accommodation:** 8 rooms, from £135.

WHITSTABLE, KENT 3–3C

Birdies £ 38 ❸❸❷
41 Harbour St CT5 1AH (01227) 265337
"Civilised", "reliable" and "buzzy" – the sort of terms reporters
invariably apply to this "lovely", "friendly" bistro; prices are
"surprisingly reasonable" too. / **Details:** 9.15 pm; closed Mon L & Tue;
no Amex.

Crab & Winkle £ 43 ❷④④
South Quay, Whitstable Harbour CT5 1AB (01227) 779377
"You eat above the fish market, so the ingredients could hardly be
fresher", at this first-floor dining room, where the culinary results are
generally "excellent"; the setting is "a bit basic", though.
/ **Details:** www.crabandwinklerestaurant.co.uk; just at the end of the high
street, on the sea front; 9.30 pm; Seasonal opening; closed Mon in winter,
closed Sun D ; no Amex.

JoJo £ 29 ❷❷❷
2 Herne Bay Rd CT5 2LQ (01227) 274591
"A totally enjoyable experience offering all the elements of a good
night out"; this "extremely cheerful" and "reliable" local favourite
(now moved to a new home) still pleases all reporters with its
"beautiful" tapas-based cuisine. / **Details:** www.jojosrestaurant.co.uk;
9.30 pm; closed Mon, Tue L & Sun D; no credit cards.

Pearson's Arms £ 44 ❷❸❷
The Horsebridge, Sea Wall CT5 1BT (01227) 272005
In a seafront pub in the heart of the town, this "first-rate casual
dining room" from the Richard Phillips stable impresses most
reporters; service, though, does have the occasional off-day.
/ **Details:** www.pearsonsarmsbyrichardphillips.co.uk; 9 pm, Fri & Sat 9.30 pm;
closed Sun D; no Amex.

Samphire £ 44 ❶❷❸
4 High St CT5 1BQ (01227) 770075
"It deserves to be on the culinary map!"; this all-day local "gem"
serves "delicious and inventive" breakfasts, lunches and snacks;
come the evening, the emphasis switches to "a small but perfectly
formed menu of traditional English dishes with a twist".
/ **Details:** www.samphirerestaurant.co.uk; 10 pm; no Amex.

Sportsman £ 50 **❶❷❷**
Faversham Rd, Seasalter CT5 4BP (01227) 273370
Stephen Harris's "off-the-chart-brilliant" gastroboozer – a 10-minute
drive into the salt marshes outside Whitstable – is "a total breath of
fresh air" ("in more ways than one!"); the "brilliantly prepared dishes
are a joy in their simplicity" and served in an "unfussy", totally
*"unpretentious" manner. / **Details**: www.thesportsmanseasalter.co.uk;*
8.45 pm; closed Mon & Sun D; no Amex; children: 18+ in main bar.

Wheelers Oyster Bar £ 42 **❶❷❷**
8 High St CT5 1BQ (01227) 273311
"A glorious experience, devoid of all poncciness and snobbery!"; this
"cramped but cute-as-could-be" high street fixture (est 1856)
continues to serve simple seafood dishes that are "always excellent,
and sometimes have a touch of the sublime"; "there's only a handful
of seats" so "book well ahead".
*/ **Details**: www.seewhitstable.com/Wheelers-Whitstable-Restaurant.html;*
7.30 pm, Sun 7 pm; closed Wed; no credit cards.

Whitstable Oyster Fishery Co. £ 54 **❸❹❷**
Horsebridge CT5 1BU (01227) 276856
The formula – "very fresh seafood in a wonderful, atmospheric
rambling building" – is "just about perfect", and this prominent
seaside spot remains extremely popular; it's "expensive for what it
is", though, and meals are occasionally spoilt by "charmless" service.
*/ **Details**: www.oysterfishery.co.uk; on the seafront; 8.45 pm, Fri 9.15 pm, Sat*
9.45 pm, Sun 8.15 pm; closed Mon .

WILLIAN, HERTFORDSHIRE 3–2B

The Fox £ 44 **❷❸❸**
SG6 2AE (01462) 480233
"A posh pub in a tiny village" – "a fantastic, every-day kind of place"
serving "brilliant" scoff, not least an "excellent" burger!
*/ **Details**: www.foxatwillian.co.uk; 1 mile from junction 9 off A1M; 9 pm;*
closed Sun D; no Amex.

WILMSLOW, CHESHIRE 5–2B

Chilli Banana
Kings Arms Hotel £ 40 **❷❷❸**
Alderley Rd SK9 1PZ (01625) 539100
"Still the best Thai in the area", this "friendly" pub dining room
continues to impress all who comment on it with its "reasonably-
priced" charms; "good take-away too – have a pint of real ale while
*you wait". / **Details**: www.chillibanana.co.uk; 11 pm; closed Mon,*
*Tue-Thu D only. **Accommodation**: 7 rooms, from £60.*

WINCHCOMBE, GLOUCESTERSHIRE 2–1C

5 North Street £ 59 **❷❷❹**
5 North St GL54 5LH (01242) 604566
Marcus Ashenford's "outstanding" cuisine – "with just about
everything locally-sourced and hand-made" – can come as
something of a surprise, at these "cosy" ("claustrophobic") premises,
which are "rather like a tea room"; however, there were a few
reports this year of the "good-but-expected-more" variety.
*/ **Details**: just off the high street; 9 pm; closed Mon, Tue L & Sun D.*

Wesley House £ 47 **❷❷❸**
High St GL54 5LJ (01242) 602366
"Accomplished" cooking and "unobtrusive" service is the gist of
almost all comments on this "relaxing" restaurant in a beautiful
Tudor building; "you either like the ambience or you don't" ("dull").
*/ **Details**: www.wesleyhouse.co.uk; next to Sudeley Castle; 9 pm; closed Sun D.*
***Accommodation**: 5 rooms, from £90.*

Bangkok Brasserie £ 34 🅣
33 Jewry St SO23 8RY (01962) 869 966
"The city's most popular new restaurant of recent times" – this "sound" and "welcoming" Thai establishment seems to be "flourishing following its move to bigger premises".
/ **Details:** www.bangkokbrasserie.co.uk; 11 pm.

The Black Rat £ 52 ❷❷❷
88 Chesil St SO23 0HX (01962) 844465
*"Don't let the rather shabby appearance deceive you!"; with its "surprisingly good" dishes and "eclectic" style, this former boozer has now established itself as arguably, in the round, "Winchester's best restaurant". / **Details:** www.theblackrat.co.uk; 9.30 pm; closed weekday L; children: Weekend L only.*

Brasserie Blanc £ 39 🅣
19-20 Jewry St SO23 8RZ (01962) 810870
*"Now well into its stride", this outpost of the Raymond Blanc-branded brasserie impresses almost all who report on it as a "reliably good" destination. / **Details:** www.brasserieblanc.com; 10 pm Mon - Fri, 10.30 pm Sat, 9 pm Sun.*

The Chesil Rectory £ 51 ❸❸❸
1 Chesil St S023 0HU (01962) 851555
*In a "beautiful old house" in the centre of the city, an ambitious restaurant fans find "utterly brilliant" all-round; the food can seem rather "safe" for some tastes, though, and quite "pricey" for what it is. / **Details:** www.chesilrectory.co.uk; 9.30 pm, Sat 10 pm, Sun 9 pm; children: 12+ at D .*

The Chestnut Horse £ 49 ❹❸❷
Easton Village SO21 1EG (01962) 779257
*"A very attractive pub in a beautiful village" just outside Winchester; most reports suggest it offers "good food and good value" too, but there's also the occasional hint that it's "somewhat trading on its reputation". / **Details:** www.thechestnuthorse.com; Junction M3 Newbury exit right hand lane; 9.30 pm, Sun 8 pm; closed Sun D; no Amex.*

Hotel du Vin et Bistro £ 50 ❹❸❸
14 Southgate St SO23 9EF (01962) 841414
The "characterful" original of a nowadays "overpriced" hotel-bistro chain that "needs to freshen up its act"; it still offers an "exceptional" wine list, and fans say the atmosphere is "lovely" too, but the food often feels "like mass catering".
/ **Details:** www.hotelduvin.com; central Winchester, top of high street, near the Cathedral; 9.45 pm; booking: max 12. **Accommodation:** 24 rooms, from £140.

The Avenue
Lainston House Hotel £ 79 ❹❸❹
SO21 2LT (01962) 776088
*The dining room of this "slightly stuffy" country house hotel looks "impressive", and the cooking is "consistently very good"; so consistent are complaints about overpricing, though, that it's difficult to disagree with those who say the customers "obviously have too much money!" / **Details:** www.lainstonhouse.com; 9.30 pm, 10 pm Fri & Sat. **Accommodation:** 50 rooms, from £245.*

The Old Vine £ 37 ❸❸❸
8 Great Minster St SO23 9HA (01962) 854616
This extremely popular pub enjoys "a prime location slap-bang next to the cathedral close"; the food is "enjoyable" too, and service "very courteous" ("no matter how busy the place gets").
/ **Details:** www.oldvinewinchester.com; 9.30 pm, Sun 9 pm; children: 6+.
Accommodation: 5 rooms, from £100.

Wykeham Arms £ 46 ❹❷❷
75 Kingsgate St SO23 9PE (01962) 853834
Perhaps it's not as polished a "gem" as it once was, but this celebrated pub, by the College, remains an "interesting" haunt, and can still dish up some "above-average grub" (plus "the longest wine list ever seen in a pub"). / **Details:** www.fullershotels.com; between Cathedral and College; 8.45 pm, Fri & Sat 9.30 pm; booking; children: 14+.
Accommodation: 14 rooms, from £125.

WINDERMERE, CUMBRIA 7–3D

**First Floor Café
Lakeland Limited** £ 34 ❸❸❸
Alexandra Buildings LA23 1BQ (015394) 47116
"The flagship store of this kitchen equipment retailer has an attractive first floor café/restaurant" – the locally-sourced food is "surprisingly good", and "the emphasis is very much on friendly, efficient service". / **Details:** www.lakeland.co.uk; 6 pm, Sat 5 pm, Sun 4 pm; no Amex.

Francines £ 37 ❷❸❹
22 Main Rd LA23 1DX (015394) 44088
By day this is a "simple café/tea room", but by night the chef of the late lamented Porthole restaurant puts on some "surprisingly good" fare; "great game specials" a highlight.
/ **Details:** www.francinesrestaurantwindermere.co.uk/; 11 pm; closed Mon, Tue D & Sun D.

Gilpin Lodge £ 81 ❹❹❸
Crook Rd LA23 3NE (01539) 488818
Recent expansion seems to have upset the tranquility of this "formal" country house hotel of long standing; fans still applaud its "perfectly-judged" cooking and "delightful" style, but there are quite a few "off-days" noted too. / **Details:** www.gilpinlodge.co.uk; 9.15 pm; no jeans; children: 7+. **Accommodation:** 20 rooms, from £290.

Holbeck Ghyll £ 80 ❷❹❸
Holbeck Ln LA23 1LU (01539) 432375
"Exceptional views" over Lake Windermere create a "stunning location" for this 19th-century former hunting lodge, where David McLaughlin continues to win acclaim for his often "fabulous" cuisine. / **Details:** www.holbeckghyll.com; 3m N of Windermere, towards Troutbeck; 9 pm; no jeans or trainers; booking essential; children: 18+ at D.
Accommodation: 23 rooms, from £150.

Jerichos £ 50 ❶❸❹
College Rd LA23 1BX (01539) 442522
"The very best steaks" are a highlight of the "deceptively simple" but "lovely" cuisine on offer at Jo and Chris Blaydes' restaurant-with-rooms, which also boasts an "excellent and fairly-priced wine list"; "well-behaved families are well treated" too.
/ **Details:** www.jerichos.co.uk; 9 pm; closed L; children: 12+.
Accommodation: 10 rooms, from £85.

Linthwaite House £ 65 🅣

Crook Rd LA23 3JA (01539) 488600

"Set above Windermere, a rather nice country house hotel" tipped
for its "good food" – "portions are by no means gargantuan, but
what is offered is beautifully presented and well thought-out".
/ **Details:** www.linthwaite.com; near Windermere golf club; 9 pm; no jeans or
trainers; children: 7+ at D. **Accommodation:** 32 rooms, from £180.

The Samling £ 80

Ambleside Rd LA23 1LR (01539) 431922

A "supreme" location with "lovely views" and "delicate and artistic
cooking" – the gist of most reports on this trendy country house
hotel overlooking Windermere; however, given the demise of its
owner, the Von Essen group, a rating seems inappropriate.
/ **Details:** www.thesamlinghotel.co.uk; take A591 from town; 9.15 pm.
Accommodation: 11 rooms, from £190.

WINDSOR, BERKSHIRE 3–3A

Al Fassia £ 39 ❷④④

27 St Leonards Rd SL4 3BP (01753) 855370

"Still ticking the boxes" – this long-established Moroccan is yet again
praised in most (if not quite all) reports for its "friendly" style and its
"excellent-value" food, which includes some "first-rate tajines".
/ **Details:** 10.30 pm, Fri & Sat 11 pm.

The Greene Oak £ 47 ❷❸❷

Deadworth Rd, Oakley Grn SL4 5UW (01753) 864294

"Slightly off the beaten track", a "welcoming" boozer in a "lovely"
setting where the food is always "solid" and sometimes "excellent";
prices are "reasonable" too, "especially for such an expensive part
of the world". / **Details:** www.thegreeneoak.co.uk; 9.30 pm.

WINTERINGHAM, LINCOLNSHIRE 5–1D

Winteringham Fields £103 ④④❸

1 Silver St DN15 9ND (01724) 733096

"How the mighty have fallen!"; this once-acclaimed restaurant-with-
rooms does have its fans, but there's a widespread feeling among
reporters that it's "living off its former reputation" and is "way too
expensive"; "fussy" service does it no favours either.
/ **Details:** www.winteringhamfields.com; 4m SW of Humber Bridge; 9.30 pm;
closed Mon & Sun; no Amex. **Accommodation:** 11 rooms, from £180.

WISWELL, LANCASHIRE 5–1B

Freemasons Country Inn £ 46 ❷❸❷

8 Vicarage Fold Clitheroe BB7 9DF (01254) 822218

"Much improved" in recent times, this is a gastropub which displays
"great flair" all round; Steven Smith's ambitious cuisine ("everything
has a twist") raises the odd concern of "trying too hard", but all-in-all
he carries it off. / **Details:** www.freemasonswiswell.co.uk; near the central
phone box and postbox; Tue-Thu 9 pm, Fri & Sat 9.30 pm, Sun 8 pm; closed
Mon; no Amex; 8+ have to pre-order.

WOBURN, BEDFORDSHIRE 3–2A

Paris House £ 93 ❷❷④

Woburn Pk MK17 9QP (01525) 290692

"Fine dining in a deer park is a treat!" and this offshoot of Alan
Murchison's (L'Ortolan et al) empire delights most reporters with Phil
Fanning's "wonderful" cuisine – "beautifully presented with amusing
twists"; shame about the "austere" decor, though, which lets down
the "truly wonderful" location. / **Details:** www.parishouse.co.uk; on
A4012; 8.30 pm; closed Mon, Tue L & Sun D.

Inn @ West End £ 45 ❸❸④
42 Guildford Rd GU24 9PW (01276) 858652
"Very easy to get to, just off the M2", this "welcoming" gastropub offers "a mix of good old-fashioned pub fare and eclectic desserts" ("such as South African vinegar pudding"), complemented by a wine list that's "extensive" and "well presented".
/ **Details:** www.the-inn.co.uk; 9.30 pm, Sun 9 pm; no trainers; children: 5+.

The Trout Inn £ 42 🅣
195 Godstow Rd OX2 8PN (01865) 510930
Fans of Inspector Morse's favourite local adore its "lovely waterside location" and "flavoursome pub grub"; it's "too busy at peak times", though – it gets "crowded", the food can be "awful" and you endure "long waits" for it. / **Details:** www.thetroutoxford.co.uk; 2m from junction of A40 & A44; 10 pm, Fri & Sat 10.30 pm, Sun 9.30 pm.

Bilash £ 45 ❶❷❸
2 Cheapside WV1 1TU (01902) 427762
"Head and shoulders above the competition in a gastronomically-challenged area!" – Sitab Khan's city-centre Indian (hitting 30 this year) remains well "worth seeking out" for its "superbly spiced and imaginative" Bangladeshi dishes, which feature "strong and unusual" combinations and tastes. / **Details:** www.thebilash.co.uk; opp Civic Centre; 10.30 pm; closed Sun.

Crown £ 42 ④④❸
Throughfare IP12 1AD (01394) 384242
Despite a refurb, this ancient inn still generates mixed reports; fans praise "above-average" food in "elegant" and "inviting" surroundings, but critics say the scoff's "ordinary", service "sporadic" and the setting akin to "a large cupboard"!
/ **Details:** www.thecrownatwoodbridge.co.uk; up Quay Street from the station or harbour; 9.30 pm. **Accommodation:** 10 rooms, from £120.

Terravina
Hotel Terravina £ 57 ❷❶❸
174 Woodlands Rd SO40 7GL (023) 8029 3784
With "the World's Number One Sommelier" (official!) in charge, it's no surprise that it's the "outstanding" wine list ("easily the UK's best") which headlines in reports on the Bassets' "classy" and "secluded" New Forest hotel; the food is "subtle and carefully executed", but can still seem a bit of a supporting attraction.
/ **Details:** www.hotelterravina.co.uk; 9.30 pm. **Accommodation:** 11 rooms, from £155.

Bryce's Seafood Brasserie £ 40 🅣
The Steyne BN11 3DU (01903) 214317
"Excellent locally-caught fish" makes this "restaurant-in-a-pub" popular with all who comment on it; it's "reasonably priced" too.
/ **Details:** www.seafoodbrasserie.co.uk; 9.30 pm; no Amex.

Pant-yr-Ochain   £ 40   🅣
Old Wrexham Rd LL12 8TY (01978) 853525
*"A lovely place to take the whole family", this upscale gastropub in a
small country house is tipped as a notably "attractive" destination
(complete with lake!); even fans, though, can find the overall value
"not as good as it used to be".*
/ **Details:** www.pantyrochain-gresford.co.uk; 1m N of Wrexham; 9.30 pm, Sun
9 pm.

The Mulberry Tree   £ 43   🅣
9 Wood Ln WN6 9SE (01257) 451400
*Tipped for "a vast menu, stretching from simple dishes to more
haute cuisine", this dining pub outpost of the Northcote empire is a
culinary (if not atmospheric) hit for most reporters who comment on
it.* / **Details:** www.themulberrytree.info; 2m along Mossy Lea Rd, off M6, J27;
9.30 pm, Fri & Sat 10 pm; no Amex; booking recommended.

The Hand and Trumpet   £ 39   ❸❷❷
Main Rd CW3 9BJ (01270) 820048
*"Dependable food and service in a relaxed country setting" – that's
the deal at this "friendly" outpost of the Brunning & Price group of
food-led pubs (which are notable for the general consistency of the
reports they generate).* / **Details:** www.handandtrumpet-wrinehill.co.uk;
10 pm, Sun 9.30 pm; no Amex.

The Wife of Bath   £ 48   ❸❷❷
4 Upper Bridge St TN25 5AF (01233) 812232
*"A lovely restaurant-with-rooms run by a charming Frenchman with a
sense of humour" – this popular institution continues to please most
reporters with its "high-level cooking" (served in "tower and drizzle"
style).* / **Details:** www.thewifeofbath.com; off A28 between Ashford &
Canterbury; 10 pm; closed Mon, Tue L & Sun D. **Accommodation:** 5 rooms,
from £85.

Crab House Café   £ 43   ❷❸④
Ferrymans Way, Portland Rd DT4 9YU (01305) 788867
*"Simple but very well-executed fish and seafood dishes served within
a stone's throw of the sea" – the "lovely, jolly and unpretentious"
formula that's won a big following for this "odd-looking" place.*
/ **Details:** www.crabhousecafe.co.uk; overlooking the Fleet Lagoon, on the one
road to Portland; 9 pm, Sat 9.30 pm; closed Mon & Tue; no Amex; 8+ deposit
of £10 per head.

The Berkeley Arms   £ 42   ❷❷❸
59 Main St LE14 2AG (01572) 787 587
*A "handsome village pub" whose fortunes have been restored by a
couple formerly of nearby Hambleton Hall – a "friendly" place with
"reliably good food and a decent wine list".*
/ **Details:** www.theberkeleyarms.co.uk.

Ate O'Clock £ 42 🅣
13A, High Ousegate YO1 8RZ (01904) 644080
"Tucked away down an alley opposite All Saints Pavement, but well worth finding" – this small modern bistro serves *"great value proper home made food at excellent value prices"*, the top deal being the 'B4 eight' menu after which the place is named.
/ **Details:** www.ateoclock.co.uk; 9.30 pm; closed Sun.

Bettys £ 41 ❸❷❶
6-8 St Helen's Sq YO1 8QP (01904) 659142
"Fulfilling all your 1920s fantasies about what a tea room should be like" – this *"classy"* institution has made a huge name for its *"high-quality classic dishes served in nicely traditional surroundings"*; it's *"expensive for what you get"*, though, and *"queues are long"*.
/ **Details:** www.bettys.co.uk; down Blake St from York Minster; 9 pm; no Amex; no booking, except Sun.

Café Concerto £ 39 ❹❸❸
21 High Petergate YO1 7EN (01904) 610478
This *"haven"* by the Minster is a *"convenient, cosy, cheerful and reasonably-priced"* spot that's *"brilliant for a coffee, sandwich, snack or cake"*; even some fans, though, concede that *"its interior could use sprucing-up"*. / **Details:** www.cafeconcerto.biz; by the W entrance of York Minster; 9.30 pm; booking: max 6-8. **Accommodation:** 1 room, at about £175.

Cafe No. 8 Bistro £ 44 ❷❸❹
8 Gillygate YO31 7EQ (01904) 653074
Near the Minster, *"a lovely, small and intimate café/bistro"* where the food is *"home-made and delicious"*; not everyone agrees, however, that the recent expansion – and greater emphasis on dinner rather than breakfast – is an improvement.
/ **Details:** www.cafeno8.co.uk; 9.30 pm; no Amex.

City Screen Café Bar
City Screen Picturehouse £ 28 🅣
Coney St YO1 9QL (01904) 612940
"A cinema café may not sound the most promising venue", but this riverside venture is tipped for its *"nice location"*, and it's the sort of place that does an *"excellent burger"* too.
/ **Details:** www.picturehouses.co.uk; 9 pm; no Amex; no booking.

Hotel du Vin et Bistro £ 51 ❹❸❸
89 The Mount YO24 1AX (01904) 557350
It occupies a lovely building, but otherwise this is a pretty *"ordinary"* outpost of the rather variable hotel/bistro chain; the *"huge"* wine list, however, is always an attraction. / **Details:** www.hotelduvin.com; 9.45 pm, Fri & Sat 10.15 pm. **Accommodation:** 44 rooms, from £110.

J Baker's Bistro Moderne £ 43 ❶❷❹
7 Fossgate YO1 9TA (01904) 622688
Jeff Baker's *"revelatory"* cooking – often served *"grazing"*-style – comes at *"surprisingly reasonable"* prices at the city's most culinarily ambitious restaurant; the shop-conversion setting, though, *"does let it down a bit"*. / **Details:** www.jbakers.co.uk; 9.30 pm; closed Mon & Sun.

Le Langhe £ 43 ❶❹❸
36 Peasholme Grn YO1 7PW (01904) 622584
"A surprise in the heart of the city" – a *"gorgeous deli, with restaurant attached"* whose *"brilliant"* (if *"limited"*) menu includes *"delicious"* antipasti and pasta (plus *"scrumptious"* wines imported direct from Italy); for the summer, there's even a *"stunning"* garden!
/ **Details:** www.lelanghe.co.uk; 9 pm; closed Mon-Thu D & Sun; no Amex.

Melton's £ 43 ❷❷④

7 Scarcroft Rd YO23 1ND (01904) 634 341

Michael Hjort's "trustworthy" restaurant of long standing – "in an unfashionable suburb, on the way to the racecourse" – is still often tipped as "the best in town"; some fans fear "it suffers in comparison with J Baker's" nowadays, but all reports applaud its "self-assured" and "imaginative" cooking.
/ **Details:** www.meltonsrestaurant.co.uk; 10 mins walk from Castle Museum; 10 pm; closed Mon & Sun; no Amex.

Melton's Too £ 34 ④④④

25 Walmgate YO1 9TX (01904) 629 222

Some reports of "disappointing" food of late at this large café/bar/bistro (which is "less sophisticated than the other Melton"); for most reporters, though, this remains a place for a "tasty, cheap 'n' cheerful meal". / **Details:** www.meltonstoo.co.uk; 2 minutes from the City centre; 10.30 pm, Sun 9.30 pm; no Amex.

Middlethorpe Hall £ 72 ④❸❷

Bishopthorpe Rd YO23 2GB (01904) 641241

In extensive and "lovely" grounds on the the fringe of the city, this "very smart and traditional" hotel – complete with panelled dining room – is a "friendly" place, particularly recommended for its "perfect" afternoon tea and breakfast.
/ **Details:** www.middlethorpe.com; next to racecourse; 9.30 pm; no shorts; children: 6+. **Accommodation:** 29 rooms, from £199.

Mumbai Lounge £ 32 🅣

47 Fossgate YO1 9TF (01904) 654 155

"Already very popular", this Indian two-year-old is tipped for "gorgeous" cooking and service that's "very attentive and friendly" too. / **Details:** www.mumbailoungeyork.co.uk.

10

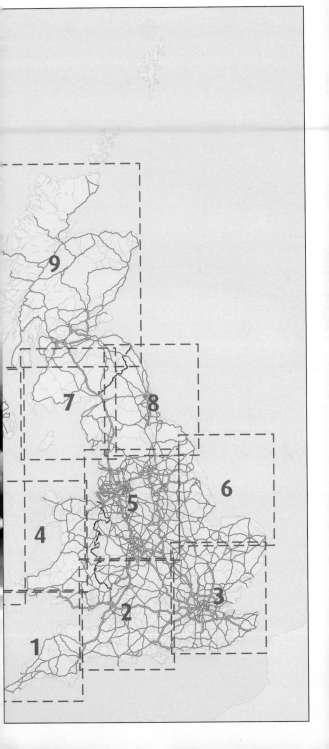

MAP 1

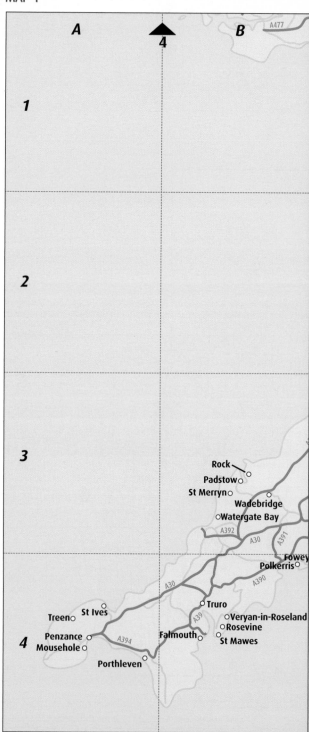

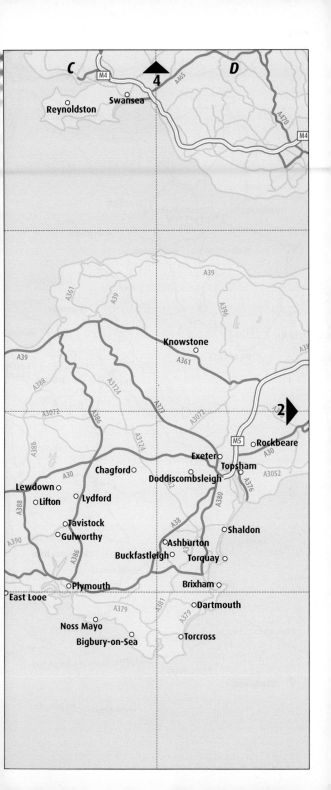

MAP 2

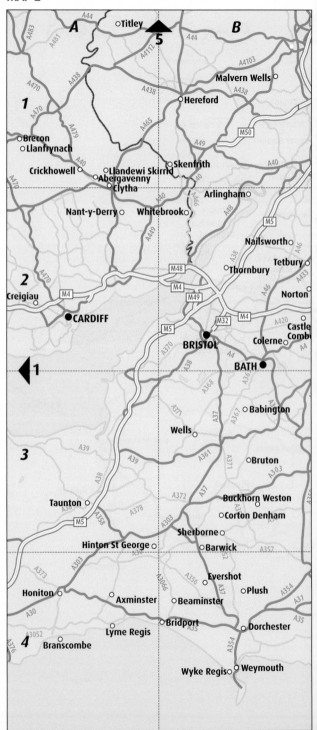

MAP 3

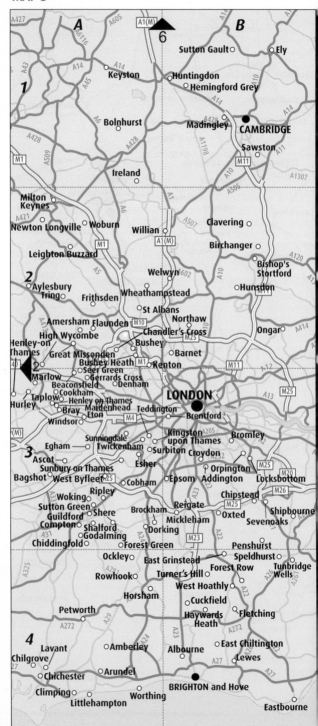

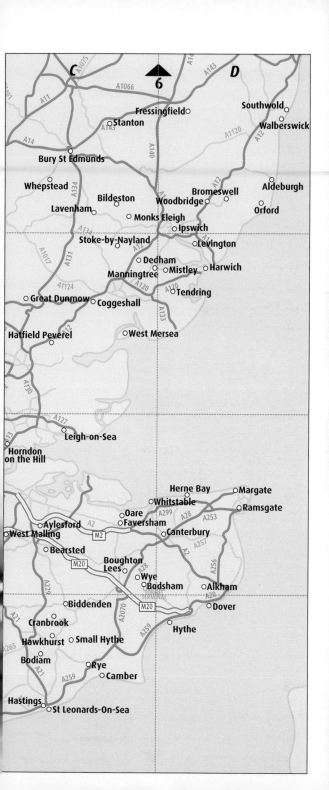

MAP 4

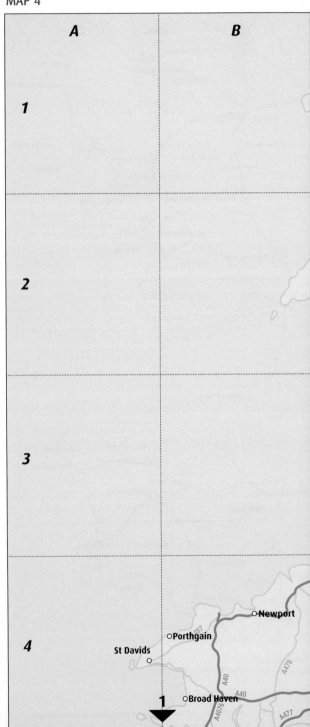

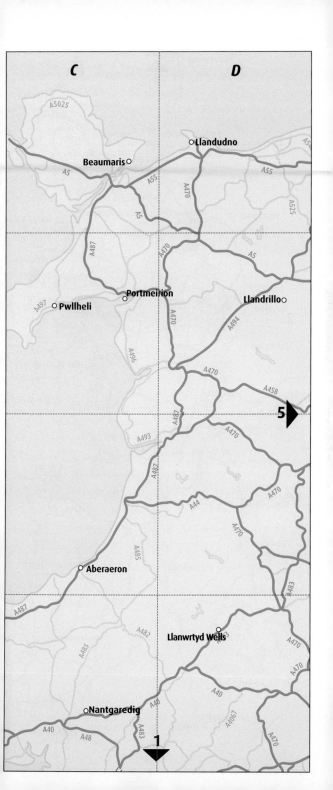

MAP 5

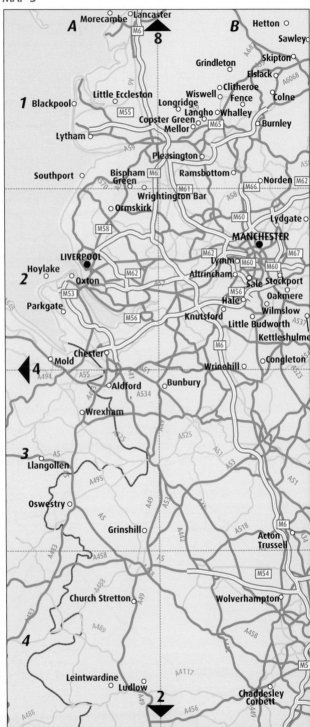

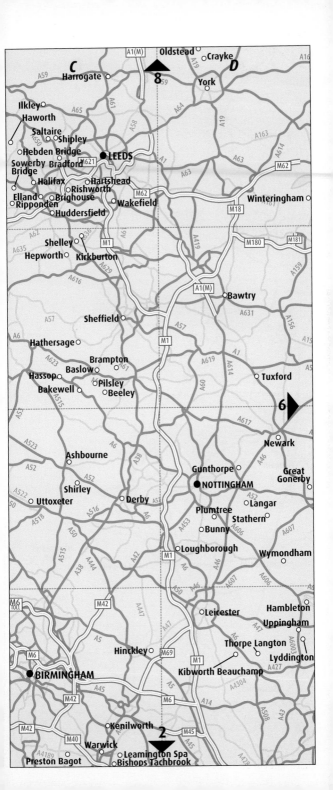

MAP 6

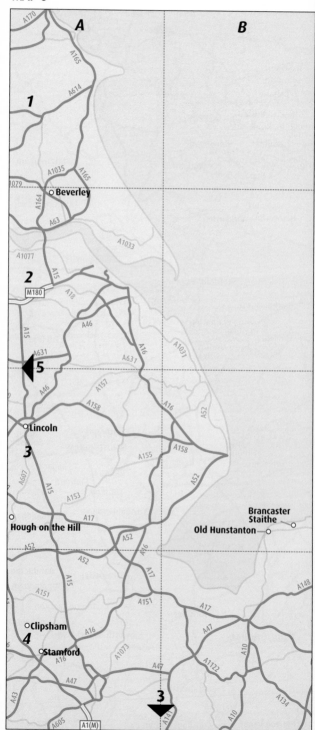

MAP 7

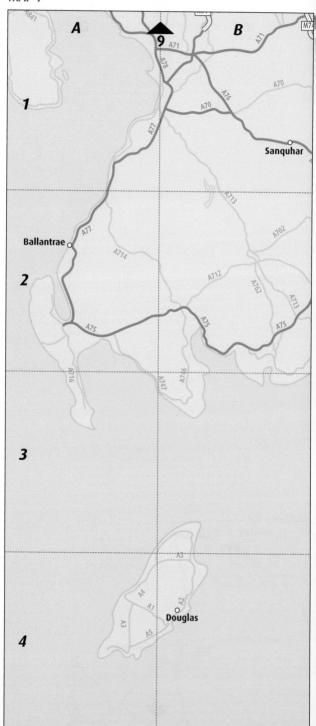

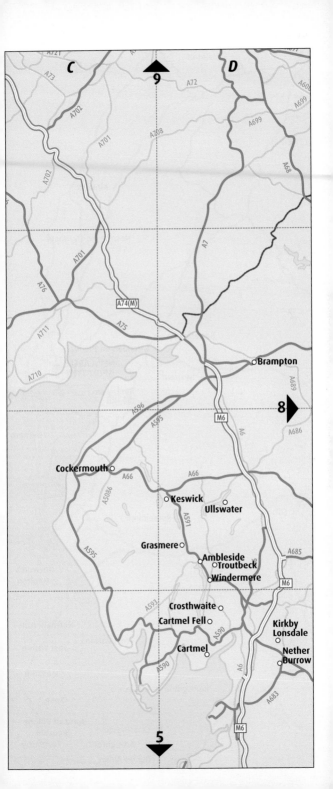

MAP 8

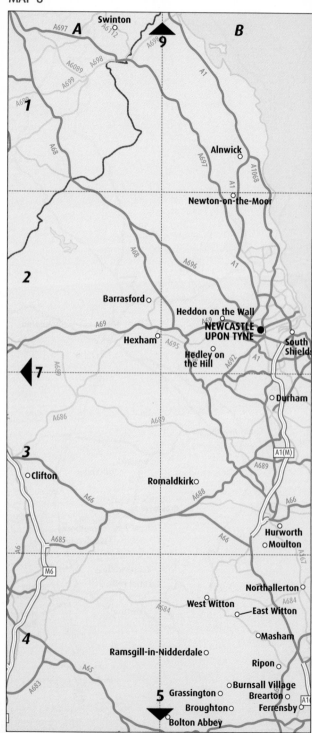

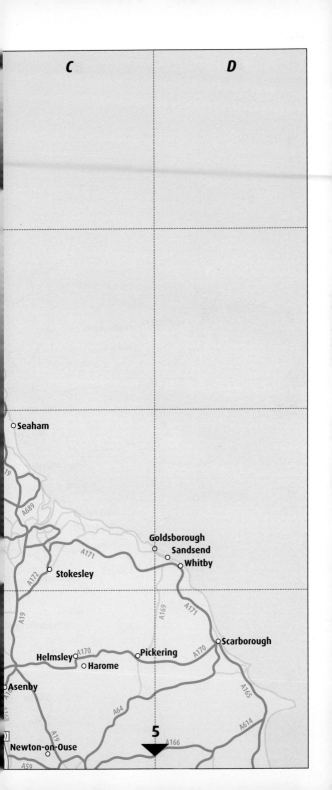

MAP 9

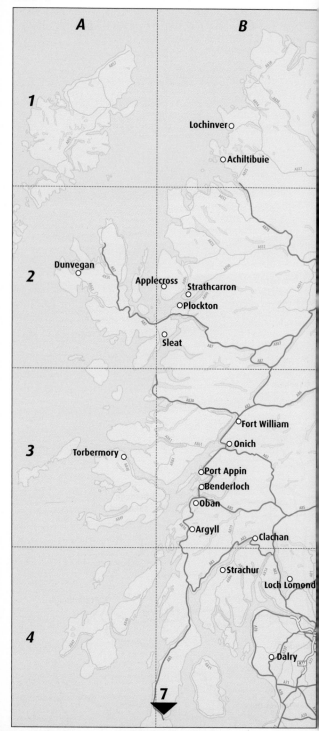

A

B

1

Lochinver ○

○ Achiltibuie

2

Dunvegan ○

Applecross ○ ○ Strathcarron

○ Plockton

○ Sleat

3

Torbermory ○

○ Fort William

○ Onich

○ Port Appin

○ Benderloch

○ Oban

○ Argyll

○ Clachan

○ Strachur

Loch Lomond ○

4

○ Dalry

7

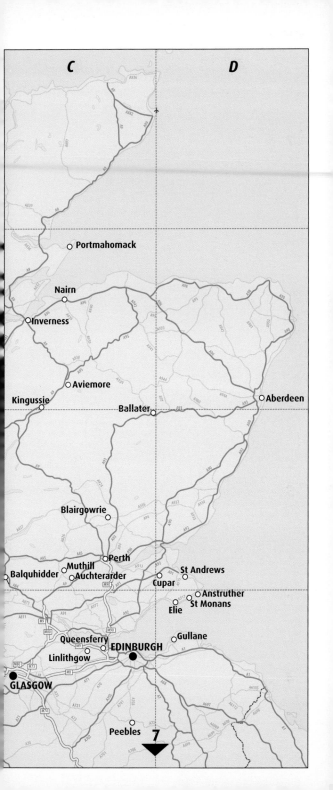

MAP 10

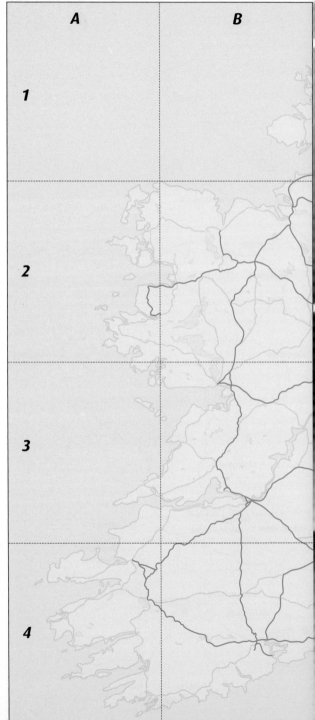

A

B

1

2

3

4

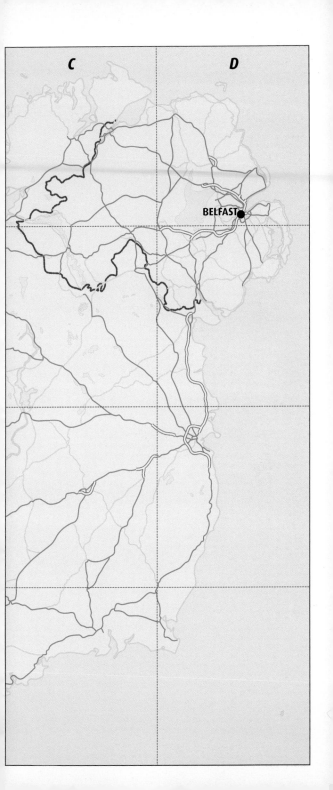

THE BEST OF

If it's Monday it's the Sobell Centre. Flora goes there every week for her gym class, along with twenty or so other six-year-olds. I also take Sarah and Jessie from our local streets which in theory means I should only be ferrying them every third week but you know what it's like, working from home, hanging about, so I seem to spend half my life dashing to the Sobell. It's a huge sports centre in Islington and getting there after school is easy, but coming back is murder, throwing them in the back of the car, counting the seconds, cutting illegally down back alleys, desperate to beat the rush hour.

I always stay while they have their hour's gym, though when the other two mums do their turn, they usually come home in between. Well, what else have I got to do? I'm actually too mean with the petrol to do a double journey. I also like wandering down the Seven Sisters Road while I'm putting in the hour. It's probably the ugliest, noisiest, dirtiest street in north London, but I know a fruit shop where you can get nine lemons for 25p. I admit they're rather small and usually soggy and my wife says she won't use them, but it thrills me every week to bring them home.

About the author

Hunter Davies is the author of over thirty books,
ranging from biographies of the Beatles to William
Wordsworth, plus an awful lot of journalism,
notably on *The Sunday Times* and in *Punch*,
where he wrote the Father's Day column for ten
years. He also writes books for children, including
the Flossie Teacake stories and the S.T.A.R.S.
series for teenagers. He has three children, all still
speaking to him, a wife (the novelist Margaret
Forster), and flits between London and the Lake
District.

THE BEST OF FATHER'S DAY

Ten Years of Teenagers

Hunter Davies

CORONET BOOKS
Hodder and Stoughton

For Caitlin, Jake and Flora,
with further fatherly
apologies.

First published in Great Britain
in 1990 by Coronet
Paperbacks

The piece entitled 'My first
teenager' first appeared in
The Sunday Times and is
reproduced by kind permission
of the Editor.

All of the other pieces in this
book originally appeared in
Punch and we are grateful to
the Editor and publishers for
permission to reproduce them.

British Library C.I.P.
Davies, Hunter *1936–*
    The best of Father's day:
    ten years of teenagers
    I. Title
    828.91407

ISBN 0-340-52551-7

Printed and bound in Great Britain
for Hodder and Stoughton
Paperbacks, a division of Hodder
and Stoughton Ltd., Mill Road,
Dunton Green, Sevenoaks, Kent
TN13 2YA (Editorial Office:
47 Bedford Square, London
WC1B 3DP) by Richard Clay.
Typeset by Avocet Robinson,
Buckingham.

Contents

Introduction

For ten years, when the world was young and the bedrooms full, I did a weekly column about my family which appeared in the magazine *Punch*. Nothing remarkable about it really, just the odd jottings by a dad about his children, no tragedies, few dramas, hardly any pack drills, though lots of names, real names, the names of my own dear children. I suppose in a way that was vaguely remarkable: the fact that someone should apparently expose his loved ones to even a very small shaft of limelight.

When I began, I decided not to use any soppy euphemisms, such as Child Number One, or the Son and Heir, or Our Last Little Treasure, as I always suspect that once people make up names, they make up stories and incidents to go with them. So from the beginning, I wrote about Caitlin, Jake and Flora, real members of the planet, who were aged around thirteen, eleven and six when the articles first appeared. Should I have spared them? Should I have disguised their identities? Perhaps. You can judge for yourself.

I remember when I was at school in Carlisle, oh not the olden days again, give us a break, you haven't even begun the book yet, we had the Mayor's Son in our class for a while. Name dropper. Yes, that's the sort of silly remark we used to make. In a place like Carlisle, there weren't any well known people. There was no chance of someone's dad being in a pop group, or Parliament or doing something really famous, such as reading the weather forecast on television. So we picked on the Mayor's son instead. Every time he came into the class room we all stood up and said

Arise, It's The Mayor's Son. How pathetic. We must have made his life hell, but he took it well.

My three children, at inner London comprehensives, have had far worse problems to cope with in their life, as any parent with children at such schools in the last ten years will know, and I don't honestly think I made it worse for them with their peers by drawing attention to them. Who reads *Punch* anyway. Certainly not their school friends. At Caitlin's school, which was Camden School for Girls, see I can name it now as she's long since left, there were girls with really famous parents, such as Cabinet Ministers and Women Novelists and TV Presenters, so it was not done to make mention of parents or their doings. Jake's school, William Ellis, also had a share of the passing famous. Flora's school, which I will not name, as she's still there, is not quite the same, but it's equally not done to enquire about parents.

What did happen, though, over the years, was that one or two teachers would pick up old copies in a dental waiting-room, or even turn out to have a subscription, and they would make elliptical comments in the corridor. This really annoyed them, especially Jake, and for a while he insisted that his name had to be changed. For a few months he became Jimmy, then he forgave me. But all the time he was at University I was not allowed to name which one, though I did when he finally left, as you will see, hurry hurry to page 217.

I saw the articles as Letters to my Mum, the sort of weekly chitchat we all pass on to our own parents, picking on the nice things, flamming up the little incidents, carefully avoiding anything too nasty or tragic. I was simply economical when it came to anything unhappy, and naturally, like all families, over ten years, we have had our share.

They were written every Saturday night, a consideration of that week's domestic highlights, or low lights, or just any flickers I could latch on to as we all struggled through the Eighties, not knowing where we were going, except into the Nineties, so we all hoped. Looking back, patterns did emerge, characters did develop, a sort of narrative grew up, mainly because of the three children. There were surprises, especially to us, when Caitlin did things we never expected, or Jake turned out to be rather different from the image I might have given about him in the early years. Readers seemed to identify with them, especially those with similar aged children, going through similar aged problems, what am I saying, similar pleasures. A series which was meant to run for only six weeks, when it began on October 17, 1979, ran and ran till 1989, till I was out of breath, and practically out of copy, as by then the older two had become students, and almost, if not quite, going out into the big wide world.

Readership surveys indicated that it became the most popular column in *Punch*, so Alan Coren used to tell me. (And it was his idea in the first place, so I always believed everything he said.) It even became a TV series, with John Alderton starring as me. I got fan mail from all over the world, and so did Caitlin at one time. While the kids at their own schools took little notice, there was a following from public schools, and in student common rooms.

In all, I wrote 428 columns, how did I spin it out, which explains why I'm now sitting here exhausted, after chucking out nine-tenths of them for this definitely the last, never to be seen again, ultimate appearance of Father's Day.

Actually, it was quite easy. What I chucked out was Me. I was surprised how often in these last ten years I have been grinding on about my health. In a dull week, it's what I always seemed to come back to, whether my dodgy knee or my sore jaw. I also chucked out columns that were mainly about my obsessions or collections, dead exciting though they are, as I think no one will be interested in them in book form. Perhaps they never were, in *Punch*, but readers put up with them as they waited for the latest on les enfants. I eliminated all the holiday columns, even though they were about family holidays, such as us in Russia, which I was very fond of, and the Lake District.

There were no columns about my wife. She can do her own, and correct any false impressions. I never knew what to call her. Having said I'm against soppy euphemisms, I found myself in the early years calling her my Lady Wife, or Mrs Davies. I didn't want to use her real name. Dunno why. Spare her, I suppose. The column's title referred to me, and my views and experiences on being your average sort of middle-class, middling caring sort of Dad. When I began, there seemed to be more than enough stuff being written by the nation's *Guardian* Women about their family lives and heroic struggles. For a while, I classed her as a Wrinkly, along with me, then I fell into the habit of calling her the Old Trout, and then just the OT. I had thought, till I ploughed through these 428 columns, that I had used that term from almost the beginning, but I see it didn't start till about half-way through. I got a lot of complaints about calling her the Old Trout, from people saying it was nasty, unfair, disrespectful to a wonderful woman and human being. She never minded. Honest.

I've decided here to concentrate on the three children, to follow them through, as they grew up, so that the book has in fact a sort of shape, even a story, to keep you turning the pages till you come to, well, I can't say the end. There is never an end, once you become a father or a mother. As long as you're here, and they're here, the family sagas go on. I stopped at a pause mark, when Caitlin and Jake, touch wood, look as if they are about to leave home. If you are really desperate, when you've read this offering, to know what happened next, send me a stamped envelope and I'll do an update every Christmas. Personally, I can't wait. Every evening, over the cocoa, we still come out with the same old stuff which all parents do. 'Whatever will become of them . . .' Here is the story so far, about what became of them, over the last ten years.

Hunter Davies
London NW5
Jan. 1990

My First Teenager

Caitlin is thirteen going on twenty-four and she's my first teenager. I've always felt completely prepared, being a man of the world, having read all the articles about teenagers, having made vows never to be restrictive like my parents, having been such a terrific dad all these years, etc.

'Dad,' she said on the phone one day last week, 'I'm in a boy's flat in Kilburn. OK?' It was seven at night and I was on my own as my wife was in hospital. I felt a sense of panic, but I took it in chronological order. First of all, why was she calling me Dad when for thirteen years I've been Hunt? I decided it was part of the barriers going up, keeping me in my place as an outsider dad figure. Which boy's flat and were his parents there? Well, one mustn't pry. At least she'd rung. And then Kilburn! My God, it's miles away, full of bomb factories. I realised she'd told me nothing. No phone number, no address, no return time. And she's only thirteen.

I was in bed when she came home, just after 10.30, very pleased with herself—pleased that she'd done me such a huge favour by dragging herself to a phone. Great. When you wake up drugged in Buenos Aires I'll at least know it all began in some anonymous boy's flat in some anonymous part of north London. I didn't actually say that. Jokes can rebound. I just muttered my thanks, terribly grateful, very good of you, what a thoughtful girl, your worship, oh great one, just as long as you can manage a quick ring to tell your old dad. What a creep I am. But that's what we've both become, me and her mum. Ever so thankful for any crumb. If we're very good, she tells us things.

1

She did give us all the gen about the punk rock concert last Sunday at the Roundhouse, after it was over. She'd crept out and got dressed at someone else's house. Avoiding me, the great permissive dad. Yet I gave her everything money can't buy. She'd gone in an old man's shirt and tie, pins and chains everywhere, a mask of make-up on her face and her hair red rinsed. ('It's only cochineal—it washes out.') She came back exhausted; what with spitting at the group on stage. If the group spits at the audience, as they did, then naturally you spit back. Her shirt was blood-stained, or so it looked. Turned out to be tomato sauce. Another group had used sliced loaves in their act, pouring ketchup all over them, then thrown them at the audience. Very musical. The dye had run in her hair, thanks to people emptying beer glasses on her. She also came back with more badges than she'd gone with. Some badge seller got himself mugged and she just happened to pick up a few lost badges. Just a joke, she said. I'm not a punk, not even a closet punk, but if you go to a punk concert, you've got to wear the clothes haven't you. Quite right, I said.

When I was thirteen I used to sneak my school trousers to a woman in the street who narrowed them for a shilling and pinch my dad's Brylcreem to grease back my hair. Not that boring story again, she said, and she was gone. I remember him once trying to stop me riding my bike on Sunday. I was always determined not to be like my dad. But the kids these days want to do more than the things we weren't allowed to do. (Gee, thanks, you mean I can go on my bike to next Sunday's punk concert . . .) Life has all moved on.

It suddenly happened two months ago, these lads started hanging round the door. I thought at first they were wanting me to come out and play football and went to look for my boots. Then Caitlin's gang of girls appeared, all enormous, ho ho ho, ha ha ha, dwarfing and dominating almost every boy. That's how it always starts, I thought, they go about in gangs for a few years before they eventually pair off. Gangs lasted ten days. Then she

2

went off with one lad, his school's star footballer, to the pictures. That too lasted ten days.

When we were thirteen, back in the dark ages, you idolised the sports stars for years, till you were at least in the sixth form and you realised the sports stars were jerks and the intellectual weeds took over. Yet she's only third year. Last week she went with a boy shopping in Hampstead to buy herself a jumper. Such intimacy. I didn't do that till I was married.

She doesn't sit demurely by the phone, waiting to be asked. Oh no. She harangues boys' mothers on the phone, telling them exactly where she has to be met. She's so cool and clipped, totally beyond being humiliated. What a hussy I seem to have bred. Women's Lib has a lot to answer for. I married the school swot and it took me about three years to hold her hand. I thought Caitlin would turn out the same. Now we sit over our cocoa of an evening with my wife saying she's *your* daughter and I say, no, no, she's *your* daughter. To my horror, I have to admit she's the teenager I tried to be. Now with the modern morals and methods, I daren't think what a good time, I mean bad time, she could have. Jake, who's eleven, will probably turn out the anti-social swot.

All the other corny things have happened. You can't get on the phone. I waited six hours the other day while she and a girl friend took turns to scream down the phone at some boys and afterwards I had to pour out half a gallon of drips like a trumpet. We only see her at meal times and I have to bite my tongue to stop myself saying you treat us like a bed and breakfast place, as dads are supposed to do. One word out of place and it's the big sigh treatment followed by some heavy door slamming. She doesn't want a party this year, not unless there's boys and I lay on drink, and I said no, it's against the law until you're eighteen and you should have heard the sighs being slammed. She's not had boys at a party before, not since she was four, and that was bad enough. We still have the marks. She's scheming at present to stay in an empty house while we're in the Lakes at half term, but I've put my foot down. Gas leaks, I said. For some reason my wife thinks this is terribly funny.

She has this job on Sundays, which on the face of it I approve of, having delivered papers myself at her age. (Papers? You mean get up early in the morning? You must be joking.) She trolls out about eleven, dressed for *Top of the Pops*, to help a man on a stall in Camden Lock sell badges. It's a big status thing in her class, actually being paid to hang around Camden Lock. Everyone else just hangs around. It's this arty crafty junk-stall place, jammed with arty crafty people. What about this man, I said, the bloke who pays you? Oh, he's really old, but he's very nice. He's half Russian. We discussed it for days, me and the wife. You go and see him. No, you go. So I hung around one morning, casual like, in my lumber jacket and Kickers, festooned with badges, trying hard not to look like a closet. This old man turned out to be twenty-seven and he thought I was a right joke and treated me like I was her grandad. But he did seem nice.

The thing is, it's all nice. She's so happy and so enjoying herself and I don't want to give the impression we're unhappy either. We've had no real rows. It's all so terribly normal and ordinary for her age. Her school work hasn't been neglected. I'm just jealous, I suppose, that I didn't have such fun and liberty when I was her age. At any age, come to that. A council estate in Carlisle in the Fifties wasn't exactly Soho. She's of a different class, a different age, a different society.

My dad knew what it was like to be me because society hardly changed in those days, but I've no idea what it's like to be Caitlin. It's natural she should want us kept out of her life, but should I worry when we're so excluded that we don't know where she is for six hours? I feel I should work out a plan now, well before anything really happens, getting ready for what everyone warns me lies ahead. I don't know nuffink yet, so parents of fifteen-year-old girls tell me, saying they've not seen their daughter for six *nights*, never mind six hours. I feel I must draw lines, make rules, if only for her to break, even though

4

I'm not quite sure what the game is. Do I say she must always be home at ten o'clock? Do I say she must always tell us who she is with and where? Or do we just smile, lay out the meals, accept any crumbs, and say nothing. Any advice gratefully received. Yours, Worried Brown Eyes.

Come on you Spurs

20 nil

Spurs 10 Arseggal 0

Teenage Jake

When Jake was born, one of my first thoughts was oh good, someone to go to football matches with. In every town there are middle-class, middle-age dads going on and on in their terribly manly ways about how they and their sons just live for Saturday and the footer match and of course they always stand though actually we missed last week, fact haven't been this season. I like to think my response was genuine.

I'd lived for football as a kid and one of the regrets of my teenage years was not that we lived in Carlisle, where not many all-time greats greated, but that my dad became an invalid and unable to take me to matches. It was obviously a regret to him as well. He once played, when in the RAF, for Hearts, the Edinburgh club. Boast boast.

I first took Jake to Spurs when he was six and I said never again. He was bored stiff, fidgeted all the time, wanted the lav or drinks every five minutes and thought that every corner was a goal. I took him the next week, and said never again again. He soon got all the gear, of course, like primary school kids everywhere, though in our area mums preferred Arsenal to Spurs as white shirts are a load of trouble and get filthy in minutes. I should have spotted the first signs. When boring old Arsenal won the double, and every half-witted, fashion-following kid suddenly sported their shirts, Jake was still sleeping in his Spurs top. Even in the Second Division, he never wavered, though by this time all his contemporaries were following Liverpool which pleased the mums as they were still washing red.

His school work has always been unbelievably scruffy, finger marks and smudges everywhere. He doesn't just read books—he attacks them, grinding back the spines so they break instantly, punching them in the face, kicking hell out of their insides. It's a one-sided fight. Jake always wins. You can tell he's read a book by the debris. Wordsworth was much the same, about books I mean. He upset Thomas De Quincey for ever by giving him back a virgin copy of a book with jam stains on every page. He'd sliced open the uncut pages while having his tea. No wonder De Q was so horrid about him in his *Recollections of the Lake Poets*. Anyway, Wordsworth was neat enough when it came to things he cared about, and so, it transpired, was Jake. We discovered in his bedroom a beautifully arranged pile of every Spurs programme I'd every bought him, in pristine condition, and even more amazing, the most incredibly detailed charts about Spurs' season so far, with graphs and lists on every player. There wasn't a smudge anywhere.

It's all your fault, she said. Why couldn't you have channelled his energies into Latin, just look at that exercise book, or Physics, only twenty per cent yet again. You're making one discipline more important than another, I said smugly. There is no intrinsic advantage in learning Latin verbs as opposed to learning Spurs' pre-war Cup runs. It's one of the mythologies of traditional education, along with the idea of team games being good for the character. Well, when you have a Dip. Ed. you've got to use it some time. Rubbish, she said. They do Latin at O-level not football results, thank God. Stick around, I said. By the time he's eighteen, they'll be giving Ph.D.'s on Tommy Doc and his middle QPR period.

When we came back from our holiday in Portugal last year, we arrived at Heathrow late in the evening and Jake immediately started grubbing in the debris under some chair and found a torn copy of the *Sunday Express* . . . Liverpool 7, Spurs 0. I thought he was going to have a heart attack. The awful groans and the looks of absolute agony all the way home. Jokes were impossible. He simply couldn't take it.

The early part of this season has been terrible. Spurs are playing badly and I have to handle him with such care all the way back from matches. He screams and swears when we tune into *Sports Report* and the reporter says Middlesborough deserved to win 3-1. He's still convinced all those seven Liverpool goals were lucky, when he hadn't even been there, so anyone who dares to report a match he *has* seen and doesn't agree that we was robbed, is a —— stupid —— and he'll never buy their paper again or listen to their report. And he never does.

I happened to say, one Wednesday evening, how about going to Arsenal as I see they're at home. Watch Arsenal? You must be —— joking! Go in disguise, I said, so any school friends won't see you. That was typical of me, making a cheap joke. The point was he would *never* want to see such a load of ——, whether he was spotted there or not. I promised him drinks and goodies at half-time, and I also said I would stand. I prefer sitting down any time, which I always do at Spurs, and, as I'm paying and driving him there and back, he always unwillingly agrees. In his code, only phonies sit. Real supporters stand. I eventually got him to go with me by saying I wanted to see Arsenal *lose*. That surely would be a pleasure . . . Arsenal beat Leeds 7-0. He's never going to Highbury ever again.

I've been tarred since then as disloyal. He's brought my own liking for Spurs into serious doubt. I secretly think they've deserved to lose every game I've seen them lose, though I can't say so, not out loud. I'm beginning to think I want to see a good, skilful, exciting game played, regardless of the teams. Such abstract discussions are pointless. He's too busy kicking the furniture, banging the doors, doing his Just William scowl. I fear for his wife in years to come and begin to wonder if I've bred a monster. Because I have equivocal thoughts, murmur heretical observations, follow disloyal actions, I'm now branded as a —— traitor. I'm not fit to touch the hem of Glen Hoddle's jock-strap. Glen can be a luxury, so I think, a nice player, but not much good when the going's hard, though the merest mention of such an opinion leads to more door slamming.

I've had to tell him the bad news that I probably won't be able to take him to the Forest home game. I'm working on it, but I rashly promised the rest of the family we'd have a day out in the country, probably at my sister's in Leighton Buzzard. I got caught, agreeing without looking up the fixture list. You neglect the rest of the family at weekends anyway, my wife says, with boring old football all the time, so it's about time you thought of us. Jake has taken it like a man. He's decided he'll go on his own. Right across north London, on endless buses and complicated connections, then that huge walk up Tottenham High Road with all the Forest hooligans looking for little lads of thirteen wearing Spurs scarves. I'm still going, he says. I'm a true supporter. He's never been on his own before. Most lads of his age are hopeless at going places anyway, though when Caitlin was his age she'd practically been in orbit, but then London teenage girls are rather advanced. Last night as I went into his bedroom—well, I have a last look at them all, even now, to make sure they're still alive, and at home—he'd fallen asleep with the light on. Over his face, half in his open mouth as he snored away, was the London bus map.

If he does get thumped, then of course it will all be my fault, having started him on this stupid football fanaticism. If he doesn't get thumped, and manages it all safely, then I know what will happen. He has hardly liked going with me all season as it is, as I moan on about having to drive all the way to places like Crystal Palace, and I often decide not to go at all if the weather's bad. If he manages it, it will be the end of an era. He won't have to come with me anymore, nor will he want to, not now that I've been revealed as just another middle-class dad . . .

Meanwhile, Flora

If it's Monday it's the Sobell Centre. Flora goes there every week for her gym class, along with twenty or so other six-year-olds. I also take Sarah and Jessie from our local streets which in theory means I should only be ferrying them every third week but you know what it's like, working from home, hanging about, so I seem to spend half my life dashing to the Sobell. It's a huge sports centre in Islington and getting there after school is easy, but coming back is murder, throwing them in the back of the car, counting the seconds, cutting illegally down back alleys, desperate to beat the rush hour.

I always stay while they have their hour's gym, though when the other two mums do their turn, they usually come home in between. Well, what else have I got to do? I'm actually too mean with the petrol to do a double journey. I also like wandering down the Seven Sisters Road while I'm putting in the hour. It's probably the ugliest, noisiest, dirtiest street in north London, but I know a fruit shop where you can get nine lemons for 25p. I admit they're rather small and usually soggy and my wife says she won't use them, but it thrills me every week to bring them home. Do you know how much lemons are in normal shops? Well then.

It's a terribly good gym class, and it's terribly good for them, and my wife is terribly pleased that Flora goes every week. I tried to get another little girl in last week and there were 170 little girls' names on the waiting list. I saw it with my own eyes. You get a very nice class of mum at the Sobell. You'd expect that, of course. It takes the middle-class mums to suss out what an area has to offer, and get little Emma

11

and Lucie on the list before anyone else has cottoned on. So that's Monday.

I think I'm free on Tuesdays, sorry I mean Flora's free, though there's a terribly good pottery class somewhere in Hampstead. The ballet class is on Wednesdays, but that's within walking distance. Thursday there's a standing swap. Sunday morning it's swimming. Thank God she's too young for the Brownies. That will start in the New Year.

As my wife can't drive, I've now had ten years of these arrangements, getting kids back and forward across the planet. The older two gave up their numerous activities just as Flora started hers, and in these ten years I don't think there's been a spare week in which I haven't had a hall or someone's home I've had to deliver to or collect from. I'm not very good at taking in arrangements and I'm constantly finding myself in the middle of some strange neighbourhood, unable to remember where I'm going or why or when. I've often dumped them in empty halls, and driven away, leaving them for a class which doesn't start for another week, or walked up and down some strange street with one of their little friends who is playing silly buggers and refuses to tell me which house she lives in. I go mad if a parent doesn't turn up on the dot to collect from our house, and then hangs around for drinkies, but I'm usually late myself, and I'm always looking for an excuse to get a foot in the door and have a look round their terribly clever kitchen.

We try to restrict their activities to a maximum of two a week, but there are some parents who are in transit every day, round the clock, especially if they're driving kids to school as well. These are the ones who cause all the accidents, driving their cars blind, trying to stop Tom and Ben fighting in the back or Sophie and Louise from moaning that they're bored with ballet. No you're not, darlings, you love it. 'Sboring. The teacher was just saying how well you're doing. No, I'm not. 'Sboring.

It is very annoying if they want to pack it in after only a few weeks, especially if you've begged and pleaded and lied to get them accepted. You've also boasted to other parents who only have two classes lined up that yes, Flora simply adores fencing/drama/cookery/tap dancing, course we were very lucky to get her in. The worst is when they pack it in when you've just got all the gear. Getting all the gear is often the prime attraction of any activity. They can't do ballet in vest and knickers, even for just the first lesson to see if they like it, but have to have real ballet shoes, leotards, leg warmers and cross-over cardigans. We have a green shirt lying around somewhere which Jake got when ñe was in the Woodcraft Folk. I think he thought it was going to be the Hitler Youth Movement at least, as he was very keen on iron discipline at the time, but he left after half an hour when all they did was sit in a circle and think about trees.

It's always the weediest kids who join the clubs with the most impressive gear. I took Jake along once to a Judo class with his friend Orlando who had so much junk it almost needed a trailer to get him to the hall. I helped Orlando get ready for the judo lesson, while Jake worried whether he should join, and it was bad enough getting his ordinary clothes off. He was only two foot high but had this enormous six-inch-broad buckled belt round his non-existent hips. His mother, who was very trendy, wanted him built up strong so that he could knock bullies down with one finger. So far, he still hadn't got enough strength to take his own trousers off. Luckily, Jake decided he would join the Cubs instead.

The only club I was ever in as a boy was the Scouts. I can still smell the mixture of dust and adolescent sweat in that grey church hall. The camps were terrifying. Bigger boys tried to do unmentionable things to you in the back of the tent in the middle of the night and I was always racked with asthma with sleeping in damp clothes. Today, there are so many different clubs for children—catering for every predilection, I shouldn't wonder.

We've just started a new class for Flora, piano lessons on Friday after school. It's the end of the week, so it won't make her too tired for school. No one ever thinks about how tired I might become. But the big advantage is that the teacher, Fred, lives just opposite. I agreed at once. What a dawdle. No more driving across London or hanging about. The first surprise was that on his door, in a little note saying come straight upstairs, he'd signed himself Frederic. For years I've called him Fred, but I suppose Chopin's neighbours were equally familiar. The next surprise was that I have to stay with her, throughout the whole of the lesson. My wife had muttered something about him being a Suzuki teacher and I thought that meant he sucked tangerines while he played. What it means, amongst other things, is that a parent can learn with the child. My wife, being a tone deaf, non-driver, has all the luck.

Flora's had four lessons now, and has started playing with two hands, chords and all, so my fury has softened rather. The parent doesn't actually play, just watches so that you can help them at home, doing the practising with them. I'm a bit behind with my practising and, if I hear 'Twinkle, Twinkle, Little Star' once again I'll scream. I'm not just learning the piano, but the French, German, Spanish and Japanese for the dreaded 'Twinkle'. I had to trail down to Soho to buy the book and I was furious at first to find it was all in foreign languages, with English being only a minor part. I know the Japs have taken over the motor-car trade but who'd have thunk they would also take over the lives of little men in back rooms giving piano lessons. I can't actually help her much with her practising. She thinks I'm useless and ignores everything I tell her, slamming the lid one day so hard that my fingers got caught and I couldn't type for two days. One can't teach one's own children anything, doesn't one find?

All these mums who are trailing their kids round these endless lessons are hoping somehow to keep them occupied. They're desperate for them to learn something, anything, knowing that in this permissive, indulgent age, parents aren't able to teach their own kids, not if it involves discipline. I'm only hoping this fellow Suzuki doesn't get on to gym and ballet next. I refuse to do cartwheels with six-year-olds or wear black leotards. I dunno. Being a caring father is so terribly tiring.

On the Record

When Caitlin was a very little girl we used to measure her every month against the wall, marking her height with a pencil, even when she couldn't stand and had to be hung there like washing. We were so proud of every inch she put on and we would ooh and aah and ring the grandparents and they would aah and ooh. Then we would go over the figures in our next letter, often managing to drag out the details for at least a page.

Every family is a museum. That's one of the things Marshall McLuhan never said, though it sounds like him. Every family is unique and is the same. I think T.S. Eliot said that, or something like it. Because every family is different, and is identical, every family should have its own archivist to keep tabs on all the events, the facts and figures, past and present. In our family, I'm the Keeper.

Then we re-decorated. At a stroke, Caitlin's monthly heights were obliterated. The world will never know what an amazing example of the human race she was between the ages of nought and 24 months. In January 1966, I decided henceforth to do posterity a good turn and not rely on pencil marks on the wall to survive the holocaust but commit everything to paper, just as Gutenberg said we should. I also borrowed a leaf from Mr Xerox and ran off copies for all the grandparents.

Did we have Xerox in 1966 or is my memory playing tricks? Excuse me while I look in the files. Hmm. I sit corrected. I used carbon paper from 1966 to 1971, but from then onwards I used a duplicating machine. You see. If I hadn't kept these records, I wouldn't have these records, would I.

15

As well as recording all the family's heights, I also do the weights and occasionally a few graphs, to show the spurts, and the plateaux, so we can compare one against the other. Jake has for years been consistently behind Caitlin in his height for his age, but this year, aged fourteen, he has put on an enormous increase. He's shot up by 4½ inches in one year. It's a world record, for our house.

At the same time, Caitlin has flattened out. No, I haven't been hitting her. We noticed last year she had only increased by half an inch, having for the previous nine years put on an average of two inches. This year, she has put on nothing. At the age of sixteen, her height race is over. She's retired at 5ft 9ins, undisputed champion, for our house.

The strange thing is, she *looks* taller than me. On the records, and I'm in charge of them so there's no fiddling, apart from my fiddles, I'm also 5ft 9ins. Yet everyone swears she's now bigger than me. I don't allow swearing in our house, so it must be wrong.

It must have been my second operation. Two years running I've had a cartilage operation and two years running I appear to have lost a quarter of an inch in height. I don't count that. House rules. I'm determined to stay at 5ft 9ins for ever, whatever the tape measure says. So that's final.

Family records are like the truth. There's no such thing. Just as there's no such thing as The News. We record what we feel like recording, or all that we happen to be able to record, or all that someone will let us record. Instead of here is the Nine O'clock News, they should say It's Nine O'Clock and Here is Some News, at Least we Think it's New, Anyway, it's all We've Managed to Get Together Since We Last Spoke to You. It would make a great title.

Because facts can not be trusted, for the simple reason that we can never know *all* the facts, I have also taken it upon myself to record the thoughts and impressions in our family every January 1 since 1966. It was rather haphazard in those early years, but now I do it under separate headings.

There's the Highlights of the year, things at that moment which stand out in our minds about the year just finished. There's Predictions for the coming year. In this section, we never allow bad predictions. That's another house rule. We stick to things like who might have babies, when and what sex. Who will be their best friends next year. It's not just about members of the family and close friends, but the world at large. We predict what the Royal Family will do, and Prince Charles has got married every year since 1969, or who will win the World Cup or the General Election. I told you this was invaluable material. I should really send copies to the BM.

The records for the early years are now all yellow with age. My writing was so big in those days. It's got smaller, just like me. Who said that. I have certainly not got smaller and I have figures here to prove it.

I see that in 1966 I predicted that Caitlin would have a sister with blue eyes and blonde hair. That turned out to be Jake. I predicted the car would be stolen twice. I have to concentrate hard to remember that I had a Mini in those days, which was always being stolen. I said that the roof would leak once again. Looking through the records, I said that every year till 1975, getting it right each time, till we got a new roof. One of my best predictions was in 1976 when I said that Carlisle United would get into the First Division. I'm afraid this year I've tipped them for the Fourth; though that might be classed as a bad prediction and not allowable.

On January 1st each year we seal up the predictions and put them in a safe place, usually so safe I can never ever find them. A year later, I ceremonially open them on New Year's Eve. By that time, I have forgotten almost everything I wrote. In fact we often find it hard to remember some of the names of people because they have moved out of our lives, or out of the area. If they only knew I have them stashed away for ever.

The Highlights of one year often seem unbelievable when read the next year. I see for 1980 I have said that one of the year's events was Flora and my wife both having their ears pierced. Surely we did more exciting things than that in 1980. But, in our little family, that was one of the happenings that came into our little heads, as we sat down and reminisced about the year just finished.

17

The most interesting section is usually Present Concerns. These are all the things in our heads each New Year's Eve, the topics we are currently grinding on about, the little things bugging us, the endlessly discussed subjects we never seem to resolve. Should I go and see a proper physiotherapist about my knee as it's sore again or should I wait? Every January for three years it's been a Present Concern. I can't bear to think about it.

Should we open up the fireplace in the sitting-room? This is a new subject, but it should run and run. We blocked it up in 1963, as we blocked up every fireplace when we moved in, as everyone did, back in 1963. But now so many people have got lovely open log fires and we could easily have one, if we hacked back the brick, or is it a steel plate, and will we need a chimney-sweep, but where do you get chimney-sweeps today, and then we'll have to buy a grate and a fender but who sells logs round here. With a bit of luck, she'll have forgotten all about it by the spring. Then next winter, the same topic will come round again.

What about the kitchen lights? Oh God, that's become another hardy annual. We have these spot-lights on a track, see. Which SHE HATES. She had them put in. Not me. Now I have to organise someone to take them out, which will mean ripping up the pine ceiling. She's not quite sure what she wants in their place. But SHE HATES them. Well, I did get the roof mended in the end, seven years after it first started leaking.

We do have a larf, as we look back each year at the things we once worried about. Like old photographs, they bring back so many memories you've forgotten you had. I also collect old photographs. I don't actually do much with them, but I have them all, somewhere. And piles of drawings and poems which all of them did when they were little. And I've got their school reports, in a drawer marked school reports, waiting for the day one of them is Prime Minister. And my ciné films. They're a legend in the family.

I often stand beside Flora, when she's at her table, and grab her scribbles, fresh from the felt pen, and have them framed and on the wall before they're dry. I'm continually giving them diaries, urging them to start keeping their own records. Jake did do one last year, just to please me, and faithfully recorded every meal. Every day, he listed the food he consumed. For a whole year. Gold dust.

There is a danger that I am so busy recording the present while it is happening that I haven't got time to live it. I do try to limit myself. I only reminisce about things that happened yesterday, not today. I wait for tomorrow to do that.

They think I'm potty, but they'll be grateful, they'll see. I wasn't interested as a child in who I was or where I'd come from. Now, I'm furious that my mother never kept my school reports or clinic cards. Was it true I wrote to Captain W.E. Johns and got a hand-written reply from him? If she'd kept it, I would have proof, wouldn't I, instead of just making idol boasts all these years.

In my wife's family, they burn everything at once. No letter is kept. She is much the same. Is it deep insecurity or just a squirrel mentality that makes me hoard every scrap? I'll be forced to retreat into a corner as soon as the archives grow bigger, leaving me no room to live and create more archive material.

I have had a notice up on the house notice-board, situation vacant, Assistant Keeper wanted, but I didn't get one reply. The notice is now in the filing cabinet.

Party Politics

We were terribly pleased when Flora was born. Not just because she was a surprise, which she was. Not just because she arrived safely and soundly, which she did. Not just because she was a girl, which she still is. We'd had enough sleepless nights with her baby brother Jake and didn't want another boy baby. No, the main reason why we were so thrilled when she entered the world on October 31, 1972 was because she had entered the world on October 31, 1972.

My wife, whom I'd chosen to be the one to give birth, as it was more than her turn, let out an extra scream for joy. Hallowe'en! The Irish nurse said no no, it's not a boy, but a little girl. She thought she'd said Hello, Ian. When we'd got that cleared up, and everything else, she lay back like a contented cow, one of those who used to get a mention on every tin of condensed milk, and smiled happily, thinking how clever she'd been in solving the problem of Flora's birthday party from now and for ever more, amen. No no, not twin boys, just a little wee girl.

We've just had Flora's eighth birthday party. Once again, the house has been full of witches and turnip lanterns and apples hanging from the ceiling and broomsticks in every corner and it's going to take us almost the next year to clear up, by which time it'll all have to happen again. It's like putting on *The Romans in Britain* every year, just for one performance. I didn't notice Mrs Whitehouse this time, and there was a lot of rude words and bare flesh. Perhaps she'll make it next year.

I don't know why you go to such trouble, which is what I say after every children's party. She just loves organising them. It's ridiculous, the amount of work and the expense, all for a load of kids. Next year we'll hire a conjuror. I just say that to annoy. You couldn't hold your head up in the neighbourhood if you had *paid* entertainment. Certainly not. What kind of caring parents would want to rent film shows or hire donkeys or bring in comedians or even worser, spend money and take them all out to a restaurant and then to a show. You might as well not have children, if you're going to take the easy way out. Tut tut. You'll be suggesting printed invitations next.

Our invitations are always works of art done by contented children, and they only take 51 weeks to create. That spontaneous childlike quality takes time to capture. It's educational, see, which is how my wife always replies, after she's pointed out that the expense is minimal. It's simply a matter of imagination, organisation and cunning.

The large black plastic cut-outs of witches, which cover every downstairs window, and will be there for months as they're hell to unstick, are on their fifth year now and were made from those plastic rubbish bags, 10p each, or ten for 90p. That's one of the many things about always having a Hallowe'en birthday party. You can re-use almost everything.

I wasn't quick enough this year. We bought a large load of paper napkins with witches on, which came from Party Mad but I'm not allowed to know the price. They'll last for ever, she said, eating the bill. I hovered round the tea table, grabbing little arms every time some dum-dum eight-year-old attempted to wipe crumbs from her mouth. 'Just for show,' I said. 'And if you want to blow your nose, use your dress.'

Most of them are now in the bin and I've only saved three, and they're rather soggy, but I've managed to wash the witch paper plates and untie every witch balloon. It's amazing how many items you can get with witches or other Hallowe'en symbols on them. All it costs is money. Sorry, it just slipped out. How many amazing things you can *make*.

We didn't get many turnips this year, as they were so expensive. Last year we bought sixteen and carved out one lantern for each child, and the smell and debris lingered on till well past Christmas. I think somebody must have cornered the market in turnips this year but, surprisingly, pumpkins were very cheap. (You are making notes. I'll be asking questions afterwards.) We got a huge seven pound pumpkin for only £1.16. Every year so far a pumpkin of that sized has been about £5. Well, fancy that.

On the same hand, Caitlin and Jake's birthdays provided endless challenges, having to think up a new theme every year. They're finished now, thank goodness. God, another mistake. I mean such a shame we no longer give jolly children's parties for dear little Caitlin and dear little Jake. One day when they awoke the good fairy had been kissing the ugly duckling while the Prince lay sleeping and lo and behold, come the morn, overnight they had turned into teenagers and the world was never the same again. We've got cine films, though.

That's the one when Jake was seven and we organised a football game for him and his twenty little friends. We'd planned to have half-time, when oranges and drinks would be brought on but the fighting was so intense that we had to have quarter time, then eighth time, then sixteenth time, slicing the game thinner and thinner in an effort to calm everything down. At full time, which I blew hours early, my wife rushed into the house to grab Dr Spock and find out if seven-year-old boys could have heart attacks.

The next year we had a great wheeze. The party began out in the garden, which Jake's parties always did, before proceeding to the Royal Free. His birthday is May 24 and it was always hot and sunny, in those far-off days before the War. The first game was called Houdini. We split the boys into two teams, and it was pure chance that all the thugs were in the same team and all the drips in another and even more of a coincidence that the game began with the thug team being tied up, very very very securely with ropes, while the drips had to watch carefully and make sure no one cheated while trying to escape. That put in almost half the party.

The year after we had a Robin Hood party and turned

23

the climbing-frame into a castle. It looked incredible. You can see the cine, if you promise not to show yours. It only took ten rolls of lining paper, which is still the cheapest paper on the market, and Jake himself helped to paint the battlements. The drips had cardboard swords and had to attack the thugs who had to stay in the castle. In the end, they all joined forces to tear down the castle between them. What a denouement. Dennis Potter couldn't do better.

I think we lost complete control of Jake's parties by the time he was ten. That was when we put our foot down and restricted the numbers to six. It wasn't the guests, who in the main were well behaved, but Jake himself. There was a tantrum if any other boy won a prize, had first go at a game, was first served at tea, got the biggest ice cream. We couldn't even give going home presents. Jake had to have them *all*. Well, it's my party.

Who would believe he's now turned into such a lovely teenager, so kind, so considerate. I said hasn't he turned out well, when you think what a sod he used to be. If I say it a third time, he might be nice to me.

On the other hand, Caitlin's parties got easier. I know it's all a matter of brainwashing and that they're all alike and there's no real difference between the sexes and it's all our fault, forcing them into rolls, even when they're not hungry, but we did honestly try to get Jake and his boys to sit quietly with pencils and paper and play Kim's Game or I Spy, but all they wanted was a rough-house. It's the girls who love guessing games of all sorts, and respond to being treated as if they were in school, though they also like a rough-house.

Caitlin's party themes were always indoor ones, as her birthday is March 6. Now you know them all. They'll expect presents next year. We had an Alice in Wonderland party one year, for which they all had to dress in an appropriate costume. They entered through a huge cardboard tunnel in the middle of which they had to drink from a little glass of magic water and everything from then on was back to front. They got going-away presents on arrival and ate their tea under the table. I'm exhausted, just remembering them.

We also had a Gypsy party and an Arabian Nights Party, though not in the same year. In the cine films, they look much the same, with many of the little girls in identical costumes and the living room on each occasion turned into what looks like a tent. In those days you just needed to *pretend* the theme was different. Nowadays, as Hallowe'en is always Hallowe'en we have to work twice as hard to make it the same, but better.

I think I will get the rest of those torn paper napkins out of the waste bin. If I iron them out carefully I can say next year that they're witches' handkies. We've never had *them* before.

House Keepers

I'm sitting here worrying about Caitlin. She's just rung from a motorway service station near Doncaster to say she's at a motorway service station near Doncaster, so that's a relief. She set off with her friends at 6.30 this morning to drive to Edinburgh for half-term. Don't ask me why. I'm just the Dad round this place. She hates driving long distances by car as it makes her feel sick, so she says when I'm driving her, but oh yes, when it's with her friends.

It's now after 3 o'clock. The car must be giving trouble. By the time they get there, half-term will be over. I'll have to lie to my mother when she rings tonight. Letting a sixteen-year-old go all that way, it's ridiculous. Seventeen, mother, on March 6, remember. That counts as an O.A.P. these days. But it won't do any good. And if I mention that they're being driven by some boy, she'll go spare. I'd better stick to the weather and what colour to paint the bathroom this week.

There's only one thing more worrying than Caitlin away on one of her jaunts and that's Caitlin at home while we're away on one of our jaunts. It's one of the unsolved problems of Western civilisation, one which unites all parents everywhere: at what age can you leave them behind in the house on their own? It's OK for the jesting pilot. He never stayed for an answer but just flew off.

They start at fourteen, moaning on about how draggy it is having holidays with the family, but you can usually coerce them for another year. In the end they become a drag on the holiday for everyone else. How can you push little Flora out in the driving rain and up a frozen fell-side for a six-

27

hour tramp when her big sister proposes to spend the day in bed, just like she did yesterday. She *hates* long walks up hills.

So we gave up about a year ago, agreeing that Miss could stay at home in London, as long as someone was in the house with her. God, the complications and confusions and hagonies we've had trying to fill the house with someone responsible, or an adult, or anyone, just to keep an eye on her, no I don't mean that, just to keep an eye on the house. Look, it's not that we don't trust you. It's a big responsibility, having a big house to look after. And we don't trust you.

My parents never had this problem. We never had holidays, ah, what a shame, although there's a rumour in the family that I was once taken to a boarding-house in Troon when I was three, just before my two younger sisters and brother arrived, and then that was it, for ever. We stayed at home for the next hundred years. We could have done with some of us going away, just anyone, as the house always seemed so full and crowded.

When I left home for the first time at eighteen, to go away to Durham, I came home unexpectedly in the middle of term and found a stranger in my bed. I arrived back late, crawled into bed, which I'd always shared anyway with my younger brother, and there was another bloke on my side. He was called Tony, a very nice lad, from an orphanage or some sort of home. I don't want to make my mother sound mercenary, taking in lodgers the minute my bed was vacant. It was just that she was doing him a good turn. No one ever got turned away, not at our house.

We spent last year pleading with complete strangers to have a free summer holiday in our lovely London house, ringing up distant relations, friends of friends. We eventually got this Scottish couple, who turned out to be Seventh Day Adventists, and they were absolutely thrilled as they were being forced to come to London with a sick child having treatment and had nowhere to stay, until they heard we were looking for someone.

'The Lord has provided,' so they said. What they didn't

know, till they arrived, was that the Lord had also provided Caitlin. It needs a strong Christian constitution to put up with her noisy records and noisy friends.

They filled in for two weeks, and then my brother and his family came down from Carlisle for the other two weeks, which was a great success. In fact I often think Caitlin would like it as a permanent arrangement. It's her idea of happy families. We go to bed at ten o'clock each night, as you well know, and if she wakens me up on her arrival home, I go berserk, staggering around in my jamas to scream at her. I can hardly sleep anyway, wondering where she is. It's all my fault, I know. I'm not normal.

When my brother Johnny is staying here, Caitlin comes home happily at twelve o'clock without any need to creep upstairs in the dark, scared to put a light on or creak any floorboards or worry about the old ogre. At that hour, Johnny is still watching TV, like any ordinary member of the population. Then when the tele goes off, the frying-pan comes on. You see, Dad, that's how ordinary families behave.

We've booked Johnny for the whole of this summer, which is lucky, and pleases everyone, as his kids love doing the London museums and sites and sights. Well, you can go off Carlisle Castle on a rainy Saturday, fascinating though it is. That still leaves Easter, when we plan to be in the Lakes, but we're working on it. Applications in triplicate please, with bank references and religion.

Can't I just have Fig and Sophe to stay? No need to get someone else in at Easter. I explain the awful complications of kicking the central heating boiler and the Miele's on the blink and the upstairs lavatory might overflow again, then what would you do, not to mention burglars. I know every teenager's ambition is to have a friend with an empty house. It was my ambition, after all, I can remember it all too well. So the answer is no. Most certainly not. You're too young. I mean it's too much of a responsibility.

All around, I talk to parents with the same problem. We've just had Poo, one of Caitlin's friends, to stay the night, doing her parents a favour while they went to Paris.

They have a housekeeper, this family, so you would think there was no problem. Turns out the housekeeper says that on no account is she being left alone in the house with Poo. She's a perfectly nice girl, very friendly, a bit untidy, not at all wild, but the housekeeper said that if she was left alone with Poo, she would resign. As they value their housekeeper more than their daughter's comfort, Poo was forced to wander like a gypsy round the houses of her friends.

Ah, that was Caitlin again. She says they've got to Scotland at last. 'It must be. I can see a big notice in the mist saying Scotch Corner.' Then she rang off, having run out of money. Scotch Corner! That's miles from Scotland. And the mist has come down. What fools they are.

I suppose it's better than hitch-hiking. When I was her age, me and her mother once spent a whole day at Scotch Corner, ending up in tears, failing to get even a lorry to stop and take us over the Pennines back to Carlisle. I used my lucky left hand as well, but it did no good. I finally hid behind a wall, so it looked as if it was just a girl on her own hitching, but that failed. What fools we were.

Now I'm a Dad, I don't allow that sort of thing, do I. Hitch-hiking is very dangerous and I don't approve of it. Little did I think one of her friends would turn out to have his own car. I don't know where they get the money from. Parents these days are so indulgent. Aren't we.

She has tried to argue that she and Jake being left on their own together would be safe enough, but I don't like the idea of that either. All the brothers and sisters I hear about who are left jointly in charge cause even more problems. You have two sets of hooligans, I mean friends, invading the house, and they all blame the other lot for wrecking the joint.

It's her general standard of housekeeping that is as worrying as anything else. No plants get watered, no floors get Hoovered, no windows get opened. If you do tell her specifically to open windows, they remain wide open, night and day, an invitation to all.

But I've agreed that at eighteen she can be in charge of the house when we're away. She'll have to learn sometime.

Or I'll have to learn not to be a fusspot and take things as they come and not get upset and imagine awful things.

Hurrah. Final phone call. She's arrived safely in Edinburgh. Well, it's actually a cottage in the wilds in Berwickshire. Yes, it's freezing and wet but we're now going to have a long walk up a hill. Such fun.

Rabbit, Rabbit

We've been very nice to Flora for a whole week now. I played cards with her all yesterday morning which seemed sinful, doing such a thing on a weekday morning while all respectable members of the human race were at school, almost as sinful as going to the pictures in the afternoon and coming out while it's still daylight. You can go to the Bad Fire for that sort of thing.

My wife even stopped shouting at her about the ice cubes. Flora has this passion for making herself stupid home-made drinks, half lemonade and half orange, topping it up with ten ice cubes. She's not really against Flora's concoctions, but the number of ice cubes is rather excessive, especially as it's winter. I don't mind. Ice is cheap enough. Let them have their fun. We never had ice cubes when I was young, etc., or a fridge, etc., unless you count the one we lived in six months of the year, etc.

The thing which bugs her most of all is that Flora will decide to start making her stupid drink *after* we've all sat down for a meal. It's one of the basic rules of civilisation as we know it, engraved on all the wall tablets in our kitchen. Everyone has to arrange their drink *before* the meal begins.

Jake is worst. He gets up, shoves his way past the back of everyone else's seat, and then starts a fight to the death at the door of the fridge, as if he's in the last reel of *Jaws*. He seems incapable of getting ice out of the ice tray. We have those clever rubber ones, easy peasy, except for Jake who ends up trying to bash their brains out, then they fly all over the kitchen like nuclear missiles and the meal becomes a screaming match.

Anyway, Flora has been allowed to get away with this heinous crime for a whole week. It's led to very quiet mealtimes. I've quite enjoyed them, in a sadistic sort of way, watching my wife close her eyes and grip the sides of the chair while Flora has stood at the fridge door and messed around with the bloody ice cubes. She's ill, see. You can't be rotten to a little girl of eight when she's poorly. Fair do's.

It started with a cold and developed into a terrible wheeze. I began to fear it might be asthma, which I had all my childhood, or bronchitis. I rang the doctor and luckily a locum was on duty so I jumped at the first appointment. We love our family GP dearly, and have been with her for over twenty years, but so does everyone else. When the normal patient, convinced he's about to die, rings up and finds the doc is away, he'll decide to put off dying for another week, till the doc returns. It's hard luck on the locums, not being trusted, but the result is a very quick appointment system.

He tapped her chest through her vest, which perplexed her, as how can you hear anything through an Aertex vest, oh, I see Hunt, he hears through the holes, and pronounced it wasn't bronchitis but a chest infection. There's a lot about, he said to her. No, no, I'm the only one in my class with these sort of vests, though Sarah might have one, and perhaps Claudia, even Chlöe.

She was five days on the first lot of antibiotics, and the wheezing got worse if anything, till she sounded like a little old man with a death rattle. I took her back and he went through the vest again, and said the chest infection is still there, we'll try another antibiotic.

The know-all in the chemist, and as know-alls go, chemists are at the top of the barrack room lawyer league, said tut tut, hum hum, once you fail on one antibiotic, you could be on them for weeks and weeks. The best thing is this vaporiser for the bedroom, you mark my barrack room words. I said we'd just stick to antibiotics. I didn't like the price.

Later that day, I went to see if she fancied Scrabble, or even Monopoly, which I hate, as it gives me a headache, but she loves it and she is poorly. And I found her in tears.

After a lot of coaxing, I got out of her that the problem was a rabbit. I said I didn't know how to play that game. Was it like Rummy. No, a real rabbit. That's what I want more than anything else in the whole world and if you really love me you'll buy me a rabbit. Dear God, give me strength. I breathed in deeply and said what about a goldfish. They make great pets. More tears. You can't cuddle a goldfish.

It's Sarah, you see. She's got a rabbit and Flora hasn't. We've been through the whole topic of pets millions of times. She was just coming the abdabs, knowing we were being unusually kind to her as she was ill. Look, we go away to the Lakes every holiday, so who would look after them? You'll soon get bored anyway. Then who will clean out and feed and water the poor little hamster, monkey, gerbil, snake, elephant, giant panda, tarantula.

Caitlin was exactly the same at Flora's age. She was once in floods of tears for days because she wanted a dog. It was the only thing that would make life worth living. We were so horrible to her. Everyone has pets except us, it's not fair, we're so selfish. What a state she worked herself into. I reminded her of this the other day and she swore blind it had never happened.

When Caitlin got over the dog, she then got it into her head that I was going to buy her a pet mouse. She'd convinced herself I'd promised, which was a lie. She got a second-hand mouse cage from somewhere and cleaned it, painted it up, put in fresh straw and water, and every night for about six weeks slept with it beside her bed. Pathetic, isn't it. Perhaps we *were* horrible parents. She also has no memory of that.

We come from a long line of non-pet owning families and I suppose the habit becomes ingrained. That's a lie. When we lived in Dumfries for a while we did have a cat which lost one of its legs in a trap. It ended up with a stump and we used to hear it going round the house at night. Pad, pad, pad, thump.

We have, of course, our tortoise, now safely asleep for the winter, missing all the fun. Wait till he wakens up in

May and I tell him about Charles and Diana. He's the
perfect pet as he takes no looking after whatsoever. I didn't
even put him down for the winter. Once again, I failed to
find him in October and he just disappeared. Perhaps we'll
never see him again. Or he's queuing at St Paul's for the
wedding.

A rabbit, now. I don't think they go on heat, whatever
that disgusting phrase is they use about dogs, but I bet
they're a load of trouble. Please, please, Dad, say you'll get
me one, wheeze, wheeze, wheeze.

They do say that having animals does children good.
Teaches them to be kind and caring and responsible for
others. They can express their love openly, with no
complications. Perhaps we *have* been horrible all these years,
thinking only of our own comfort and convenience.

I went into Sarah's to ask them about rabbits, where you
buy them, can you eat them, I mean what do they eat, and
I found they'd brought their huge rabbit cage into the living
room. Derek, the dad, had spent the best part of a day
making this terrific cage, special wire and wood and a
terribly ingenious escape door. As if a pet wasn't bad
enough, you also have to build a housing estate.

Smokey, for such is this wretched rodent's name, or are
rabbits something else, had been brought in from his lovely
cage in the back garden as he was found to be suffering from
hypothermia. Oh, such consternation and worry. It's one
thing having your children ill, but having to fret about a
bloody pet being poorly, who needs it.

Smokey had made a good recovery in the house, except
the room now had rabbit shit where he'd been allowed to
run around, but not to worry, that would soon be cleared
up. I ran straight home without hearing any more,
determined that we were not having rabbits. But how was
I going to tell Flora.

The second dose of antibiotic finished this morning and
this afternoon I took Flora across to the locum once again.
I think the doctor must be on her yacht. (God, she'll have
me for that. Justa joke. We all know how the National
Health ill-treats and badly pays all GPs. Sorry.)

Flora's wheezing seemed just as bad to me, but this time, through a vest darkly, he pronounced the chest infection had greatly cleared. The noise didn't mean much. Just a bit of stuff in the windpipes. She can go back to school tomorrow. Hurrah. No more cards for me. No more ice cubes for Flora.

And oh, by the way, said the locum, you haven't got any pets have you. That could have been the cause of the chest infection. If I were you, I wouldn't let her stroke or play with any animals. I thought Flora was either going to burst into tears, or hit him.

So that's it all settled. It was the doctor who said it, not me. Very clever, these locums.

Teacher's Pest

Name me six of Caitlin's teachers, said my wife. We were in the car driving to Caitlin's school for the annual assessment and I was really wondering whether I should have put on an ordinary jacket, and looked like a real Dad, instead of my plastic battle-jacket which I think makes me look pretty sharp, in a Sixties sort of way, but probably makes me look like her Granddad. One doesn't want to be an embarrassment to one's children, does one.

Go on, name three of them then. I pride myself on being a caring, committed parent, clued up on their little worlds, tuned in to their educational progress, knowing about all their activities, but yes, a sports-jacket, my Marks and Spencer grey one, would have been much more suitable.

OK, I knew I'd catch you out, after all that boasting. Name *one* of her teachers, then. What, I said. What are you on about? One teacher? Chris, isn't there one called Chris? Ask me another. Easy peasy.

As he's her only male teacher, no wonder you remembered his name. And what are you wearing that stupid jacket for. You look like a jerk. You don't want to embarrass Caitlin, though God knows, after these years.

I don't think my mother ever went into any of my schools in her whole life. She knew her place. Standing outside the school gates, ready to jump to attention should one of the Gods happen to go past. Parents were not seen and not heard in those days.

Now parents have practically taken over, especially in the primary schools, hanging about the classrooms all day, getting in the way, foot in the staff-room door, oh yes,

I will have a cup of coffee, these slow readers are a right drag, I think I'll help you do Maths next week, that's if it's not my turn to do Assembly, or am I interviewing the new Head that day.

I do know all the teachers in Flora's primary school, and so I should, as both Caitlin and Jake have been that way, and left marks to prove it, and given a starter for ten I could probably name every child in Flora's class, but I am a bit hazier on their secondary schools. They still have a slight mustique, as Princess Margaret might say.

With secondary schools, you have to wait till you're invited in, though there are enough opportunities, such as Open Days, school plays, jumble sales and most important of all, the annual chance to meet each of their teachers and hear, man to man, or man to woman, or mantovani, how the little treasures are progressing.

The very first one I ever went to was when Jake was four and in nursery school and they decided to have the parents in and discuss each child's educational development, which was a bit daft, as all they did was cutting and sticking, but I heard the mother ahead of me distinctly ask the nursery teacher if Jason was Oxbridge material.

The secondary meetings are the ones that matter, especially when O-levels and A-levels are coming up, and the teachers can enjoy their little bit of power, bollocking parents for their child's bad reports, saying it just won't do, and I really think Darren would be better off doing CSE. No, no, they scream. Anything but CSE. I promise to beat his little head in every evening from now on if you'll only please, please.

We'd been to Jake's the previous week. That's a boys' school, which is what Jake happens to be, this week anyway, and it was formerly a grammar school though Jake is part of the first comprehensive intake. It's highly disciplined and rather traditional and we all queued up obediently to take our punishment like men. It's almost like a prison visit, sitting silently waiting in rows, and the teacher sticks strictly to the facts when it's your turn to put your nose against the grille, going through the latest marks without much time for any old psychological chat.

At Caitlin's school, the system is arranged in much the same way, with the teachers at desks around the hall, and little numbers so you can find them, but there's always a party atmosphere, with much shouting and laughing and arguing and a coffee bar and cakes available. Her school is also now a comprehensive, all girls, or have I already said that, but they don't have uniform. It's known as a rather enlightened girls' school, full of enlightened girls.

'You must be joking,' the girl ahead of me was saying to the teacher. She was with her parents and the teacher in question had been saying that she really must pull herself together and work harder. The usual stuff.

'Prove it,' said the girl.

'Don't be cheeky, dear,' said the mother.

'No, no, she's quite right,' said the teacher, getting out her marks book.

There was then a good-humoured argument between the teacher and girl, though it might have been two girls arguing in the playground.

I love listening to all the discussions, which isn't hard, as they all talk so loudly, comparing each girl with her parents, searching for likenesses, remembering how they looked six years ago. I only ever see most of them on this annual visit so in a year you can see huge changes. That's when I realised that Caitlin's clothes aren't as unusually scruffy as I'd thought, or that hat as ridiculous or those plimsolls so stupid. In fact, when I looked around, I could see she was wearing a uniform.

Then you sit down, face to face, with the teacher. Hmm, that explains a lot, you can see them thinking, eyeing you over. Well, I'd never expected *him*. Now I understand.

The parent in turn is thinking: so this is the bugger who has been so horrid to my child, giving her extra homework, marking all the essays badly, the queen of the beta minus minus. Hmm, now I understand. She doesn't look like a nut-case, or is that the Latin one, or has that one left, or am I getting completely mixed up.

41

They were all terribly kind about Caitlin, much to my surprise, pleased with how she is working. It seems to me all she does is play, but then all I did *was* play at her age, so I do tend to moan at her a lot. As if she listens to anything I say.

One of the teachers told me all about UCCA, which is not a trade union, or a branch of Express Dairies, but is the University College of California. No it's not. Got you there. I asked her what happens if you apply to a university and it turns out to be one of those which closes before you get there. That's what I heard some Vice-Chancellor going on about on the radio. We've got a dum-dum Dad here, I could see her thinking.

Women teachers, on the whole, tend to be more interested in the personality of the child and will indulge any parent who wants to try out their theories. It's also interesting to hear their theories. Most men teachers tend to go blank when you come out with your little worries, the minor things we caring parents concern ourselves with. While a woman might recommend the Tavistock, a man might suggest cold showers.

You can often learn surprising things. The mother ahead of me at Jake's school was amazed to learn that her son hadn't been at school for three days. We're all surprised every year to be told that Flora is shy in class. It must be true, as three teachers have now said it, yet all we see at home is this raver in a boob tube and make-up prancing about like a Pan's Person.

By going into the school at least once a year, and meeting the legends, the centres of their firmament, you do at least get some sort of insight. It's often the only time some parents learn anything, as a lot of adolescents don't talk to their parents about their school life. Caitlin tells us a lot, if you catch her in the right mood when she comes in from school, and so does Jake, though you have to listen hard. Having shouted his rotten head off for the first thirteen years of his life, he's now polishing a mumble.

Talking to their teachers saves you saying, 'What did you do at school today?' which is the question you must never ask but is by far and away the question most parents want answered.

'What did you do at school today, Dad,' said Caitlin when we came home. I mumbled, too tired to go through it all. She didn't come with us, you see. She can't stand my old plastic jacket.

Hammering Tongues

We had a terrific row at supper this evening. It used to
be called tea, then high tea, then when it was two sittings
it was *their* tea followed by *our* dinner, and now it's supper,
tout la famille, just as the Advertising Standards
Association says it should be. All friends together, round
the camp fire, the nuclear unit. Happy families.

We seem to have had a lot of rows recently. Well, not
rows, intellectual discussions, the sort which flare up when
they try to lay down the law. After all, they're at school
and know everything and we're just pensioned-off lodging-
house keepers, here to make meals, clean the floor, give
out the pocket money and do other menial duties.

The other evening, we, the servants, happened to say
that Napoleon's mistake was marching on Russia. What
fools we were, what a simplistic approach to history, how
out of date can you get. Caitlin gently, but firmly, as if
dealing with an idiot, explained that Napoleon's big mistake
was not Russia but Spain. Apparently he messed around
in Spain, buggered it all up in fact, and that was the real
beginning of the end. I should have known. Sorry I spoke.
Your majesty. Should I clear the dishes now or wait till
you've finished your thirds of the apple tart.

I only happen to have a degree in history, a very poor
one, mind you, from a provincial university but their
mother got an open history scholarship to Somerville, so
she should know a thing or three, shouldn't she, but of
course we don't know anything. That was eons ago. When
you're in the lower sixth, you do know everything, don't
you. And did you say Somerville. Bloody hell. Nobody goes

there any more. An all-women's college. You must be joking.

Then there was an intellectual row about hair. I said hair was alive, otherwise how does it grow. Caitlin and Jake both said that hair is dead. Hair has no cells, so technically hair is dead, see, Dad, don't you know anything, or didn't they have cells when you were at school. No, just attics I said. That got them.

Anyway, this evening's little contretemps was an unintellectual one and concerned Flora, still aged eight. She's never been keen on meat and naturally we don't force her to eat anything she's not keen on. That's what being a parent is all about, Brian. It's a very simple game. Play the easy ball.

To make up for her lack of meat, we always give little Flora a double helping of French beans. It's like eating pound notes at the moment, eating fresh French beans, but the are delicious and worth every morsel morceau of 80p a pound. Actually, what she had this evening was a full plate of lovely French beans, gently under-cooked, as her main dish. Caitlin had apoplexy. Why should Flora have all those. If she doesn't like lamb, that's her fault. It doesn't mean to say she should have double French beans. You just spoil her.

'Oh shut up, you old witch,' said Flora.

'Take that,' said Caitlin. And hit her.

It was a horrid thing to say. Flora, why did you say that horrid thing. Mind you, in those old jumble sale clothes, she does look a bit like Worzel Gummidge, though that is a thought I keep to myself. I don't want to be thumped. On the other foot, it's not very kind for a sixteen-year-old, sorry seventeen last month, to hit her eight-year-old little sister.

We all watched Flora carefully, waiting for the floods of tears and the RSC perfomance. She paused, looked around, felt her arm where it had been soundly slapped by Caitlin, and burst out laughing. She knew she had won.

So we all laughed, ha ha, which infuriated Caitlin. She flounced out, saying it was bloody unfair. Flora was the favourite, we let her get away with murder, just because she's only eight.

Jake also sincerely believes that Flora is the favourite. You indulge her all the time and let her do things we were never allowed to do. Why don't you tell her off for a change, or even hit her. Oh, no. You never touch little Flora.

It's all true. We were much tougher on the first two when they were young, keeping them in their place, being very strict, allowing no nonsense. Now, when Flora does something awful, we tend to laugh rather than scream at her the way we did with them. She's only little, we say. Then to ourselves we mutter, she is our last.

At eight years old, Caitlin's life revolved round the Brownies, getting house points at school, watching *Blue Peter* and keeping her room neat and tidy. Flora at eight won't even contemplate the Brownies, that's just for babies, but wants to go disco dancing or even better, down the pub. She already has her ears pierced, which Caitlin never had till she was fourteen, and uses eye-shadow. Actually, it's Jake's chalk for his snooker cues and we've told her not to and she'll get some terrible infection, but what a funny idea, look at Flora, see what she's done now.

This afternoon she went to Winchester market, which is a marvellous open-air market near Swiss Cottage, though rotten old Camden Council are about to sell it off, and spent all her pocket money on a pink velvet jump suit. The big ones were horrified at us, the so-called parents, letting her do such a stupid thing.

Yet, on the other feet, Flora eats her heart out to be Caitlin. She is insanely jealous that she is not the oldest in the family. Last Saturday evening, when the usual hordes of seven-feet-high yobs, I mean young gentlemen, called for Caitlin, and they all went out of the front door, going ya ya ya, on the way to the pub, no that can't be right, they're only seventeen, they must have been on the way to the Rechabites.

Flora stood watching them from the upstairs window and cried. Why can't she go out with boys on a Saturday night

47

and have fun. Why should she have to clean her teeth and go to bed at eight o'clock. The world is so unfair. She can see no hope whatsoever of ever being sixteen.

I tell her that when that time comes, Caitlin will be an old maid. All that scruffy punk stuff will be completely out of date and she and Sarah and Chlöe and Claudia and Imogen and all the other eight-year-olds round this part of the Western world will come into their very own with their very own style. Perish the thought. Flora is never interested in this thought. She wants to be sixteen *now*.

However, one of Caitlin's boyfriends, Danny, happened to see this little figure with her nose pressed against the window and took time off from going ha ha ha, ya ya ya, in the street, wakening everyone up, and blew her a kiss. Wasn't that nice. Otherwise, we would never have got her to bed.

I suppose Flora is bound to be more advanced than they were, if that's what it is. Being the youngest, she has all their examples ahead of her. She's living in a hot-house. Caitlin, when she was young, was on her own. None of us knew what lay ahead and we took each step very slowly. On the other toes, Caitlin got our undivided attention, all our energies and devotion, being our first-born. That is a thought she in turn is not interested in.

I keep telling Caitlin that the oldest always does best in the world. I'm an oldest child. Look how brill I've done. OK, ignore me. Read any psychology book and you'll see that the first-borns are the most advantaged.

I didn't think so at the time. I seemed to get lumbered all my childhood with looking after my two younger sisters and younger brother, making toast for them, boiling potatoes for them. It didn't seem much fun at the time, being the oldest.

Caitlin has been spared all that. She's hardly ever had to look after Flora. On the rare occasions she babysits, and after all where do we go, Flora's usually asleep. In my humble opinion, I think she's had all the fun of being the first-born, with none of the disadvantages. But of course who asked me. She'll never believe it, not till she herself is a parent.

Jake is a middle-born. I don't think I'd like to be a middle-born. You get bossed around by the oldest, or contemptuously ignored, and then when you get to man's estate, and become a teenager, you have to put up with the younger child being grossly indulged and having all the fun and licence you never had. At least Jake is a boy, born between two girls, which makes a difference, though try telling him. He's convinced the world is against him. They all think that.

My wife is a middle child. Her ambition in life was to be an only child. She thought that would be the most marvellous position to be in.

I'm an only parent. I only have one set of children. It's not fair.

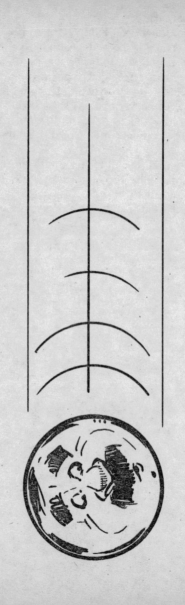

Games People Play

They've been sunbathing in the garden all day while me and Jake have been getting progressively paler, crouching inside over the snooker table. I've always loved games with the family, though I pretend I'm doing them a huge favour, but this snooker thing has become an obsession and I'm well on the way to a misspent middle age.

We've been playing it for what seems like centuries, long before it became fashionable. Oh, it must be well over six months since I treated myself to the table, I mean bought it for Jake's birthday. I don't think we've missed a game every day since then. Now where are those scores. Jake hides them when he gets behind.

We normally play every evening after supper. Wannagamehunt, he says, and I grunt, playing hard to get. I don't care, he says, I'll go and finish my homework. Hold on Jake, just coming, if you insist.

We drag the table out, then we drag it away again. Almost every evening we forget that we've pinned the rest of the family in the kitchen. Snooker is very anti-social, in a normal family-sized house, as the table dominates our whole living-room. So we let the others decide where they're going, then pull the table out again.

Setemupjake. No, it's your turn. We have a row every evening before we begin and the bickering continues all the way through. We are always getting into the game when he decides he must go to the lavatory. When he gets back he plays a shot, then decides the table isn't level and gets down on the floor and starts fiddling with the legs while I throw the cue on the floor and say that's it. I'm not playing any more.

I do of course, as I want to win. When we play beach football on our summer holidays, or when me, Jake and Flora play cards, the only object as far as I'm concerned is to win. What's the point of having children if you can't beat them at everything. Actually, Jake is ahead this month on snooker. But I have got a sore knee.

My wife hates all games, either with other adults or with the children. There are some families who seem to spend all their spare time playing games together, one big happy unit, just like the TV commercials. It makes her cringe, especially the ones doing it in public on their summer holidays. She maintains they're working on their image and it's always self-conscious and most of all it's hearty. She hates anyone who's hearty, apart from Russell, and we all know he's a lovely bloke really.

Yet strangely her hero in life is Sebastian Coe. You thought it was me, didn't you. No chance. One is never a hero to one's wife. Flora has put up Seb's photo on her noticeboard, beside her desk, which was kind. I think she even likes him more than Prince Andrew. Haven't seen his photo recently. Wonder what he's done to offend. We don't discuss such things. One must have some privacy in marriage.

She will play certain family games on occasions, if we're really stuck, such as Scrabble. She puts down the first word that comes into her little head and smiles and gets an average of three points every time and they very soon don't want to play with her any more. Who wants to play someone who doesn't care whether they win or not. I know it's terribly British, and that the taking part is supposed to be the thing, but she's not really taking part, just indulging us till she can get back to her book. She can't understand how anyone can ever want to play any sort of game when they could be reading. Or talking. They're the two occupations she prefers.

I try to explain that snooker is multi-disciplined. We do a lot of reading all through the game, rushing to the rules to stop the other cheating. And the talking never stops.

Jake has a phrase he repeats all the way through every game: 'That counts as in.'

I've gone off table tennis at the moment, which was our previous family passion. I just never seem to get any better. Sboring, I fink. But we still play chess every other day, except when I feel a headache coming on. I'm too old really for all that concentration, Jake. Your mind is young and fresh and empty. I've got all that wisdom and experience packed in, haven't I.

Flora's favourite game is Canasta. She thinks Rummy is for babies and last summer holidays she got it into her head that Canasta was pretty smart but it led to endless tears as her little eight-year-old hand couldn't hold thirteen cards at a time. I would arrange them for her and she would accuse me of looking at her cards and cheating and throw them all down and we'd have to start again. Now she copes very well, or perhaps the cards are getting smaller. I do *let* her win sometimes. Her disappointment is so utter that I have to.

Have I made them so competitive or is it inherent and is it bad or is it good? Look, let's just get on with the game and cut the chat. It's your go.

All children love games, at least up to the age of around twelve, even when they're not very good at them. Caitlin was in the netball team when she was at primary school and I was convinced she'd play for England. Then, at secondary school, I thought she would be a hockey star and we got her this brilliant pair of hockey boots, two sizes too big to allow for growth during the many sporting years ahead. I don't think she played for more than two weeks.

At one time, girls' schools were as dominated by sports as most boys' schools still are, but they seem to have given up the ghost now. I feel sorry for the PE teachers. You never see anyone queuing up to talk to them on Open Evenings. Miss Buss and Miss Beale would have a fit if they could see today's teenage girls, slouching around, pale and unhealthy, though their shiny, glowing hair might impress them.

I suppose in a few years time Caitlin will return to an

interest in outdoor sports, when she begins to equate physical activity with exercise and keeping slim and healthy and I'll say see, you should have kept those hockey boots. When you're in the sixth form of course it's not done to move if you can help it.

She can't believe that for years she came swimming with us every Sunday morning, and loved it. Even Jake won't come now. So it's just us oldies and Flora. Family games do have a natural life span. The children either give up, feeling it's beneath them to play with the family, or the parents give up, worn out and not much use you know. I now realise that after my two cartilages I'll never play football with Jake again, but I won't start that or I'll be in tears.

Snooker is of course sweeping the country. Even Caitlin has started playing. I thought at first it was just to show off to her boyfriends, or because she liked the image of the smoke-filled saloons in the late-night movies, but now I think it's because she's heard rumours that there's Big Money in snooker. She takes it very seriously. When she plays, the games proceed in silence. If you dare to make any comment, suggest a ball she should go for, or which way round to hold the cue, she storms out of the room.

Jake is currently agitating for a better table. It's one of those cheapo ones, so he says, though it cost £80 which I think is a fortune. He moans about the tin legs, hardboard sides and the chipboard top which has now warped and the balls never run straight.

I've been to look at a slate one, second-hand, as advertised in the local paper, but it was in a bloke's second floor flat and even with three people we couldn't move it one foot. We'd need a crane to get it into our living-room. And if we did, that would be it. The rest of the family would have to live permanently in the kitchen.

Smoke Less Zones

I don't know what made me turn round and look towards Caitlin's room. Call it a premonition if you will. All I know is that some sixth sense seemed to guide my eyes in the direction of her window. Call it spinning out the first paragraph if you will.

My room is at the back of the house. Slides will be passed among you later. We had this back addition built over an old coal cellar and my room is at the top, stuck out in the garden with two large windows. I feel like a ship's Captain on his bridge, surveying the scene, looking out at the au pairs, I mean admiring all the lovely gardens.

I was actually thinking about the gardens, wondering if we have a flower thief in the locality. I'd just come back from my morning walk and in the window in the next street I saw a woman sticking up the following notice. 'I hope whoever stole our flower pot is looking after the gardenia. Thank you.' The controlled middle-class fury that must have gone into that wording. I bet it makes the burglar laugh every time he sees it.

I turned towards Caitlin's window and there she was, sitting in full view, for anyone to see as she has still not mended her blinds even though I have been on at her for months to pick them up off the floor but if that's the way she wants to lead her life, then I'm certainly not running after her any more. She was sitting reading, so that was good. I like to see them working. In her hand was a cigarette. Never in my whole life have I seen any of my children smoking. I couldn't believe it.

She suddenly looked up, realising she was being watched,

as if some seventh sense, etc, and guiltily took the cigarette from her mouth. By this time I was racing up the stairs in a rage. Yes, I know you can't believe it. Mild, unassuming, friendly, permissive old me, loves all children, helps animals across the street, pats old people in their pram. This was not the image of myself which I have carefully created.

You can't get into Caitlin's room. The junk has so taken over that it blocks every surface and jams every doorway. She deliberately manoeuvres objects to keep out intruders and she herself takes ages pushing and pulling things, every time she goes in and out. I didn't even try to get in. I just banged on the door and shouted like a loony. 'That's it! That's it! You've done it now!'

I wasn't quite sure what she'd done, or what I was going to do about it, but I felt absolutely furious. It was that fleeting image, suddenly catching her smoking in such an abstracted manner, turning over the pages, as if unaware of what she was doing. It certainly didn't appear to be a novice trying out her first fag.

We've suspected for months but every time I've said there's a funny smell of smoke around here she's blamed it on her boyfriends. We don't normally allow smoking in this house, thank you. Please kindly put it out, thank you.

I even stop my sister when she asks, though I know she hates me doing so. I don't think Social Workers should smoke, do you. If I'm feeling good, I might let her stand at the back door, with it wide open, and have a few drags, as she is my sister. But that's all.

We lost the battle some time ago to stop visitors smoking inside Caitlin's room. As we've said it's her room, to keep as she likes, then we can't really interfere when she has her own guests in, can we. She doesn't mind them smoking in her room, so she says, so why should we. However, they're not allowed to smoke anywhere else in the house. And they don't.

I come from an all-smoking house. Both my parents and my two sisters and brother smoked, which drove me mad.

I suffered from asthma all my childhood, and the slightest whiff of cigarette smoke made me wheeze, so I was never even tempted to try a cigarette, and these fair lips have never been sullied. My father was an invalid, bed-ridden most of my childhood, and yet right to the end he was smoking away, despite choking and spluttering. It became one of his few pleasures in life. (And he died of multiple sclerosis, not lung cancer.)

I've always been determined that my children won't smoke, but I didn't think I would have to lay down any laws. Our self-righteous example, as non-smoking parents, would do the trick. When parents smoke there's not much you can do to stop the children.

I tell a lie. I once did put a cigarette between my lips. I was doing the Beatles biography and Ringo, when he heard I'd never had a reefer, said here's one, have a go, it's really great, you'll love it.

We got the children to bed early. Oh, this must be fourteen years ago now and Caitlin and Jake were babies then. We took the phone off the hook, locked the front door, closed the curtains and settled down to be really wicked. I'd decided I would say it was research, if we got raided, but I was very worried, thinking it's usually the beginners who get caught by the police while the regulars get away with it.

It was hard lighting up, as neither of us had ever lit a cigarette before, and inhaling was even more awkward, but at last we managed it. We lay back, waiting to feel really good, but nothing happened. Perhaps we were smoking the wrong end. Perhaps you ate them. After an hour in which nothing happened we put on *Kaleidoscope* on Radio 4 (OK, don't tell me it wasn't called that) made some hot cocoa and toasted cheese and carried on with our normal exciting evening and were in bed and asleep by ten past ten.

When I next saw Ringo I said I didn't think much of his reefers. I knew all this getting high was just a myth anyway. He said I got you there. It was just cabbage leaves. Was he lying or was it true? Perhaps we'd just failed to smoke them properly. I don't know, but we never tried again, remaining pure and prissy for ever.

Caitlin came down to my room about half an hour later, after a lot of rustling and scuffling, and asked sweetly and politely why I'd been banging on her door. I said that was it. She was getting no money from me when she becomes twenty-one. Those savings are for non-smokers only.

It was a pretty rotten trick and rather a stupid way to react. I have these National Savings Certificates in each of their names, and when they eventually reach twenty-one, they'll get about £3,000 each. Until that moment, I'd never decided that they were for non-smokers only. It had just come into my head. So it was a bit unfair on Caitlin.

One of her girlfriends harangued me next day, saying it was horrible to cut Caitlin out of my will, just for having a smoke. The threat had obviously increased when she got to school. 'And I thought you were a liberal father,' she said cunningly. One of her boyfriends, who actually is a heavy smoker, said he thought it was a good idea. He wished he could stop it now before he gets really hooked. He's heard that when you get old, such as nineteen, then it's impossible ever to stop.

Caitlin is now seventeen so we don't have many rules these days. She *thinks* we do, but we don't. At that age, there's not much a parent can do anyway. In a year she'll be going away to college, or I hope so. I need her room for my stamp albums. Any influencing we've done is over. She's accepted it or not. At eighteen, she'll be off. The final baton change will then take place and she'll have to run the rest of the race on her own.

I think I've got that metaphor from *Reader's Digest*, or have I made it up. Anyway, there's some more mileage in it yet. You see, friends, a clumsy baton change can make you lose the whole race. (Like it? You can borrow it yourself. No charge.)

So, in these last few months of trying hard to be a responsible parent, I feel I should stick to at least some of my standards. I handled the whole smoking thing badly and was very silly, but I made my point. I now believe that she doesn't really smoke. She says it was only a passing thing, trying it out. She can't afford it anyway and she agrees it is a health risk. So, she's now a non-smoker.

P.S. I did hear of one parent who promised his son £10,000 at twenty-one if he was a non-smoker. He made it. Then spent all the money on cigarettes. I don't believe my petal would do such a thing, do you.

Domestic Notes

It's so exhausting going away on holiday. My wife has been madly cleaning everything, as if the inspectors were coming in, not just our relations, and I've got a list of all the lists of things I now know I'll never get done before we leave.

We have so arranged it that we have friends or relations here for the whole of the time we'll be away. They're very grateful, poor things, but if they muck up anything, after all the preparations I've done, I'll go spare.

It's only when I've gone round that I've realised the house is falling to bits, kept together by the fact we know it's falling to bits and have learned to live with it. Strangers won't possibly know how to cope, as it's taken us eighteen years to get to grips with our inadequacies, so I've just spent a whole day labelling all the items, sticking on handy hints for careful users. It looks as if everything is up for sale.

I've re-written the notice on the Miele three times because even I couldn't understand my own instructions. Put simply, the hinge on the door has been broken for two years so when you let it down, the whole thing collapses on the floor, unless beforehand you stick one of the kitchen chairs underneath it. Quite easy, really. We do it without thinking.

It does mean you have to climb over all the furniture to load up the dirty dishes, as once you have the kitchen chair in position you can hardly move. I know it's ridiculous, but we can't face having the Miéle service people in. Have you tried to ring them? On the other hand, if some fool just opens the door, the whole thing would collapse, then we would be forced to ring Miele, if not 999.

I'm a bit worried about my note with regard to window

cleaning, instructions for dealing with, in the event of his miraculous appearance, see over page, please note. If it fell into the wrong hand I could be sued for thousands.

Our regular window cleaner went off to Canada last year. I dunno why. How do I know? Flora has a friend whose total conversation consists of How do I know. Very catching.

There's a highly recommended window cleaner who does one or two chosen people in our street, and we're on his list. Well, his probation list. We have conditional acceptance, depending on our good behaviour, if we're kind to him, fit in with his routine, achieve good A-level results and get the fees together. Even then, he's not promising. It must be easier to get into Oxbridge.

He's been several times, but on completely different days. He just arrives, when he's got a gap, and should we be out or not ready for him or asleep, then bingo, he's off. That's us finished. It would be our own fault, of course. He's already dropped one house because they weren't in when he chanced to call. Serves them right. People really don't know how to treat window cleaners these days. All it takes is subservience.

The position is complicated by the fact that there are two cowboy window cleaners going the rounds, both tramps, who also arrive at strange times. On no account must they be let in.

I went down to the front door the other day to find this scruffy old bloke with a rag who said he was our new window cleaner.

'What's your name,' I said, having been warned by the house bulletin to be prepared.

'What name do you want,' he said, looking sly.

'No, you tell me your name first,' I said, looking slier, or is it slylier.

He said he was called Ron and I said ha ha, we're waiting for Fred and he said oh yes, Fred sent me and I said, oh no, I just made up Fred, so thank you very much, my good man. When you work from home you learn to cope with such intellectual problems.

When I'd written out these complicated window cleaner instructions and dire warnings, I realised I'd done it all before—at Easter when we were away and some American friends had the house. Dear God, has it gone on that long. On that occasion we left a £10 note to pay the real window cleaner. (His price is £8 which is for three storeys, inside and out, compared with 15 shillings in 1963 when we arrived. Let's have the facts.) My instructions got our friend Karen so confused that she went off to California with the £10 note. And she still has it.

In the living-room, the TV sound still doesn't work, but my brother Johnny knows about that, as the button's been broken for four years now. It's on permanent low, which suits us but drives everyone else furious. The brand new Junior Hoover is on the blink so I've warned campers that the bag might have to be emptied regularly and the contents disposed of. If in doubt, try the Royal Free Hospital.

Don't try to close the curtains, as you'll never get them apart again, though I am going to mend them soon. If I didn't have all these notes to write I could get so many jobs done.

Please be careful with the washing-machine. *There is nothing wrong with it*. It's an expensive German one, an AEG, because the bloke next door said English washing-machines were a load of rust. We have it on every day of our life. Such dirty people in our house. If we hear that some idiot has buggered it up, we'll probably not come home, ever again.

Oh yes, that funny wire cage behind the front door must on no account be removed. I happened to be coming down our street the other day and I saw one of Caitlin's friends going straight to our house, open the door, walk in, yet the door was closed and she hadn't got a key. Answers in a plain envelope please. She'd simply put her hand through the letter-box and opened the door from the inside. My precious Penny Reds. Anyone could have got in and stolen them.

So I've fixed up this sort of wire barricade, a temporary arrangement which we'll have for the next twenty years. The postman hates it and our letters now arrive shredded, but it does mean no one can get their hand through.

Going upstairs, unless you want to lie down for a bit, have a rest after all these notes, don't be alarmed if the sitting-room phone appears to start bells ringing all over the house. It *does* start bells ringing all over the house. That's the answer. As for the cause, how do I know. I can't face ringing the Post Office Engineers. Not this decade anyway.

You will notice under Jake's bed three copies of *Rothman's Football Yearbooks*. They may look interesting, and Simon might want to read them, but *don't* let him. He could get killed. These books hold the bed up. Perhaps the roof as well.

The very modern, architect designed shower on the top floor is a joke shower. Yes, I know we've had it fifteen years, and for fifteen years it hasn't worked. We should have had the plumber, and the architect, either back at once or hanged. Don't tell me. I've got enough problems. It's all to do with water pressure. Look, you're getting a free house, you don't expect things to work, do you?

Now the plants. Something strange has happened in our little domestic life in the last year. I am no longer OC/Plants. My wife has taken over. She can write all the boring instructions. It all started when my sister Marion was in charge one week and watered them once only, on the last day, despite my instructions on exactly what to do. They were swimming down the hall when we opened the door on our return. My fault, of course. Oh yes, always blame me.

The smell of gas is the smell of gas. You are quite right. Don't ring the fire brigade. It's that stupid Parkinson Cowan. The pilot light on the grill never worked from the beginning and that's something else we should have complained about. You'll notice it first thing in the morning. Just open the windows. Pick up any dead bodies. Life goes on.

I think that's everything. If anything else goes wrong, don't ring me. You're on your own. Oh God, I had better write down the name of our good plumber, and our nice builder, and that cheap electrician. Otherwise someone might contact one of those ten thousand cards which come through the letter-box every day. And they're just the roof menders.

We're now away on holiday for three weeks. Everyone needs a holiday. It's the only way to recover from getting ready to go away on holiday . . .

Hero Today, Gone Tomorrow

I had to pick up Flora from a friend's house the other evening. She doesn't go to this house very often but when she does it's all high jinks and over-excitement, and she won't come away and I have to stand there in the hall like a dum-dum, trying to be the father figure. I hate going for her, but when you work from home, that's the sort of job you get landed with.

I decided to walk, to give myself a bit of exercise, though knowing I was taking my life in my hands. No car! That would start it all off, with Flora in the hall stamping her little foot and me saying no car, dear, I thought the walk home would be good for you, now come along, please, don't mess daddy about.

It was a good walk. This is the time of year for urban street walks, between six and seven in the evening, with everyone coming home, the lights full on, the curtains apart, living their lives on an open stage. It was one of the first strange things I noticed, when I came to London twenty years ago. Nobody ever seemed to pull their curtains. No shame, these Southerners. In the North, we had our curtains tightly pulled from about four o'clock onwards. And that was in summer.

The smells and sounds and sights are so exotic in an inner London street. The middle classes with their Habitat pine and open-plan minds or the Greeks and the Indians arguing over the kitchen pots and pans. I often gape for hours. You could press your nose right up against the windows, and they still wouldn't mind. In the North, you're only allowed to admire the lawn. And they do have some immaculate front lawns in Carlisle. Dare to peep at the window, even when the curtains are drawn, and they'll call the police.

So, I had a v. interesting walk, noting the different wallpapers, the new bedroom carpets, the teenagers breaking out, the living-in friend now doing all the cooking, and got to the house at the appointed time, determined to be strong and get Flora out with no arguments.

She was half-naked, jumping around to some awful Adam Antics with her little friend, but they put the record off when I arrived and Flora quickly got her clothes on and said thank you for having me. What a treasure. What a credit to her father.

She put her coat on, without being told, but left it hanging open so I said come along now Flora, button it up, it is a cold night and you have got the sniffs. She went back inside to get her school bag, and various notes and bits and pieces which she had to bring home from school, and gave them to me to carry. One likes to be useful.

As we opened the front door, her coat was still unbuttoned, so I remonstrated. Well, I quietly pointed out that I had told her to button it up. It's no fun for us, Flora, if you're off school with flu and sniffing and oh, the usual stuff one says when trying to convince the world that you're a caring parent.

'Oh shut up, you,' said Flora, turning on me. 'Just shut up. I'm *not* buttoning up, so there.' And she flounced off into the street.

I turned and tried a half smile, just to show I was not upset, not one of these hooligan fathers who lash out, but I didn't get a half smile in return.

'Isn't it awful,' I said. 'These kids today. I would never have said Shut Up to my father.'

'*Ours* never do,' said the mother, firmly closing the door.

They have older children, apart from their nine-year-old girl, and it is true they are all very well behaved. But bloody hell. How self-righteous.

On the walk home, I ignored all the open-plan widows and stripped pine graduate wives, and decided it was me at fault. By this time Flora had buttoned up her coat and said she was sorry, and we were all friends again.

It's parents like me who are ruining the country. Go on, say it. Yes, I know, we were to blame for the Toxteth riots and those Chelsea football hooligans. Sorry, Mrs Thatcher. But for me, I'm sure there would be no unemployment and inflation would not exist. If only our generation of parents had been *authoritarian*. That would have solved everything. Probably would have won us the World Cup as well. As it is, we're all wets and softs.

I can't remember my children ever being in awe of me. Caitlin so often treats me like a half-wit. I just have to get some small point wrong in the latest UCCA saga, or ask a question she's already answered, or refer to some teacher who left decades ago, don't you ever listen, and that's my lot. No more stories for me, unless she's in a good mood and I am indulged.

I've told Jake I have actually met Steve Perryman, in the flesh, and do you want to hear about when I was at the World Cup Final at Wembley in 1966, but he hasn't been impressed. And what about the time I saw the Beatles recording every track on *Sergeant Pepper*, sitting in the Abbey Road studios with them, but does that get me any house points. Does it heckers.

I did a little chat at Jake's school not long ago, telling them how to run a school magazine, and one boy came up to Jake the next day and said it was a good chat, really interesting. 'You've been conned,' said Jake.

Until he was aged thirty, William Makepeace Thackeray thought his mother was a saint. That is a bit old to get wise to the world. It is normal for the scales eventually to fall from the eyes of children and parents to be revealed as after all having feet of clay, and other complicated clichés, but it usually happens well before adulthood.

I have done my children a great favour. There will be no shattering revelations in their lives. My feet of clay have been leaving muddy prints all over the place since they were born. They can never be disillusioned. I have never been a hero to my children.

I didn't want to be a hero, of course, I haven't got the

muscle. As a parent, I'm a seven stone weakling, but I've tried to be quick enough on my pins to avoid too much sand being thrown in my eyes. Sometimes I've got myself in a bit of a mess, but then anyone would, with clay feet and sandy eyes. Where have all these mixed metaphors come from. It's only January, and I've already used up my annual allowance. Right, that's the last one.

I wanted to be their friend. Ah. But Oh God, the long explanations that has led us into over the years. We're the Dr Spock generation, we caring parents of the Sixties. We believe in reason. He never told us that being reasonable would take up so much time. It would have been so much quicker and easier to have slapped them down and allowed no discussion.

Next time, I think I'll come back as a tough, no-nonsense parent, just to see what difference it makes, and treat them instead like dogs. I could keep Caitlin in a kennel, outside of course, then I wouldn't be awakened when she came home late. If I fed Jake on Pal he would be so much smarter, with a lovely shiny coat, and it would save a fortune on the housekeeping. And transport. I'd make him run to Spurs, not get the bus. I'd keep Flora in a basket and rent out her room to lodgers. All conversation would be in whistles, plus kicks to emphasise certain points. They'd probably love it. Consider me a real hero.

As it is, I don't know how this being reasonable system is going to work out, whether the final relationship will be any better than mine was with my parents.

I spent half my time as a child hiding things from my parents, even dopey things like chapped thighs. I wore short trousers as a boy, till I was about twenty-five, well, almost. I can hardly believe it now, as even babes in arms these days wear jeans.

Every winter the tops of my legs used to hurt like hell. I suppose it was with rushing when I went to the lavatory, and not drying myself properly. The gales coming in from the Solway Firth would head straight up my trouser legs and that was it, red raw till the spring. For some reason I thought this was terribly embarrassing, and wouldn't tell my parents.

Jake as a little boy insisted on telling us everything, showing us everything, and we would say no, no, Jake, please spare us that. We *know* what it looks like. Go and put your rotten clothes on, at once.

We haven't been as open as some parents I know, the real liberals and permissives and other rude words, who have utterly no secrets from their teenage children, who talk happily about their lovers, and then listen to the children talking about their lovers, then bring the lovers in so they can *all* talk about it. There's no need to go into further details. Let's leave that to *The Guardian*, or the cartoonists, or *The Guardian* cartoonists.

It could be that with my children things will happen in reverse. Having received so little respect from them so far, being told to Shut Up or Drop Dead, the scales will fall *over* their eyes when they do grow up. I'll suddenly be looked upon as a wonderful human being, which secretly I have been all the time anyway.

They'll hang on my words of wisdom and bow to my superior knowledge and never say anything horrid to me and be utterly respectful. I can't wait to be an Aged Pee.

Late Night Movers

I am lying in bed, wondering how much longer I can go on lying in bed listening to the noises down below. Probably all night. Oh God, I'll never sleep. We only have two teenagers, and they haven't been teenagers all that long, but it seems to me that for the last hundred years I have lain in this bed either listening to their rotten noises or *waiting* for them to come home and start making their rotten noises.

Nobody is having a party. There are no records being played. No one is shouting or screaming or crying or laughing. And it is only ten past ten. So what am I moaning about?

For a start, I should have been asleep five minutes ago. That's what we normally aim for. We hear *Kaleidoscope* and then the News headlines, and that's it, lights out, heads down, like decent, ordinary, well adjusted, completely average, run-of-the-mill adult people.

We, by the way, means me and my lady wife. She's here as well. She usually is. I know that me lying here, all bitter and twisted as I listen to the noise down below, is keeping her awake. Any minute now she'll blame me. If I just relaxed and went to sleep, then she could get to sleep. But how can I relax? There's that noise again. Ping, ping, pong, pong. Can't you bloody hear it? I dunno. What the hell is he doing downstairs?

Now I can hear furniture moving, a table being dragged across the kitchen floor. So that's what he's doing. Playing table tennis with himself in the kitchen, bouncing it off the walls. Has he no consideration? What have I done to deserve

73

this? How can a fifteen-year-old make so much noise on his own?

Shall I get up and bang on the floor and tell him to shut up. That will just lead to more noise. I'll really have to shout to make him hear. Then Flora will wake up. She was in bed as usual at eight o'clock. She made a slight song and dance about it tonight, maintaining she wasn't tired. 'I wish I *was* tired,' she said. 'But I'm not.' I went to tuck her in, precisely one minute after she had gone into her bedroom, and she was fast asleep. What a good girl. Why couldn't they all have stayed nine years old for ever?

The ping ponging has now stopped. He'll be walking across to the kettle, to make himself some more coffee. Yes, I can hear it being switched on. Now there's silence. Boing, boing, boing. What can it be this time? He's started singing to himself. How can he be happy when I am lying here so unhappy? It must be snooker. He's playing himself at snooker. 'That counts as in.' I can almost *hear* him winning. I wish he'd hurry up and get the black in and give me a break. Ho ho, break. Gerrit.

He must be waiting for the late night movie. What sort of strange creatures have we bred. I've never watched a late night movie in my life, or any film on TV. Of course we're the normal ones. Doesn't the whole world go to bed at ten?

Bang! Bang! God, what a fright, just when I was dozing off. No, that's not true, how can I be dozing off. It's Jake banging on our bedroom door. What the hell does he want?

'There's no toothpaste.' Jake's hoarse whisper, which he thinks is so low it won't waken us up, just in case we might be asleep, can probably be heard all over North London.

I pretend to snore. So he repeats his query. Louder this time. Why does he want to clean his teeth now?

'The toothpaste's finished,' he says again, almost in my ear-hole this time.

'Gerrout! You don't have to clean your stupid teeth. Just shurrup and gerrout.'

His mother tells him that there's some in the upstairs sink, but go up quietly so that he doesn't waken Flora. Fat chance. All the hall lights have now been switched on so that our bedroom is suddenly like Blackpool Illuminations.

Now he's gone into the lavatory. He's like Pavlov's Dog. Cleaning his teeth means going to the lav. He's just had to pull the chain, hasn't he. No consideration at all. I'll have to lie in agony for the next half-hour now. That upstairs lav is sticking and if the ball cock doesn't cut off soon I'll have to get up and go up into the loft and I've left the ladder in the side passageway and where's the torch? I haven't seen it for months. I think I'll move into an hotel. Hurrah. The cistern has stopped flushing.

'I've got no clean socks.' Bloody hell. He's back again. 'I need them for school.'

'Go in your bare feet, you half-wit,' I say.

'Wear a pair of Hunt's,' she says. 'They're clean.'

What a really stupid thing to tell him. He's now lying on the floor in a heap, having come into our bedroom and fallen over the chest of drawers where I keep my clean socks. Perhaps this *is* the late night movie. Ciné verité. They're filming it all with hidden cameras.

At last. He has gone back downstairs again. All I can hear now is silence. That's the trouble. That sort of silence will keep me awake all night, waiting for the next noise.

Where is that Caitlin. She promised she wouldn't be late. About six o'clock this evening she said she was going round to Jane's for an hour. That was four hours ago. It seems like every night for the last two hundred years that I've been lying here, waiting for her key in the door.

Our nocturnal curves coincided for about half an hour something like five years ago when she was twelve years old. For one brief moment in time, we *all* went to bed by ten o'clock. Oh, bliss it was and to be asleep was very heaven. Now she's shot past us into the stratosphere, still going strong. Goodness knows when or where she'll land. Our metabolisms are just so different. She thinks twelve o'clock is an early night.

Several times recently, Jake has locked the front door when he's come in, not knowing Caitlin was still out. Naturally she has to ring when she gets back. More hysterics. I now have a new system when they're both out. I leave a special notice on the hall stairs which tells them to Tick Name When you Come In. So, whoever is last in, locks up for the night. The trouble is, I don't trust my own system. I feel it will all go wrong and I lie fretting that I'll *still* be wakened up.

Very often, I have fallen asleep, somehow, then wakened with a start, wondering what the time is and whether Caitlin is home yet. How awful if the police ring and we don't even know where she is. So I get up and check that the front door has been locked. Then I know she's in. Or do I? Has Jake locked it by mistake?

I could go up to her bedroom, and see if she's asleep, but her bedroom is such a mess, with cushions and blankets all over the floor. There might be dozens of them asleep there, none of them Caitlin.

The other night she came home in agony as a car had run over her foot. It wasn't as bad as it sounded, though bad enough. She now has boyfriends who have cars, just sixth formers from the local boys' school, where do they get the money from, how do their parents allow it. This night they were going to a party and they ran out of petrol so Caitlin got out to help push the car. Someone decided to push it the other way, and it ran over her foot. Nothing was broken. Except my sleep.

When I'm listening to house noises, which I have done for three hundred years, I can cope much better. Walls collapsing, pipes bursting, the roof falling off. I've heard all these signs for years, but I just turn over and think, well, it's an old house, you've got to expect such night-time noises. I'll investigate in the morning. The night the ceiling in Caitlin's room *did* fall down was such a surprise. Especially for Caitlin. She was in bed early for once. It was a dreadful warning to her. She knew from then on that no good could ever come from early nights.

They do try to respect our bedtime habits. They never bring people back into the house after ten o'clock, not these days. Me appearing in my pyjamas at 10.15 and slobbering at the mouth like a loony soon stopped all that.

Did I ever stay up late as a teenager? I can't really

remember, though I often used to miss the last bus and have to walk right across Carlisle from my wife's house in what *seemed* like the middle of the night. Perhaps it was only ten. All life in Carlisle stops at six o'clock.

On one famous occasion, famous in our family anyway, oh not that again, we once walked all through the night from Keswick to Carlisle, a distance of some thirty miles. We got home at seven in the morning. I was a wreck and she carried me the last few miles. A tramp scared me. Not my fault.

There goes the front door. Yes, and I can now hear it being locked. Our oldest and dearest is at last home for the night. All's right with our little bit of the world. It can't be more than eleven o'clock. I'll just give it a few more minutes. I have known Caitlin come home and have a bath, put on her pyjamas, then the phone rings, and she's out again in a flash.

That sounds like the phone being dialled. Our three phones are all on the blink. It's like a burglar alarm going off whenever anyone dials. She's probably ringing Jane, having seen her all of one minute ago. She'll be on for hours. I often come down in the morning and find the phone on the floor, the cushions in a heap with three empty tea-cups beside them and steam still coming off the receiver. If I ever find out she's been ringing abroad when my back is turned. By the left.

She and Jake will now be settling down to watch the movie. At least they watch it happily these days. Last year, they used to argue all the time. Caitlin would accuse Jake of making noises with his mouth when listening or asking silly questions about what's happening. Then he would get bad-tempered. At close of play, they would both rush up the stairs still arguing, saying it was the other's turn to switch the telly off. It was so stupid. Then I'd have to get up and go down and put it off.

Silence, real silence, at last. They must have the volume right down. How kind. They do enjoy these late night movies together. Perhaps I should get up. That would solve everything. Have I been missing something wonderful all these years? Such as midnight.

Stout Party

It's over at last, Caitlin's eighteenth birthday party. It seems to have been the only subject of conversation in this house for the last three months. Actually, it's not over yet. Somewhere outside there, in the world beyond, it's still going on.

Flora and I have just arrived home, having been present for the first two hours. When we left, one of the managers had taken over the disco microphone to warn that the party would stop if anyone started smoking. Smoking jobs, is what he said. What can this mean? Flora had no idea what he was talking about. Neither have I. I only hope they all behave themselves. Don't want it to end in tears. Not after all that preparation.

The first problem was where to hold a party. Over my dead body would it be held over my dead body. The party in our house for her fourteenth birthday was more than enough, thank you. Never again, I vowed, and the marks on the wall still haven't gone away. But being eighteen is a bit special, as they say on *Match of the Day*.

We decided to treat it as her coming of age. She's been grown up since she was thirteen, if you ask me, as if anyone asks me anything, but I agreed a proper party now would be instead of a twenty-first. Eighteen these days is the Big One, the watershed in a young person's life, after which everything is exactly the same as it ever was.

I suggested the Music Room of Burgh House in Hampstead, a really lovely room, with old panelled walls, very tasteful, where I held my famous stamp fair in the summer, the sort of place which would be perfect for the young ladies in their long dresses and the young gentlemen in their bow ties to clebrate with a glass or two of cider.

Might be a few rough ones, see Hunt, don't want anything too posh. Cos of breakages. And if it's too near home the word gets round and you get a lot of gate-crashers. If you're paying, Dad, you don't want gate-crashers, do you?

So we spent several weeks investigating likely rendezvous and decided on the Rock Garden, a fashionable and very noisy but cheerful hamburger restaurant in Covent Garden, right on the Piazza. Flora and I had lunch there and gave it our seal of approval. My lady wife refused to go inside. She hates hamburgers and pop music.

We arranged to hire the upstairs room for tonight, Saturday March 6th, from 8 till 12. The manager kindly agreed that all the guests at Caitlin's party could then go downstairs to the basement and get in to see the live groups for free. The place itself is open till six in the morning. What a strange world it is out there.

Caitlin had said there was no need to order food. People didn't eat food at parties these days. What they do at Caitlin's parties these days is *throw* food at each other. Oh, what jolly fun. As long as you don't have to clean the walls up afterwards.

We agreed on a maximum of seventy guests and I ordered fifty bottles of the house wine, though I didn't reveal this to Caitlin, and seventy hamburger meals, which I didn't reveal either. I thought providing food would keep down the drinking.

We were going to get a live group for our party, perhaps Miles Over Matter, they're very wonderful, at least according to Caitlin, but decided instead just to hire their disco, £40 extra, a bargain already.

Invitations, that put in another three weeks. Caitlin was going to hand-paint each one, but did three before flaking out. She then wanted them printed in four colours, and I agreed, till I discovered the price, so I bought a pad of coloured paper and went to the copying machine at our local post office and duplicated seventy invites.

There was some argument about putting *my* coloured paper inside *their* machine, in case it would be too thick and block up the intestines. The invites came out looking great, but I failed to get a discount, even though I pointed out I'd used my paper, saving them their white stuff. Oh, the expense. Should I tell you how much it has all cost? No, let's not be churlish. It is a happy day. Least I hope it still is.

Caitlin then scrawled an extra message over each invite, thereby mucking up all my beautiful handiwork on the copying machine. She had decided at the last moment that each guest should come in 'kinky fetish clothing'. Whatever is the world coming to. If Grandma hears about this, bang goes your present, my lass.

That put me in a fix, as I'd agreed to take Flora for the first two hours. What was I going to wear? Could I go as Glen Hoddle?

Flora went as a sort of gypsy and looked terrific and I went in my best black trousers and a white shirt like Manuel from *Fawlty Towers*. That was not intentional, to look like Manuel, and I only said it was after several cheeky young persons had pointed it out.

Have you been to a teenagers' party? I mean in the last hundred years. Desmond Morris would love it. Very anthropological.

I wonder what happened to dancing. You know, two people together, waltzes, dinky two-steps, Valetta, Dashing White Sergeants. I asked the bloke on the disco but he hadn't heard of any of them. Not even a quick-step. All the fast girls did the quick-step in my day.

Most of the girls and the boys were in fancy dress, and none looked too kinky, so that was a relief. It did give it a festive atmosphere from the beginning. Caitlin was in fur. One boy came as a vicar. I noticed a Brownie and a nurse and one girl in cling-flim. The first load of hamburgers, which came with chips and salads and lots of dressings and other bits and pieces, went in a flash. Caitlin had the grace to say you were right, papa.

I showed them how to jive, no, really I was pushed into it, public demand, and the old magic was still there, thanks to practising these last six weeks with Flora. The Sixties is high fashion with teenagers, so they do know what jiving is. They've seen it on the late-night movies, along with crinolines and bustles.

When my eyes and ears had settled down, I realised that some things had not completely changed. Groups of lads still sat around together, watching groups of girls, sitting around watching. Quite a few were obviously in couples, ah, isn't that sweet, and they seemed ever so clean and healthy. Everyone was kind to Flora and to me, a visitor from another planet.

The thing that did surprise me was the open affection the girls felt for each other, all such good friends and showing it in such a natural way. The boys seemed more hesitant, watchful, far less confident and mature than the girls. The party was being given by a girl so there was a hard core of her life-long girl-friends there, going back to primary school.

I knew many of them from the days of pushing them in prams with Caitlin, playing on the swings, digging in the sand, though if I hadn't been told the names of some of them I would never have believed it. Very slowly, through all that drastic face change and body metamorphosis, I could just make out the relics of a little girl, smiling thinly through. Will I recognise my little Flora when she is eighteen? Will she be a bigger version of the same or will she too be a completely different human being?

We left at ten, by which time the party was well established. The Rock Garden had done us proud, with good service, attentive waiters, but I hope no gate-crashers get in, or silly people do silly things.

Flora has gone to sleep, thrilled with her little self, what a lot of boasting she'll be able to do on Monday morning, and I'm waiting for Jake. He was allowed to take three of his school friends, as a special treat, even though they're all just fifteen and sixteen.

Jake was a bit worried when he heard that Caitlin wanted fancy dress. I just don't want you being ordinary, said Caitlin. I know, said Jake, I'll wear gloves. In the end, he arrived in dark glasses and a beret. Wow.

Comings-of-age in the old days were family occasions, with all the generations joining in, but I thought one person from the older generation would be more than enough. Me. My wife made an excuse and left herself at home, very happily curled up with a particularly good novel, a big log fire and soppy thoughts about this time, eighteen years ago tonight.

Jake has now just arrived home, very pleased with himself. He got the last bus home and says there was no trouble whatsoever and the party was a big success. The manager bloke ended up chanting soul music over the disco. Jake left promptly at midnight, leaving the eighteen-year-olds to, well, whatever eighteen-year-olds do. I don't expect to see Caitlin for days. Probably not till she's nineteen.

Making Tracks

It's been Flora's Sport's Day today so I felt I should do my bit and turn up and hang about and shout for Raleigh which is the house she's in. It makes you feel sort of proud, know what I mean, brings a lump to the old froat, to hear these lovely little primary school children screaming their heads off for Raleigh, Drake, Grenville and Howard, even though at least 40 per cent of the little treasures come from the West Indies, Cyprus, Pakistan and points East and think that Raleigh is the bloke that invented bicycles.

We true Brits know better, don't we Flora. They're the names of Houses at Brookfield Primary. Yes, but what else, my petal. I dunno. Was they teachers at the school? How do I know. Come on Ra-lee.

I don't do a lot for the school these days and I feel suitably humbled and embarrassed when other parents do so much. I was on the governing board for years and ended up Chairman, but that was when I was young and fit and in my prime. I also ran the School Magazine for several issues, but now I'm old and grey, at least I was till this morning when I carefully took the grey hairs out of my moustache. I have become rather disorientated. A sort of Anouilh has taken over. How do you spell that word? I bet he's a House in a Frog primary school. Come on On-ee.

I think I've been to every Sports Day for fifteen years, ever since Caitlin started there. Jake went through the same school. Neither of them has their name on the programme as holder of the all-time record for 50 yards, sorry, 50 metre races or first year girls high jump. Perhaps Flora will give us immortality.

One year I did do the loudspeaker which meant being shut up in a little box beside the track, which is a very good one, on Parliament Hill, and I was on a real microphone, as used by Highgate Harriers, and I kept up a running commentary, as kids brought me the results of every race, and I exhorted people to get ready for the next event, as instructed by the teachers, and after three hours I realised that after all David Coleman isn't the dum-dum I'd always suspected. I collapsed afterwards. Then I was told nobody had heard a bleeding word. It's a big track, and we're only a little primary school, and all the mums and dads and kids were sitting where there happened not to be a loudspeaker that was working. I immediately retired from all thoughts of being a professional sports commentator, deciding after all I will be a brain surgeon when I grow up.

They can make a lot of noise, even in a little primary school, and I always enjoy my afternoon walks on the Heath when sudden bursts of hysterical screaming waft over the grassy slopes in the stillness of some far wood and the dodgy-looking blokes behind trees, about to be up to no good, don't half get a fright.

'One condition,' said Flora. She's so bossy these days. Whatever will she grow up to become. Answer, Caitlin. 'You can come on one condition.'

What's that, my sweet. I'm so reasonable, all the time, one of my faults, don't tell me.

'As long as you don't wear your shorts,' she said, standing foursquare, putting on her Miss look. 'I don't want to be shown up. You look stupid in them. Is that clear?'

Yes your majesty, your honour, Roger and out. They're quite nice shorts, actually, made them myself, cutting them down from an old pair of jeans, Bermudas I think they call them in American primary houses. I did at least get the message that at forty-six it was time I gave up real jeans but I thought a baggy pair of Bermudas, rather amusing, look at old Hunt, what a card, but of course he has got good legs, I mean, for a bloke of his age.

I never quite know what to wear with them. Obviously not black socks and ordinary shoes, I'm not that stupid, this

86

isn't Blackpool, do you mind, so I wear my blue training shoes or my Green Flash Dunlop plimsolls though they are a bit cacky, as we used to say in Carlisle. I agonise. Do I have bare legs or not? Shoes, even gym shoes, look a bit silly without socks, but if I wear my only pair of white socks they get filthy the moment you even look at them. Decisions, decisions.

Flora had at least spared me all those problems by her dictat so I set off for the sports in my normal grey trousers. I only have grey trousers, some of them not as normal as they used to be, or even as grey, but all of them began that colour. Over the decades, I've been through the full range of grey. Remember Charcoal Grey. What a craze that was. I can still recall longing for a Charcoal Grey suit when I was at Durham in the Fifties. *Everyone* had one, with any pretensions to be fashionable. The trousers got so shiny in the end that it was like wearing a plastic suit. Plastic hadn't of course been invented back in the Fifties. Don't be stupid, Dad, plastic has always been invented.

I sat with various mums and dads on the grassy slopes while the kids shouted and shrieked and drank disgusting orange juice, that sugary stuff that comes in ten-gallon plastic petrol cans and we don't allow in our house, certainly not, we drink unsweetened orange juice from Sainsbury's which is like drinking pound notes only the taste is much sourer. Various smaller kids were being screamed at, for getting on the track, and several mums were clutching their stomachs, feeling as sick as a parakeet, knowing that their Darren or Jeremy or Winston, we're very mixed in our school, was next on the track and would he let the family name down.

From a distance, these little end-of-term school sports days appear totally disorganised, totally boring and utterly pathetic. It's only when you know the dramatis personae that you understand how genuinely dramatic, nay hysterical, some of the personae are becoming. All human life. Is there?

Our sports were terribly well organised this year, and everything ran completely to time. I've been to them in the past when we've run, or dragged, two hours late, and never got half the events finished. The headmistress or the PE person has had to bring them suddenly to a halt on the final straight when it's realised that every Mum and Dad has gone home and this year children, it's a dead heat between Raleigh, Drake, Grenville and Howard, thank you, have a nice summer holidays everyone.

I somehow missed Flora's long jump, which she didn't win, though she was second ('me ankle was sore'), but I was looking the right way when her relay started and her team won. Well done, Ra-lee, Ree-lay.

Then the most awful thing happened. They'd done so well, the teachers and parents in charge, their efficiency being beyond reproach, that they decided to put on an extra event. A fathers' race. I tried to hide. Then I said I've got a neighbour's dog to take for a walk, but I'd been grabbed by a bossy teacher, or it might have been Flora, the differences are slight, and found myself standing on the track with eleven other embarrassed dads, of all shapes and sizes and colours, all cursing themselves for having taken the afternoon off work.

It seemed like a Wembley Cup Final out there. Any thought I'd had of it being a pathetic little school event, watched by a few dozen parents, vanished as I felt the red plastic turf beneath me and saw the white lanes of the track curving ahead. I was convinced the eyes of millions were upon me. I do of course tend to go through life thinking everyone is watching me, which is why I'm a bad actor and a poor public speaker and self-conscious and what am I doing, running myself down, I'm the hero this week.

We were lined up and told it would be two circuits of the track and I said that's it, count me out, you must be choking, I know the Royal Free is only minutes away, and they're all watching from the windows, but I'm not giving myself a heart attack, not when the tickets for Gatwick have just come for our summer holidays. That's 800 metres or yards or miles and certainly far too much for me. Shut up and get in line. Then the starting pistol went.

All the kids were screaming, but I could hardly hear them, just a faint buzzing in the ears. I wondered whether I could turn out to be Alf Tupper, who trained on fish and chips and just arrived and beat the world in his pit-man's clothes, or Wilson of *The Wizard* who lived in a cave. While I'd been thinking about them, I found I'd done one circuit and was still alive, surprise surprise, though four other dads had dropped out, flat on the ground, hoping for oxygen. *Chariots of Fire*, that's it, I thought, lifting up my knees.

Just before the final bend, I put in an extra spurt and I overtook the bloke ahead and I realised it was Andy, the school's PE teacher. He was in the last Olympics. This is not a fib, not even an exaggeration. Look him up. Andy Drzewiecki. He's a weight-lifter, British champion in fact, very famous.

On the last stretch, I found myself waving to the crowd like mad which I knew as soon as I did it was a mistake. Flora would be furious. One must not be flash.

The first Dad home was called Guy Ogden. Now, he is a great runner and recently came 200th in the London Marathon. He won our race by miles. Second was another Dad, John Carrier, who is also a good runner and he too was in the London Marathon, though he came a bit further back, 8,247th to be precise. I didn't recognise the Dad who came third. But guess who came fourth. Yup. Autographs later.

Just think what might have happened if only I'd been allowed to wear my shorts . . .

On His Bike

I don't like interfering in Jake's life. At sixteen he is old enough and wise enough and big enough to make his own mistakes. But today I went along with him to give moral support. Call it being bossy if you will. Thank you. It was a big decision for a young lad to make, so I said I would like to be there. My advice might be useful. Also my cheque book.

He has saved £150 in the last few months, giving it all to me to keep for him. Naturally, when he suddenly wanted it, I didn't have it in cash. I don't keep that amount lying around, not unless I'm expecting to have to spend it on some mad piece of extravagance, such as getting the windows cleaned or buying a pound of French beans.

Jake has had a week-end job since Easter, but I'm not allowed to mention any details. Some things are private. He's been very diligent, working away at Marine Ices for £1.25 an hour. After all these months, he then goes and spends all his £150 in one go. I tell a lie. The bill came to £149.73 and I have it here in front of me, which means I owe him 27p. Considering how long it took, the mental and emotional strain, the aggravation and concentration and wear and tear, I hope he has the decency to let me off the 27p. It was more like going to a psyche shop than a cycle shop.

When I was his age, you could run a family of six, have holidays at Troon, a week-end bungalow at Silloth, keep a Model T in the bath and still have change out of a Penny Farthing. The very thought of ever seeing £150 in one's life was pure fantasy. Whatever has happened to the world. Who would have thought oh shut up Dad and just get on with it.

I can remember my first bike as if it was yesterday. It was a Raleigh Lenton Sports in green and I got it at TP Bell's in Carlisle, paying it up on the never-never at 13/11d a week. What a strange sum. They didn't have calculators in those days. I earned all the money myself, doing a paper round in the morning and delivering groceries on a bike after school, or have I told you all this, children. Flora, surely I haven't mentioned this to you, well not recently, I mean in the last half-hour. Sorry.

I walked it all the way home as I was too proud, too shy, too worried about riding it. It had a Sturmey-Archer three-speed and I wasn't quite sure how it worked. When I got it home, I cleaned every part, just in case. Kids these days never clean anything, etc. I went to school on it every day from then on, my face a mass of tears in winter as I free-wheeled down this steep hill, Stanwix Bank, and the ice and the rain and the wind was like a terrible torture which I had to overcome by will power.

I had one summer holiday on it, cycling to Cambuslang in Glasgow to my grandmother's house, a distance of some ninety-nine miles. I did it all in one day, which I find hard to believe now. Today, when I happen to be driving along that route, which is now all dual-carriage and motorway, lolling back in my automatic 2.3 Granada, I point out to the family the precise spots, just by that little stream, over there in the heather and bracken, where Daddy rested thirty years ago. Yes, you've told us that as well. When I got to Cambuslang, absolutely knackered, I stayed in bed for a week. Then I cycled home again.

Caitlin and Jake and Flora all had bikes, brand-new ones, bought when they were younger, spare no expense in this family, yes we do spoil them, but they were children's size bikes, bought as birthday or Christmas presents. If you want a bigger bike when you're older, so I told them, then you'll have to work and save up your own money, just as we did, tra la. You're on your own.

I'll handle this, Jake, I said. He'd seen one he fancied, a Carlton Grand Prix, priced at £118.00. I had to read the price several times, thinking at first it might be £11.80 or even £18.11. My eyes are not so good these days, especially reading prices which in my mind's eye have stayed firmly in the 1950s.

I had to queue for quite a while to get any service as the place was full of people with half bikes or bits of bikes speaking in what seemed like a foreign language to the bloke behind the counter. There were two people serving, but all the customers seemed content to wait for the Boss to serve them. I could tell who the Boss was. He was the one shouting into the telephone, while attending to his customers, while reading the price catalogues, while testing a wheel.

'How much discount for cash,' I asked quickly.

I presumed that most kids, as in my day, would be paying up their bikes. I wanted to say look here, my good man, I happen to be one of the big spenders, I will pay it all now, but for something off, after all, when I bought my new car, I got 14 per cent off for cash, but I could see he was a busy man.

He gave me a quick look, then turned to serve someone. I had to repeat my question, much to Jake's fury. *All* sales were cash, he said. Positively no discount. Take it or leave it. Next please.

I told you, muttered Jake. So I had to queue up again in order to say, very humbly, yes I would take it. He had a Smike-like youth doing the man-handling of the bikes, and also repairs in some sort of workshop at the back, and he was ordered to get out the bike we wanted and check it over. That seemed to take ages, as Smike was constantly being given other orders, most of which he seemed to get wrong.

No pump, I said to Jake, showing off my knowledge of cycle technology. Look, it's missing. So I queued up again, only to be told to keep quiet a moment, please. The Boss was up a ladder this time, counting sprockets, and I'd interrupted him at a vital point. He came down, giving me the big sigh treatment, and said of course there's no pump, that model doesn't come with a pump.

Stupid old me. I might have guessed that at £118 you couldn't expect any extras. Jolly lucky to have wheels.

He eventually handed me something which looked like a spray for killing insects in the garden, nothing like a pump as I know it, offering it in metal or plastic, quick, there is a queue. I chose the plastic at £2.83. Then I had to queue up again to ask him how to use it. There seemed to be no adapter.

It's a funny thing about age. I have no inhibitions about asking stupid questions. I don't mind at all displaying my ignorance. I am more than willing to concede stupidity and bow to the expert, as long as he will kindly explain or, best of all, do it for me. He gave the pump a quick blow, to show how it was done. Then I tried, and the whole thing seemed to explode, and he had to return and do it again. Jake, meanwhile, was trying to hide, hoping no one would think I was with him.

A bell, I said. I see there isn't a bell. Not one of the extras, ha ha, so we better buy one.

· 'I don't want a bell,' said Jake in my ear.

The man smiled. *Nobody* buys bells these days, he said. Certainly not boys. Only little kids on trikes buy bells. Where have I been all these years.

Then we agonised over lights, and got them at £7 for two, then a carrier frame, a bargain at £4.50, deciding to save up later for the pannier bags as they all seemed to cost a fortune. Oh, and a water bottle, Jake said he had to have one, but that was a snip, compared with all the other essentials and cost only £1.25.

I never had a lock for my bike, back in the olden days. No one stole things, when I was young. Ask my Mum. Nor did we have homosexuals, rapists, nasty books, violent films, trade unions, strikes, bombs or bad language on television. And it was hot and sunny every summer. We were happy then.

Jake said he would have to have a lock. Bikes are always being pinched in our area. The woman opposite got her rear wheel stolen last week, even though she'd locked the bike to a railing. The Boss sent his assistant to explain Locks to us, the theory of, and we were told the best one was £23. At that price, I said, you would need a lock to lock up the lock. He was off at once, sighing with his eyes, to serve elsewhere.

We finally chose a lock at £4.15, one of those chain things, long enough to go round both wheels. Very cunning. Then we had a long and earnest talk about Insurance. With a good lock, was it worth it? Or should we take out Insurance, and give the lock back? I think six people got served while I pondered Insurance.

I asked the Boss if the £12, which was what he quoted, covered theft from anywhere, and he handed me a pile of leaflets and forms.

'You can read, it,' he said, 'I haven't got the time. I've got people to serve . . .'

At long last, we got all the necessary accessories assembled, and the bill totted up. Only two hours had elapsed from first walking into the shop.

I was looking at the bike seat and it did seem abnormally narrow, like sitting on a piece of steel wire. I would find it hellish to sit on, not of course that it's my bike, or my money, and it is the modern style, and if Jake's happy, why should I make any comments, but of course I couldn't stop myself.

'What?' said the Boss. 'Too narrow? That seat too narrow?'

The whole shop was enjoying his declamatory style, perfected over decades of dealing with dum-dums.

'They don't come any broader than that. Unless *you* want a *woman's* seat. Is that what you would like . . .?'

I paid the cheque at once and followed Jake out into the street. I should really have let him buy it all on his own. He probably could have done it in a tenth of the time. I have promised not to interfere any more.

It stands gleaming in the hall, so sleek and sophisticated and scientific. It has ten gears, none of which is a Sturmey or an Archer. I didn't dare ask about them.

Oh Levels

Flora has decided what she wants to do after Primary School. She wants to take a year off before she goes to Secondary School. Oh, you know, the usual things. Bum around Europe. Perhaps India. Discover oneself. Just see how it goes, but anyway, a year off, that's what I really fancy doing.

She hasn't actually put it in those exact words, as she's only nine, but she has heard the Big Ones, now that O- and A-level exams are over, going on about their future plans and the plans of all their contemporaries, and a year off sounds pretty good to her. It could be catching. Why should Sixth Formers have all the fun. It would help the economy and keep down the unemployment figures if everyone had a year off, every second year. You do feel rather exhausted at the age of five when you fly up to the first year Infants. You deserve a break. Then when you go up to the Juniors, wow, take it easy, let's sit back and think about things.

It is an established fashion once you've finished A-levels, to have some sort of year off, even if all you're doing is taking a year off before commencing a lifetime off. We never had such indulgences. On the conveyor belt, we were, back in the Sixties. Heads down. Ours was not to reason why. With one's nose to the sticking place, one put one's best foot to the grindstone and hoped that a 2:2 would impress Mr Marks and Mr Spencer sufficiently to offer a start as a management trainee.

Some things don't change. There's still a strange feeling at this time of the year as the nation waits for the O and A results. You start off in June convinced you've made a mess of them all, then time passes, hopes spring, and by August you begin to think yes, I *could* get A in French, perhaps even in Maths and English, that was quite a good answer really, even though I should have done the other one.

Jake has said goodbye to Biology for ever. Whatever happens, bye bye, Biology. His notes have gone, even though I've screamed at him. What if you have to re-sit. What if years ahead you decide to take up Biology again. What if Flora, when she's sixteen, just loves Biology and could use your notes? It'll all be different by then, he says. Oh, yeh.

We'll probably be in the Lakes when his O-level results come through, but he won't have his results sent up there. You're only allowed to leave one stamped addressed envelope, so his school says, and he wants it left here. He'll pick it up himself, when he gets back, in his own good time, from wherever it is he might be going.

We're also waiting for Caitlin's A-level results. Caitlin? I can hardly remember her. The moment her last exam was over, that was it. This is the strangest feeling of all. Eighteen years of non-stop chat and action and bingo, it seems to have come to an end. Usually, friends, things happen slowly in life. It's only when you decide to look up that you see, yes, a new pattern has been slowly emerging. Now we do this. Then we did that. However did the change take place. But with Caitlin, our oldest and very dear one, it has happened not just overnight but overminute.

She is staying at present in Islington with some friends. Who isn't. One feels sort of out of things, living this boring old suburban, domestic life. It's not quite a squat but something called short-term community housing. I've been there, and it looks like a squat to me. But then what do I know. Mortgages, rates, doing the garden, digging the weeds, who could ask for more, now I've got older, saying my prayers, when I'm sixty-four, I mean forty-six, tra la. You've got to larf. It's either that or calling the Police.

She does ring us every day, which is very kind, and drops in every second day. Today she came for some soap, so she can get a wash at Caledonian Road baths. She also took some tins of tomatoes, some rice and probably other things, but I was too polite to stop her at the front door and search all her carrier bags. We've actually gained since she left us. The food bill has dropped. We should be so lucky.

The bell on a string which I rigged up five years ago when she became a teenager lies there in tatters. I shed a little tear every time I pass it. I devised a complicated method of pulling the string every time the phone went. With her being on the top floor, rotten records on at full blast, we got sick and tired of going up the stairs or screaming every time it was for her, which it seemed to be all the time. This bell on a string was a brill idea. You can use it yourself. I won't need it any more. Not for a while. It broke four weeks ago and we never got round to mending it. Why should we. Life moves on. Sick tempus parrotus fugit.

Has she left for ever? Or is it just for the summer? We don't know. I sit in the corner, doing my knitting, waiting to be told. She won't let Flora move into her room yet as she doesn't know her definite plans for the next few years, till we see what the A-levels bring. But Flora has not to touch anything, do you hear that, or else. That room is private.

I can now close the front door at ten o'clock every night, bring the cat in, put the milk bottles out, put the cat back out again. What am I doing. We don't have a cat. Who let that beast from next door in our house. I've told you. I'm so disorientated. This is a betwixt and between whiles. A marking time sort of phase. The days are in a daze.

Then I go upstairs, having locked up, safe in the knowledge that no one will be coming in at one in the morning and banging around. After all these years we've lain there, wondering, should we wait up, no you go, no I'll go. Now we can get back to normal, the long battle is over. Bloody hell. Jake still isn't in. I'd better unlock it. Any moment now Flora will be starting all those high jinks.

I've told Flora no, my petal, *you* will be going straight back to school in September, no messing for you, my lass. I don't care what Caitlin might be doing. She's eighteen, getting on twenty-nine, and it's her life, anyway.

What Flora is dreading next term is the Normans. No,

not that scruffy family in the flats. You know, those blokes that came over with William the Conk. Her teacher began the year which has just ended by telling them, now children, we're going to do the Normans. There was a tremendous groan all round, much to the teacher's surprise. 'We've dunem. We dunem last term, Miss.'

The teacher thought hard and said ah yes, but, children, listen to me. *This* time the Normans will be different.

'It wasn't,' said Flora at the end of last term. 'It was *exactly* the same.'

Little does she know that she could be doing the Normans for ever, till she's twenty-one. I did the Romans every year when I was at Primary School. Jake fears he will be doing the English nineteenth century next year, once again, if he chooses History as one of his A-levels. My Jake, the Sixth former. Yup. Come September.

I wonder what it will be like when we don't live our life in school terms. That will be the strangest thing of all. I can't wait.

Youth Opportunities

Now that Caitlin and Jake have got their A- and O-levels behind them, conversations round the table have become a bit limited, with none of those boring GCE things to grind on about.

Caitlin has got the next five years lined up, at least in theory, depending on acts of God and whether the call of the wild gets too strong or some new and amazing squat comes up. She doesn't seem all *that* thrilled, but when you've done so much, what new thrills are there. I'm v. pleased. Perhaps in five years time there might be some jobs around. How nice to be able to have something to do till then.

She got through her three A-levels, which I thought was very good, considering her fun-filled life, with more than enough to get into the University of her choice. She got two Bs and a C. I like to think that in my day I got three Bs, but I've taken a few liberties with my memory over the years, especially as when I did A-levels they didn't give you grades. I got three marks of around 60 per cent. Honest. The master said. As, you think? With inflation, they must be that by now.

She has deferred this university of her choice, which shall be nameless, to protect the innocent, until the following year, as she wanted to take a year off, don't we all, and I said fine, but you won't get no dosh from me, sweetie pie. So she is going to Art College, starting next month, to do a Foundation Year. Lucky beggar. I'm all for extra education, of any sort. Keeps them off the streets.

After that, she can do her four-year university course, which includes a year in America as she is going to read

American Studies. Hmm. That could be a clue. Then after that, she won't have many years to put in before her old age pension.

Most of her friends seem to be taking a year off, if not a life off. I have two of her boyfriends in the house at the moment, two unemployed young gentlemen, squatter types, perfectly content to have nothing whatsoever planned for the next five years, or the next fifty, and they can't understand why any father should even think about such things. Shows my age, doesn't it.

They're not staying here, I'm not that daft, although from the silence upstairs they could have fallen asleep. I decided I would offer them a little job, help out, what with a car to run. Yes, they each drive a car, proper wrecks, one which cost only £15, but bloody hell, how on earth can they even pay for the petrol. I was lucky to get them as it's so hard to get staff these days. I am convinced that we must be living in an age of *full* employment, despite those nasty newspapers putting around horrid rumours to discredit lovely Mrs Thatcher.

For example, and I'll come to Jake's O-levels in a minute, do hold on, I went on the train yesterday to York, on the famous Inter-City 125, and both going up and coming back the dining car was cancelled. Buffet only. 'Staff shortages,' so I was told. Our football pitches on Hampstead Heath, for which I pay a fortune every year on behalf of our Sunday morning football team, are two weeks late this year as they can't get them ready in time. 'Staff shortages.' I asked at Sainsbury's for a boy to help me with the £130 worth of groceries we had just bought, I have the bill here, as long as a roll of wallpaper, but they said sorry, staff shortages. In an ice cream parlour in Chalk Farm, and in a tea shop in South End Green, both on the same day, I heard them asking for staff, pleading for anyone to work, part time or full time. And have you tried to get a plumber to turn up or someone to mend the roof? There you are. Sobvious. They just put out those terrible unemployment figures to divert the public's attention from the Royal Family.

These two jokers upstairs are redecorating Caitlin's room,

ready for Flora to move in. It was either that or getting it fumigated. My wife agreed they could do the bedroom on two conditions. One, no HP sauce. She caught them eating a packet of chips in the house the other week, how disgusting can you get, then they had the affrontery to ask for some ketchup, missus. Certainly not, said she. So they went round the corner shop and got some, carrying it over a doorstep which never in its life has known such aromas. Secondly, no smoking. Surprisingly, they agreed to both conditions.

They were due to start work here at ten this morning, so I rushed round buying all the paints, sandpaper, brushes, rollers, you don't expect workers to have tools do you, and of course they didn't start till twelve. Then they asked for tea, toast and yes, perhaps a boiled egg, Hunt, sokay, we can make it, fanks. They did work till three, then went for dinner. They're hard at it again, whatever it is they're hardly at up there. Lovely lads. Great workers. So lucky to have them. I might lock them in so British Rail or the GLC Parks departments can't pinch them.

We've had endless moral arguments, round the camp fire of an evening, because so many of Caitlin's friends who are going to University in a year's time are taking social security on their year off. No, I won't start that again. Gives me a headache. Am I becoming reactionary in my old age? When I was, I had to struggle, for every, etc, please fill in your own blanks.

Jake also did well in his exams, passing all nine O-levels, including three grade A's, which was exactly the same as Caitlin, wasn't that strange, Flora, are you listening. We've had agonies about which three A-level courses he should take and they have changed almost every day, but the latest call over is English Literature, History, Politics, which are the ones he got As in. My son the sixth-former. I'm still practising. My daughter the art student. I feel a hundred years old. I'll be lying about their ages soon, just to make myself seem younger.

Jake's sixth form sounds trific. His boys' comprehensive has just amalgamated at sixth form level with the girls' comprehensive next door, which is something that should have happened years ago, and it's like being at a sixth form college by the sound of it. Some of these girls did brilliantly and got A grades in everything, so that should keep the boys on their toes which is a useful position to be in if the washroom's crowded and you can't see to comb your hair in the mirror.

Now little Flora, just nine years old, sorry, but I can't type out nine years and eleven months every time. On Hallowe'en she'll be into double figures. My daughter, the ten-year-old. Something terribly complicated has happened to her, as if I haven't got enough problems trying to understand sixth-form time-tables and how to get a mandatory grant from our local education authority for a foundation art year. Have you ever filled in a form for a grant? I'm just going to apply for the basic minimum. Life is too short. I could lose a fortune in time, just trying to understand it.

Flora is in a mixed third and fourth year class. Most of her class are really fourth year children, in their final year at primary school, but Flora and some others are only third year in age, I do hope you are folllowing all this, and will therefore be in a top class two years running. I might have got a few details wrong there, but it has been a long summer and I'm not quite as quick as I used to be.

'Must we have an imbecile sitting with us at meals,' said Jake the other evening when all I'd done was ask the same simple question, admittedly twice, about his History syllabus.

So, that's the latest progress report on the three of them, bang up to date, as of this moment. Oh no, don't bother to ask about me. I don't count. No no, please. I'll just sit here in the corner knitting. And paying the bills.

Toy Symphony

Flora has given up the piano. Another stage in life over, another milestone, my how they fly past, goodness don't they grow up quickly, whatever happened to that little gurgling baba, who is that stranger at the door. I don't mind time pushing on, squire, it's the detritus left behind that bothers me. What the hell am I going to do with that piano.

It's been in the local paper all week-end but not a sniff, not a tinkle, not even a wrong number. We bought it seven years ago for Caitlin and then she gave it up, having passed two exams, or was it three, I can't remember. She burned all the certificates the other day, along with her life-saving badges and certificates for gym and a letter saying she was runner-up for the Green Cross Code. Some people have no respect for history. I did try to save them from the bonfire but no, gone for ever, all that effort, up in smoke. Flora took over the piano and passed no certificates, as her teacher did not believe in exams, this is the 1980s, not those meritocractic 1970s. That's the end of the line. From now on, folks, we're a non-piano-playing family. Downhill all the way.

We bought it for £350, paying £50 for a six-month hire in the first place, to see if Caitlin liked it, and then the balance later, which is a good system. Seven years, so, let me see, beautiful bit of wood, well cared for, made by the famous R.G. Payne, over-strung, underpriced, yes, I'll take £700 for it. It must have doubled at least in seven years. So I rang the firm we bought it from and after endless delays the bloke turned up and said £200, take it or leave it. What a cheek. So it's in the paper at £400. We shall see. And if we don't see, I suppose I'll have to eat my humble tail between my legs and beg him to take it.

Flora has now started the clarinet. For a brief moment in time, she was doing only *one* activity. I could hardly believe it. At her peak, she had up to five different things I was rushing her to every day, or so it seemed. They have all finished, except for Funky Disco, or Dunky Fisco as my mother insists it's called, which is on Saturdays at the Pineapple Studios in Covent Garden. *Everyone* goes there. And now we also have the clarinet which is to be on Sundays at midday.

For a whole week we've sat and worshipped this new instrument, a brand new, shining clarinet, made by Boozey and Hawkes, so it says, whom I thought were just music publishers. We've paid £24 for a six-month hire and if she hasn't given it up by then and gone on to brain surgery or hang gliding, we will pay in all £154. She's had one lesson so far which consisted of putting it together. I could hardly believe that such a little thing could take so much assembling. Flora loves it. Best part of it. All you did with the boring old piano was open the lid. This is like putting the GPO Tower together from Lego.

I have been allowed to have one blow, after I'd washed my hands and begged and pleaded, and I couldn't get a sound. My wife has tried and failed. Jake couldn't do it either. My sister Marion, social worker of this parish, maintains she got a little sound, but she's a fibber. Only Flora has proved that it actually is alive and works. Five notes she's got. In order. We've got a prodigy on our hands. My daughter, the clarinettist.

It has a neat little case, takes up no room, whereas that piano is just a lump, what are we going to do with it. My wife has already re-allocated its space, working out where a blanket box will go, that a new lamp will be bought, how the plants can go elsewhere. I half expect to come down in the morning and find the piano in tears. It must have heard us talking about it by now. The unwanted lodger. Letting out its bed before it's even moved on.

I would really like to keep it, memories of such happy

times, tra la, part of our legend, but she is ruthless. Out, never darken our carpet again and the filth behind it really is disgusting.

At every stage, I always want to keep hold of the artefacts as proofs of the paths we've been along. My memory is not what it was. I look at the children, all enormous now, and find it impossible to believe I pushed them in the pram and rolled with them on the carpet. Yet when you *are* at that stage, you appear to be stuck in a groove, time stands still and you can never imagine them not being little, or that the next stage will ever come, other than the one you are in now or some such tosh, what has happened to this paragraph.

She said that the climbing frame was dead. Jake, it is true, had not played on it for several years and Flora had become bored with it, far too big, so it was out, damn spot, I mean damp spot. I tried to move it and bits of green mould came away in my hand. I was able to face getting rid of that, if only just, as I have it preserved on our cine films, all those marvellous parties that Jake had when it was turned into a castle or tent or tree and all those innocent little boys scrambling over it, those lads now six foot and either working in shops or claiming social security.

I did manage to salvage the first toy that we every bought in our whole parental life. I got it several months before Caitlin was even born, which is now over eighteen years ago, when I happened to see it at Ostrobogolis, a local toy shop. It's a big floppy sort of animal, made of brightly coloured felt. We called it Fattybo and we used to sit and look at it, our best loved possession, but wondering if perhaps I was tempting fate by buying something for our unborn first-born. We even decorated Caitlin's room round it, matching its main colours, dark brown and orange, a room that doesn't exist any more. Our ground floor is now one long room and Caitlin, where is she these days. We have colour snaps to prove it, but snaps don't tell the real story. Caitlin did want to take it to her squat, could she be a romatic, deep down, but I refused. I've seen her place, and her friends, and they won't care for Fattybo the way we will care for Fattybo.

The toy chest has long gone. That was a fitted unit, a sort of little bench against a wall that you lifted up and put the toys inside then sat at to do your little drawings. No bottom in this house is ever going to be small enough again to fit it, so it had to go. But we kept the building bricks, for our grandchildren, ahh, and also a box of Galt farm animals because they look so decorative, even the ones that Jake used to eat. Then there was the doll's house which I used to love playing with as it had all the rooms covered with little bits of different wallpapers we have had in this house in the last twenty years. It's out on loan. No, not the V&A, though they did ask. The cradle, a very posh one made of cane which cost a fortune at Heal's, has subsequently seen the birth of another twenty babies. It was last heard of in Muswell Hill. I always ask the parents to leave their baby's name on it when they borrow it. Must have all the records.

We still have the swing, though it is far too small for Flora. It stands forlornly at the bottom of the garden, a sign at least that we are not yet a childless couple. We did offer it to the family next door, when we decided to get rid of it, for their little girl Jessica. They very smartly said no, how kind, but it would be nice if Jessica could come over our wall, from time to time, and play on it. Which is what happens. So we have this old swing, cluttering up our garden, just for Jessica to use, when I could be using the space for, oh I dunno, wholemeal bread, goats, potatoes, chickens, spinach, muesli and all the other stuff right-thinking people are growing in their gardens in these hard times. I know I never will, so come on over Jessica, you can keep using it.

My wife's main concession, when we were throwing out all these time capsules, was to go through all the children's books and keep the best. Jake has every Biggles, and intends to keep them, but it's the ones for younger children we particularly wanted to keep, by John Burningham and Maurice Sendak. We're also keeping the Beatrix Potters, though they all hated them. Our great-grandchildren will love Beatrix Potter, or else they'll get a belt round the lughole. When you're a great-grandparent, you're allowed to do that. This is a Golden Age for children's fiction, not just because I've got my first children's book out this week. It's for Flora, about Flora, and I intend to surprise her with the first copy for her tenth birthday which is Hallowe'en. What a great father. I never cease to impress myself.

I fear the next thing will be the snooker table. She is already measuring it up, working out which sofa can take its place. I admit Jake and I don't play as passionately as we did last year, but hardly an evening goes by without us having one gameroo after supper. We men go straight from the table to the table, a tradition I greatly enjoy. (Clear up or wash the dishes? Do me a favour, what do we have all these women for.) Snooker signposts in the evenings.

I know this ritual won't go on for ever and Jake will become bored and so another stage will be over. But what's the hurry. It's not doing any harm. She wants it out now or folded away. Some people have no feelings. Family life moves on quickly enough without giving it any little pushes.

Visiting Time

Has Caitlin left home? We watch and wait and look for signs and examine tea leaves, which is very hard these days, since tea-bags came in. Is this the beginning of the end, we ask ourselves over the cocoa, and is our first-born bird about to flee the nest and leave us all forlorn, ha ha, ho ho.

Everywhere round our area I meet people who say is it really true, your teenage daughter is gainfully occupied *and* she's not living at home, snot fair, some people have all the luck. So I preen myself and take the credit for this marvellous coup. After all, not only do most school-leavers not have any work, they are at home in bed for ever till the last syllable of recorded TIM, being too lazy to look under the bed at their rotten watch.

Since July, when Caitlin got her A-level results, she has been in this awfully nice squat with these awfully nice people over in Islington. Technically, it's community housing, or some such, but it looks and feels like a squat to me. She pops in for a bath and for packets of spaghetti and other vital vittels and she and her boyfriend have a meal here once or twice a week. Usually, it's Sunday lunch and usually she's late but of course we don't moan and groan any more, being so pleased to see her. Who cares if it's an hour after we've all finished and the roast is cold and Jake has finished his thirds and I'm asleep on the couch. Take it easy, action.

Every morning since she started her Foundation Year course at Art College at the beginning of October she has got my stupid wife to ring her at eight o'clock sharp, wakey wakey, rise and shine, this is your early morning ogre speaking. Yes, even squats have phones these days, though it's just a box in the hall and they have to pay to get out which of course means we sometimes get reversed charge calls, not that I mind, me, moaning and complaining, you've got the wrong person, missus. I just smile and think well, I am saving on all those TIM calls since she left home.

She's working very hard at art college, and enjoying it, though I worry that she might enjoy it too much and not go on to University next year, as arranged, but let's take one thing at a time, squire, we'll cross our bridges when they're hatched.

I left home for good at eighteen, the age Caitlin is now, though I didn't realise it at the time. I went orf to Durham for four years and never came back, except for a few weeks during the long summer holidays. Unlike Caitlin, I didn't have my own room to leave behind. I shared a bed with my younger brother, plus the lodgers my mother took in the minute I'd left home.

Caitlin has always had her own room, oh we spoiled them rotten. They've got all their own teeth as well, nothing shared or second-hand, own towels, own toothbrushes, own face-cloths, own plates. I'm the only one who eats out of dirty dishes, that's if no one else is watching. Saves a fortune.

Caitlin's room is now empty and waiting for her, should she decide she needs it. It's not the room she used to have, as Flora has now taken that over, but it's still a room of her own, though slightly smaller than her first room.

She has spent about a week in this room so far. She arrived home one evening feeling rotten and after a good meal and bath went to bed, but in the night she woke with terrible pains. Even I got up, and I'm a sod when it comes to getting up in the night, whether it's poorly children or poorly wives or poorly tortoises. I'm only interested in poorly me. After long discussions, I decided I had better ring the Emergency Doctor. Have you ever done this? There's a list of top ten numbers I hate ringing, which begins with British Rail Enquiries, followed by London Transport, then any taxi or minicab or plumber, followed by the doctor in fourth position. That's the ordinary doc, of course. When it comes to the Emergency version, it's straight up to Number One.

I was transferred by recording machines all round London before I reached a human voice at last and I poured out all my troubles, I mean Caitlin's troubles. 'Don't ask me, dear. I'm the worst person in London to ask. I know less about medicine than anyone. I'm just the telephonist.'

Forty minutes, so she said, that would be the quickest an emergency doctor could come. At least in London there is such a system. Whatever would we do in the Lake District. Or in Bulgaria. That's where Caitlin was on her summer hols. What if it had happened there.

I sat looking out of the front window, my nose pressed against the panes, staring into the darkness. It was two o'clock in the morning. I've never been up that late for years. Even the burglars had gone home. I was watching for the doctor's car, ready to pounce, in case he gave one light knock at the door, then disappeared again.

He was an Indian gentleman, very solemn, no nonsense. I was hoping to have a bit of a chat, wanting to find out what sort of doctors opt for this emergency work, for ever going to strange places in the dark, called out by some very strange people, such as me, this bloke in his 1960s dressing-gown with his inane grin, asking dopey questions, keeping him back from his medical duties.

He spent most of his brief visit filling in forms. He could not believe Caitlin was called Caitlin and asked her to repeat it four times, writing it down wrongly each time. It is a daft name, I know, and few people ever get it right first time, or know its origin. I notice these days that her new friends call her Kate, what a liberty, who do they think they are, then I remember, she doesn't live here any more. She can call herself anything now. After the doctor had written it down a fifth time, and I was beginning to think I'd called out the Emergency Gallup polster by mistake, he then examined her.

There's always the worry when you call out a doctor that the rotten child will have recovered by the time he comes and be jumping all over the house and you'll be marked down in the black book as dum-dum parent. This happened to us twice with Jake when he was little, then of course when we didn't ring in time, it was *Emergency Ward Ten* and he had to be rushed direct to hospital for an abscess which we had been laughing about, accusing him of making it up. He'll never let us forget that.

He gave her some pills and she quickly got back to sleep. In the morning, I had to go with a prescription to the chemist but he had only half of these particular antibiotics in stock. Emergency docs prescribe stuff which no one else ever uses, so this jaunty chemist johnny said. I went back the next morning—and he wasn't so jaunty. His chemist shop had been wrecked overnight. Some gang had got in, looking for drugs, then smashed up the place. It gave me some good chat to tell Caitlin. I said of course they'd been after her pills. These emergency docs use hot stuff.

She has now gotten over whatever it was, poor lass. I think it was cystitis, spelling an optional extra, or did he say an inflammation of the stomach or kidney. I'm mentioning it now that she's better, although, touch wood, one should not go around talking about children being ill, or boasting they are never ill. She was always a good patient, stoical and resigned, no bother, never demanding attention or treats, not like some people I could mention. Me, for example.

We were the ones un-stoical and un-resigned when she was very little and we weren't used to children's illness. We had one of those stupid Cry Calls when she was a baby and I was always convinced she had stopped breathing when she was ill and I would rush up to find a wire disconnected or the battery dead. By the time Jake arrived, we had disconnected the Cry Call. With Flora, we had thrown it away.

I now realise that one will always worry about them being ill, even when they are groan up and living away from home. I could never understand my mother being interested in my movements when I'd left home and it was a right drag to tell her, even if it was just some old story. I'm all for old stories. I hope they'll always tell me good fiction. They can keep the truth a secret.

114

Caitlin's visit was only a short one, and she returned to the squat once she had recovered, so I didn't have time to discuss things, nor was it really the right atmosphere to talk about plans and the future and arrangements. What an old fuss-pot I am becoming. Those tea-bags are only for Caitlin's use, so what does it matter if they never get used. Those black plastic sacks can surely stay unpacked for a few months longer. Plans? People don't have plans these days. We all live from one morning call to the next morning call.

School Journey's End

There were quite a few tears in the playground, which was strange, not because it was the playground but because the tears were coming out of the eyes of those sorts of kids I'd put down as toughies, know what I mean, usually full of old lip, always effing and blinding, but when the chips are down they've got very little sauce and they are quickly revealed as marshmallow souls and what a menu this is turning out to be.

It was a scene which happens once a year in every playground. I have witnessed it myself twice already. All the little ten-year-olds getting on the coach, ready for the school trip, waving bye-bye to the mater and pater, mum and dad, auntie and nan, Gran and Grandad, Her Feller and His Fancywoman.

I suddenly had a vision that they were all wearing gas masks, with labels round their necks and very long short trousers and old-fashioned caps and the memories came flooding back. No, I was never an evacuee, but I've seen the films. I was an evacuator, if that's the word. We received evacuees in our council house in Carlisle during the war and I hated them, flash Cockney gits who got all this sympathy from teachers because they'd been in the London bombing, lucky sods. Nothing exciting like that ever happened in Carlisle.

It's been so quiet all week, not having Flora at home. Books do make a room but children make a home. I don't count teenagers as children, far less human beings, in fact what are they, you might ask, there must be a reason for them, a purpose to their lives, I'll let you know when I get any clues.

Only three round the table has made mealtimes so polite and civilised. You really need four to make a crowd, then you have two-way conversations, or more, as each person holds two, their own conversation and the one they are trying to interrupt. I was talking first, that is not true, what a liar, oh shut your glump.

Jake has been remarkably quiet this week anyway, but then so would you, if you were going to a White Party. Of course he wasn't going at first, stupid idea, who do they think they are, I'm not wearing white. Stupid.

When Caitlin was sixteen, all her parties seemed to end in tears and terrible scenes. And that was just the parents. There did seem to be a spate of vandalism at the time, gate-crashers causing havoc, breaking windows, wrecking rooms, but that seems to have subsided now. I'm talking about a long time ago. God, it must have been 1981. So hard to remember that far back when so much has happened since. Perhaps Jake's contemporaries got the party-wrecking craze out of their system when they were fourteen.

He went to one party the other week where you had to wear jackets. Amazing. What a terrific wheeze. Most original. I suppose jackets and ties are very eccentric these days. I'm surprised the police didn't run them in.

Remember when drapes were not allowed at dance halls? And DAs were banned. Course, I'm really going back now. There's a good sociological survey to be done on prohibited dress throughout the centuries. Entry will be refused to the cave ball to anyone wearing woad. Gentlemen will not be served in powdered wigs.

Jake has his white bowling shoes, so that's a start, but should he wear his white Spurs shirt or not? He doesn't care about them much these days, what a turncoat, and hasn't been all season, oh no you haven't, I'm the true supporter now, but then he does have his Saturday job.

The big problem has been trousers, as you're supposed to wear *all* white. He is now halfway through bleaching a pair of old jeans and the kitchen smells like a laundry. It's working brilliantly so far, and the blue has almost completely gone. I came down this morning and found little patches of denim, about four inches square, all along the radiator, drying out. He got started on the jeans, then realised there were some holes, so he had to start getting patches bleached to the same colour, or lack of colour. Not easy, you know, going to a White Party.

I wish Flora had been here to witness this little cottage industry. She loves the idea of Jake going to parties and is constantly picking up the phone, hoping to hear conversations she's not supposed to hear, or watching him get ready to go out.

For a few weeks now, Jake has had his hair in a middle parting. He looks just like my dad. He always wore his hair like that, in the style of those pre-war footballers, which of course he was, after a fashion. I missed out on middle partings. Wouldn't do me much good now, even if I tried. Not with my hair. I'm getting a middle spacing, rather than a middle parting, a sort of thin bit at the front, but we don't talk about it.

We have had no communication from Flora all week, though we did tell her not to bother anyway. Far better to send postcards to the grandparents in Carlisle. Much more important. Oh no, I tell a lie, we did get a note on Monday, saying sorry this is a boring letter, but Mrs Pyne (the headmistress) says we have to write home *now* and I've nothing to say as the activities haven't started yet, it's not fair, I've got nothing to say.

They've been at Butlin's at Clacton, or Claque-de-Nancy as they say in France. I met a postman once who swore he saw that written on an envelope. And also Arich Arbor. Go on, you can work that one out. Don't be lazy.

All week I have talked to parents who have had a letter or postcard every day from their loved ones which means, boast boast, what a loving family. So in reply I boast about the *lack* of letters, oh we don't care, we told Flora not to write, meaning that we bring them up to be independent, not clinging. It's very complicated, parental boasting. The ones who run them down are often showing off most.

The weather has been poor, but then it's traditional at all school camps to stay soaked and muddy all week and never change your clothes, gosh what fun. There was some incident involving a tiger at Colchester Zoo, so one Mum told me, and a boat trip when the water came over their wellies, but of course we haven't been told anything, I mean we *instructed* her not to tell us anything till her return, that's the sort of family we are, don't you know.

She did ring last night, Friday night, the last night of her holiday, which was a bit daft, having waited so long, but they'd all just discovered how to ring reverse charges. She got through two minutes after we had gone out, so she got Jake. Hard cheese, Flora. It's yeh, whatjawant, yeh, grunt, grunt, yeh, then he hangs up. Not exactly a polished telephone conversationalist, our Jake.

Flora came home half an hour ago. I went by car to school to pick her up, and ended up parking practically back home again, as every parent had done the same. There we all were, exactly one week later, standing in the same little groups, wondering and waiting. No tears this time, though I could sense a few worried thoughts. Luckily, the coach was only a few minutes late. Jake was on one school trip when the coach was four hours late and there were nearly heart attacks all over the playground.

They all looked so embarrassed and self-conscious, getting off the coach, half-catching their parents' eyes, then looking away, laughing with their friends, especially if it was the friend they had wanted to sit with. What a worry that is for every child on a school trip. But they did look clean and tidy, even glowing, a perfect advert for the Welfare State. They don't wear uniform, at our primary school, but for this trip they all had on identical woollen pom-pom hats in blue and green, knitted by parents, so that our school would be easily identified amongst the other two thousand schoolkids who were at Butlin's last week.

We haven't heard the full sagas yet, but they will be to come. She just caught sight of Jake, before he went off to his party. I like your grey jeans, Jake, are they new? Just a week away, but you can miss so much.

Prodigal Daughter

We had a surprise visitor last week. I got this phone call, saying could I pick her up and give her a bed, the sort of phone call which used to drive me round the bend. For years, we seemed to get them on the hour. Living in London, you are at the mercy of everyone in your whole life you have ever met, or to whom you might be remotely related, who happens not to live in London.

I did it myself of course, and I am still very grateful to Squire Barraclough for giving me room on his settee in Archway for two weeks in 1958. I wonder where he is now. I wonder what that settee is doing. I wonder if I've spelled his name right.

I went downstairs to tell my wife, heh up, lass, get kettle on, look sharp, by the right, think on. I've promised someone they can sleep in our spare room. I'm on the way to pick them up. She's homeless, poor thing. Could be just one night. Could be for ever. You have got tea-bags in the house? Right, see you later.

And I ran out of the front door and into my car and went zoom, zoom, as she stood there with steam coming out of her ears.

'I've got my feminist book to finish and it's all right for you but I have other things to do and you might have consulted me and anyway who is it?'

I zoomed back again, a few yards, and wound down the window.

'It's Caitlin,' I said. 'Remember her?'

I went off chortling into the night, though it was actually two in the afternoon on a very rainy, very freezing, so-called spring afternoon but I like the look of the words, 'chortling into the night'. Has an archaic ring, pre-war school stories, what.

Caitlin's squat is nearer her art college than we are and she is nineteen and got her own life to lead. So it goes. Depending on whom I'm telling, I can make it sound like the pits or gosh what fun, so you think she must be in the Lady Di set at least in some little bijou flat in Kensington. She does pay rent. It is official.

Zoom zoom. I had been to it once before, helping her move in, but it was dark, definitely night on that occasion, and I didn't manage to have a nose around. Now I was looking forward to casing the joint, or joining the cases. Her worldly possessions were in a line of black plastic bags, waiting in the hall for me to collect. There was also a hatstand, a plastic chrysanthemum, a kite, a broken mirror and an enormous portfolio which I could hardly carry into the car. She must have been working hard.

It was obviously a condemned house, with the walls bare, holes in the ceilings, all bannisters removed, junk in corners, no water or electricity, gosh, this really is fun, but I said nothing, not wanting to put my foot in anything and trip over. I do feel sorry for many of these poor homeless people. However can they go back to their lovely warm middle-class homes when they've tasted the good life.

Then she took me upstairs to the room she has been using as a studio. I admit that has been one definite advantage. We don't have such a room here, nothing quite as large and light and spacious. We *could* create one, of course. All it means is taking the windows out, knock a few walls down, rip a few floors up, but I don't think her mother would approve. She's frightfully fussy that way.

There seemed to be no one else around, unless they were hiding. One by one, all the people have moved out, into different accommodation provided by the Council. Caitlin and her boyfriend are the last survivors. Now, at last, even they have to get out.

But she had some very good news, hence her excitement. In this day and age it's like winning the Pools, being lucky in the draw for the Nobel Prize, your number coming up to be interviewed on *Desert Island Discs*, all those things that we mortals only ever dream about. Yup. It has happened. She is moving into a council flat. Open the champagne, folks.

I have to go along with all this delight, not wanting to be a spoil-sport, but inwardly I am shaking my head and thinking what has it all come to, Hunt. You struggle and work hard to become a property-owning capitalist, a fully paid-up member of the middle classes, someone Mrs Thatcher can be proud of as she goes about the planet bestowing her blessings, then this happens.

I know I ought to be thrilled, but old prejudices die hard. They tell me things have changed out there, status symbols have altered, and it is true that I do know lots of teachers and social workers and artists and other respectables who now live in council property, but gee whiz and by the left and who'd have thunk it. Council house to council house, in just two generations.

At Caitlin's age, which is nineteen, my ambition in life was to get out of our council house. Now the world's ambition is to get into a council house. Should I have my head felt or send her on a brain-washing week-end with Giddy and Giddy, Roy Brooks, Knight, Frank and Rutley, Jackson Stops and Starts.

It is only a temporary thing, of course, before she goes off to university in the autumn. She is part of a housing co-op and is not depriving some poor homeless family. There is not exactly a rush any more for those sort of decaying monster council blocks around King's Cross for reasons we need not go into and really I don't want to describe it at all. The sight of the vandalised lift will give me nightmares for weeks.

It is good for the young to get away and do whatever the young do and terribly good for the middle-aged to be left in peace with their hot-water bottles and two pairs of spectacles, supping their cocoa and trying to find *Kaleidoscope* on Radio 4 knowing that no one has been interfering with their rituals and turned the stupid knob to Capital. But into a high rise council flat?

123

Hobby Horses

Jake and my wife are not talking at the moment. Well, it's the season. Every year at this time, these things come round, the same old problems, same old decisions to be made, same old arguments and agonising. We were spared the Big One last year but God, the year before, it went on for ages.

No, it's not about whether we should have the central heating boiler serviced this time or miss a year and hope to save some money, though of course if we do it'll go wrong. Nor is it hunt-the-tortoise time. Any moment now it will disappear and we'll never know whether it's dropped dead on us or gone off early to hibernate.

The number one topic of the moment, which it must be in thousands of homes just now, is college entrance. Jake has been twitting on about his UCCA stuff and university entrance forms and how to permutate five from any fifty. Now that he has started the Upper Sixth, it's real decision time.

Upper Sixth. God, it seems only yesterday he was trotting off in his clean blazer, polished face, new shoes, leather briefcase, no I must have made that up. It was in the Victorian daze that they had archaic things like briefcases and satchels. Modern schoolchildren have all the advantages of the latest technology when it comes to carrying their belongings to school. They're called plastic carrier bags.

Jake is actually very well organised and has read all the university handbooks and brochures and made several visits already and decided the sort of offers they might make. Caitlin, two years ago, got bored very quickly and would only pick two, instead of the five which Uncle Ucca allows you. Luckily she got into one of those of her choice and after a year on a foundation art course, she starts university on October 2nd. Lucky University.

The bit that has upset my wife seems pretty trivial to me. On one of these application forms which Jake is currently dog-earing and cat-licking, he has got to fill in his Hobbies and Interests. Nothing unusual about that. But my wife picked it up and found that Jake had put down three hobbies—Cycling, Spaghetti Eating and Harmonica Playing.

Oh Jake, you can't put that. All you do is cycle half a mile down the road every Saturday to Chalk Farm to do your week-end job as a waiter. Then you come back again. Apart from that, you don't actually *cycle* anywhere. What if the admissions tutor picks on it in the interview and asks you how many races you've won and were you in the Tour de France this year?

Jake just smiled. He thinks it's quite funny. I suppose it is slightly more interesting than Reading. Everybody in every Sixth Form puts down reading on their university application forms. I suppose the most boring of all is walking. You might just as well put breathing.

His spaghetti eating *is* quite funny, though I doubt if the admissions people will think so. At the school camp this summer, which was for First Years but Jake went to help out, he was first in a spaghetti competition. He's rather proud of it. Several kids at school have come up to him since to ask about it. There was this race, see, to get through a bowl of spaghetti in the fastest time. Several masters took part, as well as First Years and Sixth Formers, and our Jake won. What a hero. Gee, Jake, tell me again how you did it.

But not on your university entrance forms, Jake. Be sensible. They haven't much sense of humour, these university people.

As for the harmonica playing, that is just dopey. He can't play for toffee, though he'll thump me for saying so. But *he* thinks he can. When he's in a soulful mood, he puts his records on in his room and plays along with them. On his bleeding harmonica. You can hear cats howling all over the neighbourhood.

It is a problem, though, having to have Hobbies and Interests. I am surrounded by them and I now wish I didn't have so many. My room is piled high with all my collections of stamps and books and postcards and autographs and newspapers and memorabilia and other junk which is all terribly precious and must not be touched by anyone. Including me. I buy the stuff, then leave it there.

I put football down as my hobby when I was Jake's age, applying to Durham. I knew it wasn't smart or intellectual, but having kept records of all Scotland's matches back to 1936, and acquired dozens of scrapbooks still soggy with pink and green coloured newspaper photographs of my heroes, I was ready for any question, should the subject come up.

In the actual interview, all this superior being asked me, sitting on his chaise-longue, showing no interest in me at all, or in any of the stuff I'd written on my application form, was which operas I had seen. Coming from Carlisle, I found that very easy to answer.

When I left Durham, trying hard to get a job, I was much more concerned to have some respectable sounding hobbies and interests to put on my forms. I remember the week before the end of the term joining the Fine Art Society, whatever that was, and being made secretary. That filled up a lot of space. Pity it didn't impress the Shell interviewing board when I was called before them in Newcastle. Turned down flat.

Should you tell the truth about Hobbies? Do they care? Does anyone actually read that section? They keep shoving it on, so there must be some reason. At seventeen and eighteen, you look around and see other people with apparently all-consuming interests in life and you feel rather jealous and out of it. You have to think up some, or you feel naked, an empty, boring person. But if you put the wrong ones, you can sound a jerk or a pseud or a wet.

When Caitlin was filling in the same forms, two years ago, my wife was equally scathing when she found that Caitlin

127

had only put down one hobby—Jumble Sales. This was perfectly true. It was by far her number one interest at the time, providing her with endless excitement and rubbish. God, that reminds me, if she doesn't clear that side passage out by October 2nd, I'm burning everything.

My wife was not against her telling the truth, one must never encourage one's children not to do that, tut tut, but she did try to suggest that Caitlin might use rather different words. 'Curio Collecting.' That would sound slightly more upmarket.

Caitlin got her own back on me when she was filling in those forms. I think I'd been trying to press her to apply to Durham, and generally giving helpful hints, oh no, I couldn't possibly have been interfering, and she said certainly not. I don't want to go to anywhere you went.

You always have a section in these entrance forms where you fill in the name of your parent or guardian. Caitlin refused to put down my name anywhere. Instead, she put her mother's name. But Caitlin, I said, they'll think you're an orphan or from a one-parent family or we're divorced. It's just routine. When they say 'parent', you always put in your Dad's name. That's how nature intended it. But she wouldn't change the entry.

Then of course there's Occupation. I remember that causing a lot of consternation when I was at school. All the lads whose dads were fitters insisted on putting down Engineer. What cheats. Or postmen came out as civil servants. My dad was a clerk, but I always made him spell out exactly what grade he was—Higher Executive Officer was the highest he reached—as it looked much more important.

Jake is now threatening to get his own back on my wife for being so critical about his hobbies. You know how busy she always is, writing books, doing reviews, little broadcasts, generally organising the literary world. He says he's going to put her occupation down as 'Housewife'.

Hello Campus

Today was a watershed day. A small hurdle for UCCA but a giant leap forward for our family. Today was the day, mark it well, Hunt, try to write clearly in your diary, that your first-born started university.

We took her there in the car, me and the old trout, plus another girl from Caitlin's school who was starting at the same place, plus her Dad. We have now just got back and my headache is worser than it was when we started. All day I have felt rotten. Withdrawal symptoms, you will say, and you will be wrong. Nothing has given me greater pleasure for a long time.

First of all, we have spent nothing on her school education, so I managed a few smug smiles to myself as we drove out of London. Imagine having sent your child to Dartington, then have him or her or it turn out just like any other comprehensively educated child of the Eighties. All that money, I wouldn't have been able to bear it.

What have I done with the money I haven't spent? Search me. OK, I have some nice stamps and we do have good hols and Augustus Barnett must have had a fortune from us and I have bought you that new Miele, sorry, us the new Miele, I know, I know, it's for the house, it just slipped out.

If you spend £5,000 a year on a child's education for ten years, which is apparently what some dopey parents do, think how much the same money would make on a simple insurance policy. At the age of nineteen, let me see, you could present them with a cheque for £100,000, tax free, and say, 'Here you are, off you go, have fun, don't upset the horses and give us a ring at Christmas, one of these

129

decades.' With that sort of money, you wouldn't need O-levels, never mind a posh accent.

I was also pleased, as we drove through the London suburbs, going very slowly 'cos I couldn't see a thing out of the back with the trunk and all the boxes, to think that Caitlin was actually going to start university. You know what it's like when they insist on taking their ridiculous Year Off. Caitlin did do something useful, but I wondered all the time if she might change her mind.

The lovely trunk in the back of the car, all brown and shiny, was not Caitlin's but her friend's. Caitlin has decided to go through life with the minimum of possessions, don't you know. Who needs all these materialistic things. She came out of the council flat where she has spent most of the summer with a few black plastic sacks, then some friends threw a cushion down from the top floor, and we were jolly well orf.

Her dear mama had washed a few of her things, then ironed them beautifully, but not too beautifully, so she would still recognise them. My contribution towards the first day has been to stay up all last night screaming. That was why I started and ended the day with such a headache.

Caitlin rang two days ago to say she needed her passport or birth certificate, otherwise she couldn't start. Something to do with Enrolment or getting the keys of her room, anyway, it was vital, you *had* to have them. Oh God, I turned the whole house upside down and failed to find her passport. She had it last, I knew that, oh yes you did, but I had to try searching for it before I could blame her. She has now decided it must be in the rubble of that squat she was in earlier this summer, the one the Council knocked down.

I hate looking for things. It makes me so bad tempered. Normally, I'm ever so easy-going, honest, ask anyone, but when I lose something and fail to find it, I see so many other things in chaos, stuff I'd failed to find on previous searches, vital documents I know I should put away more safely, then my mind goes blank and I can't see or think straight and I just rant and rave and rush round the house blaming everyone. Who's stolen it. That's my favourite.

Now, Hunt, just sit down quietly and think clearly about where you last had it, says my wife, ever so sensibly, and that makes me froth and foam even more. In the case of the birth certificate I knew it was all my fault. I have a special folder for all certificates and no one, but no one, is ever allowed to touch them. That's it. It's either you lot, or burglars. No one leave the planet.

I had every drawer in the whole house emptied, before I found it. At the *back* of the drawer I had put it in. I must have overfilled the drawer and forced it shut at some time and the folder had slipped down behind, hidden from view. Oh God. I went to bed, very late, still in a temper, and hardly slept.

We found the campus, despite having forgotten to bring a map, and eventually located the rooms which Caitlin and her friend had been allocated. There was a good atmosphere, friendly and welcoming, with lots of older students detailed to help the newcomers. Most of the new students seemed to have come with their parents and there was a great deal of carting and carrying boxes up and down. Then back again as we all got lost.

Caitlin's room looked quite nice, not much space but an attractive shape and well designed. She's in a unit with twelve students, male and female, and they share the same cooking facilities. Gosh, what fun. We didn't stay long. No one wants their aged parents hanging around. I feel eighteen and I'm convinced I look no more than nineteen, but for some reason the rest of the world doesn't think so. I can never understand this.

The first weeks in a new institution are always very strange, so we said wisely, nodding our aged heads, as we drove into the town then had a long walk along the sea. There you are, a location clue, but that's the last one. Must give Caitlin some privacy. At last.

We tried to remember our own first days as students. I went on the train from Carlisle to Durham with three other blokes from school. No parents came with us. Parents didn't have cars in those days. And they were *always* very, very, very old.

131

I can remember the same confusion about trunks and how to get them to the room, wherever that was. I can remember the smell of the Castle, rather sweaty I thought, soapy and moist. Some of the same smells came back today, down all the years.

I can remember that the older students looked so ancient, such men of the world, so mature and worldly, which of course many of them were. This was 1954 and many had done National Service first. I was one of the callow eighteen-year-olds, straight from school. Still am.

My wife went from Carlisle to Oxford all by herself on a train which took for ever and she arrived late and went straight to bed, then woke up having decided to get out of college as soon as possible. She hated being cooped up with girls all her own age inside a building with endless regulations, and was determined to have a flat of her own. Which she did.

On my second day, I rushed out to buy a college blazer, a college tie, a college scarf and a gown. I would have bought a duffle-coat, the other essential of student life in the Fifties, but I'd run out of money. Sounds like the 1850s, doesn't it. Remember how people of the opposite s−x had to be out of the rooms by seven o'clock? Standards and attitudes and conditions of student life have changed so much in thirty years. I'm sure Caitlin will enjoy it. She has got her black plastic sacks.

Comprehensive Cover

We've been looking at schools. No, not to buy one, though quite a few are ripe for development with some fine playing-fields and bits of greenery, and would fetch a fortune, if ever schools went out of fashion. Not much chance. I feel that schools are with us for quite some time. Keeps them off the streets. What would those teachers do without them.

It's all the emotion that keeps them going, all this passionate concentration and deliberation which parents put into the Great God Education. Then the rows and scenes to come. There's always some parent in our area who hasn't got the school of their choice and refuses to send the poor kid to any other school and they're down at the education offices every day, or camping on the pavement outside the school they do want, or chaining themselves to railings.

Now that Flora is aged eleven and a few days, we must put our great minds to the problem of her secondary education. Our Local Authority, which happens to be ILEA, Division 2, has sent us a bumper bundle of possible comprehensive schools, twenty-one in all, just to confuse us. How do those parents straight off the boat ever cope.

The list includes the London Nautical School, whatever that is, though I'm sure Flora would like the uniform, oh no, it's for boys only. Or there's a boarding school out in Suffolk she could go to, Woolverstone Hall, which is where the writer Ian McEwan went. Completely free, I see, for parents living in Inner London. But of course we couldn't part with our little Flora, the last of our lovely brood. Oh well, two down, only nineteen to wonder and worry about.

We have been through all this process twice already, with Caitlin and Jake, eight and six years ago, so many of the possible schools are household names. But a strange thing has happened in eight years. Those once spoken of with contempt, dismissed as sink schools by the know-alls, are now oversubscribed. Some of the one-time rubbish schools are now so snotty that if you don't put them down as your first choice, then it's no chance, please leave the pavements clear and don't touch those railings.

Three good things have happened during my lifetime in London. No smog. That was amazing. I used to come home in the early Sixties and be unable to find my own street and end up driving on pavements, completely lost. Then the Thames is now clean, the cleanest metropolitan river in the world. Thirdly, we have at last got proper comprehensives. OK, don't scream, I know your little Kevin is down for Eton and Tracey is down for Roedean and you did try the local primary, but it didn't stretch them. What are they, made of rubber or something? Yes, I know you can't bear *your* local comprehensives, have you *seen* them, shocking I agree, and the language, tut, tut.

I try not to argue about education these days, life is too short, but isn't it lovely the way public schools now feel prejudiced *against*. You hear these parents moaning about their Darren and Craig, upon whom thousands have been spent at Westminster, unable to get into Oxbridge because, so they say, Oxbridge is letting in comprehensive kids with much *lower* grades. All true. And it will get better, or worser, depending on your point of view. Hey ho. What a larf.

Yes, we were rather fortunate when it was Caitlin and Jake. Our area was in the throes of changing and the schools which had formerly been grammar schools naturally had the edge. They were everybody's first choice. Nobody then wanted the schools which had been secondary modern schools. There was no Eleven Plus, but we were in agonies waiting to see if they would be sent to their first choice, which they were. Phew.

With Flora, we have felt no worries at all, as the choices seem equal, even though for the last few weeks some kids in her class have been boasting about their school for next year, ooh horrible, that stinks, that one, come with us Flossie, it's really good, no no, my sister knows the *really* best one.

Round the cocoa, just a quick cup, we decided we would look at only two, the two nearest possible schools to our house. We decided against the one Caitlin went to, excellent though it is, as that means a short bus ride. Why impose travelling on her when there's no need. Jake is at an all-boys, so that's out, though it's mixed at Sixth Form level.

Last Tuesday we went to school A, which is a ten-minute walk away. I've never liked the building, but it was marvellous inside. We were taken round by two very laid back Sixth Formers, a girl and a boy. It didn't matter which classroom I said we would like to look in, he drawled Yeh, why not. Eight years ago, I don't remember being able to walk into any classroom while lessons were going on. I wonder if Eton allows that. There was an air of great excitement and the enthusiasm from the pupils and the staff. In a Maths class, the teacher even stopped to explain to me what SMILE is. Don't ask me what it is, but I was told. I did Old Maths at school.

School B, which we visited on Thursday, is even nearer, in the next street, just three minutes away, and has terrific grounds, but it is much more traditional. It even has a uniform, which worried Flora, but she has been through the rules and realised it's fairly flexible, with several colours and choices, so she'll be able to stun them.

At both schools, all the parents seemed pretty ordinary, brows knitted, worried and harassed looking, while their children turned up as if in some fashion display. Well, the girls did, out to impress their future classmates. During one of those boring addresses which a head gave, droning on in a vast hall, coming out with the usual clichés, I sat behind two girls of Flora's age who spent all the time doing their nails, arranging their hair and fixing their jewellery.

The written stuff they give out tells you so little. All nineteen schools in the handbook have a section called Aims, and they all say much the same. 'To develop the full potential of each child . . . to provide a caring community . . . standards are high . . . a sound general education.' Yawn, yawn.

Having worked out the uniform rules, or lack of them, Flora went straight to the section marked Jewellery in each school's own prospectus. Let's have the right priorities. Then she wanted to inspect their Dance and Music facilities, both very important to her. There seemed to be a better organised orchestra in one school, but the other had better sounding Dance groups. Not a word from Flora so far about learning. Not even a smile.

One school was very violent eight years ago, and the corridors were like jungles, but they have transformed it. The only nasty graffiti we noticed was in the more traditional school, though the teacher taking us round at the time rushed into the classroom ahead of us and sat on top of the worst desk, hiding a particularly juicy bit of modern football slang.

Although we were so relaxed, we experienced parents, with no worries about the possible choices, there were lots of parents making endless notes, asking scores of questions. I met one dad, a bloke who used to play in our Sunday morning football team, who had two private schools on his list, plus four local comprehensives. Poor fellow. He's been at it almost full-time for weeks and will hardly have a spare moment between now and Christmas.

So we came home and tried to take it very seriously, compiling our own list. Do we go for ethos? Let's not. We can't even agree what the word means. Academic work? They both seemed the same. For attractiveness? One definitely has a much prettier setting, with enormous greenery, but are kids aware of such things? It's coming down to nearness in the end, and which one most of her friends from primary school will go to.

Which will suit *Flora* best? Oh God, that is hard. Having been through all those teenage traumas, I can't begin to imagine that Flora at eleven will be the same person at sixteen. Should we save her from herself, or encourage what we think is in her?

There was one thing to be said for the Eleven Plus. No arguments. That was it. The only thing wrong with parental choice is parental choosing. Pass the pin, Alice.

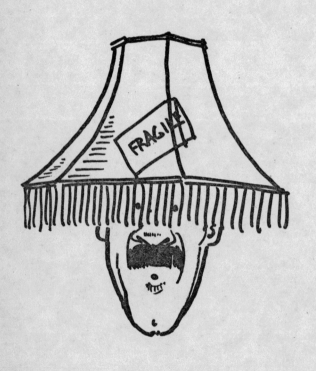

Flat Rates

We've been playing at students this week-end, not the glamorous bits like throwing eggs at walls and being sick out of windows, surely there must be people out there still doing that, but the more humdrum stuff like carrying endless plastic carriers full of old crockery, old clothes, pots and pans, books, broken lamps, stupid ornaments, silly notices, wondering where on earth all this junk came from, wondering where on earth it will go.

You've guessed. We've been helping Caitlin. All students seem to spend most of their time these days wandering around, trailing their bags and belongings, looking for some place to lie down. Caitlin has had two different dumps, I mean rooms, since she started her student life six months ago.

When I was a student, the state paid everything for me, being so poor, tra la, but it at least gave me freedom and some wealth. I have to pay all Caitlin's maintenance fees, and I'm not moaning, just stating a fact, so I've spent a lot of time trying to get back deposits from landlords. This time I decided to take on a short lease of a small unfurnished flat, which she is going to share with a girl friend.

As landlord, I suggested I would go down first and knock it into shape. Okay, I *insisted*. I don't think Caitlin wanted us anywhere near it, as our standards and styles are not her standards and styles, but me and the old trout and Flora decided we would go down on our own for the week-end and christen her new room. Gosh, what fun.

I had ordered a bed on the phone from Debenhams. I know, it was mad, the last thing Caitlin wanted was a new bed. She much prefers an old mattress on the floor or something found in a skip, but her mother and I, do note the royal we, wanted her at least to have a proper bed. Everything else could be second-hand. It was really me what did it. Even if I'm just sleeping there for the week-end, I want to be on a proper bed. Everyone else can sleep on the floor. When you get to my age, the old back needs as much support as it can get.

I slept on a bloke's sofa once, for six weeks, when I was young, back in the dark ages before Mr Ortho had invented his Paedic beds, and it was hellish. And as for camping with the Boy Scouts, sleeping on groundsheets, bloody hell, that was agony. I'm surprised I ever grew up to be 5' 10". OK, 5' 9½".

Rotten Debenhams wouldn't deliver it on Saturday, so I had to go straight to their store the minute we arrived in Brighton to pick it up, then get it in the car to Caitlin's flat and up two flights of stairs. And me with my dodgy knees. But I did it. She's a lucky girl, that Caitlin. All week-end we said that. Good job she didn't hear. She would have said the opposite.

Then we went to buy a second-hand chest of drawers. Yes, I know she would be quite happy hanging her clothes on the floor, as she normally does, but I wanted to get one bit of real furniture, before she fills the whole place with rubbish.

I fancied a pine chest of drawers and we eventually found one—at £300. Ridiculous. We have about four here in London, in each of the bedrooms, and they didn't cost more than £30 each. All right, I know, don't say it, this was twenty years ago.

There was no shortage of places to look as the staple industry of Brighton is antique shops, that's apart from those people running bijou French-style restaurants. In the end, we found a place selling cheap utility stuff, 1950s junk, all fairly nasty but all fairly cheap. I saw this chest of drawers marked £26 and offered the bloke £20 cash, take it or leave it, in my fast London way. 'No chance,' he said, even faster.

I then rose to £22, hard cash, and he said cash is nothing to me. I followed him to a backyard, where there was more stuff lying around, and he went mad, ordering me out. No one was allowed in that backyard. He had two terrified assistants who both looked at me, pityingly.

It was by now late on Saturday afternoon, our only day for shopping, so I was forced to pay what he was asking. My usual principle is that they will always take less. I asked him if I could leave it in his yard while I went and got the car. Parking is hell in Brighton. I have never been to a worser town. Even in the residential districts, you can't park. And the meter maids are fiends. It was going to be very awkward anyway, getting near his shop, as it was in a trafficless lane.

'Look,' he said, as I handed him the full amount, in cash, through clenched fingers, 'will you stop causing problems.'

My wife looked away. If I had been a man, not a London mouse, masquerading as a real man, I would have told him to piss off, keep your rotten chest of drawers. In the film version, I'd definitely do that. Probably even hit him as well. No one messes around with Big Hunt, not when it's me who's landed the job of writing the script.

But I was tired and fed up and hoping that my wife had not heard the full extent of his bad temper and rudeness. So I slunk off, humping the stupid chest myself. Oh, she's a lucky girl, that Caitlin.

Back in the flat, I had to stop my wife rushing around and doing her Mrs Tittlemouse tricks. There were at least ten other vital jobs to be done, but she had thrown herself at the kitchen wall and pulled off sixty-two brown vinyl tiles. They were doing no one any harm. Caitlin might have loved them, by the very fact of being so gross.

All week-end I had to stop her rearranging things. She even tried to get me to move the kitchen, the actual sink unit, because it offended her. She was longing to take over and do it her way. She's so lucky, that Caitlin. Wish we all had a new flat to play with.

We then had to go round Brighton collecting bits of

Caitlin's stuff which she had left in various people's flats and rooms. We were horrified by one place in Kemptown, the supposedly posh part, so it looked from the outside, though I think every street in Brighton looks interesting. She's so lucky, etc, imagine having three years in such, etc.

Anyway, we had to go into this communal kitchen to try and find some of her plates, such as those rather nice blue ones her dear mother had given her last term, and that non-stick pan I had bought in a sale at Christmas, but we had to give up in the end. Every utensil in this kitchen was covered in congealed food. Some of the mould must have dated back to Alexander Fleming.

We met another couple of parents in the house, bringing food parcels for their precious offspring, and we had a good moan together, oh you know, you bring them up the right way, give them bedtime stories about Brillo Pads, introduce them to Squeezy at an early age, tell them inspiring stories about Mr Hoover's inventions, point out that that funny thing is called a tap, turn it on and you'll be quite surprised, but why bother, life is too short.

But we did get Caitlin's new room into some sort of order, all the bags and bits of furniture gathered and arranged, and we settled down for the evening, we three in Hippodrome, not working for the BBC. Do you remember that radio show? I thought I hadn't. God, it must have been forty years ago. I'm far too young to remember it.

That evening was the strangest part of the week-end. These days, in our middle-class, middle-aged, London home, we have space, room to live and breathe, which is what social scientists say we all need. I can always escape to my own work room or the upstairs sitting-room.

But in Caitlin's one room there was Flora watching TV and playing her Michael Jackson tapes, my wife trying to read, and I was trying to get *Sports Report* on a bashed-up radio. We had a meal, sat around, chatted, then we all went to bed, all in the same room. Yes, I know it's how most of the world lives. It's how I used to live, in my childhood. Doing homework at the dining-table with

142

ITMA on and the clothes drying in front of the fire and people shouting at each other to close the door.

Perhaps I don't want to be a student again after all. I couldn't put up with living such an inconvenient, communal, one-room life. We're so lucky, we parents of Caitlin's.

All Party Risk

Jake is eighteen tomorrow. What on earth am I going to get him. He went off to school this morning quite unperturbed about my worries, smiling to himself, the way they do at that age, and then he came straight back again. School's closed. He'd forgotten.

For the third day this week all our local schools have been on strike, which means that Jake and Flora have been at home. What are they playing at, these teachers. I've managed to struggle on somehow with the miners' strike, closing my eyes and hoping it will never affect me, but the teachers' strike has got me where it hurts. Hunt, so she shouts from downstairs, I'm working, so if Flora wants anything, *you* will have to be in charge. As if I haven't enough problems.

Yes, it is true that for eighteen years I have known that Jake would be eighteen tomorrow, so I should have prepared myself. But you know what happens, things crop up, decades come along, dramas intervene, taps need new washers, and you suddenly wake up and blow me, it's tomorrow.

All I've got for him so far is a balloon which says Eighteen Today. Yes, I do spoil them.

I happened to be passing this shop in Hampstead when I saw these balloons, so I rushed in, thinking that will give me something, bound to be cheap, I mean how amusing. They had them with all the years up to Twenty-One Today. But that was all. I also wanted to buy one which said Forty-Six Today, but they didn't have any. Sorry, we only go up to Twenty-One. What a swiz.

I wanted a balloon saying Forty-Six Today because that will be my wife's age, the day after tomorrow. I know. Haven't I been lumbered. Every year I have Jake's birthday to agonise over, followed the next day by my wife's. You would have thought they could have talked things over and spread things out a bit.

Tomorrow, I can think about tomorrow's concerns. Today, I'll just concentrate my mind on Jake. Now, would he like one of my old suits? Would *anyone* like one of my old suits? Hmm. That didn't get me very far.

Flora has just come into my room. My wife has at least done the decent thing and organised a morning's activity for Flora. She does have good ideas, my wife. Wish I had good ideas, apart from that balloon. She had suggested that Flora and her friend Sarah make our lunch today, all on their own, thinking of the menu, shopping, cooking and serving it. They are having the run of the kitchen and have got to come to me for the money, once they have decided on the menu.

It looks like a £10 job, judging by their shopping list. Double Cream, Basil, Bacon, Four Oranges, Ice Cream, Tuna Fish. What on earth can they be making. By the way Flora, I said as she left, clutching the tenner, when you're in George the Greek's see if there's anything for Jake, you know, my petal, for his birthday, about a fiver, I dunno, no, not pittas, he is eighteen.

I can't remember my eighteenth birthday, I must have been there, but in those days eighteen didn't seem to matter. Most of us were still at primary school at that age, at least mentally. Flora is so grown up at eleven I honestly do think, now and again, when Jake is chuntering on about A-levels, that she must hurry and get her UCCA forms filled in, or has she already sent them off?

I do remember being twenty-one. I had a do, a little intimate dinner party at the Central Hotel, Carlisle. I'm sure they still talk about it. I invited six friends, including my wife, then my best friend, she still is, I'll rephrase that later. I haven't got time to worry about such things with Jake's birthday looming.

Anyway, I paid for this little dinner party, all by myself, having saved up the money from my holiday job as a bus conductor on the Ribble, but throughout the whole meal I was in a panic that I wouldn't have enough to pay for it. I also wore a bow tie. God, that just came back to me. I've never worn a bow tie from that day to this.

Jake has been going to eighteenth birthday parties for months, some of them very grand, but when we suggested one for him, he said no fanks. Oh Jake, you've been going to all these parties, taking all this hospitality, especially from all those lovely girls and their parents, why don't you let your mummy organise something rather nice for you, hmm, knife and fork, tablecloth, four courses, the full treatment, Hunt can buttle, Flora can be a waitress? Get lost.

Jake has not had a birthday party since he was nine. Isn't it strange. Caitlin had one every year of her school life, and Flora has so far. Is it a female thing? Come on, don't tell me girls have simply been brainwashed all these years, conditioned into loving parties.

Since he was nine, Jake has always refused parties, though his nine-year-old party was pretty momentous. Jake's body was so convulsed and his face was so scarlet we were sure he was a gonner.

He is talking at present, but only talking mind you, nothing is settled, about having a joint party after A-levels with two other people from his class, but not in this house. I am quite relieved. He estimates if he did have a party, and he's not promising, then he couldn't invite under eighty people, so they're thinking of hiring a local hall. I did pick up the phone yesterday and a voice said bouncers, what about bouncers, do you want any, but I hung up, not wanting to eavesdrop on Jake's private calls. You never know what you might hear.

That will give him something to look forward to after A-levels. Have you noticed the weather improving. Once those Os and As start, then it will be heat-wave time. You mark my words.

I could buy him a watch. That would be useful in his exams. You're supposed to buy long-lasting presents for important birthdays. Jake goes through life watchless, just like my wife. I don't know how they can manage. It's like going around half-naked. Caitlin doesn't wear a watch either. What foony people.

A ring? God, no. I am a ringless person. I don't want to encourage that sort of thing. It will be monogrammed hankies next. Perhaps a season ticket for Spurs for next year? We don't know what he'll be doing or where he'll be next year. Nor Spurs. They could get demoted. He has been talking about a motor-bike, or a scooter thing, but I'm not encouraging that either. He can buy his own. He's very rich, as he's saved up all his earnings from his Saturday job.

I could get him a few shares, an interesting speculation, or some premium bonds, but it's a bit soft, giving money or financial presents on birthdays. My wife would never forgive me. She believes birthday presents should be carefully thought out to suit the person. People who give money, so she says, are pathetic, showing no imagination. Caitlin went through her teens saying money, money, that's all I want, but she had to smile and say, thank you Mummy for the very thoughtful present.

I can hear Flora in the kitchen now. The smells are good. I bet she hasn't opened the window and the whole room will be steamed up. I hope she doesn't want any help. I gave up cooking after I had mastered toast. There was somehow no challenge any more.

I've got it. When they've done the lunch, I'll send Flora back to the shop to get stuff to make Jake a special birthday cake. I dunno what stuff. Stuff you make cake with. That will keep Flora and Sarah occupied this afternoon as well.

So that's not bad, a birthday cake *and* a special balloon. I'm quite looking forward to tomorrow. Yes I know my two little offerings will not be much, but what I'm really looking forward to is finding out what my wife has bought me to give Jake. It's bound to be something good and imaginative and just what he's wanted, and I'll smile smugly, having been so clever.

She's done that for eighteen years, why change the system now. We all know that women love birthdays.

Driving Ambition

I'm teaching Flora to drive. What kept her, I hear you say. She's already eleven years old, surely she can drive by now. Very funny.

No, really, she is seriously learning to drive and I am teaching her. It began about a year ago, on holiday in the Lake District, when she asked to take the controls up this little private lonning, or path I suppose you'd call it, for those people who've never been north of Kendal.

I have an automatic car, a Ford Granada, so it's quite easy to drive. If I can manage it, anybody can manage it. Well, nearly anybody. My wife is a non-driving person. I did try to teach her, about ten years ago, but we had words and she got out of the car rather suddenly. It was moving at the time, and she was supposed to be in control, but she just opened the door, swore at me, and got out, leaving me to stop it running into a river.

I have a friend who was teaching his wife to drive and they came to this big roundabout and she said which way, left or right, and he said straight on. So straight on she went, up the kerb and straight over the Corporation's prize flower garden. Moral, learn the language before you learn the driving.

I had vowed to teach nobody nothing no more, neither my wife nor the children. All you get is abuse or calluses on your knuckles. God, the years I spent running behind Caitlin when she was learning to ride a bike, holding on to the back of the seat to stop her falling off, while she screamed and said don't leave go, don't leave go. There's nothing more awkward than running behind a bike, trying to hold on to it. I bet that's how my dodgy knees started. Sorry, just slipped out. Yup, feeling very fit today, thanks for asking.

But Flora and I haven't fallen out yet. She does what she's told. No teacher can ask for more than that, but I suppose at eleven most kids are fairly biddable. She's just so thrilled to sit behind a driving wheel that she's content to let me boss her around. My wife could learn a lot from Flora.

Caitlin always was willing, and would grit her teeth and try hard, even when it was something for which she had no natural ability. I'm talking about the Child Caitlin, up to, say, the age of fourteen. After that, well, things were never the same again. You know what it's like with teenagers. Can't tell them anything. But when she was young my wife taught her to swim and she practised hard and had a trific style. It's my wife's only accomplishment of that sort, swimming, and there's a legend in the family that she once swam for Cumberland and Westmorland. I wonder if she ever got there.

Jake was always hell and would refuse any help or tuition or even advice. He *looked* like a swimmer, which he believed was enough, so he'd throw himself in and wildly wave his arms about. Never got anywhere, except into a frenzy. Now it's too late, of course. He just thrashes about in the water. There you are Jake, if only you'd listened to your Mummy and Daddy, or gone to those lessons when we told you, you could have been huge by now. Don't care, so he says. Anyway, I'm going to be a cyclist.

He wears a racing cyclist's shirt, to which he is devoted, and we hate the sight of it, but that's about all. I don't think he's been on his old push-bike for months now, but when people ask him what he's going to do in life, he still says a professional cyclist. 'After my A-levels,' he says, 'I'm shaving my legs.'

This has him convulsed. Listen, son. I make the jokes in this house. Perhaps it's not a joke.

He was worst of all when learning to read. He was convinced he didn't have to be taught that either. Caitlin and Flora were so keen and eager and willing to learn. It was me that used to tire first, well no wonder, having to listen to them struggling through that stupid *Janet and John*. I suppose they must be grandparents by now, old Janet and John. Modern primaries probably use computers or videos for all teaching.

In the end, we discovered an excellent way of teaching Jake to read. I pass it on for what it's worth. You might use it some time. It's called Hitting Them. Have you tried that? Just a clip round the ear'ole when they say 'sboring, I don't want to read no book. It did work with Jake, I used to bash him on the head with his reading book till he got to the end of the page. I'm amazed he ever grew as tall as he is, but it did work. That'll be ten guineas.

Now look at him, reading *and* writing and joined up handwriting, after a fashion. He's halfway through his A-levels, as I write. I think it's History tomorrow.

Over supper this evening we were talking round the table, as one does, about the origins of the First World War, driving Flora mad. For four years, all she has had to listen to at meal times is talk about O- and A-levels. Poor lass. No wonder she takes her escape by driving my Granada. She deserves it.

Anyway, Jake was talking about Archduke Ferdinand and Flora asked him who he was. Jake explained he was Heir to the Phone of this little country. Flora thought he said that, I was sure he said that, and so was my wife. All our children speak with what we consider to be Cockney accents, and you know how all Londoners strangle the Queen's English, while we speak of course with perfect Northern pronunciation. We are always accusing Jake of saying Fink and Fanks, but Heir to the Phone, that was the best he's ever come out with. Must have been a small country, said Flora, if he was Heir to the Phone. Jake refused to explain any further, if we were just going to mock.

How about Railways then, I said, I'll ask you some question on Railways, that's bound to come up in your Nineteenth-Century English paper. I started my set lecture on what a wonderful genius George Stephenson was, but he wouldn't listen.

'They won't ask *that*.' It's about all Jake ever says, if you even attempt to tell him anything you happen to know a little something about. Me and the Old Wrinkly have been on this planet a lot longer than him and we both did History at University, OK it was a long time ago and OK there was a lot less history to learn in those days, but we do pride ourselves on having picked up a few tit-bits which we are perfectly willing to pass on. But does he want to hear, does he heckers.

I don't know how these sporting children manage, the ones who get taught by their parents, such as Sebastian Coe and Sharron Davies. How did they survive all the rows and temper tantrums, the laziness and contrariness. Hitting them, perhaps. Get in that water, back on the track, or I'll thump you again with this rolled up, soggy copy of *Janet and John*.

But Flora is coming on a treat. She can even do three-point turns. I have high hopes she could make Le Mans. Over this last year she's done ever so well, on this private lonning, but at half term in the Lake District I decided to show her off to her grandad, Arthur, who is aged eighty-four this year.

It came out in passing that I was teaching Flora to drive, and we thought he would be against it. He's a funny bloke. You can never anticipate what will make him shake his head and go tut tut, you shouldn't allow that, ooof. He went tut tut when we allowed Caitlin to go to Geneva with her friends at fourteen, yet encouraged her to dye her hair purple.

He was shocked when he heard Flora had climbed Helvellyn at the age of six ('very bad for the heart') but he approved of her having her ears pierced at seven.

But he laughed aloud at the idea of me teaching Flora to drive and said yes, he'd love to see it, so we drove miles across Cumberland to a disused aerodrome at Kirkbride, a place we remembered from our childhood. It was still disused, but it took me some time to find a gate in to it. It was obviously now owned by a local farmer. I eventually found a way in and it was trific. For the first time, Flora had a proper track to drive on, for over half a mile, instead of the little bumpy lonning. I sat at the back while Arthur sat beside her, urging her to go faster.

It was my wife who didn't think it was at all amusing. We'll get into trouble, she said, if the police catch us and anyway it's obviously someone's land. Don't be silly, woman, I said. When we finally drove out of the old aerodrome, with Flora and Arthur beaming, we found the gate closed and the farmer's wife standing there, arms crossed. I thought about blaming Arthur, hoping they might let an OAP off with a light sentence.

The best method of defence when you are caught in this situation is simple: grovel. So I jumped out and ran up to her and poured out endless apologies, terribly sorry, up visiting from the South, strangers round here, thought it would be OK. Her arms were in fact holding a paint brush and pot as she had arrived to put a quick coat of paint on the gate. She was absolutely charming. No bother. Don't worry. But she warned us to be careful, if we ever do it again. A plane could have landed on us. Turns out a local flying club is now using the airfield.

So that's the next thing. In the summer hols, I plan to teach Flora to do stunt driving. Catch them when they're young, I always say.

On the Levels

We came back from holiday specially early for Jake's A-level results, to be there at that fateful moment which would decide his future, ready to hold his hand and pick up the broken furniture, or be over the moon and open the bottle of Waitrose champagne I have been saving secretly all year.

Most of all, it was vital to be there with him in case his grades were not up to scratch and there would be a mad rush to ring UCCA and UNCLE and any other set of initials which might help him to get a university place.

So we rushed down the M6 on the Wednesday, to be with him on Thursday morning, well in time to open the dreaded envelope. Guess what. Jake wasn't there. The bugger. And we could have had another two days in the Lakes.

Oh yes, he had got back to London OK from his round Europe rail jaunt, goodness the tales to tell, but now there was a note saying he had gone sailing with two friends, somewhere on the south coast, and would be back on Friday. DON'T OPEN THE ENVELOPE, so his note said. Nor had we to go to school and try and find out his results. I dunno. I've been his Dad for eighteen years. That's all you get.

We had arranged the whole summer round being here in the flesh, to be present for the family's last GCEs, well, of the old sort. It will be another five years before Flora's time will come, as she's only eleven, but by then the system will have changed. They're just going to test you on pop song titles and hair-styles in future. Honest. Someone told Flora.

Luckily, I had enough to occupy my mind with when we arrived back on Wednesday. What am I saying. Bloody unlucky. Four weeks away, and the world had collapsed.

Some idiot had over-wound the kitchen clock, when for years I have made it clear that it's a hanging offence for anyone, repeat anyone, and that means any of your boyfriends, Caitlin, even to breathe on that clock. It is so temperamental that if you look at it twice it curls up and stops.

Then the sitting-room ceiling. We have closed our eyes to the cracks for the last ten years, but in just four weeks they had become chasms.

Then, even worser, the rotten washing-machine door wouldn't close. We brought back enough dirty clothes to supply a school jumble, or Caitlin's flat. It's an AEG and we have had it ten years. Oft, of an evening, when things were slack, time hanging loose, we have mused on what single modern invention could one *not* do without. My wife has always said, quick as a flash, her washing-machine.

Her life could go on without the fridge, certainly without the dishwasher, and definitely without the telephone. I have usually hawed and hummed and said the car, I could survive without the car as I hate cars and loathe driving, but I would quite miss the phone. My vintage Olympia electric typewriter, that's what I would miss most. And the radio. All good harmless conversations round the cocoa. You can keep your late-night movies and videos.

I went to bed in a lather. It's always like this, coming home after the summer hols, but this time seemed worse than normal. Oh no. Don't say it's a sign! Would Jake's A-level results be the next thing to go wrong? Or was all the bad luck now over.

There was no letter next morning, which was just as well. In my mind, I had already been working out if my best magnifying glass would work on it, the one I use for my stamps, though not too often as all it does is show me just how many thins there are in my cheap Penny Blacks. Mrs Davies is very good at steaming open envelopes and then sticking them down again, only took years of practice, but Jake would suspect. He always does.

We then discussed, for the millionth time, his possible grades. He had accepted two conditional offers, which is what everyone does, but they did seem rather high. For his first choice University, to read Modern History, he had to get an A and two Bs, plus a pass at S-level, though Jake's comprehensive is not normally organised for S-levels. For his second choice, to read History and Politics, a course he was coming round to thinking sounded much better anyway, he needed only one B and two Cs. Surely that would not be beyond him?

We had begun to think so, till the lousy *Guardian* did that story about the fact that only 3 per cent can separate an A from a C grade. All the country's A-level students must have had absolute panics on reading that. What a lottery, these exams, what a con, why do we all put up with them. Then another newspaper, *The Sunday Times* I think, said that this year half the students would fail to get the grades needed for their conditional offer. I wonder if AEG need some young, trainee engineers, with reasonable O-levels?

And once again we discussed the interview he had had for his first choice place. He had refused point blank to wear a collar and tie. It would be false, Hunt, it wouldn't be me, I never wear them fings. He also insisted on going off carrying his bits in his Waitrose plastic carrier bag, the one he takes to school, like all the smartest sixth formers.

Yes, the obvious thing happened. The tutor bloke interviewing him asked what he had in his plastic bag. So out came a worn copy of *Asterix*, a copy of *Cycling News* and a history book, thank Gawd for that.

I suppose these tutor people do get desperate for something to ask the nation's youths. At one of Caitlin's university interviews, the bloke was fascinated by the number of bracelets she had on her right arm and wouldn't stop asking about them. All these taxes I have paid all these years to keep these university johnnies going, and that's all they can think of to talk about. From memory, let me see, she had thirty bracelets on that day. OK, even you might have commented.

About midday on Thursday the phone rang and it was a friend of Jake's, bubbling over, full of himself, anxious to talk to Jake. He had been to school, seen his own results

157

on the board, and was dying to discuss them with Jake. On the board? Jake had assured us no one would hear till the envelopes came on Friday morning, if not later. What the hell is going on? Where is he anyway?

Then another friend rang, who had also seen her results. Each time I managed not to let them tell me what Jake had got, but very soon the whole area would know.

I studied Jake's scrawled note he had left. No clue about where he had gone sailing. No address, phone number. Not even the town. Just the south coast. What a dum-dum.

After a third person had rung, I decided to have a little walk, perhaps near Jake's school, as it's only four minutes away and I have to pass it to get onto the Heath. My wife said no. Flora said don't. Jake had told you *not* to look. It's *his* results, not yours. He should know first.

I went off, making no promises, but honestly, Jake, I couldn't help it. Just as I was passing the school, a girl came out and told me what he had got. I didn't believe it. I had to go into the school and look at the board for myself. Didn't I. Stands to reason.

Dear God. The scenes of human emotion. It brought it right back, all those years at school and university when I strained my eyes each year to see what marks or grades those half-wits had given me, unable even to see them at first, or even find my own name for the tremors throughout my body.

I could hardly bear to see all those nice young eighteen-year-olds standing there shaking. As the newspapers had predicted, half were utterly shattered, many in tears, many frozen to the spot, numb and unable to take it all in. While the other half were immediately elated, struck by instant joy, tremulous with pleasure. Why do they have to go through all that. Either way, the ridiculous flow of adrenalin is unsupportable. I am surprised there were not any heart attacks, though there was a great deal of swearing and shouting and people rushing off in a blind fury, their whole life apparently ruined by a few dots on a large sheet of print-out.

Later that night, Jake rang, off-hand to tell us he would

be back sometime Friday morning, muttering something about having ruined someone's yacht. We let Flora tell him the news. We had decided that someone else would be bound to tell him his results before we did.

Jake got his grades. Even more than he needed, managing two As and a B, plus two S-level passes. What a relief, but was it worth it to see the misery of so many of his friends?

I like to think I deserve a bit of the credit. Oh come on. All those years when he could hardly speak, least not so's anyone could understand him properly, when he jumped on tables and was a monster and wrecked every occasion and ruined our night life for so long and bashed the hell out of the furniture, who was it who got him interested in Spurs? Oh yes, it was his collecting programmes and sitting for hours analysing their league tables that made us realise he might find an interest in life apart from shouting and screaming.

So, that's it till 1989, when Flora will be sitting her first public exams. Of some sort. By then, I hope to have got the washing-machine working and the ceiling done . . .

Up to the Back Teeth

Jake has been in hospital this week. Yes, McLaglan Ward in the Royal Free Hospital, Hampstead, London, England, has had the pleasure of his company. Lucky people. Not often they get such distinguished scholars.

Nothing very serious, of course, though I had better not say that too loud as he thinks it was a major operation which he took terribly seriously, even if some of his friends did not. He made some dopey young medic write down every little detail of his medical history when they came round with the forms.

Turns out Jake has got a v. serious history of diarrhoea, which was news to us. He had the runs in Europe this summer for five days, so you see, Hunt, I had to tell them. Then he insisted on telling them about the v. bad asthma I had as a child. It all counts, Hunt.

He has been having three wisdom-teeth out, a painful enough thing, as anyone who has had it knows, but one which he was able to save up for a relatively convenient time. At this very moment the country's dental wards are probably full of teenagers having them out, now that all their O-levels and A-levels are safely over.

Mrs Davies has also not been 100 per cent this week, cos of her ear. Got it bunged up with showing off her brilliant breast-stroke at the very posh Luz Bay Club in the Algarve. It was probably the sea water which did it. Anyway, she has been deaf in one ear since we came home, so this week I spent a fortune at the chemist's and bought her some drops. I've quite enjoyed putting them in. I could have been a surgeon. People have said I have the fingers.

161

Despite her sore ear, she spent a whole morning this week writing out a long list of the virtues which a good headmistress needs. It is Flora's first week at her comprehensive and it so happens they've got a new headmistress as well. She has asked for views on what makes a good headmistress, so my wife, in her caring way, got out her best fountain-pen and quickly itemised twelve desirable things. Oh, you know, a headmistress must be inspirational, discreet, humane, fair, calm, principled, all the usual guff. On my list, I said that the only rule for a Good Headmistress is that she must be nice to Flora, but my wife wouldn't let me send it in.

She went off and posted her list, which was really daft, as the school's only four minutes away, and have you seen the price of a second-class stamp now. She happened to mention what she'd done when Flora came home from school—and Flora went wild. It was only the *girls* in her class who had been asked for suggestions. Not parents. My wife had completely misunderstood.

Oh God, we'll have a really rotten name now, won't we, Flora's only been there a week, but we'll be marked down as interfering parents with you sending off your bossy rules for being a Good Headmistress, unsolicited and out of the blue. Real mess you've made of things. What will she think when it suddenly comes through the post.

She quickly wrote an apology and I ran round with it by hand. As second-class post takes about a week, we should be OK. She blames it all on her deaf ear.

I'm fit and well, by the way, thanks for asking. Rather surprising. Counted everything and, at this moment in time, no complaints, squire. Not that I have time to worry about myself, what with ear-aches and the boy scholar's operation on his jaw.

We rang the hospital on Monday morning at midday and a nurse told us he'd had the operation and was fine, fine, in fact he was up and walking about, so we strolled across the Heath feeling very pleased. No matter how simple an operation is, it can also go wrong. Did I tell you about the time I ended up with a thrombosis when all they were doing was taking out a cartilage? Oh, sorry. I forgot.

He looked absolutely terrible, lying there as if he'd been run over. His face was all swollen and he couldn't speak because of swabs in his mouth. He was spitting blood and moaning that his chest and mouth were in agony. My wife made an excuse and left. She went to the lavatory where she promptly fainted.

Now, it was a very hot day, close and humid, and she has got a poorly ear, but even so, it did seem a little bit excessive.

So I told Jake about our honeymoon. This was in Sardinia in 1960 and I developed a boil on my bottom. Very common on honeymoons, ask anyone. The hotel called a doctor who arrived and got me on the bed. She was an Amazon of a woman and she proceeded to pummel the boil, saying all modern drugs and injections were a waste of time. My wife watched for only a few moments, then there was a crash— and she had fainted on the floor. The doctor left her there. When she came to, the doctor simply said, 'Un peu de courage, madame.'

Ah well, that's the role of men in life, Jake, I said. We bear all the pain and the women pass out. But he was in no mood for philosophy. Two of his friends arrived at that moment, a girl and boy, calling "Jakey-poo" and even daring to smile when he asked for a pen to write down things as he couldn't talk.

He did eventually manage to grunt a few words and told them the only good thing had been the Pre-med, that was really good, you felt terrific, they should try it some time. 'Why do they give you cold eggs, Jakey?' asked the girl.

That was when things got a bit complicated. Gawd knows how you can miss-hear Pre-med for Cold Egg. As Jake was in agony with his mouth, it took ages to explain, by which time everyone was shrieking, and the sister said we were all making too much noise and should go soon.

Later that evening, I went over on my own and took him Flora's Walkman, which she had kindly agreed to lend him, and her best tape, her Bob Marley.

He seemed physically in better shape, and could talk more

easily, but he was very miserable, having read *Cancer Ward* the night before, waiting for his Pre-med, and he was now thinking of all the really ill people in hospital. I gave him a bottle of Sagres beer and a Sumol, saved from Portugal, just to cheer him up, but he pointed very gravely to a notice above his head. Nil by Mouth. Stupid Hunt.

Jake has always like proper attention when he has been ill, even as a little boy—attention in the sense that he likes due concern from one and all, an audience if nothing else, to hear his latest reports on himself or, if half an hour has passed with nothing new to report, then someone to take his temperature.

Caitlin was always much more stoic when she was young, going off and being very silent, staying quietly in bed, making no demands. But once she began to get slightly better, then she was suddenly up and off, refusing to be sensible or be cossetted any more, deciding to get up straight from her sick-bed and trail to some party miles away.

Jake came out of hospital today, and he appears to be enjoying doing everything by the book. He had arranged to play golf later this week, at least have a go at it for the first time with some friends, but my wife said was it sensible, Jake, just two days out of hospital? He thought hard and said you're right, perhaps I won't. What a sensible lad.

But he is now taking things a bit far. He says he won't have any casserole at dinner tonight, all because he saw my wife putting a spoonful of wine in it. Bad for me, Mum. The doctor said no alcohol while I'm on penicillin. So she threw something at him.

Flora likes treats rather than an audience when she is ill. If I can bring her a Marathon or a Slush Puppy on the hour, then she gets better very quickly. Touch wood, she's had nothing too serious, apart from all the usual childhood stuff. Oh, there was that pneumonia in America in Bicentennial year. What a way to celebrate. She now rather likes to boast about it.

Jake once did have an emergency dash when an abscess suddenly burst on his bottom when he was about ten. For months he had been complaining, wanting to show us where it hurt, and we all said oh shut up Jake, go away, not at the dinner table, we don't want to see it, thinking it was yet another trivial spot. In my mind he spent the whole of his childhood with a sore bum. But after that emergency rush to hospital, he has never let us forget our cruelty.

So how's the old jaw, Jake, getting better all the time, hmm? He was just about to give me a blow-by-blow reply, when there was a knock at the front door. Two of his friends had sent round an enormous bunch of gladioli. How kind. He was very touched. I wanted to suggest it might be a joke, but I didn't dare.

He now wants me to make him a cup of coffee. I dunno. When you work at home, I sometimes think people take advantage of you. So I'll have to rush. In ten minutes it will be time to put another five drops in the old trout's ear.

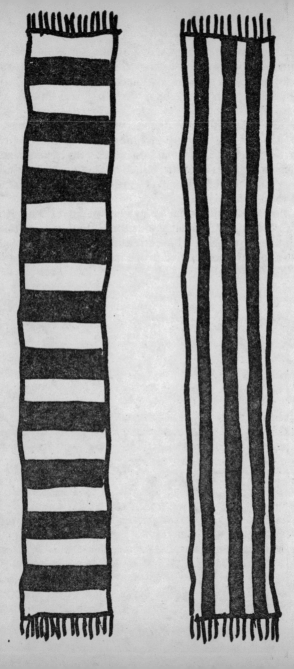

Dad and Daughter

I never feel autumn has really started till I go to Spurs for the first time in the new season. I always miss the first few matches, as we're away, but anyway who wants to watch football in August. The hooligans never look the same without shirts on.

The problem was who to take with me. Jake this week started a job and he has to work Saturdays. No consideration at all for my needs and pleasures. He's working full-time in a bookshop till he gets enough money to go abroad. It's his Year Off, don't you know, before University. Wish I could have a year off.

I tried several friends around the street, but John was in bed with his foot strapped up, just had an operation on his Achilles Tendon, and other excuses, and Derek was playing tennis. So should I go on my own? Now I'm grown up, or pretending to be, I should be able to cope. If I leave chalk marks on the ground, I can usually find my own way home.

I hung around the house all morning, wondering what I would decide to do. My lady wife says she always knows what I'll end up doing, when I'm apparently prostrate with indecision, but I never do. So often I surprise myself. By this evening, Hunt, I wonder if you'll have been?

I went out to talk to the tortoise, hoping for clues, some indication of what I should do, but there was no sign of him. Must be hiding already. Summer is a-comin' to an end. I picked up the last handful of rotten, squelchy pears. For twenty years, we've had this lovely pear tree in the back garden which looks marvellous for a few weeks in spring, then we pay for it all summer as the fruit turns overnight from rock hard to dead soft and we become a host nation for ten million wasps. Next stage, it will be the falling leaves. Yup, the nights are drawing in.

Arthur, my father-in-law, has been saying that the Nights Are Drawing In since June 21. You would have thought at 83¾ he would not be so keen to watch the seasons rushing past, but the weather gives him such pleasure. Living in Carlisle, you don't get too many excitements.

I watched the lunch-time football previews, as I always do, with my bottle of Guinness, but Mrs Davies had let me down completely and there wasn't a crisp in the whole house. I'm quite prepared to eat mouldy ones, which have been at the bottom of the cupboard for decades, but there was not a sausage, not a nibble.

There are poeple in football, half-wits like football league officials, who say that having football on television stops people coming to matches. What rot. It whets or is it wets the appetite. When I do watch on TV, I feel I'm already half there. Come on the lads.

So by sitting there, ah ha, that was a real clue. I must be verging towards going after all. Or was I? Gawd, the suspense.

I'd forgotten I'd said I might join my wife and Flora for lunch at Marine Ices, so when the programme finished, I went off to meet them. That was it. Driving in the complete opposite direction. A decision had been made.

They were surprised to see me, convinced I would have gone off on my own to the match. They'd had a rotten morning shopping. Oh, some stupid argument over shoes with Flora refusing all the sensible ones.

At two o'clock, I looked at my watch and said that's it then, folks, I am obviously not going. Two o'clock is always the deadline to get to Tottenham.

'I'll come with you,' said Flora.

Woosh. Why did I never think of it. What a sexist piglet. We tore home and Flora tore into her track-suit, to keep warm, and I tore into a bottle of duty-free whisky, to fill up my little hip-flask which had a funny, sour smell as I had obviously not cleaned it out since last season. Ah, all the memories came flooding back.

As usual, I spilled some whisky on the kitchen table as I tried to fill it in a hurry and I had to bend down and slurp it up with my tongue with Flora shouting oh do come on, Hunt, we'll be late. That was what Jake used to shout, every second Saturday from the age of eight till sixteen. Then he started his draggy old Saturday jobs.

We parked in the same Tottenham side street I have parked in since 1958. It's miles from the ground, but it means it's easier to get away. I used to play a game with Jake whereby we guessed what the gate would be, just by how much space I had to park the car. It was pretty tight, so I guessed 31,000. Flora, being a newcomer to all this intellectual stuff, was unable to hazard a guess.

We ran up the High Road, weaving in and out amongst the massed ranks of supporters, all of them still looking straight from a Lowry drawing. Jake, when he was a little boy, used to waddle along, as he was a bit f−t at one time, humming Tot-ing-ham, Tot-ing-ham. He could never get the right pronunciation. Ardilles at least had the excuse that he was a foreigner.

I bought Flora a scarf. Was it bribery? I always made Jake buy his own, all those years ago, but Flora is my last. You have to spoil them. I know she's only eleven, but I already feel at times that that's it. Heads down now till the grandchildren come. She chose a nasty one in vertical strips, give me the good old horizontal stripes at time. And it was £2. Bloodyhell. Then the programme was 50p. Remember when you could watch Carlisle United, have a hot pie and a Bovril, and still have change out of a packet of Woodbines.

A tout offered me two £7 seats for £10 each, but I declined, even though it was only five minutes to kick-off. I'm not that daft. I went to the Ticket Office, just in case, and got almost the last tickets in the family section, £5 for me and £2 for Flora. What a bargain. They've now got a computer thing with whirring machinery which prints the tickets and the girl working it was having trouble, but it eventually spat out two for us.

The seats were in the North Stand, so we had to run like

hell. She was red in the face with all the rushing. It'll be a rotten match now, I said to Flora, but hasn't it been exciting, just getting here.

I could see quite a few people glancing at us. It still is fairly unusual for a Dad and Daughter to go to football matches. I know many dads who would not take any children, boys or girls, under the age of sixteen, because of the crowd violence, which is a great shame. Flora of course is in her first year at Comprehensive now. Doesn't mean to say she'll have a better chance than anyone else, should we get mixed up in a fight, but at least the crowd language will not come as a surprise to her.

We got to our seats two minutes after the game had started, which was bad luck, but from then on, boy, or should I say girl, what a match. It was non-stop excitement and incident and cheering and applauding, that's if you happen to be a Spurs fan. We beat Queen's Park Rangers 5−0. By we, I mean me and Flora. You pays your money, so naturally you are allowed to take some of the credit. Come on you Lilly Whites.

Afterwards we raced to the car and got the radio on just in time for the familiar tune of *Sports Report*—and we heard some even more amazing news. No, not that Princess Di had had a baby boy, imagine breaking into serious things like football to tell us that, have they no sense of priorities. No, they announced that Arsenal got beat and Spurs were top of the League, if only on goal difference. Oh rapture.

You will be able to boast about this day for years, I told Flora, not just on Monday morning at school. Was it Young Kaspar who was told to remember a famous victory? Well, that was one. You are unlikely ever again to see Spurs win 5 nil in a League match.

What an old pessimist I've become, but I thought I'd better not overdo the excitement of that freak match. Wait till it's January and it's freezing cold and the team plays like a load of Wallies and gets beaten in the Cup by Darlington. What I really wanted to say was would you like to come to the next match, Flora, hmmm, my sweet, but I said nothing. Hoping she would.

My wife had baked a cake for our arrival home, not knowing the result, nor yet the boring old Royal baby news, which was all she really wanted to hear about. That used to be Flora's job, all those winters when me and Jake went together. Something nice in the oven for when the Men return.

So have I found a new friend for this new season? Am I to be given a new lease of life?

After tea, she said it had been trific, thank you for taking me, but nothing else yet. I'll have to wait and see. Just take each game as it comes, Brian. The crowd, by the way, was 31,655.

Italian Read

The phone rang at half-past eight this morning, which was rather unusual, it being a Saturday, Flora not going to school. When it rings at that time on a week day, then we know it must be for Flora. Is it dancing or PE today, Flos?

But Flora was still in bed, these twelve-year-old teenagers, so I picked the phone up, my mind miles away, thinking serious thoughts about muesli, should I try some or will I ruin my teeth and jaw for ever. We have home-made stuff, don't you know, but the old trout fills it with half logs and it sticks in the old toothypegs, yes they are still playing up something rotten. I've already stopped having crisps, peanuts and chewing gum, in an attempt to give my jaw as little work as possible, but it now looks as if I'll have to give up muesli. I will soon be reduced to sops at this rate.

'Meester Daveez? Theez eeez Eee-tal-ee calling.'

Then it went peep peep, followed by a lot of other funny noises, and the line seemed to go dead. I thought at first it must be some dopey foreign person ringing up about our advert in the local paper. We're looking for a granny sitter for my Mum, fat chance so far, but then no one seems to want to help oldies these days. All we've had so far is people fresh off the boat ringing up and not being able to say anything when they've got through.

Something about Eee-tal-ee, I said to my lady person in the kitchen, who was shouting at me to know who it was, which is what always happens when people are on the phone. We all shout at each other, saying what to say or what not to say. The person *not* answering is always so bloody clever at knowing exactly what should have been said.

It'll be Jake!

My wife had suddenly rushed through from the kitchen, oh if I don't watch her, she often does this, getting very forward these days.

I'd forgotten all about Jake. He has been away in Florence for three weeks now, studying at the British Institute on a four week course. I have written four long letters to him so far, great letters, full of family chat, plus every football result carefully cut out of the papers, and all we've had from him so far is one post-card. And that was 90 per cent full of the details of his journey getting there. As if we want to know that.

All Jake's journeys, even getting to school, have been dramas, so we knew that going on his own across Europe would turn out to be a saga. He had been given the wrong tickets by the travel agent, the stupid train times were not right, he didn't get a sleeper, nearly lost that, almost missed the other, yawn yawn.

All that me and his dear Mama have been wanting to know is what is it like in Florence. We've heard boring travel stories before. In fact, in my last letter I did him a Multiple Choice Questionnaire. To keep it simple, all he had to do was tick off one answer for each question, then return it, just to keep us happy. Jake always did like exams.

Your Landlady: Is she old/young/nice/not nice/just like your Mama?

Your Bedroom: Is it big/small/cold/hot/full of Italians?

Have you seen: Prince Charles and Lady Di/Sir Harold Acton/Graeme Souness/Rossi/the English Cemetery/nine o'clock in the morning/that old razor I left in the hotel when we were on holiday in Florence last year?

Your Fellow Guests: State their age/sex/home town/ class/school/character. Photos will gain extra marks.

In this one post-card we have received so far, he mentioned that there were five other English students in his lodgings, but with no clues to them whatsoever. Call me nosey if you will, but Dear God, I expect a bit more gen than that.

My wife looked worried. If it really was a call from Italy

at this time of the morning, perhaps it was because something was wrong with Jake. He'd fallen off his Vespa, if he'd bought his Vespa, which was one of his daft ideas before he went. It might be a hospital trying to get through. Or the police.

I picked up the phone again and went hello, hello, hello, as one does, while my wife screamed at me for having hung up. Shurrup, I said. What's the Italian for hello? I tried Ee-lo a few times, then suddenly Jake's voice came through, bright as a new-born button.

He was ever so excited, fair panting to tell me his news. He had got a job. And secondly, he probably wouldn't be home for another three months.

My wife was waving her tiny hands in the background, having heard the reference to three months, but not knowing the rest.

Jake had just come that moment from having an interview for a job in a big posh house in Florence, with massive grounds and a swimming pool. In exchange for four hours a day gardening, he is to get free accommodation. Gardening? Our Jakey? He wouldn't know a spade if he met one in his muesli.

The hours I've screamed at him, just to get him to cut the lawn, but I've always failed. I don't think he's ever killed a weed in his life, nor would he recognise one. I did manage to get him to move some paving stones last month, and they're still there, dumped at the precise spot where his mind wandered and any moment Jessica from next door is going to climb over the wall and do herself an injury. He doesn't even *know* what gardening is. He was reading this book not long ago and asked us this hard word he had come across: primrose. Imagine getting to eighteen and not knowing what a primrose is.

On the phone he explained that when he finishes his course in a week at the Institute, he'll then stay on as a gardener, though first of all he is going to Elba for the weekend. Elba? Yes, twenty of them are going to sleep on the beach. My Jakey? Sleep on the beach? What will his Mama think about that. She's already been twitting on about who is doing his washing and has he really taken enough clothes for four weeks and is he getting enough to eat.

Apparently, only one of my letters has got through so far. What a drag. After all my effort and that v. clever Questionnaire. The post is taking twelve days, so he said I needn't write again for the moment. I started to tell him about Spurs, but he said he knew. You can read the English papers that same day in Florence. Why did I bother.

I asked him about the five other students in his digs, and he said oh yeh, they're all girls, real Sloanes. Many of the girl-students just sit about drinking all day and hardly go to lessons. He said the Italian was coming on well, least he was quite good at understanding, but not the speaking. I said Italians have much the same trouble.

There was then a sort of clicking on the line, and I thought he was putting in more money, but he said no, it was Call Collect. You know, transfer charges, Hunt. Hadn't I understood that when the operator had come through in the first place? It would probably cost £10 a minute. Bloody hell. That's a fortune. Sorry about that, he said, then he started to tell me about his journey to Florence, and I shut him up at once. Probably hurt his feelings. At that price, I'm willing to take the chance.

I didn't spend too long chatting after that, but arranged that his Mama would ring him next Friday, direct at his digs, and he could give us the address of this Palazzo he's going to move into. Then I hung up.

I went over all the details, so nice to have an audience hanging on one's words, but all his Mama wanted to know about was this posh family he's going to live with. I said the woman of the house had just interviewed him that morning. I think he said the husband was French, or something. She looked rather worried. Look dear, you've read too many novels about sensitive young English boys being taken up by mysterious Italian contessas. He is eighteen. Nineteen next month. Oh no, we'll now miss his birthday, what a shame.

When Flora came down to breakfast, I said heh up, have you heard the news about Jake.

He's getting married? It was such a quick reply, and the old trout for a moment looked so startled, that I laughed till my jaw started aching again. He's obviously having a trific time, I said, must be loving Florence, if he's thinking about staying another three months, and hadn't he shown enterprise, getting himself fixed up with a job.

You jealous? That was Flora again. Probably true. Can I be jealous of my own son? I never had a year off before University. He's having such fun in his, doing exciting, exotic things. My pre-University holiday job was stacking wood in a timber yard in Carlisle. Oh yes, very cultural.

This woman who's hired him, surely you can remember other things he told you?

Listen dear, when you ring him on Friday, *you* can cross examine him this time. And ask them if they need an assistant gardener out there. I know someone who could do with the break.

Red Letter Day

Flora is burning her homework. No, it's not a ritual act, the children's liberation movement making a public gesture of their contempt for the work ethic. She's simply burning the work she's just completed. That's what Miss said they might do. When you've finished, try putting it in some flames.

I dunno. All seems potty to me. Mark my words, Flora. It will all end in tears. Both sorts. Your homework will be in shreds, if it survives the flames, then you'll start crying.

Keep out of it you, she replied. You're no help at all when it comes to homework, so just shurrup, eh.

What she's been doing, for this last hour, is writing a letter from Jane Eyre to Mr Rochester. Are you with me. Do concentrate. Well, when you're a first-year at comprehensive, you dive straight into the classics, none of this *Janet and John* or *Just William* juvenile stuff. Bring on the greats. The whole class of twelve-year-olds, apparently, has been loving *Jane Eyre*. Not the book, stupid, They watch it on the video. Charlotte Brontë would be surprised. (Or was it Emily? I always get them mixed up. I daren't say it out loud or Flora will scream at me. She thinks I'm a dum-dum anyway.)

Flora has written a lovely letter. I know because I sneaked a look at it when she was out of the room, very neat, dated 1826, which she says is the year the book took place, and who am I to argue. She did ask about how you would finish a letter, back in 1826, either See You Soon, Love Jane, or would it be Cheerio for Now? My wife suggested making it very simple, signing it just from Your Dear Friend, Jane

Eyre. I didn't suggest anything. I just get shouted at if I suggest anything in this house.

The object is to get the style right, for 1826, and the sentiments between Jane and Mr Rochester right, and then, wait for it, this is the bit she has looked forward to most, they have to try to make the paper on which the letter is written look as old as possible. Crease it a bid, add a few stains, and then perhaps, so the teacher suggested, discolour the edges by putting it in flames. What a daft thing to suggest. I think some of these teachers need shottin'.

We don't have no flames in our house, being CH, although at week-ends we do have our illegal little log fire upstairs, just for me and the old trout, a pick-me-up after the put-me-downs of the week, a treat for good behaviour, and every Saturday evening we sit before it with our drinkiepoos, watching each other carefully, no, none of that soppy stuff, just to make sure the other does not take more than the fair share of the Fleurie. That's my new passion. I buy it for the name. Reminds me of Flora. But at that price we drink only one bottle a week.

There is no fire on yet, that comes later this evening, and Flora naturally can't wait, which is why she's standing in the kitchen holding her beautifully written letter over the gas stove. I'm not allowed to interfere. But I know at any moment the whole lot will go up in flames.

For once, it is the sort of homework I could help with, we literary folk, but she wants to do it all by her own. That was a Jake phrase. 'All by my own.' She is just like Jake with her homework. She will insist on doing it in the living-room, right amongst all the noise, with the telly going, my lady wife in the kitchen, Grandma wandering up and down reciting Burns.

Flora has got her own perfectly nice bedroom upstairs, room enough and more for her homework, with a desk and a lamp, utter peace and tranquillity, with no one to disturb her, but will she go there, will she heckers. We spent years shouting at Jake to go up to his own room to do his homework, but he never would, not till he was fifth-year. I suppose he thought he was missing something. Can't think what. We all know Grandma's recitations by now.

'Do you know any poetry, Flora?' She says that every five minutes, ever so brightly, with no knowledge at all that she asked the same question five minutes ago. Flora is very good with her and never gets bad-tempered. Well, she is doing her homework. Got to concentrate. I suppose it must teach you something, managing to do homework in the middle of all this.

When I was a lad, no don't go away, we only had one room. Well, there was a bathroom, inside as well, what a boaster, but that was full of packets of Woodbine.

At this time of year, the bedroom was always freezing. You could skate on the bare lino and there was enough ice on the inside of the windows to stock a freezer. In the end, when I got to the fifth year, and was on to serious stuff, I used to go down town to the Reference Library to meet the girls, what am I saying, to get some proper work done, Mum, I can't work in this place, with that stupid Tommy Handley on the radio and all those clothes steaming in front of the fire. And why can't you keep coal in the bath like normal people.

I know I *could* help Flora with her English, but she won't let me. Nor am I allowed ever again to sign for her homework. A good system this, getting a parent to sign to say the homework has been done and how long was spent on it. We never had that system at school.

Last week, feeling a bit frivolous I suppose, anything to brighten up this dull old life, I signed her homework 'H. Davies, Esq'. God, the scenes when she came back from school. Seemed to me a perfectly harmless thing to do. For weeks now I've just signed H. Davies and it was getting a bit boring. You'd have thunk I'd written some obscenity. What harm can a little Esq do, Flora? But that's it. Her mama has to sign from now on. Has some teacher made a teacher-like comment? I still don't know what I did wrong.

The strange thing is that Flora, egged on by my lady wife, has decided that I can do maths. Every time she gets stuck, she gets sent to me. We all know my wife isn't much good, but I'm not much better. It's just that I do all the sums and paperwork and bills and finances in this house, don't say I don't help. Flora thinks I'm some sort of genius at maths and she will insist on coming up to me, when I'm typing or reading, plonking her work card under my nose and saying, quick, how do I answer that one.

New Maths are hellish. The whole language has completely changed. They even seem to count a different way. So many of her work cards are based on premises I don't understand and can never enter. We were brought up to count in tens, but they have exercises in which you go up to five, or seven, or nine, and then you add on extra numbers, though they call them modules or nodules or matrices or some such. They start off with words I don't follow, and then numbers and examples and drawings which don't make sense.

So I turn off the electricity, as my typewriter humming drives me mad, unless I'm actually typing, and very slowly I ask Flora if I can read the other work cards, or take your hand away, dear, let me at least see the previous questions. I stare blankly, wondering where I am. She then grabs it from me and flounces away.

With a bit of time, such as a couple of years, I probably could work out what the hell is going on, but she expects me, as a grown-up, as someone who's supposed to be able to count, to know at once what is going on. It's like coming into a film in the middle, one made in Poland, or perhaps Paris, Texas, and trying to get hold of the plot. Very hard for anyone. But Flora, she won't give me a chance.

Oh no! It's happened. I can see flames in the kitchen. Jane Eyre's letter, in her best joined-up handwriting, has gone up in smoke. I better not say I told you so, but I did tell you so, Flora.

She's now settled down to write it out again. Taken it very well, considering. This time she's going to use a candle. And I am being allowed, oh rapture, to hold the candle. We'll do it over the sink. Let's hope we don't bung up the drains with the candle grease.

As a little surprise, while she's been writing it out again I've just been upstairs to my room. You know I collect stamps. Well, I also collect Postal History, which means envelopes, though we call them covers, we professionals. There were, of course, no stamped envelopes in 1826, as stamps did not come in till 1840, but a few weeks ago I bought a bundle of Free Fronts at an auction. These are envelopes which MPs and Lords send from Parliament. I buy them for the signatures.

Guess what. I've found a real live envelope, the genuine article, with the postmark on it saying 1826. And it's addressed to Yorkshire.

When Flora has finally got her letter finished, and then together we manage to get it suitably aged with a candle, fingers crossed, I'll present her with this wonderful 1826 envelope to put her 1826 letter in. What a good Dad. Nobody can say I don't help with homework. Sometimes.

Fresher Fields

Jake started college today. We've just got back from driving him there with all his junk, finding his room and carting his stuff from the car.

All week there's been great excitement, with endless farewells to his friends, as if they were never going to meet again, but at the same time a lot of moaning and groaning. Clothes. That's been a right bugger. He's got through his entire school career without wearing a collar and tie, or a jacket, and as for a suit, I don't think he's even seen one. Yet in this pile of Freshers' literature that came for him, outlining all the good times ahead, it clearly says that a suit will be useful for formal occasions.

I remember buying my first suit the minute I got to Durham in 1954, charcoal grey it was, Burton's best, what a scorcher, didn't I feel smart, and I wore it constantly for four years till it was so shiny you could see your face in it. I wore it for informal hops, don't you know. As for formal dances, your actual balls, that was evening dress, or perhaps the college blazer. Gawd, it sounds like the Dark Ages.

Against my principles, Hunt, I'm not buying no suit.

Up to you, my petal, but your dear mama has worked out a clothes allowance for you. She thinks you'll need two new pairs of trousers, two shirts, two pairs of shoes, and you should be able to get all that lot for £140. As for the suit, I'll come with you if you like. Price to be negotiated. I'm not a hard man. Want you to look presentable, don't we. Not really, he said.

He was out for a whole day and did every shop in London and returned with a pair of jeans and a sports T-shirt. That's all he's worn throughout his school life, so goodness knows why it took so long. He bought the T-shirt in Take Six, of blessed memory. Twenty years ago, newly arrived in London, I used to haunt Take Six in my lunch hours, looking for cheap T-shirts. In fact, hold on Jake, stand still, was it at the end of the rack, near the door. Thought I recognised it.

He *nearly* tried on a suit in Take Six, but decided against it. One of his friends, who also started college today, actually put on a suit, thanks to his mother standing over him, then chickened out.

So we all met up in the Oxford Circus Marks later in the week, as if I haven't got enough to do, and he trailed round making faces at every suit, every coat-hanger. What about a jacket, just to give yourself cover? You might get invited to sherry with the chaplain, that's what happens, Jake, on your first week at university. Then you never see him again.

In the end, thanks to the Old Trout's endeavours, he did buy some new trousers, shirts and shoes, but he held out against any jacket or suit. Sometimes I think he takes not being a posho too far.

I did notice, though, when we were loading the car this morning, that he had packed an old jacket of mine. Just for emergencies. And the OT had forced one of my ties into his plastic bags. A lot of good that will do him. Who's going to tie it for him. Can't shout for his Mummy, now he's at Varsity. He did once wear a tie, correction, when he was lower down the school and the Queen came on a visit, but a master tied it for him.

The car was loaded, which I was very pleased about, as at last I've got rid of all my petrol station tumblers, the free ones I've been saving for yonkers, except that she won't let me save them in the house, they are so vulgar, so I've been keeping them in the side passage. I did try them on Caitlin, two years ago when she started university, but she saw them just in time and put them straight back in the side passage. That old kettle which is all furred inside, also got rid of that, and some crockery which we always hated.

When we took Caitlin to Sussex for her first day, I had

to park miles from her room and it took ages carting all the stuff back and forward. Today, we got really close to Jake's place, which was handy. I'm two years older now, and not nearly as strong as I was. (Can't mention which university Jake's at, by the way. I'll get thumped if I do. You'll just have to search for clues.)

He took one look at his room and decided he hated it. Oh Gawd. Just like Caitlin. She didn't like hers for the opposite reasons to Jake. She wanted to be *away* from the student high jinks, off the campus, in a room of her own in Brighton itself, which she organised after just one term, and was immediately much happier. Jake doesn't like his room because he's not, apparently, with the bulk of the first year, where all the action is. Or so he thinks.

At the same time as Jake started today, Caitlin has begun her year at the University of California at Davis. It's part of her American Studies course, to have a year in America. Another lucky beggar.

We've always been led to believe that where Jake has gone today would be trific, as everyone always says so, but advance reports about Davis, a place we'd never heard of, had indicated it was a Cow Town. But Caitlin loves it, judging by her letters. There's a pool just outside her apartment and Davis itself is supposed to be the Berkeley of the Eighties, very popular and desirable, clean and bright, where everyone cycles and is into cleanliness and hard work. Sounds every parent's dream.

The town's main industry seems to be canning tomatoes. They're working on the world's first square tomato. Or have they already done so. Her letters aren't clear. I do hope she sends Flora some for Christmas.

Guess what the main cannery is called? Caitlin has sent me this little cutting from the local paper which I'd like to share with you:

> At the extreme north end of town, but still on the East side, sits the beautiful Hunt's cannery, where on foggy mornings the whole town can partake of tomato soup simply by breathing.

Due to long lines of tourists—not to mention tomato trucks—on week-ends, it is best to arrange your tour of Hunt's early on a weekday.

Not content with misspelling the name of their town, they also take my Christian name in vain. Well, it amused Caitlin. Oh, here's another little cutting she's sent. It looks as if she's perhaps been looking for jobs, to eke out the miserable money I allow her.

HELP WANTED
London Fish 'n Chips Part-time position available for persons who can speak a little Chinese. Please come to 129 E St, Davis. Tel. 753-7210 for interview.

Her courses have just started, and she's got on the ones she wanted, after hours of queuing. Her tutor has written a book on Willa Cather, who happens to be one of Caitlin's heroines, and has his room plastered with photographs of her.

I know it will take a week or two for Jake to settle down. It always does. Being a Fresher is pretty draggy. All those crowded meetings and nasty instant coffee and over-excited second year half-wits trying to con subscriptions. You hang around with people you don't particularly like, as they just happen to be in the same corridor, or same classes, then you spend the rest of the year trying to shake them off.

But I still envy him. I told him this all day, so he was probably glad to see the back of us. All these new people and activities, Jake, the experiments that can be made, new sensations tried, and if you don't like it, try another. It was thanks to the student newspaper at Durham, Jake, are you listening, that by chance I got into writing. Huh. So they're to blame, are they.

We had a poor lunch, but then he's at a place which is surprisingly rotten for restaurants. (There, that's another clue.) And then we came home. It's now just after six o'clock and Flora is already in her pyjamas. Well, what else is there to do.

I might feel envious of our older two, and all their studentish excitements to come, but back here we could have a v. boring term ahead. This old house rather creaks. Listen to those echoes. For the next ten weeks, Flora is an only child.

Davies v Forster

I am often asked, as I go about the planet addressing Women's Institutes, talking to Masonics, lecturing under-graduates, advising Royalty, assisting at soup kitchens, talking to myself, if I am ever jealous of my wife. The quick answer is, yes.

At the moment, I certainly am. Her latest novel got on the bestseller list and I'm sick as Flaubert's parrot. Wish I'd had a novel in the hit parade. Lucky beggar.

The slow answer is, no. What people are really suggesting is that, with two writers in the same house, husband and wife, shifting the words all day, there must be some, er, how can we put this, Hunt, tensions.

I suppose an actor and actress living together might feel some domestic strain, if one is out of work more than the other; or two dustmen, if one can no longer hump the heavy loads; or two teachers, if they advance at different rates or strike on different days. But I have to say, hand on wallet and pen on heart, that me and the Old Trout have never had a cross word or ill feeling about our respective jobs.

But we do have gentle sparring on one topic, the way all parents do, regardless of whether they are in the same line of business. For twenty-one years, as we have observed *les enfants* growing up, or trying to, we have looked at them, and our own respective families whence we have come, and said THAT'S YOUR SIDE COMING OUT.

Well-defined characteristics have emerged, traits which we all accept have come from one set of genes. Outsiders might not spot them, but we think we can see these family distinctions very clearly. Every seven years or so, when new skins seem to be uncovered and come to prominence, we stand back and say, heh up, that's the Davies coming out. Or, look at that, isn't she a typical Forster.

So in our little house it's Davies v Forster, in the nicest possible sense, as we calculate the odds, examine the ratings, see who's leaping up the Top Ten.

Forsters have standards. They could drive you mad, these bleedings standards, but they are definitely there, in so many parts of their life. For a start, they're always tidy and organised and well turned-out. Her Dad, at eighty-five, keeps himself and his house and his life spotless. Her brother and sister are the same. I've worked on her over the years, of course, to get things in proportion, and at first glance our house does look Forster fit, with everything in its place. But unlike true Forsters, a second glance will reveal the dust, things shoved in corners. I am winning. Slowly.

Flora is following the Forster pattern, and likes to be immaculate, even when it's casual. She folds her clothes the way Mummy thinks the world should, and has drawers that could be inspected at any time. Oh, these Forsters. They're so fastidious.

By comparison, Davieses are sluts. I blow my nose on my scarf without thinking, well it is *my* scarf, while my wife and Flora recoil in genuine norror, how can you, that's disgusting. I will use someone else's toothbrush if I can't find mine, wipe my hands on any towel, put on yesterday's clothes for ever, drink straight from the milk bottle, and other gross habits too horrible to discuss. And as for my clothes cupboard, please don't look. I'll never get it closed again. I've just jammed it with a sleeve.

Caitlin, at the last count, and we haven't seen her for six months, is a Davies in that respect. Imagine a Forster even contemplating living in a communal squat. Ugh. Oh yes, I get the blame, she gets all that from me, all my fault, don't say it. At least in her work, Caitlin is a Forster. Terribly organised.

Jake is sort of in-between. His college room is very untidy and scruffy, but it's also fairly bare. Unlike true Davieses, he doesn't go through life trailing clouds of clutter.

Forsters have standards of behaviour. There are things they will and will not do. You can't budge them. Once they've made up their minds, that's it. She won't lower these standards, whether refusing to go on a programme she disapproves of, or having a cup of tea when she's already said no. If the latest cheap wine turns out to be not so good, she'll say no more, thanks, while I'll say yes, it's not so good, then I'll finish off the whole bottle. I'll always accept second best, even third and fourth. I'm not proud.

They're so decisive, these Forsters, which I do admire, well, mostly, while we Davieses twit on for ever, tying ourselves in knots, going back and forward, hiffing and havering, rehearsing all the possibilities, driving everyone mad, including ourselves. Jake and Flora are very decisive. You always get a yes or a no, whatever the topic. No messing. Me and Caitlin usually say yes, then no, then yes again. Well, if I knew my own mind, I might follow it.

But is this decisiveness so wonderful? I've noticed with Jake, and now with Flora, that they will not go to certain places, join certain clubs, deciding instantly, usually for good reasons, that it will be draggy. So they stay at home, moaning that they're bored.

Caitlin always had a hectic social life at this stage, though the Forsters will sneer, saying this was because she often accepted second best. We Davieses like to think that we say yes to life. We're sociable and gregarious, even if we come back and moan and wish we hadn't gone.

She thinks I would have survived in a Prisoner of War camp, yes, that's the sort of chat we have over the cocoa when times are slack. I'd eat the rats and lick other people's greasy plates. She'd stick it out. She'd maintain, like Sidney Carton, that it's a far far better thing I am doing, and go to the guillotine, while I'd say me sir, yes sir, anything you say sir.

In our house we have Davies Time and Forster Time. I like to catch the train as it's leaving the station, or the post as the van is about to disappear round the corner, or be at the pictures as the credits begin. It gives me such pleasure. I often come home glowing at 5.31 of an evening, having

193

run after the postie and shoved my letters in his surprised hands as he's driving, catching the last post once again. Clever old Hunt. My lady wife, and Flora, consider good time-keeping to mean being ready, if not actually there, one hour before the off. Potty, I call it.

Forsters are artistic, I will say that. They do surround themselves with lovely things. Well, I have to say that or I'll get thumped. They can turn dumps into treasure-houses by their presence alone, rearranging a few leaves, putting plates a nice way, turning round the furniture, chucking out that repulsive object at once, who on earth put that there. My lady wife, Flora and Caitlin all have that Forster gift. Me and Jake, well, have you seen our drawers? That used to be a family phrase when Flora was very little. You keep rubbish in your drawers, so she would say to me, following me round the house.

Davieses are usually popular, so we like to think, never having rows or arguments with people. They, on the other hand, will allege that this comes from being spineless. As for the Forsters, they will give their personal opinion, and insist on it, whether they have been asked or not, and one of them has been known, in her time, to leave people quaking.

No, that's not quite true. I had a row with a woman the other week, about education, while she hasn't had a violent argument for ages. She's becoming ever so nice, almost Davies-like.

That's what has happened over recent years. We've picked up bits from each other, swapped the genes, copied traits. Now we tend to sit back and see what we've done together, identifying the elements which the baton-carriers of the future will take with them.

Yankee Doodles

Would we recognise Caitlin? After all, we haven't seen our oldest, and these days our most reasonable, for over seven months. She might have changed her hair, her clothes, her accent. Her clothes are bound to have changed, said Flora. She left the UK carrying a plastic bag full of her worldly possessions. She'll have stocked up in local thrift shops by now.

Would she recognise us? I don't think I've changed much—few more wrinklettes, couple of grey hairlings. The Old Trout, well, she's always looked the same to me, ever since I first saw her, aged fourteen. Wonderful.

Jake, so we like to think, has become much more mature in the last six months, now that he's an undergraduate. Doesn't cry at all when you take his toys away. Even does his own shoe laces. But Flora, wowee, Caitlin really might not recognise her at all. She's shot up, and it's not just her mama's shoes. When I see her coming down the street these days, I think who's this young lady.

We set off from San Francisco first thing after breakfast, heading for Interstate 80, the OT clutching the map, Jake and Flora clutching their Walkmen, me clutching my eyes as we seemed to have been driving for yonkers and still hadn't crossed the Bay Bridge, are you sure we're heading the right way, woman, don't want to end up in Japan, chop chop.

The town of Davis is only seventy-five miles inland from San Franny, but it seemed to get hotter and more tropical with every mile. The rest of the world, which included us till five days previously, assumes that everywhere in

California is hot, they all have swimming-pools, sun-tans, brilliant teeth, their own hair. But in San Francisco and the Bay area they get a lot of rain, cold weather, mist, baldness, just like us.

Caitlin is at present at the University of California, which has nine campuses in all, including Davis. It's in a little country town also called Davis. All year I wanted to send her a letter addressed to Davies, Davis, Davis, till I found out there were 20,000 students there, probably hundreds called Davies, thousands called Davis. Not that we ever speak to them. We're the pedigree people.

America doesn't look much like America these days, not on the roads. They seem to have cut down on those monster roadside adverts, and the cars have positively shrunk. They're all titchy Japanese or European ones. Only the poor still drive big, old-fashioned, Yankee cars. Just as only the poor are fat. Only the deprived eat hamburgers. Only children chew gum. Only the working classes smoke. How's that for generalisations. Marvellous how, in five days in one town, you can sum up 250 million people. No problem. You're welcome.

We'd booked into a motel just outside Davis, as Davis is too tasteful a campus to have such vulgar things, but we took one look at it and the OT said drive on, I'm not staying here. I thought about driving on to New York, just to show her, but that could have taken five months, and Caitlin would be back in London by then. Come on then, clever clogs, where should we stay?

In the end we found a motel which passed the OT Test, if only just. We got the receptionist to take us to look at two possible rooms first, to check for noise. Very obliging, American hotel people. You'd get the bum's rush if you tried that in London. You're lucky to get them to speak to you.

Each room had a colour telly, fridge, bathroom, lashings of space and quite good soft furnishings, plus a microwave oven. What's all this then, I said. All I want is a cup of tea in the morning. I'm not cooking for a regiment.

Look, stop messing around, you fool, we've come 10,000 miles to see Caitlin, not to have you clucking like an old

196

hen about your stupid morning tea. What a pain you can be.

Caitlin used to lived in one room in I Street, when she first moved to Davis, which I rather fancied visiting, if just for the name, I mean the letter, but a few months ago she moved to her own place, self-contained, in somewhere called Olive Drive. Very English-sounding. In her letters, she's been thrilled by it, very pleased to have got it, and for about the same rent as before, $185 a month.

I'll have to take this next bit carefully. You know I never like to offend people, always sensitive to moods and feelings. Okay, Old Trout is not a very nice way to refer to one's wife, but come on, it's an old joke between friends, everyone knows that, she doesn't mind, honestly she doesn't.

So I'll say at once that Caitlin looked trific. Best we've seen her looking for several years, so brown and healthy, glowing and radiant, and doing ever so well. Do you know, while we were there in Davis, she was offered a position as a TA. Isn't that great. Yes, we didn't know about this either, but in American universities there's such a thing as a Teacher's Assistant, usually someone doing graduate work, who helps the professor, doing things like marking students' work. And she gets paid. I didn't find that out till after I'd given her the cheque for her next term's bills. Not that I would have given her less. I'm not that mean, well, not quite. She will have to work for it. But what an honour.

Anyway, her abode. One morning we arrived to pick her up and there was this smart little van outside with a uniformed chap knocking on her front door. He looked as if he might have arrived from the Davis version of Harrods, bringing a hamper for madam. Then we saw the writing on the side of the van: TERMITE CONTROL.

Oh, just a few cockroaches, look Flora, here's a dead one. Whoppers, aren't they. All that white powder round every room, just chemicals I've been putting down to stop them taking over.

She has, I admit, got two fairly large rooms, plus a kitchen and shower room. All of them bare. Absolutely bare. Yes, there is a fridge, big enough to hold parties in, and a cooker. But that's all. Nothing on the floors. No furniture. No bed, even. She seems to do her essays sitting on the bare floor.

But who are we to criticise? Pathetic specimen that I am, twitting on about needing a kettle and tea by my king-size bed in my luxury fitted motel room. She loves her apartment. What does it matter to us if it seems worse than the squat she once lived in near King's Cross. That did have a table. She is obviously very happy. I'll move on quickly, in order not to give more offence.

We loved Davis, the campus and the town, so attractive and green and such nice students and a nice atmosphere. Every parent would love to have a child studying at Davis. And such yummy houses, all low two-storey buildings, with trees and gardens, all beautifully kept. I Street was in the heart of the town and seemed very pleasant to me, but of course you've done trif, Caitlin, really good, getting a whole place to yourself, right by the railway line, on the wrong side of the tracks, sorry, I mean on the more interesting side of the tracks.

We had some very good meals all together, once I'd sussed out that not every restaurant in Davis was vegetarian. Caitlin, you see, is. Naturally, she veered that way, when she was thinking of places. Me and Jake, real men both, like to eat quiche, now and again. Underdone, of course, so you can see the blood.

Luckily, Caitlin, despite her few possessions, had bought real coffee for our visit, and found a bashed-up, red coffee-pot in some thrift shop, so it was a pleasure to be invited into her wondrous home and be treated. And, in the end, we got used to her place. Interesting. Yes, I think that's the word I should have used in the first place. Just like the whole visit.

Veggie Burgers

They're so selfish in this house. Here's me trying to keep the economy going single-handed, helping my fellow workers to increase production, hoping not to cause further unemployment, and I suddenly seem to be surrounded by people who are GIVING UP.

At supper this evening, Flora pushed away her glass and said, that's it, I'm not having Coca-Cola any more, I've given it up. She'd only taken one sip, and there were at least fifteen cubes of ice in her rotten glass, as she has this passion for ice. All that waste, all the electricity that went into running that fridge, and the floor space it takes up, and now she says she doesn't want it no more.

But you always said it was poison. You always said it was full of sugar, bad for your teeth and bad for your health. You should be pleased I've now given it up.

No, I'm not. It's the last straw. Hold on, we've got a whole packet of straws in the cupboard. Who's going to use those stupid straws if you've given up drinking Coke. And they're those dopey bendy ones, double the price of straight straws. I dunno.

I blame the Old Trout. She's completely changed her drinking habits, so Flora is now starting to do the same. No, I don't. I really blame that Gorbachev. Ever since we've gotten back from Russia, she's not been her normal self.

I count a normal self as someone who drinks at least half a bottle of wine a day, perhaps more if there's something to celebrate, such as getting to six o'clock without having a drink.

In Russia, we could hardly get any drink, so she decided

not to try, and now the habit has stuck. Days and days pass without a drop going near her, in fact it's now a whole week since she last had any wine. She might, or she might not, have a glass at Sunday lunch. Just depends. From now on she'll ask herself, do I really need it, do I really want it, is it just habit, should I really. Oh shut up, you old bat, just don't expect me to be so sensible, that's all. You go your own way, and I'll go mine. Where's the corkscrew?

I've been determined not to moderate my ever-so-moderate habits. I'm just a social drinker, truly I am, I just drink to be social. Hello Hunt, you've had a hard day, pull up a crate and sit down, take the weight off your wallet. But a strange thing has happened. Because *she* has cut down, *my* intake has been reduced as well. Though Gawd knows, I have tried hard.

I now realise that much of our drinking was competitive. We'd mark the bottle, half each, make sure we had exactly the same sized glasses, which is very hard in this house as they are all different sizes, I blame that Shell garage. Then we'd watch each other like hawks, making sure no one got more, no one cheated, no one drank from the other person's glass when they went to answer the phone, oh I've seen it done, stop at nothing, some people.

Half the fun has gone out of it. I can now drink a whole bottle, if I like, but what's the point. There's nothing or nobody to stop me, so there's no sense of achievement, no real savouring of having won an extra half-inch while she was on the phone. OK, it was me.

Drinking half a bottle all on my own has resulted in half a bottle being left. When you buy the sort of cheap plonk I buy, it turns to vinegar by the next day. Sharing a bottle together meant it went in one go. Bottles have now been lying around with bits in them for days, when previously twelve minutes was a record for an un-opened bottle. In the end, I've been chucking stuff out. Yes, I know I'll go to the Bad Fire, as my mother used to say.

Even worser than the drink situation, both Flora and her mama have announced they have given up meat. Oh yes, all right for them to indulge themselves, think only of their own pleasure. Every bloomin' night this week, we have had veggie food.

Look, lasses, I do man's work, it's not easy at the typewriter face, shifting all those heavy words. When I come down of an evening, get washed, take my dirty clothes off, God, the struggle changing that ribbon today, I want to tuck in to good old roast beef or good old steak or good old veal, but bloody hell, not stir-fried vegetables again.

You're right, Hunt. It's not stir-fried vegetables today. It's pasta.

I'm not totally prejudiced. I'm willing to have some pasta now and again, such as once a year, as a first course. This was naked. Bare pasta, just as it came out of the womb, or wherever pasta comes from. Any meat-balls, you guys? What, not even tomàto sauce? Oh, come on then, get the grated cheese out, stop messing around. As a huge concession, I was eventually allowed to put something on my plateful of naked pasta—salt and pepper. Big deal.

That's another thing she gave up in Russia. Salt. There was a third bit of idiocy, now what was it? Oh, that's right. I just read about it at the end of her Russian diary. 'In Russia, I did without alcohol, salt and a pillow.'

Well, bully for you. Well done, my petal. Just don't blame me if the pillow manufacturers have a deputation on our doorstep. I expect the salt mines have already closed.

She's always had this weakness in her. As a little girl, when she was a fervent Christian, her favourite time of the year was Lent. She looked forward to it so much. I thought I'd knocked some sense into her, these twenty-six years. Now I fear it could always be Lent from now on.

Look, what are you trying to prove. No one thinks any better of you. Just a fashion, that's all. You're one of the health freak herd. All this veggie nonsense. Any minute now they'll prove that vegetables are bad for you, then you'll all come rushing back, ha ha.

Flora has never been much of a meat-eater, but now she too has given it up. She's in the third-year. They get these notions. I saw a report last week which says that 20 per cent of our school children have become vegetarians. The nation's dinner-ladies must be going spare. Who wants seconds of these spam fritters? These words had them stampeding across the gym when I was a lad. I wonder why we ate in the gym. Always meant to ask. Now they probably can't get rid of the firsts. It's all salad bars and other soppy stuff.

They're causing me to cut down on my food and on my drink, that's what I'm really furious about. Yes, I do feel pretty healthy at present, thanks for asking, and the old jaw has been goodish for some time now, but that's not the point. I like stuffing myself. It gives a shape to the day, looking forward to a grand tuck-in, eh lad, can't beat it. I'm sure I've years of eating left in me.

They say that with age you naturally cut down, as the body's metabolism bla bla bla, but I'm not at that stage yet. I'm as greedy as I ever was. Is that your cold toasted cheese over there? Bags me, if you're leaving it.

Where will it all end, this cutting down nonsense. She asked if we truthfully needed a car, living in London, all those nasty fumes, so much healthier to walk everywhere. And what about Caitlin's bedroom, and Jake's bedroom? Now they're away at college half the year, should we let some poor person have them? We don't need all that space any more, it's time we cut down.

On your bike. Yes, that's a good idea, she said. You could mend that old one, then we could really do without the car.

I'm going to bed early. I get so tired these days. I think it's lack of meat and drink. I start yawning the moment I've had my stir-fried pasta. So, I'm off. Let's hope our bed is still there. If she's bought a futon behind my back, she's for it.

Late Night Reveries

We were lying in bed last night, my Good Friend and I, when I turned to her and said where's Flora.

No, she doesn't sleep with us, not no more, well she is fourteen. I meant where is my little Flora, my own little petal, whereabouts on the planet is she at this very moment?

That party, you know, we both agreed she could go, perfectly harmless, we know the house and all the people, what are you fussing about.

I had locked and double-locked all the doors and windows, thinking it's so nice to have Caitlin and Jake safe at college, rather than coming home in the middle of the night. I'd forgotten Flora. She'd gone out to her first late evening event, but I'd told her I wanted her back here at 10.30, pronto, no messing. Oh no, life is repeating itself. This is where we came in with Caitlin.

I can be a hard man, especially talking to myself, which I mostly am, in this house.

And it was then, at 10.31 precisely, as the cat flies, that I said to the GF, where is that Flora? Note the use of the word 'that'. How could you translate that 'that' into a foreign language? It's an admonishing 'that', yet with a hint of affection.

Look, are you going to listen to *A Book at Bedtime* or are you going to twit on all night.

Sorry, your ladysmith. It's just that I told her 10.30, so where the heckers is she.

And I told her 11 o'clock.

Oh Gawd, here we go, here we go, here we go, again. Don't say she's going to play us off, just as the Big Two did.

I lay awake, fuming, I do make rather strong cocoa, and before my eyes there stretched ahead the Next Four Year Plan and I thought oh no, I can't go through that once more, I'm too old, too tired, please let me off, I promise to be awfully good if You do.

I pulled the blankets round my head, tried hard to think of something nice, such as chocolate cake. Yes, that was interesting. I hate all cakes, but the other day Flora came out with a little childhood memory; when her grandmother was babysitting for her, she woke up one night terrified and her gran sat by her bed and said there there Flora, you'll soon go to sleep, just think of your favourite cake. And it worked.

For years and years, I used to lie awake in this very bed wondering where the hell either Caitlin or Jake had got to. It is London, they have to learn, survive this and they're fit for anything in life, such as being a traffic warden.

You know what it's like. You imagine awful things. You wait for the police to call, the hospital to ring, or even worse, falling asleep with the radio still on. Have you seen the price of PP9 batteries these days.

I don't know why you are making such a song and dance. It is our fault, said the GF. Not their fault. We are the ones who are unnatural, going to bed at ten o'clock every night.

It is true that Caitlin used to come home and tell us about the parents of her friends who would still be up at one o'clock when their offspring came home and say have some tea, some sandwiches darlings, shall I cook you something, come on, tell us what you've been doing. Then they'd all talk, late into the next morning.

I am told this is common. In fact, I am told there are many, many parents like this. I don't believe a word of it.

In our house, I expect our children either to stay in all their lives, until they leave home, or if they must be out in the evening, to come home by 10.30, creeping up the stairs in absolute silence, without pulling any lav chains, putting on any kettles, banging any doors, and I'd be obliged if they went to sleep in the dark, preferably without breathing.

Flora's bedroom is exactly above our bedroom. The

floorboards are more like sounding-boards. The slightest movement, and our whole room shakes. I went through years of agony when Caitlin had it, suffering the monstrous regiments of her friends. Flora's friends look like being even bigger. I blame that National Health. (Note that 'that' again.)

Should we change the bedrooms round for the next four years? Or fix silencers. Or how about moving into a flat or a hotel till the war is over. I've seen the past, and I fear it's going to be the future all over again.

Experience never seems to do you any good. The new version hits you when you least expect it, and in a slightly different way. Oh, it's okay telling other people, passing on advice. Surgeon, heal thyself.

All right then clever clogs, what are the rules going to be this time round. Let's make it clear from the very beginning, before we have to bring down the heavy hand, not that we have to yet. My goodness no, Flora is still my little petal, all five feet six and a quarter inches of her. I measured them all in on New Year's Day, and I measured them all out again.

It depends what *you* decide, what *you* want to do. You're the father. Try to act like one for a change. But before you start thinking up half-baked regulations, just remember what you were like at her age.

Come off it. Do me a favour. Carlisle in the 1950s. You were there. It was like being in a monastery. 'Sleep-over' meant sleeping in late and not delivering the papers on time. There was none of this late night partying, far less staying out all night with friends.

Did you spare a thought for your mother? Did you ever realise what it must have been like for her, you the oldest, her with an invalid husband, huh?

Look, I've told you. I was nae bother at 'a, for the simple reason I didn't go anywhere.

What about Keswick, August 4, 1956?

Cue for moody music, skiffle in background, Brylcreemed hair, radios with fan grills, Woodbines at tuppence a pint. Need I say more. I'm sure yous all have been there, or thereabouts.

205

Yes, that was a famous victory for a radical chick behaviour. Even now I am amazed by our daring, our flaunting of all known conventions. What we did was walk home. I knew you'd be shocked. Alone. Yup, not one chaperone.

It had been a beaut day in Keswick, typically marvellous Lakeland weather, no rain for minutes on end, and we'd lolled by Derwentwater, ambled up Catbells, and when the time came to catch the last bus back to Carlisle, we said blow it, let's deliberately walk all the way home. Only thirty miles. We can do it. Hand in hand in the moonlight.

Every August 4, we still say to each other, remember Keswick. It's our secret. We haven't got many, gawd knows. Like living in a goldfish bowl round here, with them tramping upstairs all night long with their seven-foot friends and then jumping on those floorboards and turning on their awful thumping Reggie beat.

Did you think about your mother that night?

Do you know, from that moment until then, I never had. I've got through all these chapters of my life so far without ever stopping for one second to imagine what it must have been like for my Mum. She must have been going spare all night, imagining we'd been drowned, or fallen off a crag, involved in a bus crash, abducted, eaten alive by tramps.

When I dragged myself in at seven o'clock in the morning, she said never a word of admonition. Not even: That Hunter.

Photo Finish

I'm always saying and thinking heh up, another stage in life has been reached, another bench mark on the family table, even when it's just a grey hair in my 'tash or a new crack in that kitchen wall.

But this time I feel we have clambered over a milestone. Caitlin, our first-born, has just gone off abroad for two years. When will we see her again. Even more remarkable, she is self-supporting.

Goodness, I never thought that last phrase would ever leave my typewriter. Not many of us around who can say that, who can boast that any offspring is not costing us something. No, she is not quite earning, not in the normal sense, but for the moment, and I hope the next moment, she is in charge of her own finances.

From now on, it's up to you Caity-Cateyes. Gosh, I haven't called her that for twenty years. Over and out.

She should by now be in Clark. I dunno where Clark is. The map is in the other room. Don't universities in the USA have funny names. It was strange when she had that year at Davis, which turned out to be in a town called Davis, out in sunny California. Until a few months ago, she was going to a place called Smith. I suppose there must be a University called Jones, and Brown, probably an Evans and a Thatcher, even a Shufflebottom. How provincial we are, thinking universities must be called after towns, just cos we in the UK do it that way.

She announced about a year ago that she wanted to do research in women's studies in the US, no comments please Hunt, and I said fine, whizzo, you may do it on Third

Division North Football Teams, or Penny Black Plates for all I care, good luck to you lass, but once you have graduated, that's it, my petal. You are on your own. (Did I really mean it? It sounded to me as if I did. I was terribly stern. Well, at twenty-two, they have to push off in their own boat sometime.)

The problem has been to get funding. I began to feel sorry for her and all American parents of college-age children. These prospectuses came in from places like Smith and the fees and expenses for a year come to around 15,000 dollars. How can parents ever manage. We moan in little ole Britville, but ours are nothing like that. Tuition fees are free over here for natives. You just have to pay to keep them alive. Bread and gruel can be rather pricey these days.

We've had to advance some cash, as she'll have to live till the monies come through, and pay her air fare, but are we moaning, are we heckers. I've gone round the streets boasting. Our Caitlin is being paid to study in America. Beat that, you lot.

I'm sure we'll manage a trip out there, if just to prove that Clark exists. Hold on, it's in Mass. Not a religious place, I hope.

Oh, I see, it's in a town called Worcester. She'll find it cold in the winter, compared with California. Has she taken enough woollies, I wonder. She won't be able to go bare-footed there. I hope her money really covers everything. Heating bills will be high. Should I have advanced more. Will food parcels help. What about vests.

What are we twitting on about. She's jolly well orf. The nest has been flown from. Our daughter the graduate has moved on.

Yup, she got a Top Second. Good huh. Better than me or her Mama, as we got Seconds. They were not officially graded at our places, though I bet mine was pretty good, probably a very High Middling To Top Second, might even have been a Top Super Out Of Sight Second. It could even have been an Almost First, but they didn't want to shame everyone else in my year.

She didn't go to the degree ceremony. Doesn't approve

of that sort of thing. My Mum came through from Carlisle to celebrate my Degree at Durham, with the next-door neighbour for company. My Dad was an invalid, confined to bed by then.

He never witnessed, alas, that touching moment when I was handed my Almost First on Palace Green, Durham, 1957. I then got my photograph taken by a lady called Daisy Edis who specialised for a hundred years in taking spotty Durham graduates in their hired gowns, then touching up their portraits so they looked like Robert Redford.

I have that very photo on my wall in front of me. My Mum used to have it over her bed, ahh, but there is no space for it where she is now. Nor would it mean very much to her either. I have the most remarkable, pure, lovely complexion in this photo, and such lush clean hair. In reality, I was all spots and had greasy hair. The Old Trout frequently reminds me of this, but I prefer the Daisy Edis version. That's me for ever, folks. Just don't change, Hunt. We like you as you are. Or almost were.

Jake has got one university photograph so far, in his college football team, but they're all mucking around and looking stupid and his face is rather blurry. I hope he gets a proper one taken next term.

I would have liked Caitlin to have gone to her Graduation ceremony, if only for the photograph. I know she would have hated to put on the stupid robes, and would probably have refused to be photographed, but she would have made an old man rather happy. I could have hung it over my bed for the next two years, while she's away. Ahhh.

Pardon My French

We arrived at Victoria with a screech of brakes, and then a screech of passengers, you stupid fool Hunt, look at the time, we're late, typical of your time-keeping, we'll probably miss her now and it will be all your fault.

Look, if you are going to be silly, we'll never find her, stop messing around and concentrate. She could already have come out of the side entrance, so pay attention. You have memorised what she looks like.

We were waiting for our French exchange, the very first our family has ever had. Caitlin and Jake never wanted an exchange, though at one time I was willing to swap them for anything, but Flora is much keener on French than either of them, and especially keen on getting herself to Paris for the next hols, rather than being dragged to the Lake District by the Wrinklies, do I have to.

Look at all the lonely people, where do they all come from. So many do seem dodgy, but are they the ones you read about, waiting to lure away innocent young provincial girls, or are they the young innocent provincial girls. There were hordes of them resigned and exhausted, single girls, standing by their belongings, now and again dragging their little mobile bags, their mobile lives, a few yards along to pretend to the world and themselves that they were not lost or stood up or runaways.

Battered mini-cabs fluttered around me, dropping people, chancing their hairy arms with the single girls, till they saw the juvenile cops and rattled off. The scruffiest, most dejected girl suddenly lit up and bounded into a Range Rover, screaming at Mummy and Daddy for being late. I'd become convinced she was a really deprived runaway Slav, not a bleedin' Sloane. You never can tell.

Not more corny philosophy, said the OT, opening the back door and letting in Marion, our fourteen-year-old French friend, our *petite amie* for the next *semaine, bonjour ma petal*. She's come here to speak English, Hunt, so give us a break, huh.

It's rather strange, the way we got her. That makes her sound like a mail order supply, or something we won in a raffle. I mean how we came to be having Marion with us. We'd put the word around for months, writing to people, asking at Flora's school for any contacts, with no luck; then we remembered that almost twenty years ago my mother in Carlisle used to have French assistants from the grammar school. Gawd knows why, as there was hardly room in our council house for us, never mind frogs, but my Mum loved having them, and they liked staying.

She kept in contact with many of them for years, especially one called Madeleine, so we dug out her address and said heh, remember us, the family Davies from Carlisle, have you by chance a child of Flora's age, no swots or weeds please, must like clothes, reggae music, be mature for her age, artistic, interest in saxophone a plus, interest in sports a minus. We did not of course tell Flora about this dopey list—she would have screamed—but you have to begin somewhere if you're swapping human beings.

In a fortnight, it was all fixed up; they'd exchanged letters and photies and here she is. Most amazing of all is her name. Marion. Pronounced in the French way, of course, with a lot of rolling of the arse at the end. We did not know she existed, yet it turns out her name is partly in memory of my mother. Spelled exactly the same way. My mother has just died, two weeks before Marion arrived. One Marion has gone. A new one has come into our life.

They're in Flora's room now, what a noise of records, what a noise of talk. They've not stopped all week. Marion does not care much for reggae, and does not like Sade, one of Flora's all-time favourites. She loves David Bowie, yuck. She also liked Rupert Everett, whoever he is. We had this conversation this evening at supper about handsome men, goodness knows how the topic came up—my presence, I shouldn't wonder—and Marion said she would like a poster of this Rupert creature in her bedroom. Flora said that in her opinion there were no beautiful men, they just did not exist, while she could name loads of beautiful women. (Must tell Caitlin that. Right on, sister.)

The OT, just to get her half-franc in, said what about Jean-Paul Belmondo, was not he handsome, she'd always liked the look of him. Flora and Marion stared at the OT as if she'd crept out of the Ark, or the overnight bus from Carlisle. Marion said Belmondo was not only old, but ugly. So that was him out.

And that's when I came to a surprising conclusion. I don't actually think Marion is French. Firstly the language. She doesn't understand a bloody word I say. How can this be. I did get O-Level French, Xmas resit I admit, but that's always harder. Even my trifically cunning bilingual jokes completely failed on her. An *oeuf* is an *oeuf*, I said at breakfast one morning. Not a glimmer. Not a titter.

Then the wine. She wouldn't have any. Just wanted Coke and that sort of rubbish. I thought you French took in wine with your mother's milk, *au lait* to bed, *au lait* to rise. Are you listening, Marion, that's actually a three-way jokeroo, you do speak Spanish, don't you. No, my other language at school is Russian.

We got on to films and we discovered she did not seem to know anything about M. Hulot, or have seen any of the films. All she wanted to talk about was *Room with a View*, which she loved. So we took her last night to *Maurice*. Said she liked it, but can one be sure. Not even sure we did. One afternoon Flora took her to *Wish You Were Here*, which she says she found harder to understand than *Maurice*, with the speed and slang, but is looking forward to going home and telling everyone she saw Emily Lloyd, in English.

Then the food. She was completely flummoxed by garlic bread, swearing she's never had it before, foony people these pretend Parisians. I know the Chinks never eat Pot Noodles and the Eyties don't know what spaghetti rings are, but you'd have thought the French would understand garlic, mon dew.

Last night we took her to a French-style restaurant in Camden Town, the Brasserie, awfully nice, and we suggested to Marion that she had the *Crème Brûlée* for pudding, terribly good. She had no idea what I was on about. I'd realised by then she has a problem with well-spoken, Fifties French, so I held up the menu and pointed to the writing. Still she'd never heard of it, so I ordered one for her, being dead fluent. No sign of recognition. Quite liked it, but her favourite pudding is still one they have all the time at home. Her mother is always making it. Perhaps we'd heard of it. 'Ahpel croombul.'

You what? We made her repeat it several times, and suddenly that long low "a" in a croombul sounded familiar. She's got a Northern English accent, picked up from her mother, picked up from my mother. In her corner of Paris, there will always be a foreign field that is for ever Carlisle.

The Finals Solution

I am a proud parent. Must be. For the last week people in the street have been saying well done and shoving cards of congratulations through the letterbox. Close friends have been stopping me on my walks and saying is it true, goodness, you must be proud.

I have always been a proud parent. I remember the Cutting of Caitlin's First Tooth. I rushed from work, there that shows how long ago it was, and bought her a little present on the way home. Jemima Puddle-duck. Inside there is still the inscription I wrote. To Caitlin Louise Penelope, on the Cutting of her First Tooth, August 14, 1964. I will cherish it for ever, even if no one else does, along with the actual baby teeth she later discarded and the locks of her little girl hair when it was so black she looked like Cleopatra. If not Cleopatra, Elizabeth Taylor acting Cleopatra. If not her, oh forget it.

When Caitlin started to read *Janet and John*, that was trific, but I think when she went on to be able to paint and draw and act and in fact do most artistic things ever so nicely, then I was well proud, being totally without artistic talents myself. Wonder whose side of the family she gets it from.

Caitlin showed from an early age one particular skill which knocked me out. She could understand instructions, the written sort, when you buy a new gadget and it comes with twenty pages of gibberish. You say I know, let's play this new game, then you open the box, see the rules, and say no, let's not play this new game. Caitlin always rescued us. And always won.

Jake, our second born, was not such a proud-maker when he was young, in fact he drove us round the bend till he was five. Never slept all night once, in five long years. So hyperactive we were permanently exhausted. His aim in life seemed to be to shove his fingers in the light plugs and electrocute himself. He was so late at learning to read we did consider having him tested.

He drove many of his primary school teachers potty as well, as no class could be taught till Jake was settled. But by the end of his primary days, he had become a Tower of Strength. Not through being big and strong; in fact till he was thirteen he was, now, how shall I put this, I could still get thumped, he was chubby. What happened was that he became Responsible. He could be relied upon. He became captain of his primary school football team, not through being the best player, but by being dependable. And that year they won the league. Good, huh.

Flora, our little flower, our youngest petal, also has the artistic talents denied to the males in this family. Sometimes I feel a mere passenger. The OT, as a gel, was good at everything, the creep, so now you know where these skills come from. Personally, I don't believe in heredity. It's like astrology. Looking back, you can make it prove anything.

I'm always vee proud when Flora picks up her saxophone, which she is teaching herself, and gets a sound out of it, any sound, how does she do it.

Last year, when she was in the school play, *A View from the Bridge*, my little cup was overflowing, just to see her up there, acting in an American accent. I can't do any accents, never mind act. The OT, don't get her started, but her Oz accent is quite good, for someone from Carlisle.

These talents, these skills, are not of course exceptional, just that all parents are amazed when their children can do anything, most of all when it's something they can't do themselves. And the nice point about having them is that they are interests, outlets, amusements for life, whether they are developed or not.

That was one of the drags about Jake, in his middle-teen years, moping about the house, refusing to do anything, join anything, go anywhere, whereas les gels were never in, always usefully employed. It wasn't till the Sixth Form that he had another change of persona. Now I believe in that. Every seven years, they move into a new skin, a new character. You can't see it ahead, can't predict exactly what will happen, but when you look back, you see clues which you never quite understood at the time, signs that did not quite make sense.

Our news, this week, concerns Dear Jake. Close followers will know that he has been at university these last three years. But ah-ha, even very close followers, reading between the lines, studying Hunt's tea-leaves, will not know where. He has not allowed me to name it. It doesn't matter, Hunt, so I don't want it mentioned, is that clear?

I have referred to him being in a college, but that left the field open, as there are several collegiate universities, from London to Durham. Hold on, it could not have been Durham, alas, as I said I was ever so sad that none of our lot wanted to go there. Hmm, perhaps I did give some hints, drop a few clues by chance, oh stop messing around Hunt and just get on with it. Jake has been at Cambridge.

Note the past tense. As I write, he has another week to go, then after that he is an ex-student, ex-dependent on his poor parents, out into the world, that'll really larn him. So as you read this, he has finished. It doesn't matter any more where he was, even if it ever did.

I was over the moon, Brian, when this year he became captain of his college football team. Good, huh. But he rang last night to tell us something even more remarkable, something his dear mama and certainly not his poor papa ever managed. Or expected. He's got a First.

Meaningless to many people, unless you are up on or in these things. We rang Arthur, his grandad in Carlisle, aged 87¾. And he said, 'Is there money in it, then?' We had American friends with us, the day he rang, and it meant little to them either, as their system is different.

I went for my evening walk, hoping to meet neighbours, hoping they'd say heh, isn't it Jake's Finals, how did he do, but I kept on meeting remote people, a doctor we used to have twenty years ago, a bloke I once played football with, then the daughter of the local grocer, and I failed with all of them to turn the subject round to Jake. Pathetic, isn't it. Nothing to do with me, yet here I am, looking for reflected glory, coming on the pride. As if after all these years I didn't know it wasn't English, not middle-class, to boast. One must do it elliptically.

The OT says she is not a Proud Parent. She is not unproud, just that proud is not the word she would use. Happy for Jake, pleased for him. She prefers to reserve pride for different achievements. Oh, you know, being very kind and understanding and helpful to someone, being morally brave, making a stand, that sort of Boy Scout stuff. I just think it's good, huh.

The Graduate

We were just leaving for Cambridge, going to see our dear son graduating, when the phone rang. It was our dear son, panicking.

'Fank Gawd I got you,' said Jake. 'Was beginning to fink you'd gone.'

Yes my petal, my wonderkin, my baba, what can us do for you.

'I haven't got a shirt, so can you bring one. Must be white. And I ain't got no shoes. They must be black. Fanks.' Peep, peep, peep.

I fell to wondering what would have happened had he read English, whether his North London tones might have been held against him, or would that fortune I didn't spend on his comprehensive education have been a handicap. Meanwhile, the OT bustled around, doing women's work. I'm not looking for his stupid shoes, do you mind. We're going to be late, hurry up.

She came out to the car holding a pair of vintage trainers, once white, in the distant past, chuntering on about dyeing them black, had she got time, would they do, would they be acceptable. Give me strength, I said, getting out of the car.

I found an old pair of my shoes at the bottom of my cupboard and my one and only white shirt, that one with the long collar, you must remember it, rather fetching I always thought, worn with a kipper tie. (I'm about to win a bet with Flora. Kipper ties are coming back, oh yes they are. Next we'll see the return of flares. Then I'll really clean up.)

On the way to Cambridge, I reminisced. I do this constantly, looking back on this time last week, or heh, remember what we were doing yesterday. Having a whole three years, wow, what a feast of nostalgia. Now which was the pub we went to the day we took him up, back in October, 1985. What about his first room, wasn't that weird.

Cambridge has been part of our life, these last three years, taking him up at the beginning of each term, lugging his 2,000 reggae records, then bringing him back at the end of each term, and his 2,000 stupid records. We've always made a day of it, walks up the river, walks to Granchester, plus lunch, then a look round the bookshops. Brighton was also part of our life for three years, when dear Caitlin was a student. Much preferred that. Cheaper bookshops, longer walks, far better restaurants. Much more fun in Brighton.

Now both towns will disappear from the routine of our life, if not from our memories. Unless Flora goes to either of them. Hope she goes somewhere different. With even cheaper secondhand bookshops. She says she's not going anywhere. She's pig-sick of the topic of universities. Had it up to here, every bloody meal for the last five years, give us a break, for God's sake.

You've also moaned for the last five years, said the OT, oh yes you have. You've complained non-stop about the driving, suggesting they should get the train or the bus. Such a short time in their life, and you've been so selfish.

It's true I hate driving. In our day, tra la, with car-less parents, it never arose. You relied on trunks which arrived each term, just as you were leaving. Mummies and Daddies were well out of it, in our day.

Hold on, wait for it, the old mind is turning over. My mother did come to my graduation, in Durham in 1957. Mrs Forsyth, a neighbour, came with her. I can see her now, having tea in the Master's Garden afterwards.

The OT has no real memory of her own graduation, from Oxford in 1960. She says she went, but her best friend from college, who happens to be staying with us at present, says she didn't. Nobody went in those days. The OT has a clearer memory of my graduation. She can see herself sitting in the

Cathedral for the ceremony beside John Davies's dad.

'This is the proudest moment in my life,' he said. Then fell asleep.

We reached Cambridge and went up to Jake's room. What a midden. Even worse than usual. There were flies hovering over the empty milk cartons and mould on the filthy cutlery. He'd just had his hair cut, so short it was practically a skinhead. And he refused to wear the old shoes we'd brought. Said they had holes in. He can talk. What a cheek.

There were worse moans when I produced my video camera and put a new tape in, ready to capture a lovely day. Oh Gawd, no, stop it Hunt, I don't want to be filmed. I got out my camera, my sturdy Olympus Trip. And I don't want to be photographed either.

So selfish, the younger generation. Our three are all the same. The moment I try to snap them, they go mad. I don't really enjoy it, but it's got to be done, it's what modern memories are all about, innit. Oh yes, you moan now, but when you're old and grey like me, cut grey, grey I'm certainly not, who mentioned grey, then you'll thank me for having captured some of the wonderful moments in your life.

They all assembled in one of the courtyards for their official college photo. All 130 or so of the people from his college, graduating that day. Jake was about the last to climb up on the tall benches at the back. He'd finally got all his posh gear on, with a lot of bending and twisting, moaning and groaning. He looked pretty impressive, in his gown and hood and funny tie thing they wear, and for a moment I thought what have I spawned, he could be a skinhead Etonian.

Then I saw his feet. He was wearing his old slippers, my old slippers, in fact I think they were my Mum's old slippers, Carlisle Co-op, circa 1971. Horrible brown mocassin things. The Head Porter was checking all the students, making sure they were properly dressed. Jake managed it, just in time. One of his friends came rushing up with a pair of shoes in a plastic bag. Looks brill on my video, but not a word to

221

the Young Master. He doesn't know I caught him, ha ha. Could be coming to your local Odeon soon.

We were not allowed to film or photograph in the Senate House, for the actual ceremony. Pretty boring anyway. An old gadgie in a red gown muttering miles below in Latin. Who wants to capture that. Thank goodness Flora didn't come, though she'd half fancied the day off school. It was like a conveyor belt, all the colleges going through, one by one. The OT had forgotten her specs, but it was quite easy to spot Jake, even from above. Look for the headful of skin, my dear.

The best bit was afterwards, tea in one of his college's many beautiful quads, God they're so lucky, these Oxbridge people. I got in early with my camera, just as the long trestle tables were being set out, the starched white tablecloths gently billowing, the maids and butlers standing waiting in their black and white uniforms, ready to serve the Young Gentlemen. And Young Women. All equal now.

The parents were all dressed up and loving it. I even wore a suit, my old Marks and Spencer lightweight one, blue with stripes. As the Father of a First I really thought I had to make some extra special effort. No tie, though. There are limits, even on a special day.

So that's it. The end of Jake's student life. Another graduate, ready to do whatever graduates do. Don't ask me. Everyone in the street already has. He says his ambition is to go south, live on a beach, play football and never wear a tie.

Swan Song

This Is It, the Big News, the thing you have all been dreading. I'm calling it a day. Goodbye Father's Day. Pause for little tears.

Flora turned sixteen on Hallowe'en while the other two are out there, somewhere, practically at pensionable age, so can I really call myself a Father of Children any more? Can I keep turning this out, when my raw material, my home-grown copy, keeps running away.

If only I'd made this all up, created a fictional family, I could by now have started recycling all the old stuff. I have a friend, just died, Charles Norman de Courcy Parry, who did a hunting column in a magazine for fifty-three years. Every five years, so he boasted, he used the same material again. He maintained that the memory span of all readers lasts only five years. Lucky.

I suppose I could hang on, treading water, till Grandfather's Day, but goodness knows when that will come, if ever, not the way this lot is carrying on. The OT has put her favourite children's books away, and carefully cleaned that ever so nice coat Caitlin looked lovely in and that felt hat which Jake wore. We've just got back from a friend the wickerwork cradle they were all born in , which has now seen twenty babies in twenty-five years. It sits in our bedroom, mocking us. When will it be used again? And what about my best stamp swaps and the old trains I've been keeping so lovingly. Will any new little members of the human race make use of them? Fat chance.

It all began ten years ago. Alan Coren, of blessed memory, said try it for four weeks, let's have a Dad's view, as a change from all those *Guardian* women. I've always looked upon it as a letter to My Mum, another Blessed Memory. You know how you rabbit on about the family tittle-tattle of the week, flamming up the smallest things, not actually telling lies, just missing out the horrible things which happen, the sort which would just depress. We've had our share of those.

This is column number 428. I've numbered them all, since 17 October, 1979. Never missed one through illness, just hols, hardly any bad language, nothing to offend Old Trouts of any age or sex, guaranteed safe and germ-free. You could take Father's Day anywhere. It even became a hardback book, then a paperback, then, blow me, a TV series, which I refused to write, saying the idea is stupid, how can such a skittery thing go on the telly, but it ran for two years. John Alderton was me. Bet you don't remember that.

Right, a few unfinished bits of business. My bread, as you've asked, did not win first prize or any prize at the Loweswater Show. But am I deterred, am I sulking, certainly not. I'm still at it, the OT's pride and joy, baking away. So think of me, from henceforth, of a Sunday morning, turning out my three treacle loaves, one round and two long.

Of course, the real unfinished business is les enfants. We still don't know what will happen to Jake, nor does the world. After three weeks as a porter at Harrods, he got a better paid job, as a labourer. He now waits for the call, expected any day now, to go abroad to teach English somewhere, possibly maybe Italy, perhaps just for a year. Then what? Maybe possibly something else. Is he too well qualified, with his brillo degree. I can't wait to find out, whatever it is he will find out, about life, the universe, and wearing a tie.

Dear Caitlin has been home for Christmas from Worcester, Mass., hurrah, and is now applying to do further research at various American universities. Will she get a place. Will she get the funds. Will Big Hunt be asked to help. What will he say. Can't wait to find out, whatever it is he is going to find out.

And this is Little Flora's GCSE year, the first exams in

her life, after all that industrial action which her generation has suffered. How will she turn out when it comes to the things that really matter, such as life, the universe and Oxford Street. Still says she won't try for university. Pig sick of that subject.

The Old Trout swims on, one thing at a time, nothing stupid, doing things properly, with another novel offering out soon. Not got a new biog subject, so far. Who will she think of. Whose life will we have to share at meal-times for the next five years.

I have so much on, don't ask me, okay thanks, feared you never would. Apart from my Columbus biog, which is for the 1992 celebrations, so I'm well ahead, I've taken on a really mad project for Penguin. It means writing a teenage book a month for a year. Don't say it. I must be off my trolley. But it is a most exciting, nay unique creation. That's really the reason I'm packing up now.

My wrist is knackered already.

But the big problem is, what am I going to do on Saturday evenings from now on? That's when I've always knocked this out, my little bit of fun, two hours of pleasure, after a week down the mines.

For a whole decade, I've built a life round it. If it's Saturday, it's jumblies in the morning, football in the afternoon, then I have a run, a bath, put on my track suit which everyone hates, and at six o'clock sharp, bingo, time for Father's Day, and I go up to my little room, and talk to myself.

Now what? How can I fill Saturday nights? Read, says the OT. Rave, says Flora.

They're all pleased, the three enfants. They're fed up with me embarrassing them. So that's another reason to retire. Oh well, I suppose I'd better say sorry to them. Sor-ree.

But we've had some fun, you and me, haven't we. And the fan letters, mon dew, sackfuls of them. Fanks, but can't say I'll miss replying to them in the future.

Tell you what. Possibly maybe, I'll do a round robin letter, once a year, for ever, just to tell you what happens to Flora, Jake and Caitlin, on the rest of their road through life. If you send a stamped addressed envelope. I'm not paying. Bloody hell. I'm giving up an income.

What have I learned? Not a lot. When it comes to parenthood, you can't teach much, can't pass on experience, just amuse, let people know they're not alone.

It won't last. That's one Christmas cracker motto I don't mind passing on. Every seven years, they change, not just physically, but their personalities. Looking back at our big ones, I can hardly recognise them at seven, or at fourteen. Will they change again? Or is this it? That's what I don't know. But up to 21, don't bank on anything. Don't either boast, because aren't they doing well, so polite, so lovely, or get too depressed and blame yourself. Either way, the chances are it will change.

I don't think Philip Larkin got it right. If you believe 'they fuck you up your Mum and Dad,' gosh first rude work in ten years, then by the same token, we got fucked up by our Mums and Dads, so it's a pointless observation, unless you want to use it as a cop-out. I think on the whole they don't, your Mum and Dad. It's what's inside that matters most. When it comes out, you can't do much about it. Just keep smiling, be there, take each game as it comes, etc, but you know all that.

Ten years then. Goodness. In any family it's a pretty long time. It seems only yesterday that Caitlin had her first teenage party, and you'll never guess what happened when these yobbos found the fridge was still full of stuff oh no Hunt, don't start that again.

So I won't. Bye.

MICHAEL CAINE

MICHAEL CAINE'S MOVING PICTURE SHOW

MICHAEL CAINE
Britain's own Oscar-winning superstar takes the lid off
the movies in this hilarious and revealing bookful of
fascinating facts and outrageous out-takes . . .

In their 1953 movie *Abbott and Costello Go to Mars* Bud
and Lou actually end up on Venus!

Oscar Levant claimed he'd known Doris Day *before* she
became a virgin!

Sophia Loren's mother once won a Greta Garbo lookalike
competition . . . but when Charlie Chaplin entered a
Charlie Chaplin lookalike contest he came third!

Winston Churchill worked as a scriptwriter for London
Films in 1934 and Edward VIII is the only British monarch
ever to have acted in a screen drama . . .

NOW, NOT MANY PEOPLE KNOW THAT

AVAILABLE AT BOOK SHOPS

Post·A·Book

A Royal Mail service in association with the Book Marketing Council & The Booksellers Association.

Post-A-Book is a Post Office trademark.

DEREK NIMMO

UP MOUNT EVEREST WITHOUT A PADDLE

A little travelling music, maestro, please . . . Derek Nimmo offers an in-flight feast of traveller's tales with the maximum duty-free allowance of laughter.

Travelwise enough to avoid such hazards as playing in *There's a Girl in My Soup* in Papua New Guinea, the long-distance Nimmo is no stranger to the traumas of travel. Indeed, his first flight on a Jumbo was sadly marred when he was told: 'I'm sorry sir, you can only see a dirty movie if you're a smoker.'

His gloriously funny global guide is spiced with such gems overheard as the American lady's complaint on ascending the Parthenon — 'You'd think with all these tourists about, they would build an elevator . . .'

HODDER AND STOUGHTON PAPERBACKS

RONNIE BARKER

IT'S HELLO FROM HIM

When, a little while ago, Ronnie Barker decided to retire, he just left a message on his answer phone. No Positively Final Appearance, no press statement, no fuss.

After nearly forty years, a 'jobbing actor', in his own phrase, was leaving the stage. Farewell Norman Stanley Fletcher, goodbye Piggy Malone, Arkwright, Clarence . . .

The end of a career that began in 1948 when a seventeen-year-old bank clerk handed in his notice. He was off to join the Manchester Repertory Company, based for obscure reasons in Aylesbury.

'You're mad,' said the bank manager. 'Stay five or six years and you could be a cashier.'

Instead he, and the rest of us, had to settle for a stage, film and TV career as a brilliant comic actor — and writer. A very professional, well-liked man who made us laugh and laugh.

Bank managers do make mistakes.

'His own good humour shines through on every page'
The Stage

HODDER AND STOUGHTON PAPERBACKS

MORE TITLES AVAILABLE FROM
HODDER AND STOUGHTON PAPERBACKS

MICHAEL CAINE

☐ 50827 2   Michael Caine's Moving Picture
Show   £2.99

DEREK NIMMO

☐ 50610 5   Up Mount Everest Without
A Paddle   £2.50

☐ 43072 9   Not in Front of the Servants   £1.99

☐ 41537 1   Oh, Come on All Ye Faithful   £1.95

RONNIE BARKER

☐ 50813 7   It's Hello From Him   £2.99

DAVID RENWICK

☐ 50809 9   But I Digress   £2.50

All these books are available at your local bookshop or newsagent, or can be ordered direct from the publisher. Just tick the titles you want and fill in the form below.

Prices and availability subject to change without notice.

HODDER AND STOUGHTON PAPERBACKS, P.O. Box 11, Falmouth, Cornwall.

Please send cheque or postal order, and allow the following for postage and packing:

U.K. – 80p for one book, and 20p for each additional book ordered up to a £2.00 maximum.

B.F.P.O. – 80p for the first book and 20p for each additional book.

OTHER OVERSEAS CUSTOMERS INCLUDING EIRE – £1.50 for the first book, £1.00 for the second book, plus 30p per copy for each additional book.

NAME ....

ADDRESS ....

....